THE MORPHOLOGY OF THE EARTH

Splendidly preserved landscape of the " post-Gondwana " (Cretaceous) cycle of erosion, cut across Stormberg (Triassic) basaltic lavas at 9,300 feet above sea-level, Sani Pass, Basutoland. The higher country, approximately 11,000 feet, also bears planed remnants of the Gondwana (Jurassic) landscape.

Lester King.

THE MORPHOLOGY OF
THE EARTH

A STUDY AND SYNTHESIS OF WORLD SCENERY

LESTER C. KING

Professor of Geology
University of Natal, Durban, South Africa

OLIVER AND BOYD
EDINBURGH AND LONDON

OLIVER AND BOYD LTD

Tweeddale Court
Edinburgh 1

39A Welbeck Street
London W.1

First Published .   .   .   1962
Second Edition .   .   .   1967

PRINTED IN GREAT BRITAIN
BY OLIVER AND BOYD LTD., EDINBURGH

INTRODUCTION

Our realm of study is the outer part of the earth, and our subject is its evolution, principally from the Mesozoic era to the present day. In a spirit of patient enquiry we seek to find order, system and if possible explanation amid the major topographic features of the globe.

The synthetic study of such a realm has required field work upon a scale that only modern transport could have provided, for very early in the research a principle emerged that is more important than the research itself; that while the geologist may often be in error the Earth is never wrong. It was necessary for the author to see as much of the earth's surface as possible, yet not to interpret it in terms of preconceived philosophies; often to sit passively upon hills just letting the scenery " soak in " and teach the beholder —when he was sufficiently humble.

But even in this age no man can cover the entire earth and recourse had to be made to libraries for further information. This has exposed fearful inadequacies in the coverage of certain regions, even admitting the insufficiency of sources available to the writer. For these and other reasons no attempt has been made to provide even coverage for the earth's surface. Much useful data has been assembled in F. Matchatschek's *Das Relief der Erde* (Borntraeger), and the reader may be well advised to proceed with the present volume in one hand and Matchatschek in the other. Students are further recommended A. K. Lobeck's *Physiographic Diagrams* (Columbia Geographical Press) of the several continents.

Very early, an optimum of about 500 pages of text was set for the book. To approach this the original manuscript has been cut time and again, and many topics have been omitted on the assumption that the reader was already sufficiently familiar with them. Always the attempt has been to provide data that are less familiar but withal to adduce a series of comparative examples illustrating principles that the reader could then apply to his own experience.

The research is set out in no spirit of idle iconoclasm but in a bright seeking of truth from the earth itself, and if at the end our path is strewn with broken, though cherished, hypotheses—a cooling, shrinking earth, growing continents, immobile continents, compressional mountain ranges, cyclic denudation by downwearing and others—why so much the better for Geology, so long as the new hypotheses explain the facts of earth structure more truly. Their turn to retire gracefully will come with equal certainty.

My gratitude is here expressed to the University of Natal which has granted special study leave for field work on a number of occasions. Also, the University and the Council for Scientific and Industrial Research have contributed towards the cost of preparing the illustrations. Credits for figures have been scrupulously assigned, though I have not always been able to contact their authors for permission to publish. To them also my thanks are due. The courtesy of the following publishers is also acknowledged: Geological Society of America, *Geographical Review*, American Association Petroleum Geologists, Messrs. Harper and Brothers, Geological Society of London, Scottish Geographical Society, Messrs. Pergamon Press, *Revue Geographie Physique et Geologie Dynamique*, American Museum of Natural History, New Zealand Geological Survey, Illinois State Geological Survey, Columbia Geographical Press, (C. S. Hammond and Co.).

Lastly, this preface would be incomplete without acknowledgement of the deep enjoyment that I have derived from the research: not only from the lands and peoples that I have visited (and may hope to visit in the future), but also in my home. Into a tiny study roughly ten feet square have entered mighty vistas—sunrise upon great plains, tangled tropical jungles, towering snow-clad mountains and tempestuous seas. It has been fun to spend an occasional weekend in the Andes, or snatch a rare visit to Cambodia before dinner. And though I have not been exempt from " language difficulties " these foreign travels at home have usually been without " let or hindrance " which is much to be appreciated in these official-ridden days.

NOTE TO THE SECOND EDITION

In the short time since the first edition was published great additions have been made to geological knowledge—chiefly in the Antarctic, the oceanic basins, and in studies of the upper mantle. These have entailed some revision of the text.

The bibliography has also been revised, and the spate of new literature has caused —for sheer lack of space—many worthy references of the first edition to yield place to new authors. I have regretted having to pass by old friends in this way; but have sometimes left their names and dates of publication in the text. Devout bibliophiles of geomorphology can trace them through the older edition.

It remains, however, better to travel and study the earth at first hand

LESTER KING

CONTENTS

vii

PART A

THE BASIS OF SCENERY:
THE BEHAVIOUR OF THE EARTH'S CRUST

CHAPTER I

THE STRUCTURE OF THE EARTH'S CRUST

Genesis. Fundamental Rock Types. The Layered Crust. Properties of Sub-crustal Matter. Isostasy and Isobary. Crustal Temperatures. Igneous Action. Radiothermal Energy of the Rocks. Sub-crustal Convection Currents. Continental Drift. Some Dead Wood : a Digression. Palæogeography. Model of the Earth.

GENESIS

" In the beginning . . . the earth was without form and void." It was born of a heavenly body about 4,500 million years ago; and for a long period thereafter no record remains of earth's nature or of its behaviour. But more than 3,000 million years ago rocks existed, physically and chemically similar to sedimentary rocks that are forming today, which suggests that geological and meteorological conditions at the surface of the globe had then stabilised and were similar to those now prevailing.

If sedimentary rocks were forming, then scenery existed, with mountains and valleys and plains and deltas, and a primeval ocean beating upon a primeval shore. The aspect of those early lands was stark, for the terrains were devoid of life and the transition from one landform to another, from rocky hill to gravel plain or desert dunes, was abrupt without true soils or plant cover to smooth out the contours. Everywhere the aspect of the lands was such as we now find only in the great deserts—the Sahara, the Mohave or the Namib.

Of those early landscapes no vestige remains and we shall consider them no further, but ever since there has been scenery, and the earth's face has been remade from each geological age to the next as global forces have periodically elevated new regions into mountains which in turn have been torn down and levelled into plains by the forces of erosion. The rival tectonic and denudational powers, predominantly constructional and destructional respectively, share in fashioning the surface of the solid globe and their constant interplay forms the theme of this book.

Although most of our scenic study, as developed in the sequel, deals with landscapes which have existed only since the Jurassic period at earliest, we must never overlook the long processions of kaleidoscopic landscapes that have evolved throughout earlier geologic time; for the structural traits and limitations inherited from earlier periods frequently influence modern scenic evolution. Thus the Appalachian folds of Palæozoic time still control the ridge-and-valley topography of that province in North America; and in my own sub-tropical city of Durban visitors are frequently taken to see the glacial

3

pavements polished by glaciers of Carboniferous age, now being exhumed from beneath thick Dwyka tillite by modern erosion or by human activities. Scenic studies must therefore often take cognizance of geologic events that long precede the development of modern landscapes.

We shall first consider in this chapter the nature and behaviour of the earth's crust, which constitutes the very basis of scenery.

FUNDAMENTAL ROCK TYPES

The materials of the earth-body are rocks. Of the three main categories of rocks—igneous, sedimentary and metamorphic—the second and third are patently remade from previous rocks, so that only igneous rocks can be regarded as primary or in a pristine state. Even so, researches upon " granitisation " have shown that at crustal temperatures of 400-500°C. almost any kind of pre-existing earth material—clay, sand or even basalt—may be altered by " emanations " of sub-crustal origin, through intermediate schists, migmatites or amphibolites to feldspathic end-products of granitic type. Much supposedly primary igneous rock is thus earlier rock-material that has been plutonically metamorphosed even to the stage at which refusion has occurred (Sederholm 1923, 1926; Read 1955; Reynolds 1949, 1958). Whether much primary igneous rock (in the strict sense) is now visible at the earth's surface may be doubted. The most likely examples are among the plateau basalts and peridotite intrusions. But at greater depths within the crust the proportion of pristine igneous matter may increase.

Natural division of igneous rocks into three distinct chemical groups acid, basic and ultrabasic, represented respectively by granite or granodiorite, gabbro (basalt) and peridotite, is widespread. Each type has its own characteristic mode of occurrence and appears distinctively in association with certain tectonic conditions (Chapters I, II, IV). In a general way too, each type is associated with certain levels in the earth's crust; granodiorite in the high-standing continental masses, basalt at the level of the ocean floors and beneath the continents, while peridotite exists typically at still greater depths. All igneous rock types other than these three are developed only to a minor extent, and many are plainly derived by magmatic differentiation or assimilation from one or other of the three main types.

The distinctive importance of these three types has promoted enquiry whether they represent three primary magmatic types separated one from another very early in the earth's cooling history, or whether they may be derived from one another by processes of magmatic differentiation acting progressively throughout geological time to produce ever greater segregation. Abundant evidence (Tyrrell 1926) leads to the conception of acid and basic magma types as distinct throughout known geologic time. Even where they have used the same volcanic vent, they often appear to have been immiscible (B. C. King 1965). To these types Hess and his co-workers (1932) have added primary peridotite magmas which they regard, indeed, as the principal heat-bringers of all igneous activity.

The earth is a globe, and its radial structure is a product partly of its original composition and partly of processes active during geologic time. The bulk of the earth-body (the mantle) is believed to consist of olivine or peridotite, about which is a thin envelope of basic material like basalt. In the continents appears a light acid or granitic portion. Layering is concentric according to density. The outermost layers behave towards stresses of short period as though rigid, and are termed the earth's crust. Below this the earth-body is apparently weak for hundreds of kilometres, material even in the crystalline state being deformed plastically (p. 13). The crust is relatively thin, its base, known as the Mohorovičić discontinuity, being situated at an average depth of about 35 km. beneath the continents and of 5 km. beneath the oceanbeds. Sharp downwarping of the " Moho " is thus characteristic beneath continental margins (Fig. 1).

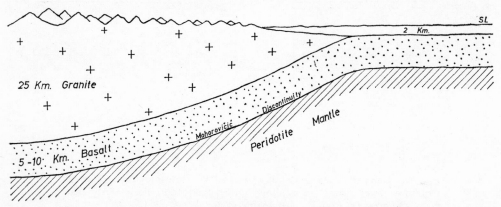

FIG. 1. Simple interpretation of a crustal section at the margin of a continent.

Much information upon the structure of the outer earth has been derived by analysis of both natural and artificial earthquake waves transmitted through it. Earthquakes originate at any level from the surface down to depths of 700 km. and this affords a classification of shocks into: *Normal* earthquakes originating above a depth of 100 km., *Intermediate* shocks from that depth down to 300 km., and *Deep-Focus* earthquakes known to originate from between 300 and 700 km. The great majority of shocks belong to the shallow class, and are tectonic in origin, often being demonstrably connected with present faulting or volcanic activity. The intermediate shocks are generally associated with zones of Cainozoic folding and faulting. The deep-focus earthquakes, which may be connected with early-Cainozoic or late-Cretaceous events about the Pacific border are registered from four regions only, the Mediterranean, the island arcs of the western Pacific, the Caribbean Sea and from beneath Andean South America. In three of these regions they are associated with abundant normal and intermediate shocks in such a way that all could be thought of as originating on deep-reaching shear-zones extending from the Pacific side towards and beneath the landward areas. Benioff (1954), who points out that stress may accumulate even in the deep zones for more than a decade, has interpreted the shears as compressional but evidence cited later in connection with island arcs suggests rather a tensional origin (Fig. 2).

The structure of continents, as deduced from the passage of earthquake waves, has been expressed by Gutenberg and Richter (1951): " The typical continental structure consists of a series of layers, the uppermost of which is of the sedimentary rocks (including metamorphosed sediments). The elastic constants within this layer, as well as its thickness, are subject to much local variation. Over large areas the sediments are completely absent, whereas in deep basins of geosynclinal character they may extend to depths over 15 km. Where the sediments are absent, the exposed rocks are usually granitic (basaltic in volcanic regions); moreover in many localities granitic rocks

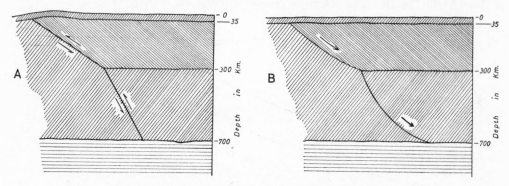

Fig. 2. Compressional (A) and Tensional (B) interpretations of earth structure from records of shallow, intermediate and deep earthquake foci. (A) *after H. Benioff*. (B) *Reinterpreted*.

are known to underlie the existing sediment. Investigations still in progress indicate that the velocity of longitudinal waves in that upper part of the continental crust which is commonly called the 'granitic layer' increases from about 6 km./sec., near the surface to (locally) as much as $6\frac{3}{4}$ km./sec., at a depth of roughly 10 km. and possibly decreases below this to about 6 km./sec. This decrease may be attributed, at least partly, to an effect of increasing temperature on the moduli of elasticity. Most of the earthquake foci seem to be in this low-velocity layer ".

Below the 'granitic layer' one to three crustal layers have been identified. Their thicknesses and elastic properties differ notably in the various layers. It has been suggested that in this intermediate layer (or layers) the material is basaltic; but recorded speeds of seismic waves differ from place to place (*e.g.* within some of the island arcs and other peri-oceanic areas). Whether this is due to change of materials, or to variation of elastic properties within the same material has yet to be demonstrated. The lower boundary of these layers is the Mohorovičić discontinuity.

Estimates, based on seismic analysis, of the thickness of the granitic crust, and of the whole continental thickness, have been given by Gutenberg (1936) (Table I). Crustal thicknesses for shield areas (Chap. III) of the continents are all about 35 km.

Analysis of trans-oceanic earthquake waves (Angenheister 1920) reveals the floor of the deep Pacific Basin as devoid of granite—perhaps from primordial time. Its floor is heavily basaltic, perhaps of an oceanite type, though Tilley (1951) has preferred tholeiite for the actual floor with more olivinic types below. An earthquake shock in the Aleutian Islands, recorded at Lwiro in the Congo was noted by Kovach (1959) to have complementary paths that were almost entirely continental and oceanic respectively (Fig. 3). Dispersion data indicated an average crustal thickness of slightly less than 40 km. for the continental path and a mean sediment thickness of 0.8 km. for the oceanic path.

Below the " Moho ", in the substratum or upper mantle, the velocity of longitudinal waves is between 7·9 and 8·2 km./sec.* corresponding with a density of about 3·3. Shear waves are less often recorded, perhaps indicating abundant interstitial fluid.

TABLE I.

	Granitic Layer	Whole Crust
Continental edges	? km.	20-30 km.
England	10	20
Southern Germany	30	45
Eastern Alps	40	50
South-east Europe	about 30	about 45
Caucasus	?	about 45 ?
Central Asia (40° N, 70° E)	about 20	40-50
Philippine Islands	?	about 50
Japan	about 20	about 50, decreasing toward the Pacific
South and Central California	15	30-40

The transition at the " Moho " may be sharp, or take place over a zone several kilometres thick perhaps corresponding to a change in physical properties induced by temperature and pressure, rather than an abrupt change in chemical composition (p. 672).

The subcrust, or upper mantle, was formerly thought to be of uniform composition, but seismic analysis of waves from controlled explosions shows locally intricate patterns of mantle velocities due evidently to local variations of composition or of temperature. The latter are identifiable on other data also at the boundary between the oceanic crust and the mantle.

At about 140 km. depth, moreover, is a low velocity layer (Gutenberg 1954) of apparently world-wide extent. It is deeper beneath the oceans than under the continents, and may later be found to be plastic.

The conclusions derived from seismology find strong confirmation from field geology. The dominance of two igneous rock types and their derivatives, granodiorite among the plutonic and basalt among the volcanic types, surely postulates a fundamental

* The densities for various layers adopted by American geophysicists are : seawater 1·03, sediments 2·30, granitic crust 2·70, basaltic lower crust 3·0, average for crust 2·87, and 3·27 for the substratum just below the Mohorovičić discontinuity.

division of crustal matter. Intermediate rock types are mainly mixed, granodioritic to gabbroic, and hosts of special rock-types have been shown to derive from the parent types either by differentiation or by assimilation. Despite many attempts, notably by N. L. Bowen, no satisfactory derivation in bulk of one major type from the other has been demonstrated.

Molten basalt has been erupted abundantly at intervals from the earliest Pre-cambrian to modern times, and at points well distributed over the globe, oceanic and

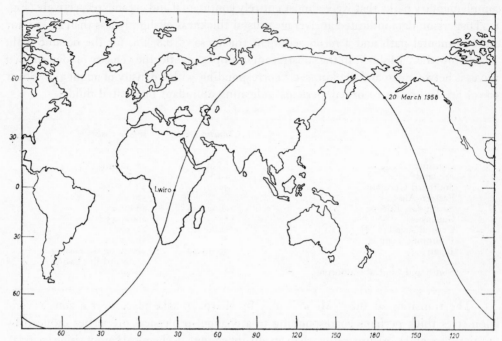

FIG. 3. Continental and oceanic paths of seismic waves from an earth-quake in the Aleutian Islands that was recorded at Lwiro, Belgian Congo *after R. L. Kovach.*

continental sectors alike, thus showing that it has been derived from a subjacent world-embracing shell.

Plateau basalt and tholeiite* represent, according to Backlund, Holmes, Walker and many others, contamination of primitive olivine basalt either by melting and assimiliation of granitic materials, or by emanations already present in the basalt magma or added from the subcrust below. Their distribution about the globe is so ubiquitous, in the ocean basins as well as on the continental bucklers, as to suggest an almost complete earth-shell of eruptible, parent basalt already charged with emanations capable of a degree of feldspathisation.

About the base of the granitic layer and the upper region of the basaltic shell, extensive metamorphism is thought to transform rock systems that have been carried

* Feldspathic basalt with mesostasis.

downwards by folding, into denser forms. Seismic waves apparently travel more slowly however, through metamorphic rocks enriched in basic minerals (*e.g.* biotite and hornblende), and a low-velocity layer is sometimes detectable in the crust. Below Iceland such a layer, of continental origin, is apparently buried deeply beneath the plateau basalts; areas within east Asiatic island arcs sometimes produce anomalous results; and analysis of certain earthquake records from Kamchatka led Stander (1960) to conclude that " in some earthquakes a mechanism not previously detected may operate at these [40-60 km.] depths."

Du Toit (1937) cites among xenoliths from the deep-reaching kimberlite pipes garnetiferous amphibolite and pyroxene granulite perhaps produced from rocks like granite, gabbro and hornblende schist.

Holmes and Daly have also made researches into this subject, and the latter has made the point that " under high stress crystalline basaltic material is not stable as ordinary gabbro or diabase but may be stable as garnet-bearing gabbro or as amphibolite or as an allied type of rock ". This is in conformity with the findings of metamorphic geology.

Several investigators (Lovering 1958) have further considered the possibility that the Mohorovičić discontinuity corresponds not to a chemical change from basalt to ultrabasic peridotite but represents a phase change from basalt to the denser, but chemically similar, form known as eclogite. But eclogite, with which diamond is sometimes associated, is so rare that it fails to qualify, on geological observation, as a possible universal substratum. Perhaps layers or lenticular bodies of it exist within the ultrabasic materials of the mantle. Peridotite, on the other hand, has appeared wherever conditions in orogenic belts have permitted it to rise towards the surface, and must be abundant in depth—a conclusion fortified by Washington's observations on stony meteorites. Below 500° C., in the presence of water vapor, peridotite readily transforms into serpentine. Modern researches suggest that the 500° C. isogeotherm may be situated not far on either side of the Mohorovičić discontinuity the physiochemical changes at which may be related to this transformation (Hess 1955).

Within the Andesite Line which rings the Pacific Basin (Fig. 4), the only rock types known are basalts, differentiates of basalt, or occasionally peridotite. Typical andesite is not directly obtainable from basalt (Tilley 1951), which on crystal differentiation yields trachyandesite or phonolite. It can arise only by an admixture of continental rock types with basaltic media. The andesite line thus marks the boundary of the Pacific Basin proper. This boundary is highly seismic and of special significance, quite different from the Atlantic boundaries which show no fundamental differences in earthquake transmission from the land to the oceanic sectors, transition from the continents to the ocean basin being seismically continuous (Gutenberg).

Authorities prior to 1950 (*e.g.* Umbgrove 1947) considered that the Atlantic Basin was thinly floored with a layer of granitic composition, but first Rothé and later Ewing have stated that beneath a thin (1 to 2 km.) of sediment the floor corresponds essentially

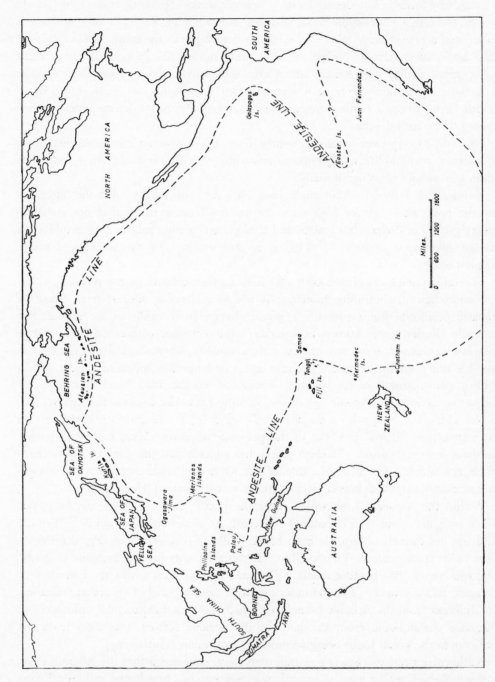

FIG. 4. The " Andesite Line " about the Pacific Basin. Within this line no rocks of continental derivation are known.

with the top of the basaltic layer. Nevertheless, patches of granitic composition rest upon this in islands and suboceanic plateaus. The western half of the Indian Ocean, which resembles the Atlantic floor in physical characteristics, also possesses many such masses ranging in size from Malagasy to small coral islands resting upon rocky foundations, with submarine ridges also in the depths (Fig. 249). Similar too, is the floor of the western Pacific Ocean between the Marianas island arc and the Asiatic mainland, and about western Polynesia and New Zealand (Fig. 250). All these oceanic regions are characterised by the presence of large submarine ridges, and sometimes also by islands, e.g. New Zealand, Malagasy, built of continental-type rocks. The conclusion seems inescapable that such regions possess some affinity with the continents, and we shall find strong evidence that these regions were indeed formerly the sites of continental masses (p. 581).

Ultra-basic rocks, though rare superficially compared with the two types already mentioned, are nevertheless widespread, with a distribution that plainly suggests derivation from some deeper-lying substratum, and not as local differentiates in each case. Heavy material from such a deeper earth-shell would naturally find its way to the surface only under special conditions, and therefore crop out in relatively subordinate amount. There is no clear consensus of opinion regarding the precise chemical and mineralogical constitution of the subjacent ultra-basic matter. Some authorities have considered it to be dunite, others peridotite and so forth, but all agree that it is ultra-basic, and that it constitutes the bulk of the earth-body below the crust (mantle).

The occurrence of peridotite belts in regions where deep-reaching crustal structures have passed downward right through the basic envelope (Hess 1939), confirms the presence of a deep-seated layer of this material. As no other samples representing still deeper zones have been recorded at the surface, it is surmised that peridotite composes the primitive earth-stuff to very great depth.

PROPERTIES OF SUB-CRUSTAL MATTER

The peculiar functioning of the outer rigid envelope of the earth, which allows for vertical and horizontal movements of rock strata in the upper crust, for volcanism of various kinds, for the transmission of earthquake shocks, and for isostatic compensation at depth (p. 15) lays a heavy rôle upon the substratum. It behaves with both rigidity and mobility, it exercises motive forces of various kinds, and it must be tolerably uniform below a certain depth all around the earth, for the velocity of earthquake waves is uniform below the Mohorovičić discontinuity, an horizon which occurs at minimal depths of 5-10 km. under the oceans and at maximal depths of 40-50 km. beneath the continents.

A pioneer contribution to the study of sub-crustal matter by Barrell (1916) pointed out that the strength of the crust is dependent upon (a) the nature of the material,

(b) cubic compression, (c) the relation of the temperature to the point of fusion, (d) rapidity of application of the stress.

As illustrations of the behaviour of different materials granite and basalt may be contrasted. Granite is about half as rigid as basalt, and hence deforms more readily under stress difference; whereas under uniform compression it proves somewhat the stronger of the two. Any stress acting upon a heterogeneous crust must therefore give rise to local unequal strains and concentrations of stress, due to the heterogeneity itself, independently of other variable factors. Local stress may rise far higher than regional stress.

Cubic compression increases in fairly steady ratio downwards. At 40 km. depth it approximates to 11,500 atmospheres, or more than 75 tons per sq. in. Like stress, the influence of cubic compression is variable according to the amount and direction of the applied forces.

Barrell has offered (1916) some estimates of strength at different depths within the outer envelopes of the earth, and though his figures stand in need of revision, we quote them in the original as a tribute to this pioneer thinker.

TABLE II

Depth (km.)	Strength per cent	Layer
0	100 ⎱	Granitic Crust
20	400 ⎰	
25	500	Basaltic Crust
30	400	
		Mohorovičić Discontinuity
50	25	Sub-crust (or Upper Mantle)
100	17	Mantle
200	8	
300	5	
400	4	

Barrell's " asthenosphere " or " level of no strength " would now be considered to begin below the Mohorovičić discontinuity, at depths of 35 km. or so below the continents. Rapidity of application of stresses is important in assessing the behaviour of sub-crustal matter. As we have seen, to rapidly applied earthquake shocks sub-crustal matter behaves as a normally elastic solid. But a variety of other observations emphasise its mobility with respect to long-continued stresses and indicate for it a marked quality of plasticity. In contrast with the lithosphere, which is decidedly strong, the sub-crust appears to be, for long-continued stresses, nearly or quite devoid of strength. The problem is one of viscosity, and the homely example of pitch which flies into pieces when struck with a hammer, but flows outwards into a pool under its own weight when left standing for several days is often invoked in illustration of the reactions of the substratum.

PLATE 1

Deformation as a rheid: laminar flow in ice of the Malaspina Glacier, Alaska.
R. P. Sharp.

Deformation in the solid state* is accomplished under physical laws which may be expressed in a tripartite equation:

$$S \qquad = \qquad \frac{p}{\mu} \qquad + \qquad f(P) \qquad + \qquad Bt^{\frac{1}{3}} + \frac{pt}{\eta}.$$

(Total deformation)   (Hooke's Law)   (Plastic deformation)   (Creep)

The first term on the right-hand side expresses Hooke's Law and relates to elastic deformation under which, if the stress is removed, the deformed medium tends to return to its original shape. But if the stress limit is exceeded the material ruptures and there is no return and permanent deformation results. The second term expresses plastic deformation whereby material deforms by flow and the stress is dissipated. All such deformation is permanent. Towards the surface of the earth the typical mode of yielding is elastic, by jointing and fracturing, accompanied in sedimentary beds by folding. Intergranular movements typify fracture plus flow. But the rocks of deeper layers yield by flow alone (the second term)—fracturing is absent and deformation is spread more uniformly throughout the mass. This is shown by the gneissose structures present in certain, formerly very deep-seated, rocks. Riecke's principle of crystal growth in positions of least stress is operative, and molecular changes also occur. Distortions are *plastic*, the deformed media show no tendency to return to the original shape, and the degree of plastic deformation is expressed in the second term of the equation.

The third term expresses the rheidity or " tendency to deform in the solid, with time ". Unless the time factor is very large or the material very weak the expression is negligible, and it is seldom considered. But time is one of the largest factors in geology, and given geological time the third expression may become the most important in the equation. Solid deformation over a long time is therefore expressed as $S=pt$ which is the formula for deformation of a fluid. Many substances are known to flow in the solid state, *e.g.* ice, salt, gneiss. For stress periods longer than a few days ice acts as a fluid (Plate 1), for periods over 10 years salt is a fluid, and for periods exceeding 100,000 years granite is a fluid. Given sufficient time, all stressed substances flow and deform plastically in the solid state. This type of deformation is termed *rheid* deformation. As defined by Carey (1953), " A rheid is a substance whose temperature is below its melting point, and whose deformation by viscous flow during the time of the experiment is at least three orders of magnitude greater than the elastic deformation under the given conditions."

The factor of *time* is critical, and as geological time is of high order, it follows that the whole earth functions ultimately as though it were fluid, though for short-term stresses, such as are relieved by earthquake shocks, major portions of the earth may behave as perfect solids.

Rheid deformation is always accomplished by laminar flow, with the volume

---

* An extended programme of laboratory research into the deformation of rocks is reported by D. T. Griggs, chiefly in *Bull. Geol. Soc. Am.*, vols. 46-66.

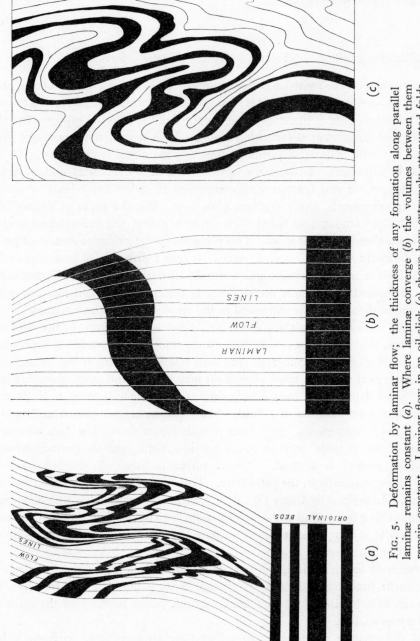

Fig. 5. Deformation by laminar flow; the thickness of any formation along parallel laminae remains constant (*a*). Where laminae converge (*b*) the volumes between them remain constant. Laminar flow in an oil-slick (*c*) shows how extremely attenuated folds may form. *after S. W. Carey.*

remaining constant. Folding of this type is typical of salt domes and of the deeper-seated schists and gneisses (Fig. 5), but many kinds of rock including basalt and serpentine are known to exhibit it. Unquestionably it is widespread in the deeper parts of the crust, and it is probably typical of all the earth-body except for the most superficial layers.

ISOSTASY AND ISOBARY

The peculiar constitution of the rigid outer crust, resting upon a weak and potentially mobile substratum,* is responsible for several characteristic elastic and plastic responses. Well-known among these is isostatic recovery, a response in the vertical sense to the horizontal transference of load, whether positive or negative (Fig. 6). For isostatic

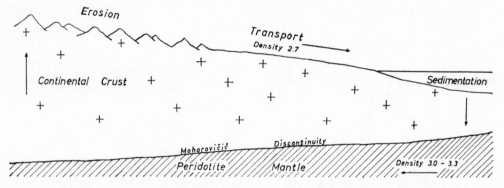

FIG. 6. Isostatic relationships between areas undergoing erosion and areas undergoing sedimentation, showing compensation for superficial transport of land waste by reverse movement in the substratum.

recovery to occur, horizontal displacement is necessary in the substratum, below the Mohorovičić discontinuity, in the opposite sense to the transference of load at the surface; and as the density of sub-crustal matter approaches 3·3 whereas that of near-surface materials averages 2·8, vertical recovery occurs in a proportion only of the material eroded or deposited.

Isostasy is a direct consequence of plasticity in the substratum, by which material may be deformed in the crystalline state (Carey 1953), and implies that regional topography may be completely compensated in the substratum. Continental regions stand high because they are light, the ocean basins stand low because their floors are heavy—sial is thin or absent. The difference of elevation between continents and ocean basins, involving two frequency maxima of elevation at the surface of the globe (Fig. 7) is thus a direct response to the isostatic principle and a demonstration of two distinct media in the construction of the earth's crust.

* In this text the term substratum is used for the mobile upper part of the mantle, directly below the Mohorovičić discontinuity.

The isostatic condition of any part of the outer crust may be determined by local variations in the force of gravity. Theoretical values for the force of gravity at an observing station are calculated; and the actual force of gravity is measured at the same point. The difference between the theoretical and observed values affords a measure of the excess or deficiency of crustal matter beneath the point of observation, which is

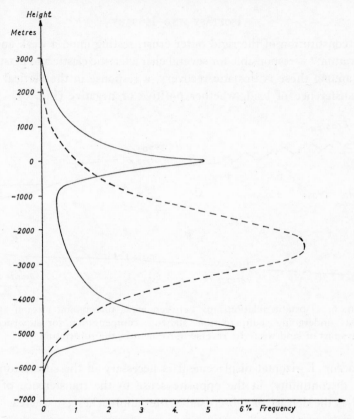

FIG. 7.   Frequency curve of elevations of the earth's surface. The two maxima indicate two fundamental types of crustal materials. The broken line is the expectable curve for a single material. *after A. Wegener.*

termed the *gravity anomaly*. The anomaly is positive when the observed value exceeds that obtained by calculation from the figure of the earth and indicates an excess of mass beneath the station, probably to be attributed to excessive volume of denser rock below. Thus over Europe several regions are discernible, defined as they compare with the general lowland value of +15 milligals (Tanni 1942). In the geologically older parts of the continent positive and negative anomalies occur without grouping into belts or districts. Anomalies greater than 50 milligals which may be accounted for by differences of surface density, do not exist. The region has long been stable. Positive anomalies are grouped in broad districts including most of the western Mediterranean, the area within the Carpathian Arc, and also the Balkan Peninsula, and Asia Minor, with the south-eastern Mediterranean. The northern foreland of the Alps is generally positive, and the Caucasus and Pyrenees form some positive strips. Negative anomalies appear markedly in a strip which borders the Cainozoic mountains and in parts of the Mediterranean Sea. Only in the Alps, which represent a coalescence of two fold-directions, does the strip broaden into an area.

Wide regions of the globe showing only small gravity anomalies, which include the plainlands of the United States and of Europe and the high-standing plateaus of Africa, are deemed to be in tolerable isostatic equilibrium; and Heiskanen estimates that " about 85-90 *per cent*. of the mass deficiency of oceans and of the mass surplus of most high mountains is isostatically compensated ". Older mountain ranges such as the Harz and Reisengebirge are generally in equilibrium and even later mountain systems such as the Alps, with their bordering lowlands, not infrequently approach a balance. The Caucasus, however, are reported as great excess loads, both in span and intensity.

Sundry wider regions also are not in isostatic equilibrium. In India, for instance, Hunter has shown that the anomaly is greater than the whole topography to be compensated, so that an average negative anomaly extends far west over the Pamirs and the Arabian Sea. Not only so, but there are pronounced differences of sign over India itself that Niskanen (1948) has attributed to rising of the Himalaya and profound sinking of the Ganges trough. " Because of this strong depression the Hidden Range southwards of the trough has expanded upwards, and to the south of this again the southern trough has sunk downwards " (Fig. 8).

The greatest anomalies known, occasionally exceeding -150 milligals, are associated with the arcuate oceanic deeps of eastern Asia (Fig. 9) situated in strongly seismic regions. Indeed, wherever seismicity is high due to recent tectonic activity, the gravity anomalies usually indicate that reverse, compensatory flow in the substratum has lagged or is shallowly present only.

Modern deltas, surprisingly enough, are generally reported as in good equilibrium, but the ideal case for testing isostasy is provided by the Pleistocene ice-caps, now everywhere shrinking away and permitting estimates to be made of the isostatic recovery of the crust following removal of the ice load. For the Fennoscandian ice-cap, theoretical formulae show that the sinking of the earth's crust in the centre of the area was nearly in accord with Archimedes' Principle. With a small weight-load, the sinking is less than the Principle supposes; thus lesser weights upon the crust are more rigidly supported. Small areas, such as the Hawaiian Islands or Cyprus are supported regionally, and this partly explains the large positive anomalies sometimes associated with small mountains. Local subjacent crustal masses are, however, sometimes responsible. The $+250$ milligal anomaly (one of the largest on earth) over the Troodos massif in Cyprus is attributed by Gass and Mason Smith to " a rectangular, near-surface, sub-horizontal slice [of

B

high-density rocks] which measures 120 miles east-west by 70 miles north-south ".
Considerable stress is, indeed, chronic in the lithosphere.

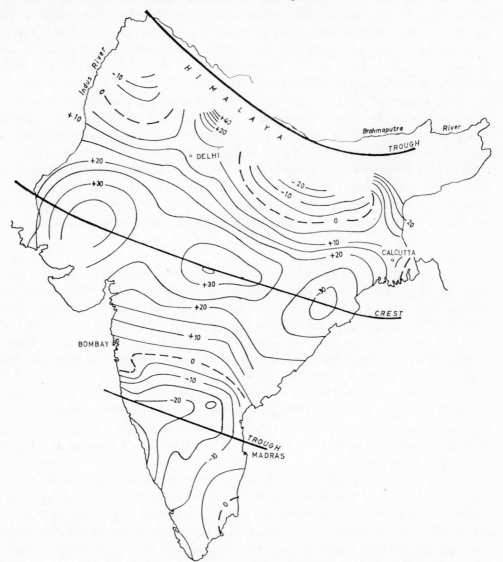

FIG. 8.   Gravity anomalies over India, interpreted as due to tectonic
movements associated with the Himalaya.   *after Hunter*.

For ideal isostasy the crust would need to consist of an assemblage of frictionless
prisms each standing at an elevation appropriate to its mass and cross-section.   As the
columns are not frictionless, the crust possesses marked rigidity.   In other words, the
crust deforms elastically and is itself capable of spreading stresses to a distance from

19

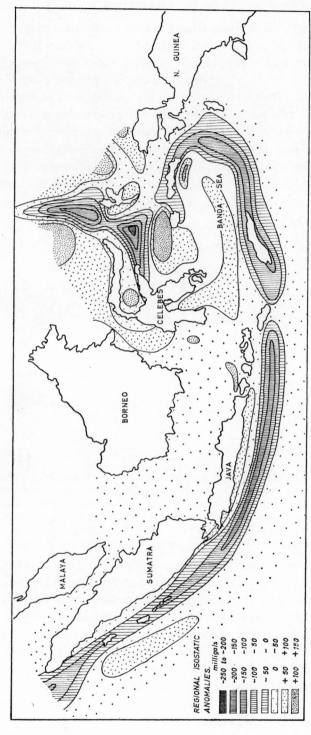

FIG. 9. Gravity anomalies in the Indonesian region. *after F. Vening Meinisz.*

beneath an excess load. Ross Gunn (1949) has afforded a neat analogy with a skater (load) upon ice (crust) over water (substratum). If the ice is thick it supports the mass of the skater elastically with relatively little bending, thus transmitting the load over a wide area (Fig. 10). Even so it will bend and displace beneath a mass of water equal to the mass of the skater (Isobary). Upon thinner ice distinct depression of the surface may be observed about the skater whose mass is compensated more directly below him. Equality of mass between load and displaced substratum (Isobary) is still maintained, though over a smaller area. If the ice is very thin the skater breaks through and the whole of his mass is then supported isostatically by an equal mass of displaced water. This is a special case of isobary when the ice (crust) is deemed to possess no finite elastic strength.

(a)   (b)   (c)

FIG. 10. The adventures of a skater upon ice representing (a) a strong crust which spreads the mass compensation of the skater to a considerable distance; (b) a thin crust which by bending secures compensation by displacement of water from below the skater; and (c) complete isostatic compensation below when the skater breaks through the crust and displaces directly his own mass of water. All are instances of isobary.

Isobary is the term applied to stress systems involving elastic deformation of the rigid crust of the earth; and by treating the strains and stresses on a section of the earth's crust as though they acted on a beam supported plastically from below certain deductions may be made as to the nature and behaviour of the earth's outer envelope. Thus while the earth's crust rigidly supports very considerable excess loads over short distances, widespread loads are generally supported isostatically. The maximum width of sedimentary belts that may be rigidly supported is thus, according to Gunn, approximately 480 km. Likewise mountain ranges, commonly 20-50 miles in width, need not develop deep compensatory " roots " directly below, but may have their " compensation " extended to 240 km. on either side of the centre line.

Excess loads carried by the crust may thus be enormous. Basaltic islands of the Pacific, rising from the floor of the ocean through a vertical height of perhaps 7,000 m., and with a base a hundred miles or more in diameter, are built of material drained from below them and therefore constitute excess loads on weakened foundations. They usually show positive anomalies ringed about a zone of negative anomalies. Some compensatory sinking of the floor may be indicated by the widespread drowning of such islands, yet their very abundance, often in lines or groups, is an indication of the local strength of the crust, even at its thinnest beneath the oceans.

Conversely, the great ocean deeps, narrow, linear troughs perhaps 10,000 metres deep, constitute negative loads, maintained by the rigidity of the crust which currently prevents the floor rising and the sides squeezing in. The floor beneath these trenches does not appear, upon seismic data, to be thinner than normal oceanic crust.

The concept of isobary, in which finite strength is assigned to the crust, adequately covers most of the departures from the isostatic state. But neither the isostatic nor isobaric principles, however they may reduce topographic and gravitational anomalies, produces new states. They are balancing mechanisms, functioning rather like the governor on a steam engine to maintain uniformity of action, not to produce fresh action.

Fresh evidence indicates that regional isostatic anomalies are often not related to the composition of the earth's crust, but record the amount of geologically recent deformation of the crust and may actually reside in the substratum below the crust (p. 659).

CRUSTAL TEMPERATURES

Observations by geologists leave little doubt that surface temperatures have varied within only very narrow range practically throughout earth history. The oldest known rocks are aqueous sediments that must have accumulated in temperatures between 0° and 100° C., and probably accumulated at normal diurnal temperatures. Life has existed continuously for more than 3,000 million years during which time it has never been inhibited, other than locally, by extremes of either heat or cold. *The earth is, therefore, an uniformitarian earth, neither cooling nor heating immoderately throughout the entire period of known geologic history.*

To maintain this balanced state (around 40 calories/sq. cm. lost per annum) there must always have existed a close approximation between the amount of heat radiated into space and the amount of heat generated within the earth body and conducted thence to the surface.

The temperature gradient observed to depths of 6 km. in mines and boreholes, and the temperatures of emission of lavas, testify to sources of heat within the earth. These sources may be in part residual from the primitive state but are mostly generated by radio-active disintegration. The temperature gradients vary both vertically and horizontally in accordance with geological structure, especially with depth to the granitic basement of each continent; and even local measurements such as those by Benfield (1947), Bullard (1939) and Anderson (1939) are of limited help in obtaining an overall picture. An average gradient in mines is 1 ° C. per 30 metres of depth, which is sufficiently rapid to ensure that at 30 km. depth the temperature could be 900°C., and at the 60 km. level possibly 1,500°; which means that material there is not likely to be crystalline in the ordinary sense. But as averages these estimates are almost certainly too high; and thermal conductivity within the subcrust is indicated as very low indeed.

Nor are adequate data available from laboratory investigations, though as an example experiments at the Carnegie Institution of Washington showed that two granites tested " would certainly flow below 800 ° C. if given time enough, for we formed 50 per cent. glass at that temperature and of course the fluxing had not reached completion.* We formed only a small amount of liquid in the basalts at 1,100° C., although those that we worked on were completely liquid at about 1,185 ° C."

Experiments on highly heated Pyrex glass (700 ° C.) show that it transmits sound waves almost as at 20 ° C., therefore it is almost certain that basalt or peridotite in the vitreous state may transmit the rapid transverse vibrations of earthquakes such as are recorded. Values for the elastic moduli of rock glasses heated up to 300 ° C. have also shown that accumulation of breaking stress is not dependent upon crysatllinity.

As basalt is regarded as forming a global shell of potential primary eruptive matter (p. 8) the derivation of basalt is a fundamental problem. Reay and Harris (1963) examined glasses made by the partial fusion of peridotite (4 per cent glass at 1,250° C. to 20 per cent at 1,355° C. after one week's heating) and found the composition of the glass to range from a basalt more or less saturated in normative silica at a temperature of 1,310° C. (15 per cent fusion) and below, to picrite basalt at higher temperatures. The experiments were conducted under anhydrous conditions at atmospheric pressure.

The Mohorovičić discontinuity may thus consist of a peridotite with its more fusible portion continually in the fluid state as a minor interstitial material. This, Daly believed, would permit the known weakness to long-continued loading of the layer at this depth, while exhibiting a high rigidity to forces of short period such as earthquake waves or tidal forces. Rheidity is not opposed to these views, though it simplifies the conditions.

Recent results in crustal thermometry indicate that heat outflow from beneath the oceans is about the same as beneath the continents, meaning that any blanketing effect of continents is negligible, and that heat dispersal from the earth's interior is sensibly uniform; which predicates, of course, ready dispersal of heat in the subcrust; and affords a physical basis for many of the observations that follow in this text—that tectonic events largely controlled by thermal conditions in the substratum are likely to be world-wide in their effects. Of course there are large local variations both on land and beneath the oceans—high in volcanic areas, low beneath the deep trenches bordering

* Other researches give much lower temperatures.

the Pacific Basin. Mid-oceanic ridges (Chap. XVI) generally have high heat flow, indicating perhaps shallow and local heat sources.

While geologists have customarily sought the energy for crustal deformation in deeper regions of the crust or subcrust, and primarily in the transfer of heat outwards, this heat outflow is controlled not only by temperatures at depth but also by temperatures at the surface. As heat energy from the sun is more than 5,000 times that from the interior (Holmes 1964), the global release of internal heat and the major world-wide cycles of crustal activity upon a spinning earth are not improbably governed by extra-terrestrial influences, leaving local tectonic activity as the special expression of force from local concentrations of crustal and subcrustal heat. A question emerges whether Heaven or Hell exercises the greater control over the behaviour of the earth's crust ?

IGNEOUS ACTION

Igneous action is endemic in the earth's crust, where magmas express the acme of mobility in rock materials. But whether plutonic injection at depth and surface volcanism are always or often inter-related is a moot point, and Kennedy and Rittmann, at least, have queried that either is dependent upon the other. Thus while acid plutons seem to be almost ubiquitous wherever formerly deep levels of the continental crust are now exposed at the surface by denudation, " Volcanoes ", to quote Williams (1953), " are, and always have been, concentrated chiefly along continental edges and within ocean basins ". Large intruded masses are only occasionally of mafic composition and even if lopolithic usually have a proximal floor, which is not often the case with true granitic batholiths. By far the most abundant eruptives, on the other hand, are basalts and their differentiated derivatives, with mixed types (andesites) suggesting that originally mafic rocks have been contaminated during their ascent through the granitic continents, perhaps when secondary reservoirs were established within the upper levels of the continental crust.

Williams has summarised these views, " Few, if any, of the concordant, foliated, synorogenic batholiths were connected with volcanism, though some of the massive, cross-cutting plutons undoubtedly served as volcanic reservoirs ".

" A few ' migma plutons ' formed by granitisation of sial may have served as feeders to volcanoes, but the ultimate source of most, if not all, volcanic magmas lies in sub-sialic and sub-oceanic shells of basalt and perhaps also of peridotite."

What have basalt and peridotite got that makes them rise from substratal depths ? What energy sends them surging and pulsating upward, even through the apparently lighter granitic uppercrust, in seeming defiance of the power of gravity ? The answer lies apparently in their content of volatiles which act not only to lower the specific gravity of the magma but also to flux the mass and transfer the heat readily upwards to the points where the magma—by wedging, stoping and engulfing the roof—drills its way to the surface. With plateau lavas these upsurges appear to pass almost without interruption right through the continental crust, and the same is true of peridotite belts. Central volcanoes, on the other hand, often eject xenoliths which suggest secondary reservoirs at depths of four or five miles, which in turn probably derive nourishment from below.

Of the presence of volatiles during eruptions, abundant evidence is at hand from all over the world. Volcanic activity is rarely anhydrous, and emission of steam usually takes place at pressures up to 300 atmospheres. At Asama volcano Minakami (using muzzle velocities of ejecta) calculated an emission at 563 atmospheres. The efficacy of volatile agencies is seldom questioned by observers of volcanic phenomena, and though nothing is yet known of the derivation of these volatiles at depth the quantity of gases that can be compressed into a molten rock can apparently be enormous (p. 673).

But buoyancy is not the whole story. Gussow (1962) points out that this alone does not initiate upward rise of deep-seated fluid or plastic media. He regards the mechanics of igneous intrusion as similar to the emplacement of salt domes (p. 119), and regards both as originating in relatively deep-seated, extensive, horizontal sheets of mobile material under geostatic load. The critical depth for activation of salt tectonics is 12,000 feet; but, for magmas it may be tens of miles. Behaving hydrostatically, the magma is forced into a localized rising structure or focus of lower pressure in the roof to initiate a state of rising intrusion wherein buoyancy becomes progressively more important as piercement attains to higher levels. At shallow overburden depths with decreased geostatic load or pressure, the diameter of the intrusion generally increases, *e.g.* kimberlite pipes.

" The intrusive magma or salt should spurt into pre-existing joints or fractures, speedily rising towards the surface, slowing down on reaching shallower depths, so that gentle flow may occur at the surface. When the hydrostatic pressure of the salt or magma column balances the geostatic overburden pressure of the rocks on the reservoir, upward movement will cease. Thus heavy basaltic magmas, and even salt domes, frequently never reach the surface. Intrusion would also cease on exhaustion of the reservoir fluids or on solidification of the intrusive mass. Violent explosions exhibited by some volcanoes are a near-surface phenomenon due to superheated steam from underground waters . . .

" In conclusion, the prime motivating force for all intrusions is the weight of the overburden or geostatic load, supplemented by the buoyancy effect caused by a density differential ".

The environments of volcanism have been expounded by Williams (1953) :

" Volcanism in eugeosynclinal troughs [*q.v.*] is generally characterised by discharge of spilitic magmas and intrusion of serpentinites, chiefly during early stages of evolution, and by eruption of calc-alkaline magmas, principally during the later stages. Beyond the eugeosynclines, in the ocean basins proper, volcanism is marked by predominance of olivine basalts, though tholeiitic basalts may also be erupted, and differentiation leads generally through andesites and trachyandesites to discharge of small residues of alkaline magma, mostly trachytes and phonolites. Explosive eruptions are normally restricted to the waning stages of volcanism; at other times they are vastly outnumbered by quiet eruptions of fluid lava."

" A second important locus of volcanism is and always has been along the edges of the continents where, by gentle folding, batholithic invasion and uplift, eugeosynclines have been annealed to the major land-masses. To this locus belong, for example, the Cascade, Central America and Andean volcanic belts. Here all the erupted magmas are calc-alkaline. Andesites, though generally subordinate to basalts, are widespread, probably because of assimilation of sialic material by primary basaltic magmas. Explosive activity is far more common than in the ocean basins, and often predominates over quiet effusions."

" A third locus of volcanism is in the forelands and backlands of fold mountains. To this theatre belong, for example, the volcanic fields of the Auvergne, southern Germany and Italy. Here the erupted magmas are chiefly alkaline. . . . Volcanism is generally short-lived, and the characteristic volcanic forms are explosion diatremes, viscous protrusions and stumpy flows."

" A fourth locus of volcanism is along and close to rift zones traversing relatively stable continental blocks. Here belong, for example, the volcanic fields of East Africa. The dominant magmas are alkaline, and here are to be found most of the world's ultrabasic lavas. Signs of sialic contamination, however, are plentiful."

The only regions long exempt from volcanism are certain continental interiors.

RADIOTHERMAL ENERGY OF THE ROCKS

Researches concerning radiothermal energy within the earth have established the existence of a vast source of energy which is expressed mainly as heat. So great indeed are the radiothermal resources of crustal rocks that the quantity of radioactive minerals must fall off rapidly in depth, all the energy necessary to match the heat lost into space by radiation from the earth's surface being supplied by the outer earth-shells alone. Three-quarters of the radiation is indeed met from 40 km. of granitic and basaltic materials, leaving less than one-quarter to be supplied from the underlying 6,330 km. of the earth's radius. As shown by analyses of plateau and oceanic basalts, the lower crust is significantly radioactive; the peridotite layer much less so, yet geological events that we shall review proclaim the peridotitic substratum also as a source of energy, including heat, for many tectonic phenomena. The outer earth appears to function, indeed, as a heat engine, and most of the unstable physical changes induced in the crust and subcrust from time to time appear in response to thermal controls.

The basaltic lower crust, deriving a large proportion of its energy from radioactivity, cannot everywhere be equally heated, and part of this caloric must escape sooner or later through the crust by processes additional to conduction. Of these, igneous action is important, and we note the great outpourings of plateau basalt in this connection.

Tilley has, in addition, recently expressed the opinion that much of the heat present at the production of large granitic and granodioritic batholiths is derived from the upsurge of subjacent basalt.

Holmes (1933) likewise: " Any local increase in the thickness of radioactive layers of the crust (*e.g.* in belts of geosynclinal sedimentation and subsequent mountain-building) must lead to considerable rise in temperature in depth, thus favouring the production of magma by refusion and the initiation of volcanism. But the flood-basalts and plateau-basalts have commonly ascended in regions like the Deccan where the crust has already been deeply denuded; that is to say in regions where the radioactive sialic layer had been thinned. The source of the excess heat necessary to generate magmas in such a geological setting can be looked for only in the substratum, which must therefore have within itself an excess of heat, at least in certain times and places."

The frequent injection of basic material into the sediments of geosynclines while they are still subsiding also argues a temperature of irruptivity in the substratum.

The sum of modern researches into the thermal state of the earth's outer envelopes appears to be that, though most radioactivity is resident in the earth's crust, sufficient is available in the substratum to allow of a potential eruptivity, and also to maintain there a state of thermal convection, actual or potential. But the dunite constituting the bulk of earth material, and almost the entire mantle, is almost non-radiogenic.

SUB-CRUSTAL CONVECTION CURRENTS

Of the reality of subcrustal currents there has long been no doubt—isostasy as a mechanical response to surface changes would be impossible without them—but the present problem is the isostatic one in reverse, can currents be activated in the substratum that themselves produce surface changes? May not unequal heating, stress or composition in a plastic substratum, for instance, lead to slow convection currents?

Tilley has argued (1951) from the effects of convection present in the Skaergaard and other large intrusions that we are now " assured of the operation of a convective circulation in a large pool of cooling basaltic magma " so that " we may feel confidence in an appeal to a process of this nature at depth as providing one effective means of mixing "; while de Sitter (1928) quotes, as proof of subcrustal convection currents moving either towards or away from the poles, two sudden changes in the length of the day, occurring in 1897 and 1917, that imply a change in the moment of inertia of the globe. Still better evidence is afforded by large-scale wrench-faults (megashears) like the San Andreas and New Zealand Alpine faults (*q.v.*). Holmes's view (1933) regarding the possibility of convection at depth is summarised, " to prevent convection in a layer extending far down towards the core a viscosity exceeding 10^{26} [poises] would be necessary. As we have good evidence that the actual viscosity is well below this limit there is no physical improbability about internal convection "; and Runcorn has indicated that to stop convection the substratum would need to be 10,000 times more viscous than post-glacial isostatic recoil indicates it to have been.

At the beginning of the 1960's evidence began to accumulate of regions showing abnormally high or abnormally low mantle velocities. Whether these are caused by differences of composition or of temperature is unknown, but they constitute inhomogeneities of great importance for potential sub-crustal activity.

The theory needs developing, perhaps on the lines indicated by Holmes (1964). Several types and systems of convection are, of course, possible, each governed by a primary cause involving thermal, chemical or mechanical heterogeneity. The relative importance of these processes remains unknown, both in general and in specific instances.

Gutenberg entertains the hypothesis hospitably despite a belief that the state of matter and other physical conditions are insufficiently known to decide on certain points regarding plastic flow at depth; and Vening Meinisz (1964) considers that thermal convectional currents take place in the mantle by pseudo-flow in crystalline material with velocities of a few centimetres a year.

Present-day discussion centres around possible energy sources to maintain sub-crustal circulation, for the radioactivity of the mantle is low and there is a necessity for heat to be accumulated (which could make convection an intermittent function). An overall agency which could, through long ages, act in this way by affecting the thermal gradient from the other end is solar radiation (see pp. 23, 656).

Daly was dubious of thermally-controlled convection because he thought the density differences produced by unequal heating were probably small and the potential convectivity was correspondingly low. He preferred to think of the asthenosphere (which he compared with the larger igneous intrusions visible at the earth's surface) as " stratified according to intrinsic or chemically-determined density ". This, he thought, might offset the feeble effect of the temperature gradient on density.

Chemical convection could be induced where change of state from vitreous to crystalline prevails or *vice-versa*. Tilley (1951) has pointed to the gravitational convection that has demonstrably taken place in large cooling basic intrusions such as the Skaergaard intrusion. How much of this convection is thermal and how much is due to crystal separation is not clear.

Carey's (1954) studies on the rheidity of the earth (p. 13) allow a period of 10^4-10^7 years as the time during which rheid flow must take place in all bodies. Stress convection is virtually compulsory in a heterogeneous earth body and is doubtless a normal condition between different localities. When rheidity is combined with differential thermal gradients extensive convectional systems may be set up in the subcrust.

Does evidence exist of present day movements in the substratum ? Possibly certain of the crustal megashears that extend for hundreds of miles, and exhibit lateral or transcurrent displacement of scores or even hundreds of miles, are controlled through the full thickness of the crust by differential movements in the substratum. Such megashears, which appear to penetrate the entire thickness of solid crust (de Sitter 1956), are extremely long, relatively straight and dip nearly vertically. In some instances the vertical component is so small as to have little topographic expression, and even where this amounts to thousands of feet it is small relative to the horizontal displacement. According to Betz and Hess (1942) such transcurrent faults can be both normal and reversed along their course, and intermittent movements, occasionally accompanied by basaltic eruptions, take place over a long span of geologic time.

Examples of such features are: the San Andreas fault of California (350 miles of lateral movement since the late Jurassic) and the " Montana Lineament " of the Rocky Mountains. Kennedy has postulated 65 miles displacement along the Great Glen fault of Scotland, and 200 miles has been quoted along the Alpine fault of New Zealand. The median tectonic line of Japan which crosses northern Kyushu, central Shikoku and Honshu until it reaches the Fossa Magna is also transcurrent with southward displacement of the western side perhaps amounting to 160 miles. In lands surrounding the Pacific Ocean all major wrench (transcurrent) faults are right-lateral as though a gigantic anti-clockwise rotation had taken place within the oceanic basin.

In the oceanic basins where the crust is thinner, such features are more numerous. In the Antilles 60 miles of displacement has been estimated by Betz and Hess along the Bartlett Trough (p. 600) and Anegada fault, and the Philippine Trench (p. 642) may be a similar megashear. The floors of the oceanic basins are diversified for hundreds of miles by east-west lineaments (shears in the east and rise-and-furrow topography in the west) that find their simplest explanation as response in a thin crust to streaming of the material below. Curiously, such features trend north-south under much of the Indian Ocean (Heezen and Tharp 1965).

Convection in the mantle would seem to be by large scale eddies with laminae flow over thousands of kilometres (Runcorn 1965).

CONTINENTAL DRIFT

If large scale convection currents, however induced, exist within the substratum then they may find expression at the earth's surface in such phenomena as transcurrent faulting, orogenesis and epeirogenesis, continental disruption under tension, continental drifting, continental approaches and so forth. Indeed the activation of most tectonic changes is indicated to have come from below.

Fortunately, much light has been shed on these problems for post-Algonkian time by the hypothesis of continental drift, based upon a multitude of field observations, and particularly by that portion of the theory dealing with correspondence of geology between opposed shorelines, which has enabled reconstructions to be made (Figs. 17, 166). The drift hypothesis has solved many problems difficult of explanation under other hypotheses, while at the same time its tenets are often subject to more rigid controls and checks than apply to other hypotheses, so that its validity can be tested severely (Chapter II).

Under any likely system of convection, vertical currents would ascend in certain places and spread out laterally towards the top of the substratum. If the currents are thermal they will supply heat to the lower crust, perhaps to the point of fusion.

The horizontal flow may be deemed to exercise a powerful viscous drag on the base of the crust, and if the dimensions between the ascending and descending currents be of continental dimensions then the horizontal drag may produce continental displacements, with tension over the rising currents and compression over the sinking currents. As Holmes has pointed out, drift of continents in convection currents provides naturally and inevitably for simultaneous tension and compression in the tangential direction. He cited as example, " the opening of the Uralian geosyncline at the same time as the crumpling up of the Caledonian mountain systems of Scandinavia, and the formation of the North Atlantic while the Sierras, Rockies and Coast Ranges of North America were growing ". This placing of simultaneous local tension and compression in clear causal connection represents an advance on theories involving world-wide epochs of crustal compression or tension.

Convecting systems may be global, or they may be local and dependent upon the positions of the continents and oceanic basins. Global systems were doubtless present in primordial time, and as Hills (1947) has shown, their influence on a crystallizing earth could well have been to create two sub-equal proto-continents in opposed or polar positions. Evidence suggesting that such was the original condition of the sialic masses accumulates from several sources. But by the Palæozoic, at least, the proto-continents had clearly abandoned any original antipodal positions and were nearly in contact along an east-west line.

The disruption of the two proto-continents and the radial flight of their fragments (the modern continents) suggests very clearly two local systems of subjacent convection currents operating in Mesozoic time beneath Laurasia and Gondwana respectively, each with strongly rising central currents and radial dispersion towards the periphery (Chapters II and XIV).

There are few data to indicate whether the drift of most of the continents has ceased, is slowing down, or is continuing. Doubtless, the original energy of Mesozoic disruption is largely spent, but the continents may well have ridden into other convectional systems, as is suggested by the anti-clockwise rotation of Australia involving a retrograde motion to the west in New Guinea (p. 668).

The hypothesis of continental drift has recently received strong confirmation from studies of remanent magnetism in rock masses (Runcorn 1956, 1956A; Creer 1958; and Irving 1958) which show not only that the continents have changed their positions relative to the geo-magnetic poles progressively during geologic time; but that they have also moved with respect to one another (Fig. 11). As between Europe and North America this amounts to a rotation of 25° or more corresponding to opening of the North Atlantic Ocean. For the South Atlantic, Creer (1958A) postulates a clockwise rotation of South America relative to Africa of 22 ° post-dating the Rhaetic lavas of both regions.

FIG. 11. Disposition of the North Magnetic Pole with respect to North America and Europe progressively through later geologic time, showing opening of the North Atlantic rift basin during Mesozoic and early Cainozoic time with relatively little movement in the late Cainozoic. The Indian data show that at least one part of Gondwanaland moved independently of Europe and America. *after Runcorn, Irving, Deutsch et al.*

There is already a large measure of agreement between the results achieved by the new method and the continental reassemblies postulated on the earlier geologic data. Certain discrepancies remain to be resolved, but these do not appear to be serious. On the whole, geologic evidence is coarser but at present more reliable, palæomagnetic studies promise more precise and accurate data for the future, if a method can be found for estimating, during the geologic past, aberrant wandering of the magnetic relative to the geographical poles. This movement, which has amounted to 300 miles (or 5 degrees of latitude) shift of the south magnetic pole during the past 50 years, is ignored in relating palneomagnetic measurements to a hypothetical dipole at the centre of the earth—but is nonetheless real.

At present the geological analogies between regions now sundered form the only visible and compelling evidence for adoption of the drift hypothesis (King 1953A) (Fig. 12). The test is critical: if the apposed regions do not correspond geologically then the driftist has lost his case; if they do correspond, then the probability of drift being true becomes immense as the matching details increase in the several categories of evidence.

In this connection the magnitude and detail of du Toit's (1937) correlation between the geologies of South Africa and South America seem not yet to be adequately

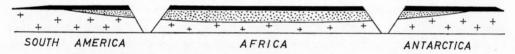

SOUTH AMERICA   AFRICA   ANTARCTICA

FIG. 12. Diagrammatic section through Karroo type sediments and lavas of South America, Africa and Antarctica (see Fig. 17). Later Cretaceous monoclines, in which the strata have subsequently bent down to sea-level at edges of continents, are neglected.

recognised by many geologists. Formation after formation in ordered sequence, through many varieties of rock types and to a great total thickness, covering many thousands of square miles, may be said to bridge the gap of the South Atlantic on to either side. Corresponding structures run directly and obliquely across the gap, and sometimes intersect one another, recalling Bailey's famous phrase that " the crossing of the ranges begun in the Cape is completed in South America ".

The lines of evidence adduced by du Toit (1937) include:

a) general similarity of coastlines,

b) fracture patterns as fault-line scarps and monoclines,

c) abruptly terminated plateaus or elevated erosional plains with disturbed or reversed drainages,

d) submarine features such as the mid-Atlantic and mid-Indian ridges,

e) equivalent formations on opposite coasts with due regard to their mode of origin and subsequent history,

f) similar variation in formations when traced along opposite shores,

g) contrasted phasal variation when traced away from opposed shores,

h) unconformities on comparable horizons,

i) comparable geosynclinal troughs in each mass having more or less similar trends and histories,

j) comparable fold systems passing out to sea at opposed shores,

k) crossings of fold- or fault-systems of specific ages,

l) synchronous intrusion of batholiths in equivalent fold systems,

m) plateau basalts and associated dyke-swarms,

n) petrographic provinces with similar eruptive suites of different ages,

o) comparable zones and periods of ore-genesis, especially such as may contain rare or distinctive minerals,

p) strata denoting a special environment, particularly extreme climatic types such as tillite, varved shale, laterite, evaporite, æolian sandstone, coal, and coral limestone. These must be fitted into a rational scheme of past climate,

q) terrestrial faunal and floral palæontologic provinces with identical or allied species.

The sum-total of evidence (and subsequent investigation by Maack (1952), Caster and Mendes (1948), Martin (1961) and others has shown that the comparisons are often even stronger than du Toit made them out to be) is vastly impressive, the more so when we consider that for the case cited by du Toit it appears down the whole length of opposed coasts from West Africa to the Cape, from the Guianas to Patagonia, transecting many, if not most, of the structures for a distance of 3,000 miles. Not before the Cretaceous period did marine formations follow the existing coastal outlines of eastern South America and western Africa.

The stratigraphic correlations between sundered regions such as South America and Africa, India and East Africa, are not susceptible of explanation under any other hypothesis than that of former contiguity of the now sundered lands, while other regions such as the eastern United States and western Europe seem to have been much closer during Palæozoic and early-Mesozoic time. Palæogeographic reconstructions, properly executed, thus afford the clearest demonstration of the scenery of former times.

Some Dead Wood: a Digression

Hypotheses, once promulgated, tend to become dogmas that are sometimes difficult to discard, and it is now our painful duty to reject certain current beliefs of wide acceptance among geologists that have outstayed their leave as working hypotheses. This we do not in criticism of our predecessors who invented those hypotheses, but solely in order that the reader may approach the review of earth data that occupies the main place in this book with as few preconceptions as possible, letting the data themselves freely develop their own explanations instead of forcing them into moulds of already set opinion. In a final chapter is offered a fresh working hypothesis incorporating the sanctions that the various classes of data prescribe for us, and there the reader shall be free in turn to criticise or reject the proffered hypothesis.

There is no merit in discussing outmoded hypotheses at length, and so the relevant evidence that compels the rejection of each hypothesis is stated as briefly as possible.

a) *A Cooling and Shrinking Earth* formed the basis of Suessian mechanics for the development of major earth structures, and notably for the crumpling by tangential forces of rock strata in orogenic welts. Doubtless the earth may have cooled during the initial stages of its formation; but the nature of fossils shows that there can have been little cooling of the seas since Cambrian time, and even the earliest known sediments of Archean time are such that they must have accumulated at the surface under physical conditions closely resembling those existing at various parts of the earth's surface at the present day. If the earth's surface has been thermostatic, temperatures within the general body of the earth have probably not varied greatly either; though it should be remarked that surface temperatures are controlled principally by solar heat received which is more than 5,000 times as great as heat-flow from the interior.

Measurements of radioactive disintegration within the earth's crust, coupled with measurements of the heat lost from its surface into space, show that the earth is not cooling significantly at the present time; so that a physical basis for the hypothesis is lacking despite its recent revival by some authorities (*e.g.* Lees 1953).

b) *Crustal Shortening.* If the earth is not cooling and shrinking then the whole basis of Suessian tectonics involving immense tangential pressures within the crust is invalid. Fold mountains must form by some process other than by lateral crustal compression, and phrases such as " 250 km. of 'crustal shortening' in the Alps " are utterly meaningless. Indeed, it is extremely improbable that rocks have the strength to transmit lateral thrust to distances of 50 miles or more in recumbent folds and sheets. Rather one must envisage a force that is operative at every point such as gravity down an incline or a crustal scum over a freely flowing subcrust.

Moreover, during later geologic time compressional phenomena in some parts of the earth's crust seem always to have been synchronous with tensional phenomena in others. Global cycles of crustal tension or compression seem not to be demonstrable.

c) *Phantom Continents* were often invented by geologists and biologists to explain curious discrepancies in the distribution of fauna and flora, both existing and fossil. These continents were deemed formerly to have occupied areas of the present oceans and to have since sunk. They were often postulated to be of large size, even Trans-Pacific. The complete absence of continental matter from these situations, as proved by post-war geophysical exploration of the oceanic floors (Chapter XVI), is sufficient to ensure rejection of these concepts.

But there remains a class of former land area, of much smaller dimensions, in borderlands from which sediments were shed on to the present continents. Certain of these were island arcs which have since been welded on to the appropriate continent, or which now form part of the shelf area, as along the western side of North America (Eardley 1962). But other examples (*e.g.* the postulated land of Appalachia off the eastern coast of the same continent, are not covered by this explanation either because the bulk of sediments is too large or the sediments are of the wrong type, or because the continental shelf is too narrow to accommodate such a landmass. These instances

C

are often explicable under the hypothesis of continental drift (p. 28) and several are discussed in Chapter II.

d) *Growing Continents*. The frequent parallelism of mountain ranges and continental margins, and the occurrence of younger chains parallel to older mountain structures has led some geologists to a belief that continents have grown by the deposition of land waste offshore and the creation of new mountains from this material in subsequent ages : thus adding to the general land area. North America and Australia are often quoted in this regard. But the hypothesis of growing continents fails because (i) most of the waste derived from the lands is deposited in depressions on, and not beyond, the continental shelf, and (ii) all known fold-mountain systems are founded upon continental, not sub-oceanic, basements. Even in Indonesia or the Aleutian island arc the oldest rocks exposed or penetrated by drill are of continental affinity. Moreover, (iii) as in the Appalachians, the clastic sediments building certain of the marginal ranges can be shown to have been derived from the oceanic and not the continental side. (iv) Nor are mountains always successively upon the seaward side of earlier ranges. The Rocky Mountains lie on the continental side of the ancestral Sierra Nevada and the concept of a bigger and better America progressively with geologic time is therefore unsound in principle. (v) Even where mountain ranges have been added successively away from an original nucleus of geologic " shield ", continental growth is no more than an optical illusion. Southward from the Siberian shield, for instance, appear early-Palæozoic (Sayan and Altai), late-Palæozoic (Kuen Lun), Cretaceous (Karakorum) and Cainozoic (Himalayan) ranges. But the shield area (Fig. 159) could not possibly have provided an original source of rock materials for all these mountain systems; and it is in any case broadly covered with sub-horizontal Cambrian and Ordovician sediments. Australia has been quoted as the ideal example of a continent that has, since Algonkian time, grown successively to the east from an original coastline extending roughly from Darwin to Melbourne. The great Palæozoic and Mesozoic rock systems of the east, however, rest upon a continental foundation that from seismic observations is 30-40 km. thick. Unquestionably, ever since Archean time a foundation of the continent has existed in the eastern as well as the western half of the continent.* (vi) Lastly, though many of the world's coasts are significantly paralleled by mountain ranges, quite as many others are devoid of parallel ranges, *e.g.* Africa, and some such as western Europe, have their ranges intersecting the coast at large angles so that the structures are transected at or beyond the shore. This last category of evidence adverse to the concept of growing continents affords, however, singularly critical evidence upon the subject of Continental Drift (*q.v.*). Truncation of geological formations and structures at many coasts, such

---

* Even under the latest development of the continental growth hypothesis wherein Ewing and Worzel (1954), noting the occurrence of sands interbedded with red abyssal clays in the floor of the Puerto Rico Trench (Chapter XVII), have emphasised the rôle of such trenches at or near the edges of continents as traps for land-derived waste and have pointed to the existence of such trenches around much of the Pacific Ocean, there is no guarantee that this is even a typical phenomenon, and no explanation is offered of the initial sinking of the trench nor of its shape and location. Nor are sediments of abyssal type commonly associated with arenaceous formations in mountain ranges.

as the Variscan mountains of Brittany, or the Cape Ranges, positively prescribes formerly adjacent continental land for their continuation.

e) *Permanence of Continents and Oceanic Basins.* The view that the continents and oceanic basins were created in primordial times and, apart from shallow, epi-continental floodings, have not since changed either their outlines or relative positions significantly is opposed by the known shedding of waste on to the continents from surrounding areas which are now oceanic. Examples are the Devonian delta of the Appalachian region as described by Barrell (Fig. 168), and the shedding of immense quantities of waste from east, south and west on to South Africa to build the Karroo system.

The hypothesis affords no adequate explanation of the shapes of the continents nor of the different types of continental margins. It does not explain certain remarkable stratigraphic similarities between the continents; nor of itself does it explain the distribution of past climates in different regions of the globe (Chapter II).

f) *Sialic Roots to Mountain Ranges.* The classic theory of sialic roots beneath major elevations of the earth's surface, involving a local thickening of the earth's crust projecting down into the substratum is oversimplified. Some mountainous zones even seem to have (on seismic information) a thinner crust than some adjacent areas of low elevation. Often the belt of negative gravity anomalies deemed to represent the root departs notably from the elevated zone *e.g.* the Alps. The mechanics of a root " thrust down " into denser material are incomprehensible, though perhaps crustal matter could be " sucked down " into a more mobile substratum. Even where the base of the crust, as defined by the Mohorovičić discontinuity, is believed from seismic data to descend beneath mountainous regions, the amount of descent is generally far less than what would be required under the straightforward concept of isostasy. Moreover, the negative anomaly over the Puerto Rico Trench is situated where crustal thickness is known from seismic data to be a minimum—only 4 km. The levity of such regions must possess some further cause beyond mere unevenness of the continental base, and may even be sited partly in the subcrust.

PALÆOGEOGRAPHY

The several variables already reviewed, crustal and subcrustal constitution and structure, intra-telluric heat, continental form and distribution exert controlling influence upon the physical geography of our planet. From age to age as the continents rise, sink or drift, and as the ocean basins deepen, shoal or change in shape, the oceanic waters encroach upon or retreat from the lands the outlines of which are necessarily in a state of flux. A large extension of South-east Asia has recently sunk beneath the sea until only islands and peninsulas (Borneo, Sumatra, Java and Malaya) remain visible where formerly land was continuous. So recent is the subsidence that drowned river valleys can still be integrated (Fig. 13) into a former drainage system; and the distribution of river fish upon the islands still follows the former hydrography, *e.g.* Sumatra. The whole seaboard of eastern Asia, is indeed, drowned in varying degrees, and the true margin of the Asiatic block is to be traced along the island festoons which are so marked a feature of that region. The Sea of Japan is a deeply subsided basin, the East China and Yellow Seas are really shelf, covered by less than 100 fathoms depth of water. These inundations have doubtless been caused by subsidence of the continental mass, but everywhere the oceanic basins are overfull, and the waters have encroached upon the continental margins

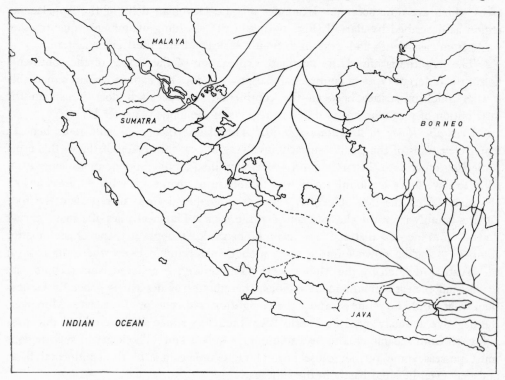

Fig. 13. Drowned former landmass in South-eastern Asia showing the integrated river systems of late Cainozoic time still identifiable across the sea floor. *after J. H. Umbgrove.*

to a general depth of 70-80 fathoms, the submerged regions corresponding in part with the continental shelf.

Inconstancy is indeed the most striking feature of the shoreline as it has existed in the geologic past, and the areas and shapes of the landmasses have fluctuated widely through antiquity. Maximal limits are set by the fundamental outlines of the sialic continental blocks themselves, but any reduction of area is possible down to final submergence of the land beneath the seas. The history of these changes is to be read—though in an imperfect manner—from the record of stratigraphic geology, and the interpretation of that record in this light is termed Palæogeography. Many savants have constructed palæogeographic maps, either of individual continents, *e.g.* Schuchert for

North America, or of the entire globe (Gregory, Haug, Arldt). Owing to fluctuating shorelines and topographic changes such maps are seldom valid for more than one-third of a geological period.

None of the great exponents of Palæogeography has expressed belief in continental drift, an astonishing fact when one considers how well many of their compositions exemplify the drift principle (Fig. 14).

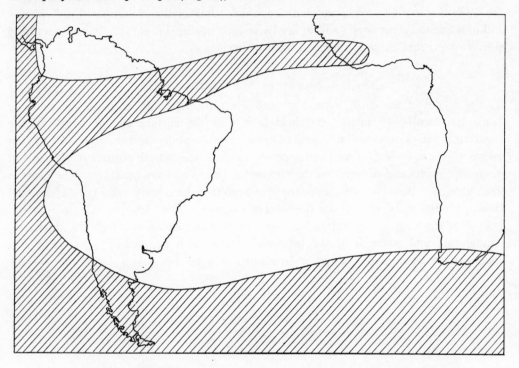

FIG. 14. Distribution of land and sea (lined) between Africa and South America during Devonian time according to Gregory and Barrett. The data would be better explained if the two regions were then in contiguity. *after J. Gregory.*

Philosophically, the concept of two primordial continental masses, Laurasia in the north and Gondwana in the south, of similar size and originally in opposed semi-polar positions, is satisfying. It is easier to derive as a primitive state on the young earth than almost any other pattern. It involves little more than differentiation and convection currents in the young, cooling earth (Hills 1947). Under the drift hypothesis all the granitic envelope was originally concentrated in these two oval, primitive masses. There is an economy of material that imposes a rigid check upon later distribution of landmasses for the bulk of granitic envelope cannot be added to significantly in later geologic time. Continents may fragment or coalesce, but they cannot " grow " significantly.

The conception of drift harmonises with what is known of the physical conditions of the earth's crust: high-standing lighter continents, deeper, heavier oceanic sectors, isostasy involving horizontal transfer of material at depth in the sub-crust.

The more the philosophy of drift is examined with its many and rigid stratigraphic controls, the more attractive it becomes (Chapter II). It is no idle armchair theory; but stands upon hard work in the field, upon literally thousands of facts garnered upon the rocks that can be seen, measured, sectioned, hammered and compared individually and in sequence, structurally and in age by anyone qualified to do so. It makes a fitting climax to our first chapter upon the Basis of Scenery.

MODEL OF THE EARTH

So the model of the earth with crust and substratum permits through the ages the horizontal transfer of matter and load both near the surface and at depth in the substratum; it permits regional and plutonic metamorphism and the uprise of molten magmas. It can undergo a wide range of vertical movements both positive in plateau and mountain uplifts and negative in the sinking of basins and geosynclines. The crust is weak enough to permit isostasy and strong enough to make isobary a reality. The model favours continental drift. It fits the facts of magmatic differentiation and assimilation. It evolves from age to age through a series of transmutations in which the thickness, temperature and strength of the lithosphere alter with denudation, orogenesis and epeirogenesis, and igneous activity. In a word, it is *mobile*.

CHAPTER II

THE UNITY OF GONDWANALAND DURING THE LATE-PALÆOZOIC AND MESOZOIC ERAS

Late-Palæozoic and Mesozoic Continental Deposition in Gondwanaland. Late-Carboniferous Deposition. Early Permian. Late Permian. Triassic Deposition. The Jurassic Regimen. Cretaceous Fragmentation of Gondwanaland. Conclusion.

Late-Palæozoic and Mesozoic Continental Deposition in Gondwanaland

The former unity of Gondwanaland is best demonstrated by the mighty sequences of late-Palæozoic and Mesozoic continental sediments that are characteristic of all the southern continents, with India (Fig. 15). In each of these theatres the several stratigraphic series total some thousands of feet in thickness, and cover scores of thousands of square miles in the same horizontal attitude in which they accumulated. They are quite uncomplicated and could not possibly have been derived from within the areas wherein they now occur. Minor original structures such as current bedding and glacial striae, indeed, often prescribe sources beyond the present borders of the continents, including the continental shelf. From observed field data Blanford in 1890 and Suess a little later expounded the concept of a former gigantic *terra australis*, and several authors embodied it in palæogeographic maps whereon the South Atlantic and Indian oceanic basins were substituted, wholly or in part, by hypothetical landmasses.

Modern geophysical research beneath the oceans has demonstrated the impossibility of evoking granitic continental masses from the basaltic oceanic floor, or, conversely, of causing pre-existing continents to founder into the depths without trace. So the concept of a Gondwana supercontinent might well have become untenable were it not possible to reorient the existing continents by continental drift. When this is attempted they are seen to fit in a remarkable manner into a simple ovoid landmass (Fig. 17).* It is this reconstruction that we shall now test by considering the remarkably simple and diagnostic strata of late-Palæozoic and Mesozoic age. Only very locally and for restricted time intervals do these record marine incursions upon the interior of the supercontinent; the formations are overwhelmingly of continental facies, and this in itself is powerful evidence in favour of a single landmass (King 1958).

But it is in the palæoclimatic interpretation of the sediments that the most striking confirmation is obtained not only of the essential correctness of the reconstruction spanning in its great breadth a number of climatic girdles *precisely similar to those existing at the present day*, but also of the majestic drift of the Gondwana continent with

---

* All the reconstructions figured in this text were made with curved perspex shapes upon a globe.

39

time through the climatic girdles—as revealed in appropriate facies changes, both sympathetic and antipathetic, in the several parts of the reconstruction.   On the whole, most regions of Gondwanaland experience a cooling from a warm climate in the Silurian period to a cold, or even frigid, epoch during the late Carboniferous.   Subsequently, amelioration of climate proceeded until the Triassic when some parts experienced a desert or even tropical regime.   That these changes were not due to world-wide variation

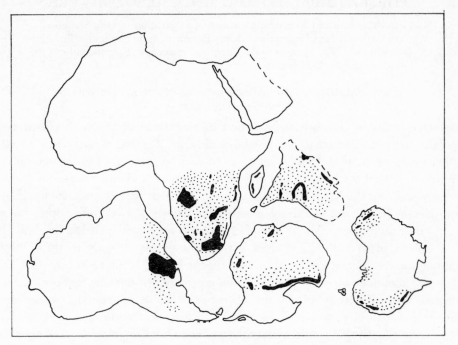

FIG. 15.   The present distribution of Gondwana and correlative formations (black) with their probable former extent (stippled) plotted upon a reassembly of Gondwanaland.

of climate is proved by the fact that neither heating nor cooling take place everywhere at the same rate, they may even occur in the contrasted sense on opposite sides of Gondwana, the west warming up for instance while the east was becoming progressively colder.   Something much more complex than global temperature changes is implied by the evidence (King 1958).

LATE-CARBONIFEROUS DEPOSITION

Our synthesis, stage by stage, of the salient stratigraphic facts from the several regions of Gondwanaland begins at the late-Carboniferous epoch* when all the constituent continents experienced heavy continental glaciation.   The present scattered distribution

* Synthesis might well begin in the late Silurian, for rocks of this and of Devonian age are now known in four of the " Gondwana " continents.

of the glacial formations, with India north of the equator, is incomprehensible, especially in view of Simpson's demonstration (1956) that an austral, polar ice cap should not extend beyond latitude 55° S. The reconstruction, however, brings these scattered remnants together into a coherent whole that is emphasised by the directions of ice-radiation plotted from striations of the sub-ice landsurface. The pattern for most of Gondwana is, indeed, similar in many respects to the pattern for modern Antarctica (Fig. 17). A peripheral fringe of varvites and ice-front phenomena is detectable in South America, the Congo Republic, Northern India and Western Australia.

Antarctica. Positive evidence of Gondwana glaciation in Antarctica comes from the Horlick Mountains of the central region (Long 1962), where 900 feet of Carboniferous* tillite rests upon striated pavements truncating early Devonian† and basement rocks. Precisely similar occurrences have been described from the Beardmore Glacier region by Grindley(1963), and from Dronning Maud Land and Victoria Land come other records. Antarctica, indeed, seems to have formed the chief gathering ground from which the main ice sheets of the late Carboniferous dispersed, and morainal debris was deposited not only over the Antarctic but also peripherally over other sectors of Gondwanaland. As the directions of ice radiation show (Fig. 17), its influence on ice-flow may then have been paramount.

South America. Palæozoic glaciation is manifest locally in Brazil as early as the Silurian, and Devonian occurrences have been reported from a number of places. These are all local and sporadic within the lower, middle and upper divisions of the system. The great glaciations began in the early Carboniferous, and in western Argentina the lowest tillite of the Sierra Chica de Zonda in San Juan lies beneath beds containing the *Rhacopteris* flora. Nowhere else in Gondwanaland is such a relationship, implying early Carboniferous age, known. This is assessed by Caster (1952) as the most " thoroughly glacial record " of Argentina. The direction of ice-travel as shown by striations was (in the modern sense) towards the north-north-west, which on the reconstruction for the late Carboniferous (Fig. 17) is precisely north.

In Eastern Argentina tillites near the Sierra de la Ventana of Buenos Aires are overlain by the Bonete Series with molluscan and *Glossopteris* fossils, and appear to be somewhat younger. In Uruguay too are multiphase glacial formations resting unconformably upon smoothed pavements of older rocks. The directions of ice-travel, ranging to west and north-west, concur with those of Eastern Argentina.

Most extensively studied of the South American frigid deposits, however, are the Itarare tillites (with associated rock types) disposed sub-horizontally over four million sq. km. of the broad Parana Basin, in Southern Brazil (Leinz 1938). The formation increases in thickness from a few metres in Rio Grande do Sul to 500 metres in Parana,

* Permian spores have been recovered from the upper tillite, above striated pavements within the tillite itself.

† Devonian rocks of Horlick Mts. are marine, with abundant brachiopods, those of Southern Victoria Land are continental, with fossil floras.

and attains 1,000 metres in certain developments in São Paulo. Over the same distance the single tillite present in Rio Grande do Sul is multiplied to two or three phases in Santa Catarina, four or five in Parana, and five or six in São Paulo where there was pronounced fluctuation of the ice-fronts and much fluvio-glacial outwash. Beyond this state, sporadic and thin occurrences appear in western Minas Gerais and Baia. " The ice sheets came from the east and south-east. Their movement was controlled by the slope of the floor of the Parana Basin. They originated on a land mass . . . situated in an area occupied today by the Atlantic Ocean" (Martin 1964). Pre-glacial valleys, some 100 m. deep, preserve earlier marine sediments at a few localities.

The date of glaciation in Brazil falls within the late Carboniferous; but not to the end of that period for the coals of the Rio Bonito stage, superior to the tillite, yet underlie the *Mesosaurus* horizon of the Irati shale, which marks the passage to the Permian. So far as can be ascertained the glacials of Uruguay and Buenos Aires are of essentially the same age or perhaps just a little later, certainly late Carboniferous. The direction of ice movement shows, moreover, that though the ice sheets were different from the Brazilian sheets, from which they were separated by a high range of hills against which is banked the entire thickness of Santa Catarina sediments including the Triassic eolian sandstone, nevertheless the main source of the ice lay outside South America to the east.

In the Andean belt peripheral to Gondwana, normal marine and terrestrial Carboniferous sediments are known and in Northern Brazil continental beds of Westphalian age, with a bed of anthracitic coal in the Poti series, fill a large sedimentary basin in Para, Piauhy and Maranhão. A cool temperate climate is perhaps indicated by these formations.

Southern Africa. The oldest Karroo formation of the Congo Basin (Lukuga series), includes glacial deposits equivalent to the Itarare series of Brazil and the Dwyka series of South Africa. The sequence is thinner, however. The original extent of the Lukuga series is not known, for much of it was removed by denudation before the succeeding series of continental deposition were laid down in the Congo Basin. It seems, however, to have been quite wide, for similar beds, including tillite, appear at the base of the Lutoe series in Angola. The glacial formations of Angola (Cassanje) and the Congo Republic are similar in most respects to those of Brazil, and a striking feature near Lovoy River is the abundance of varved shales recalling the similar development in São Paulo. Cahen (1954) has shown that in the eastern Congo the ice moved both east and west from a ridge trending along the 28th meridian between the first and sixth parallels of south latitude. For Katanga the centre of glaciation was on the site of the Hakansson Mountains, and here piedmont glaciers may have spread out at lower altitudes. The fluctuations of the ice front, together with the marked irregularity of the sub-glacial floor, which projects through the glacial deposits in many places, suggests a mountain or highland glaciation rather than a mighty continental ice-sheet.

Cahen opined that " The glaciation seems to have begun towards the late

Carboniferous, and to have reached at this epoch its maximum expansion. Local recurrences of glaciation may have occurred in the Permian ".

Of recent years varved shales and tillite 100 feet thick have been identified towards the base of a Karroo sequence faulted down in the middle Zambezi Valley (Bond 1952). The direction of ice-travel, as judged from erratics, is probably towards the south or west. Bond thought that the nature of the deposits did not warrant the assumption of a continental ice-sheet; so the occurrences are evidently like those of the Lukuga series in the Congo Republic.

No trace of Carboniferous glaciation has yet been reported from East Africa and it is probable that very little, if any, ice accumulated there. In the Sakoa area of south-western Malagasy, however, boulder beds which are followed by black shales and coal-bearing strata with *Glossopteris* are considered to represent the glacial epoch (Besairie 1953).

In the Republic of South Africa conditions were quite different. Thousands of square miles of country are underlain by tillite (Dwyka) leaving no doubt whatever that large tracts were formerly covered by a gelid carapace. du Toit has rendered (1922, 1937, 1954) very full accounts of this refrigeration showing that the deposits thicken markedly from the Southern Transvaal, where 30 feet or less of tillite appears, to the Southern Karroo where the thickness is 2,500 feet. The tillite is usually unbedded for hundreds of feet vertically but bedded varieties and fluvio-glacial sands sometimes appear towards the top, or indicate a break of deposition within the body of the tillite, *e.g.* at Laingsburg where five stages may be seen. Striated tillite also appears in such situations, recording renewed advance of the ice over frozen tundra; elsewhere shaly laminae indicate a transient waterbody over previous till. The floor usually shows gentle relief, but it may be markedly uneven and ridges of ancient rock sometimes protrude upwards through hundreds of feet of tillite.

The great thickness of the Dwyka in the Southern Cape required marked subsidence of the floor for its accommodation if it was to remain below the level of the country supplying ice and moraine. Related subsidence is indicated towards South-West Africa where a shallow incursion of the sea during the melting of the ice is recorded by marine fossils including " *Eurydesma* " and palæoniscid fish which are of assistance in correlation with India and Australia. Continued subsidence after glaciation is also prescribed by the immense thickness (over 20,000 feet in the south) attained by the remainder of the continental Karroo system.

Du Toit has demonstrated from the distribution of " marker types " of erratics, some of which have travelled several hundreds of miles, and from the directions of striation upon the abundant pavements, that the ice rode towards the south and south-west from highland gathering grounds about Windhoek, Griqualand West, and the Southern Transvaal. The direction of ice movement was clearly controlled by the fall of the ground from high gathering grounds in the north towards a subsiding basin in the south. The matrix of the northern tillite is, moreover, sandier than that of the south. None the less, more recent work by the Geological Survey (Haughton 1952) prescribes a southerly source (beyond Africa) for the tillite of the Southern Cape Province, where it is thickest; and from the north-east, where the Indian Ocean now flows, a fourth ice-sheet drove into and over the vestiges of the Transvaal ice-sheet (Fig. 16), constituting another " Gondwanaland problem " to the seeker after its source.   Crossing striæ and conflicting depositional structures where the two directions of ice movement impinge

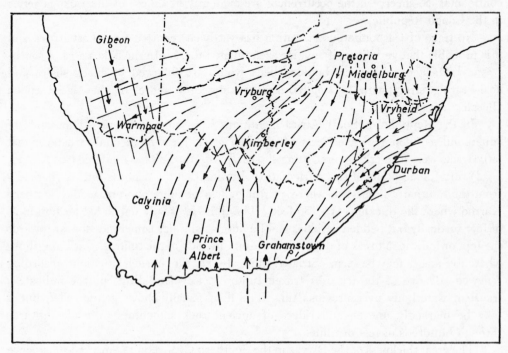

FIG. 16.   Directions of Dwyka ice radiations in South Africa.
after A. L. du Toit and S. H. Haughton.

in northern Natal suggest that the Natal sheet was either later or more powerful than the sheet derived from the Transvaal.

Beyond the present line of the equator through Africa, a broad arch of country made a smooth watershed between endoreic and exoreic drainage systems of late-Carboniferous time.   As it underwent denudation, much of the debris was washed northward across the Sudan and Libya where it accumulated in vast piedmonts to form the lower members of the Nubian series.   Intermittently the sea transgressed from the north leaving after its withdrawals intercalated marine strata with appropriate fossils. Over parts of the former French West Africa these incursions were more extensive and prolonged, and perhaps linked up with the incursions already noted in the Amazon region.   The palæogeography of North Africa remained essentially the same from the late Carboniferous until the Cretaceous, when marine incursion reached a maximum.

India. Late-Carboniferous glaciation is recorded in all the localities of India where Gondwana rocks are found " from the Rajmahal Hills to the Godavari and from Raniganj to Nagpur " (Wadia 1939; Krishnan 1949). The Talchir boulder bed at the base is 50-100 feet thick, and contains characteristic soled and striated erratics, often brought from afar, embedded in a fine silty matrix. Much of it is thought to have accumulated in lakes dammed up by earlier moraine, and apparently striated pavements are scarce.

Though no trace of glaciation has been recorded from Southern India (which has since been uplifted and eroded) any assessment of the distribution of late-Carboniferous glaciation in Gondwanaland must envisage the probability that Southern India was beneath an ice-sheet of which the northern developments with their extensive lakes were merely outliers. In the Salt Range, according to Fox, the glaciers deposited the material directly into a shallow sea. Greenish " needle shales ", 500-800 feet thick, which follow the conglomerate contain the earliest local specimens of *Glossopteris*, and the Umaria Marine bed which overlies the Talchir boulder bed in the north corresponds with the *Eurydesma* and *Conularia* stage of other parts of the southern hemisphere, the fauna being stunted by cold, and possibly by dilution of the sea-water (*cf.* South America). In Orissa, also, we meet again the familiar problem that part, at least, of the ice must have come from beyond the present boundaries of the subcontinent.

Australia. Every state of Australia retains traces of the " Permo-Carboniferous " ice age, leaving no doubt that during the late-Carboniferous period, and part of the Permian, ice-sheets of sub-continental dimensions waxed and waned over the greater part of Australia, extinguishing the earlier *Rhacopteris* flora as they did so.

The first hints of diminished temperature in New South Wales were apparent even before the Kanimblan orogeny, and with the rise of mountains glaciation came immediately into being " reaching the acme of its intensity in Upper Carboniferous time " (David 1950). " The general movement of the ice was from the south [present orientation of Australia] and much of it must have come from high land lying to the south of Tasmania, but there were doubtless other important gathering-grounds in the mountains of the Kanimbla geanticline. Much of the tillitic and fluvio-glacial material was clearly derived from local volcanic rocks and from a neighbouring granitic landsurface. Varved shales are ubiquitous, and the accumulation of paired laminae to a thickness of more than 200 feet must have spread over many thousands of years ". At least six glacial advances and retreats, with inter-glacial stages, are known in the Hunter Valley, N.S.W., and five in Tasmania. This evidence of fluctuating ice-fronts over Eastern Australia, is surely due to a marginal situation with respect to the Gondwana glaciation as a whole. The close relationship of this region to the probable position of the main ice divide situated in Antarctica (Fig. 17) also should not be overlooked.

A broad zonal distribution characterises the phenomena. In the southeast the glacial imprint lies heaviest, the most striking pavements and roches moutonnées being those of the Inman Valley, South Australia, where also erratics up to 23 feet in length have been found, and Bacchus Marsh, Victoria, where the ice over-rode high as well as low-lying ground. Above the pavements are at least eleven beds of tillite with fluvio-glacial conglomerate, sandstone and shale totalling 2,000 feet in thickness. Through New South Wales the glacial phenomena continue strongly, only fading away far to he north in Queensland where rather dubious evidence of ice-sheets is found in 17° 20′ S., almost to the latitude of Cairns.

These East Australian sequences also reveal a lateral transition from terrestrial to marine facies in keeping with the marginal position of that continent in the Gondwana reassembly. In Western Australia most of the occurrences are fluvio-glacial. They are not certainly known to be of Carboniferous age but may belong to the later, Permian phases of the glaciation, thus comparing with developments in Northern India; unless, indeed, the Sakmarian deposits of both areas are rewashed Carboniferous glacials.

Summary for the Late Carboniferous. All the southern continents, with India, present concrete evidence of glaciation on the continental scale and this long ago led to the conception of a late-Palæozoic Ice Age. *The maximal centres of glaciation were, however, not contemporaneous in the several continents but were sequential from west to east.* The tillites of western Argentina are dated as early Carboniferous and there are none in eastern Gondwanaland of this age. The tillite of Brazil and Uruguay is late Carboniferous, but the ice had melted away long before the end of the period as shown by the accumulation of the Rio Bonito coals which *antedate* the *Mesosaurus* zone at the top of the Carboniferous. In South Africa the tillites are late Carboniferous and though the tillites accumulated before the *Mesosaurus* zone the coals did not follow until some time *after*. The Talchir conglomerates of India appear to be of much the same age as the Dwyka tillite of South Africa, though the coals (as will be seen) come in earlier owing to lower latitude in the reassembly. Glaciation in Australia did not begin until very late in the Carboniferous period and continued well into the Permian. After the Greta coals, indeed, there was a further accumulation of erratics in shales during the Permian; and in the Collinsville area of Queensland coals actually appear *before the glacial beds* (Hill 1952).

In other words, the climate was cooling over Australia towards glaciation in the late Carboniferous while it steadily warmed up in South America because the glaciation was past.

Clearly, no simple hypothesis of global temperature changes fits the facts of tillite distribution in space and time, and though such temperature changes may have been responsible for, or contributory to, glaciation in general, they require supplementing in order to explain the spatial and temporal phenomena recorded. Either pole-wandering, or its more probable converse, wandering of the southern continents across the polar zone needs to be invoked in explanation.

In this regard, drifting of the Gondwana reassembly from east to west across the polar region affords a coherent pattern for the facts of tillite distribution. It is probable, however, that the actual pole at no time lay within the Australian landmass.

Peripheral areas, moreover, fall into latitudes (or climatic girdles) appropriate to the environment of sedimentary deposits found in them. The cold temperate (*Glossopteris*) coals of Northern Brazil appear to have accumulated about latitude 50° S.; the dry-climate Nubian sandstones of North Africa appear about latitude 30° S. (the desert belt); while the cold lakes of India are between 40° and 50° S. latitude. At this time, glaciation was extending over Australia where the climate was formerly warmer. The pattern is coherent throughout.

EARLY PERMIAN

When the ice had melted from Gondwanaland (except Australia) leaving a plaster of boulder clay far and wide, there remained large basins which served as foci for deposition of dark, unfossiliferous shales in bodies of inland (non-marine) water, often of wide extent.

Antarctica. In the Horlick Mountains of Central Antarctica 550 feet of dark shales overlying the Gondwana glacials (Long 1962) may represent this stage and indicate a cold temperate climate, though Plumstead (1962), on the fossil plants, thinks them late Permian. Other deposits at Whichaway Nunataks and in the Ross Sea area are, however, allotted to this stage by the same author. Over much of East Antarctica further sediments, totalling 2,000-5,000 feet in thickness, are arkoses, sandstones and shales with lignites and rare, thin limestones $\frac{1}{m}$ all characteristically of shallow-water continental environment. Coal beds are widely known in the lower part of the formation indicating swamp environments. *Glossopteris* leaves, found at Buckley Nunatak on the Beardmore Glacier and elsewhere, specify a Permian age for the lower part of this Beacon formation, while the South African plant fossil *Rhexoxylon* indicates that the youngest beds are Triassic (*q.v.*).

South America. With the advent of the Permian in Southern Brazil, in the Itapetininga stage of the Irati group, comes the useful little zone fossil *Mesosaurus*, recording a true " geological moment " on both sides of the South Atlantic basin. Of special importance is the appearance of *Mesosaurus above* the Rio Bonito coal measures whereas its representatives in the Republic of South Africa occur *below* the Ecca coal measures of that country, thus demonstrating clearly the different ages of the coal formations in the two continents though both belong to the general *Glossopteris* flora.*

The lower Permian formations of Argentina, Uruguay and Southern Brazil usually begin with dark, cold-water shales (*e.g.* Irati) consonant with the cool-temperate climatic conditions that must have succeeded the glacial episode of the late Carboniferous. The accumulation of the Irati group occupied the greater part of early Permian time, and there is no record of large scale arkosic accumulation such as is found in Antarctica at about that time. Instead, the succeeding lower members of the Estrada Nova series are of more muddy facies.

* In the Kaokoveld of South-West Africa, however, coals are known *below Mesosaurus* as in South America ! (Martin 1961).

Farther north, as the Permian advanced, *red* shales appear in the Estancia series (de Oliveira and Leonardos 1943) and the Aquidauana facies of Matto Grosso (Caster 1952). The arid environment which they imply is consonant with the situation of Baia and Matto Grosso in the desert belt (30° S. lat.) upon the reconstruction.

In Western Argentina the " red " facies, perhaps confined on the west by mountain ranges of which evidence appears in the roots of the Andes, is encountered some ten degrees farther south than the Brazilian outcrops of the same facies. But upon the reconstruction both are seen to have lain almost in the same latitude at the time of accumulation.

Other Permian basins formed peripherally to Gondwanaland in the northern States of Brazil. These were at first occupied by swamps wherein flourished a flora with " *Psaronius* " typical of the northern continents and indicative of a warm or even tropical climate. Upon the reconstruction (Fig. 18), indeed, the region falls for the early Permian around lat. 20° S.

Most of the Argentinian Patquia formation (which covers the whole of the late-Carboniferous and Permian periods) is, however, of cooler climatic type, and even includes rewashed glacial material from neighbouring isostatically rising areas well into the Permian.

Southern Africa. Following upon the Dwyka tillite and limnoglacial shales, the lower-Permian formations are represented by the lower and middle portions of the Ecca series, the deposition of which corresponds very largely with periglacial outwash plains. Glaciation persisted into the Permian in parts of Antarctica and Australia, so the dark, unfossiliferous cold-water lower Ecca shales of the Cape and Natal are appropriate to their position in Gondwanaland.

Still within the lower Permian of Natal and eastern Transvaal are the arkosic and gritty coal measures of the middle Ecca derived from north-easterly and easterly sources[*] (du Toit). The reconstruction suggests that these sources lay in the Dronning Maud Land sector of Antarctica where Roots (1953) has discovered just such a thick sequence of unfossiliferous mixed sandstones overlying granitic basement.

The occurrence of coals is apparently a feature marginal to the great sheets of grit and sand, and " Over much of the Transvaal, throughout Rhodesia and along the Zambezi these middle Ecca coal measures were laid down directly on the floors of the depressions of an ancient landsurface. In the extreme north . . . conditions for coal formation were not properly attained until a somewhat later date " (du Toit). The low temperature *Glossopteris* flora was the chief contributor to the coal, but soft-wood lycopods and rushes are also abundant. Widespread silicified trunks of *Dadoxylon* with marked annual growth rings record deciduous forests like those about the modern Arctic, to which the landscape of much of Permian Gondwanaland probably bore a marked resemblance.

A different facies of the Ecca, devoid of useful coal, is present in the west of

[*] Modern Directions.

Southern Africa. This is the " Red Ecca ", of red and green shales and mudstones with weak brown or red sandstones, which show affinity with the Estancia series and Aquidauana facies of central Brazil. Two major basins of distinctive facies thus overlapped on to Southern Africa from both the west and the east respectively and the distribution of early-Permian deposits in three of the southern continents becomes intelligible upon the reassembly (Fig. 18).

Farther north, in Angola (Serie de Lutoe) and the Congo Republic, black shales succeed the glacials. These are ascribed by Cahen to the Permian, and they are followed by beds with coal, equivalent to the Ecca. Similar beds have been recorded upon a small scale in Uganda (Davies 1952).

In Southern Tanganyika, also, coal beds are preserved in the Ruhuhu graben. In a sequence totalling nearly 10,000 feet in thickness, the basal group of sandstones and conglomerates, 1,690 feet thick, is not known to contain tillites but may be partly of Dwyka age. Two series of coal measures and the Ruhuhu beds with the *Glossopteris* flora record the Ecca. In Malagasy, black shales and coal-bearing strata with *Glossopteris* flora are again exemplified in the upper part of the Sakoa series. Marked intra-Permian tilting ($10°$-$15°$) permitted a slight marine incursion at the top of the series.

Beyond the Equator a broad arch of country extending from Nigeria to Lake Rudolf seems to have existed continuously since the Carboniferous period. To the north of this arch deposition was intermittently maintained as piedmont plains, continuing to build the Nubian facies. Deposited upon the Archean, in broad basins that deepen northward, these sandstones range in age from Carboniferous to Cretaceous. Except in the north where marine inundations appear, they are wholly continental in type, and overlap in southern Egypt and the Sudan on to the denuded flanks of the arch of Archean and other ancient rocks.

India. After the glacial Talchir series (which continued into the early Permian) is a distinct, though brief, interlude before the accumulation of the Barakar stages of pebbly grits, sandstones and shales containing much carbonaceous matter as streaks, lenticles and beds of coal. " In the Jharia coalfields, the Barakars include at least 24 seams of coal, each more than 4 feet in thickness, and it has been calculated that over 200 feet of coal are present in the total thickness of 2,000 feet of strata " (Krishnan 1943). Current opinion is that the Barakars accumulated in an interconnected series of shallow lakes and swamps, an environment perhaps resembling parts of modern Canada. The Barren measures, sandstone and ironstone shales which succeed, indicate a distinctly warmer climate.

Comparison with the South African Ecca (Table III) shows that the coals appear earlier in India (at the lower Ecca stage of South Africa), relatively soon after disappearance of the marginal, limnoglacial conditions of the Talchir. Later, when South Africa accumulated its middle Ecca coals, low-grade ferruginous shales of a warmer type of environment were deposited in India. These facts are in harmony with the lower

D

TABLE III—CORRELATION OF LATE-PALÆOZOIC AND MESOZOIC FACIES IN GONDWANALAND

	SOUTHERN BRAZIL AND URUGUAY	SOUTHERN AFRICA	PENINSULAR INDIA	ANTARCTICA	EASTERN AUSTRALIA
	Fragmentation of	*Gondwanaland*	*into modern*	*continental*	*masses*
EARLY CRETACEOUS					
LATE JURASSIC	? Red sands of the interior	Lualaba series of Congo. Marine series in East Africa cyclic	Jabalpur (continental), marine beds of Cutch continental	Formations known	Freshwater beds of Artesian Basin (sauropods and dinosaurs) denudation
JURASSIC	"Gondwana"				
RHAETIC	São Bento basalts	Drakensberg basalts and dolerites	Rajmahal basalts	Kirkpatrick Basalts and Ferrar dolerites	Tasmanian dolerites
LATE TRIASSIC	Botucatú red desert	Stormberg series ending in "Cave Sandstone" desert	Mahadevi series (tropical environment with saurischia)	Unknown	Wianamatta. Beginning with cool-temperate environment, rapidly warming up. Hawkesbury
MID TRIASSIC	(*Buenos Aires folding*) Santa Maria (reptiles)	(*Cape Province folding*) Upper Beaufort; hiatus in Transvaal and northward	Hiatus		
EARLY TRIASSIC	Hiatus	Middle Beaufort (reptiles)		Falla Formation	Narrabeen
LATE PERMIAN	Grupo Rio do Rasto	Lower Beaufort (green) mudstones with (*Dicynodon, Taeniopteris*)	Panchet series (*Dicynodon, Taeniopteris*)	Coal beds	Upper coal measures
EARLY PERMIAN	Estrada Nova Series (green mudstones) Estancia Beds (partly red). Irati dark cold-water shales. *Mesosaurus*	Upper Ecca shales (red in South-West Africa) Middle Ecca coal measures. Lower Ecca cold-water shales (rare *Glossopteris*). *Mesosaurus*	Raniganj (coals) Ferruginous shales. Barakar series with coal. Tillite	Lower Beacon Sandstone and black shales. *Glossopteris*. Tillite	Upper marine series (with tillites). Greta coal. Lower marine series (with multiple coals)
LATE CARBONIFEROUS	Rio Bonito coal measures. Itararé Series including glacials	Dwyka tillite with overlying fine dark cold-water shales	Talchir glacial and fluvio-glacial beds	Buckeye and Pagoda Tillites in Trans-Antarctic Mountains	Late Carboniferous glacials and associated beds of South-eastern Australia
EARLY CARBONIFEROUS	Glacials in Western Argentina				

latitude (10° farther north) in which India appears on the reconstruction, and the palæogeography depicted by Ahmad (1958).

Australia. The lower Permian of Australia is aberrant in that while continental glaciation had vanished by the end of the Carboniferous period from most other sectors of Gondwanaland, renewed advance pushed ice fronts north of Fitzroy River in Western Australia. This re-advance is well dated as Sakmarian upon the evidence of ammonoids in marine intercalations and Thomas has suggested upon similar evidence that some of the Indian glacials also continued into the Sakmarian. One is uncertain, however, to what extent some of these latter may be rewashed late-Carboniferous glacials. Permian downsagging along the west coast of Australia persisted until between 10,000 and 20,000 feet of mixed marine and continental strata had accumulated.

Eastern Australia continued to be heavily glaciated throughout most of the early Permian. The direction of ice-travel was from Tasmania towards Queensland, and the severity of glaciation diminished steadily over the same range of country. This anachronism of frigidity is confirmed by the coaly formations, the appearance of which is also delayed. The first coals (Greta or lower coal measures) formed at the close of the early Permian well before erratics ceased to be dropped from floating ice, but the major coals did not accumulate until the late Permian (*q.v.*), when they became increasingly abundant through the Tomago and Newcastle stages till the end of the Palæozoic. In these late coal measures logs of *Dadoxylon* are common, though we have noted them much earlier in other regions of Gondwanaland.

As Eastern Australia occupies a semi-peripheral situation in Gondwanaland, an extensive development of marine Permian formations interdigitates with the paludal coal accumulations.

Summary for the early Permian.   There is demonstrated, from the early Carboniferous until the mid-Permian, a clear progressive movement, first of glacial phenomena and then of cold-temperate coal measure accumulation, from west to east across Gondwanaland (Table III), with all facies and phases fitting into climatic girdles appropriate to inferred latitudes at the several portions of the reassembled super-continent. *There is no simple climatic change affecting the globe, nor even Gondwanaland, as a whole, but local progressive, and sometimes contrasted, changes.* Such contrasted changes can be achieved only by a progressive movement of climatic controls across the area, either by polar-wandering from west to east, or by drift of the reassembly across a fixed polar region from east to west. The manner of such movement, whether in a single, slow, majestic drift, or in a series of pulsations of varying amount and direction is indeterminable at present.

Late Permian

No great physiographical changes occurred between the early and late stages of the Permian period in Gondwanaland. Most of the great sedimentary basins of the early Permian continued to function in a similar manner during the latter stage of the period and there is often no significant break between the two sets of deposits. But on the whole, with the withdrawal of the supercontinent as an entity from the neighbourhood of the geographical pole (a statement we now permit ourselves after the synthesis of evidence in the two preceeding sections) continental deposits of the late-Permian and Triassic periods generally show, in their lithological characters and fossil content, evidence of warmer climatic environments consonant from place to place with the fresh latitudes and climatic girdles into which the several parts of the reconstruction locally move (Fig. 18).

Antarctica. Below the Beacon Sandstone, which spans upward into the Triassic, *Glossopteris*-bearing formations of the Horlick Mountains have been assigned to the late Permian (Plumstead 1962). The beds are grits, sandstones and shales of the type general in the Karroo-Gondwana continental sequences, with the *Glossopteris* flora sometimes making coal as at the Amery locality in 68° E. (Crohn 1959).

South America. The late Permian is recorded in Southern Argentina by the Tuna series but far better known is the Estrada Nova series of the Santa Catarina System in Southern Brazil. This predominantly argillaceous sequence, greenish in fresh exposures is towards the top quite indistinguishable lithologically from the lower Beaufort series of South Africa, though according to Caster (1952) it is somewhat earlier in age. The presence of sapropel is attested by small seepages of natural oil which have caused searches for petroliferous shales. A persistent feature is the abundance of concretions, a characteristic also of the South African Beaufort series.

Following accumulation of the Estrada Nova series a stratigraphic hiatus is now recognised in São Paulo by de Almeida and Barbosa (1953); but Caster (1952) considers this to have been short and includes the Rio do Rasto group, exposed in the Brazilian states of São Paulo and Parana also within the late Permian. An almost exactly similar hiatus is known in the Karroo System of South-West Africa (Martin 1961).

Southern Africa. Late-Permian time was occupied in South Africa by accumulation of the Upper Ecca (shales) and the Lower Beaufort series. In the sandstones, feldspar is altered to kaolin, an indication of a warmer climate than had prevailed during the early Permian. Thin, shaly " drift " coals with sparse flora are known in the upper Ecca over a wide area about Rhodesia, and the uppermost horizons of the middle Ecca include sapropelic torbanites which are now exploited in the Republic, so that environmental conditions seem to have resembled those in Brazil. The resemblance becomes even more remarkable in the lower Beaufort which is lithologically indistinguishable from the upper part of the Estrada Nova stage of São Paulo, Brazil. The climatic environment of both seems to have been warm temperate, and this is confirmed for the Beaufort by the entry of an abundant reptilian fauna. Fish remains, freshwater mollusca and crustacea are known from shaly bands representing temporary lakelets. The Beaufort as a whole thins away to the northward. It is lacking over the Transvaal, but the lower stage is represented by the Rhodesian Madumabisa shales in a separate basin of deposition. Lower down the Zambesi River, the Karroo sequence for

Moçambique begins with beds assigned by Borges (1952) to the Ecca and continues with an equivalent of the Beaufort (the Grès du Tete) containing large feldspars. Limestones appear in the upper part. Red beds which follow are also thought to belong to the lower Beaufort.

In the Congo Republic formations of this time are conglomerates and coarse sediments, vari-coloured and reddish towards the top. These possibly indicate a desert regimen within the torrid zone. Equivalent in Angola are the " Fish Beds " with more than 200 well-preserved specimens indicating a passage from the Permian into the Triassic; and in Songea, Tanganyika, the lower Permian coal measures are succeeded by the lower Bone horizon (300 feet thick) corresponding to the *Endothiodon* and *Cistecephalus* zones of the lower Beaufort with similar reptilian fossils. Farther north, in the coastal strip of Kenya, the Duruma sandstone series continues the Karroo facies (Temperley 1952). The lower half of this 10,000 feet thick series is referred to the late Permian. It is mostly a massive, current bedded, feldspathic grit with pebbles of gneiss, and obscure plant remains embedded in sandy, micaceous shales.

Malagasy possesses a similar continental late Permian sequence in the south-west (Sakamena series) with reptiles (*Tangasaurus*), amphibians (*Rhinesuchus*), fish and *Glossopteris*. A marine facies appears towards the north which shows a sea connection with India. This gulf was maintained during the Mesozoic until the final break-up of Gondwanaland, so that interdigitation of continental and marine facies is well displayed in Malagasy.

Quite clearly, the end-Permian deposits of Brazil, South-Central Africa, Malagasy and India (*q.v.*) are all of warm temperate to tropical environment appropriate to a change in position of the reassembly on the globe from the frigid zone towards the warm temperate girdle (Fig. 19).

Whereas much of North and West Africa had been covered by a shallow shelf sea during the early Carboniferous, a great part of it became emergent following the Variscan earth movements and underwent denudation. Sedimentation was resumed during the late Permian with red sediments in the high Atlas and meseta of Morocco and in Algeria. Krenkel (1934) assigns these to a warm temperate environment, which is confirmed by the occurrence of warm or tropical flora of northern aspect, including *Equisetites*, *Pecopteris*, *Ginkgo* and *Walchia*. The latitude of 20°-30° N. indicated between Figs. 18 and 19 for this region is perhaps appropriate.

India. Two stages in India may be assigned to the late-Permian; the Raniganj stage and the Panchet series. These are as distinct as the upper Ecca and Lower Beaufort of South Africa with which they are contemporaneous, and indeed the Panchet succeeds the Raniganj with slight unconformity or over-laps on to the Barakars. In the Raniganj and Satpura areas the earlier series attains a thickness of over 3,000 feet and is noted for its abundant plant remains and coal seams. The flora is chiefly the " *Glossopteris* " flora without the coniferous, annually-ringed *Dadoxylon*. Of considerable interest is the appearance of the labyrinthodont *Gondwanasaurus*; but no reptiles are known yet. The climate under which it flourished must have been relatively warm as indicated also by kaolinisation of the feldspars in the sandstones and the red and brown coloration of many of the shales, *e.g.* in the Kamthi and Hingir beds.   This coloration appears earlier in the sequence than it does in South Africa and indicates a possible 20° of lower latitude in India during the late Permian. Indeed, the beds correspond lithologically much better with Karrooid formations in the Congo Republic, which share the same latitude with India upon the reconstruction (Table III).

The Panchet series, 2,000 feet of greenish, buff and brownish sandstones and shales succeeded by greyish, micaceous and feldspathic sandstones and shales, is important for its fossil labyrinthodonts and the first reptiles, including *Dicynodon*. *Glossopteris*, though present, appears to be waning and to be supplanted by the *Taeniopteris* flora, of Mesozoic aspect, thus dating the Panchet accurately with the lower Beaufort.

Australia. In the eastern states glacial erratics continued to be dropped into more normal sediments until the mid-Permian. Some of these may well have been carried by icebergs drifting in a cold easterly current from the main centre of Gondwanaland glaciation about the Ross Sea area, (upon the reconstruction the region falls into the westerly wind belt between latitudes 50° and 60° S.); though David (1950) has noted that " Some may have been left behind by ice-sheets pushing out from the coast but resting upon the sea-floor ". Many erratics are, in fact, of relatively local rock types.

During the late Permian the same region underwent pronounced hinge-line subsidence, a marine sequence containing a cold-water assemblage of shallow or littoral life-forms thickens towards the coast, but basins in the coastal hinterland were kept full of sediment including coal-seams of the Tomago and Newcastle stages. The insects that flitted over the swamps were dwarfed, and groups associated with a forest flora are absent, as are also sub-tropical types. Amphibians, too, were rare, and reptiles are unknown until towards the end of the period.

Thereafter, warming up was rapid and, according to David, the climate had at the end of the period so far ameliorated in the south that " stately forests of lofty trees abounded ". All this is completely in accord with the positions of Australia in Figs. 18 and 19 and the necessary transition between them. Australia during the late Permian apparently moved faster out of high latitudes than any other part of the reassembly (Fig. 19).

Late-Permian strata do not crop out in Central and Western Australia save in the North-west Basin and Bonaparte Gulf where abundant floras and faunas indicate possibly a warmer environment than in Eastern Australia.

Overlying early Permian glacials in Tasmania are grey shales of Ecca facies with glaciated pebbles dropped into them. The top of the Permian becomes more sandy in good strong beds lithologically resembling the Ecca, not the contemporaneous lower Beaufort of South Africa. The feldspars also are mainly fresh. This tardiness of warmer facies (see Table III) continues with the middle and late Triassic Langloh feldspathic sandstone of the Derwent Valley which resembles the earlier, lower Beaufort facies of South Africa.

Following a sudden retreat of the early-Permian ice, the western edge of Australia became a gulf similar to that which extended from India down to Madagascar. The *Eurydesma* fauna which it contained is identical (Thomas) with that of the Salt Range of India and the Urals, but local conditions changed rapidly owing to alternate shallowing and deepening.

Summary for the late Permian. Reviewing the evidence from Gondwanaland as a whole, we find two outstanding facts (a) the general increase of temperature indicated by changing lithologies and fresh fossil forms (*e.g.* reptiles) and (b) the long continuance of cold conditions in Australia as contrasted with the semi-tropical conditions of India and the Congo Republic. While a general calefaction could be the result of global climatic controls, the persistence of cold conditions in Australia to the very end of the period tells against this view, and favours instead a drift of the super-continent through normally-defined climatic girdles like those of modern times. Indeed, *the Permian continental deposits of all parts of Gondwanaland fall into climatic girdles consonant with the latitudes in which those parts necessarily appear in relation to one another.*

TRIASSIC DEPOSITION

By the early Triassic period topographic relief in Gondwanaland seems to have been relatively slight, most of the inequalities, either inherited from the ice-age or induced by its subsequent isobaric readjustments, having been eliminated. From this monotonous terrain the *Glossopteris* flora had vanished, being replaced by the Mesozoic " weeds " *Cladophlebis*, *Taeniopteris* and *Dicroidium* (*Thinnfeldia*) with cycads. Reptiles became abundant in the warm temperate environments recorded in the lithological successions of the period, and their fossils are widespread. During the Triassic period, a vast expanse of Gondwanaland remained subject only to broad epeirogenic movement creating low axial upwarpings that under denudation shed quantities of land-waste into intervening basins which thereby became wholly or partly filled up with shallow-water or sub-aerial sediments. Thus some regions show continuing sedimentation across the Palæozoic—Mesozoic boundary, others show an hiatus. On the whole the early Triassic afforded widespread non-deposition and even denudation over the western half of Gondwanaland; but relatively thin deposition, under desert or tropical conditions, supervened almost everywhere in the latter half of the period.

Antarctica. The presence of *Rhexoxylon* has caused the upper part of the Beacon system in the Ross Sea area to be regarded as Triassic in age; *Dicroidium* and cycads are also present in the Fall formation about the head of the Beardmore Glacier; but the sequence probably ceased to accumulate before the end of the period. The climatic regimen of Antarctica at this time, seems to have been mild.

South America. Following non-deposition during the early Triassic, the basin of São Paulo and Parana was filled up by the reptile-bearing Santa Maria Red Beds which de Oliveira and Leonardos cite as of early and middle Triassic age; but Caster continues the deposition well into the upper part of the system. This formation is not known northwards through Brazil, where the landscape seems to have undergone broad planation; but a remarkably similar zone is known in the lower Etjo beds north of Windhoek, South-West Africa. Martin (1961) has shown that these occurrences are brought into aligned positions on the Gondwana reconstruction.

The late Triassic witnessed a new, and very characteristic, phase of deposition. Beginning with the Red Beds of the Piramboia formation (from o to 300 feet thick) laid down in ephemeral desert lakes, the sequence is of eolian Botucatu sandstones (sometimes as much as 600 feet thick) which covered an enormous area of country by the close of the Triassic period. de Almeida describes it as one of the greatest deserts in recorded earth history. The geographic location indicated for south-central Brazil at this (Rhaetic) epoch is thus within the great belt of deserts situated about the southern tropic (Fig. 19).

Triassic orogenesis appears upon the South American portion of Gondwanaland along the line from the Sierra de Cordoba to the Sierra de la Ventana in the State of Buenos Aires. Both the formations involved and the manner of folding were matched by du Toit with the fold mountain systems of the Cape Province in Africa, and other authorities have concurred.

Southern Africa. The Triassic deposits of Southern Africa are similar in type and distribution to those of Brazil. In the Republic of South Africa the middle and upper Beaufort beds (analogous with the Grupo Rio do Rasto) continue the Permian sequence without break into the lower Triassic. They contain abundant reptilian fossils akin to those of Brazil.

The Beaufort series thins northwards from the Cape and cuts out entirely over the Transvaal (*cf.* Brazil north of São Paulo). Over a vast area of Africa south of the equator therefore appears the sub-Stormberg hiatus, and during this time most of the landscape was eroded to a plain of great monotony, as was Brazil. Even where Beaufort beds are locally present, *e.g.* in Rhodesia, they belong only to the lower part of that series.

Towards the end of the period extreme aridity prevailed from Central Africa to the Cape, as attested by the accumulation first of red lacustrine beds with early dinosaurs (*Plateosaurus*) *cf.* Piramboia formation; and then by widespread desert sandstones passing under a variety of local names (*e.g.* Cave sandstone, Bushveld sandstone, Forest sandstone).

Rhodesia has 800 feet of these desert sandstones west of Bulawayo; and in Angola the Lunda series of reddish mudstones and sands (overlying the Cassanje series which corresponds locally with the middle and upper Beaufort) may likewise represent the Stormberg. But the whole of the Congo basin seems to have been exempt from deposition (Cahen 1954) and to have been an extensive plain of slow denudation.

In the south, where marginal desert conditions prevailed, the corresponding (Cave) sandstone is a loessic deposit 300 feet in thickness.

The close similarity in lithology and age between these arid Stormberg deposits of Southern Africa and the Botucatu of Brazil is remarkable. In the far south, again, occur the Cape Ranges, folded simultaneously (and upon the reconstruction collinearly) with the Sierra de la Ventana of Buenos Aires (du Toit).

Towards the East African coast, after an unconformity like the sub-Stormberg hiatus, both continental and marine sedimentation were resumed. Thus between the Zambezi and lower Shiré Rivers in Moçambique sandstones with *Rhexoxylon* are followed by red beds with dinosaurs. In Songea also, the period ended with the Tenduru beds, containing *Scaphonyx* as in Brazil. The Sakamena series in Malagasy shows reptilian and plant fossils towards the top of the series corresponding to the early Triassic. Then after a discordance, many thousands of feet of cross-bedded Isalo sandstones in which the only fossils are silicified wood record the late-Triassic desert phase. A marine incursion at the top (Bajocian) testifies continuance of the aridity until the mid-Jurassic. The late-Triassic desert of Gondwanaland was immense.

For North Africa (Morocco and Tunis), also, the Triassic was a time of great aridity with salt and gypsum deposits amid red sandstones of Bunter type (Krenkel 1934). For this, the location in the desert belt (lat. 30° N.) on the reconstruction is entirely appropriate.

The vast extent of Triassic desert covers a breadth greater than the modern arid girdles and is followed (Arkell 1956) by evidence of warmth in the fauna and flora of the Jurassic to far northern latitudes, *e.g.* Greenland.* To some extent an enormous landmass like Gondwana or Asia makes its own climate (*e.g.* monsoons), and it is possible that the desert belt becomes more extensive the more land is concentrated in that belt.

India. The early and mid-Triassic hiatus was represented on the same horizon in India by a stratigraphic discontinuity between the Panchet and Mahadevi series.

Before the close of the Triassic, simultaneously with the Botucatu and Stormberg series, deposition was renewed over India with the Mahadevi series. The lowest (Pachmarhi) stage of this series consists of red and buff, unfossiliferous sandstones with some red clays near the base and top. Evidence of wind action is not recorded. The Maleri stage, which follows conformably, indicates a more humid (equatorial) environment in which labyrinthodont amphibians flourished in company with late-Triassic rhynchocephalian and saurischian reptiles. Upon the reconstruction, indeed, the Triassic equator passes across this portion of the Indian Peninsula.

Australia. Only in the eastern cordilleran belt are Triassic strata known in Australia (David), so that the general denudation regime of the period that we have

---

* But both Seward and Berry rejected the oft-repeated statement that the Cretaceous flora of Greenland was *tropical*.

already reviewed over a span of three continents covered almost all of Australia too· Those Triassic formations that are known in New South Wales (Hawkesbury sandstone, Wianamatta shale) record by their facies a temperate environment assessed by David : " The Triassic climate was probably in general mild, and at times it was certainly pluvial, while the pronounced growth rings of the conifers tell of well-marked seasonal changes ". Confirmatory evidence comes from Tasmania where Banks (1952) has described the early-Triassic Knocklofty formation as laid down in shallow lakes which evaporated in the dry season. The wet season maintained the abundant fossil flora. Later in the period the climate became more pluvial and hotter. Here appears a swifter warming up than anywhere else in Gondwanaland. The difference of climatic environment is indicated by the position of Eastern Australia in the reconstruction for the Triassic where this region is found in latitude 35 ° S., contrasting with 50 °-60 ° during the early Permian (Figs. 18, 19). The observations we have quoted could well correspond with a passage from a latitude of prevailing westerly winds to a girdle where the dominant winds were easterly Trades.

In Queensland 15 ° farther north, the Triassic carries abundant flora, with fossil insects (Hill 1952), which though indicating warmer conditions than in New South Wales is nevertheless far removed from the desert environment that afflicted so much of the interior of Gondwanaland in similar latitudes.

Summary for the Triassic. The unity of Triassic history is apparent throughout large tracts of Gondwanaland (Table III). In some interior regions the continental type of deposition widespread during the Permian continued into the early Triassic, but by the middle of the period the landscape generally was undergoing widespread arid planation carried across the sedimentary basins and their slightly elevated rims alike (Dixey 1956). This almost universal denudation removed, however, no great thickness of material and the smooth landsurface was lowered only imperceptibly. There is, indeed, scarcely any record of detritus from the vast steppes of the early and mid-Triassic, and the late-Permian sediments in the hollows remained with little loss. The terrain of low relief extended over the greater part of Gondwanaland until, towards the end of the period, earth movements (strong only along the Sierra de la Ventana— Cape Ranges belt) produced minor swells and desert basins across which, in the latitude of the southern tropic, a wide swathe of eolian sands shifted back and forth under the influence of the wind. A study of the fossil wind systems under which the sands were distributed might provide interesting results. India, on the equator north of this belt, had reptile-haunted swamps; Eastern Australia to the south had sediments appropriate to a cool then warm temperate environment.

The evident quiescence of Gondwanaland throughout the Triassic period was rudely shattered in the Rhaetic when basaltic eruptions from the subcrust burst through the basement in vast dyke-networks, and plateau lavas spilled out far and wide across the interminable plains. Sometimes briefly heralded by central eruptions, the highly mobile lava sheets spread to surprising distances. The volcanic details need not detain us, but the distribution of the lava-sheets and intrusive phases within the Gondwana reassembly is instructive. These are the São Bento lavas of Parana and São Paulo in Southern Brazil, and the Stormberg basalts of South-West Africa dipping gently eastward beneath the Cainozoic deposits of the Kalahari Basin. Xenoliths in the Kimberley diamond pipes, and the basaltic sheets of the Transvaal Bushveld and the region from Victoria Falls to Bulawayo, demonstrate that the lavas were formerly widespread across the interior of Southern Africa, while the testimony of the dyke systems of " Karroo dolerite " which were the feeders covers most of the areas where the actual lavas have since been removed by denudation. In Basutoland the lavas still preserve a thickness of 4,000 feet, and more is present in the Lebombo Range along the Moçambique border. Altogether, the lavas spanned east-west from side to side of the sub-continent south of lat. 20° S. and north of the Cape Folded Belt. Of especial interest are several lopoliths or high-level magma chambers in Griqualand East (*e.g.* Insizwa). Both the persistence of the dykes and the Lebombo structure prove the original extent of the lavas and associated intrusive phases well beyond the present eastern coast. The reconstruction, of course, suggests that a continuation of the irruption should be sought in Dronning Maud Land of the Antarctic where a continuation of the Karroo sediments has already been demonstrated upon the work of the Norwegian-British-Swedish Expedition in 1948-50. The specimens recovered by geologists of the expedition did not include basalt, but basic plutons analogous to those of Griqualand East were identified. Cropstones from penguins captured by the German *Neue Schwabenland* Expedition in 1939 included basalt. On the other side of Antarctica, in Victoria Land and Adelie Land dolerites of a similar suite have been known, in great sills totalling 4,000 feet in thickness, for half a century, and these have been closely compared with the abundant dolerites of the same age in Tasmania. The (Kirkpatrick) basalts, too, are known in the northern part of Victoria Land (Gair 1965) and about the head of the Beardmore Glacier (Grindley *et al.* 1965). Thicknesses exceed 1,500 m. and 1,000 m. respectively.

Nor did India escape the conflagrations: the Rajmahal eruptions spread the basaltic magma far and wide.

The essential similarity of the extrusive and dyke rocks in the five Gondwana continents has, indeed, long been a subject of agreement among petrographers who have studied them (du Toit, Edwards, Walker).

The Rhaetic volcanic episode, distributed in a broad girdle across almost the full width of Gondwanaland, thus affords a remarkable confirmation of the correctness of the reconstruction already deduced from stratigraphic geology. It affords also (see Table III) useful evidence of volcanic contemporaneity as distinct from facies resemblances of the sedimentary series. More, as Martin (1961) noting the great thicknesses of the basaltic outpourings in South America and South Africa wrote: " The two continents seem at this time literally to have floated on temporarily molten cushions of basalt . . . In this respect actualistic arguments against the possibility of drift seem decidedly unsafe "!

The Jurassic Regimen

In most respects the Jurassic palæogeography of Gondwanaland resembles that of the early and mid-Triassic when denudation operated shallowly over a vast steppe of low relief.   Jurassic continental-type sediments are few (Arkell 1956) and generally unfossiliferous, their age often having to be defined by reference to other stratigraphic units.   On the other hand denudational landforms were supreme in a vast planation to which the name " Gondwana cyclic landsurface " has been given (King 1950) (p. 197).   Where it is still preserved, this landsurface nowadays appears as an erosional bevel upon the highest plateaus, such as Basutoland.

One new factor of prime importance entered the reconstruction.   Between India and Somaliland, and reaching down to Tanganyika and Malagasy, appeared a fresh mid-Jurassic arm of the sea (Fig. 20).   This marks the beginning of the split which, by the earliest Cretaceous, extended down the whole east coast of Africa to Uitenhage, and which heralds the break-up (accomplished by the mid-Cretaceous period) of Gondwanaland into the several continents with the outlines that we know today.

Antarctica.   Little is known of Jurassic formations in Antarctica.   Much of the main body of the continent, East Antarctica, may have been under denudation at that period though lower Jurassic plants have been recovered from the uppermost part of the Beacon sandstone of Victoria Land by Gunn and Warren (1962).   From Graham Land (Hope Bay) 61 species of fossil plants have been recovered (Plumstead 1962); and animals of warmth-loving types have elsewhere been recorded (Fairbridge 1952).

South America.   " After the emission of the Rhaetic lavas denudation prevailed over practically the whole of Brazil.   Only locally did red sands (Uberaba series) accumulate.   Prolonged throughout the Jurassic period, the erosional phase reduced the landscape everywhere to an extraordinarily smooth plain, which sometimes includes already-razed fragments of the Triassic or sub-Botucatu landscape ".   " While much of the Gondwana landscape now lies buried in the fossil state beneath a Cretaceous cover, in other regions such as the mountainland south of Belo Horizonte it appears never to have had any sedimentary cover and has been exposed continuously to the elements from Cretaceous time until the present day. . . .   Where the bedrock furnished suitable materials, the Gondwana surface is frequently armoured with surface ironstone or ' canga ' some of which is rich enough to have been worked for iron ore " (King 1956).

No continental accumulations of Jurassic age are known with certainty in Eastern Brazil.   " The red Uberaba series of Triangulo Miniero, and the Cayua red sands of São Paulo both contain tuffaceous materials that may well have been supplied during the dying phase of the São Bento lavas, on which they rest, when the lavas were less fluid and mobile.   This would suggest an eo-Jurassic age for these formations ".   In other places lithologically similar beds may represent the first sands resting upon the Gondwana landsurface, which would make them early Cretaceous.

Southern Africa. Remnants of the Gondwana cyclic surface still survive in the modern landscape, and Dixey (1938) first correlated these remnants through all the territories south of the equator. Sediments of Jurassic age are unknown over the Republic of South Africa and Rhodesia; but in the Congo Basin and neighbouring Angola, where Triassic deposits are absent (Cahen 1954), continental sedimentation was resumed upon a wide scale (the Lualaba series) during the latter part of the Jurassic period.

The coastlands of Kenya and Tanganyika and also the western seaboard of Malagasy as far south as the Onilahy River, are broadly covered by marine Jurassic formations, arenaceous and calcareous, beginning with the Bajocian stage. The gulf in which these accumulated did not, however, extend to Moçambique where the earliest marine sediments known are lowest Cretaceous. The materials were derived from the west in Kenya (Temperley 1952) and from the east in Malagasy (Besairie 1953).

The marine mid-Jurassic rocks of south Kenya lie upon the Triassic Karroo facies, but in the north this facies is absent and the Jurassic overlies a Gondwana landsurface carved across Basement gneisses.

India. Opinions are divided (Krishnan 1949; Jacob 1952) upon the precise ages to be assigned to the Jurassic Gondwana beds of India. Plant fossils are plentiful but usually indecisive. The chief series following the Rajmahal basaltic lavas, is the Jabalpur which consists of white and light coloured clays and massive soft sandstones. The terrestrial Gondwanas of the east coast, preserved chiefly in depressions along the major rivers, pass laterally into marine facies with fossils indicative of a latest-Jurassic or earliest-Cretaceous age. Thus at the end of the Jurassic period an arm of the sea had begun to define the eastern coast also of the peninsula.

Australia. David (1950) describes Jurassic conditions: " In striking contrast to the Triassic the Jurassic period was characterised in Australia by the existence of vast expanses of freshwater lakes, which must have invaded nearly half the total area of the continent ". At the same time the great western shield seems to have been updomed and furnished, under denudation, flaggy and current-bedded, soft, calcareous sandstones and clays, which somewhat resemble the Jabalpur of India. Rarity of sauropods and dinosaurs has been taken as indication of a cool climate, but this does not accord with the latitude assumed by Australia upon the reconstruction. Other explanations may be valid.

The western coastline shows a history similar to that of East Africa and Malagasy, for a gulf which began to open during the Permian, became very pronounced during the Jurassic. Both marine and continental strata are associated.

Conclusion. Gentle arching and doming with concomitant erosion, seem to have been characteristic of the central portions of Gondwanaland during the Jurassic period with a garland of basin depressions (Northern Brazil, Congo, India and Eastern Australia) upon the northern flank of the arch. These downsaggings generally conform to a new pattern of deformation different from the basins that had existed following the Carboniferous ice-age.

Quite new amid all the deposits of continental facies that have been developed from Carboniferous to Trias within the interior of Gondwanaland are the marine coastal deposits that fringe the modern outlines of East Africa and peninsular India: a new conformation of the southern landmasses is heralded, and attention shifts from mighty continental stratigraphies to marine realms of shelf and geosynclinal facies, the complex story of which cannot be summarised here but which the reader may follow for himself in Arkell's authoritative *Jurassic Geology of the World* (1956).

CRETACEOUS FRAGMENTATION OF GONDWANALAND

During the prolonged period of geologic time already reviewed, Gondwanaland behaved as an unity. Only following the mid-Jurassic did the sea begin to penetrate that tremendous super-continent along modern coastlines. With the Cretaceous period, however, several splits opened up successively and by the middle of the period all the modern continental outlines were established. Upon the lands fresh basin-subsidences developed, sometimes in new, sometimes in old positions; but these were small when compared with the vast basins of Permian time (*e.g.* the Kalahari as compared with the Karroo Basin). Attention focuses instead upon the fascinating partition of the old super-continent, which had been so satisfying in its ovoid outline, into the family of curiously-shaped southern continents, and their centrifugal flight from the original centre of gravity of Gondwanaland—South America to the west, Africa slightly to the north, Antarctica to the south, India to the northeast and Australia away to the east. Generally the smallest fragments seem to have travelled the farthest (Fig. 247).

This fragmentation may best be followed by examining the penetration of the oceans along the new coasts. The first disruption, as judged by the marine deposits, took place along the eastern side of Africa, separating off the eastern realms of India, Malagasy, Australia and possibly Antarctica in one piece. As early as the Permian, shallow incursions of the sea penetrated from the Salt Range southward to Malagasy and adjacent Tanganyika. The stratigraphic sequences remained dominantly continental (Karroo facies), however, during the Triassic and Lias. The mid-Jurassic (Bajocian) then witnessed the development of a clearly-defined gulf from which continental accumulation was henceforth excluded, and a fully marine sequence of coastal limestones and shales is characteristic of the later Jurassic. No marine Jurassic formations are known, however, from Moçambique or the east coast of the Republic of South Africa. The earliest marine deposits there are Neocomian in age. The fission between the eastern and western halves of Gondwanaland, begun in the mid-Jurassic, was therefore completed by the earliest Cretaceous.

The two halves seemingly soon drifted apart into new positions where they fragmented again. The western half (South America with Africa) may well have occupied a position where the cleavage between them corresponded with the site of the South Atlantic submarine ridge (Fig. 225). The date of this second rupture is again clear. Except for the shallow epicontinental incursions of the Permian sea with *Eurydesma*, only sedimentary rocks of continental type have been recorded as forming along the opposed continental edges from the Carboniferous until the Jurassic period; and Arkell (1956) is emphatic: " South of the points where the Atlas Mountains in Morocco and the Caribbean Coast Range of Venezuela and North Range of Trinidad strike so spectacularly out to sea, no Jurassic rocks are known on the Atlantic side of either Africa or South America ". By itself this is negative evidence only, but with the positive evidence from earlier periods of former contiguity of these landmasses (R. Maack; A. L. du Toit and others) the only reasonable conclusion is that at the beginning of the Cretaceous period the long-established unity between what are now two continents had not been destroyed. The earliest marginal sediments related to the present outlines are lagoonal Aptian, followed by marine Albian in Nigeria, Brazil (Sergipe) and Angola. Whether the cleavage was completed by the Albian is not known as appropriate formations are not exposed along more southern coasts, but it cannot have been long delayed.

Meanwhile the continental type of sedimentation continued, though often in fresh depressions, upon the lands. The Serie de Kwango of Angola and the Congo (Cahen 1954), the earliest beds of the Kalahari Basin (du Toit 1954) and the plateau formations of Equatorial and West Africa (Nickles 1952) are newly located in this way, and are matched across the Atlantic by the Urucuia and similar arenaceous series in Brazil (de Oliveira and Leonardos 1943).

The eastern segment of Gondwanaland may likewise have been sited at the time of its further disruption appropriately to the mid-Indian submarine ridge (Figs. 21, 226). Between India and Western Australia a waterway had long existed, for a Permian gulf allowed marine formations to accumulate. This is less pronounced in the Triassic; but mid-Jurassic (Bajocian) subsidence admitted the open ocean to south of Geraldton. Several hundreds of feet of deposit have been proved in bores. Farther south, near Bullsbrook, late-Jurassic or early-Cretaceous plants occur in sandstones which show that the depression was extending southward, and complete emancipation, with marine conditions along the full length of western coast, was accomplished by the Albian, when also marine conditions appear upon the Coromandel coast of India. From Antarctica no adequate data concerning these events are yet available; but in New Zealand significant new conditions at this epoch are recorded by fresh sedimentation (following the Jura-Cretaceous Hokonui orogeny) in the Albian with an Indian fauna. The known data are therefore consistent and suggest that the final opening of the Indian Ocean Basin was synchronous with the opening of the South Atlantic Basin—both of them Albian. *By the middle of the Cretaceous period Gondwanaland had ceased to exist.*

CONCLUSION

The former unity of Gondwanaland has been established, and the manner of its disruption demonstrated, from highly diagnostic stratigraphic evidence that has been compared and appreciated by Gondwana geologists for over half a century. More recent studies indicate that the local differences are no less important in the basic palæo-geographic reconstructions. They show that there was no global pole-wandering and no change in the major climatic girdles of the earth, only changes in the positions of the continents and a refitting such as their very outlines prescribe. The evidence is ample enough: formation after formation in ordered sequence through thicknesses of many thousands of feet, spread without complication over more than a million square miles in five continents. It is the clearest demonstration in all geology.

From the Carboniferous period until the mid-Jurassic all fragments of Gondwana-land drifted as an unity; disruption and flight of the several fragments occupied only from the mid-Jurassic until the end of the Cretaceous period; after that no evidence of further drift during the Cainozoic era accrues from geology. If there was drift of continents it must have been slight.

A similar conclusion, though not unanimous, has been expressed by palæo-magnetists. Thus Irving and Green (1957), after discussing postulated movements up to the Jurassic, write for the Cretaceous and later : " Relative continental movements of the type just described have been negligible since the Upper Tertiary, but appear to have been operative through the Cretaceous into the Tertiary ". They continue, " Australia and India have undergone translation movements with respect to each other and to Europe and North America during Cretaceous and Lower Tertiary times ". They also conclude that the continents have rotated. A palæomagnetic survey of African Karroo sediments and lavas by Nairn (1960) also, after indicating " a movement of the African continent from a near polar to an equatorial situation during the period from late Carboniferous to late-Triassic times " noted " an anticlockwise rotation of nearly 90° " (cf. Figs. 17, 18, 19).

From the palæomagnetism of Cainozoic and Quaternary rocks from Europe Hospers (1955) concluded that " If polar wandering has taken place at all, it has not exceeded 5°-10° since Eocene times ".

But the northern continents do not afford a single system of rock formations like the Gondwana upon which a case for their former unity as another super-continent (Laurasia) can be made. This demonstration awaits evidence of another kind (Chapter XIII) (Fig. 166).

As Chapter I established the possibility of continental drift under what is known of the physics of the earth's crust and substratum, Chapter II has demonstrated from geologic data the actuality of that drift, for the southern continents at least, during the late-Palæozoic and Mesozoic eras.

Furthermore, as the palæoclimatic girdles for Carboniferous till Triassic time prove to be similar in distribution and in width to those at present existing, there can have been no undue pole-wandering; and the Earth is shown to have been an uniformitarian earth, neither contracting nor expanding significantly during the latter part of geologic time.

CHAPTER III

CONTINENTAL STRUCTURE : (A) SHIELDS

Altitudes of Continents. Major Continental Structures. The Shield of
Africa. Shields of South America. Peninsular India. Antarctica. The
Foundations of Australia. The Precambrian Grain of Gondwanaland.
The Laurentian Shield. The Foundations of Europe. The Angara Shield.
The Chinese Nuclei.

ALTITUDES OF CONTINENTS

The average altitudes of the continents (Table IV) are apparently a function of their
respective areas. Antarctica alone appears to be exceptionally high, but Daly's estimate
refers to the level of the inland ice-cap and is speedily corrected when allowance is made
for the thickness of the ice, beneath which the isostatically depressed bedrock surface
sinks from 10,000 feet or so in the containing peripheral mountains to low levels in the

TABLE IV

	Area (millions sq. miles)	Average Height (feet)
All land	57	2,500
Antarctica	5	6,000
Asia	17	3,150
Africa	11	2,460
North America	9	2,360
South America	7	1,935
Australia	4	1,115
Europe	4	1,115

after R. A. Daly.

interior (Fig. 22). Thus an ice-free topography in Antarctica would probably stand
isostatically at a plateau level around 2,000 feet.

The altitude of any locality is the resultant of two opposed sets of earth forces, one
constructional the other destructional. The first set, tectonic, is concerned primarily
with raising or lowering of the surface to new altitudes. The denudational agencies,
opposedly, are directed to the tearing down of landscapes that have previously been
elevated above base level. Locally in basins, and beneath the sea, the surface may be
built up by aggradation, but the dominant expression upon the lands, at least, is degradational. The complex interplay of the tectonic and denudational agencies upon the
earth-body has been responsible for the topographic expression of the lands and ocean
basins throughout the ages, and forms the main theme of this book.

Thus topography, though a surface phenomenon, reflects also deep-seated actions,
and though the precise nature of the earth's crust is not the subject of our present enquiry

we cannot fail to take cognizance of those profound effects which, even in a later age, may find surficial expression. This point has been made by Penck (1953); "*Every crustal movement leaves its traces in the superstructure, and the sum total of these make up the structure of the earth's crust*". "Not only does this structure differ from place to place, but also it was produced at very different periods. It is preserved as a disturbance of the bedding; but the other effect of the crustal movement, the altitudinal modelling or

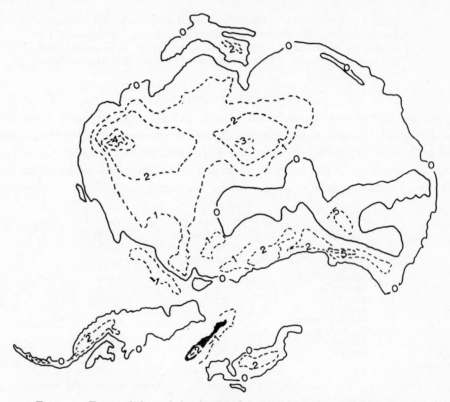

FIG. 22. Form of the sub-ice landsurface in Antarctica. Elevations in thousands of metres. Bentley Trench, black.

the vertical upbuilding is not durable. Should the movement die out anywhere, denudation removes all the parts that had been left projecting, and the depressions are filled in; the structural features alone remain ".

So we pass to a brief examination of the structure of the earth's crust in so far as it affects topography.

MAJOR CONTINENTAL STRUCTURES

Since the analysis of Edward Suess (1885-1904) revealed two contrasting types of post-Cambrian continental structure: (a) apparently-rigid, dominantly-gneissic nuclei or *shields*, and (b) folded mountain chains or mobile *welts*, much effort has been expended in defining their relative areas with exactitude, and dating the episodes of mountain-making with geological precision. For Precambrian time the distinction is less obvious, for even the shield areas show welt-like successions of folded and metamorphosed rocks recording ancient orogenesis, complete with granitisation and intrusion.

Despite the crustal mobility insisted upon in Chapter I, huge areas of the continents have been exempt from strong orogenesis since Algonkian time at least, and in some instances practically since the Archean. Thus, upon the Siberian shield Cambrian and Ordovician rock series lie with essential horizontality over wide areas, whereas in the Sayan mountain arc rocks of similar age have been crumpled and now dip steeply along a well-marked zone of folding.

Viewed upon the world scale (Figs. 23, 24), the pattern of " shields " and " welts ", or areas that have not failed under tectonic stresses and areas that have failed, since Precambrian time, is a familiar one to engineers. Even apparently uniform structures do not fail uniformly throughout, but failure is complete along definite zones whereas the remainder of the body under stress is not deformed at all.

Wherever they are known, Archean rocks are regionally and intensely metamorphosed with strong and steep banding in the gneissic members. They are often closely folded and sliced in the manner typical of rheid deformation. Such deformation of later date appears also in the cores of fold-mountain systems (*q.v.*) and geologists have not been slow to draw the inference that all the shield areas underwent complete orogenesis in Archean time. But there can be no guarantee that the steeply-inclined rheid structures ubiquitous among Archean rock systems originated in the same way along narrow belts of deformation. Instead, the rheid structures visible in several of the Archean shields were clearly produced over broad areas rather than narrow zones (though these occur too). McCutcheon has indeed shown (1957) that self-induced gravitational strains within the earth must themselves produce a radial earth structure, (near-vertical in the shields).

Such broadly-disposed rheidity may well be a response to cymatogenic activity on a large scale (p. 656), wherein the crust accommodates itself to vertical movements which are regional but which at the same time often involve considerable differential components as along axes of maximum uplift, rift valleys, and coastal monoclines. The suggestion is that accommodation takes place at depth by flow in the solid state, expressed in steeply-dipping gneisses, as may be seen in regions that have been differentially uplifted by great amounts since Palæozoic time (Rio de Janeiro, Benguella Highlands). Such regional gneisses are poorly furnished with ore-bodies. Though the shields are often metalliferous the ores are associated with independent igneous intrusions: the great gneiss areas themselves are usually barren. Such gneissosity is therefore not to be attributed to orogenesis (Chapter IV) with its accompanying irruptions of liquid and volatile matter; but to profound, and broad, vertical laminar movement of the shields, with recrystallisation often producing large augen of microcline feldspars (p. 656).

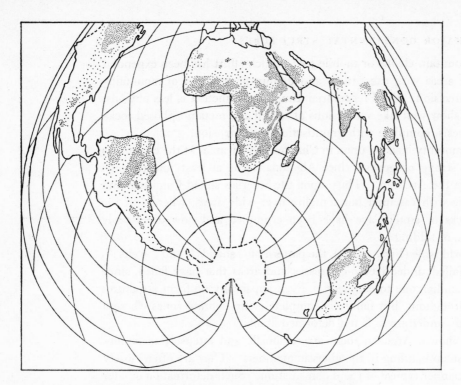

FIG. 23. Distribution of "shield" areas in the southern hemisphere. Exposures of basement rock heavily stippled, later deposits resting upon basement lightly stippled.

FIG. 24. Distribution of "shield" areas in the northern hemisphere. Exposures of basement rock heavily stippled, later deposits resting upon basement lightly stippled.

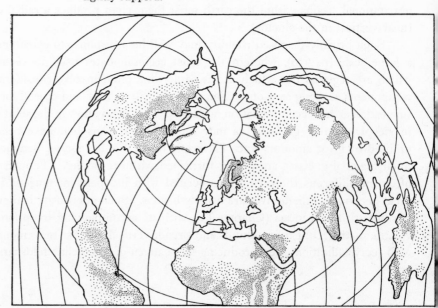

Whether or not "shield rocks" (which "the world over consist mainly of quartzo-feldspathic gneiss and amphibolite, roughly in proportion of 4 : 1 ") now crop out at the surface, geophysical studies have shown them to underlie all younger rock systems on the continents. There is no evidence from the shields of lateral accretions to the continents. All the shield areas of the globe were in existence as such immediately following Archean time, and even the roots of later deeply-eroded orogenic belts sometimes display similar materials as a floor. Demonstrably, the sum total of continental matter has not been increased significantly in post-Archean time. Right to the edges of continental shelves beneath the oceans, geophysics has demonstrated the existence of the continental basement.

The vast granite batholiths that intrude the Archean rocks, and which often appear intimately related to the transformation and deformation of these rocks, themselves form an integral part of the many shields in various continents. Without denying the possibility of primary magmatic granite, many of these " granites " have been derived from pre-existing Archean rocks by processes of granitisation, a topic expounded of recent years by H. H. Read and others. In so far as the structures of shields are concerned, the results of magmatisation, which is the action of liquids, or of migmatisation, which is the action of volatiles, are often remarkably alike. This is well brought out in the charnockites, a coarse-grained granitic rock suite typical of shield areas, which range from plutonic metamorphic to igneous in origin, and which Wilson (1954, 1959) has considered " due to either heat-transfer up deep-seated thrust-faults and plastic shearzones or to slumping of blocks of the basement into hotter zones by normal faults ". A huge province of charnockites in the Antarctic has been described as hydro-metamorphic, " perhaps homogenized from quartz-feldspar gneisses ".

Large ultrabasic intrusions within shield areas are commonly layered (e.g. Bushveld), thereby contrasting with the peridotites of orogenic welts (p. 112).

Frequently, several distinct nuclei are grouped into a single shield, when they behave under most conditions as an unity, e.g. the West Australian shield, where the nuclei are described by Hills (1945) as having a swirling pattern of Archean strikes. In the intervening zones between the nuclei uniform strikes prevail over long distances. Guimarães (1951) has also referred to " agglutination " of separate Archean nuclei as having built up the Brazilian shield in Precambrian time. The several component nuclei of China and South-East Asia, however, seem to have behaved with a measure of independence during the epoch of Mesozoic foldings. Similar activity may have been associated, at a much more remote date, with the granite piercement domes of Rhodesia described by MacGregor (Fig. 25). The contorted Archean rocks are now disposed in narrow strips and triangular segments between the adjacent " domes ". Similar bodies are recorded also in Canada and about the Gulf of Bothnia, indeed they seem to be fairly typical of the shield regions.

Though in many regions the basement rocks of the shields are amply exposed, e.g. Africa, nonetheless they are elsewhere widely blanketed by a veneer of terrestrial or shallow-water sediments, which span any interval of time between the Proterozoic and Recent.   A modern example is Lake Chad in Central Africa which for an area of 2,400 sq. km. has a depth of at most 2-3 metres.   Its bed is a bluish mud of unknown thickness, and surrounding deposits show that the lake had a far greater extent in the

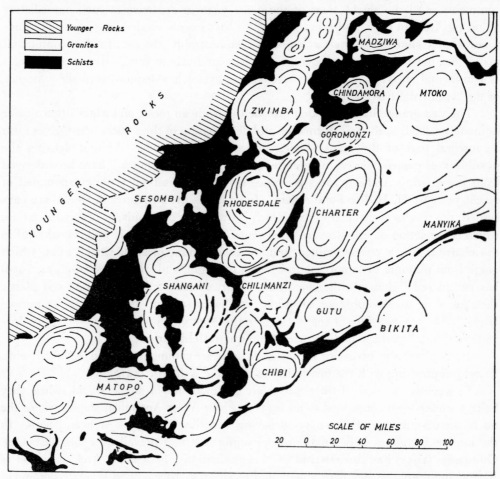

FIG. 25.   Domed structures in the gneissose basement of Rhodesia.
after A. M. Macgregor.

recent past.   Much deeper and larger is the Caspian-Aral Basin of the southern U.S.S.R. Where continental foundations have subsided deeply thicknesses of sediment laid thereon may amount to several hundreds or even thousands of feet.   Examples are: the continental strata of the Congo Basin, the marine formations of the Gulf of Mexico and the Yellow Sea with its adjunct the Gulf of Pohai.   Though hiatuses representing phases of non-deposition are common in such sequences, they are seldom sharply folded.   The sequence covering European Russia, for instance, spans from the Cambrian period to the Recent, and displays quite ten hiatuses, but no strongly angular general unconformities (Nalivkin 1960).

The boundaries of continental basins may overlap one another in space or time, giving rise to various structural relations. Umbgrove (1947) has classified such basins from the structural point of view: (a) basins which are concordant with the strike of the surrounding rocks and (b) basins whose boundaries are discordant to the older

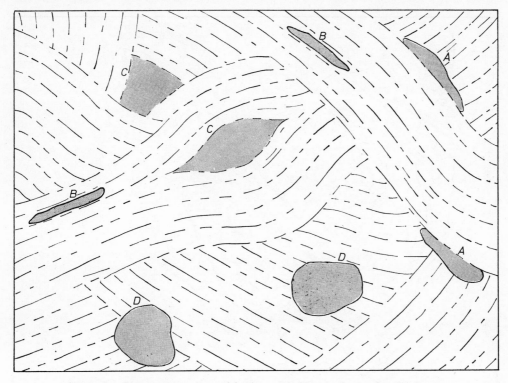

FIG. 26. Types of continental basins: (A) Marginal troughs, (B) Intramontane basins, (C) Nuclear basins, with isochronous and anisochronous frames, (D) Discordant basins. *after J. H. Umbgrove.*

structures. The former type is also subdivided into basins with isochronous frame and basins with anisochronous frame (Fig. 26). Such broad continental basins conform well with the aspect of expansive plains and plateaus characteristic of shield areas (*e.g.* Western Australia or the interior of Africa).

The tectonic activity of shield areas is expressed chiefly by the intermittent uplift of large regions (epeirogenesis), usually by a few hundred feet at a time. Uplift is not necessarily uniform: axes of maximum upwarp often separate equidimensional basins of lesser rise (cymatogenesis) (p. 196). du Toit has given an excellent illustration from Southern Africa (Fig. 27). At successive tectonic episodes the same differential effects are generally reproduced, so that the axes are repeatedly rejuvenated and the basins repeatedly lag behind. As the upwarped axes are most eroded, and the basins commonly serve as receptacles for land waste, a complementary record of denudation and deposition is sometimes available for local study, and many of the conclusions reached in Part C of this book derive from this circumstance.

Along the crests of axial upwarps that have been long maintained and greatly uplifted special tensional effects may accrue. The crest of the arch breaks and subsides

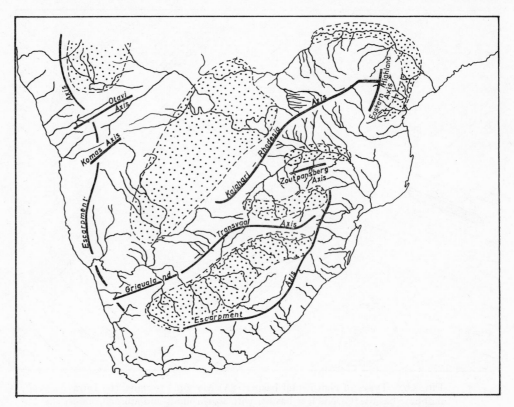

Fig. 27. Upwarped axes and basins of depression resulting from Plio-Pleistocene deformation in Southern Africa. *modified from A. L. du Toit.*

to form a rift valley and such structures are found in relation to the shields of Africa, Brazil and Angara. In a later context appears the Rhine graben (p. 395) of Europe. The dislocations of the rifts are in every case due to crustal tension, and the rifting may be renewed from time to time in concert with the general arching. Gravity fields generally show negative anomaly over the rifts, positive beneath the flanks. The existing rifts of Africa and Brazil (São Francisco Valley) are of Pleistocene generation; but older, and probably just as extensive, rift forms existed in both theatres during the late-Cretaceous period. Deposition in the Nyasa rift of Africa has yielded dinosaur bones; and the Cretaceous rifts of Baia, Brazil, have afforded plant remains at Araci.

The Benue Rift of Nigeria contains a thickness of sediments totalling 15,000 feet much, if not most, of which is supposedly of Cretaceous age. Under erosion the original boundaries of the Benue rift have retreated considerable distances on either side and faults are difficult to find in the gneisses of the floor, though some are known in the Gongola; but their disappearance in the basement is thoroughly in accord with the rapid loss of all trace of such features elsewhere in Africa, *e.g.* where the basement is exposed along the abundantly faulted axis of the Natal monocline. Laminar flow, not fracture, apparently takes place in the steeply inclined gneisses.

Similar elevatory movements, with fracturing, sometimes afflict zones of previous mountain building from which great volumes of rock have been removed by denudation. The Basin and Range province of the Western United States wherein appears a multitude of fault-bounded earth-blocks, stands over the site of the Jurassic Nevadan ranges, and the Cainozoic fault-systems of New Zealand are developed over the Mesozoic foundations of a great fold-mountain system. In Queensland, Cainozoic faulting is related not only to the uparching of Eastern Queensland along the Great Divide but also to subsidence of the neighbouring basin of the Coral Sea, so that it greatly resembles the state of Rio de Janeiro which, being elevated during the Cretaceous period alongside a subsiding oceanic sector, was likewise broken steeply by faulting at that time. The blocks, in their original state may indeed almost have given the impression of tumbling into the sea. The later, (Plio-Pleistocene) Paraiba graben of this region is associated with strong renewed monoclinal outwarping of the same coast at the close of the Cainozoic era (p. 333).

Thus, where displacements are sharp, and where stretching of the superficial arc is implied as in the upper limb of monoclines or at the crest of axial upwarps, deep-seated rheidity may be aided superficially by tensional fracturing as in the pre-Cretaceous fault-block systems of the Natal and Rio de Janeiro monoclines and by the rift-valleys of Africa and Brazil. Such faults die out rapidly downwards to be replaced by flow phenomena in the shield rocks. Hence Lees's inability to find faults associated with the Cretaceous rifts of the lower Niger and Benue Valleys in West Africa is readily understandable.

In contrast with the smooth, broad deformations of the shield areas, only occasionally accentuated by tensional faulting, the earth's greatest tectonic elevations and depressions are restricted to long, narrow zones, the former making mountain chains, the latter ocean deeps. Such mountain chains are composed chiefly of great thicknesses of sedimentary rocks with or without volcanic contamination. Even the final pyramid of Mt. Everest, surmounting 29,000 feet above sea level, is composed of erstwhile marine sediments. By their steep attitudes the rocks of these *welts* record violent earth movements and deformations in the vertical sense, so that since the time of Suess geologists have customarily considered such welts as distinct from the broader features of the shields. Yet no such mountain welts are known to extend beyond the true boundaries of the continents into the deep ocean basins; none is known without an ultimate floor of continental matter, and none appears entirely without relation to other continental features. Their floors thus appear to be parts of older continental extensions, their sedimentary constitution is drawn from neighbouring continental materials (as shown by the predominance of siliceous and argillaceous rock types) and their structures are always developed with relation to neighbouring shield or continental areas which usually, indeed, have participated in the earth movement in modified form. Nor are shield rocks intrinsically more rigid than those of the welts, for they are often found in the cores of mountain ranges folded and squeezed equally with younger sediments of the welts. The arbitrary distinction between shields and welts thus largely falls away and the welts are understood, in essence, to be continental areas that have behaved rather more violently in the vertical sense than the remaining or so-called " shield " areas. Discussion of them is deferred to Chapter IV.

There are often, however, marked differences between sediments derived from shield areas and those from mobile welts that require notice. Whereas the waste from new orogens gives rise to coarse, mixed debris of greywacke type, or to the rapid alterations of sandstone, limestone and shale that constitute the *flysch* facies (p. 101), erosion of flat, shield terrains usually supplies cleanly-washed, quartz sands, often even-grained and cemented into sandstone by silica. Feldspars are lost by chemical weathering and clays are sometimes interstratified with the sandstones. Limestones, partly of chemical origin, are also frequently associated with the sandstone series, and cherts are occasionally prominent, especially if there be nearby acid volcanic activity. Where differential uplift has been pronounced, and dissection is active, feldspars are fresh, the grain is coarse, accumulation is rapid, and arkoses result.

Correlation amid ancient rock systems is difficult because of their sporadic occurrence and the similarities of plutonically metamorphosed rock types; but of recent years radiometric datings have furnished sufficient information for a tabulation (Holmes 1964).

We now summarise the salient features of individual shields (Figs. 23, 24) paying particular attention to those traits that exercise some control over modern scenery.*

The Shield of Africa

The Archean framework of this great plateau, of which Arabia also forms a part, is exposed over about one-third of the whole vast territory, and everywhere the facies is similar : a complex assemblage of plutonic rocks, both igneous and metamorphic, whose structures stand steeply as a result of intense laminar flow at extremely remote date. These ancient structures have in some places guided the trends of later deformation

---

* Only the briefest summaries can be given in a work dealing essentially with the evolution of modern scenery, but the reader who desires more detailed information will find the following general texts helpful: Krenkel *Geologie Afrikas*, de Oliveira and Leonardos *Geologia do Brasil*, Wadia *Geology of India*, Fairbridge in *The Antarctic Today*, David *Geology of Australia*, von Bubnoff *Fennosarmatia*, *Geological Survey of Canada* Memoir on Economic Resources, 1957, Nalivkin *The Geology of the U.S.S.R.*

throughout the rest of geologic time.* Even the Pleistocene rift valleys largely follow the grain of the basement (Dixey 1946; Grantham 1937) though Teale (1936) notes that in Tanganyika the dominant rifting cuts, in many places, " across old tectonic lines of shear and foliation ". According to Krenkel's analysis Africa, together with surrounding ocean floors, is dominated by two sharply-contrasted systems of structural trends, and Cloos (1937, 1939) has rendered a similar theme with greater complexity. Nevertheless, these syntheses are over-simplified and should neither be accepted too literally, nor extended beyond the margins of the continent.

The most complete subdivision of the Archean is established for Rhodesia where the Sebakwian system comprising several thousands of feet of highly metamorphosed sediments and basic volcanics is intruded by serpentines and older gneiss dated radioactively as over 3,000 million years old. Then the monotonous greenstone (30,000 feet thick) of the Bulawayan system (2,800 million years) is intruded by the younger gneiss and includes all the principal auriferous belts of the Colony. Lastly, the fine-grained arkoses of the Shamvaian system (2,600 million years) are intruded by younger (Matapos) granite 1,900-2,150 million years old. Similar divisions based on lithology and to some extent on radioactive dating are possible also in East Africa and the Republic of South Africa; but in both these regions many uncertainties attend correlation of the ancient rock systems. Ancient rocks also make the rim of the Congo Basin and lie beneath the fill of younger systems. Most of them (Kibara and Katanga systems) are younger (1,400 and 600 million years respectively). The pre-Kibaran is folded from the north-east to south-west and an age of 2,630 million years has been assigned to the folding.

Archean rocks crop out also in a chain of major anticlinals from the Moroccan Anti-Atlas via Ahaggar and Tibesti to the Sudan, Egypt and Arabia. Three separate systems of Precambrian rocks are exemplified in Morocco and two elsewhere. Thus an Archean system of gneiss, crystalline schists and serpentines in Egypt, is overlain by further systems deemed of early and late Proterozoic age. Across the Red Sea, in Sinai and Cis-Arabia (apart from some metamorphic rocks of dubious age) are only Proterozoic rocks (Picard 1941).

Another axial " rise " in the basement extends from Sierra Leone by the Guinea Coast to Nigeria, the Cameroons and Oubangi, most of which consists of gneiss and crystalline schist previously foliated roughly normal to the present coast. The relations of these systems to the succession in Rhodesia are still obscure.

Macgregor has drawn attention to a number of mantled gneiss domes, closely crowded together, in Rhodesia (Fig. 25). Between these domes, the Archean rocks are disposed in arcuate or triangular areas, with steep foliation parallel to the curving edges and gneissosity of the intruding domes. The whole pattern resembles a strongly heated convective system, and seems to indicate a stage beyond simple

* A principle demonstrable also in other continents : as by Rudemann for North America, Hills for Australia; and as Schwinner has indicated for the Palæozoic and later trends of Europe.

laminar flow in the solid state, with a higher temperature than is necessary simply to form gneiss.

Early Palæozoic marine rocks are scarce in Africa. In the north the Cambrian is known only near Tetuan, in Morocco, and the Ordovician is confined to a small area within the Sahara. Marine Silurian and Devonian are known, however, sporadically across the full width of North Africa. Mild orogenesis followed the Silurian, and after the Devonian epeirogenesis raised most of the region above the sea, as is shown by the very extensive continental Carboniferous of the Nubian series, with only minor and temporary marine incursions. Essentially similar conditions prevailed in Arabia (Picard 1937) where upon the Archean rock basement stand tabular terrains of early-Palæozoic continental-type sediments passing up into marine types in the late Palæozoic. In South Africa, where the formations probably accumulated in inland seas, palæonto-logical evidence of Cambrian and Ordovician series is lacking. A Cambrian age is currently accepted for the Nama system, on the basis of obscure fossils but this is liable to revision. Reddish Silurian sandstones are widespread from the Cape (Table Mountain sandstone) to the Congo Republic (Upper Kundelungu) where fish scales and crustacean fossils are reported. A Devonian shelf sequence is known in the Cape.

With the Carboniferous in South and Central Africa, began a phase of almost universal continental deposition, at first glacial. This is the Karroo system, already described in Chapter II.

SHIELDS OF SOUTH AMERICA

The ancient nucleus of the South American continent exposed in the Brazil-Guiana massif is composed principally of ancient crystalline rocks. On a geological map the Brazil and Guiana crystallines appear separately, for the ancient plateau has been bisected by the Amazonian lowlands in which mainly alluvial formations crop out, but the Guiana and Brazilian shields are structurally a unit which extends from the Orinoco River to the Sierra de Tandil, south of the River Plate. The visible western boundary of the shield may be traced along the courses of the Paraguay and Parana Rivers, themselves defined by mid-Cretaceous lineaments, but the actual westward extent of the shield is much greater, being marked by the folded ranges of Palæozoic rocks (e.g. Sierra de Cordoba) which make the farther border of the alluvial plains of Paraguay. Nor is this all, Steinmann records that in Peru Precambrian rocks underlie the younger structures of the Andean cordillera both along the Pacific coast and in the eastern foothills, while in Chile and Western Argentina also portions of the basement have been carried upwards in the cores of Palæozoic and later mountain ranges. Thus the ancient continental basement has extended from the east coast of South America to the west.

Through the Guianas the 2,500 million year old Barama-Mazaruni assemblage of rocks strikes approximately parallel to the coast. It was in part granitized and converted into gneisses around 2,000 million years ago to produce the Bartica group of rocks with equivalents in the Rupununi formation to the South. Upon the basement rests, through Venezuela and British Guiana, the flat-lying, Proterozoic, Roraima covering formation.

General accounts of the Brazilian Shield are given by Guimarães (1951) and by de Oliviera and Leonardos (1943). The following brief notes are taken from these sources : the basement is a great mass of gneisses and granites (themselves rendered gneissose). With the former group are classed marmorites, quartzites, amphibolites, with graphitic, talcose and micaceous schists of sedimentary origin, and darker gneisses possibly in part of volcanic derivation. Many of the rocks classed as diorites, grano-diorites and monzonites may at one time have been sedimentary but in the majority of cases uncertainty exists whether they may not also have originated as primary batholiths. Doubt thus attends the deciphering of stratigraphy and tectonic movements in some localities owing to the intensity and extent of granitisation (Guimarães). The features of the shield are displayed in the chain of great mountains directed north-south between the Serra Geral and the coast, the most common rock types being acid gneisses, with orthoclase or microcline feldspar. Other large areas where the Archean basement is exposed are to north and south of the Amazon Valley, the upper Araguaya Basin and the borders of Bolivia.

Resting upon the Archean, after a long interval of erosion which resulted in the planation of vast areas, are several series of less ancient sediments. Earliest of these is the Serie de Minas, which is separated by a succeeding (Huronian) diastrophism (accompanied by magmatic intrusions, metamorphism, granitisation and mineralisation) from the newer Proterozoic. The newer Proterozoic includes the Itacolomi Series and the Serie Lavras, ending with a glacial tillite possibly equivalent in age to the Numees Tillite of South Africa and the Sturtian Tillite of South Australia. The Huronian diastrophism was directed upon lines trending north 40° E, and this, with a succeeding Cambrian diastrophism which was directed north 40° W., governed the trend of the later Caledonian folding of Silurian rocks (the Bambui Series) in the vicinity of the São Francisco River. The folds produced were of the open Jura type.

Upon the southern part of the Brazilian-Uruguayan shield, disposed in an open, discordant basin, lies the Late Palæozoic and Mesozoic sequence of the Santa Catarina system, similar to the Karroo system of South Africa and the Gondwana system of India. This has already been discussed in Chapter II.

In Patagonia, at the southern extremity of the continent, is a second ancient massif composed of several small nuclei welded together by the Cretaceous orogeny which gave rise to the Patagonides. Patagonia itself stands at a lower elevation than the crystalline massifs of Brazilia and South Africa, the crystalline rocks appearing as high as 1,200 metres only in the cores of certain Mesozoic ranges. Windhausen (1931) has indeed considered Patagonia as an element not belonging to the original framework of South America, a view that accords with a wide variety of data.

The general aspect is that of a flat, shield terrain, with local, vertical dislocations as at Gastre. In addition to the Precambrian rocks there are folded Palæozoic systems and the structure owes much to the Palæozoic diastrophism. Mesozoic porphyries are widespread, and lastly appear Cretaceous and Cainozoic rocks, little deformed. With the exception of the Cretaceous dinosaur-bearing sandstones and the deposits of Entre Rios, none of these formations penetrates the Brazilian region—Patagonia, as a shield has operated in a manner different from that of Brazil. A great part of this Patagonian mass is, indeed, now submerged in the broad continental shelf, directed towards the Falkland Islands.

Between the two fundamental units of Brazilia and Patagonia is a " negative element " which represents the scar where these two structural entities were joined together, and which provided an entry for marine inundations of the Meso- and Cainozoic. Its origin goes back to the remote times of Gondwana, for folding in this zone occurred during the early Palæozoic. A similar feature in South-West Africa admitted the sea during Nama time and again later with the *Eurydesma* shales of the Karroo system. Farther to the south was a Palæozoic intracontinental geosyncline the contents of which were rudely disturbed in the Permian when a set of folds caused the original rise of the Argentine Precordillera and the southern cordon of the Sierra de la Ventana.

The present asymmetry of the South American continent is very marked, and 90 per cent. of the drainage is directed to the Atlantic. This is, of course a reversal of the original hydrography inherited from Gondwanaland when the rivers flowed westward from the eastern highlands. The intermittent rise of the Andean chains since the mid- or late Jurassic (Chapter XIV) produced, however, an impassable barrier in the west that diverted the outfall from westward to eastward, and transferred the bulk of detrital accumulation from a situation peripheral to Gondwana to the meridional, intra-continental depression extending from Amazonia through the Chaco and the pampas to beyond the River Plate.

PENINSULAR INDIA

Archean and other Precambrian formations are exposed over more than half the area of the Peninsula, and more youthful formations covering the remainder are everywhere disposed sub-horizontally. Marine rocks are seldom represented in the covering formations : the Peninsula has experienced only very local and brief incursions of the sea since pre-Palæozoic time. Over the same interval it has also escaped orogenic movements, though the presence of typical Gondwana strata " at several places along the sub-Himalayan zone eastward from Nepal up to about long. 95° E. in the Abor Hills, where they are found generally crushed by the mountain-making movements and over-thrust by older rocks " shows that the northern borders of the Peninsular mass have been overridden by the youthful ranges of the Himalaya. The full extent of the Indian shield in that direction therefore remains uncertain. A continuation beneath almost the whole of Tibet to the Kuen Lun and into Yunnan seems by no means impossible. Russian seismologists have indeed recorded evidence of deep level thrusting, perhaps combined with transcurrent movement, beneath the Pamirs, Hindu Kush and Tien Shan that is " consistent with the interpretation that India is still moving northwards, or central Asia southwards " (Holmes 1964). Krishnan (1953) remarks, " The effect of the Assam wedge is seen far to the north-east in south-eastern Tibet and south-western China. The mountain chains of that region show a sharp north-eastward flexure or convexity ". This Assam wedge is a plateau of ancient basement rocks about which the mountain chains of Himalaya and Burma connect at a sharp angle. Separated from the main Archean mass of the Peninsula by a broad strip of the Ganges—Brahmaputra alluvium, the Assam wedge has been uplifted by the Cainozoic forces that built the

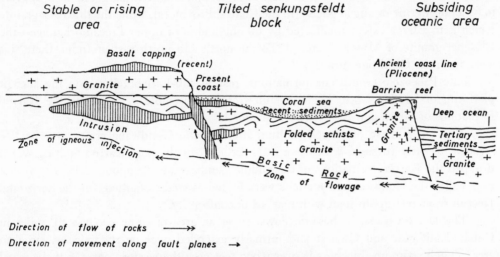

FIG. 28. The eastern extension of Australia as a " senkungsfeldt " beneath the Coral Sea. *after Jensen.*

encompassing ranges and was sliced by faults in such a manner that each slice has been shifted slightly to the south of the one immediately on its west (p. 481). A full analysis by Soviet or Chinese geologists would be welcome.

The oldest rocks of the Peninsula (Aravalli and Dharwar systems) have been rendered strongly gneissose. Among the older rocks also are the peculiar charnockites, hypersthene-bearing rock-types which are sometimes associated with zones of repeated and persistent uplift, and hence may represent deeper, palingenetic zones of the earth's upper crust. Such rocks are found extensively also in Malagasy, Southern Africa, Western Australia and Antarctica all of which regions are deemed (Fig. 17) to have been primordially in close proximity to one another. There is also great similarity in mineral suites from these regions: garnet, sillimanite, graphite, monazite, thorianite, ilmenite, zircon, etc., and du Toit has contended that analogies exist in the strike patterns of the ancient rock systems (Fig. 29). In India, along the eastern side of the Peninsula and in the Aravalli Hills the predominant strike is from north-east to south-west, but through Bombay, Hyderabad and Mysore the trend is at right angles to this. The two directions conflict about the tip of the Peninsula and in Ceylon, which according to these strikes may originally have been sited off Cape Comorin.

Younger Precambrian sequences include the Cuddapahs and Vindhyans, the latter bridging over into the Cambrian like the Adelaidean of Australia and, possibly, the Lavras System of South America. Some of these formations contain obscure fossils that are probably of freshwater habitat.

The older rocks are much intruded by granites, divisible (Krishnan 1953) into three periods. " The earliest of these is generally a highly-folded gneissic complex for which the term ' Peninsular Gneiss ' has been used in South India. The next appears to be a porphyritic or augen gneiss (in the Central Provinces), while the third is a granite which is to a large extent unaffected by folding and is of upper Precambrian age—the Closepet granite of Mysore " etc. " To the north and north-east of India, there was a sea from the Cambrian onwards."

Late Palæozoic Gondwana formations, resting sub-horizontally upon the ancient platform, or let down into it along fault troughs, resemble very closely the Karroo formations of South and East Africa (Chapter II).

The chief phase of trough faulting affecting the Gondwana strata may be late Triassic to early Jurassic, which is a little earlier than the post-Karroo faulting which dropped the Karroo formations of the middle Zambezi and Limpopo Valleys. In the Son Valley the Gondwana formations were folded as well as faulted, for the horizontal Deccan traps rest upon them with marked unconformity.

The Deccan traps, or basaltic flows, cover an area of some 200,000 sq. miles in Cutch, Kathiawar and Gujarat and formerly extended over nearly twice as large an area. The maximum thickness is over 6,000 feet near the western coast, but the usual thickness is less than half of this. Of late-Cretaceous and Eocene age, these great outflows are deemed to have issued from numerous fissures, though centres of acid eruption are known in Kathiawar and the Narbada Valley.

" The traps were erupted and spread over an uneven pre-existing topography. Their base is now found at different levels above or below sea level " from over 3,000 feet in Jashipur to 1,800 feet or more below sea level in Kathiawar. Many of these differences of elevation are due to post-eruptive warping and faulting.

Throughout the late-Mesozoic and Cainozoic eras, only the coastal areas were invaded by the sea. The shield as a whole remained above the ocean and received on its erosionally-planed landsurfaces merely an armour of laterite. Only up the Narbada Valley did the sea penetrate to the interior, in late-Cretaceous, and possibly again in Pleistocene, time.

ANTARCTICA

Inaccessible though most of the continent may be, expeditions to the Antarctic have been well served by geologists and the data already obtained are decisive (Adie 1965). Antarctica consists of two portions: West Antarctica where mountain ranges forming a continuation of the Andean structures extend from the Antarctic Peninsula in long. 40° W. to Edward VII Land and Marie Byrd Land on the Ross Sea at long. 170° W., and East Antarctica on the opposite side of the line joining the great indentations of the Ross and Weddell Seas. This latter, and much larger, area is sharply defined, and beyond a narrow continental shelf plunges rapidly to 4,000 metres beneath the encircling ocean. The oldest rocks known are Precambrian gneisses, schists, limestones and greywackes, vastly intruded by granites. These crop out at many places about the periphery from Coats Land to Victoria Land and thence to the Queen Maud Range at the head of the Ross Sea inlet (Grindley and Warren 1965). Some of these rocks are amazingly like basement rocks of other southern shields, *e.g.* the widespread charnockites of Enderby Land (McCarthy and Traill 1965; Klimov, Ravich, Soloviev 1965), which resemble those of India and East and South Africa, with Malagasy. The gneisses and amphibolites recorded by Roots (1953) from Dronning Maud Land may also link up with the abundant examples of these types in Natal. According to Starik, Ravich, Keylov and Silin the Antarctic charnockites are 915-950 million years old and a later series of migmatites is 700-780 million years old; but a late intrusion of charnockitic granite in the Vestfold Hills (Crohn 1959) is only 500 million years old.

The known data suggest that the crystalline basement of ultra-metamorphosed gneisses and schists, granulites, amphibolites and granites, extends under all of East Antarctica.

Capping the basement above widespread unconformity are both flat-lying and folded sedimentary rocks. Boulders of limestone containing *Archaeocyathinae* from both the Ross and Weddell quadrants suggest that the oldest sediments are Cambrian, like the beds of that age in South Australia. Devonian strata in the mountains of South Victoria Land, and in the Horlick Mountains towards the Pole, appear sub-horizontally upon the basement as forerunners of the Gondwana-type Beacon System of which the characteristic basal tillite member appears in the Ohio Range (Buckeye tillite). Higher in the sequence are sandstones and shales, in places thousands of feet thick, which at Buckley Nunatak in the Beardmore Glacier (lat. 85° S.) have yielded the characteristic plant fossil *Glossopteris*. The youngest beds, containing *Dicroidium* and *Rhexoxylon*, are Triassic. Moreover, the sedimentary rocks of Victoria Land are topped off with basalts, and are intruded upon a grand scale by dolerite intrusions, presumed to be of Jurassic age, that have been compared closely with the dolerites of Tasmania and South Africa (Chapter II).

On the other side of the continent, in Dronning Maud Land, a thick series of unfossiliferous sandstones shows characters that could well dub it as the marginal facies of the great Karroo Basin of South Africa, the eastern extension of which is missing, cut off from that continent. The sediments of Dronning Maud Land are the hosts for large gabbroic intrusions as well as basic dykes and sills, the whole strongly reminiscent of the gabbroic lopoliths of East Griqualand. These facts go far to justify the position assigned to Antarctica in our Gondwana reconstruction.

F

The shield, as already noted, is strongly deformed by the weight of the inland ice but it had already been deformed tectonically at the end of Cainozoic time. In South Victoria Land relief from strain has been achieved by monoclines with downthrows towards the coast of perhaps 10,000 feet. Some of these have been recently revived, with faulting, and active volcanism which may be correlative is avouched by the famous cones of Mts. Erebus and Terror formed of alkali-rich trachytes, kenytes, phonolites and basalts (King 1966).

THE FOUNDATIONS OF AUSTRALIA

Australia is an ancient landmass, the Archean foundations of which are amply exposed in the western half of the continent which may have been land since Precambrian time. But towards the middle of the continent the basement sinks down and is wholly concealed beneath a mantle of Cretaceous and Cainozoic deposits, most of which are non-marine in origin and all of which are undeformed by tectonic movements. Apart from the Macdonnell and Musgrave Ranges of Central Australia, Palæozoic mountain systems are encountered only in the eastern highlands, where no trace of the basement is visible, and the continent might be deemed to have come to an end. Australian geologists, however, have long insisted that the eastern coastline by no means represents the original limits of the continent. They have considered part of the floor of the Coral and Tasman Seas to have belonged formerly to Australia. This is entirely acceptable under our reconstruction of Gondwana (Fig. 29) and will be further examined in Chapter XVIII.

The most complete sequence of Precambrian rocks is in Western Australia where three principal groups, the Yilgarn-Kalgoorlie, Mosquito and Nullagine formations are separated from each other by immense unconformities and granitic intrusion cycles, so that they may correspond to the Archean and the Older and Newer Proterozoic eras respectively. The Yilgarn System consists of highly metamorphosed rock types such as garnet and sillimanite gneisses, charnockites, staurolite-kyanite schists, quartzites and granitic gneisses with satellitic pegmatites and basic intrusions. Correlative formations which show the further extent of the shield are gneisses and schists (micaceous and graphitic) at Darwin, in the Macdonnell and other ranges of Central and South Australia down to the Eyre Peninsula, at Broken Hill, N.S.W., and at Mt. Isa in Queensland.

The Mosquito is mainly an altered sedimentary system of schists, jaspers and dolomites. Formations of similar age are the Pine Creek series of Northern Australia and some of the schists at Mt. Isa, Queensland, both of which contain annelid burrows. At the end of Mosquito time came the greatest irruptions of granite in the history of Australia, including the vast compound batholith of Western Australia. With their hoods of pegmatitic dykes, these batholiths were the chief mineralisers of the continent.

David (1950) describes the Newer Proterozoic (Algonkian) formations as perhaps the most extensive sedimentary system of Australia. " It now covers an area of about 310,000 sq. miles, and the sea in which it was deposited formerly covered fully half the entire area of Australia." Land lay to the north (in the modern orientation) and from heavy (Nullagine) conglomerates in the west the facies changed to thick limestones with *Cryptozoa* of a clear sea at Boulia (Queensland) in the east. In the south-east are the rocks of the Adelaide series, continuous from the Precambrian up into the Cambrian.

A number of separate nuclei (*e.g.* Kimberley, Pilbara, Nullarbor, and the Barkly Tableland) have been recognised in the shield from variations in strike of the Pre-cambrian rocks, and the deformation in belts of the Nullagine formation. Hills (1945)

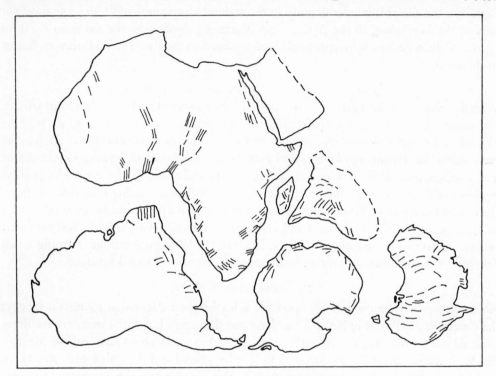

FIG. 29. Trends of basement rock structures in Gondwanaland.

has conjectured that such foldings and thickenings of the crust about centres and axes could be caused by subcrustal convection currents. He was unable " to envisage any mechanism whereby such structures could result from regional compression, but they could readily have been caused by differential vertical movements among a mosaic of blocks ". Vertical deformation on the rheid principle may then be responsible for the zones of strongly folded Nullagine formations in the Ethel Gorge north of the Ophthalmia Range and in the Bangemall district. Wilson has demonstrated that the dominant Archean lineations are north-south, though the dominant post-Archean trends are east-west.

Western Australia has the Permian glacial rocks and other terrestrial formations of Gondwana type, suggesting a close connection with India. This connection cannot have been wholly by land for Teichert has shown that Devonian, Carboniferous and Permian marine rocks run down the West Australian coastal area to lat. 30° S. but it accords magnificently with the relative positions on the reconstruction of Gondwanaland and agrees also with the east side of India where Gondwana rocks of continental type pass laterally into marine Permian as the late-Palæozoic gulf extended into the parent landmass.

The central lowland of rolling plains, from the Gulf of Carpentaria to the Australian Bight was the site of immense deposition throughout Cretaceous and Cainozoic time, yet only at the beginning, in the Aptian, was it actually flooded by the sea from north to south. Cainozoic seas were ephemeral and confined to the Eucla and Murravian Basins in the south.

THE PRECAMBRIAN GRAIN OF GONDWANALAND

With due regard for the swirling strike patterns often encountered in Archean formations, the major Precambrian strike directions in the various southern continents may be plotted and compared with one another in the Gondwana reconstruction. As may be seen in Fig. 29, certain agreements and patterns are displayed as between one landmass and another, and while it would be premature to claim such congruences as positive evidence of former continental unity, the comparison favours, rather than detracts from, the concept of a unified Gondwana. Especially impressive is the enormous development of charnockites in the Enderby Land sector of Antarctica with notable and evidently related occurrences in South-east Africa, Madras and Western Australia, forming a vast province of reconstituted plutonic rocks about the centre of Gondwanaland.

THE LAURENTIAN SHIELD

North America is encompassed upon all sides by post-Algonkian mountain ranges: the United States Range in North Greenland and Ellesmere Land, the western cordilleras from Alaska to Mexico, the Marathon and related systems about the Gulf of Mexico, the Appalachian garland from Alabama to Newfoundland and the Caledonian structures of Eastern Greenland. Everywhere within this framework the continent presents evidence of a stable foundation or shield that has reacted without orogenesis since the Precambrian. The stand of the continent has generally been low, so that epicontinental seas have flooded over it from time to time, leaving on their retreat extensive mantling formations in the central United States and the Canadian Arctic.

Outside of Canada only small portions of the basement are exposed (Fig. 24). It is to the Dominion therefore that we turn to examine the foundations of the continent. Not more than about 20 per cent. of the Canadian shield has been explored in detail resulting, with the usual difficulties and limitations of work in Precambrian rocks, in many uncertainties of correlation. These rocks have been classified by the Geological Survey of Canada (1957) into two main groups: the Archean, including basement survivals in Minnesota, Ontario and Greenland (3,200-3,400 million years), the Keewatin (2,500-2,700 million years) and the Timiskaming. Younger are the Proterozoic groups,

Huronian and Keeweenawan ranging from 2,000 up to 500 million years ago. Additional are enormous volumes of intrusive igneous rocks. All these are disposed (Wilson 1948; 1949) in the usual Precambrian patterns with linear features, strike swirls about less disturbed nuclei (*e.g.* Yellowknife) and so forth which, on the stripped portions of the shield, often show with great clarity in air-photographs.

For the Archean, over the central part of the shield the Keewatin formations are almost wholly volcanic in origin and consist of basic lavas and ashes with very subordinate acidic material and banded cherty ironstones. The limited horizontal extent of the latter indicates that they were probably laid down in ponds and lakes of the volcanic landscape. In Saskatchewan and Quebec to west and east, an increasing amount of ordinary sediment suggests the presence of open water or even the sea, but volcanic detritus continues in the sediments which, though in part quartzites and slates, are frequently converted into para-gneisses. Even older than the Keewatin is a series of sediments (the Couchiching) which at Rainy Lake appears to underlie the Keewatin.

" The sedimentation of late-Archean time was brought to a close by an intense diastrophism, by which the lava flows and sedimentary beds were thrown into near-vertical positions and in places overturned. At the same time, approximately, immense bodies of (Laurentian) granite were injected, and stoped away or otherwise destroyed great parts of the older surficial rocks . . . Throughout most of the shield the general strike of the ancient rocks varies between east-north-east and east-south-east. In the North-west Territories, however, the general strike is northerly.

The Proterozoic formations are very thick and represent a very long span of geologic time. They record a diversity of events such as glaciation in the Gowganda formation, the Algoman orogeny with renewed intrusion by granites, and more than one epoch of planation. The concluding Keeweenawan consists chiefly of shallow-water sediments with tuffs, probably laid down in broad basins between mountains, and the accumulation seems to have been followed by a widespread interval of erosion which reduced the region to an almost featureless plain above which rose only a few scattered hills and broken ridges representing the roots of the Proterozoic mountain ranges. All this was accomplished before the beginning of the Palæozoic era.

The early-Palæozoic formations covering the main shield area are Ordovician and Silurian which are widespread, still in the horizontal position, not only on the mainland of Canada but also across the Arctic Archipelago as far as Ellesmere Land. The epicontinental sea withdrew temporarily during the late Silurian, and again in the Middle Devonian after which the region may be supposed to have remained as land until the Jurassic or Cretaceous. Over the area of the Canadian Shield Palæozoic epicontinental seas waxed and waned as the shield rose or subsided, but the vertical range of movement was small and the total thickness of strata deposited does not exceed 1,000 feet in Manitoba and Hudson Bay. Even these are mainly limestone and dolomite, with subordinate shales and sandstones showing that adjacent land areas shed little terrigenous waste towards the centre of the continent.

The essentially undeformed nature of the Cretaceous and later strata of the Great Plains province between the exposed shield and the western cordillera leads to the supposition that the Archean shield extends far westward, at least to the Rocky Mountains. Southward through the United States, the shield is almost everywhere concealed beneath a cover of younger rocks, but a number of domes (*e.g.* Cincinnati, Nashville, Ouachita Mountains) in which rock series as old as Ordovician are exposed suggest that the real foundations are not far beneath. The shield rocks do crop out, far west in the cordilleran belt, and in the resistant knot of the Colorado Plateau sliced through by the Grand Canyon to display not only the flat-lying Proterozoic strata but also the contorted Archean below. Of the occurrence of basement rocks beneath and within the orogenic welts of the Cordillera and Appalachians we shall treat later, but in these regions its general rigidity has been overcome and it has behaved in a mobile manner.

In basins such as those of Texas, Louisiana and Arkansas mantling rock series sometimes attained a thickness of 10,000 feet but on the arches between, these series commonly thin or cut out by overlap. The later series are more restricted spatially and are frequently of continental facies, especially the Cainozoic sequences associated with denudation of the evolving cordilleran system. These sequences extend eastward from the mountains to the Missouri River.

The Foundations of Europe

Very little of the Archean basement of Europe is now visible. Virtually all the western and southern part of the continent was re-made orogenically in post-Algonkian time (p. 442) and even in the undeformed region of European Russia, Palæozoic and later sedimentary formations hide the basement from view. The most important exposures are about the Baltic Sea where in Sweden and Finland several Precambrian rock systems, mostly crystalline, are exposed in a cluster of nuclei (Murmansk, White Sea, Karelia, Southern Sweden—Finland). In the last-named, granite domes with gneissose margins are separated by narrow strips of tuffs and leptites like the granitic domes about Bulawayo, Rhodesia (Fig. 25). Oldest rocks (3,200-3,400 million years) are the gneisses and schists of the " Basement Complex " heavily intruded by granite and themselves strongly granitised by plutonic metamorphism. A closely allied group is 2,600-2,700 million years old. These rock types continue eastward in the Kola Peninsula to another small area on the shores of the Arctic Ocean east of the Pechora River. Several later rock systems (Bothnian, Kalevian *et al.*), progressively less meta-morphosed with lesser age, range up through 2,100 to 1,150 million years in age. Later is the Jotnian system of red, desert sandstones comparable with some types of the Keeweenawan of Canada, and like them of late Precambrian age. In the U.S.S.R. deep exploratory boring has discovered beneath the Devonian a late-Proterozoic system like the Sinian of China (Nalivkin 1960).

The ancient shield is sharply bounded on the west by the early-Palæozoic mountain structures of Norway, but a western corner has been considered by sundry authorities to project across the North Sea and to underlie the English Midlands in the angle between the crossing of early- (Caledonian) and late-Palæozoic (Variscan) mountain structures that meet from the north and south-east respectively to cross in South Wales. Beyond the Caledonian structures, in the Western Isles of Scotland, Archean rock types reappear. These Lewisian gneisses include rock systems of 2,700 and 1,700 million years old respectively. The late Precambrian rocks of Britain include the Dalradian system and end with the red torrent-bedded Torridonian rocks of Scotland.

From the Baltic Sea, eastwards and south-eastwards the basement rocks are concealed beneath an ever-thickening accumulation of unfolded, transgressive rock systems ranging from early-Palæozoic to Recent in age. von Bubnoff has assigned these blanketing formations to no less than eleven cycles of sedimentation. Because of the blanket which affords a relief seldom more than 100 metres, the limits of the shield in this sector are difficult to define; but geophysical observations show (Bogdanoff 1957) that the crystalline basement dips continuously from the north below the post-Algonkian strata. The surface of the basement shows broad undulations down to a depth of about 2,000 metres near the western Ural and the southern limit of the Central Russian Tableland. " These boundaries are marked by the profound downfaults in the basement" (Fig. 158). On the west the Carpathian structures show the loss of basement rigidity while on the east the Urals provide a similar limit; on the extreme south the Caucasian and Crimean folds continue the boundary, but to the south-east the buried shield reaches almost to the Aral Sea. Most of European Russia thus appears to be underlain by an Archean basement, which nevertheless appears at the surface only in two relatively small areas: one in the Arctic north and the second forming the Podolian-Azov massif built partly of Precambrian gneisses (with charnockites), in the extreme south beyond the River Dniester and towards the Crimea and the mouth of the Danube. Here the rock systems fall into much the same age groups as the Baltic Shield.

The European basement has suffered a chronic tendency to subside in basins sometimes geosynclinally (Chapter IV) but also epeirogenically. The Paris and London Basins of the late-Mesozoic and Cainozoic are familiar, and the North German Basin had a subsiding tendency from the late Trias until the Quaternary, with the basement now sunk 3,000 metres or more. Currently in existence is the Baltic Basin, and three further depressions occur across Russia between northern and southern belts of elevation. Local structures: " ramparts and domes, anticlines and flexures " are numerous therein (Nalivkin 1960).

THE ANGARA SHIELD

The extent of the shield has been investigated by Obruchev (1931), who made the following points: (a) The ancient shield of Siberia consists of Precambrian (Archean and Proterozoic) rocks, metamorphic and eruptive, strongly folded. Cambrian sediments surround the shield to the west, north and north-east lying transgressively upon the older rocks. (b) The basal layers of the Cambrian, where found upon the shield, are conglomeratic passing upward into sandstone and are derived from the ancient shield. (c) The Proterozoic of the ancient shield has two rock series of different ages. The former is strongly folded and metamorphosed to schist, especially in the mountainland of Olekma-Vitim. On the older Proterozoic the newer lies unconformably and transgressively. It is not known upon the inner shield, but is distributed in small zones to the west, north and north-east where it has been strongly folded and intruded. (d) The Caledonian foldings (light middle Cambrian and stronger late Silurian) were, Obruchev expressly states, not of geosynclinal type. He thus tended to think of the shield as extending over the greater part of northern Asia, but left the question open, ending with the title " Older Shield or Caledonian Folded Zone ".

The block of the Angara Shield, as described by Obruchev (1926) and Bogdanoff (1957) is an aggregate of three separate massifs. First is the mass of Primitive rocks, mostly hidden beneath epicontinental Cambro-Silurian strata and Cainozoic lava-flows, which makes the Middle Siberian Tableland, and reaches from the Yenesei River to the Verkhoyansk Mountains beyond the Lena, and from Lake Baikal to the Arctic Ocean in Taimyrland. Eastward from its vertex in the Amphitheatre of Irkutsk a succession of crystalline horsts extends to the Great Khingan; westward, similar massifs appear in the Sayan and adjoining mountains. Both Archean and Algonkian groups are present, the former being heavily intruded and metamorphosed. Suess considered all these crystalline rock masses to be of Precambrian age, but Soviet geologists now prefer an early-Palæozoic age for the crystallines associated with the Sayan and other folds. Second is the probable extension of the basement at low elevation, and beneath a smother of transgressive beds, far to the west below the Siberian Plain, almost to the Ural Mountains where appear marine Jurassic, Cretaceous and early-Cainozoic rocks. The contours of the crystalline basement, which have been followed by geophysicists, rise in a monoclinal warp towards the Central Siberian highland; but elsewhere the floor has low relief. The overlying Cainozoic sediments reach a maximum thickness of 6,000 metres where the river Ob crosses the 60th parallel north latitude. The third massif is the nucleus of the Kara Sea, most of it submerged, but with the Precambrian basement appearing in Taimyr and with its outline confined within the island groups of Novaya Zemlya and Severnya Zemlya.

With the nearby Baltic Shield, northern Eurasia presents one of the largest aggregates of nuclei on the globe. With Mongolia and the Sino-Korean massif, Angaraland has long played the rôle of a *terra-firma* invaded only by shallow seas, of which the Kara and Yellow Seas are substantive examples, or by sporadic inland waters. Three times during the Mesozoic, when the area stood much lower than it does now, the sea transgressed shallowly over the least elevated parts, during the late Trias, the middle Jura and the early Cretaceous. Between each of these incursions were strong regressions. As in China, Jurassic continental formations with coal are known in many places, *e.g.*

along the east side of the Urals (early Jurassic) and on the Dzungarian borders where *Unio* and *Estheria* are common, and about Irkutsk (mid-Jurassic). The plant fossils of the various basins indicate a colder climate (conifers) in the west and warmer climate in the east (cycads). The basins probably represent sporadic tectonic basins rather like the later shallow tectonic basins of modern Mongolia but without the same aridity.

The continental Jurassic of Siberia is very little folded but may be faulted. The thick Jurassic formations of Mongolia (Berkey and Morris 1927) are, however, isoclinally folded, apparently under vertical rheid control. This coal-bearing series of Jurassic and early-Cretaceous age is unrepresented on the Russian platform.

Conversely, the late-Cretaceous—Paleogene marine deposits which extend across the southern part of the Russian platform on to the south-western corner of Siberia are otherwise absent from the entire Angara shield (Nalivkin 1960). Except peripherally in Western Siberia and in the Amur River Basin, the region continued as land throughout the Cainozoic era, and the continental rocks of this era lie horizontally everywhere over inner Siberia. The only dislocations make horsts and grabens as in the valleys of Irkutsk, Urjum, Ungurga, and Bureja.

A further Siberian nucleus appears in the Kolyma region, including the New Siberian Islands and the lower reaches of the Indigirka and Kolyma Rivers (S. Obruchev 1934). Precambrian rocks are there overlain by sediments of a " shelf " facies. This nucleus is separated from Angaraland by the Mesozoic chain of the Verkhoyansk Mountains. The nucleus is remarkable for the abundance and variety of its igneous rocks, effusive and intrusive, including several alkaline types. The Kolyma nucleus did not behave as an entity. It is broken into several pieces which have been elevated or depressed independently. The New Siberian Islands appear from the evidence of terraces to have been elevated, while on the mainland two great sinkings mark the Indigirka and Kolyma Basins and two horsts build the Alaseiski and Jukagirka Plateaus. The Caledonian fold system rims the nucleus in the south but is welded on and equally affected by later epeirogenic movements.

The Chinese Nuclei

" The physical evolution of China has been largely based on a framework that was already laid down in Precambrian times. The existing features, though they came into existence at much later dates, conform in their general arrangement with that ancient framework " (Lee 1935). The widespread occurrence of Archean schists, highly metamorphosed apparently in a deep-seated zone, is indicative of post-Archean rheid tectonics. The trends of fold axes accord with the Baikal and Sayan trends, and, farther south with the Altai ranges so that these directions, repeated many times in later geologic history, seem to have been decided almost from the continental beginnings.

The Wu-tai geosyncline in Northern Shansi typifies the older Proterozoic phase. In it were deposited sediments, the progressively finer grain of which corresponds with a cycle of erosion in a neighbouring highland, and ends with marine transgression. At least one unconformity has been recognised in the system and there was probably more than one cycle of erosion.

"At a period which may be described as mid-Proterozoic, the zone of early Proterozoic sediments was sharply and intensely deformed (Willis). The disturbance was apparently accompanied by granitic intrusions of large volume, which were then or afterward rendered schistose in common with the folded strata. The events were complex. The movements may be classed as orogenic, since they resulted in deformation of strata in an apparently well-defined zone. The strikes follow the Baikal direction (northeast-southwest) in North China, change in the Tsinling Shan to east-west and north-west and extend to the Kuen-lun. Thus they form an arc outside that of the Baikal-Sayan embracing Mongolia. . . This period of orogeny was for the provinces affected equally as important, apparently, as the intense orogenic disturbances which mark the Permo-Mesozoic period in Central Asia ".

There followed a long period of which apparently no sedimentary record is known, until a new sequence accumulated in a trough which traversed Eastern China. In Mongolia an immensely thick series of greywackes belongs to this phase. The Precambrian was closed by a minor episode of diastrophism which, followed by erosion, causes the Sinian (late Precambrian or Cambrian) formations of China and Mongolia to lie with clear unconformity upon the pre-Palæozoic.

A comparable unconformity exists, according to Willis, throughout Central Asia, " but the superjacent strata are probably Devonian or Silurian ".

In and about China appear four resistant nuclei: North China-Korea, Ordos, Tarim, South China-Vietnam. These have not coalesced to the same degree as did most other shields, but are separated by wide zones of younger folded rocks. The edges of the nuclei are extensively overridden by the lesser, marginal folds of these younger rocks. Several of the boundaries of the nuclei are faulted. Away from the intervening geosynclines the deposits of the nuclei are continental, often red beds, demonstrating how great a portion of China has remained rigid throughout long periods of geological time.

The Sino-Korean nucleus appears in Inner Mongolia where continental Mesozoic and Permo-Carboniferous rocks rest with profound unconformity upon a crystalline basement which extends from Alashan and Ordos in the west past Jehol and Moukden into east Soviet territory (Kirin), thus constituting a great barrier which prevented Palæozoic seas from entering Mongolia (Huang 1945). A down-dropped segment through Manchukuo, the Gulf of Pohai and the great Plain of China now separates the mountainous east Manchurian and Korean massif from the Mongolian portion of the nucleus but the two must be deemed continuous. The trough is akin to the Baltic Sea, which lies shallowly upon the Fennoscandian shield. In Korea the crystalline rocks are widely overlain by Cambro-Ordovician, like the similar Shantung Peninsula and its twin Huaiyan massif which also belong to the shield.

Southward from Mongolia crystalline rocks of the ancient nucleus crop out through the cores of the Western Hills of Peking to the provinces of Shensi and Shansi joining with the massifs of Wutai Shan and Heng Shan. Westward, in the vast territory encompassed by the loop of the Huangho, is the platform of Ordos upon which Cambrian rocks still lie horizontally. Little of the basement rocks appears from beneath a mantle of formations from Cambrian to Cretaceous which are exposed in cuestas westwards from the Huangho towards the Liupan Shan. There is also widespread eolian sand and loess, for Northern Ordos is a desert. Southward again, the Precambrian basement emerges in the fold axes of the Tsinling Shan.

Prominent in the tectonics of Asia is the almond-shaped Tarim massif of Sinkiang. Here the basement is obscured by the abundant debris poured into the basin (which has no outlet) from the great ranges which confine it. But the attitudes of the rocks composing those ranges leave no doubt of the hard core against which they thrust.

Smaller than Tarim is the Ferghana Basin to the north-west, a crystalline basement, according to Leuchs, hemmed in between the mountain chains of the Western Tien Shan and the Alai.

From Sikang to Central Yunnan is a belt of basement rocks termed by Huang (1945) the Kam-Yunnan axis. It is of great palæogeographic significance as it divides two geological provinces.

Gneisses and schists, probably of Precambrian age, occupy large areas in the extreme south-east of Yunnan and in northern Tongking. This is the North Tongking massif.

Cambodia and Eastern Thailand possess yet another nucleus, which has played a controlling part in the shaping of the ranges of Annam on its eastern flank, and the Indo-Malay chains to the west, as has also a crystalline mass on the Yunnan-Burmese border.

The distribution of these various resistant knots through Central and South-east Asia has governed the grain of all subsequent orogenies. Their control upon the physiography of Eastern Asia has been tremendous, special local effects appearing throughout that region caused by the sporadic occurrence of the nuclei instead of their welding into a single mass like the Angara and Fennoscandian shields.

CHAPTER IV

CONTINENTAL STRUCTURE : (B) MOBILE WELTS

Mobility of the Earth's Crust. Orogenic Mountain Types. Geosynclines.
The Lithogenic Phase. Facies. The Orogenic Phase. Igneous Activity in
Geosynclines. Geotectonic Environment of Geosynclines. The Manner
of Failure. Behaviour of the Basement during Orogenesis. Tectogenes.
The Physical Nature of Tectogenes. The Orogenic Cycle.

MOBILITY OF THE EARTH'S CRUST

Nowhere is the mobility of the earth's crust better displayed than in the structures of
mountain ranges, for these have all been uplifted far above the average elevations of
the continents by intracrustal and subcrustal forces *that have been resolved vertically.*
Whatever the geologic structure of the mountains : volcanic, upwarped, fault-block or
intensely folded, the tectonic forces have *elevated* crustal segments that formerly stood
at much lower levels. The seat of the tectonic forces is therefore indicated as beneath,
in depth. Indeed, McCutcheon's (1957) analysis of strains induced by self-gravitational
forces, and attendant deformations as applied to the earth, " shows that an extension
type of strain, characterised by radial extrusion of material,'exists in the upper mantle ",
and there doubtless originate the fundamental forces of orogenesis.

Uplift may, of course, be repeated from time to time upon the same, or other,
axes; and the type of deformation may change in accordance with local alterations in
the mobility of the crust. Thus garlanded basic volcanic eruptions have frequently
heralded the production of extremely mobile fold-mountain systems and the destruction
of such mountains under erosion may be succeeded after an interval by re-elevation of
fault-block (horst and graben) systems, as exemplified by the Harz and Erzgebirge of
Central Europe or the Basin and Range Province of the Western United States.

A certain amount of horizontal displacement, too, is represented in many mountain
structures. Geologists tend more and more to interpret this displacement not as the
prime cause of mountain making, but as a secondary consequence of the fundamental
uplift (p. 119).

OROGENIC MOUNTAIN TYPES

The relation between deformation consequent upon the application of tectonic forces
and the local mobility or rigidity of continental basements is well brought out in a
general classification of orogenic mountain types.

Suess, Argand, Stille, Obruchev, Huang and others have put forward classifications
of orogenetic mountain ranges. Table V follows the system of Huang (1945), itself

an elaboration of Argand's classification (1922). Any structural type may originate in any geological period.

Orogenic mountain systems marginal to, or between, the lands generally show the most intense deformation and make the largest mountain chains; systems crossing the continents show greater complexity and variation. They are frequently of the " posthumous " type, mimicking the structure lines of more contorted and more ancient structures below.

Crustal mobility displayed in mountain welts reaches a maximum in the fold systems without ascertainable basement. Therein rock strata that accumulated to great

TABLE V

A. Folds without ascertainable basement (Alpinotype).
   1. Geosynclinal folds (Nappe mountains and folded mountains) (Himalaya).
   2. Offshore folds (Indonesia).

B. Folds on ascertainable basement (Germanotype).
   1. In ancient geosynclinal areas.
     (a) Fold-block mountains (Tien Shan : New Zealand).
     (b) Fault-block mountains (Kirghiz).
     (c) Parageosynclinal (Hunan).
   2. In continental masses.
     (a) With thin sedimentary cover.
       (i) Thin mantle-folds, often overthrust (Tatsing Shan).
       (ii) Fault-block mountains (Shantung).
       (iii) Synorogenic (Epeirogenic movements, synchronous with orogenesis).
     (b) With thick sedimentary cover.
       (i) Faulted and folded mountains (Saharan Atlas).
       (ii) Folded Mountains (Jura).

thickness within subsiding troughs called *geosynclines* are crumpled, and perhaps metamorphosed into schists or even gneisses. The structures of these rocks are often complex, involving successions of anticlines and synclines on both major and minor scales, overthrusting, fracturing by steeply inclined faults, and occasionally in the higher structural levels by horizontal translation of sheets (nappes) and masses of rock. Always, however, the deeper structures (root zones) of such major mountain ranges are disposed nearly vertically (Fig. 30). In Alpinotype orogenic belts the whole section of crust available to geologic study partakes profoundly of the deformation.

In Germanotype deformation, however, the general structure subjected to deformation is of a younger-mass or cover, resting with unconformity upon an older-mass of already folded or crystalline rocks that reacts with a high measure of rigidity.

The Tien Shan, for instance, is an ancient Palæozoic chain which after being denuded acquired subsequently a thick cover, piedmont and intermontane, of Mesozoic and early-Cainozoic rocks. Exceptionally, the piedmont deposits reached a thickness of 15,000 feet, and their folds are almost of geosynclinal nature. The fold axes are similar to those of the original Tien Shan, and Huang writes of an Alpine movement " so intense that a *reformation* of the old Variscan structure was accomplished, and consequently the morphological expression is distinctly Alpine ".

In New Zealand, however, the lines of Cainozoic orogeny, affecting locally a considerable thickness of Cainozoic rocks, conform with the trend established in the earlier (Mesozoic) Hokonui Orogeny, but show much less intense deformation (Fig. 181). The folds often pass into faults and thrusts cutting the pre-existing geosynclinal folds without altering the grain of the country.

In ancient parageosynclinal areas still less disturbance may be found, as in the folded Hengyang Red Beds of Hunan which merely accord weakly with the stronger Mesozoic structures below.

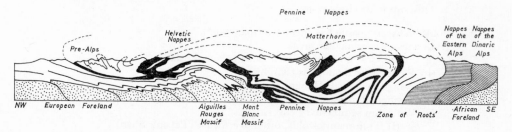

FIG. 30. Section through the European Alps showing rooting of the Pennine Nappes in nearly vertical structures. *after R. Staub.* (Later opinion (Fig. 36) regards the Pennine and Helvetic nappes as independently generated from two distinct zones of major uplift.)

Folds in covering strata resting upon crystalline basements may be extremely varied. In a thick and extensive sedimentary cover disharmonic mantle folds may be developed which slide along the rigid foundation, or else folds conformable with the basement structures. The Jura Mountains are often quoted as of the former type; the latter is exemplified in the Western Hills of Peking. In both types the foundation is either not visible or only partly exposed.

Blocking into horsts and grabens, from which a thin cover may largely be removed by erosion or buried under detritus is a common type of deformation on the shield areas. Under extreme stress thrusting may take place with the formation of overthrust sheets. Huang quotes the Tatsing Shan of Inner Mongolia as of this type.

In a normal orogenic cycle the order and intensity of deformation first follows geosynclines, then platform areas or parageosynclines, and lastly crystalline massifs. Within these massifs the intensity of deformation decreases from the margin inwards. Well-protected areas surrounded by rigid masses are deformed least or remain immune *e.g.* the Ordos platform which is protected by the Tsinling axis and the inner Mongolian axis. Areas nearer to the applied force are said to be folded first.

The rock formations composing fold-mountain systems originate as clastic sediments deposited to thousands of feet thickness in subsiding furrows of the earth's crust called *geosynclines*. The furrows need not always be continuous troughs but rather " a string of elongated basins which might be arc-shaped or straight, and in many examples arranged *en echelon* " (Holmes 1964).

The bulk of terriginous sediments derives from adjacent highlands, rather than from broad plains.

The early history of a geosyncline, therefore, involves slow, intermittent crustal subsidence, prolonged perhaps through several geological periods. The Alpine-Himalayan geosyncline, for instance, was extant from Carboniferous till early-Cainozoic time, and the Appalachian geosyncline from the beginning of the Palæozoic era until the Carboniferous period. Later, the geosynclinal floor and contents are subjected to orogenic spasms, under the influence of which the contents are crumpled, perhaps thrust, and finally uplifted to form new mountain chains.

Though rock systems filling geosynclines are more often than not laid down in marine environments they are originally terrigenous, and no past geosyncline has been described that did not have an association with continental (granitic) crust; nor has modern geophysical research within the great oceanic basins revealed the presence of existing geosynclines far from land. True orogenic deformation has been absent from oceanic basins throughout geologic time; geosynclines are essentially continental features; which is possibly one of the most significant facts concerning behaviour of the earth's crust.

The variety of features which may occur in association with geosynclines has prompted many attempts at classification and over forty names have been proposed for various types (Glaessner and Teichert 1947). For clarity, we define briefly a few of the more important: *eugeosyncline*, a very deep and narrow trough in which the sediments (mostly shales) may be invaded, first by basic igneous rocks (ophiolites or greenstones) and later, when the mountains rise, by granitic batholiths; *miogeosyncline*, a shallower type, perhaps marginal to an eugeosyncline, at other times independent, only lightly intruded by igneous rocks; *orthogeosyncline*, a major trough such as the Alpine geosyncline, often marginal to the continents with perhaps an eugeosyncline phase along the axis and miogeosynclinal phases along one or both sides; *parageosyncline*, a shallower trough situated within a continent and often kept full of sediments so that coal beds and other continental rock sequences appear.

Sometimes the collapse of a major geosyncline gives rise to new geosynclines, usually miogeosynclines, alongside its newly-formed mountain ranges. Thus the rise of the Sierra Nevada from a Jurassic eugeosyncline through western North America produced the Cretaceous Rocky Mountain miogeosyncline to the east and the Cretaceo-Cainozoic Coast Ranges geosyncline to the west (Fig. 31). Likewise the modern rise of the Himalaya was accompanied by depression of the foreland, now filled with alluvium as the Indo-Gangetic Plain (Fig. 32).

Bucher (1933) has made a useful distinction between " homogeneous " geosynclines, which are areas of quiet, long-continued subsidence with marked longitudinal zones showing littoral, shelf and deep-water *facies* continuous for great distances, and " hetero-

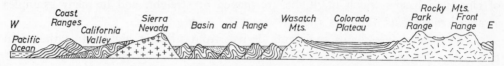

FIG. 31. Section through the Coast Range, Sierra Nevada and Rocky Mountain geosynclinal belts of North America. *after A. Holmes.*

geneous " geosynclines characterised by a lack of uniformity in the sediments when followed from place to place. The latter show much local movement during the period of sedimentation, and even reversals of elevation are common, parts of the geosyncline being emergent for a while. The Cainozoic Coast Range geosyncline of North America was of this type ; and the conditions described off-shore in California, where amid several local basins of thick deposition islands (Santa Cruz, Santa Catalina) rise to above sea level (Emery and Shepard 1945), imply that part of the geosyncline still remains

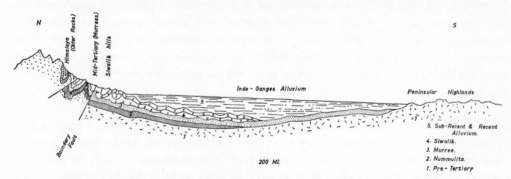

FIG. 32. Relation of the Himalaya to mid- and late-Cainozoic sediments, the Punjabi alluvia and the foreland of Peninsular India. *after D. N. Wadia.*

within the continental shelf (Fig. 213). The vertical oscillations of heterogeneous geosynclines (p. 103) provide an illustration of the dominantly vertical manner in which orogenic forces are applied.

THE LITHOGENIC PHASE

The ultimate cause of geosynclinal sinking is unknown; but the phenomena imply some controlling tectonic condition deeply in, or below, the crust, for the sinking, though normally quiet and progressive, may occur paroxysmally or even be reversed. Once subsidence is initiated the sediments which accumulate in the hollow assist isostatically to depress the crust still farther. The rate of sinking and of accumulation of sediment are sometimes well balanced, giving rise to a great thickness of strata almost wholly of shallow-water type, as in the Appalachian geosyncline. In the lower delta of the Mississippi River, such conditions exist at the present time. Russell and Fisk have pointed out that the load of sediments here deposited should cause an accretion of about 30 sq. miles of land annually. Yet a comparison of surveys made about a century apart shows neither appreciable gain nor loss. The Gulf floor in this vicinity must therefore be subsiding at a rate identical with the building up of sediment. This sediment is deemed now to be 30,000 feet thick in the vicinity of the present coastline, accumulation having begun late in Jurassic time, presumably at about the epoch of orogenesis found in the Sierra Nevada.

The sediment has not accumulated evenly. Regional studies of the emerged part of the Delta indicate (Murray 1952) " that strata have accumulated repeatedly in the depocentres to thicknesses of 3,000 feet, more or less, after which the depositional locale shifted. This thickness of deposit thus appears to constitute the maximal load that can be supported by the elasticity of the crust in a specific area and time. Not allowing for these shifts, the cumulative maxima of formational thicknesses for the western Gulf region totals: Jurassic 111,000+ feet, Cretaceous 131,000+ feet, Cainozoic 211,000+ feet, though for no locus is the actual total of all three known greatly to exceed 30,000 feet ". This illustrates what false conclusions can be drawn for the subsidence of geosynclinal floors by summing maximal thicknesses of individual formations.

Volumes, however, are enormous: Guzman (1952), estimated " the total volume of sediments contained in certain Mesozoic and Cainozoic stratigraphic units in the Mexican Gulf Coastal Plain (excluding the Yucatan Peninsula) is of the order of 303,900 cubic miles ".

The floors of the Welsh and Lake District geosynclines, of early-Palæozoic age, appear also to have sunk by 35,000 feet (Jones 1938). Where the floor of a geosyncline sinks more rapidly than the sedimentary fill thickens, seas (either shallow or of moderate depth) result. The seas of Eastern Asia are geosynclines of this type.

A modern double geosyncline (mio- and eu-) off the coast of North America is described by Drake, Ewing and Sutton (1959). " Many geophysical measurements, including seismic refraction, gravity, magnetics and echo soundings . . . along the continental margin of eastern North America north of Cape Hatteras . . . have revealed the presence of two sedimentary troughs, one under the shelf, the other in deeper water under the continental slope and rise which are separated by a ridge in the basement near the edge of the shelf. The sediments in the shelf trough have been drilled to a depth of 10,000 feet and are of shallow-water character. Cores of the upper part of the sediments of the outer trough (in which sedimentary thicknesses between 15,000 and 20,000 feet are attained) have revealed features attributed to slumping, sliding and turbidity current action, and, in part, to the greywackes of Pettijohn's (1949) classification ".

G

This double trough (Fig. 34) bears a striking resemblance to the double geosyncline of the Appalachians as described by Kay (1951) and seismic data from other continental margins suggest that it may even be a standard type for geosynclines; yet other continental shelves possess only a single trough.

For the future evolution of the North American offshore geosyncline into a mountain system Drake, Ewing and Sutton visualise: " The major process necessary to convert the present continental margin into a mountain system is the one which thickens the crust under the outer, or eugeosynclinal trough. Since the miogeosyncline is already based on a crust of continental proportions, its deformation requires only a means of folding and thrusting the surficial sediments ".

As the base of a marine geosyncline ceases to subside the trough may fill up, and coarser and ultimately continental sediments lap over the marine. This is so in the late Ordovician of the Allegheny geosyncline where sediment became progressively coarser through the Ordovician to the Taconic orogeny, and progressively finer and less extensive through the succeeding Silurian period. May (1942) estimated from the quantity of material that the volume of rock eroded in the Ordovician was much greater than that in the Silurian. The mass raised before the Taconic (post-Ordovician) orogeny was therefore greater than during the orogeny. But it need not have been higher. Typically, however, the bulk of coarse waste (molasse type) is shed after the new mountains have been heaved up into position in the orogenic phase.

Not all geosynclines are marine. Great thicknesses of freshwater beds accumulated in the Rocky Mountain geosyncline, and thousands of feet of alluvium are known to have accreted in the Punjab geosyncline, south of the Himalaya. Indeed, the opinion has been expressed that all geosynclines have had sialic floors, and hence, even though temporarily invaded by the sea, they are always really continental features. According to this view, the coastal geosynclines are interpreted as features of the shelf and slope surrounding the continents, and form part of the continental structure. Umbgrove has remarked (1947) that " The Precambrian basement is also known to crop out in almost all the larger Palæozoic, Mesozoic and Tertiary mountains, proving clearly to what extent the younger part of the earth's history is engraved across the existing records of earlier ages ". These Precambrian basements had the same general properties in those mobile regions as in the visible stable shields (Chapter III) and prove conclusively that those mountain systems were not welded on to a continental nucleus at a later date, but were sited from their beginnings upon already existing continents. This viewpoint may be appreciated better when the chapters dealing with the oceans are studied, for the present we note that it rules out the curious concept, long current in geological literature, that continents " grow " by lateral accretion of successive geosynclinal margins. Without a foundation of continental matter, indeed, it is probable that true geosynclines could never originate, much less function. Whether the great thicknesses of sediment are accommodated by subsidence of the crust into the substratum, or whether the crust itself is thinned by lateral migration of matter from beneath the geosyncline into neighbouring regions is quite unknown; but isostatic equilibrium, as observed, is essentially maintained, which suggests that the excess of mass in the geosyncline must be compensated by a deficiency in the substratum.

FACIES

The history of a geosyncline and its bordering regions derives chiefly from study of the geological formations that it contains. "The clastic sediments accumulated during a given period of time vary from place to place in thickness, grain-size, degree of sorting, bedding and the distribution and kind of organic contents. These characteristics together constitute a facies, and were controlled by the conditions of sedimentation and the life, if any, in the area of deposition ". Normally, of course, the distribution of faunal and of sedimentary facies is related.

Shallow-water marginal zones, adjacent to the lands, show great variation both horizontally and vertically with bedding planes usually sharply defined. Breaks of faunal or lithologic sequence are common, frequently with signs of erosion. Materials are usually well-sorted so that the argillaceous constituents have been cleanly separated from the arenaceous often in alternating bands. The coarser bands frequently display strong and variable current bedding. Conglomerates are typical. Ripple marks are also common. Calcareous materials are abundant, either as reefs, or as banks of shell and shell debris. Oolitic structures appear, and occasionally bands of phosphate.

In the deeper water farther from land, the sediments are more mixed so that the sandstones are usually argillaceous and carry finely-divided chlorite or muscovite, while the mudstones are correspondingly arenaceous, with abundant quartz grains, sometimes angular and of large size. Deposition appears to have been continuous, the beds are uniform and marked bedding planes are few or widely spaced; conglomerates are uncommon. Organic remains are distributed sparsely throughout the sequence rather than concentrated in bands, and carbonate rocks are usually absent, though nodules and concentrations are frequently present. The thickness of the sequence amounts generally to several thousands of feet.

In the axis of the geosyncline, distant from land, dark mudstones and shales may accumulate (the Ordovician graptolite facies for instance). They are generally free of sand, and carry little or no carbonate. Evidence of slumping in the original muds is not unusual. Graded bedding sometimes indicates that the sediments in these deeper zones have arrived in turbidity currents, when the trough may be found to have filled from the end rather than the sides.

At any one time facies pass by gradation laterally into one another, and as the boundaries may, for various reasons, migrate from one geologic epoch to another, the sediments of a given facies in a given period may overlie these of another facies, and be covered in turn by those of a third facies.

The thickness of sediments at any one point is governed firstly by the sum-total of the vertical movements which occurred there to make way for the deposition of sediment (only in a continuously subsiding area can sediments accumulate without interruption), and secondly, by the amount of sediment which arrived there. This is largely a function of the distance from and the physical nature of adjacent land. A rugged terrain supplies abundant coarse clastics, a subdued terrain only small quantities of fine material. In both the mineral constitution of the sediment reflects that of the land of derivation, and perhaps the climatic regimes operating there (Dapples *et al.* 1948).

The presence of conglomerates and breccias grading into arkoses shows the rapid erosion of adjacent highlands, possibly recently risen into position within the geosyncline itself. Thus arose the coarse *Nagelfluh* outwash of the Alps which passes northward into finer grades of sediment. Molasse, which may be deposited in advance or in rear of, or within, the mountain chains according to the situation of the secondary troughs, records the main upheaval of major anticlines from the axis of a geosyncline. Stages in the rise of the Alpine chains are thus recorded by temporary greater abundance and wider spread of the nagelfluh facies. The chief of these phases was in the Vindobonian. Likewise, in front of the late-Cretaceous ranges of the Rocky Mountains appear the Palæocene local conglomerates of the Arapahoe and Denver formations.

Appraisal of facies in the European Alps has also been instrumental in the interpretation of the complicated fold and thrust structures which build the ranges. Thus where sheets of rock (nappes) have been forced over one another, Arnold Heim has been able to demonstrate the direction of origin of the sheets and to restore in continuous section the deposits of the geosyncline (Fig. 33).

The importance of the concept of facies is well brought out also by studies of the early-Palæozoic geosynclines of Britain and the United States. For the former, O. T. Jones (1938) has been enabled to reconstruct from the intricate facial detail both the physiography of those early times, with at least three basins (Welsh, Moffat and Durness) forming simultaneously, and the earth-movements associated with the sinking and deformation of the various basins of deposition. In the United States Kay (1942) has rendered similar service, showing that the greatest stratigraphic thicknesses were laid as extensive semi-lenses of detrital sediment in depressions complementary to uplifts of the Taconic and Acadian orogenies. These he calls deltageosynclines. They were confined by the Cincinnati and Adirondack axes which were " arches for limited times, were hinges of oscillation, and at other times were more depressed than the central part of the Allegheny belt ".

Isopachs, or lines joining places of equal thickness of sediment (Fig. 34), normally make oval or elongated shapes about the centres or zones of maximum deposition. Changes in the shapes and location of the isopachs as revealed from formation to formation reflect the physical changes taking place in and around the geosyncline.

Sedimentation does not proceed undisturbed. In addition to punctuation by minor orogenic disturbances, there may be effects due to regional movement (epeirogenesis), tilting and warping, eustatic movements of sea level, and isostatic depression under loading. All these may be found recorded in changes of facies in the sediments accumulating here and there in the geosyncline.

A profound change of facies is brought about when newly formed mountain structures first begin to rise above sea level. Masses of soft rock are freshly exposed to severe

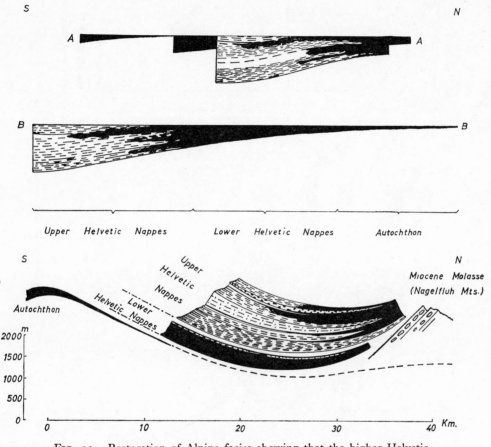

FIG. 33. Restoration of Alpine facies showing that the higher Helvetic nappes derive not from the north where they now appear but from the south. *after A. Heim.*

erosion and the detritus is poured rapidly into the remaining basins, marine or continental, to accumulate as the " Flysch " facies, a series of rapidly alternating beds of sandstone, mudstone and limestone, in some regions attaining remarkable thickness. With the heaving of the mountain chains to their full height this type of deposition ceases, and is succeeded by the yet coarser, wholly continental facies of the " molasse ". The flysch of the Alpine System, extending from the Pyrenees to Tibet, is Cretaceous-Eocene in age, the molasse is mid-Cainozoic, the mountain chains having attained their full height and majesty in the Oligo-Miocene.

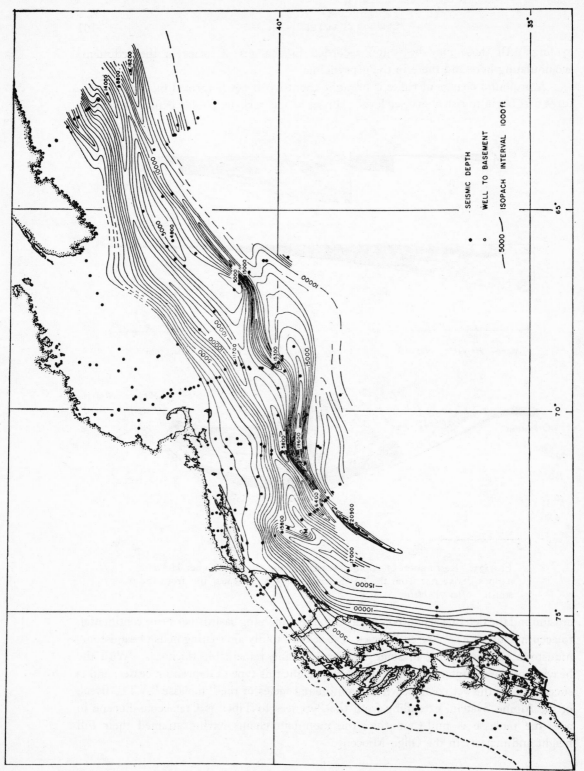

FIG. 34. Isopachs showing thicknesses, in feet, of sediments in the double geosyncline

Thick greywacke sequences have been regarded as equivalent to the flysch sequence in the orogenic cycle. They contain much fragmentary phyllite, slate and chert in contrast to the clean quartz grains of a normal sandstone, which suggests that they were derived upon erosion of previous orogenic terrains composed of clastics that had undergone low-grade metamorphism to slate and phyllite. Greywackes are abundant about the Pacific margin being dominant rock types in South-east Alaska, Japan and New Zealand. The enormous thickness of late-Palæozoic and Mesozoic greywackes and argillites of New Zealand predicates a source in a rising region to the west in Gondwanaland. If surmises on continental drift are correct this land may have been the Palæozoic mountains of Eastern Australia (p. 453).

Greywackes are generally regarded as " dirty " sediments, carrying a considerable amount of volcanic material, usually andesitic in composition. In the cordillera of western North America such deposits have been interpreted as related to garlands of formerly existing island arcs (p. 441).

Certain of the widespread coal-bearing formations in the depressions of earlier Hercynian chains, from the Mississippi through Europe and Central Asia to China have also been described as corresponding to flysch deposits.

The long-continued subsidence to which a geosyncline is subjected stretches and weakens the floor and carries it down into regions where rigidity may be overcome by increase of temperature and new stress conditions, sometimes accompanied by basic igneous intrusion.

Deformation brings an increasing relief of the sea bottom, accompanied by accelerated sinking of minor basins, into which abundant new material (flysch) is poured from islands as the rising anticlines appear above wave base. This stage may be reached at different times in different parts of the geosyncline. Finally, the floor and contents of the geosyncline become mobile (p. 105) and deform with elevation of its contents into fresh mountain ranges (Fig. 35). The main lithogenic phase is then over, and the principal activity centres about crumpling and elevation of the sediments. This is the orogenic phase.

The Orogenic Phase

The final yielding of the crust beneath a geosyncline is usually sudden compared with the prolonged lithogenic phase which precedes it, though the final collapse is usually heralded by premonitory shudders which may from time to time interrupt the lithogenic phase, to be followed in turn by renewed quiet sinking and detrital accumulation. Such early movements have been demonstrated in the Alpine geosyncline, where the sediments of individual areas sometimes show changes from bathyal to shallow water. It has, indeed, been described as at times " a highly mobile zone, full of archipelagoes, shallow seas, deep basins, and long troughs ".

Heterogeneous geosynclines have, moreover, a complex interplay of the lithogenic and orogenic phases, which succeed and replace each other repeatedly. Sedimentary formations thicken and thin rapidly and locally.   Thus the Cretaceous formations which total over 7,000 feet north of San Francisco Bay are missing completely beneath the Eocene beds of San Pedro Point south of San Francisco, and the Miocene formations behave similarly.   The Eocene and Oligocene, on the contrary, thicken in the opposite direction by 4,000 feet and 2,500 feet respectively.   Whether in the positive or negative sense, activity in heterogeneous geosynclines is expressed almost wholly in vertical planes, and

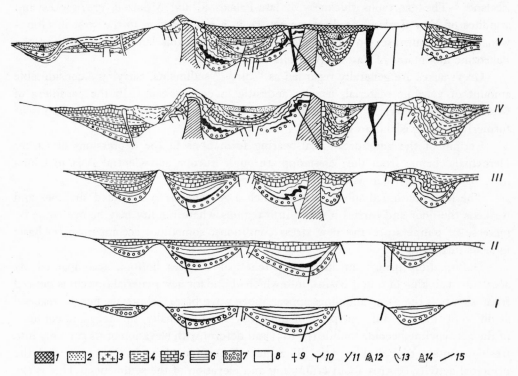

FIG. 35.   Rock series accumulated in the development I-V of a geosyncline.   *after V. Belussoff.*   1. Molasse, 2. Coal-bearing sands and mudstones of intramontane and marginal depressions, 3. Salt and gypsum deposits, 4. Carbonaceous sediments, 5. Limestones, 6. Grits, sandstones, shales, 7. Basal grits and conglomerates, 8. Basement, 9. Dykes connected with volcanoes, 10. Basic intrusions (ophiolites), 11. Metalliferous intrusions, 12. Granitic batholiths, 13. Small alkaline intrusions, 14. Salt domes, 15. Faults.

even during failure verticality is expressed in powerful fault-block movements (*e.g.* Californea, New Zealand).

The history of major geosynclines may thus include several alternating phases of accumulation and deformation.   The Sierra Nevada-Rocky Mountain (Nevadan and Laramide) orogenies are viewed thus by Eardley (1944) as a single main event, with at least ten minor deformations ranging in age from late Jurassic to mid Oligocene.

The several orogenic crises of a single revolution seem generally to increase in intensity to a maximum, and then rapidly decrease. According to Stille (1924), the individual orogenic pulses are of short duration, and are essentially synchronous throughout the world, though not necessarily of the same intensity. Detailed strati-graphic work does not seem wholly to support this view, though the broad principle may perhaps be admitted. Within large divisions of time, say one-third of a geologic period, synchroneity of major orogenic impulses in different parts of the world does exist, but it breaks down for shorter intervals of time.

The deformation undergone by rock systems involved in orogenesis ranges from simple anticlines and synclines to highly complex overfolds and flow structures. Many of these latter have been diagnosed as due to gliding, under gravity, of geosynclinal contents down the flanks of geanticlines raised within the orogen. Thus the great Helvetic nappes (Fig. 30) are deemed to have slid off the northern flank of the Aar-St.

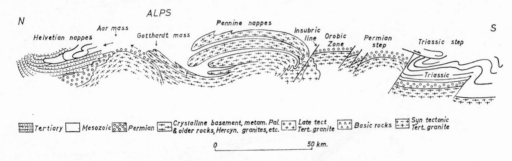

FIG. 36. Structural analysis of a cross-section through the Alpine-Dinaric belt of Southern Europe. *after L. V. de Sitter.*

Gottard massif towards the neighbouring depression, partly tectonic and partly erosional in origin (Fig. 36), while the Pennine nappes were generated from a still more uplifted zone in the south. A similar explanation has been proffered for the flysch nappes of both the western and central Alps, and it is clearly applicable to fold and thrust structures within mountain ranges in many parts of the world. Instances are known of sliding induced not by super-elevation but by denudation of neighbouring areas. Such morpho-tectonic deformation is described for Haute-Provence by Gohan and Veslin (1959) (Fig. 37). All grades of deformation are known from an undeformed slab sliding over a rigid basement to a highly mixed mass of incompetent strata wherein most of the movement is accomplished within the gliding mass itself. During translation, the *Argille scagliose* of the northern Apennine foothills, for instance, must have moved as a veritable rock glacier (Merla 1951), and the front edges of Himalayan *nappes* have even flowed into gorges through the frontal Siwalik Hills (p. 528). The presence of low rheidity salt and mud-stone, and the transformation of anhydrite into gypsum, greatly aid in flowage; thus folding in the lower Fars (Miocene) series of Iran (wherein these materials are abundant)

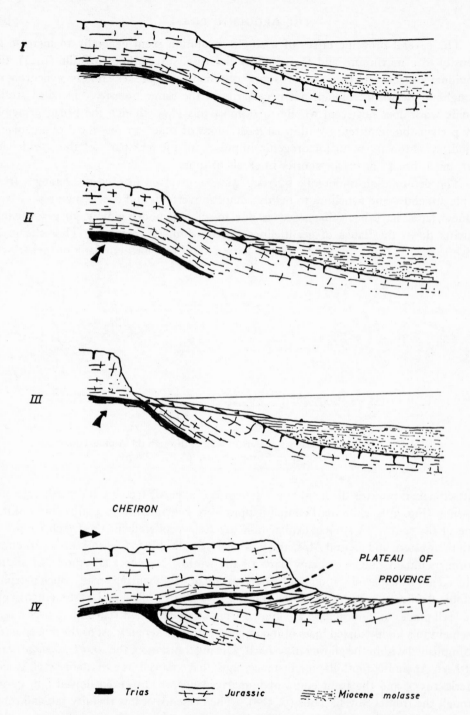

FIG. 37. Production of an erosion thrust in southern France.
after G. Gohan and J. Veslin.

is highly complex and even involves flows over neighbouring areas of younger (Bakhtiari) formations where these stood at lower elevations (de Bockh *et al.* 1929).

On the whole, the larger the moving mass the more coherent will the structure remain. Also, the larger the mass the smaller the dip of the gliding plane need be.

But not all lateral displacements of strata are due to gravitational sliding. Many examples are known (*e.g.* Rocky Mountains) of masses which have ridden *up* an inclined thrust plane. In general such masses are of stronger formations than are involved in gravitational sliding, and granite or other basement rock is not seldom involved in the thrust mass. Followed back to the root zone these thrusts commonly steepen to quite high angles suggesting that the fundamental force is one of *levity* in the axial zone of deformation with secondary lateral extrusion of part of the super-elevated mass into adjacent sectors. If this is so, and even granite appears to have flowed laterally upon some of the Rocky Mountain thrusts, then both forms of deformation find origin in a single basic cause; the abnormal elevation of a segment of the earth's crust followed by lateral *flattening out* of the mass under its own weight by flow (above) and thrust (below) (Fig. 38).

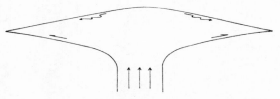

Fig. 38.   Lateral spreading under gravity of materials in an orogenic welt involving (*a*) gliding and folding in upper sector, (*b*) thrusting in lower sector.

As a result of experiments Bucher (1956) described the process of orogenic deformation : " As the orogenic welts rise to elevations greater than can be supported by the strength of the rocks they flatten under their own weight, turning into recumbent folds which, advancing, produce the tectonics of marginal folding and thrusting, the peel thrusts and the wholly superficial phenomena of thrust flows and tilt flows. Where more mobile magma bodies reach higher levels in large volumes, they dominate the structure. Flattening under their own weight, they produce similar though more localised and irregular effects on the foreland ".

At a maximum of deformation schists are produced by mineral transformations which may be multiphase and widespread. During static intervals other suites of metamorphic minerals may be produced as in the late-Mesozoic (Rangitata) orogeny of New Zealand (p. 471).

Belussoff (1959) has given a synopsis of various types of orogenic folds and their development in association with vertical displacements of the crust. The orogen, he postulates, is divided by faults or steep flexures into sectors (Fig. 39) in each of which a characteristic mode of deformation occurs. Successive sectors are often elevated and depressed like the keys of a piano (*e.g.* the " coffin folds " of Ferghana (Fig. 40) or the calcareous terrains of Dagestan, or are arranged stepwise as in the Tien Shan or perhaps the Jura. Straightforward folds of great variety may originate within each sector.

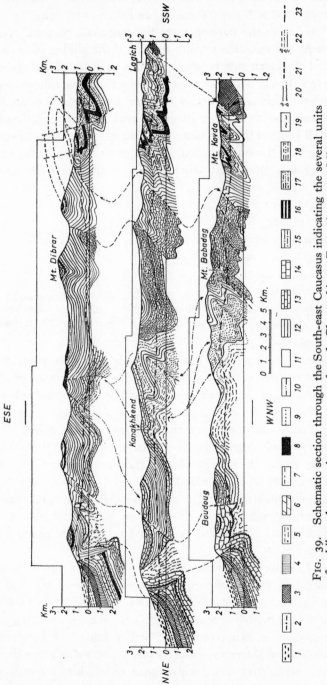

FIG. 39.   Schematic section through the South-east Caucasus indicating the several units of a bilateral mountain structure.   *after A. Chouryghine.*   Formations 1-4. Miocene to Palaeocene, 5-13. Cretaceous, 14-18. Jurassic, 19. Gliding planes, 20. Stratigraphic contacts, 21. Lines indicating corresponding structures.

More complex fold systems, including "injection folds", may result from interactions between the sectors. Where sedimentary sections are thick the rock often behaves plastically. Flow also occurs where incompetent members are present such as the Trias of the northern Jura; and clay *diapirs* (p. 119) form, even in regions so little disturbed as the Mississippi delta, where there are marked differences of density between formations subjected to stress. Within structural arches extrusion tectonics operate with horizontal as well as vertical component.

Elevation of geanticlines within the axial zone of a geosyncline likewise exercises lateral pressure upon adjacent sectors, causing folding therein. If sectors are arranged stepwise, as may well happen upon this scale, there will be a tendency (Belussoff 1959) for each sector to react unilaterally upon its lower neighbour causing thrust phenomena as well as folding. Under injection tectonics, nappes of Alpine type may be generated at higher crustal levels, while steeply dipping schists record the fundamental vertical displacements of the axial zone.

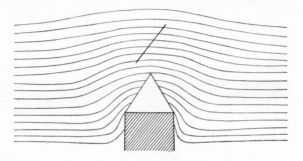

FIG. 40. Deformation of "coffin" folds. *after A. Sytcheva-Mikhailova.*

The general pattern of folding by sectors within an orogen is expressed by Belussoff (Fig. 41), whose orogenic history of a geosyncline also appears in Fig. 35.

Folding probably occupies a long period of geologic time, with episodes of greater activity or of rest. While the fundamental activation doubtless arises in depth (p. 669) it is probably aided by repetitive erosion and isostatic rise of the original geanticlines. Belussoff has indeed remarked that phases of folding coincide with the appearance and development of geanticlines centralised within the geosyncline.

Modern tectonic theory points more and more to the general near-vertical attitude of many axial orogenic structures, and minimises the effects of lateral compression within the earth's crust. Under this concept, the forces controlling orogenesis must be deep-seated. As long ago as 1918, R. D. Oldham observed of the Himalaya and Pamir that "The broad features of the major relief, as well as the determination of the more restricted zones of greater uplift are not the result of processes apparent in the structures visible at the surface, but of more deeply seated, and possibly quite independent processes which are not accessible to surface observation". He sought the chief cause of elevation in phasal changes "localised, or at least concentrated in the lower part of the crust, or [prophetically perhaps] in the layer immediately beneath it". Of late de Sitter (1956) has drawn attention to the "remarkable independency" of many younger with regard to older orogenic zones "in the sense that trends may be perfectly independent". Crossings are quite common, as in the younger and older Appalachians, and de Sitter quotes the westerly plunge of the High Atlas structure cutting " perpendicularly through the strong north-south Caledonian and Hercynian trends of the Moroccan meseta ". Such relationships could only be normal, as they appear to be, if the intersecting structures marked the outcrop of steeply standing zones of deformation within the crust. Being nearly vertical, such orogenic zones might well be conceived as passing through the entire crust, and serving as conduits for the radial transfer of energy from the substratum towards the earth's surface. Where lateral compression occurs in association with orogenic zones, it should then be regarded as secondary and due

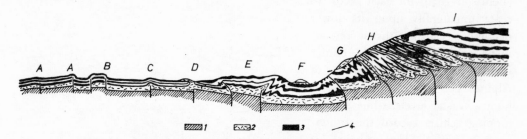

FIG. 41. Idealised structure of a zone of folding involving: 1. Crystalline basement, 2. very plastic formation, 3. stratified sequence, 4. Faults. The various sections separated from one another by steep fractures are: A. Monoclinal folds. B. Fold on a block bounded by two faults. C. Injection fold. D. Piercement structure. E. Folds in a block bounded by two reversed faults. F. Gravitational Nappes. G. Gravitational Nappes with discordance. H. Zone of "crushed" rocks. I. Median Block relatively undisturbed. Each block reacts on the one at lower elevation. *after V. Belussoff*.

to the resolution of forces by imbalance, either original or produced by heterogeneity, of the earth's crust. van Bemmelen (1949) has adopted a similar viewpoint that the primary movements are vertical and due to processes of a physico-chemical character embodied in " hypo-differentiation ".

Before pursuing the topic further we note that, following the major deformation of rock systems, broad uplift elevates the newly-formed fold structures so that they form a mountain range at the surface. As they come under erosion coarse waste is shed to accumulate as molasse partly in shallow seas, partly in lakes, and partly in piedmonts. The flysch troughs are then above sea level, but while the main mountain ranges rise the molasse basins tend to sink.

The great heights of major mountain ranges, such as the Rockies, Alps and Himalaya were attained only long after their respective crumplings. In some instances final elevation was accompanied by profound, nearly vertical faulting. While the complexity of structure is usually a result of the deformational stresses applied, the height of the ranges often depends more upon the thickness of the sediments than the strength of the diastrophism.

The maximal depth to which orogenic folding extends within the crust is uncertain but steep synclines are known to carry sedimentary formations to depths approaching 60,000 feet into crystalline rocks. Lees quotes as examples infolds of Mesozoic rocks penetrating the Variscan basement of the par-autochthonous massifs within the Alps.

What happens at the base of a geosyncline, when basal rocks and lower sediments are carried down into depths where rule temperatures and pressures to which they are foreign? Clearly the rocks must be altered, and this is perhaps a typical condition for the production of regional metamorphic effects.

Wahl (1949) has pursued this topic far into the speculative realms of rock genesis. He deemed the rock matter of the geosyncline, both contents and floor, to pass through successive stages of metamorphism appropriate to successively new temperatures and pressures as it is carried down. These changes may be zonal and correspond to the metamorphic zones of Grubenmann and other authors. The existence of strong stress is important, for it governs to a considerable extent the order in which the minerals are reconstituted under metamorphism. Some minerals are reconstituted under stress earlier than others. Crystallisation of albite, for instance, precedes anorthite, though from an igneous melt under uniform pressure this order of appearance is reversed. Some of the earliest minerals to be reconstituted in this way are albite-rich plagioclase, potash feldspar and quartz, which tend to grow along foliation planes produced at a lower grade of metamorphism, to form a banded rock or gneiss. Some portions may be melted and squeezed out of the host along foliation planes of surrounding colder rocks as *lit-par-lit* injections. Such removal of acid constituents renders the residual gneisses more femic in constitution. Certain of the hornblende-mica gneisses so abundant in Archean rock series may well have been generated as residues in this way.

At deeper levels as heat becomes dominant, stress fades away (though not before laminar flow in the solid state has operated through the rockmass) until, if the processes be carried far enough, selective melting and finally complete remelting or *palingenesis* occurs. Palingenetic magmas produced in this way have, according to Wahl, relatively little eruptive power " since they have not acquired temperatures much above their temperature of solidification ". We may see in them the materials of the potash-rich, concordant batholiths which appear in certain favourable structures in the cores of mountain ranges.

Wahl follows this selective palingenesis further, and visualises with the expulsion upwards of still more " acid " material the production at greater depth of yet more mafic rock types such as charnockite, which being always associated with regions of repeated and persistent uplift, may represent formerly deep seated palingenetic zones. This leads to a consideration of igneous activity in geosynclines.

IGNEOUS ACTIVITY IN GEOSYNCLINES

The phases of igneous activity associated with geosynclines are:

a) Quiet intrusion of the sediments by tholeiitic basalt. These bodies enter either during the subsidence of the geosyncline or during the first orogenic spasms when the stretched floor yields along tensional fissures. They are possibly due to geostatic loading (p. 24) and the nature and attitude of the overlying formations exert a degree of control over the manner and extent of intrusion. Flat-lying formations above continental basements are dyked, but if the geosynclinal contents are very thick, and the resources of magma are not exhausted, the whole column of sediments and any superincumbent lavas may be lifted, as pressures are relieved more easily by injecting the residual lava into large sills and gently transgressive sheets, or even into lopoliths.

b) When folding has begun, with the development of innumerable vertically-disposed planes of laminar flow, possibly expressed in steep, isoclinal folds, easy passageways are provided for the upward penetration of vapours, liquors and magmas which thereby ascend with facility into higher realms of the crust.

At the main onset of orogenesis, with rapid failure of the heated crustal base, peridotitic or serpentinous rocks may be injected with great rapidity through the entire thickness of the crust. The intrusions make a long narrow outcrop (or occasionally twin parallel outcrops (p. 658)), and are never repeated within a single orogenic cycle. The mineralogy of these orogenic peridotites is simple : they consist mainly of olivine with a little enstatite accompanied by diopsidic augite; chromite or chrome-spinel is a constant accessory. Feldspars are absent. This characteristic mineral assemblage surely implies derivation from the mantle zone beneath the earth's crust.

Intrusion may be in the solid state, as with the Mount Albert dunite of Gaspe Peninsula which has a structure like a salt dome; but Hess (1955) finds this unsatisfactory as a general hypothesis because serpentines occur along the margins of alpine systems where folding has not been intense, and they sometimes form accordant sills in low-dipping sedimentary rocks. Moreover, " the internal fabric of the serpentines rarely shows evidence of flow, for the delicate network or mesh structure is very commonly present throughout. If solid flow has occurred it must have preceded serpentinisation ". As slickensided, slippery shear zones form easily in serpentines and afford ready planes of movement, however, quite considerable bodies of solid serpentine may slip into sediments by " lemon-pip " tectonics.

But the most remarkable fact is that though such rocks have normally a density of 3·2 or more they ascend with apparent violence through crustal rocks with a density as low as 2·7 ! The only possible explanation is that at the time of irruption the ultramafic magmas were so heavily charged with volatiles that their density was for the time being reduced below 2·7. The most abundant volatile component in volcanic eruptions is steam, and as the olivine of many of the bodies has been metasomatised to serpentine (a transformation that takes place below 500° C.; 13 per cent. by volume of water being required to effect the transformation, which also involves an increase in volume of approximately 25 per cent.) the conclusion is obvious that the activity is caused by accumulation of superheated water vapour in mantle rocks immediately below the Mohorovičić discontinuity.* Once begun, the release of pressure consequent upon ascent to higher levels could be expected to increase the violence of the action just as ebullience increases within the throat of a playing geyser. Fundamental forces of substratal origin are available here and we shall return to consider their general import in geosynclinal evolution in a later section (p. 675); but before leaving the subject we note a further conclusion from Bucher's experiments (1956), that *folding of materials is confined to a warmed, weaker zone no matter where pressure is applied upon the whole system.* So orogenic deformation is localised where viscosity is temporarily reduced and mobility is initiated by access of subjacent heat and perhaps volatiles (igneous action) rather than by any geometrical pattern of " forces " in the earth's crust.

c) If the geosynclinal base subsides slowly, or an early orogenic phase supervenes, opportunity arises for the fractionating processes described by Wahl to operate, and concordant plutons, rich in soda or potash, may be injected.

d) Extensive intrusion of huge granodioritic batholiths, sometimes accompanied by andesitic eruptions. In the cores of orogenic welts these intrusions, and their effusives, may be linked for hundreds or thousands of miles. Volcanics associated with the Yenshan orogeny of eastern Asia, for instance, extend along the coast for 2,500 miles from Kuantung to the Soviet Far East. The eruptions there usually began with flows of andesite, followed by trachy-andesite and trachyte and concluded with thick rhyolitic flows and pyroclastics. The first andesites of Mongolia appeared in the late Jurassic and later ranged into the Cretaceous, but rhyolites are confined to the Cretaceous, wherein they are widespread. Immense granite batholiths are associated in Mongolia and Manchukuo as well as at the coast.

Much research has been directed to phenomena of synorogenic granites and associated metamorphic rocks by Wegmann and by Read who summarises (1955): " During orogeny the basement acquires a new structure and locally becomes plastic. The development of this state is associated with the appearance of diffuse granitic material of a definite quality. The most granitised parts are found to be the most mobile, and certain characteristic patterns of deformation can be established ". " The granite rocks produced vary in form and composition with time and place [passing] from early diffuse granitisation granites, dominantly sodic, to late circumscribed and

---

* At higher levels additional water may be derived from the geosynclinal sediments themselves, and Hess has cited examples of more extensive serpentinisation among such sediments than amid relatively anhydrous crystalline gneisses at greater depths.

H

intrusive granites, dominantly potassic ". With increasing time and at deeper crustal levels they pass through the series: autochthonous granites—migmatites and meta-morphites—parautochthonous granites—intrusive magmatic granites—granite plutons. The early soaking of the country rock by volatiles to form migmatites with appropriate flow structures culminates in intrusion when mobilisation is achieved. The series plainly indicates a source for the activating volatiles and heat at considerable depth; Read places it below the granitic crust. But the activity sometimes reaches high into the geosynclinal sediments themselves: and conversions of sediments into granodiorite upon a large scale have been described from Nanga Parbat by Misch (1949). Seemingly the vast discordant batholiths of British Columbia and Alaska also transformed their way across folded structures of the mountain belt until they were relatively close to the surface. The summit of Mt. McKinley, presently at 20,300 feet, is of this intrusive granite which has burst through the intensely folded and thrust-faulted Ordovician rocks on its flanks.

Temperatures at which migmatisation takes place have been estimated by Barth (1956) using the partition of albite between alkali and calcic feldspar. He found that at 400° C. fine-grained migmatites were formed, at 430° C. the grain became coarse, and at 550° C. granites were formed capable of intruding the surrounding rocks.

Even in the migmatite front considerable mobility of suitable metamorphic rock types may be achieved. Thus amphibolites which contain an hydroxyl radicle are commonly subject to " wild folding " with " recumbent folding, crenulations, flow breccias and other evidence of plastic deformation ".

Contacts between synorogenic granites and overlying sediments show that grani-tisation and accompanying crustal displacements occur during later orogenic phases. Thus in mantled gneiss domes (Finland, Rhodesia) the gneissic core is clearly intrusive into the schist envelope of which it forms the basement. Eskola (1949) who studied these structures in many regions concluded that " As granitisation is intensified, mantled gneiss domes pass gradually into magmatic masses, or plutons that by them-selves would be interpreted as . . . intrusive masses ". The source of granite intrusives within orogenic welts is the granitic crust itself, and Read concludes : " Folding, granitisation and mobility go hand in hand. The same granitic rock is Precambrian basement in Sweden and early-Palæozoic intrusions in Norway " (Fig. 42). Crystalline massifs of orogenic welts may thus be re-activated in later orogenesis e.g. late-Palæozoic massifs of the Höhe Tauern that behaved plastically during the Cainozoic Alpine orogeny (Exner).

From studies in the western cordillera of North America, Gilluly (1963) has made an important point: that " there is no obvious correlation of tectonics, either with metamorphism or with granitic intrusion, though both metamosphism and granite are obviously associated with tectonism. To judge from both sedimentary and structural records volcanism and orogeny have been active at one place or another in the region throughout Phanerozoic time, though of course being highly episodic locally. Plutonic processes, on the other hand, have been highly concentrated in the Cretaceous, less so in the Miocene and, almost trivial at all other times during the Phanerozoic whose records we can read ". If this is general, episodic plutonism is likely to prove much rarer than episodic tectonism.

  e) Late intrusions and extrusions (often of alkaline rocks and other local differentiates) appear after the crust has rigidified and is in a condition for faulting.

As there may be several orogenic crises in the course of a revolution, the processes of the igneous cycle, like those of the sedimentary cycle, may be repeated and perhaps reversed in order.

Polycyclic magmatic activity during the revolution of a geosyncline is well shown in the Variscan Orogeny of Europe where no less than five phases of folding were

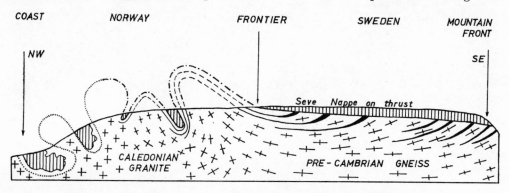

FIG. 42. Production of intrusive granite from Precambrian gneiss: the basement within the Caledonian orogenic belt of Norway. *after* H. H. Read.

accompanied by granitic or granodioritic intrusions. The Saalian (early-Permian) phase was the chief metallogenetic epoch, but metallisation may be appropriate to each phase.

GEOTECTONIC ENVIRONMENT OF GEOSYNCLINES

As the crumpled contents of the geosyncline are squeezed upwards and outwards their main form is governed by the nature and intensity of the orogenesis combined with the thickness of the sedimentary formations involved, but, as Suess long ago showed, the outline of the mountain front may be controlled, in detail at least, by the nature of the foreland against which the creeping fold and thrust structures impinge. Where the advance is obstructed by pre-existing resistant massifs of the continental shields or earlier orogenic welts, the outline of the mountain front may be moulded by the form of the ancient masses. The Alpine front of Europe is often quoted as having been controlled by the line of Variscan horsts extending from the Central Plateau of France through the line of the Vosges—Black Forest and Harz Mountains to the Sudetenland

and beyond. The Rocky Mountains on the other hand had little ascertainable resistance of this kind and tend structurally to die away into the foreland where similar rock systems to those crumpled in the mountains lie relatively undisturbed beneath the Great Plains.

The pattern of ranges is defined by the terms *Virgation, Syntaxis, Deflection, Linkage,* current since the time of Suess. They refer respectively to: the " divergent sheaf-like arrangement of several branches "; the crowding and converging of several branches (Fig. 184); change of direction in a single range or allied group of ranges (Fig. 84); and the abrupt meeting of interfering arcs (Fig. 43). Such conformations, met with in all major mountain systems, are usually a response to the forces applied

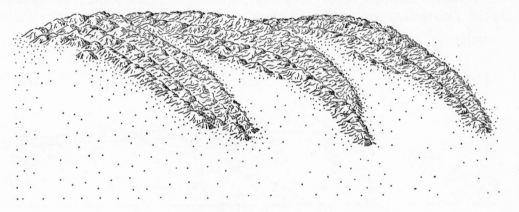

FIG. 43. *Linkage* of mountain ranges *en echelon.*

during orogenesis, such as the presence of resistant masses either peripheral or intra-montane. Occasionally, however, they reflect conditions present in the earlier geosynclinal stage, which exert local influences during the orogenesis.

With the completion and elevation of the mountain structures, fresh geosynclines often sag alongside the new mountain chains. They may be formed upon either or both sides of the new chains. Thus after the Nevadan orogenesis of western North America, the Rocky Mountain geosyncline sank to the east of the Sierra Nevada, and the Coast Range geosyncline to the west (Fig. 31). Such new geosynclines may form as deep trenches or as broad, shallow concavities, according to the resolution of the local stresses.

The development of fresh geosynclines alongside old, collapsed ones has caused some geologists to write of the " migration " of geosynclines. In Europe the procession of Caledonian, Variscan and Alpine welts has been visualised as a " migration " of the geosynclinal belt progressively southward, away from the continental shield. On the other hand the Rocky Mountain belt lies " inland " of the earlier Nevadan geo-syncline. Perhaps the outstanding example of so-called geosynclinal " migration " is in Asia where the Caledonian mountains of Sayan and Transbaikalia bound the primitive shield of Angaraland. Southward to the Kuenlun come range upon range of Variscan mountains oriented according to local structures. Then follow in succession the Karakorum (of Cretaceous age), the Himalaya (mid-Cainozoic), the Siwalik Hills (Pliocene) and the Indo-Gangetic Plain (Pleistocene). At each stage new geosynclinal material was folded, crowded together, consolidated and intruded so that it changed from a zone of weakness to a zone of greater rigidity.

Thus some authors visualised the continent as growing by accretion, and the same views are held concerning particularly Europe and North America. But a little reflection shows that the possibilities for growth in this way are strictly limited by the quantity of eroded material available to fill the geosynclines. To think of the shield of Angaraland, large though it is, supplying the material to the various quarters about it sufficient to make even the Caledonian and Variscan ranges is not feasible. Moreover, to this day most of the crystalline basement of Angara is covered by flat-lying Cambrian and Ordovician strata, which show that the region can have supplied but little sediment to mid- or later-Palæozoic geosynclines. Nor is the concept of transmission of material from one set of ranges to the next geosyncline acceptable. Hence, as we may judge, there must be other sources of detritus. Nor are they far to seek. There are numerous ancient crystalline massifs visible and buried in Central, Eastern and South-East Asia. All have contributed to the geosynclines; and doubtless the massifs were earlier connected as parts of a great Asiatic Archean basement. Likewise in Europe, though the Fennoscandian Shield is not visible much beyond the Baltic, doubtless it extends at depth far beneath the continent to the Alpine-Caucasian mountain system.

Indeed, wherever geosynclines occur, whether about or within the continents, they appear to be due to subsidence of pre-existing continental matter. As we have seen, geosynclinal subsidence is not primarily a function of sedimentation but of tectonics. Geosynclinal effects, despite Umbgrove's curious speculation (1947) on a sub-oceanic connection between the Variscan fold-ends of Europe and those of America, are not known upon the floors of the great oceans. Geosynclines, it seems, are indissolubly linked with the continents, and indeed there is a steady gradation of environments as distinguished by von Bubnoff, from shields, through stable shelves, mobile shelves and geosynclines, to marginal troughs.

THE MANNER OF FAILURE

The tectonic process by which the sedimentary contents of a geosyncline, accumulated in horizontal position, attain the folded, crumpled or even strongly overthrust situations which may be inspected in mountain structures requires explanation. The major axes of these structures, which may be scores or even hundreds of kilometres in length, are aligned along the length of the mountain chains, that is, parallel to the original trend of the geosyncline. *En echelon* alignments are also common. Our problem is to derive mechanically these typical structures : in simplest form, the question is—*how to make an anticline* ?

Current theory ascribes the production of fold-mountain structures to application of lateral crustal compression; but this often produces *parallel* folds (Fig. 44) wherein the thickness of each successive formation remains essentially constant. Such folding dies out rapidly in both upward and downward directions. Folding of this type is rare in geological exposures and cannot afford a basis for the intimate crumpling of schistose and gneissose belts in the cores of mountain ranges.*

Most crustal folding thickens proportionately in the crests and troughs and thins upon the limbs, though the fact should be noted that the thickness of each formation

FIG. 44.   Parallel folding wherein the thickness of each stratum remains essentially constant around the curves, but the folding dies out rapidly both above and below.   Contrast with laminar folding (Fig. 5).

measured vertically remains constant (Fig. 5.) *Such folds are formed typically by vertical, or near vertical shearing ; and this is the characteristic form of folds found as major and minor structures of fold-mountain welts, and in associated ore bodies.*

The only feasible conclusion is that mountain structures, in their mid- and deeper horizons at least, have been generated *not* by application of lateral pressures with resulting reduction of the earth's circumference, but principally, if not solely, by radial displacement within the crust. Quite surprising depths are sometimes reached by nearly vertical folds. Lees (1952) has recorded to the south of Trinidad that the " basement is depressed in a simple syncline to a depth of about 40,000 feet, from which it rises with the intermediate flexures, to the outcrop of the great Guiana massif of ancient schists, gneiss and granite ". The same author also records steep folds of Cretaceous strata overlying basement within the Benue Valley of West Africa (p. 271) involving possibly 35,000 feet displacement that could only have been achieved by near-vertical laminar flow of basement and cover together. The deeper structures of strongly contorted

* Among the several recent text books on structural analysis that may be recommended are : L. U. de Sitter (1956), E. S. Hills (1963), and Turner and Weiss (1963).

mountain zones are universally expressed in steeply dipping schists, gneisses and fracture zones. Only superficially, in terms of crustal thickness, do mountain structures become horizontally disposed in recumbent folds and overthrust sheets (nappes).

Fundamentally then, geosynclinal failure consists of laminar flow expressed in the near vertical direction along crustal zones wherein the topographic elevation of the mountains may be observed. The more viscous a substance is the more likely it is to deform by laminar flow, so that with the high viscosity of crustal and subcrustal matter laminar deformation must be overwhelmingly the mode of failure within mountain belts.

Near the earth's surface lateral confining pressures are much reduced, and opportunity is there afforded for the lateral spread of geosynclinal contents that have been carried upwards by the orogenetic pulsations, thus producing (Fig. 38) under gravity the sub-horizontal translations of rock materials witnessed in so many of the world's major mountain systems. The Naukluft Mountains, under the arid climate of South-West Africa, display the appropriate cascading structures admirably (Korn and Martin 1959).

These opinions are borne out by study of certain of the weaker bodies of the earth's crust such as salt beds, gypsum and mudstone which, deposited in originally horizontal positions, and subsequently buried beneath great thickness (12,000 feet or more) of younger formations, have become mobilised under static load and taking advantage initially of small overhead fissures or local lower pressures, have ascended through overlying layers of the crust as salt domes and piercement masses of gypsum or mudstone, acquiring as they did so characteristic rheid laminar structures showing intricate folding in near-vertical attitudes. At first, piercement of overlying strata is effected forcibly be geostatic load, but as the salt rises buoyancy increases in importance and becomes a powerful force as the height of the intrusion increases. Piercements commonly increase in cross-section towards the top, feeders at depth being relatively thin and flattened laterally. Mud volcanoes may appear at surface, and some in Trinidad recently formed islands (Wilson and Birchwood 1965). Some domes in the Persian Gulf area form salt mountains 4,000-5,000 feet above the surrounding plains, the salt, of Cambrian age, having risen from an original bedded position some 20,000 feet below the surface. At or near surface the same weak materials flow laterally as salt or gypsum glaciers and mudflows carrying with them immense exotic blocks of Cambrian and Ordovician rocks. All these deformations take place in the solid state, an essential quantity under the rheid concept being the time available for deformation. According to Carey (1953) salt acts as a rheid for stresses lasting longer than ten years, gypsum for one year and mud also has a low value. Where any one of these low-viscosity formations is present in a geosynclinal sequence, very complicated orogenic structures may result. Extremely deformed are the clay diapirs (Fig. 45) of Cainozoic folded belts (Burma, Baluchistan, Java, New Zealand) which have acted even as intrusives. Such movements may be repetitive at long intervals of geologic time. Thus a group of salt structures along a flexed zone from Central Utah into Colorado is deemed by Stokes to have experienced the following stages of development following deposition of the Paradox salt and gypsum formations and the Hermosa limestones during late Pennsylvanian time: (a) in the late Pennsylvanian or early Permian the salt domed the Hermosa, which was eroded until the salt was exposed. (b) During the later Permian, Triassic and early-Jurassic periods fresh deposits accumulated around the dome, which continued to be eroded until late-Jurassic

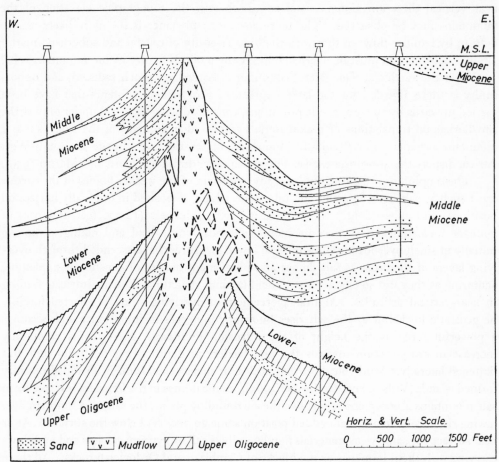

FIG. 45. Clay diapirs (mudflow) in section through the Barrackpore oilfields, Trinidad. *after G. E. Huggins.*

deposits practically covered it, and the Cretaceous passed undisturbed across the older structure. (c) Renewed propulsion of the salt during the early Cainozoic pushed through the late-Jurassic beds. (d) Mid-Cainozoic elevation and erosion admitted groundwater to the salt. Solution and collapse of adjacent and overlying strata followed. (e) Erosion has excavated the salt anticlines, leaving local residues of overlying gypsum.

A converse of " clay diapir " rise is provided where a resistant mass narrowing downward is forced up between two subsiding basins by " lemon pip " tectonics (Fig. 46).

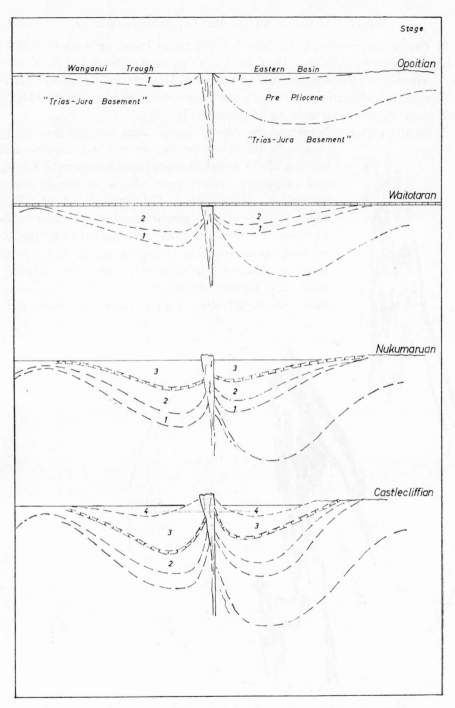

FIG. 46. Piercement structure of the Ruahine Range, New Zealand (see Fig. 182), showing "lemon pip" tectonics between two subsiding basins. *after J. Kingma.*

At shallow deformation levels lateral displacement involving weak materials may also be controlled by rheidity. Thus the gravity collapse structures of South-western Iran (Harrison and Falcon 1936) wherein masses of Miocene and Cretaceous limestone have slipped, cascaded and overturned upon Eocene marls of low rheidity which have flowed freely, even without aqueous lubrication (Fig. 187).

Along the northern border of the Alpine system, from the Pyrenees to Tibet, erosion of the slowly protruding mountain structures along the axis of the geosyncline produced between the Cretaceous and Oligocene periods great sheets of rapidly changing sandstones, mudstones and limestones (flysch) of low rheidity. These incompetent materials acted as lubricant to many of the over-folds and over-thrusts that crept outwards from the axis, sliding upon the less competent strata of shale or limestone which are often thinned out until they become discontinuous, so that the overriding mass rests locally above a shear plane upon more resistant

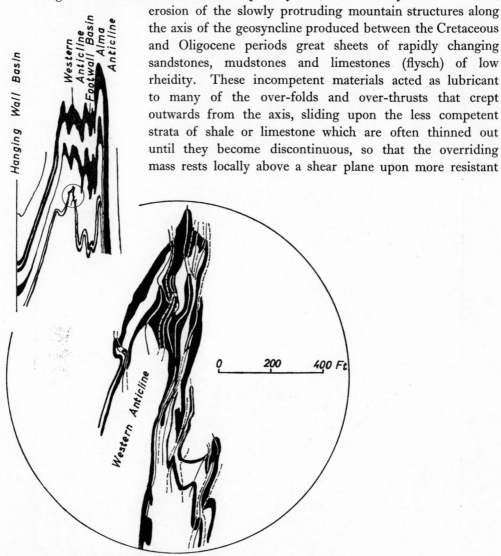

FIG. 47. Laminar, rheid tectonics in the Broken Hill mining field, New South Wales. *after J. K. Gustafson, H. C. Burrell and M. D. Garretty.*

rock formations. In the Canadian Rockies examples are known where translation took place first upon one shale formation, then the discontinuity sheared up through sandstones into a higher shale where the horizontal displacement was continued. In many ways, the travel and deformation of these nappes resembles the flow of an ice glacier which, too, sometimes develops folds and thrusts within the body of moving ice. The motion is highly complex, partly viscous, partly plastic, partly along internal thrust planes and partly by extrusion.

Lateral flow may also be induced in the lower parts of the geosynclinal contents by self-induced gravity strains. Material there tends to rise and spread laterally up the flanks of the geosynclinal basin, perhaps involving slices of the basement in laterally disposed thrusts. Such movements (McCutcheon 1957) are usually part thrust, part flow (Rocky Mountain front).

Under the concept of rheidity all earth materials flow if stressed beyond a critical time. Though no precise data are available, field relations suggest that under shallow orogenic conditions serpentine has a rheid value of perhaps only some tens of thousands of years; and even granite probably flows along laminæ in the solid state if stressed beyond a hundred thousand years. Granite has, for instance, flowed within the thrust-sheets of the Rocky Mountains. Gneisses seem to flow very readily indeed. But possibly the best examples of large-

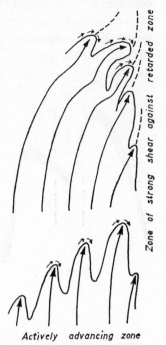

FIG. 48. Drag of fold structures against a neighbouring retarded zone. *after S. W. Carey.*

scale deformation by rheid flow are provided by crystalline schists and gneisses which were originally deformed at depths probably of several miles within the crust and which have subsequently been exposed at the surface by prolonged erosion. Carey (1953) describes them: " At Broken Hill, for example, where economic incentives have led to the identification of the original strata and their systematic tracing in great detail, it is found that the beds have been folded and extruded into flow patterns resembling in every way those of a viscous fluid. Individual beds thicken to many times their original thickness and elsewhere are attenuated to mere films for thousands of feet. Folds are involute and contorted on a grand scale. Limbs of folds are squeezed together often to vanishing point, thereby detaching altogether cores of thickened lobes forming ' teardrop ' structures. It is commonly agreed by geologists who have worked on this field and on crystalline schists generally, that such deformations are flow phenomena " (Figs. 47-49).

" Observe, however, that here we are dealing with a heterogeneous aggregate of different minerals, each with its own rheidity, perhaps differing widely from each other . . . However, in such cases the aggregate as a whole has a viscosity, rigidity and rheidity, and may be treated as homogeneous when bulk behaviour is being considered". Terzaghi, too, has shown for landslides that heterogeneous materials may possess an " average, shearing strength ". Where a heterogeneous mass is stressed below the ' average shearing strength ' of the system, the weaker materials deform like " a very viscous liquid ". Similar principles must be of widespread application during the deformation of the assorted contents of a geosyncline.

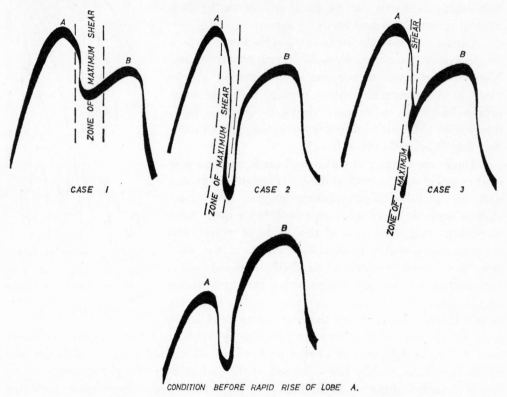

FIG. 49. Production of " tear drop " structures in folded zones. *after* *S. W. Carey.*

The behaviour of individual minerals is discussed by Carey: " When heterogeneous schists are subjected to shear, the stress across all minerals is at first equal. However, those minerals with lowest viscosities yield most rapidly towards a hydrostatic stress figure. This increases the shear stress in the more viscous minerals, increasing their rate of flow so long as the stress in them is still below their rupture strength. Under greater impressed shear the less viscous minerals may flow while the more viscous minerals suffer both flow and fracture, and are drawn out into augen in which the minerals show both fracture and strain recrystallisation. It is the most viscous minerals, not necessarily the most rigid, which first behave in this way ".

The normal development of rheid folding, as described by Carey is of separate lobes over-running one another progressively. Against lesser moving bodies a zone of strong shear develops with involution of the lobes towards the shear zone (Fig. 48).

BEHAVIOUR OF THE BASEMENT DURING OROGENESIS

Supporting evidence comes even from non-orogenic areas of simple monoclinal structure. The Natal monocline, an open fold roughly 150 miles across, which defines the south-eastern margin of Africa, involves a number of superincumbent sedimentary formations resting upon a gneissose basement. As the monocline developed, these formations were involved in numerous tension faults that broke the country into blocks superimposed upon the general monoclinal structure (Maud 1961). Mapping of these faults has shown repeatedly that though they can be traced for miles through the sediments they can seldom be followed for any distance into the gneiss. The conclusion seems inescapable that the faults disappear within the gneiss which has deformed by flow, with little fracture.

The opinion long prevalent among geologists that granitic or gneissose continental basement possessed high rigidity, and that in front of, or even within, orogenic belts it fractured rather than folded, forming a series of resistant horsts against which the more easily deformed sedimentary formations, especially those of geosynclinal thickness, were moulded, needs revision. Lees (1952) examined many regions marginal to the mountain chains of Europe, Iran and elsewhere and concluded that " A study of foreland fold zones indicates that the cover of sedimentary rocks plays a passive rôle and accommodates itself to movements of the basement beneath. Lateral pressure exerted along a sedimentary cover from a thrust mountain front . . . is not regarded as probable ". And again, " The active principle is movement of the basement and not sheared, rootless folding in the sedimentary cover produced by lateral pressure ". " A crystalline basement can flexure and form the cores of anticlines with, in some cases, little or no faulting ". Even in the Jura Mountains, the fold-structures of which (Fig. 50) have long, and confidently, been ascribed to sliding of a detached sedimentary cover, lubricated by Triassic salt, across a non-yielding basement, Lees, after personal inspection, has opined that the structures within the sediments reflect "basement folding" beneath; and Wegmann, after suggesting that the basement was broken by north-south trending horsts and grabens and by north-east striking antithetic faults, " on all of which strike-slip movements have taken place ", considered that the major tear-faults of the region resulted where movements in the basement were along narrow zones, elsewhere more diffuse movements caused folding in the cover. The long period over which the Jura folding has been accomplished, from Oligocene to late-Pliocene time, favours the idea of slow, rheid creep in the basement; but the greatest difficulty of the *Abschering* hypothesis of superficial sliding over a rigid basement is to explain how lateral thrust could be transmitted from the Alpine zone 50 miles to the south across the weak downfold of the Swiss plateau, infilled with Miocene molasse. The Mesozoic sequence (2,000-4,500 feet thick) involved in the Jura, moreover, is not itself strong to transmit lateral pressures over great distances. Only half of it, indeed, consists of strong lime-stones. And Tertiary folding is found even north of the Jura zone. Penck (1925) concluded, " The overthrusting forces here hardly came from the Alps, but were derived from the area between the Thuringer Wald and the Harz itself ".*

From these and similar studies the granitic basement may be understood not as a passive, rigid medium transmitting external pressures only by fracture and shear, but as a mobile agent responsible for much of the orogenesis seen at the earth's surface, carrying with it during mobility the superincumbent sediments that are deformed vertically in the most active zones and in part horizontally in the upper and marginal zones of lesser activity.

The experiments by Bull (1929, 1931) and by Griggs (1939), though they cannot reproduce natural conditions, express this trend of thought on crustal creep and give

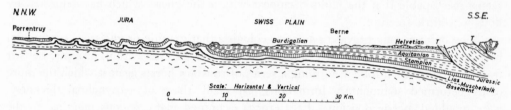

FIG. 50. Relations between the folded Jura, the Swiss plateau of Cainozoic rocks, and the front of the Helvetic Alps, showing how the crumpling of the Jura is more probably caused by creep of the basement than by lateral thrust from the Alps. *after J. Goguel.*

results not inconsistent with observed data. Scheidegger (1953), too, has discussed deformation of earth-materials from the standpoint of the physicist and emphasised their capacity for deformation under different environmental controls. While doubtless fluid convection currents are restricted to the substratum below the Mohorovičić discontinuity, deformation by laminar flow seems well established for all levels of the crust also.

Major crustal failures are generally located along zones of previous maximum subsidence (geosynclines), leading to the alternative conclusions that either the crustal stresses are relieved along a zone already possessing minimal strength, and that the weakest materials (the geosynclinal sediments) take up most of the deformation, or that the forces leading to crustal weakness that originally operated to cause the geosynclinal subsidence still operate in the same place.

In several mountain belts, *e.g.* Rocky Mountain System, marked disharmony exists between geosynclinal belts of maximum sedimentary accumulation and the pattern of deformed ranges, leading to the conclusion that the forces operating in orogenesis are

* Translation : Mr Martin Simons.

deep-seated and independent of the sites of earlier geosynclines. The same reasoning leads to the conclusion that apparently stable regions of the crust (shields) are stable not because they are stronger than other parts of the crust that have deformed, but simply that deep-seated activity has not been present to deform them.

Why certain parts of the crust should appear stable and others unstable, or in other words why the geosynclinal welts of instability should appear where they do, cannot be understood until it is clear what the pattern is and how it formed in time. The world pattern of post-Algonkian welts or zones of extreme deformation separated by wide regions of little tectonic disturbance conforms to a general pattern of failure familiar to engineers. I once saw a wartime film showing the demolition of a cantilever bridge. Only a relatively small quantity of explosive was used—at a critical point where stresses were resolved in the structure. This point failed immediately, the unequalised stresses were then transferred elsewhere through the structure, concentrating at another point which failed in turn, and so on through a whole series of successive failures, each distinct in time as well as position. At the end, existed a number of points and zones in which failure was complete, between much larger portions of the structure which had suffered no deformation though these had moved essentially as wholes at the times when the heavily deformed zones collapsed. This is the general pattern of post-Algonkian orogenesis for the earth's crust, for geotectonic processes occur in such a way that the energy used is at a minimum, so that crustal failure takes place where the stress difference first exceeds the strength of the rocks. The tectonic processes are a function of (a) the intensity of the forces, (b) the strength of the materials involved, and (c) structural conditions at the beginning.

TECTOGENES

There still remain the fundamental problems of why a geosyncline initially subsides, why its contents undergo orogenesis, what are the forces involved, what is the significance of the distinctive types of igneous rocks irrupted and of their characteristic time sequence: in short what is basically the cause of the whole operation?

Hess (1938, 1955) has drawn attention to the special nature of the ultrabasic intrusions that accompany the early stages of mountain making. In all probability these are derived directly from the substratum itself. They are usually olivinic and are frequently auto-metamorphosed to hydrous serpentine by contained volatiles. The melting point of olivine is high, but Hess thinks that olivinic masses (dunite) may be intruded with volatiles at low temperature as serpentine magmas. However, experimental researches by Bowen and Tuttle (1949) upon the system $MgO-SiO_2-H_2O$ scarcely favour this hypothesis on petrogenic grounds, for they suggest that typical olivine-orthopyroxene rocks are intruded more or less in a solid condition at about 1,000-1,200° C, and that the alteration to serpentine takes place later when the temperature has dropped to around 500° C. Nevertheless, the apparent low rheidity of serpentine admits of such mobility as to make it intrusive even in the non-igneous state. Thus several instances of probable reintrusion of Jurassic serpentine into younger rocks in the Coast Ranges of California have been described by Thomas (1951), Taliaferro (1943) and others.

The undoubted mobility of subcrustal matter which has entered the shallow regions of the crust goes far to explain the rôle of ultramafic petrotectonics. The association of " peridotite belts " with a majority of Palæozoic and later orogenic zones indeed suggests that the rôle of ultrabasics may be no passive one, but that the orogenesis itself derives, in a measure at least, from activity of these mobile ultrabasic materials. Their activity cannot be doubted for they have risen thousands of feet through the upper crust as hydrous melts, possibly of relatively low specific gravity and high volatile content (p. 112).

Hydrous ultramafic rocks have been shown (Davis and Hess 1949) to contain approximately three times the radium value of ultramafics with less than 10 per cent. of water, which suggests strongly that they are late products of differentiation in the substratum, and have ascended into the continental crust in a manner similar to the pegmatites of higher crustal levels.

If we view the problem correctly, the origin and evolution of orogenic zones may have to be sought in the substratum (pp. 670, 675).

The work of Hess (1938, 1948) upon both the East and West Indies has thus tended to minimise the rôle of geosynclines in orogenesis, and focus attention upon *tectogenes* or zones of crustal activity that may or may not coincide with geosynclines in position. The word tectogene signifies a zone liable to orogenesis though not necessarily a geosyncline; nor conversely, are all geosynclines necessarily tectogenes. In the East Asiatic island arcs (Chapter XVIII), for instance, which are thought to be orogenic zones active in modern times, the island garlands are considered to represent the folded contents of geosyncline whereas the tectogene is situated along the outer line of the ocean deeps. This separation of the passive geosyncline and the active tectogene is a valuable concept, and explains many apparent discrepancies in the behaviour of geosynclines of the kind quoted by Lees (1952) where deep exploratory drillings have revealed unexpectedly thick sequences of sedimentary rocks resting with little deformation upon apparently stable basement. Some of these sequences are thicker than the corresponding sequences in deformed zones. He cites : " (a) the unfolded Louisiana-Texas coastal plain, where Tertiary and Mesozoic formations have a thickness of the order of 30,000 feet; (b) the Bahamas, in the foreland of the thrust mountains of Cuba, where boring on Andros Island reached 14,585 feet and was still in Cretaceous; (c) the Arabian foreland zone along the Persian Gulf where Eocene to Triassic thicknesses are as much as 16,000 feet, considerably more than the average in the Persian mountain belt; and (d) southern Sind, where a boring at Lakhra drilled to 12,666 feet found an unexpectedly thick Cretaceous development ".

C. M. Raoul (1952) also working in the West Indies where the serpentinised peridotites (mainly late Jurassic—early Cretaceous) are restricted to the Greater

Antilles, though acid intrusives (granodiorites) are known in both the Greater and Lesser Antilles as well as the islands off South America, has disagreed with Hess's conclusions that (a) peridotites are intruded only during the first great deformation and (b) that serpentinised peridotites occur only along the axes of most intense deformation. He believes that it is rather the granodiorites which are associated with the main axes of deformation, though the intrusives themselves are little deformed.

Despite these objections, the rôle of peridotites seems fundamental in orogenesis. Available data do not permit the formulation of a complete hypothesis of orogenesis in terms of substratal control, but perhaps something on the following lines may be envisaged : access of heat from deep-seated sources causes local or regional rise of temperature in the substratum which already possesses considerable mobility in virtue of its low rheidity. Expansion of hydrous peridotite is followed by lateral migration of the substratum away from the zone of rising temperature and this causes depression of the surface which initiates a geosynclinal regime. With depression of the continental base crystalline material enters the non-crystalline zone below the Mohorovičić discontinuity and is transmuted into non-crystalline matter which in turn flows plastically away from the general region of super-heating. The action, of course, may take place with many changes of locale at different times.

As the crust is thinned of basic or ultrabasic material at the base, isogeothermal surfaces attain materials of relatively higher levels and *lower melting point*. The physical changes which ensue in the crust determine the future site of orogenesis. With continued accession of heat some of the lower crustal horizons receive a charge of telluric heat sufficient to cause melting which initiates the orogenic phase within the geosyncline. At the same time the hot, highly-mobile peridotite, appreciating the weakening of the crust and heavily charged with volatiles sensitive to any lessening of pressure from above (like super-heated water confined in the throat of a geyser), begins an ascent that takes it rapidly upwards in the weakest zone. (Only by some such geyser-like action is it possible to elevate masses of normally heavier substratal rock into the uppercrust, and just as geysers play only for limited periods—so the intrusion of peridotite may be deemed to occupy only a short (and initial) period of the orogenic cycle). When a sufficient proportion of super-heated volatiles has been discharged upwards the action slows and eases.

But the accretion of deep caloric may continue steadily after the initial orogenic spasm has closed and hence arise the migmatitic granites and gneisses intrusive at a later stage of orogenesis. The cycle may later be repeated (perhaps in modified form) as is often found in geosynclinal histories. Such repetitions of activity often occur upon lines not coincident with the first spasm.

The Physical Nature of Tectogenes

The frequent deficiency of gravity measured over the sites of mountain ranges early led to a belief in " roots of mountains ", or crumpled and thickened portions of the

I

outer earth shell that had " under tangential compression been forced down into the substratum ". This concept of " sialic roots " was later extended to cover similar gravity deficiencies upon the sites of oceanic deeps associated with island arcs, and the name " tectogene " was coined to cover the active principle of orogenesis thought to be associated with sialic roots.

But the physical concept of " sialic roots " is no longer tenable, for the belt of negative anomalies sometimes departs radically from the orographic features which are deemed to be compensated by the " roots ", and seismic researches (p. 604) have shown that instead of the crust being thickened beneath the troughs of island arcs (which were quoted as existing tectogenes) the crust is there of minimal thickness, and granitic crust may there be altogether absent (*e.g.* Puerto Rico trench). Moreover, many Cainozoic mountain chains of great elevation show only minor tangential crumpling compared with the Alps, and in some instances the main upheaval was not achieved until tens of millions of years after the folding.

Lastly, the assumed chronic state of tangential compression in the crust that was relied upon to develop the postulated crustal thickenings was a corollary of an assumed cooling and shrinking earth. On an uniformitarian earth model it has no validity and may, for island arcs, even be replaced by local tension (p. 575) which of itself affords explanation of the minimal crustal thickness in such situations as well as the arcuate form of the island chain.

Perhaps a fair modern estimate of " sialic roots " postulated upon gravity deficiencies is that by de Sitter (1956): " In general, it is a hazardous occupation to try to derive a tectonic reality from the mass distribution which the geophysicist has presumed in order to explain the observed gravity field ".*

Evidently sialic roots belong to limbo; but the concept of an active " tectogene " causing or related to orogenic changes is a useful one that merits redefinition. The first necessity is to place the tectogene correctly. Whereas under the crustal compression of a shrinking earth the crust itself was deemed the site of tectogene activity, our model of the earth visualises a passive crust responding to activity in the heated substratum. The tectogene must therefore reside in the substratum. What can be its nature?

In accordance with the views already developed of volatile-charged regions within the substratum, material that is buoyant and ready to levitate into the crust might develop turbulence with respect to more normal substratal substance around it, rather like the ingress of aerated water through a pipe into a swimming bath. (The " tweaks " that a swimmer feels as he passes indicate a surprisingly powerful force of turbulence.) A tectogene may therefore be redefined as a physically active, and possibly turbulent, state within the upper part of the substratum.

The material would have not only low density to be recorded as " negative gravity anomaly ", but also lower seismic speeds such as led Gutenberg to envisage sialic roots down to depths of 50 km. The concept also affords explanation of mountainous regions

* See also p. 660.

wherein seismic data indicate a shallow depth for the Mohorovičić discontinuity. In New Zealand, for instance, the crustal depth is only 20 km. so there is patently no sialic root to these mountainous islands. If the material below 20 km. is not sialic root but volatile-charged, light-fraction substratum then the present high tectonic activity of these islands as manifested in frequent faulting, tilting and earthquake shocks, receives clear and simple explanation.

Tatel and Tuve (1955) have recorded likewise a depth of only 20 km. to the Mohorovičić discontinuity at the coast of California off Santa Barbara and at Puget Sound in the most actively seismic and tectonic region of North America. The explanation surely resides in variations of density within the substratum rather than within the crust as they prescribe (see p. 672).

It is in regions of thinnest crust, too, that transcurrent faults of large displacement (sometimes amounting to hundreds of miles) are found : the San Andreas fault of California,* the Alpine fault of New Zealand, the Bartlett Trough, and several features within the Pacific Basin (p. 628). Very recent, or even current, translation along these fractures suggests the presence of subcrustal convection currents beneath, a natural corollary of decreased viscosity. Cotton (1957) also has visualised " forces generated in a subcrustal layer " as responsible for some major transcurrent faulting in New Zealand.

The volcanic effects within mobile welts (wherein, indeed, they characteristically occur) are largely caused by the agency of volatiles. Steam in huge quantities accompanies volcanic eruptions, serpentine belts are typically hydrous, and migmatite fronts with associate amphibolites and hornblende schists† indicate abundance of water vapour during their progress, and even deep granitic batholiths often fail to reveal evidence of " dry " magmas.‡ To the greatest depths of the crust the presence and even abundance of water vapour is manifest in the phenomena observed in orogenic welts. No suitable source for this water vapour seems to exist within the lower levels of the rigid crust itself, and the natural corollary is that it is derived from the mobile substratum.

The tectogene therefore appears to be some form of physico-chemical activity that ascends through the entire thickness of the crust from the mobile substratum to the earth's surface. It should possess characteristic structure. Eardley (1957) has visualised a deep-reaching shear structure and our own concept (Fig. 51) would be similar except in two respects : (a) Eardley writes of " magma " where we would substitute volatiles that are more active both physically and chemically. Volatiles can create magmas, and afford better opportunity for narrow zonal phenomena such as orogenic welts and negative gravity anomalies. (b) Eardley tends to think of such crustal shear as compressional in origin; we should prefer to think of it as tensional, not only affording more

---

* Byerley (1954) has shown that many earthquakes in western North and South America arise from transcurrent faulting, usually on faults striking west of north that have the movement on the continental side to the south.

† The amphibole molecule typically includes hydroxyl, thus indicating abundance of water vapour during its formation.

‡ That " dry " magmas do occur, however, shows that heat may be transferred independently of water vapour, perhaps even at temperatures exceeding the dissociation point of water.

rational siting for injection phenomena, but also permitting easier derivation of observed patterns of the welts ranging from linear with transcurrent movement to curved arcs, the characteristic form of simple tensional shears (p. 575). Such patterns may ultimately be determined by currents in the substratum.

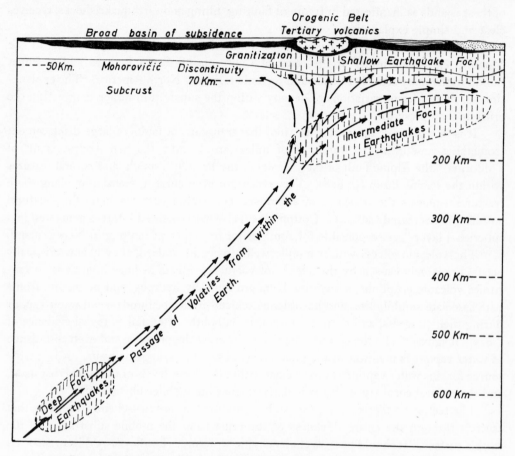

FIG. 51. Concept of a tectogene without roots. The upward passage of volatiles from the earth's interior is permitted along a curved shear in the mantle. *modified from Eardley.*

THE OROGENIC CYCLE

So the tectonic cycle sometimes culminating in orogenesis may be summarised : Under suitable combination of thermal and mechanical controls water vapour accumulates locally within the upper part of the mantle zone within the earth (substratum). This lowers the density of the substratum there, and if the action be widespread epeirogenic sagging of the earth's uppercrust may ensue over broad areas such as the Arctic Archipelago of Canada, the Congo Basin or Indonesia (Fig. 13).

If the accumulation of volatiles be particularly strong convective currents may be set up in the substratum as a result of density changes and perhaps also of heat transfer, that may draw the vapour-charged sections into linear distribution. Linear subsidences of the crust into the less dense current could form geosynclines which continue to subside as the continued production of volatiles progressively lowers the density along the current flow and the static load of the sediments themselves increases. A negative gravity anomaly may show, or may be cancelled by accumulation within the geosyncline.

Assuming that the local accumulation of water vapour is maintained, the density of substratum within the tectogene would ultimately be reduced below that of the overlying basal crust, which itself comes under tension as the crust subsides. Volatiles under static load entering the basal crust where it is stretched and under tension may mobilize a portion which then mildly intrudes the crust and lower geosynclinal sediments with basic rocks.

No further action need ensue, unless continued concentration of water vapour reduces the density of the substratum beyond the point where crustal load will tend locally to collapse into it. At this stage the major crustal shear visualised by Eardley may develop along the axis of the orogen. Immediately (in the geologic sense) a portion of the vapour-charged substratum rises into the weakened crust where, under even slightly reduced pressure, it becomes supercharged, expands and with its levity even more marked rises without much lateral spreading swiftly upward as a peridotite belt, increasing its energy by geyser action (superheating at successive levels) as it ascends, and altering to serpentine by auto-reaction in the upper levels of the crust where the temperature falls below 500° C.

Irruption of the peridotite belt presumably releases much of the volatile-pressure in the substratum and marks the end of the phase of vapour increase in the tectogene, so that geosynclinal subsidence ceases.

Instead ensues a phase wherein volatiles penetrate widely through the weakened foundations of the geosyncline causing mobility not only of the basalt but of the granitic layer above, creating palingenetic batholiths with migmatite fronts that rise diapirically up the core of the orogen even into sedimentary formations of the geosyncline.*

The rise of volatiles into relatively high levels of the crust is doubtless greatly aided by the development of near-vertical laminar tectonic structures within the more rigid uppercrust (p. 676).

If for any reason volatile accumulation within the subcrust ceases, or changes its locale, increase of infra-density should cause the orogen to rise, with considerable expression of vertical laminar tectonics along the heated zones within the crust. At

---

* Though the analogy may be far from perfect, the author is reminded of the view seaward from Durban where a few miles offshore the warm waters of the Moçambique current discharge large volumes of water vapour upward into the atmosphere. At first invisible, this vapour condenses at a height of 4000-10,000 feet into billowy cumulus that sometimes rises in giant thunderheads over the strip of warm marine current. In such a way may vapour-charged batholiths be visualised rising into the earth's crust above the subcrustal tectogenes.

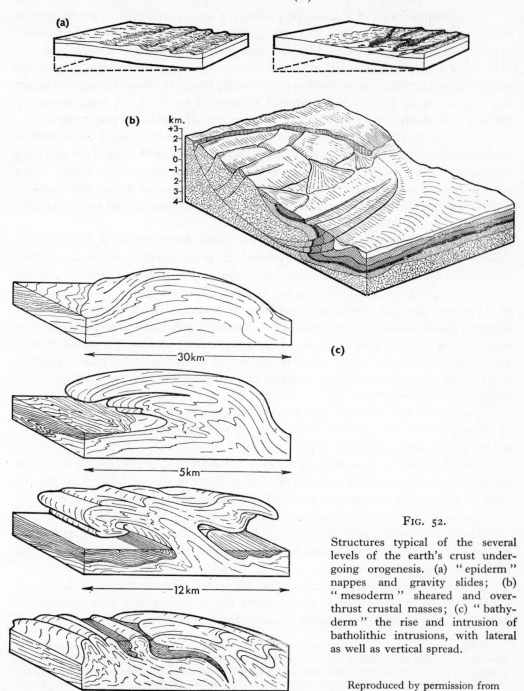

FIG. 52.

Structures typical of the several
levels of the earth's crust undergoing orogenesis. (a) " epiderm "
nappes and gravity slides; (b)
" mesoderm " sheared and overthrust crustal masses; (c) " bathyderm " the rise and intrusion of
batholithic intrusions, with lateral
as well as vertical spread.

Reproduced by permission from
HOLMES: *Principles of Physical Geology*
(Nelson, 1964)

this stage would arise the greatest mountains, and earlier structures formed at the time of irruption of the serpentine belt could be renewed, or might be superseded.

Structures typical of the several levels of the crust—" epiderm, mesoderm and bathyderm "—undergoing orogenesis have been summarized by Professor Arthur Holmes (1964) in a series of diagrams. With his kind permission we use them to bring this chapter to a close (Fig. 52).

THE DEVELOPMENT OF CONTINENTAL SCENERY: DEGRADATION AND AGGRADATION

CHAPTER V

THE STANDARD CYCLE OF DENUDATION

The Manner of Landscape Evolution. The Flow of Water over Land-
surfaces. Mass Movement of Rock Waste over Landsurfaces. The
Standard Hillslope. Pediplanation (Scarp Retreat and Pedimentation).
Pediplanation *versus* Peneplanation. The Influence of Bedrock. The
Influence of Climate on Landscape-Making. The Cycle Concept. The
Standard Epigene Cycle of Erosion (Pediplanation). Some Consequences
of Pediplanation. Addendum : Glacially Denuded Landscapes.

THE MANNER OF LANDSCAPE EVOLUTION

Following the creation of new surface states by tectonic movements, epigene landscapes
are moulded by the agencies of running water, wind, ice and mass movement operating
upon earth materials in strict accordance with physical laws. The physical basis of
denudation is expressed by Horton (1945) : " The geomorphic processes we observe
are, after all, basically the various forms of shear, or failure of materials which may be
classified as fluid, plastic or elastic substances, responding to stresses which are mostly
gravitational but may also be molecular. . . . The type of failure . . . determines the
geomorphic process and form ". Only in their relative proportions may the agencies
responsible for epigene landscape evolution vary, and then only within narrow limits.
Hence, as we hope to demonstrate in the sequel, the evolution of landforms is essentially
uniformitarian.

Except in glaciated regions where the landsurface is encumbered by a sheet of solid
ice, or in desert ergs where dunes are impelled by wind, landforms are sculptured by
the flow of water transporting debris across the surface of the ground or by slipping,
sliding or creeping of the ground itself. Unlike glacier ice or wind which on occasion
may carry land waste to higher levels, both water flow and mass movement are expressions
of gravity control. The " flow " of land waste over normal landscapes is, therefore,
downward and lateral, and this is fundamental to the development of such landscapes.
In general, the slopes of any landscape are so developed as to conduct away as efficiently
as possible the mantle of weathered waste that tends to accumulate upon them. This
is so under all climatic regimes and upon all terrains, so that a general homology exists
between the landforms of all regions, those above-mentioned excepted.

At this juncture a study of the physical laws under which water flows and debris
moves over the skin of the earth becomes imperative. Empirical study of existing
hillslopes, which has dominated geomorphological thinking hitherto, fails to give the

139

quantities that we need to know, and fails to afford a dynamic concept of the operation of the forces at the surface of the earth.

THE FLOW OF WATER OVER LANDSURFACES

The flow of water over a landsurface is a matter of hydraulics, but although the quantities have mathematical expression to be found in text books we shall eschew the exactitude of symbols and formulæ for more general statements in conformity with the constantly fluctuating conditions present upon natural landsurfaces across which water is passing.

For water flowing away from the crest of a divide, there is a critical distance over which no erosion takes place because flowing water cannot erode a slope until erosive power exceeds the resistance of the soil to erosion, or in other words, until the turbulence of the water can overcome the cohesion of the soil. At the top of each hill therefore appears naturally a zone of no erosion under water flow, with a non-concave profile. Clearly, the greater the proportion of infiltration into the soil the wider this zone is likely to be, so that on porous soils and bedrock the convex hillcrest usually attains maximum width. As examples we may quote the broad convexity of hilltops upon the boulder clay of midland Britain and the chalk country of southern Britain and France, and contrast them with the minimal summit convexity expressed on hard granite and quartzite terrains in Africa where the proportion of runoff is high.

As distance from the water-parting increases, so also does the volume and erosive power of water flowing in rills or thin sheets over the surface of the ground. Even upon a slope of originally uniform gradient, once the critical distance from the water-parting is passed, erosion by rill-wash supervenes and steepens the profile, improving still further the erosive power of the rills. This portion of the hillslope rapidly becomes steeply concave and is often sharply marked off from the smoother *crest* above. Frequently, the closely-spaced rills cut through superficial deposits to the bedrock which may be exposed either locally or in continuous exposure as a *scarp* (Fig. 53). Even where bedrock is not exposed the soil is thinnest and poorest and is removed most rapidly in this zone.

Under water wash the middle slopes of major hills inevitably become the steepest and most actively eroded part of the profile, and hence the retreat of hillslopes and scarps is equally inevitable once the critical limit from the water parting is passed.

Corrasion implies a corollary of waste removal and so the land waste that is actively produced in the upper part of a steep slope is necessarily washed downwards on to the lower part where also the velocity of the surface wash is checked as the level of the neighbouring stream is approached. Corrasion diminishes, or even ceases, and the greater part or even the whole energy of the flowing water is devoted to transporting the debris to the local stream. Its efficiency in this task is measured by the extent of debris washed down on to the lower part of the slope. Only under very favourable conditions of hard bedrock yielding little waste does the *debris zone* vanish entirely, leaving a sharp angle carved in bedrock at the foot of a steep hillside. " Bornhardt Inselbergs " afford perhaps the best and most numerous examples of this.

Following the cutting of a steep hillside by rill and gully action, and perhaps also retreat of the scarp so formed, surface water requires to be discharged across a relatively

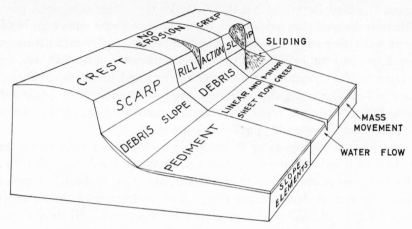

FIG. 53. The morphologic elements of a hillslope formed under the action of (a) running water and (b) mass movement under gravity.

flat terrain to an adjacent stream channel. This relatively smooth, flat zone is the *pediment* (Fig. 54). The amount of water to be discharged across the pediment is a maximum including all the rainfall of the upper slopes, minus infiltration, together with precipitation upon the pediment itself. In cross section, therefore, mature pediments exhibit

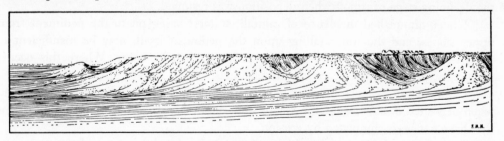

FIG. 54. A pedimented landscape formed by scarp retreat. Irdin Manha, Mongolia. *after F. K. Morris.*

the smooth concave profile of an hydraulic curve on which the gradients range commonly between $7°$ and $\frac{1}{2}°$ * Longitudinally, pediment surfaces are often surprisingly smooth with a rise and fall along the inner edge at the foot of the scarp face, the *low* points corresponding to the emergence of gullies through the scarp.† Throughout, the

* Though it can rise to a maximum angle of about $13°$ the pediment is essentially a slope of less than $5°$ over by far the greater part of its profile.

† This is the opposite of scarps fronted by fans (debris or rock) and bahadas.

pediment, a product patently of water flow, is so adjusted as to impart the maximum efficiency to disposal of precipitation and in times of heavy rainfall it may often disperse the water flow in sheets. The operation of sheet flow upon pediments has been observed in nature (King 1953) to conform with hydraulic principles and especially the operation of the quantity called Reynold's Number. Under favourable conditions true laminar flow (without turbulence) has indeed been observed towards the inner edge of pediments cut in hard rock (King 1953). But such a system cannot be perfect in nature over more than a small area and within a limited time. Hence the zone of laminar flow, dependent upon a favourable conjunction of precipitation rate and surface smoothness, is often elided, and rill-cutting and gullying appear extensively upon many pediments. The remarkable thing, bearing in mind the general irregularity of ground surfaces, is that the zone of laminar flow should appear in nature at all.

As the sheet of flowing water thickens beyond the inner zone of the pediment, laminar flow (if it existed) breaks down and rhythmic wave-trains develop. They visibly multiply the erosive power of the flowing water many times. Turbulent *sheet flood*, inches or feet in depth, supervenes. This is frequently the agent primarily responsible for the hydraulic profile developed by pediments. All these effects I have observed personally in the field, the wave trains in one particular instance coming down like tidal bores one to two inches high and spaced 30 feet apart on a sheet of water from one to three inches thick. Where incisions were made into surface deposits these were flat-floored and steep-sided, and at one stage water was observed flowing out of the sides at a level slightly above the bottom. This helped to calve relatively large masses of earlier-deposited debris and enlarge the flat floor rapidly. Lateral corrasion was not achieved by meander cutting; meander trains, very regular, formed best at the declining stage of runoff when deposition was resumed.

Under diminished incidence of rainfall, water coming on to the pediment from upper slopes, and the water falling upon the pediment itself, may be insufficient to form sheets and then passes across the pediment in rills only. Where this occurs frequently, pediments are scored by rill channels.

Land waste transported across pediments is usually in a relatively fine state, and when deposited in hollows often helps to smooth out any irregularities in the rock floor that have not been eliminated by erosion.

Pediments are best exemplified (King 1953) on hard rock in semi-arid environments, where the transport of land waste across the terrain is most efficiently conducted. Any departure towards arid or humid extremes is attended by the accumulation of waste in the landscape, and cutrock pediments may to some extent become masked or buried. Nevertheless, pediments are fundamental elements of hillslopes formed necessarily, as we have seen, under the physical action of running water, and hence they appear with greater or less prominence in all epigene landscapes. They are by no means restricted, as American geologists would have us believe, to semi-arid and arid environments but may be admirably studied even in the Appalachians as Davis's paper of 1930 showed. English landscape, too, exhibits some clear pediments in the non-glaciated southern counties, *e.g.* Wiltshire Downs.

We may now conclude that *the four basic elements of a hillslope as originally analysed by Wood* (1942) (Fig. 53) *all form naturally under the normal flow of meteoric waters across a landscape* : they reflect in form and evolution the natural results of the application of hydraulic forces.

As the manner of water flow over landsurfaces is prescribed by physical laws that are invariable over the globe, the four-element hillslope is the basic landform that develops in all regions of sufficient relief and under all climates wherein water flow is a prominent agent of denudation. This includes all regions except those wherein the dominant agents are glacial ice or wind.

FIG. 55.   Convexo-concave profile of a degenerate hillslope lacking scarp and debris slope elements.

The question now arises, *must all four elements be developed under water flow or may certain elements disappear under appropriate circumstances?* The standard example that we have considered involves certain assumptions, the first of which is that sufficient relief is available for all four elements to appear one above another. Briefly, in regions of low relief insufficient height is available for all elements to be developed, and the first to disappear is usually the scarp face followed by the debris slope. This leaves a smooth coalescence of convex crest with concave pediment (Fig. 55). Also, where streams are closely spaced, the critical distance from the water parting over which erosion by water flow is ineffective may occupy a large proportion of the hillslope profile and the inter-fluves become in consequence almost wholly convex. Wide stream-spacing, on the other hand, favours the development of broad pediments and a landscape may result wherein convexity is almost absent from interfluves and more than nine-tenths of the landscape consists of pediments (*e.g.* parts of Rhodesia).

Further, a strong bedrock affording a clear scarp face tends to provide a fully developed slope with all four elements clearly displayed; but a weak bedrock, readily breaking down under weathering, tends to eliminate the scarp face and produce a degenerate, smooth convexo-concave profile in which the crest meets the pediment in a smoothly reflexed curve. (Such slopes are common in parts of Northern Europe and are achieved principally by prolongation downwards of the crestal slope from above. In Africa, however, the pediment slope is usually prolonged upward. These differences may arise from lighter and heavier incidence of rainfall respectively, or from the prevalence of solifluction in northern latitudes following the Quaternary ice age.)

Considerable range of hillslope form is, therefore, possible under differences of relief, bedrock, stream spacing, and other variables, but none of the resultant landforms departs from the basic elements; and the fully developed, four-element slope remains the most vigorously retreating, active type of all. Other slope forms, involving **a** reduction from the maximum of four elements, are decadent and may even atrophy (as shown by a failure of active retreat).

The optimum hillform, in physical terms, is clearly to be sought in regions of hard bedrock and strong relief. It is exemplified by the bornhardt or " inselberg " in which summit convexity is small, most of the hillslope consists of bare, rocky scarp face, the debris slope is minimal, and the main hillform rises abruptly from an extensive pediment (King 1948). While many bornhardts owe their form in part to decomposition of the rock or to splitting off of slabs at curved joints, in the hardest gneisses such disintegration is suppressed and the surface of the bornhardt is channelled and fluted by rill action, e.g. in Rio de Janeiro.

On hard rocks which disintegrate to give only very fine debris, readily washed away, inselberg landscapes may appear in miniature even though the relief is very small.

The margins of inselbergs, it should be made clear, bear no necessary relation to local geological structures. The same rock types (and the strike) pass without distinction from the upper slope into the pediment.

Mass Movement of Rock Waste over Landsurfaces

In addition to transport of land waste by flowing surface water much rock detritus moves from higher to lower levels under the influence of gravity : by creep, slip, slide and flow (Sharpe 1938). Such movements are controlled by the physical laws governing the behaviour of earth materials under stress.

Data upon the behaviour of ideal materials are available in text books of physics, and describe the behaviour of perfectly-elastic, perfectly-viscous, viscous-elastic and firmo-elastic bodies, also the nature of friction—static and sliding. These are topics with which the geomorphologist must be familiar if his researches are to have real meaning; but which find scant reference in a majority of geomorphic texts.

Most geological materials are of the viscous-elastic type which means that they deform in either or both of two ways, according to the manner of application of stress. If the stress is moderate and is applied suddenly the material deforms elastically and if the stress is released the material returns to its original undeformed state. Should the stress be very great the material may be stressed beyond its yield limit (as defined by the cohesion of the molecules), when the material fractures, so that the stress is suddenly released. On release of stress there is no return to the original state.

Alternatively, however, small stress may be maintained over a prolonged time interval, when release of strain may be achieved gradually by plastic or viscous deformation within the body. The resulting deformation is permanent, and is a function not only of stress but also of time.

All hillslope studies must take cognisance of this dual mode of failure of earth materials—by fracture and by flow—especially as the superficial types of rock matter (sands, silts, clays, weathered and unweathered sandstones, shales and limestones) are generally susceptible of either mode of deformation within the lapse of time covered by a fraction of a cycle of erosion. Illuminating discussions on these topics are by Sharpe (1938), Ward (1945) and Horton (1945).

We may now apply these concepts to the study of mass movement of land waste down a typical hillslope. Towards a divide the amount of waste produced under weathering and requiring to be transported is small; in consequence the natural slope is probably gentle, and the soil relatively stable. The only lateral mass movement likely is by creep (a result of simultaneous action of both gravitational and molecular stresses), and even this may be minimized where slopes are very gentle, as is shown by the development of lateritic duricrusts (a product of advanced chemical weathering) upon very flat, ancient divides (Chapter VI).

With increasing distance from the divide, the quantity of material requiring to be transported increases in direct proportion if the bedrock weathers at a uniform rate. Hence for disposal of the waste by creep the slope must steepen progressively, *i.e.* the slope must become convex. Creep is a function not only of stress but also of time so that low divides may ultimately develop very broad convexity.

As the steepness of a convex slope increases with distance from the divide so also the stresses increase until accommodation by creep becomes inadequate. On a slope of considerable relief stress may thus be increased beyond the elastic strength of the material (*i.e.* the yield limit is passed) and rupture ensues, accompanied by slipping and sliding of material. (Motion follows because the stresses built up prior to fracture are much greater than the stresses required to move the mass once the bonds across the surface of failure are overcome.)

Slipping occurs characteristically upon arcuate (nearly circular) sections and hence such slipping leaves behind *a steepened section* in the hillside. In this way, free movement of material tends to steepen middle or upper hillslopes ; thereby producing a scarp, which will continue to retreat by calving of further slices consecutively behind the slip scar. This phenomenon is all too familiar to engineers and geologists concerned with stability of hillslopes and road cuts.

On suitably steep situations, material may not slip out upon curved fractures but may fall freely, roll or bounce from higher to lower levels. Static friction is greater than sliding friction and movements once triggered may continue for a distance and time limited only by the relief and the nature of the country rock.

The detritus from slips and slides then accumulates as a talus below, adding the third element, " the debris slope ", to the hillslope profile. This is often in extremely ill-sorted condition ranging from fine mud to huge blocks slid and crept into position *e.g.* Illawarra scarp of New South Wales, or the Town Hill scarp of Pietermaritzburg. Resting in place a talus weathers and the finer products of weathering pass downward through and over the mass, the finest being transported the farthest, so that the toe of the talus flattens into a concave profile, a pseudo-pediment or perhaps a bahada, thus adding the fourth slope element. At this stage the action of running water can no longer

K

be ignored, even in deserts, and the final transport of rock waste over the flat, lower hillslopes is seldom, if ever, by gravity alone.

Like water flow, the natural action of mass movement tends, therefore, to produce a fully developed, four-element hillslope, each component of which is capable of semi-independent evolution. Both agencies can do this even from an originally uniform slope, provided that it is large enough. For this reason we must mistrust all analyses which treat hillslopes as though they were simple landforms from top to bottom. Even mathematical treatments on such a basis possess no real validity.

We return to the former question asked under water flow, *must* all four hillslope elements arise under mass movement, or may elements be suppressed under certain circumstances? The answer is the same. Full development of all four elements is dependent upon local factors, chief of which are adequate relief and strong bedrock. Failing these, the scarp tends first to disappear, followed of necessity by the debris slope. A decadent convexo-concave hillslope (Fig. 55) then results.

Our manner of treatment has over-emphasised the independent rôles of water flow and mass movement, idealising two separate systems as it were. But in nature these seldom act independently, rather they aid and abet each other, and the phenomena appropriate to one system pass by gradation into those of the other. Thus dry materials commonly exhibit high cohesion and tend to deform elastically and slowly until the yield limit is passed, when rupture takes place and sudden motion ensues along localised planes of maximum shear. But the same materials in the wet state may lose much of their elastic strength and deform plastically by flow. Any clots of elastically strong materials are carried along upon the flow; blocks of hard rock may travel " bobbing like corks " upon the surface of a mudflow. Where a plastic substratum flows, a rigid uppermass ruptures in nearly vertical fractures. Pieces break away and even an overhang may be left.

A plastic flow will stop on a slope when the yield limit is raised or the stress falls below the yield limit. Hence most mudflows come to rest upon lower hillslopes where the gradient flattens though some may continue until they block stream channels in the axis of a major valley. Critical at this stage is the amount of water present in the mass (and consequent fluidity). When the proportion of water is very high, fluid rather than plastic flow ensues and flow does not stop until the end of the slope is reached. Thus the phenomena pass over into the water-dominant realm of hydraulics, the solid particles being carried discretely in a medium of low viscosity, that is, in suspension in water. The phenomena of denudation under mass movement and under water flow are thus amenable in the ultimate to a single, unified physical treatment.

THE STANDARD HILLSLOPE

The starting point for modern hillslope study is the analysis of hillslope form by Wood (1942) who distinguished, in a fully developed slope, the four elements (Fig. 53), that we have designated : *crest, scarp, debris slope* and *pediment*. Though locally one or more of the elements may fail to develop in a hillslope, such departures afford no contradiction of the normality of full development. This analysis applies to hillslopes all over the world, in all stages of development, and of all geological ages for, as demonstrated above, hillslopes are the result of physical forces acting upon physical materials in ways that are now established as natural laws. A further useful study is by Balchin and Pye (1955).

At this stage it may be well to define the four elements of a hillside slope more closely. The *crest* is the summit area of a hill or scarp, usually related to the zone of weathering and measuring from an infinitesimal portion to half the total length of hillslope. The profile is usually convex and is controlled by soil creep. The crest is usually longest where the depth of surficial detritus is greatest, *e.g.* in formerly periglacial regions, or where rivers and streams have recently become incised and the hillslopes have not had time to adjust to new stable conditions.

The *scarp* is the outcrop of bare bedrock exposed on the upper part of the hillslope. It is the most active element in backwearing of the slope as a whole.

The *debris slope* consists of detritus slipped or fallen from the crest and scarp and resting at its angle of repose against the lower part of the scarp face. As this debris is weathered to finer detrital grades it is removed under erosion and so the debris slope retreats in essential conformity with the scarp face above. Clearly, if the scarp retreats more rapidly the quantity of waste supplied will build up the debris slope to bury the lower scarp face, so that a balance is generally struck between these two elements.

The *pediment* is a broad concave ramp extending from the base of the other slope elements down to the bank or alluvial plain of an adjacent stream. Frequently its profile approximates to an hydraulic curve and it is unquestionably fashioned under the action of running water. Beneath the surface wash the bedrock is usually sharply truncated by erosion, but sometimes the subjacent rock may pass upward through progressively weathered mantle into soil. The concave surface profile has then probably developed only in previously weathered materials. Of course, landforms that were originally cutrock pediments may, if the cycle of hillslope development is arrested, deteriorate into the second condition as the transported mantle is slowly removed and weathering proceeds beneath it into the bedrock. Some of the concavities of lower hillslope profiles of northern latitudes may thus have originated as pediments, though their origin as such may no longer be demonstrable.

Normally veneered with detritus, most if not all of which is transported, pediments are essentially cutrock features, and bare rock is not uncommonly exposed where the veneer thins away towards the base of the commanding hillslope. Here often appears a distinct break in the profile separating the upper hillslope from the pediment. This break forms the functional base level for destruction of the steeper hill elements above. In areas of weak rocks, the break is usually smoothed out into an open curve, but where the bedrock is hard and there is little or no accumulated waste the junction between pediment and scarp face may be so sharply angular that a boot can scarcely be placed in it (King 1957). Sometimes, such abrupt transitions are sharpened by jointing, but this is not necessary, and many of the boundaries intersect the joint systems at an angle.

Occasionally, where the inner zone of the pediment is of bare rock or where the pediment extends as a rock fan into a scarp, it is convex over small areas, but such details, though not uncommon, merely represent incomplete stages in the production of the inner pediment.

Often the angular relation in the bedrock is masked by debris fallen or washed from above. Fair (1947) has regarded the zone as one in which the coarse waste of the debris slope is broken down under weathering ready for transportation across the lower declivity of the pediment. " Thus the rate at which waste is comminuted determines in no small measure the sharpness of the angle between talus and pediment ". Both Lawson and Bryan have also attributed the abrupt change of slope between hillside and pediment to a relatively sudden change from coarse debris on the hillside to finer debris on the pediment. But this cannot be the whole truth for the change is even more abrupt, as we have seen, where no debris is present.

In certain regions of the globe—e.g. the eastern and southern districts of Rhodesia—pediments constitute 60 per cent. or more of the landscape. Indeed, the author has regarded them as possibly the most important of all landforms being the fundamental form to which all most actively evolving landscapes tend to be reduced.

The best pedimented landscapes belong to late-Cainozoic cycles of erosion (Plate 2 : Chapter VIII); in more ancient early-Cainozoic landscapes later-induced, secondary convexity is now widespread. But in the pristine state, as the best preserved examples still show, pediments were almost the universal landform of the early Cainozoic, the only eminences often being small rocky nubbins. Baulig's descriptions (1928) of the Oligocene landscape of the Central Plateau of France leave us in no doubt regarding the pedimented nature of that ancient surface; and even the small remnants on Dartmoor and the Pennines have the characteristic curve of pediments when the oldest ridge crests are viewed in profile, and the famous skyline tors (King 1957) are similar to the castle-koppie residuals of the Rhodesian veld.

PEDIPLANATION (SCARP RETREAT AND PEDIMENTATION)

Wherever it is present upon a hillslope the scarp element has the property, under weathering, of breaking back and hence scarped hillslopes characteristically retreat across a landscape, reducing the crestal area above and extending the pediment below. In general, as the hillslope is worn back, the slope elements maintain the same forms so that the hillslope retreats with constant declivity. In many districts, hillslope elements exhibit remarkable uniformities of gradient, which could be so only if the hills, large and small, had maintained throughout their erosional history a reasonably stable angle

... to face p. 148

PLATE 2

Small scarp and inselberg rising above broad pediment at Naraku near Quamby, 40 miles north of Cloncurry, northwest Queensland.

C. R. Twidale.

of slope; that is, if the slopes and scarps had retreated parallel to themselves. For " stable angle of slope " there may be composite slopes where contrasted rock types appear in the valley sides—*e.g.* Grand Canyon of Arizona. Under these circumstances minor scarps alternate with debris slopes. Fair has stated (1947) that it is the outcrops which govern the form of the slope as a whole, and that the slope will be less in maturity than with a single caprock (Fig. 56).

In such districts, where scarped faces or at least debris slopes abound, the absence of overall slope flattening is clearly demonstrated. As will be appreciated, hillslopes in the early and very late stages of the erosional cycle (*q.v.*) depart somewhat from this dictum, but experience and measurement show that, from the time major hillslopes have become stabilised until they lose much of their importance as landscape features, they normally evolve without decided flattening.

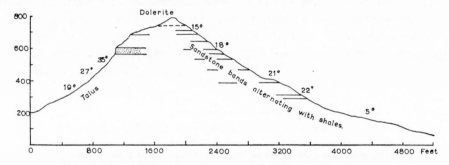

FIG. 56. Structural influence on slope form as shown by a dominating sandstone band (stippled) and a series of minor bands, each represented as a single horizontal line. The several minor bands yield a gentler slope. *after T. J. D. Fair.*

Parallel retreat of slopes is dependent solely upon forces acting upon the slope. It is independent even of minor changes of local base level; but it is greatly aided by high relief, resistant formation, horizontal structure in sedimentary rocks, and original generation as a tectonic (fault or monoclinal) scarp.

On incomplete or decadent hillslopes without scarp face, where the convex crest makes conjunction with the concave pediment, the property of parallel retreat may be inhibited. The evolution of any given hillslope is, therefore, dependent in large measure upon the presence or absence of a scarp face. Degenerate slopes of this type have been studied by Baulig and the reader is referred also to the general study of slope evolution by Birot (1949).

For a scarp face to exist adequate relief must be available; and hence most major hills and escarpments are liable to parallel retreat, smaller ones not necessarily so. Beyond a certain critical measure of relief, upon any type of bedrock (p. 153) a scarp face *must* develop under the physical agencies of rill (gully-head) incision or mass slipping discussed above.

Where landscapes have been warped or tilted by an amount exceeding this critical measure, therefore, a scarp inevitably develops upon the displaced surface and separates higher and lower portions of what were once the same landscape now appearing at different levels (Fig. 57). Where the cumulative uplift is sufficiently great such effects may be multiple, giving rise to a stepped landscape whether the uplift was intermittent or continuous, *e.g.* the second late-Cainozoic (Pliocene) cyclic land surfaces of Natal (p. 246).

Thus the piedmont-treppen concept of Penck, now demonstrated in the field in many lands, is proved valid and inevitable under the natural physical laws governing the development of tectonically active terrains. In the light of modern knowledge, the Davisian analysis (1932) which ignored different elements in the hillslope profile, is quite unsound.

The general physical relations of hillslope elements are now clear. In nature, of course, many complexities may be introduced by erosional factors such as renewed or continuous stream incision and lateral stream corrasion at the foot of slopes. Non-homogeneous bedrock, of course, may produce strongly scarped faces on resistant

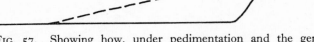

FIG. 57. Showing how, under pedimentation and the generation of scarps, local uplift beyond a " critical height " may produce apparently *two* surfaces in a single cycle of pedimentation graded to a single base-level.

rocks above, while the ends of minor spurs on weak rock below are convexly rounded. Dixey, Pallister and Fair, severally discussed the function of a hard caprock in slope form. Such structures do not involve any departure from the general principles of slope development. Infinite variation exists to delight the geomorphologist in the field, but the basic plan is surely clear and simple.

Much thought has been devoted to the mechanisms by which pediments originate and grow, and a diversity of opinion has been expressed by : McGee (1897), Berkey and Morris (1927), Johnson (1932), Rich (1935), Davis (1938), Howard (1942), Bryan (1922, 1940), Fair (1947), King (1953) and others. We conclude that pediments originate and grow by retreat of the hillside elements above them; or as Penck observed (1953) : " The gentle slope, that replaces the steeper one, thus develops at the foot of the latter; and the flattening of the land progressed from below upwards and not in the reverse direction ". Thereafter, as their concave profiles guarantee, pediments are modelled under the influence of running water. The curve so generated is obviously a function of the age and width of the pediment. Together, scarp retreat (by gully-head erosion and mass slipping of material) and pedimentation (by bedrock levelling and sheet-waste removal) are the most potent agents modifying epigene landscapes.

The miniature slopes of badlands eroded in relatively weak earth materials show curiously close analogies with the hillslope evolution described above.

Schumm (1956, 1956A, 1962) found on miniature pediments at Badlands, South Dakota, that during almost eight years the pediments were (a) lowered by sheet wash and (b) grew headward by retreat of the upper hillslope a distance of 6 to 12 cm. The hillslopes were rough and permeable; the miniature pediments smooth and less permeable.

" Calculations based on the Manning equation suggest that the velocity of overland flow on the pediments may be of the same magnitude as that on the hillslopes. The decrease in roughness from hillslope to pediment compensates for the decrease in slope angle. The pediments are swept free of debris and are regraded by a more effective utilization of run-off energy ".

PEDIPLANATION VERSUS PENEPLANATION

Penck's viewpoint expressed above is in direct conflict with the older Davisian viewpoint that landscapes evolve by downwearing of interfluves so that flattening of the land progresses from above downwards with ever-increasing extent of the convex, crestal element of hillslopes (peneplanation). Direct observation shows both types of advanced landscape in nature, and geomorphologists have generally ascribed the multi-concave, pedimented landscapes to denudation under arid or semi-arid climates with multi-convex landscapes forming under humid regimes (Cotton 1955; Holmes 1955; Baulig 1956). But the two types of advanced landscape often occur side by side, and indeed grade into one another. For instance, as divides and interfluves descend they often change in section from bi-concave where the relief is strong to convex at the distal end (Fig. 58). The difference is clearly to be ascribed to diminishing relief. Where relief surpasses the " critical height " (p. 153) for the materials of which the ridge is composed it develops a scarp face and concave profile, and where relief is less than the critical height the scarp face disappears and convexity supervenes (from above) in the profile. Much of the supposed distinction between " pediplanation " and " peneplanation " thus disappears from the consciousness of the field observer, who finds all types of gradational processes operating upon hillslopes in every quarter of the globe.

What is abundantly true from field observations is that where, in the early stages of landscape evolution, relief is ample the landforms are concave and retreating scarp faces common so that reduction of the terrain is by pediplanation. But as relief becomes necessarily low over most of the country in later stages when the uplands are reduced, a broad convexity often spreads laterally from the divides already reduced under pedi-planation, and this gives a semblance of peneplanation by downwearing which has mistakenly been thought to have operated *throughout* the period of erosion.

Thus Pallister (1956) found in Uganda the normal four elements of hillslope profile, and also that parallel retreat was typical until the final stages of degradation, when flattening occurs. This is in a humid tropical region of deep weathering and soil, and again it shows the independence of slope development from climate. The relief is only 400 feet and quite half of this is lost relatively quickly during the stage of scarp retreat

so that the remnants of laterite pertaining to the initial " mid-Tertiary " summit surface
are now scattered and small in area.   Most of the terrain thus now falls under the class
wherein relief is so small that slope flattening now dominates by both water wash (which

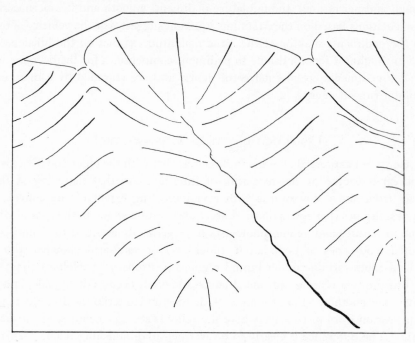

FIG. 58.   Spurs changing in cross-profile from biconcave to
convex as they become lower (relief decreases).

maintains concave pediment forms) and mass movement (which tends to cover and
obscure them and introduces convexity on the lower slopes).   Where this latter is prominent (Dixey 1955) " we arrive at a very gently undulating surface that is very close to

FIG. 59.   The two kinds of old-age landsurface (a) where water-wash is
dominant and upon hard rocks (b) where mass-movement is dominant
and upon weak rocks.   These correspond morphologically to W. Penck's
endrumpf and *primärrumpf*.

the general conception of a peneplain ".   But, of course, this is only in the senile landscape; the full vigour of change from the " mid-Tertiary " to the modern aspect of
Uganda was accomplished (as Dixey and Pallister point out) by scarp retreat and pedimentation—there was no peneplanation in the Davisian sense in the production of the
later cyclic landscape from the first.

After landscape has been reduced to low relief by scarp retreat, *two* kinds of old-age surface may appear (a) where water wash is dominant, and upon hard rocks (such as may be widely seen in Africa), the landsurface is multi-concave upwards, (b) where mass movement is dominant, and upon weak rocks, the surface may show both concavities and convexities perhaps with the latter more obvious in the landscape, as in parts of Northern Europe (Fig. 59).

These views confirm Penck's description of old-age landscapes as either *endrumpfe* or *primärrumpfe*, multiconcave or multiconvex respectively, but finds the distinguishing factor not in relation to earth movement but to the physical constant of " critical height " in the bedrock. This quantity now deserves further explanation.

The Influence of Bedrock

Laboratory study of earth materials and analyses of stress relations, as carried out by engineers concerned with the stability of works, yield data of prime importance to geomorphologists. A vertical cut, for instance, can retain its form only until the shear stress overcomes the cohesion between the particles. *As horizontal pressure (Fig. 60) increases with depth there will be a critical height beyond which any given material cannot stand unsupported.* For clean sand, which has no cohesion *per se* the height of such an excavation is clearly zero. But if the material has cohesion then the critical height may be derived from the formula:

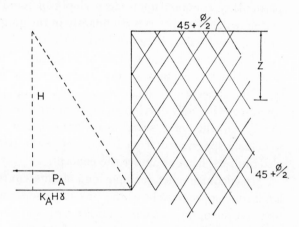

FIG. 60. The stability of earth materials in a vertical cut, showing the horizontal pressure as a function of depth. (Horizontal pressure (P_A) = 4 times the stress × half the height × a material constant (K_A) derived from the angle of internal friction ϕ.

$$\text{Critical Height} = \frac{4 \times \text{cohesion}}{\text{stress} \times \sqrt{K_A}}$$

where K_A is a determinable constant for any given material. Under this formula a dense clay (in which K_A = unity) with a cohesion of 1,000 lbs per sq. foot and stressed at 200 lbs per sq. foot will have a critical height of 20 feet. Sound rockmasses, according to the formula may sometimes stand to heights of hundreds or even thousands of feet in nearly vertical faces. *These examples show the control exercised by rock cohesion upon the development and maintenance of scarp faces.*

In nature few rocks are massive and devoid of minor planes of weakness. Where such planes exist, failure takes place much earlier and occurs not upon the theoretical planes of mechanical analysis but upon the weak planes themselves. This is especially so if these planes dip towards the face, when the problem of stability involving static friction along the plane may be solved by inclined-plane mechanics.

Virtually the only rocks in which few weak planes appear are those of plutonic origin: the granite-gabbro suite with regional gneisses and charnockites. It is amid these massive rocks, therefore, that the greatest smooth rock faces are displayed giving rise to the famous bornhardt or inselberg type of landscape wherein the scarp face attains maximum development among the tetrarchy of slope elements (*e.g.* Africa, Rio de Janeiro) (Plate 3). As I remarked in an earlier work (King 1948) these characteristic landforms are the combined result of (a) rock type, (b) scarp retreat following (c) incision in a new cycle of erosion. Also, such rock types may be expected to develop scarp faces in a minimal relief, as indeed they do. These landforms owe their existence not to any peculiarity of climate or weathering (indeed they occur in all major climatic environments) but to the massive quality of the rock with few joint planes. On the other hand, a hillslope of sound rock overlain by a profoundly weathered mantle develops " terracettes " as the weak soils cannot maintain a major hillslope. " Terracettes " are thus particularly common upon steep slopes of rapidly weathering bedrock such as basalt and may therefore be seen abundantly in the gorges of the Snake River Canyon, Idaho, or upon the Drakensberg of South Africa.

It is hoped that geomorphologists will be encouraged to employ the observations and methods of engineers more freely in future studies of hillslopes.

The concept of critical height explains clearly the necessity for adequate relief in a landscape if a fully developed, four-component slope is to be generated; and conversely the inevitability of a scarp face developing if the critical height is exceeded. The inevitable appearance of piedmont treppen in tectonically rising regions (Chapter VII) also finds explanation under the concept.

In adequate relief, juxtaposition of different rock types in various attitudes produces landforms appropriately to the physical properties of each and the structural relation between them, thus yielding infinite variation amid detailed landforms. Whatever the geological structure may be resistant formations tend to be etched into prominence as relief increases, and these often make the detail which confers local character upon a region.

The effects of geological structure are, however, subordinate and local. The fold-ridges of the Appalachians or the granite bornhardts of Africa are of such distinctive aspect as to lead superficially to the opinion that the bedrock structures are more important in landscape-making than the great continental erosion cycles; but this is not so, the geological terrains control local detail only, the geomorphic cycles of the continents (Chapters IX-XII) extend impartially on rock terrains of all descriptions etching out the appropriate detail upon each, but maintaining their own continent-wide integrity as they do so. The rare examples of structure-dominated landforms are of tectonic, volcanic or similar origins so recently created that denudation has not yet had time to ravage them.

Certain common earth materials, particularly those produced abundantly on weathering, exhibit special properties affecting the landforms that they produce. Thus even so simple and inert a substance as quartz sand exhibits quite contrasted properties when stressed, accordingly as its state is dense or loose. A densely compacted sand increases in strength when stressed for deformation implies an increase in volume. Loosely compacted sands, however, decrease in strength when stressed as the grains fit more closely together and the volume decreases. Loose sands cannot stand more steeply than the angle of internal friction (angle of repose), and this is the same whether the sand be wholly immersed in water or in air, but compacted sands may stand in

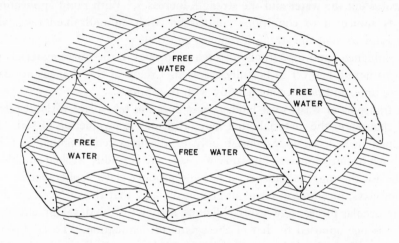

FIG. 61. Clay mineral structure illustrating (a) the flattened nature of the particles, (b) the structure, (c) porosity of clays. Bound layers of water ruled. When the structure is destroyed by overstressing, the clay loses porosity and becomes a dense, consolidated clay traversed by innumerable minute cracks. The structure cannot normally be restored.

vertical or even overhanging faces when capillary water or salts give intergranular cohesion.

Clay minerals are commonly flattened so that, fitted together, they leave a much larger proportion of pore space than do normal sands. Clays as a mineral group are, therefore, relatively porous (Fig. 61). Furthermore, the particles bear a negative electric charge which becomes large when compared with gravity or the mass of a particle. The charge is sufficiently strong to ionise adjacent water, and hence a layer of water about two molecules thick is held rigidly in contact with the grains. Because of this, clays do not compact like sand, but retain an open void structure between the grains and remain porous.

Only when sufficient stress is applied to overcome the rigidity of the bound layers of water and destroy the open structure of clay masses do clays compact. Such overstressed clays are no longer porous and lose many of the properties normally associated with clays. These properties are not regained with time, as may be observed in clays of significant geological age that have been subjected to stratigraphic loading. Destruction of the original structure leaves a consolidated clay that is widely traversed by minute fissures. Relief of load, as by denudation of overlying strata, permits the fissures to open slightly and admit water extensively through the mass. Such clays, of which the London Clay is an example, are very weak. Many details of surface weathering in stiff Cainozoic clays, *e.g.* crumbling, may be traced to this factor.

The shear strength of clays varies hyperbolically with water content; with some qualification upon the type of test or loading conditions in the field. A slowly applied load squeezes out the water and the strength increases. With rapid application of load the clay is subjected to conditions comparable with an undrained test, when with constant water content the strength remains constant.

The influence upon topography of such properties in the waste materials produced by rock weathering has yet to be fully assessed. Many of the changes are continuous over a long time, and occur concurrently with transport.

The transport of waste over landsurfaces does not take place without physical and chemical changes in the materials that may result in the production of soil. Raw soil, as developed in deserts, may consist only of disintegrated fragments of rock and crystals. Such primitive material has no coherence and is readily washed and blown away.

Under weathering, the feldspars decay and produce clay. Coherence is an essential property of clays, meaning in terms of geomorphology that the surface deposits, bound by fresh molecular forces, now exert a definite activity in the development of hillforms that is in essence opposed to that of the agents of denudation. To clay is added the binding effect of roots as plant growth is established, and ultimately the addition of humus, a fresh product with bonding properties.

The rock thus passes through a series of changes in which its physical constants, as they affect hillslopes, are profoundly modified. As coherence is in general increased with advancing soil maturity the effectiveness of denudational forces is diminished—both water flow and mass movement—and the sharp distinctions between the four elements of hillslopes and other asperities tend to blur until, finally, smoothly degenerate, convexo-concave slopes may be produced.

These changes may be linked with climatic and vegetational factors, which has led to the erroneous view of control of landforms by climate; but the basic controls are still the physical constants of specific earth materials and processes.

THE INFLUENCE OF CLIMATE ON LANDSCAPE-MAKING

Climate is in the atmosphere. A geomorphologist observes the physical results of physical forces acting upon physical materials of the solid earth and these are his legitimate field of study. To introduce climate as a controlling force in landscape-making is therefore to include inference with fact. Reverting to the use made of data upon earth materials

PLATE 3

Scarp face in gneiss of a youthful valley side, Rio Paraibuna, on the borders of Rio de Janeiro and Minas Gerais, Brazil. Such scarps are maintained in granite-gneiss during the pediplanation cycle, giving rise to bornhardts.

Lester King.

by engineers concerned with the stability of works, may we remind ourselves that though these practitioners measure carefully the physical properties of the materials with which they deal, they seldom consult the local climatologist !

Perhaps it is significant that most of the supporters of climatic interpretation of denudational cycles have come from the ranks of geographers, not geologists. Most of the landscape differences that they quote arise not from climate at all, but partly through the nature of vegetation. Thus the influence of carpet grasses, as contrasted with tufted grasses, upon the physical properties of soils and their erodability under water wash and mass movement may be profound, and productive of significant differences in the elemental proportions of a hillslope profile. Basically these are still controlled by the physical properties of bedrock and waste mantle. Currently, many slope profiles are being surveyed in attempts to probe the manner of slope development; but how seldom are these profiles related to adequate studies of the physical elastic constants of the rock and soil variants below ?

Climate is not the fundamental controlling factor at all, bornhardts (inselbergs), for instance, were first described from East Africa, and from studies in Southern Africa Passarge referred to them as a special product of *arid* denudation. The multitudinous bornhardts in the maritime states of Brazil were later attributed by de Martonne to a special kind of *humid tropical* denudation. Similar hillforms occur occasionally in the *sub-tropical* coast belt of Natal; and others in the Piedmont of Virginia and Georgia appear in regions quoted as of "*normal humid*" climate. Comparable rock faces are known in the South-west of New Zealand which is *wet, cold temperate*; and even from the Antarctic in Dronning Maud Land. Bornhardt hillforms are thus recorded from every climatic environment on earth. What are the real common factors in all these, and other, occurrences? Hard, massive rock types, and plenty of relief! The physical properties of earth materials govern the development of bornhardts (*cf.* Twidale 1964), as indeed of all hillslopes, wherever they are (*cf.* Berry and Ruxton 1961).

Again, pediments are often claimed as confined to arid or semi-arid regions, though they are by no means absent from " humid " Europe and North America (*e.g.* Tanner 1956). Davis (1930) has mentioned, for instance, concave rock floors occurring " in abundance along the belts of less resistant strata in the folded Appalachians from Pennsylvania and Virginia to Tennessee and Alabama ". These seem to differ from pediments only in that nobody has yet called them pediments. This applies also to details of the earlier Appalachian surfaces as Davis goes on to show.

Schumm (1956) has observed that in badlands near Wall, South Dakota, convex divides are developed on the Chadron formation whereas steep straight slopes develop on the overlying Brule formation. He noted: " The topographic differences appear to resemble those existing between characteristic humid and arid topographic types, or between the ideal forms postulated by Davis and Penck in their respective cycles of slope retreat ". Here is a simple example (which could be multiplied) of contrasted landforms side by side without differences of climate but with contrasted physical characteristics in the formations. Could there be a simpler demonstration of the fallacy of climatic control of landforms ?

Schemes which attempt to classify landforms dominantly upon " climatic " influences, without detailed studies of the physical forces operating and the properties of bedrock, rest upon an empirical basis only, and have little permanent value. Differences in temperature and temperature range, incidence of rainfall, strength and frequency of wind are not fundamental, they are differences of degree only, and do not overset the basic homology of landforms. *As a matter of direct observation all forms of hillslope occur in all geographic and climatic environments.*

This basic homology of all landscapes needs to be appreciated before the differences which, in literature, have been unduly magnified. Within the basic homology, as stated formerly (King 1953), the standard evolution of landscape is at its optimum under regimes of frequent and heavy rainfalls, when waste is most efficiently removed from a dry surface and retreat of scarps is perhaps at a maximum. Deviation from the mean, either towards greater humidity or greater aridity, decreases the effectiveness of waste removal either by increasing weathering and waste load or by reducing water wash. Hence, waste tends to accumulate at points within the landscape and clog the physical system (King 1953; Langbein and Schumm 1958). On the one hand is produced a soil blanket that mantles perhaps even the scarp face and debris slope, with dire results upon the active evolution of the landscape as a whole; on the other abundant waste accumulates in the hollows as fans and bahadas, so preventing the operation of the usual processes of pedimentation which are responsible for the finishing touches put to a landscape. Accumulation of waste is symptomatic of decreased efficiency in landscape evolution.

At extremes of aridity wind becomes a potent agency and may dominate over running water as in the *erg* or desert sand sea, while at the opposite extreme the action of glacial ice supersedes that of freely flowing water. These are extremes when the action of the usual physical forces is partly opposed or suspended.

THE CYCLE CONCEPT

Under the cyclic concept of denudation introduced by W. M. Davis, a landscape subjected to erosion is deemed to undergo a series of appropriate denudational changes involving: firstly stream incision with increasing relief, secondly, interfluve reduction under weathering with decreasing relief, and finally, planation. Of the general truth of the cycle concept there can be no doubt: but unfortunately the manner in which such scenic modification is achieved has been sadly misunderstood, and in nature the evolution of continental topography has preceded upon lines very different from those currently set out in text books as " the Normal Cycle of Erosion " (King 1953). The chief defect of the Davisian philosophy resides in the second stage wherein no provision is made for the parallel retreat of hillslopes—the most important activity of the whole epigene cycle and wholly undue emphasis is placed upon vertical downwearing under weathering. Yet, major divides have often been lowered but little over lengthy periods of geologic time. Thus the major Brazilian interfluves of the Amazon catchment are still capped by loose, or only semi-consolidated Cretaceous sands, though exposed to denudation throughout the Cainozoic era. The revised concept of a standard cycle of erosion is, therefore, formulated below.

THE STANDARD EPIGENE CYCLE OF EROSION (PEDIPLANATION)

Landscape is dominantly a function of the processes operating to mould it, and the major topographic features are related first of all to the erosional cycles prevailing over the continents. After tectonic events have initiated them, these *cycles of erosion work steadily across the continents, and the landforms of any given region are governed primarily by their relations to these erosional cycles.* If a major cycle has but recently encroached upon a region the topography will be rugged in accordance with the youth of the cycle locally, if the cycle has been long current planation is likely to be far advanced and the landscape will consist of denudational and depositional plains. The paramountcy of cyclic erosion in the development of landscape is displayed by whole continents (Chapters IX-XII).

When a landmass of sub-continental dimensions has been uplifted, with the establishment of new base levels to which erosion can operate, a fresh cycle of erosion is initiated and commences its labour of denudation, working from the coastlands towards the interior. The manner in which it performs its task depends upon a variety of factors such as the size and spacing of the local rivers, the nature of the uplift (whether this is uniform or involves differential movement, especially marked coastwise tilting), and to a lesser extent upon the local rock types and physical agencies. The activities by virtue of which the cycle develops are (a) river incision, (b) scarp retreat and pedimentation, (c) soil creep in low relief; and the dominance of these activities respectively and successively in the landscape may be considered to define the metaphorical stages of youth, maturity and senility. The whole process of evolution within the cycle, stage following stage, is carried progressively inland.

Within a single epeirogenic phase, continental uplift is doubtless repetitive in small amounts, so that multiple minor nickpoints are generated in the lower stream courses; but as these advance independently upstream the smaller ones are seemingly absorbed by the larger, so that within a short distance of the coast the effect, in so far as rejuvenation of topography is concerned, is cumulative and telescoped to present an appearance of major uplift only. Such nickpoints (Fig. 62) proceed long distances upstream, and may frequently be identified half-way across a continent (*e.g.* Victoria Falls). Corresponding nickpoints appear in congruent positions along tributaries (*e.g.* Amazon and Congo river systems) (Fig. 72) and are often cognate from one river ystem to another *e.g.* Aughrabies Falls on the Orange River, Rua Cana Falls on the

Kunene and the falls and rapids of the lower Congo between Matadi and Stanley Pool.

In the stage of youth the streams, rejuvenated seaward of ascending nickpoints, cut deep ravines and gorges. At first the sides of these are steep, but when the rivers have accomplished most of their rapid downcutting the maximum relief is attained, and the valley sides (at their maximum steepness) are no longer actively lengthened.

Rainwash and weathering then reduce the angle of slope to a stable declivity decided by the nature of the bedrock and the physical agencies acting upon it. At this stage is produced the slope form appropriate to the local conditions of bedrock. With the attainment locally of grade in the rivers (Mackin 1948; Woodford 1951; Holmes 1952), and of a stable gradient upon the valley sides the youthful stage of the cycle is fully developed. It occupies a relatively minor period of time compared with the rest of the cycle.

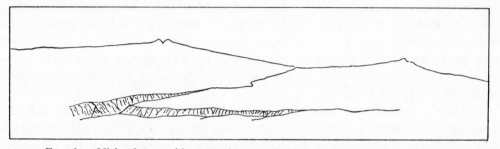

FIG. 62. Nickpoints working up rejuvenated streams into an ancient landscape.

In the stage of youth there is often considerable multiplication of insequent streams, and the texture of dissection may become fine so that the landscape is characterised locally by a maze of ramifying small valleys. Nevertheless, the incised gorges and valleys are usually zonal only in distribution. They occupy but a small area compared with the area of initial surface remaining in the continent, or with the more advanced cyclic landscapes downstream. It is within such zones, however, that the most rapid changes in the landscape are achieved.

The second stage of the cycle (maturity) is dominated by activity on the hillslopes. The rivers having ceased in all but exceptional cases to incise their beds significantly, an element of stability enters the landscape, and the river channels evolve by lateral corrasion, which affects only a small proportion of the landscape. The chief rôle in landscape evolution is then assumed by the hillslopes, which retreat at virtually constant gradient, so that the valleys open out. Every valley side becomes a retreating hillslope so that with a fine texture of dissection the interfluves are rapidly consumed: with a coarse texture and drainage mainly by a few trunk rivers the interfluves may remain broad and carry significant areas of the initial surface for a very long time. If the relief is low the natural curve of the pediment may soon take it up to meet the convex crest, so slope development by retreat may become moribund. If on the other hand, the relief exceeds the critical height, shrinkage of the interstream plateaus continues until opposed pediments meet and a biconcave transverse section to the interfluve results, *e.g.* Sacaton Mountain area (Howard 1942). A noteworthy fact emerges here. The upper surface of the interfluve remains in this case virtually without alteration until the hillslope elements of the new cycle encroach upon it. I have seen on outliers of upland surfaces quite unmistakable tiny summit areas surviving virtually without alteration though all the country for miles around had been consumed by scarp retreat in a newer cycle of erosion. Such remnants are invaluable for mapping of ancient surfaces and deciphering the earlier history of landscape. The hill called Shoshi in the Shamva district of Rhodesia, with only a few acres of flat summit area, is a superb outlier of the main plateau fifty miles away.

Frequently remarked at the mature stage, however, is the curve at the crest of the hillslope where the profile, elsewhere concave, becomes convex. Here the superficial accumulations have been left unbuttressed as the hillslope retreated and soil creep exercises a dominant function. The feature is akin to the slight incision of streams above nickpoints, due to accelerated " getaway " of the water. It affords no evidence of general downwearing: it is ahead of the main hillslope. Indeed, such crestal convexity is by no means an essential feature of a hillslope or scarp, and many a great scarp, under active retreat, intersects the summit plane at a sharp angle. Penck has remarked of this stage that " The whole slope system retreats inwards, ever further from the edge of the river, so that the higher, steeper slope units in the uppermost parts disappear one after another ".

This is the stage at which a general angle of declivity may develop upon a majority of hillsides over wide districts, even though some of these have manifestly retreated a considerable distance while others are valley sides but recently stabilised. Such congruity (p. 148) could exist only if the hillslopes had attained a common angle of declivity and had maintained it through all subsequent vicissitudes.

Between the steep retreating hillslopes and the widening pediments of mature landscapes a distinct break of slope is often apparent. This break of slope is one of the most fundamental features of landscape, and its existence has already been ascribed to discontinuity in the processes of landscape making. Upon suitably hardrock types the break may even become a sharp nick. Then are seen the steep-sided granite-gneiss inselbergs termed bornhardts, *e.g.* in Madras, Rhodesia. So striking are bornhardt landscapes that they have been regarded as distinctive in origin. But this is not so, they represent merely an extreme form of the universal type of residual mountains in pedimented landscape and the factors responsible for their development have been evaluated in the usual terms (King 1948). They occur also in massive limestones and quartzitic terrains. The secret of mature landscape evolution lies, evidently, in the mode of hillslope development combined with type of bedrock.

Hillslopes may be initiated either as valley sides consequent upon stream incision, or as tectonic features the result of faulting, monoclinal warping, or even gentle tilting

L

of considerable magnitude in a landscape. This is an important distinction upon which the evolution of landscape as a whole may afterwards depend.

Hillslopes related to river incision appear as youthful valleys ramifying powerfully through the landscape in accordance with the drainage pattern. At first they may occupy a minor proportion of the total area, most of which consists of the initial surface upon interfluves; but as the valleys open out a very large proportion of the country becomes dissected by a maze of valleys that destroy the initial surface literally throughout its extent (Fig. 63). This can happen whether the inherited drainage was arborescent or trellised. The net result, achieved chiefly in regions of uniform uplift with a fine texture of dissection is that the initial surface is rapidly destroyed and substituted by a rolling topography of a newer cycle.

FIG. 63. A landscape dissected by ramifying valleys.

In differentially uplifted regions, especially where the maximum uplift is great as in large coastal monoclines, major tectonic and erosional scarps are directed athwart the drainage lines (*e.g.* Southern Africa) and evolve quite independently of the drainage pattern. Thereafter these powerful cyclic erosional scarps maintain in their retreat the initial parallelism with the original monocline. Secondary scarps, structural or otherwise may also develop in the same orientation (Chapter VII), and a stepped cyclic landscape or *stufenland* develops that is largely independent of the main drainage pattern (Fig. 64). Once generated, the scarps may retreat virtually as fast as nickpoints advance up the rivers (Fig. 74). The rate of retreat of many of these continental erosion scarps approximates to 1 foot in 100 years. The Drakensberg (Plate 4), the eastern highland scarp of Rhodesia, the scarps girdling the Nigerian plateau, and the great western scarp bounding the volcanic plateau of the Sierra Madre Occidental in Mexico all approximate to this estimate, and further examples can be quoted from Australia, China, Siberia and possibly India and Brazil.

Under erosion, the scarps may not always remain clean and wall-like. Some degenerate into zones of dissected country separating an upper and earlier planation from a lower and later surface; nevertheless many of the major cyclic scarps of Africa impress precisely because they have not so degenerated but have remained clear and distinct throughout their history. The oldest date even from the Mesozoic, *e.g.* the

PLATE 4

The Drakensberg scarp, head of the " African " (early Cainozoic) denudational cycle, destroying by scarp retreat perched valleys and ridges of the Mesozoic " post-Gondwana " and " Gondwana " landscapes, Basutoland south of Champagne Castle.   Relief 6000 feet.

Anon.

[KING: *Morphology* . . . to face p. 163

Natal Drakensberg which is still a wall-like scarp 4,000 feet high though it originated late in the Cretaceous period and 150 miles or more to the east. One of the factors most favouring survival of such scarps is that they shall be large.

The planations which stand above such scarps are, of course, even older. Whereas, for instance, the smooth erosional landscapes of the South African highveld belong to Cainozoic cycles, the Basuto highlands 4,000 feet above them, are remnants of Mesozoic planations (Frontispiece) that have been exposed continuously to the weather since that era (pp. 230; 258). Such features have remained with only minor alteration until they are destroyed utterly by encroachment of the fresh cyclic scarp (Plate 4).

If the only effective scarps were major continental scarps like the Drakensberg an inordinate amount of time would be required for a fresh cycle to sweep across the face

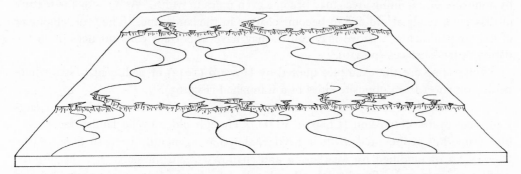

FIG. 64. Landscape evolution by erosion scarps crossing valley-systems
(see also Fig. 74).

of a continent. But other scarps are generated as the valley sides of major rivers and their tributaries, *e.g.* Zambezi and Mississippi and by retreating these also consume plateau remnants of an initial surface. Where, as in Africa, large rivers are widely spaced the spread of new cycles will be slow and the earlier cyclic remnants remain long on the higher parts of the landscape. In a more closely dissected terrain they disappear with a rapidity that is more or less inversely proportional to the square of the stream-spacing.

After scarps have retreated, both the major continental cyclic scarps transverse to the drainage and the minor scarps or valley sides, a wide development of pediments becomes apparent in the mature landscape. From either side of every stream, large and small, twin pediments extend laterally and by coalescence with others make pediment plains upon which stand unconsumed, steep-sided residuals. In Rhodesia (excluding the sand country of the west) pediments constitute probably 65 per cent. of the landscape; the rest is residual hillmasses.

As pediments widen they are subject to regrading, especially the steeper part toward the foot of the overlooking scarp. From an initial slope of perhaps 10°, they are reduced commonly to declivities of half a degree or so. This regrading is accomplished chiefly under sheet and rill wash, and even ancient and very flat pediments often show beneath a thin veneer of transported material a smoothly cut, unweathered rock surface. Fair remarked of the general smoothness of pediments in the Karroo that " sheet-wash and rills are capable of regrading them with little difficulty in response to minor changes of base-level ".   But base-level changes are not necessary to regrading as Rich (1935) has also noted: " Drainage diversions and the dissection of abandoned fans and pediments are normal and to be expected.   They do not require the intervention of diastrophic or climatic changes ".

Conflict of pediments from neighbouring streams, in which the stronger (usually the larger) extends its area at the expense of the weaker, is also a very real process causing degrading.   These interactions commonly favour the larger pediments which by annexure of adjoining areas may become even miles in width.   As a result the texture of dissection tends at old age to become coarser in the landscape.   The " development of master pediments ", as we may call it, may have important consequences upon the dating of landsurfaces (p. 226).

Interesting are the examples quoted by Howard (1942) of pediment passes where pediments meet from opposite sides of a watershed (Fig. 65).

As a matter of observation, the most extensive pediments are related to late-Cainozoic cycles of erosion (Chapter VIII).   Though older cyclic landsurfaces were often superbly pedimented in their heyday, they have generally been so dissected by later cycles or modified by weathering and shallow stream incisions that the original perfection is marred.   On the other hand only a few early-Quaternary cycles have as yet achieved widespread pedimentation.

Upon both youthful and mature pediments thin sheets of hard residual gravel are sometimes strewn.   Ancient examples may appear in geological sequences as thin, persistent conglomerates formed of exceptionally hard pebbles.   Stokes (1948) has interpreted the Shinarump, Buckhorn and Dakota conglomerates of the Colorado Plateau in this way.   " The building up and expansion of these coarse deposits apparently required long periods of time.   The Shinarump conglomerate involves the lapse of the entire Middle Triassic;   the Buckhorn conglomerate represents most of the early Cretaceous;   and the Dakota a good proportion of the late Cretaceous.   In such cases the time loss is not strictly accounted for by the unconformity at the base of the conglomerates—it is represented by the conglomerates themselves ".

In the later stages of the erosion cycle, when the hills are reduced to small, rocky koppies and the pediments stretch perhaps for miles, a multi-concave landscape is characteristic.   In Southern Africa, this advanced evolutionary stage is widely developed with respect to stable, or gently falling base levels.   Extensive alluvia or even flood plains are seldom present, and the soils may be quite different on opposite sides of even small streams.   Typical is the landscape on the east and south sides of Manda (Concession), Rhodesia, where the pediments sweep right down to the reedy margins of the streams themselves.   The Marodzi Valley west from Concession is larger and possesses a strip of flood plain 200-400 yards wide. But the bordering pediments are each over a mile wide before they abut against the rocky slopes of koppies. The general slopes of these koppie sides are nearly 30° inclination, but the lower 300 to 500

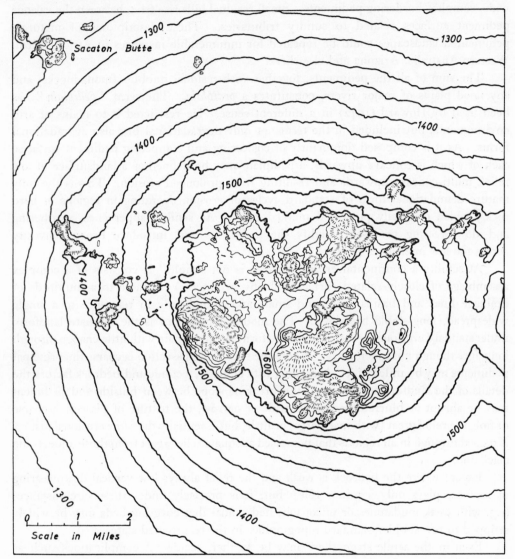

FIG. 65. Pediments and pediment passes in the Sacaton Mountains, Arizona.

feet may approach a slope of 45°. The inner, middle and outer zones of the pediment have slopes of 1°40′, 1°10′, and 30′ respectively, and these estimates are more or less standard for the district. Where the pediments pass as rock fans into the mouths of narrow side valleys they become steeper, sometimes 5° or 6°. The pediments themselves do not seem to exceed slopes of 3°, even when they are narrow and not very concave. In the Glendale-Bindura district of the same country, the Mazoe Valley, though miles in width, nowhere possesses extensive flood plains but always a narrow river channel with wide, complex, bordering pediments. Small residual hills rise from between the various pediment surfaces related to sundry tributaries. These descriptions of maturely pedimented landscapes could be repeated for innumerable instances in Africa, Brazil, Western Australia, Arizona and elsewhere.

The sum of all the pediments, together with residual nubbins (monadnocks) and any flood plains of major rivers, constitutes a *pediplain*. The term " *pediplain* " has been used by Howard (1942) in a different sense. He restricted it to plains of arid environments, but included in the term not only degradational but also aggradational forms. As it is composed dominantly of coalescing and competing pediment surfaces, each of which is concave upwards, a pediplain may be defined as a landsurface of low relief, multi-concave upwards and resulting from prolonged erosion. This is the fully mature denudational form of standard cycles of erosion operating in regions of hard rocks, which originally possessed marked relief. As senility supervenes, weathering and downwearing processes modify the pediments and introduce broad convexity across the low interfluves (p. 151).

At senility a continental erosion surface is not simple. It consists of a complex assemblage of closely-related surfaces (chiefly pediments) referable to a multitude of drainage lines and basins, large and small, and united only in reference to a single widespread, long-stable base-level. The modified pediment is the ultimate landform under standard erosional agencies, and once formed may remain with little change through long ages though not indefinitely. Where the texture of dissection is coarse the principal pediments may be miles wide. According with climatic, tectonic and bedrock factors the details of the landforms may vary; the break of slope between hillside and pediment may be abrupt or blurred, pediments wide or narrow, the texture of dissection coarse or fine, the relief great (with inselbergs) or little, but essentially the same erosional history is passed through in all regions that possessed adequate relief apart from those undergoing glaciation.

Except where the bedrock is weak and the relief always low vertical downwearing of surfaces plays only a minor rôle; but, it is precisely under these circumstances (*e.g.* with weak mudstones or unconsolidated sands) that covering beds may be widely stripped to reveal older standard topographies in the resurrected state.

Even in the senile stage there may be further, accidental complications such as the multiplication of cyclic surfaces by structure (split nickpoints), local land movement and so forth.

Observational data suggest that even at the senile stage weathering of the firm rock beneath the pediment veneer is very slow, but this conclusion may not be valid. In Africa, Pleistocene climatic changes were expressed in an alternation of arid and relatively more humid phases, causing alternate aggradation and dissection on a broad scale,

Sometimes the superficial materials overlying cutrock pediments, when revealed in the sides of dongas, contain Middle Stone Age implements, proving the synchroneity of one of these widespread depositional phases. Loess is not infrequently associated. Later came the phase of incision, when the dongas were trenched through the depositional blanket and often down into the bedrock as well.

A landscape that has been planed may remain in that state for an indefinite time with only minor alteration, until some tectonic change establishes a new base level. Then, following tilting, uplift, or isostatic recovery, the streams begin to incise themselves, and convexity enters the landscape adjacent to the stream channels. It is the initial stage of a new cycle of erosion.

Some Consequences of Pediplanation

The classic account of the " Normal Cycle of Erosion " as expounded by W. M. Davis has proved regrettably in error. With its emphasis on universal downwearing, it was a negative and obliterating conception resulting from cerebral analysis rather than from observation, and has led to sterility in geomorphologic thought and retarded progress in the subject severely. The new pediplanation approach springs from the work of W. Penck, Kirk Bryan and Jessen. In vindication of this opinion comes the synthesis of continental landscapes (Chapters IX-XII) which forms the main theme of this book, and which could not have been possible under the Davisian peneplanation concept with its emphasis upon downwearing of landscapes under weathering. We accept Davis's original idea of a cycle of erosional changes in landscape while rejecting the method of landscape development which he advocated.

Aptly at this stage, therefore, may be stated the advantages and novelties of the Pediplanation Concept.

a) Scarp production is recognised as an inherent propensity of landscape which finds expression wherever possible. Thus is explained the abundance of scarps in continental landscapes.

b) Congruity of hillslope gradients in a district of suitable rock type is an indication that stable gradients once achieved, are maintained.

c) An explanation is offered of youthful scarps separating mature landsurfaces above and below. Such scarps clearly remain youthful throughout their existence.

d) As *two* landsurfaces, one above and one below an intervening scarp are inherent in the theory, the old idea of progressive downwearing to a single planed surface loses much of its force, and polycyclic bevels in landscape such as appear in all continents become explicable.

Frequently in classic literature appears the remark that the lengths of erosion cycles must decrease or else the last would obliterate all trace of the others. Under scarp retreat and pedimentation this view is no longer necessary.

e) The abundance of virtually unaltered summit bevels in the landscapes of all the continents, even though the bevels may in some cases have been reduced to very small dimensions, receives explanation.

f) With the inherent scarp-forming properties of pediplanation, the abundant bevels and berms on the face of recently elevated mountain ranges appear as a simple consequence of tectonic activity (see Chapter VII).

g) The frequent discordance between topographic and geologic boundaries is a natural corollary of the hypothesis. The cyclic scarps have, in nearly all instances, transgressed from weak on to resistant formations, *e.g.* Pilansberg and the Waterberg Plateau of the Transvaal.

h) Valley alluvia, so important a feature of the classic " Normal Cycle ", are minimized under pediplanation, thus according with the relatively small proportion of flood-plains in most of the great erosionally planed landscapes of the world that have not been basined.

i) The multi-concave forms of certain senile landscapes are explained.

j) The non-glaciated landscapes of the world are seen to fit a single cyclic regimen. There are no separate humid, semi-arid and arid cycles with distinctive landforms, instead exists a basic homology of all cyclic features.

k) Cyclic scarps are sometimes quite independent of the drainage patterns, especially in maritime provinces. The same scarps are often independent also of bedrock structure. This is a natural result of pediplanation (Chapter VII).

l) The features of multi-cyclic continental landscapes are capable of measurement and verification by processes of mapping and statistics and can be compared throughout large parts of each continent.

m) With landsurfaces not wasting away *in situ*, the ages of existing landsurfaces may be extended backwards in time almost indefinitely; and are then found to fit the facts of geologic history accurately (Chapter VIII).

n) Intercontinental correlation of cyclic landsurfaces, as set out in Chapters IX-XII, becomes possible.

Thus the consequences of the pediplanation hypothesis and its application in the interpretation of global landscapes form a major contribution to historical geology.

In following this theme we shall largely ignore minor deviations from the standard concept of slope form and development: not because we are unaware of such deviations, or the considerable literature upon them, but because upon the global scale they cease to be of importance, as the principle of gravitation supersedes in argument observations of individual falling bodies.

ADDENDUM: GLACIALLY DENUDED LANDSCAPES

In the frigid regions towards the poles and upon high mountains precipitation falls largely as snow which, owing to the low temperature, does not melt away but accumulates as a blanket upon the earth, where also it is converted into ice. Beneath such ice the work of normal denudational agencies is inhibited. The ice itself, however, moving from higher to lower levels by laminar flow, operates as a denudational agent and carves a characteristic suite of erosional landforms. Where glacial ice occupies main valleys and hollows upon the mountain sides, leaving the mountain tops and ridges projecting above the surface of the ice, the action is to deepen and broaden the valleys and to excavate arm-chair like hollows (cirques) upon the mountain sides. The projecting peaks and ridges are sharpened into horns and arêtes, partly by frost action, as in typical Alpine regions. Even after the ice has melted away, the marks of its former action may remain in the landscape and be diagnosed infallibly by geomorphologists.

In this way, formerly more extensive ice action has been recognised upon mountain ranges all over the world, even in regions (Mt. Kosciusko, Australia) where no glaciers occur now, and an extensive literature has grown up dealing with the interpretation of these landforms (see Flint 1947) and Peltier (1950) for discussion of the cycle of glacial erosion. The opinion is generally held among geologists, however, that amid mountains the effects of glacial erosion, though obvious and characteristic, have not been decisive in the evolution of landscape but that the glaciers have for the most part occupied and modified valleys already in existence as river valleys before the episode of glaciation set in. This is so in the Alps, both of Europe and New Zealand, the Andes, Rockies and the Himalaya.

Greater effects are produced where the ice has joined into extensive sheets or ice-caps which smother the hilltops and valleys alike, grinding the whole country down to a rolling topography such as appears over much of the Canadian Shield. Beneath such ice-sheets abrasion and smoothing of bedrock is carried on extensively, numerous rock hollows are created to be occupied by later lakes; but doubts have sometimes been expressed whether the actual bulk of rock removed is exceptionally large (Demorest 1937; Gould 1940). This question might better be answered by considering the respective areas of glacial erosion and of glacially-derived products in the peri-glacial zone, but it must be confessed that several regions which have lain under ice-sheets do not appear to have suffered modification sufficient to destroy the pre-glacial conformation (*e.g.* New England Upland upon which Mt. Monadnock survived with little glacial modification).

The accumulative effects of glaciation (Chapter VI), extending over peri-glacial areas also, are more widespread and often more important in the topography than the effects of glacial erosion (*e.g.* Canadian Shield).

The most recent glacial episode in the earth's history, the " Pleistocene Ice Age ", was clearly not a single event. Four separate major phases of refrigeration have been identified in northern lands, and sympathetic variations of climate appear to have been world-wide.

Melting of all the present ice-caps would raise the sea-level 66 m. or after isostatic readjustment, 46 m. The maximum lowering of sea-level due to Pleistocene glaciation is to about 150 m. below present sea-level, or 200 m. altogether.

CHAPTER VI

DEPOSITIONAL LANDFORMS WITHIN THE CYCLE

Deposition *vis-à-vis* Denudation. Loess and Parna. Soils and Duricrust.
Soils in Succession. Modifications due to Frigidity. Volcanic
Accumulations. Depositional Landscapes in Time.

Deposition vis-à-vis Denudation

Pediplanation, revealed at its best in semi-arid or steppe regions is the most efficient
mechanism for the removal of denudational waste from the landscape. Deviation from
the semi-arid norm impairs the efficiency of the mechanism, and departures from the
standard epigene cycle of erosion are manifested by the appearance of depositional
landforms.

Degradation and deposition are, indeed, parts of one problem, for the former
produces waste of which the latter has to dispose. As an erosion cycle cannot be
mechanically perfect, some deposition appears in all epigene landscapes. Much of
this is transient. More permanent accumulations of detritus appear as the local efficiency
of transport is lowered.

Many observers have studied denudational processes and cyclic erosion under
various climatic regimes. Two excellent summaries by Baulig (1952) and Peltier (1950)
draw attention to the *differences* in various landscapes under different climatic regimes.
We have already insisted (Chapter V) upon the essential and fundamental homology
between *all* epigene landscapes, and hence regard those differences in landforms as
minor and differing in degree only. They are usually revealed by local accumulations
of detritus (soils and sediments) in the landscape. Hard-rock hillslopes are little
affected.

Thus if the climate becomes more arid than the norm with a reduction in stream
transporting power, the surplus waste tends to spread as broad sand- or mud-flats with
the streams becoming intermittent in flow and braided along anabranches. Debris
fans and bahadas may become the most extensive forms in the landscape, as can be seen
in parts of the Western United States and South Africa (Fig. 66).

The region of the Sudan, in North Africa, experiences a rainfall that is " not sufficient
to remove much sediment to the sea, yet running water produces soil erosion which is
continuous and powerful, except in the ' qoz ' region where absorption accounts rapidly
for all rainfall. Much of the surface material removed from the hills is redeposited in
alluvial fans ". These vast Sudanese plains have been described by Dresch (1953) as
undulating, with the rises flat-crested from an ancient plain of erosion (Chapter IX) into

170

which the broad, shallow valleys have been incised. Valley sides and slopes are very gentle, convex above and mostly with a well developed concavity. There are many flat alluviated depressions and the hydrography is confused. The exoreic drainage is perennial, the endoreic drainage spasmodic. During the dry season tributaries and streams cease flowing and the *harmattan* blowing ever to the south clears the uncovered muddy surfaces by deflation. Laterite formations are widespread. Following the first tropical rains—violent linear erosion develops along the middle courses of the streams, but along the upper flats sheet erosion is more apparent, while the lower flats become sites of muddy deposition.

FIG. 66. *Bahadas* surrounding the Löwenberg (gneiss) and (nearer) granite " inselbergs " in the desert of South-West Africa. *after C. A. Cotton from a photograph by E. Kaiser.*

Under progressive desiccation transport by water becomes less and less efficient, and with decreasing vegetal cover the work of wind increases in importance; sand-dunes may then appear in a typically desert landscape. Desert dunes, 100 feet or so in height often stretch parallel to the prevailing wind direction for scores of miles (e.g. Libya), but in some regions (Kalahari) the dunes are fossilised and aligned with former wind directions. Elsewhere, as in the southern Libyan Desert, the drifted sand forms mostly flat or gently undulating plains.

The hydraulic network tends often to disintegrate, and the control generally exercised by universal base-level is lost as numerous independent bolsons of centripetal drainage operate as local base-levels. Hillslopes are little affected, and evolve slowly by scarp retreat in the normal manner, as may be seen in the hamadas of the Sahara, the hillmasses of the Gobi and certain of the block features of the Basin and Range provinces; but on the lower country waste continues to accumulate, drifting under the influence of wind until the culmination represented in the *erg* or desert sand-sea is reached. Such ergs, as found in the Algerian Sahara, the Arabian Desert and the Namib of South-West Africa may show little evidence of water work over long distances. Even when rain does fall in torrential showers its effects are transient, for the water soaks rapidly away into the sand; yet even the arid regions quoted are seldom entirely without landforms due to running water.

<h2 style="text-align:center">LOESS AND PARNA</h2>

Apart from the coarse waste distributed as desert dunes, much fine dust may be exported altogether from the desert region by the action of strong wind, being distributed over surrounding lands as a blanket of yellow *loess*. This blanket lies with a meniscus surface upon the slopes of mountains and valley-floors alike. It conforms to major lineaments of the topography, but fills out the minor irregularities. Loess is uniformly fine-grained (with a particle size normally between 20 and 70 μ decreasing regularly from the source) except occasionally right at the base, and there is a general absence of stratification or other evidence of transport by water. Where it has been cut through, as by subsequent gullying, the faces of loess stand in vertical walls sometimes scores of feet in height, though the deposit itself is soft and friable. This behaviour results from its texture, the classical description for which is from von Richthofen: " On every bit of loess, even the smallest, one may recognise a certain texture, which consists in that the earth is traversed by long-drawn-out tubes, which are in part extraordinarily fine and in part somewhat coarser; which branch downward after the manner of fine rootlets and generally are coated with a thin white crust of carbonate of lime . . . the earth between them has a loose porous structure and does not possess that close texture which is peculiar to other kinds of earth; for example the clays, potter's clays and loams ". Fossils are not often present and those which do occur are suggestive of steppe regions. Nevertheless, we must note the occurrence of loesses of two contrasted origins: the " hot " loesses related to desert regions, and the " cold " loesses found in peri-glacial areas. Both are, of course, related to regions where much fine waste is produced and little vegetation flourishes.

The " hot " loesses are frequently underlain by red clays or earths, themselves waterlaid and fossiliferous. The famous loess of China is underlain by the (Sanmen) red clays or red loessic earths which Barbour (1929) describes as " mainly " a residual product from which the more soluble elements have been leached by prolonged exposure to weathering ". Often the reddish layers pass upwards by transition into the loess, and they are clearly of a similar age. In China, the presence of *Rhinoceros tichorhinus* shows the red earth to be Pleistocene, but other red clays with an *Hipparion* fauna are also known beneath the loess and have at times been confused with the red earths. A similar sequence of " fossil " loess is displayed in the Cave Sandstone of South Africa. A yellow upper portion is barren, but the reddish, bedded layers towards the base

contain dinosaur bones, and pass down into the shaly " Red Beds ". These accumulations are part of a vast Triassic desert that extended to Botucatu, Brazil (p. 318).

Four or more epochs of accumulation, separated by intervals of erosion, are
recognised in the great loess of China. The older deposits are very much weathered
and altered.

Related wind-blown deposits are the loessic cave-earths which at Chou-kou-tien in
China and Sterkfontein in the Transvaal have yielded such interesting fossil types as
the man-apes *Sinanthropus* and *Australopithecus*.

Rather distinct from loess is *parna*, an æolian clay covering in sheets thousands of
square miles in South-eastern Australia (Butler 1956). Associated mineral particles are
smaller than for loess and the grading shows that the parna accumulated as clay aggregates
derived from previously existing soils; thus while loesses are " new " soils, parnas are
" old " having already passed through one cycle of weathering and soil development.
Without being specifically named, parna has been identified by Thorp (1945) in the
United States and in European cave deposits by Zeuner (1945). It is generally regarded
as having been distributed during an earlier " arid " climatic phase.

Parnas and riverine clays cannot be distinguished by particle size or sample grading
as they are basically the same material. Grading patterns may distinguish them,
however, as riverine clays diminish in particle size to either side of water courses, parna
decreases in size from dunes or lunettes. The direction of travel, too, may be different:
thus in the Murray River Basin, Australia, the riverine clays travel westward, the parnas
eastward.

Though calcareous, parna sometimes occurs in districts far removed from limestones,
as in the vast granite plateau of Western Australia. Quite evidently it " travels " better
under wind than do sodic clays, and the answer to this problem may lie in the fact that
whereas sodic clays commonly absorb by ionisation a layer two molecules thick of water
about individual constituent grains causing them to assume a strongly bonded structure,
such linkage is lacking between the particles of lime-bearing clays which, with larger
pore spaces also, are, therefore, fluffier and blow more readily (p. 155).

SOILS AND DURICRUST

Both denudational and depositional landscapes are widely covered by soil mantle,
classed either as *residual* or *transported*. Though thin and often transient, the soil mantle
is tremendously important for its nature governs the distribution of vegetational types
to such an extent that the whole aspect of the earth would be changed if the current soil
types were altered in composition or distribution.

In general soil is an organised product of four variables: parent materials, climate,
topography and time. A majority of pedologists regard climate as the most important
of these. Climate is important for the production of soil especially from the ratio
between rainfall and evaporation. Where evaporation exceeds rainfall, soluble salts of

lime, magnesia and soda are enriched in the soil profile in excess of the amounts present in the original parent material and the soils are called *pedocals*. *Pedalfers*, on the other hand, occur where these salts have been leached away and aluminium and iron are concentrated in the residue. These are acid soils, and where silica and iron have acted additionally as cement, tough *duricrusts* (*q.v.*) are formed.

Given sufficient time for alteration, additive processes involving the production of organic substances exercise a greater function even than bedrock which decides the type of original debris and raw soil. Ultimately, the same higher grades of soil type may be produced from almost any original bedrock. This has been the theme of Russian pedologists whose flat home region, where soil-removing processes are slow, indeed illustrates the theme admirably. Soil maps for such regions conform closely to climatic charts, but in many other regions the opposite is true and geologists have been able to map invisible bedrock formations by soil characteristics, so that the geologic map forms the basis for a soils map. This is probably true more often than it appears to be: geologic maps are usually based on stratigraphical series, in each of which several lithological types may be represented, otherwise geological maps might prove better indicators of soil distribution than they do.

There remain yet other regions wherein the distribution of soil types is related directly to topography. Specific soils appear upon hillslopes, valley bottoms, uplands and other landforms. This congruence applies particularly in regions of youthful morphology where denudational agencies are active, and in regions of polycyclic topography where the several cyclic facets in the landscape are of markedly different geological ages. This is so in Angola (Diniz and Aguiar 1965) and Western Australia (Mulcahy and Hingston 1961), but in eastern Australia different major cyclic landsurfaces carry the same soils (Van Dijk 1959) owing to minor erosional modifications.

Of recent years the emphasis laid on pediplanation has led several soil scientists to re-examine the relations between soil-type distribution and the stages of the pediplanation cycle. Both in India and in Australia a close correlation has sometimes been found between these two factors. Soil profiles have been found to reach a relatively more mature culmination on older, as compared with younger cyclic landsurfaces. Even within a single epigene cycle also an acceptable degree of correlation may appear between soil type and pediment form. In general, soils are thinner and possess only the lower horizons of the soil profile on steep slopes. In Australia, Macdonald Holmes expressed this truth when he elaborated the thesis that " changes in slope set soil boundaries ", and that " many of the chief properties of a soil type are given to it by its topographic site ". In both the areas cited, of course, the general factor underlying the relation between soil-type and topography is *time*.

Soil may be defined as an organisation developed within the superficial materials of the earth by vertical differentiation of constituents such as " sesquioxides, clay, lime, organic matter and salts in a soil profile, and certain structural, consistence and colour arrangements " (Butler). The resultant soil profile developed above bedrock has usually a dark, fertile " A " horizon overlying a more clayey, leached " B " horizon or subsoil.

As soil development continues the originally mixed constituents become progressively separated and if those which are carried towards the surface are removed in solution or by suspension in water or air, a residue of less soluble or inert materials is left to form ultimately an "old impoverished" soil of low fertility. Following an early phase of surface enrichment by migration of salts and addition of humus, therefore, soils deteriorate in quality with age (p. 182).

The time required for any given soil to reach its ultimate type is generally unknown, but soils, as we see them now, may sometimes be related not to existing but to earlier and different regimes. Some of these are the *duricrusts*: thick calcareous, siliceous, aluminous, ferruginous or occasionally manganiferous superficial accumulations that cover vast semi-arid and arid regions of the globe, masquerading under a variety of names such as laterite, bauxite, surface limestone, silcrete and so forth. In three things especially are they united: they are usually relatively insoluble, they appear in the residual state on widely planed surfaces, and where they occur climatic evaporation generally exceeds rainfall during most of the year.

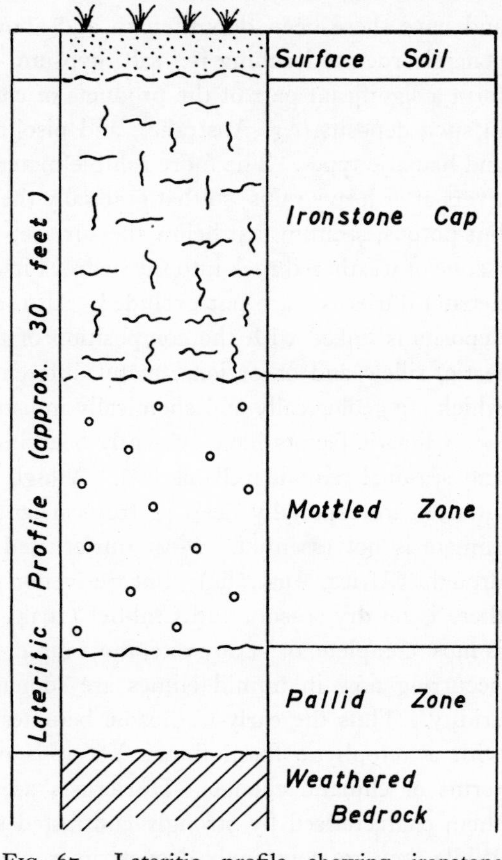

The Australian duricrust represents a soil mantle at the ultimate state of pedalfer development, residual in origin

FIG. 67. Lateritic profile showing ironstone horizon, mottled zone, pallid zone and weathered bedrock.

and formed superficially over thousands of square miles of anciently planed country. Through the long ages that have gone to its development, all but the most insoluble constituents of the original rocks have disappeared and the residue has been cemented into an intensely hard armour which either appears at the surface or lies beneath a few inches of poor soil. Beneath the ironstone cap a full laterite profile usually exhibits a *mottled zone* (found also below residual bauxites, *e.g.* Guiana), in which soil constituents are strongly differentiated, passing downward into a leached *pallid zone* resting upon deeply weathered bedrock (Fig. 67). The total thickness of altered material may be considerable. In the Geraldton district of Western Australia Precambrian granitic rocks are kaolinised to depths of beyond 100 feet, and the Jurassic Newmarracarra limestone is completely leached of calcium carbonate to nearly the same depth.

The accepted mode of origin for the duricrust is that the constituents were leached from the bedrock by groundwater, were carried upwards to the surface by capillarity and have there been deposited in and above the soil as the water evaporated. The general order of leaching is: salt, gypsum, lime, clay, iron oxides, silica. As colloids form a significant part of the products of chemical weathering opaline silica is not rare in such deposits (*e.g.* Australia), and pisolitic structures are common in the limonitic and bauxitic types. The more soluble materials (alkalies) are removed altogether to the rivers after heavy rains, so that gradually the insoluble residues accrete to form a tough, but porous, stratum just below the surface. The duricrust often grades down through a zone of weathered rock into the bedrock itself, proving its origin *in situ*, but secondary, detrital duricrusts are not excluded. Also, although the composition of these residual deposits is linked with the composition of the bedrock, and the supply of aluminous, ferric, silicic and other ions, many different types of rock may give rise to products which are geologically and chemically indistinguishable.

Climatic factors have evidently been important: evaporation rates should be high and seasonal rainfall well-marked. A high diurnal temperature aids duricrusting and laterites are especially deep in tropical lands like India and Uganda; but a tropical climate is not essential. Most duricrusted lands are subject to an annual period of drought (Africa, Australia); but Scrivenor points to deep ferricrete in Malacca where there is no dry season, and Chibber (1934) has remarked in Burma that " laterisation is most complete, or at any rate, most rapid, where the rainfall is heaviest ". Duricrusts occurring now in humid climes are sometimes accompanied by evidence of former aridity. Thus the early-Cainozoic bauxites and laterites of France are contemporary with a xerophytic fossil flora. Yet it is probably unsafe to interpret duricrusts in terms of climatic change. Duricrusts are forming now in many regions, some of them characterised by strongly contrasted seasons, some by a wholly humid climate. While they are commonly deepest in tropical regions (Brazil, Uganda, India), there is no argument that they cannot occur in temperate regions also if the period available is sufficient to allow for a slower rate of accumulation. Thus bauxite occurs on the Vogelberg in Germany and even in the cold regions of North China incipient lateritisation has been noted.

Lastly, time is needed. Though duricrusts are forming today in many lands, the building up of a thick deposit over a wide plain requires, probably, half a million years. Most of the world's thick duricrusts lie upon landsurfaces whose planation was achieved well back in the Cainozoic era (Chapter VIII). Only upon such landsurfaces that have remained for an immense lapse of time without significant lowering under erosion can thick duricrusts accumulate. In Australia, David (1950) concluded that though two periods of laterite or bauxite formation were evident in most states, the chief duricrust must be " Miocene or older ". This closely parallels conditions in India and Africa where the chief duricrusts lie upon early- or mid-Cainozoic landsurfaces of extreme planation. In both India and Africa also a lesser duricrust appears upon successively younger (Pliocene) landsurfaces. In India this lesser duricrust is largely detrital and derived from the main laterite. In Uganda where Ruhe (1954) recognised only two laterite horizons upon early- and late-Cainozoic cyclic landsurfaces respectively, Pallister (1954) was of opinion that laterite, formed at various times from early-Cainozoic to Recent previously extended as an almost continuous sheet over a topography with slopes of 10° or less. Dixey further pointed out that " the later laterites are often of true residual character, and not merely recemented detrital laterite, so that no distinction geologically can be made between the laterites formed at these different times, and at different levels ". The latest opinion is by de Swardt (1965).

Duricrusts afford proof positive of the absence of Davisian downwearing for they are invariably *accumulative* upon flat, weakly-drained landsurfaces of great age; and the innumerable instances where they are described as forming hard caps to residual table-topped hills (*e.g.* the Tent Hills of South Australia) or the scarps of broad table-lands (*e.g.* Kalahari scarp of South-West Africa) illustrate to perfection the dominant rôle of scarp retreat in the reduction of broad landscapes from one base level to another. Not infrequently such cappings of duricrust are broken away at small cliffs, where weathering attacks the soft, leached material beneath and so the cliffs remain sharp. Where the cementing medium fails at the surface, nodules and blocks are liberated that form the gibbers of desert and semi-desert surfaces. These may later be recemented and many duricrusts show multiple stages of formation in this way.

Laterite was first described from India by Buchanan, but there has since been disagreement over the connotation of the term (Scrivenor 1909, 1937; Crook 1909; Evans 1910). Cutting the Gordian knot of old controversy we may, with Chibber, regard laterite as substantially " a kind of vesicular (surficial) rock composed essentially of a mixture of the hydrated oxides of alumina and iron, with often large percentage of other oxides, chief among which is manganese ". General opinion assigns a high alumina and a low iron oxide content to typical laterite, but the name is loosely applied to allied residual products in which iron oxide content is as high as 50 or more per cent. This has been so in Africa.

With disappearance of iron oxide laterite passes into bauxite (with diaspore and gibbsite), a product of continued segregation of alumina over vast periods of time. The bauxites of Ghana show enrichment from 14 per cent. alumina in the original igneous rocks to 37 per cent. in the laterites. Secondary enrichment or " refining " may increase this to 50 or 60 per cent., or in special cases 70 per cent.

All the chief bauxite deposits of the world accumulated upon planed landsurfaces of post-Cretaceous age whereon the ground slope does not much exceed 5°. Upon late-Cainozoic landsurfaces of British Guiana high-grade bauxite most commonly occurs

M

in beds lying with sharp contact upon beds of kaolin, similarly in Ghana; and elsewhere it may be associated with alkaline plutonic rocks, as from the deep late-Cainozoic weathering of nepheline syenites in the Appalachian province of the United States. But the bauxites (*terra rossa*) of Southern Europe and Jamaica result in many instances from deep weathering of argillaceous limestones. The thickest deposits appear in solution pockets or other depressions of the karst topography.

Kaolin is often associated with lateritic and ferruginous duricrusts (Queensland) and in snuff-box shales whereof the joints have been limonitised. Undigested fragments of bedrock are commonly embedded in laterite, but it is incorrect to think of alluvia or talus cemented by iron oxides as laterite.

In Rhodesia, Mennell (1909) has recorded " laterite resting upon nearly every possible description of rock, and lists ten types in eight of which " it is due to the decomposition *in situ* of the underlying rocks, whose nature is reflected in the constitution of the resulting laterite ". Even if the analyses of some of these suggest that they are not laterites (*sensu stricto*) they are nonetheless duricrusts. The formation of duricrust can, however, be largely independent of the nature of the underlying rocks.

Ferricretes are the iron-rich duricrusts: they are far more common than the aluminous laterites. Ferricretes from Victoria Falls are almost pure limonite, and though they are derived from basalts they are free, as a rule, from alumina. The *marram* of North Africa, between 18° N. and 22° N., is a ferricrete which appears above suitable bedrock (*e.g.* shale). It forms a capping upon the high ground, especially near the continental divide, Ennedi-Erdi-Uweinat. Marram is absent from deep oasis depressions (Sandford 1937).

In Africa ferricrete appears generally as a duricrusted product above ferruginous shales and frequently assumes a pisolitic form. Some of the Somabula, Rhodesia, ferricrete contains a great deal of manganese, and approximates in composition to wad. Manganese-bearing duricrusts at Insuta in Ghana are enormously richer than any other ores of manganese in that country. In many parts of Australia also an almost continuous sheet of laterite of great extent still survives to form the surface rock. One of the largest of these residuals is the Alice Tableland, a roughly elliptical area in Queensland some 250 miles in length on the Main Divide between lat. $20\frac{1}{2}°$ and $24\frac{1}{2}°$ S. The original top soil has been eroded away and the plateau is formed partly of pisolitic laterite and partly of sublateritic leached material. The underlying rocks include sandstones, shales and limestones ranging in age from Carboniferous to Cretaceous (David 1950).

Australian pisolitic ferricretes are sometimes covered by podsolised soils suggestive of modern downward leaching. Whitehouse (1940) has described them for Queensland, and they are known also from southern Eyre Peninsula, the Dundas Plateau of Victoria and the Midlands area of North-eastern Tasmania where Stephens has regarded the laterite as passing up into the soils, but it is difficult to ascertain in how far the effects are due to podsolisation under the present regime superimposed upon opposite effects

PLATE 5

Silcrete upon a late Cainozoic landsurface, quarried near Boort, Victoria, Australia.

Lester King.

of an earlier age. The thickness of some ferricretes, 25 to 40 feet, occasions difficulty in assigning a podsolic origin, and as David (1950) has pointed out " the leached zone which in many places is found to underlie the laterite affords evidence of extensive upward translocation of material ".

In Australia erosion has widely removed any original " A " horizon for the ferricretes, and even the pisolitic layer has disappeared in many instances. Yet there remain " what appear to be remnants of a Tertiary podsol or lateritic soil in the sand-plain areas in the south-west of Western Australia within the triangular region bounded on the north-east by a line from Shark Bay to the western end of the Great Australian Bight. These occur as patches up to perhaps 20 miles in diameter on the surface of the Miocene peneplain or plateau in areas where there has been little erosion, and are of almost incredibly monotonous levelness ". In the Yilgarn goldfield the soils are residual or sedentary upon granite, greenstone and paragneiss from which they have been derived by deep weathering (Carroll 1939).

So the evidence favours original upward leaching as responsible for the ferricretes with only later superimposed surface effects in the reverse direction.

Silcretes form a widely distributed class of duricrusts composed dominantly of silica. Secondary enlargement of the grains, with interlocking of the crystals renders the rock very intractable and silcretes have sometimes been mistaken for ancient quartzites. Magnificent examples from the Cape Province have been studied by Frankel and Kent (1937) who treat of the chemical and physical processes involved in precipitation and in the metasomatic replacements of clay minerals by silica. They noted that in sands passive cementation by silica takes place but in soils and clays complex replacements *e.g.* of feldspar by silica may occur. These authors were able to determine the parent rocks (for the silcrete overlies several formations) from the heavy residues and the grain sizes of quartz, and stipulate a temperate climate during formation from the contained unweathered feldspar. Silcrete breccias are developed at the base. Nearly all silcrete is developed *in situ* (Frankel 1952).

Silcrete (Plate 5), which may be forming now, in areas of impeded drainage, is common on the floors of shallow intermittent lakes in the Kalahari. Macgregor has noted a band of silcrete locally below ferricrete in the Kalahari beds, and this relationship of the two types is not uncommon. Silcrete boulders from beneath ferricrete are known in Australia as " billy ", there also the precious opal is usually a calcite replaced by silica. Omdurman and the Southern Libyan Desert have widespread silcrete. The *meulieres* and the *argile à silex* (in part) of the Paris Basin appear to be ancient silcretes formed in earlier times on denudational terrains about the subsiding centre of the basin.

Calcrete, commonly calcium carbonate though sometimes with admixture of sulphate, occurs over rockmasses of suitable composition such as basic igneous and metamorphic rocks, limestones and dolomites. Considerable areas of Ventersdorp lava in the Vaal River catchment are overlain by calcrete deposits which may reach a thickness of 100 feet. Often the bulk of calcrete is quartz sand cemented by calcium carbonate.

The lower part of calcrete is often soft and porous, while the upper layers are hard. Almost the whole Kalahari region is underlain by a prominent calcrete of mid-Cainozoic age; and the widespread *caliche* of Texas and New Mexico is a similar accumulation. Though the bulk of these is ancient, similar deposits have been observed forming now.

On the Barkly and Alice Tablelands of Queensland, silicified limestones (sometimes chalcedonic) of late-Cainozoic age occur with clays and lateritic accumulations. The Nullarbor Plain at the head of the Australian Bight has similar deposits some of which may still be forming.

If duricrusting be acknowledged as a possibly continuous slow process, occurring upon suitable terrains more or less throughout geologic time, and not as an intensive process operative during certain favourable periods only, then it can be considered in conjunction with the pedimentation hypothesis. Thus broken pieces of earlier silcrete in later silcretes, as at Grahamstown, have led authors to postulate two periods of silicification. Whitehouse has postulated two distinct periods of ferricrete formation in the duricrust which covers much of Queensland quoting the following points in support of this view: (1) the inclusion in the Flinders Valley of boulders of " billy " (*i.e.* silcrete) of an earlier laterite in a sedimentary series which is itself lateritised; (2) silification near Bulgroo of the laterites, even of the upper ferruginous zone; (3) at several places between Winton and Boulia, the eroded plateaus of mottled (kaolin) zone show two levels of the upper more ferruginous crust. Sometimes they occur on the same slope; (4) on the Alice Tableland several watercourses cut completely through the mottled zone to the rock below, and yet have, in their beds, normal mottled-zone material.

So long as duricrusting is regarded as a process which has been confined to special, and relatively short, periods of time; and landscapes are assumed to evolve mainly by downwearing; two distinct periods are required to explain these duple occurrences. But if the duricrusting process is a slow but continuous one, then the appearance of two periods of lateritisation could be achieved by the evolution and conflict of pediments. Duricrusts, let us recall, are most commonly pediment deposits.

Duricrusts can obviously be of any age consonant with that of the landsurface of which they form a part; and though often assigned a late date because of their superficial position are in most cases immensely older. The ferricretes upon the Great Divide of Queensland had been eroded even before the late-Cainozoic basalts were poured out there, and the equivalent ferricretes far to the south-west had been eroded long before that. As will emerge in the sequel, the most widespread duricrusts are those upon the landscapes of the great continental planations which were initiated in the late-Cretaceous and were, in many instances, virtually completed early in the Cainozoic era (*e.g.* in Africa and Australia). Older surfaces are, naturally, also duricrusted in patches; while, at the modern end of the timescale, sundry landsurfaces are, under favourable circumstances, slowly receiving a capping of duricrust today. An example of relatively youthful laterite formation is described from the lower Yangtze region by Barbour who describes it overlying the Pliocene (Tanghsien) denudational surface and equivalent to the Chou-kou-tien stage of late-Pliocene, spelean accumulation.

In later chapters (IX-XII) dealing with cyclic landsurfaces the importance of many of these thick, ancient soils called duricrusts rests in their great age, often extending back to the early-Cainozoic and sometimes even to the late-Mesozoic era. Their continued existence into modern times affords proof positive that the landsurfaces which they cover have not been significantly altered by vertical downwearing since the duricrust was formed. *They certify the survival, with minimal change, of certain anciently planed landscapes into modern scenery. Where duricrusts contain identifiable fossils, they are doubly valuable.*

Soils in Succession

Development of soils implies sedentariness in the mantle of waste; but widespread removal of soils under erosion is no less real, and apart from the duricrusts no ancient soils seem to have survived from much before the Quaternary era. Mature soil profiles are only a few inches or feet in thickness, and a thin planing or skinning of the surface, almost negligible to the geomorphologist, may nevertheless result in the total loss of a soil profile acquired only after 100,000 years, or more, of surficial stability. Familiar though I was with the poverty and precariousness of African soils, I was surprised on a study tour of Australia to find in some districts how widely and how often, even in that continent of extensive duricrust, the soil mantle had been stripped in geologically recent time.

Conversely, where the land is being aggraded by alluvial or eolian action ancient soil profiles become buried and newer soil profiles are developed above them. Under favourable circumstances whole sequences of developed soil profiles may be found stacked one upon another, affording a " stratigraphic sequence " for late geologic time. Each of the soils in overlying succession may show enrichment in lime of the lower part of its profile, and as many as eight soils of different geologic ages within the Quaternary era have been recognised both in Australia and the United States of America.

Amid the unusual episodes of Quaternary time, including rapid fluctuations of climatic and denudational controls, quite remarkable reversals and repetitions of soil development and soil removal have occurred in certain regions.

The soils of the Murray River Basin studied by Butler (1959) afford evidence of a number of three-phase fluctuations (deposition of raw materials, soil formation and soil removal) which Butler has grouped into " K " cycles (Fig. 68). The cyclic status of each soil member is recognisable by its degree of " organisation " and certain of the members have a distribution covering many thousands of square miles, recalling the dictum that " soils are landscapes as well as profiles ". About Deniliquin the K_2 layer is of these dimensions though it is only 2 feet thick. Eastward of the town riverine material constituted 30 per cent. of the landscape and parna 60 per cent. for K_2 time, the former being adjacent to the river courses.

With identification of " K " cycles as time units, soil scientists in South-eastern Australia closely relate their soils to landscape, so that Butler defines a " K " cycle as " the interval of time covering the formation by erosion and/or deposition, of a new landscape surface, the period of development of the soils on that surface, and ending with the renewal of erosion of and/or deposition on that surface ". Each " K " cycle thus has an early unstable phase when the new ground-surfaces are created, and a later, stable phase when the soil profile develops. Older cycles naturally have more developed profiles, characterised by greater leaching and differentiation among the residual (clay) materials.

Butler's summary (1959) of " K " cycle data in South-eastern Australia is expressed in Table VI:

TABLE VI

K_0	K_0 materials are almost everywhere in the unstable phase of erosion or deposition. Except in desert areas, they are scarcely altered to soil and the original depositional fabric still remains in the upper six inches of accumulation.
K_1	The unstable phase involves a small proportion of the landscape: river terraces, dune parnas and suchlike minor features. In the short stable period since they accumulated minimal prairie and chestnut soils have developed on K_1 groundsurfaces. Homogeneous black soils, full of roots, with crumby structure and open texture are typical. There is no change in clay composition from top to bottom, but lime is leached from the top 9 inches and concentrated in the lower portion.
K_2	A more severe instability than K_1, involving half or more of the landscape: hillside erosion, extensive riverine deposition and parna deposition. The stable phase was longer than for K_1, and persistent groundsurfaces have red and red-brown earths and grey and brown soils of heavy texture on them. The soils are clayey, easily deformed, and may be mottled as the constituents become separated. Vesicles are characteristic and much wood may be present. The " A " horizon of K_2 soils often stands overhanging in the sides of dongas because the " B " horizon, though plastic and firm to handle, is unstable to water.
K_3	Surface instability more severe than for K_2. Persistent groundsurfaces have soils of the red earth, maximal podsolic, and solodic types and gumbotil soils on them. There is much separation of constituents by leaching and lime and iron concretions may appear.
K_4	In the unstable phase most of the countryside was stripped bare of all preceeding soil materials, and K_4 soils are generally (in South-eastern Australia) the oldest discoverable. Typical K_4 soil is a stiff thixotropic clay, very difficult to deform but once the rigidity is broken down it continues to deform readily (i.e. it is highly plastic after the yield limit has been passed). It holds up river bottoms and many streams flow upon it. No persistent surfaces are known at present, all having been buried by younger soils at some time or other.
K_5	Remnants left by the K_5 erosions occur only in the most protected accreting areas. Those described by Butler are incomplete soils, of low plasticity either calcareous or non-calcareous.

The table clearly records a waning series of phases since K_4 time when widespread erosion removed all but remnants of older soils. K_4 soils can frequently be found as burials, and all the later soils are commonly found both as surface exposures or as burials (Fig. 68). Carbon datings for the cycles at Nowra, N.S.W., indicate K_1 at 700, K_2 at 6,000 and K_3 at 29,000 years.

Butler's scheme of " K " cycles affords a competent framework for the study of soils

based on their periodicity. Within each " K " cycle subdivision can be effected by considering the mode of origin of the parent material—as alluvium, parna, " lottal "*
derived from mass-movement, and so forth. Distribution studies of " K " cycles further
focus attention upon the distribution of soils as well as profiles, a most valuable concept
in Quaternary geology.

Fossil soils formed during stable phases of landscape development are extensively
known also in North America (Frye 1949) where they are associated with glacial and
interglacial deposits of the Quaternary Era (Fig. 69).

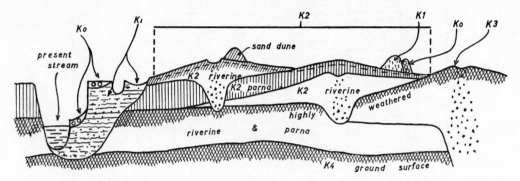

FIG. 68. Diagrammatic vertical section showing depositional systems and " K " cycles
of the riverine plain of southeastern Australia. *after B. E. Butler.*

MODIFICATIONS DUE TO FRIGIDITY

Earlier (p. 158) the point was made that landscapes of temperate regions are often
encumbered with a thick mantle of waste spread both as broad, alluviated valley floors
and as a soil mantle upon hillslopes. In these situations the abundance of waste may
so interfere with the normal processes of denudation as to hinder the normal downcutting
of rivers and retreat of hillslopes. The degenerate landforms which result evolve only
with extreme tardiness. This is shown in the clear river waters of such regions.

Where temperatures approaching frigidity are superadded, as in periglacial regions,
the quantity of waste accumulating in the landscape may reach smothering proportions.
Much of it is in a saturated condition and mass-movement (by solifluction and creep)
down even gentle slopes persistently redistributes it in ever-changing runlets like rain
over the windscreen of a fast-driven car. Landforms of periglacial regions have been
studied by Dylik (1952) in Poland, Smith (1949) and Peltier (1950) in the United States,
Hamelin (1961) in Canada and Cotton (1955) in New Zealand, and there is an extensive
and rapidly growing literature linked with *cryopedology*, the study of soils in cold regions.
Only latterly, indeed, has the extent of peri-glacial phenomena amid recent landforms

* *Lottal.* A term lacking scientific definition but used in the field by Butler and King to describe
the aqueous clayey mixtures formed by mass movement down hillslopes. Derivation : the jingle " Careful
with that catsup bottle ; none'll come and then a lot'll."

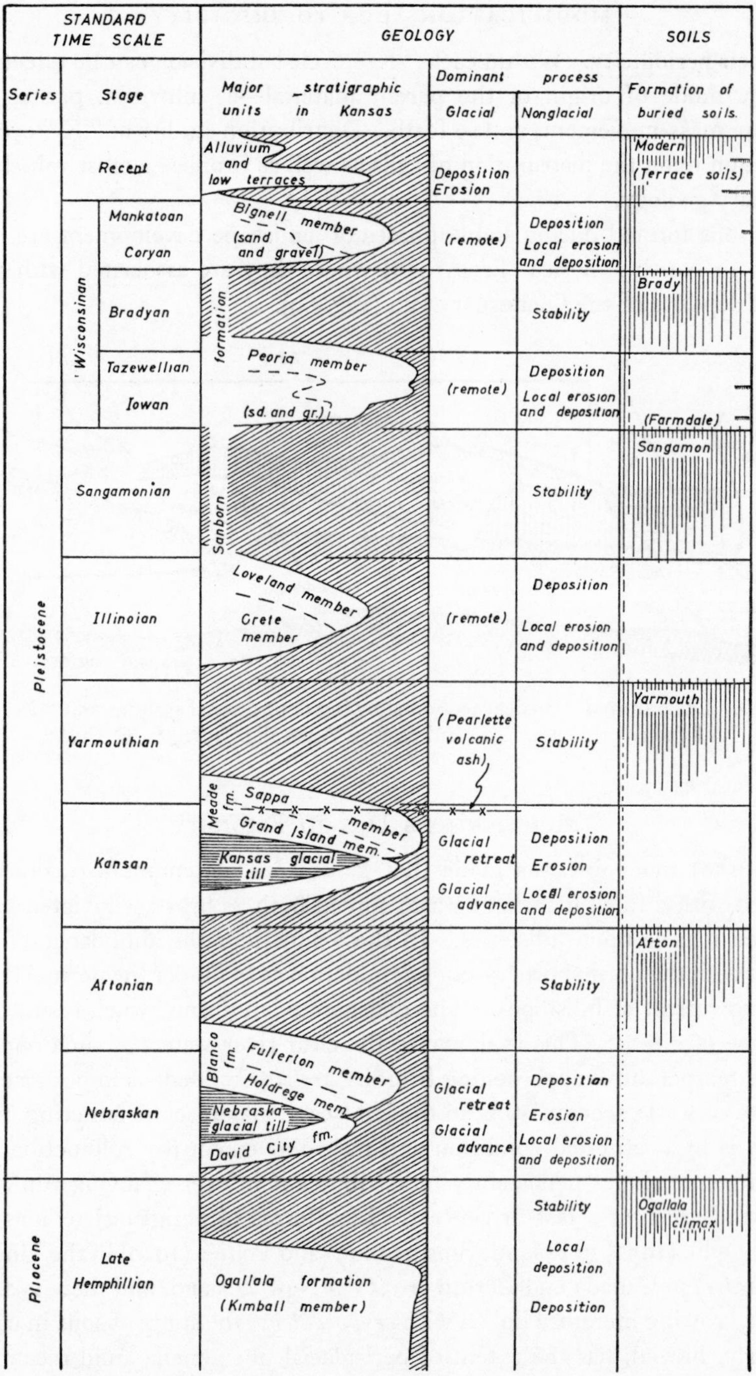

STANDARD TIME SCALE		GEOLOGY			SOILS
Series	**Stage**	Major stratigraphic units in Kansas	**Dominant process**		Formation of buried soils.
			Glacial	Nonglacial	
Pleistocene	Recent	Alluvium and low terraces	Deposition Erosion		Modern (Terrace soils)
	Mankatoan / Coryan	Bignell member (sand and gravel)	(remote)	Deposition / Local erosion and deposition	
	Bradyan	formation		Stability	Brady
	Tazewellian / Iowan	Peoria member (sd. and gr.)	(remote)	Deposition / Local erosion and deposition	(Farmdale)
	Sangamonian	Sanborn		Stability	Sangamon
	Illinoian	Loveland member / Crete member	(remote)	Deposition / Local erosion and deposition	
	Yarmouthian	(Pearlette volcanic ash)		Stability	Yarmouth
	Kansan	Meade fm. / Sappa member / Grand Island mem. / Kansas glacial till	Glacial retreat / Glacial advance	Deposition / Erosion / Local erosion and deposition	
	Aftonian			Stability	Afton
	Nebraskan	Blanco fm. / Fullerton member / Holdrege mem. / Nebraska glacial till / David City fm.	Glacial retreat / Glacial advance	Deposition / Erosion / Local erosion and deposition	
Pliocene	Late Hemphillian	Ogallala formation (Kimball member)		Stability / Local deposition / Deposition	Ogallala climax

FIG. 69. The complex Pleistocene history of Nebraska-Kansas expressed in the several types of deposition within the region. *after Condra* et al.

been appreciated. Almost all of Europe, for instance, shows peri-gracial influence: in France the only part exempt is the red soil region of the Mediterranean.

Much of the land-waste may, it is true, be contributed by glacial action, but its primary distribution is principally by water and wind action. To the former are due outwash plains, such as the Canterbury Plains bordering the Southern Alps and the flat plains of Illinois surpassing in smoothness even the most exquisitely bevelled pedi-plains; to the latter are due the " cold " loesses built of the fine rock-flour milled by glacial abrasion. To these may be added, locally or periodically, till and morainic deposits of glacial action itself. Where glaciers of continental dimensions formerly existed, the ground moraine or till left after the ice has melted away sometimes covers large areas. " Drift " editions of geological maps of Great Britain, for instance, show how widely such deposits are spread there. Over Eastern Europe and Western Siberia glacial tills extend almost as far south as latitude 50° N. Of great interpretative value are " erratic " boulders of ice-borne rock far removed from their original source into regions where they are geologically foreign. The erratics of East Anglia derived from Scandinavia form a striking example.

With the episodic waxing and waning of the ice-sheets, the operation of typically peri-glacial processes such as solifluction and congeliturbation, and the play of fluviatile and other normal agencies, all operating in successive zones which advance and retreat over the same ground and each leaving behind its characteristic sedimentary record, exceedingly complex morphologies may appear over the disputed terrains.

Thus in North America the adjoining states of Nebraska and Kansas afford a typical example of conflict between (a) an area of continental glaciation in the north (represented in Minnesota with its ten thousand lakes), (b) an area of fluviatile and eolian deposition in the west and south-west (Prairie facies) and (c) the unglaciated Ozark province in the south.

The Pleistocene glaciation in America was, moreover, multiple with the Nebraskan, Kansan, Illinoian and Wisconsin (substage Iowan) glacial maxima interspaced by the Aftonian, Yarmouth, Sangamon and Peorian (substage) interglacial phases. Not all the glacial phases are present in Nebraska and Kansas, but the history as given by Condra, Reed and Gordon (1950) for Nebraska, and Frye and Leonard (1952) for Kansas is nevertheless suitably complex (Fig. 69). We quote it here as a typical example.

The pre-glacial topography was comparatively rough, with the Seward formation (an eastward, fine-grained equivalent of the Ogalalla (Pliocene) sediments of the High Plains province) lying in the valley bottoms. The sea drained northward from the line of the Missouri River to Hudson Bay and southward to the Gulf of Mexico. Across this topography rode the Nebraskan glaciers " hundreds of feet thick ". Nonetheless, as these glaciers were wasting and were heavily charged with debris, their functions were depositional rather than erosional, so that when the ice disappeared by stagnation and marginal retreat their ground moraine formed a thick blanket of till.

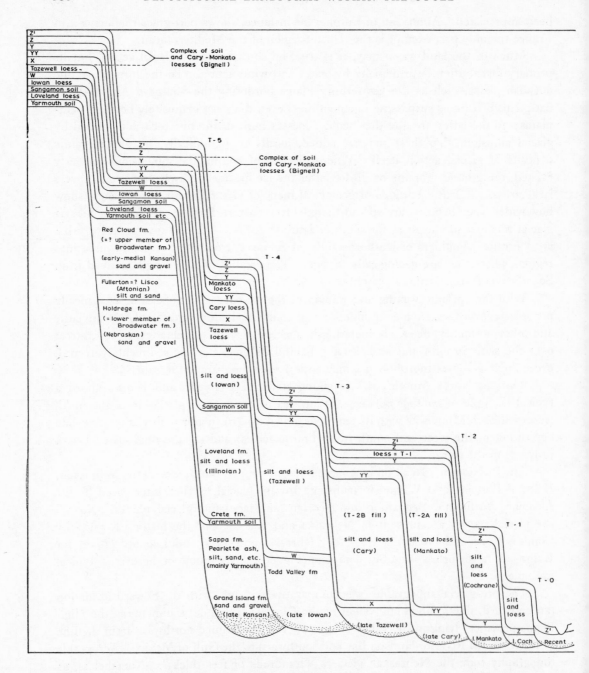

FIG. 70. Soil formation in Kansas during the Quaternary glaciation of

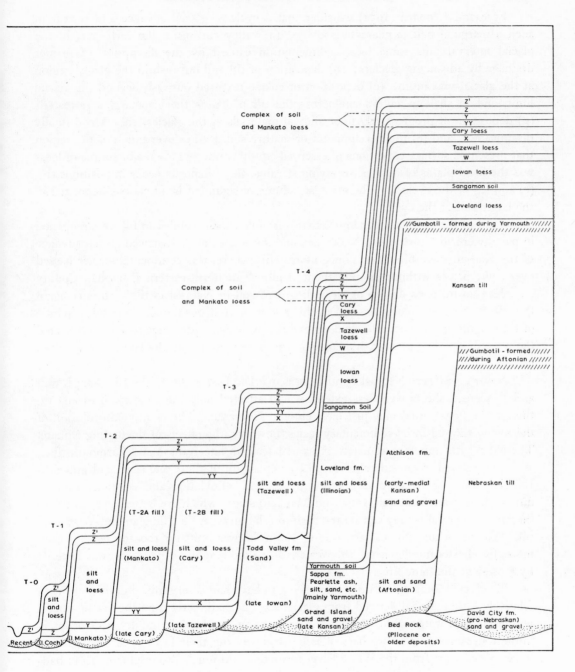

North America. *after C. B. Schultz, G. C. Lueninghoener and W. D. Frankforter.*

Frye and Leonard (1952) consider that a cycle of glacial advance and retreat in such a marginal belt is characterised by " (a) valley cutting in the early part of the glacial interval plus some local sedimentation caused by the disruption of former drainage by advancing glaciers; (b) deposition of till and outwash in the glacial region at the glacial maximum; (c) deposition of coarse-textured outwash beyond the glacial limit, and in shallow valleys cut across the till plains as the ice margins retreated; (d) deposition of progressively finer alluvial materials as the glaciers shrank and finally disappeared; and (e) the development of mature soil profiles over much of the region that presented surface conditions of essential equilibrium. As the major source of loess was the flood plains of outwash-carrying streams, these deposits occur in positions (b), (c) and (d) of the cycle ". The greatest volume of sediment is, of course, deposited in the latter half of the cycle.

Some of the pre-glacial channels that were filled with Nebraskan till were reopened in part by erosion during late-Nebraskan and Aftonian time. Renewed glacial advance of the Kansan stage filled them once more. Elsewhere, this continental glacier passed over some places without eroding them at all. " In north-eastern Doniphan County . . . Kansan till rests on top of an undisturbed soil in Nebraskan till ", so once again the effects of continental glaciation in this region were depositional. The thick mantle of Kansan till, indeed, completely deranged the pre-existing drainage pattern and altered the watershed. The present drainage pattern developed during the late-Kansan glacial retreat.

Never again were Nebraska and Kansas overlain by ice-sheets, the Illinoian, Iowan and Wisconsin sheets were less extensive and affected only the country to the north, though the first-named may just have entered Nebraska. The continued evolution of the region showed in its sedimentary facies, however, the effects of fluctuating climate. The old river channels were partly excavated again in late-Kansan and Yarmouth time, and were refilled to considerable depth by deposition of the Crete sand and gravel of Illinoian time. Further modifications by erosion, alluviation and eolation occurred during the Iowan, Tazewell, Cary and Mankato stages which are better represented to the north where also they can be traced into relation with the Illinoian and Wisconsin tills. On the whole, the eastern side of Nebraska was built up 100-200 feet, or even more, by Pleistocene deposits; the western side (and neighbouring states) was lowered by erosion at the same time.

The " cold loesses " of this region seem to have had a very mixed derivation, with relatively little material derived from glacial streams or directly from the flat till-sheets with their high water-table. Important sources were probably " the dry beds of intermittent streams and the dry bars of large rivers during their low stages. Some loess in Nebraska came from the White River formation and much also originated from badlands in Cretaceous clays as is happening at the present time. It came largely from the High Plains region of the west where the surface of the dry Tableland is insufficiently protected from deflation by the sparse vegetation ". The three main loess formations, the Loveland, Peorian and Bignell follow the Illinoian, Iowan and Wisconsin glaciations. No deposits of loess related to earlier glaciations are known in Nebraska.

Soil formation during stable periods between the many accumulations is expressed in Fig. 70.

With the retreat of ice-sheets, widespread changes occurred in the Great Lakes region where ancient shorelines (*e.g.* Nipissing) show that the lakes were formerly larger and that their basins have tilted with maximum uplift in the north.

Of especial interest in relation to glacial wasting are the varved clays which accumulate in periglacial lake basins. The classic studies of de Geer in Europe have revealed the stages of northward retreat of the last glaciation there, and Antevs has used varved clay measurements to demonstrate progressive withdrawal of the ice-border northward across New England.

On the Quaternary accumulations of Siberia is a huge literature. According to Obruchev (1926) the phases may be summarised:

a) pre-glacial, comprising alluvium and terrace formations in the valley of the Lena and sundry lake beds;

b) formations of the first glaciation. In the mountains much moraine in the north and much boulder clay and end moraine in the south; early loess accumulation;

c) interglacial. In the north, sediments of the first marine transgressions with a boreal fauna, on the lands began the tundra regime. In the south came the end of the main loess accumulation and the broad lacustrine formations. In the mountains the phase is represented by fluvio-glacial sands. Muds and boulder layers overlie the earlier moraines;

d) formations of the second glaciation. In the mountains formed the lesser moraines, with loess and the sediments of shrunken lakes in the south. Boulder clay cloaks the northlands and includes fossils of neolithic men;

e) post-glacial stage; in the north are the sediments of the second transgression with a recent boreal fauna. On the lands succeeded the tundra formation, with, in the south, the end of loess accumulation, the denudation of the loess and the spread of forests;

f) recent accumulations, and re-incision of river valleys, destruction of the forests and accumulation of wind-blown sands.

VOLCANIC ACCUMULATIONS

Volcanoes as landscape forms have been extensively discussed by C. A. Cotton (1944). Volcanic phenomena express themselves largely in accumulative phases displayed as cones or plateaus of lava or ash, in every case distinctive. Many of the world's most interesting landscapes have, or had, a volcanic episode. If this was recent the effusives and associated lake and stream beds may be present in the landscape, as in the Snake River—Columbia region of Oregon, lavas of which were poured out in the Miocene;

but where the activity was ancient, the record may be entirely secondary and consist of erosional features: dyke-ridges, sill-capped plateaus and buttes such as appear so characteristically in the Karroo region of South Africa. The distribution of such landforms is more or less sporadic in space and time, and apart from the problem of volcanism itself they pose no fresh fundamental issue in our enquiry. We shall, there-fore, not devote space to them here, but shall note their occurrence where necessary in later chapters.

DEPOSITIONAL LANDSCAPES IN TIME

Depositional landscapes, though at home within the concept of an epigene cycle of erosion, often find far greater extent and importance in relation to tectonic movement, as set forth in the succeeding chapter; but before taking up this study we may assimilate a useful principle—if erosional surfaces can, and do, survive almost indefinitely under favourable circumstances, why should not certain depositional surfaces survive also? There seems every reason to believe that the Cainozoic accretions of the prairie land-scape in regions like the Llano Estacado have remained with relatively little change (only acquiring a mantle of *caliche*) since the time of their accumulation and the same is true of parts of volcanic plateaus such as the Snake River, Deccan, and possibly even high Basutoland.

CHAPTER VII

TECTONICS AND LANDSCAPE EVOLUTION

Tectonic Movement and Landscape. Interruptions to the Cycle of
Erosion. Polycyclic Landscapes. Interruption by Differential Move-
ments. Warped Divides. Denudation on the Flanks of Cymatogenic
Arches. Basin Warping and Filling. The Paris Basin. Fossil Landscapes.
Peri-continental Deposition.

TECTONIC MOVEMENT AND LANDSCAPE

Recent sinking of the land relative to sea level is known in many parts of the world.
At present sea level is rising as the world's glaciers, swollen during the Ice Age, melt
away and their substance is returned to the oceans. Such rise is eustatic or world-wide.
But in addition to this, ample evidence attests that independent sinking of the land has
occurred upon many coasts. New Jersey is said to be subsiding at the rate of 2 feet
per century and the sea now flows where once were city streets. In the vicinity of the
Mississippi delta the remains of Indian middens and camp sites are found as much as
28 feet below sea level. The ruins of Belize, an old town abandoned in 1870, are already
below several feet of mud brought down by the same river. A large part of the Indonesian
region is shallowly sunk beneath the ocean and the courses of the former rivers can
still be traced across the sea bottom (Fig. 13).

Recent elevations of the land are equally well known. The rise of the Norwegian
strandflat has been measured at 6-12 inches per century. In the North American Arctic
ancient Eskimo camp sites now stand too far above sea level to be of use. Indeed many
of the world's coasts are bordered by flights of uplifted marine terraces rising to
elevations of as much as 1,000 feet, and some display broad coastal plains built of
fossiliferous marine rocks. Especially interesting are recorded instances of land areas
rising suddenly at times of earthquake. Wellington, capital city of New Zealand, was
so elevated 5 feet in 1855; the raised beaches still run for miles along the coast to either
side. The inner harbour of Napier, Hawke's Bay, was likewise elevated by a maximum
of 9 feet in 1931.

Altitudes observed along uplifted marine terraces sometimes show that uplift was
not uniform either between terraces or with respect to modern sea level. The marine
terraces of Cook Strait, New Zealand (Fig. 71), transverse to the grain of the country,
illustrate this admirably.

In all these instances modern sea level provides a ready reference datum. Even
small departures from horizontality become startlingly evident if traced over distances

of a mile or more. No such datum is available inland, and unless the results of tectonic disturbance are followed by a sufficiently long period for erosional or other agencies to readjust the landscape to the new conditions, mild tectonic effects are apt to escape notice in the topography. This is not always so, however. Amid smoothly planed landscapes the effects of tectonic activity may sometimes be detected even if small. Veatch (1935), observing an average slope of 1 metre per kilometre on the planed Congo-Zambezi divide, was led to pronounce (correctly) that this slope was too much, and that the surface had been tilted! The warped divide of Australia, south of the Gulf of Carpentaria, has a northerly slope of 1 foot per mile to the shore and beyond that " the sea floor maintains a comparable small gradient far out into the Gulf ".

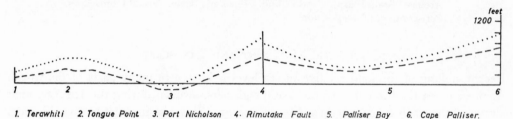

1. Terawhiti   2. Tongue Point   3. Port Nicholson   4. Rimutaka Fault   5. Palliser Bay   6. Cape Palliser.

FIG. 71. Warped ancient coastlines of Wellington, New Zealand, showing differential movement between stages of stillstand.

Throughout the east European plains from the Baltic to the Black Sea secular movements, averaging 2-4 mm. per year, and with maxima of 7-10 mm. per year, have been detected. Mescherikov (1959) has concluded: " Apparently, secular movements are a universal form of present tectonic manifestations. They embrace both mountain areas and plains, continents and sea-bottoms . . . In particular, it is necessary to discard completely as obsolete the idea of a tectonic passivity or immobility of plain-platform regions during the Quaternary period and at the present time ".

He continues: " Intense uplifts have also been discovered on the islands of Japan, in the Indus and Ganges plain and other extraglacial regions. Thus the theory of Isostasy cannot fully explain the distribution of present area of subsidence and uplift "

" In comparing the map of secular movements with tectonic maps it becomes evident that the sign of present movements is to a great extent determined by the geological structure ". Basement blocks (Voronesh, Ukraine) rise, the sedimentary basins (Moscow, Dneiper and others) sink. The same is true of other regions—Netherlands, Japan, but many discrepancies of sign do exist (e.g. Ukraine) within the major regions and, reversals also have been detected.

Mescherikov finds also that on the Russian platform the chief seismic shocks are related to flexure zones between currently rising and subsiding areas. Secular movements he regards as " controlled by endogenetic processes taking place in the interior of the Earth's crust ". Movements currently amount to several millimetres a year, with localized maxima of several centimetres or even decimetres per year.

PLATE 6

Two-cycle topography. A late Cainozoic erosional plain, now uplifted to 3,000 feet and dissected by numerous small valleys incised during the Quaternary. Near Nkomo Mountain, Zululand.

Lester King.

INTERRUPTIONS TO THE CYCLE OF EROSION

A cycle of erosion requires a protracted period of time for its completion upon the continental scale, and the hazard of interruption by tectonic agencies at some stage before completion is considerable.

In regions where uplift has been uniform the effect is that landforms of fresh cycles are induced first in the coastlands while the features of older cycles remain current in the interior. Repetitive uplift produces a succession of cyclic assemblages of landforms that may be arranged progressively in order of decreasing age from the heart of a continent outwards.

Slow continuous uplift may also produce stepped landforms seemingly indistinguishable from those due to repetitive uplift. This conclusion, first enunciated by Penck, stems from the inherent tendency of landscapes undergoing pediplanation to assume a concave form coupled with the necessity to form a scarp if the relief exceeds the critical height for the local rocks (p. 153).

Where differential movement has also been active there may be some difficulty in distinguishing the handiwork of various cycles, and deciding what features (*e.g.* scarps or erosional bevels) are of continental cyclic origin, and what are due to local deformation.

POLYCYCLIC LANDSCAPES

Polycyclic landscapes are those in which appear features attributable to two or more independent cycles of erosion, each of which is current over part of the area under examination. Most of the world's scenery is polycyclic. The simplest case is that which follows a uniform lowering of base level, achieved either by uplift of the land or by a fall of sea level.* Usually the streams of an older, planed landscape are then rejuvenated and incise themselves in youthful, second-cycle valleys below nickpoints which pass gradually upstream (Fig. 72). As the newer cycle progresses, its landforms become ever more extensive destroying the forms of the previous cycle as they do so.

The migrating boundary between the two sets of cyclic landforms is marked, in both stream and hill profiles, by sharply convex breaks of gradient, unrelated to lithologic control. These are caused by an increased intensity of erosion. All such breaks originate at the level of the hydraulic net, and recede thence outward, so that the behaviour of steep hillslopes under retreat speedily becomes independent of base-level control and the intercyclic boundary is related only to the upper edge of the scarp face, or to the pediment where no scarp face is present.

Where the earlier landscape was well planed the new steep-sided valleys, vigorously growing headward, form a striking topographic contrast (Plate 6). In time the new valley walls of main streams and tributaries achieve a stable gradient and thereafter

---

* The topographic effects of these two happenings are, in most cases, indistinguishable.

N

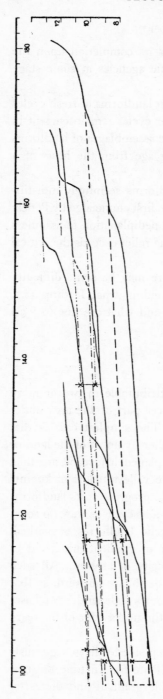

retreat as scarps, encroaching upon the landforms of the earlier planation. At their feet appears a growing complex of coalescing pediments which develops into a small pediplain of the second erosional cycle. Two-cycle landscapes of this kind are common in all continents and most countries, and it is principally from them that the geomorphology, involving the conflicting effects of erosion and tectogenesis, must be elucidated (Fig. 74).

So long as uplifts are regionally uniform, or movements of sea level are eustatic, the landforms of each cycle follow those of its predecessor with essential regularity, and the corresponding partial planations may be rendered step-wise parallel to the coast through maritime provinces (Fig. 64). Sometimes cyclic features are carried rapidly inland up the thalwegs of larger rivers into the heart of the continents, and the new inter-cyclic erosional scarps retreat laterally away from the axes of the trunk valleys (*e.g.* Zambezi) or the trunk and major tributary valleys (*e.g.* Amazon) (Fig. 63).

The combination of these two modes of development provides the master plan for the spread of cyclic erosional features on the continental scale and is reflected clearly in topographic maps covering any considerable territory (Fig. 73). It is best revealed in those regions which possess a stable foundation (shield areas), and is least apparent in regions of Cainozoic orogenesis. Much local detail is superimposed upon the general plan by differences of rock resistance to weathering, by various geologic structures, or by differences in the erosional agents, but the effects of all these are minor and subordinate to the continental plan of cyclic erosion.

FIG. 72. Synoptic profiles of the River Lot and its tributaries, southern France, with attempted restoration of the ancient stream beds below nickpoints. Crosses denote points of confluence of the ancient beds. Lengths in kilometres from the mouth; heights in hectometres. *after H. Baulig.*

When progress of the newer cycle is far advanced, the landforms of the older cycle survive, with minimal alteration, only upon the ridges and plateaus of residual highlands. The denudational forces acting upon them remain the same and they continue to develop with respect to the edge of the scarp or break of gradient which separates them

FIG. 74. Older cyclic bevel being destroyed by scarp retreat with the formation of a newer pediplain, Odzi Valley, Rhodesia.

from the more youthful, incised forms of the second cycle. Such breaks of gradient separate different slope systems as nickpoints divide different fluviatile regimes along the thalweg. As Penck has written (1953) " From the moment it arises until it disappears,

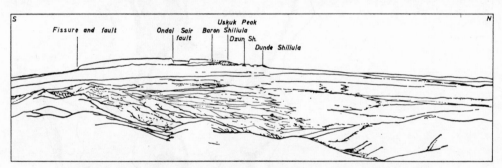

FIG. 75. Domed and dissected planation surface of the Mount Uskuk area, Mongolia. Mid-Cainozoic sediments have been strongly flexed and faulted ; in early Pleistocene time erosion developed an almost perfect plain which, still more recently, has been arched and re-dissected. Both the sediments and the old rock floor exposed in the background record the deformation. *after C. P. Berkey and F. K. Morris.*

each break of gradient forms the lower edge of a slope for which it provides the base level. So long as it lasts, the denudation of the slope, lying above, takes place in relation o it ".

INTERRUPTION BY DIFFERENTIAL MOVEMENTS

In contrast with uniform continental or eustatic movements, numerous crustal displacements are expressed in differential warping and faulting (Fig. 75). By this means broad flexures are imposed upon already existing landscapes, usually casting them into arches of uplift or basins of depression (Fig. 76) (Jessen 1943). Broadly convex uplands

196 TECTONICS AND LANDSCAPE EVOLUTION

of earlier planation may continue to register the deformation in their smooth crestlines for long periods until they are destroyed by subsequent erosion, while conversely the

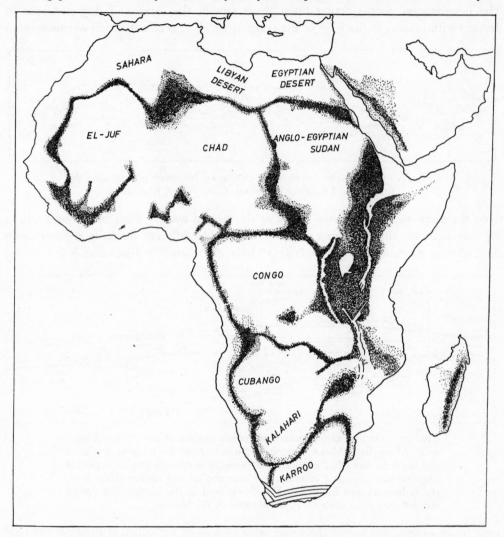

FIG. 76. Warping of the African continent along "arches of uplift" and into basins of depression. *after A. Holmes*, (1944). See also Fig. 27.

basins often serve as foci for deposition of superabundant waste derived from neighbouring uplands.

By such deformations, in which only vertical displacement is involved, the earth's surface is thrown into gigantic undulations, sometimes measuring hundreds of miles across and with vertical displacement amounting to thousands or even tens of thousands of feet. For these the term *cymatogeny* (Greek Κὺμγ=a wave or undulation) has

been proposed (King 1961). Cymatogeny, " the undulating ogeny ", defined upon
p. 659, is one of the most important concepts in geomorphology, for differential erosion
and sedimentation operating upon the elevated and depressed regions respectively give
complementary records of earth history.

Thus high on the frontier mountains between Rhodesia and Moçambique,
at more than 8,000 feet above sea-level stands an ancient erosional bevel known as
the " Gondwana " landsurface (Chapter IX). On the eastern mountain front the bevel
has been cut away by later cycles of denudation, but far out in the coastal plain of
Moçambique it is found once more, warped down to low levels as the floor of the early-
Cretaceous formations of that region. Near the coast at Inharrime it is encountered
again, in boreholes at 6,000 feet below sea level. As the surface was originally a level
plain of extreme denudation, its vertical deformation by smooth warping on this line of
section amounts to 14,000 feet since the Jurassic period (Fig. 77).

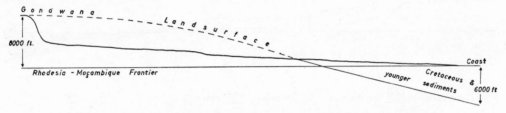

FIG. 77. Deformation of the Jurassic landsurface of southern Africa
from 8,000 feet above sea-level at the border of Rhodesia and Moçambique
(Inyangani) to 6,000 feet below sea-level at the Moçambique coast
(Inharrime).

On related sections several other cyclic denudational landscapes can likewise be
traced down from the highlands and plateaus and equated with unconformities or
hiatuses in the marine sedimentary sequence of the coastlands. The " post-Gondwana "
cyclic planation, for instance, corresponds with the unconformity beneath the Senonian
overlap; the widely planed, early-Cainozoic landscape of the African interior equates
with the hiatus and unconformity below the early-Miocene (Burdigalian) coastal sandstones; and late-Cainozoic partial planations of the land correspond with pre-Pliocene
and Pliocene hiatuses amid sandy series of the coastal belt. The oldest cyclic planations
stand highest upon the lands, and lowest (as unconformities) in the sedimentary record
of the coastal plain. Hence there exists a zone where the landsurfaces converge and
cross over into the inverted position as unconformities. This zone is not always manifest
in the flat country of Moçambique, but it occurs more clearly, with the same chapters
of denudation and sedimentation, in Zululand to the south (Fig. 78).

Repeated crustal warping of the African continental margin on a grand scale is
here apparent. The several chapters demonstrate the intermittent nature of the warping,
and serve to date and measure its several episodes from the Jurassic to the present day.
Each episode, at a maximum of uplift on the Great Escarpment (Plate 4) and a

maximum of (measured) depression near or beyond the coast,* involves displacements in both senses exceeding 1,000 feet from each previous datum to a total differential of many thousands of feet.   Southward by Natal (Plate 7) the axis of no movement has consistently lain close off shore, so the sedimentary phase seldom appears there.

Orogenesis was absent, as is proved by the regular attitude of the cyclic denudational surfaces in the landscape on the one hand, and the small and regular dips of the sedimentary series on the other.   Conversely, differential movement of such large amounts involving the elevation of a mountain range with the parallel and related sinking of a marginal trough is not sufficiently uniform to be classed as epeirogenesis.   Cymatogeny, " the undulating ogeny " for which a characteristic crustal structure will be adduced (p. 656) fits the case.

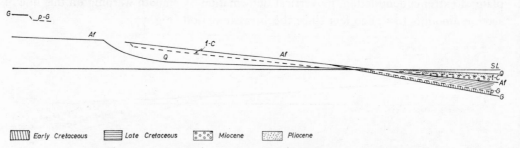

FIG. 78.   The denudation chronology of southern Africa established by relating the several cyclic denudational landscapes of the interior and marginal regions to unconformities between the neighbouring sedimentary series of the Zululand coastal plain.   Diagrammatic only.   G = Gondwana,   p-G = post-Gondwana,   Af = African,   1-C = late-Cainozoic,   Q = Quaternary.   Second late-Cainozoic surface and corresponding deposits omitted.

In mirror image, a similar set of denudational cycles and a similar sequence of marine depositions is found upon the western flank of Africa in Angola (Jessen 1936) and the coastland of the Congo Republic (Cahen and Lepersonne 1951) (Fig. 103). The necessary crossing of successive surfaces is accomplished in the coastal plain, and the vertical displacements, from 8,000 feet upon the Benguella Highlands, to far below sea level are of the same order as in Moçambique.

In the interior of the continent, the African rift valley system follows the crests of major cymatogenic uplifts wherein the uparching so lengthened the superficial arc that it cracked open tensionally (Fig. 242), and this is the explanation of rift valleys in other continents also, e.g. Eastern Brazil.†

* But localised basins of maximal sedimentation also developed upon the general tilt, e.g. in the Senonian of both Moçambique and Zululand.

† The present chapter treats only of the topographic effects of cymatogeny.   Definition of the phenomenon and its characteristic crustal structure and process, and geotectonic importance are considered in Chapter XIX (p. 656).

PLATE 7

Three-cycle topography inclined upon the Natal monocline. The smooth early Cainozoic planation is preserved upon sandstone plateaus above fragments of a rolling late Cainozoic cyclic landscape (left, right and distance), and both stand above 1,000 feet-deep valleys of Quaternary cycles. The two older surfaces incline markedly from left to right, the sandstone remnants of the early Cainozoic surface descending from 2,800 feet at the extreme left to 2,100 feet right of centre and 1,700 feet at the extreme right distance. The late Cainozoic surface is similarly disposed, showing that crustal arching occurred about the end of the Cainozoic era. View across the Valley of a Thousand Hills, behind Durban. In Zululand the same cyclic surfaces descending eastward pass below appropriate marine Cainozoic strata in the coastal plain.

Lester King.

Down faulting into troughs (rifts) produces its own crop of polycyclic riddles, one of which may be illustrated from the Luangwa Valley, Zambia. Here parts of the rift are floored with pebbly sediments, probably of Cretaceous age, which lie upon an incompletely planed bedrock, and show that the rifting was, in part at least, of probable Cretaceous age. Rising from the bedrock planation are the Chankulu and Lukonde Hills which are bevelled at 400 feet equally with the country adjoining the rift. The history (Fig. 79) seems to be that rifting affected a landscape which was imperfectly bevelled and bore residual hills, certain of which were carried down into the rift, but their tops still projected above part at least of the area adjoining the rift. The rift was speedily filled with terrigenous waste (Cretaceous ?) shed from the surrounding terrain. Later, the ubiquitous early-Cainozoic planation was carried across the

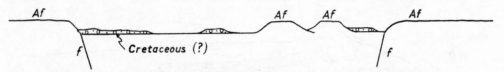

FIG. 79. Problems associated with rift faulting, the Chankulu and Lukonde Hills in Zambia. Cretaceous rift faulting let down a section of diversified country along the line of the Luangwa Valley. The rift was filled with post-Karroo but pre-Cainozoic sediments, and later the early-Cainozoic planation was carried smoothly across all elements of the landscape alike. Later, after the gravels had been partly removed by further denudation, the accordant summit bevelling of the hills and the surrounding country remained. Af = African surface, f = fault.

depositional surface of the filled trough to truncate the tops of the Chankulu and Lukonde Hills at appropriate elevation. Subsequent erosion of the gravel fill has re-exposed the flanks of the hills, and much of the bedrock floor of the rift, leaving the bevelled tops isolated.

The Los Angeles Basin which is partly faulted, shows benches carved across granite and graded not with respect to a former continental base level, but to the surface of a former infill, most of which has subsequently been removed. In this way, younger benches now appear at greater elevation in the landscape than earlier erosional levels that were buried at the time of maximum fill. The normal sequence of oldest denudational events at the top is here reversed.

A further special instance of topographic relations affected by rift faulting infill, lava flows and re-excavation, appears at Clermont Ferrand, in France (Johnson 1929) (Fig. 80).

Where unbalanced forces have operated strong topographic contrasts ensue. Thus Ruwenzori, which unlike other great Central African peaks is non-volcanic, is a huge asymmetrical block of the African basement upon which the surrounding African plain at 5,000 feet is smoothly upwarped to 14,000 feet above sea level. On the west are stupendous fault scarps, and the whole massif stands squarely in the axis of the Western Rift Valley. So recent has been the uplift (mid-Pleistocene) that the sides of the mountain are seamed with youthful ravines whose thalwegs are steeper than many hills. The geodynamics responsible involve slight transcurrent movement on opposite sides

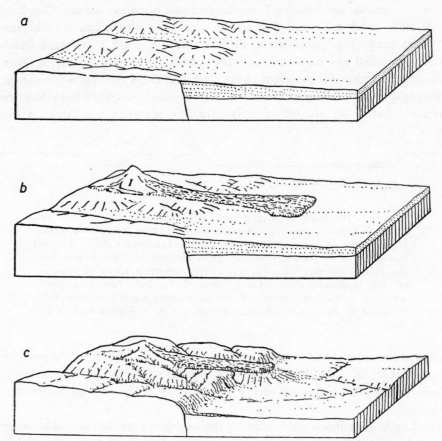

FIG. 80. Part of a former rift valley fill, elsewhere entirely removed, preserved beneath a cap of lava, Clermont-Ferrand, France. *after D. W. Johnson.*

of the rift system (Fig. 116). In similar fashion the West Indian island of Hispaniola rises out of the eastern end of the Bartlett Trough (p. 600). Transcurrent movements are indeed frequently associated with rift faulting. Quennell (1958) has demonstrated the opening of the Dead Sea depression in this manner (Fig. 81).

WARPED DIVIDES

In terrains of low relief the hydrography may be profoundly modified by cymatogenic arching and new, flat watersheds created. The Congo-Zambezi divide is situated on a featureless plain on which drainage is frequently indefinite, and water from a single area may flow sometimes to one river, sometimes to the other. This anomalous continental divide was formed by uparching of a pre-existing plain along a more or less east-west axis. Formerly, the divide was situated farther to the north, perhaps by as much as a hundred miles in some places, and back-tilted reaches added to the Congo catchment by the severance of former Zambezi headwaters are often swampy (Fig. 85).

The whole of the African watershed (Fig. 82), indeed, betrays its origin upon a warped former plain. From Cape Town the divide trends north-eastward to the Nieuwveld whence it follows the Great Escarpment east and then north-eastward along

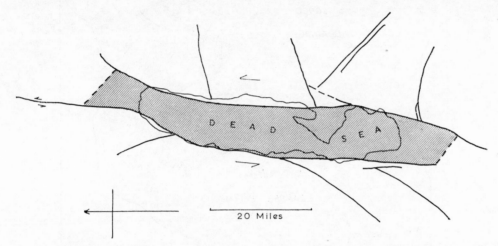

FIG. 81. Mechanics of the Dead Sea depression by left lateral transcurrent (wrench) faulting. *after A. M. Quennell.*

the Drakensberg to the Eastern Transvaal about Lake Chrissie. From this point it marches due westward, along the Witwatersrand into the Kalahari where it is temporarily lost. But it reappears once more, in the extreme west, only 200 miles from the Atlantic in the Benguella highlands. Once more the divide traverses to the east, along the Congo-Zambezi divide to the Muchinga Mountains in Zambia, and thence into Tanganyika where, with the entry of Nile drainage, it bifurcates, the two branches continuing northwards on either side of Victoria Nyanza. This is a curious watershed indeed for so stable a continent, comprehensible only under the cymatogenic concept.

Extraordinary changes are sometimes wreaked in the drainage pattern: for instance, the angular hydrography of Uganda west of Victoria Nyanza, where the rivers formerly flowing westward to the Congo were severed by an upwarp some twenty miles east of the Western Rift Valley and were back-tilted to flow sluggishly eastward through swamps to the Nyanza (Fig. 83).

This phenomenon of warped, flattish divides is commoner, and upon a greater scale, than is generally recognised. Examples of similar divides come from several continents. Thus the Main Divide of Australia often fails to follow any marked topographic feature and " takes a wavering or uncertain course across a valley or plain ". In some places it does not even occupy the highest country.

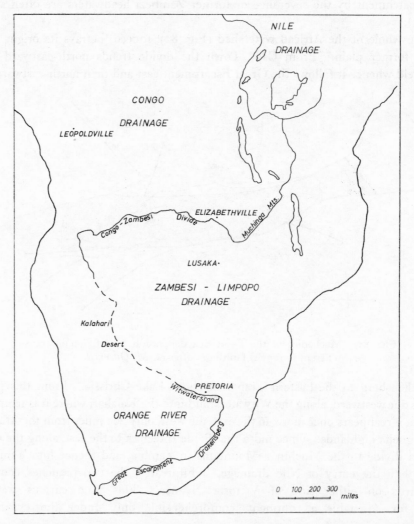

FIG. 82. The watershed of Southern and Central Africa formed by differential warping of a formerly smooth plain. From the western Cape Province the watershed follows the Great Escarpment of the Drakensberg until it traverses westward along the Witwatersrand to the Kalahari where it becomes indefinite. It is picked up again in the Mossamedes and Benguella Highlands only 200 miles from the Atlantic whence it traverses eastward again between the Congo and Zambezi headwaters to near the head of Lake Nyasa. Northward through Tanganyika it bifurcates, the branches passing on either side of Victoria Nyanza to include the Nile drainage.

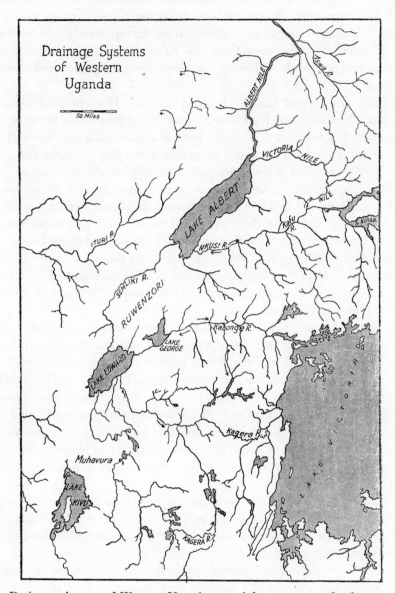

Drainage Systems
of Western
Uganda

50 Miles

FIG. 83. Drainage changes of Western Uganda caused by severance of a former westwardly-directed drainage system by uparching of the Western Rift cymatogen. Several streams were backtilted from curiously hooked headwaters to flow eastward, into the freshly created, shallow depression of Victoria Nyanza. Ancient "through valleys" still survive between rivers now flowing in opposite directions (Kafu, Katonga, Kagera Rivers).

In the far north of Queensland an indefinite divide separates the braided upper courses of the Diamantina, flowing inland, from the adjacent rivers of the Gulf of Carpentaria. Whitehouse remarks, " Viewed from the air, there seems no reason why the initial Diamantina waters should not flow to the Gulf of Carpentaria; for only a mile or two away, and with nothing but a plain between, gullies make away to the northern rivers ".

In Eastern Queensland the divide "traverses the Heberton Tableland at little more than 3,000 feet above sea level, and between it and the coast is the lofty Bellenden Ker Range rising to more than 5,000 feet. For some 700 miles it runs through tableland country, where it is in places not much more than 1,000 feet above the sea, and here it is for the most part determinable only with difficulty on the flat surface ". In the region of Mesozoic formations, laterite residuals surmount the very divide showing that when the Cainozoic mantle of duricrust was formed, the divide was non-existent and the region was a great, westwardly-inclining plain. There are even four well-defined airgaps at the crest of the arch, representing former valleys of through drainage from east to west (Wearne and Woolnough 1911). The Alice Tableland (between latitudes $20\frac{1}{2}°$ S. and 24° S.) presents the aspect, only slightly modified, of what the region of the Great Divide was like. Laterite is continuous across its 20,000 square miles, and at the very crest are basins of centripetal drainage.

Followed into Northern New South Wales, near Armidale, the divide " is 50 miles west of and 1,000 feet lower than the Snowy Mountains (5,000 feet). In the Central Highlands the divide runs east of the axis of greatest elevation and it is 30 or 40 miles east of the much higher land in the Australian Capital Territory, but at Mt. Kosciusko it includes the highest point in the Commonwealth. Valley- and plain-divides are seen at the head of the Goulburn and Cox's Rivers and between the Snowy and Murrum-bidgee. In eastern Victoria the divide has in places higher land to the north and south and at Cassilis it traverses a low broad depression at 2,300 feet between the Tambo and Mitta Mitta Rivers; in the west also it crosses broad valley depressions and swampy plains " (David 1950).

The whole of this remarkable watershed is related to cymatogenic arching of a former landscape of relatively low relief (p. 195) and shows marked independence of structural trends in the underlying rocks. In Victoria, indeed, it is directed nearly at right angles to prevailing rock strikes.

Many of the world's major watersheds have been determined by cymatogenic arching active towards the end of Cainozoic time; tectonics have therein operated to develop new hydrographic networks. But occasionally great rivers have been able to maintain their pre-existing courses by cutting profound gorges through the upheaving arches so that they now rise and discharge upon opposite sides of the arch, e.g. Manawatu River, New Zealand. Quite prominent ranges may then fail to constitute a watershed, and this is true even of the mighty Himalaya which is breached by the Indus, Sutlej and Brahmaputra Rivers all of which rise *north* of the Himalaya through which they pass in deep gorges to reach the Indian Ocean of the south (Fig. 84). In such (*antecedent*) courses river erosion has prevailed over tectogenesis.

DENUDATION ON THE FLANKS OF CYMATOGENIC ARCHES

Landsurfaces tilted upon the flanks of cymatogens experience renewed erosion by sheet and channelled run-off, and in some instances also by enhanced mass movement in the

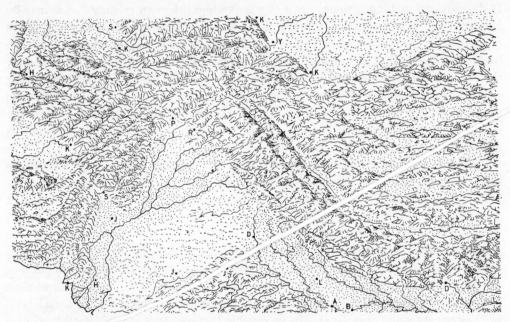

Fig. 84. *Deflection* of Himalayan ranges about Peninsular India. Wheeling through almost 180° the structure of the Hissar and Sulaiman Ranges compose almost mirror images. The modern Himalaya has risen as a mountain barrier athwart the older-established courses of the Indus, Sutlej and Brahmaputra Rivers which, rising north of the barrier, now pass to the plains of India through deep antecedent gorges. *after A. K. Lobeck.*

downhill direction. Even if the measure of tilting is small (and on many cymatogens it lies between $1°$ and $\frac{1}{2}°$), total vertical displacements are large amounting to hundreds or thousands of feet and permit redissection of the landscape in an unmistakable manner.

There are several variables in each of three categories (a) controls inherited from the parent landscapes; (b) the nature and amount of cymatogenic deformation; (c) the action of post-tectonic denudational agencies.

a) *Controls inherited from parent landscapes.* Parent landscapes may be of any kind, evenly planed or of high relief, with simple dendritic drainage or with stream patterns strongly controlled by structure, with a few powerful trunk rivers or with a network of sub-equal streams, with smoothly rolling hills or stark, angular rock masses: any known topographic pattern may become subject to cymatogeny. In many examples the parent landscape was an early-Cainozoic pediplain of wide extent that had been dissected by valley-floor planation in one or two stages prior to elevation (or depression) during the late Pliocene and Pleistocene, so that the landscapes involved were already polycyclic (Chapter VIII).

The simplest instances are provided by the arching of smoothly planed surfaces. If the maximal arching is upon previously active lines, then an existing divide may be increased and emphasised; if the crest of the arch is newly sited then a fresh divide is created, river diversions are likely and broad, shallow lakes may be impounded upon back-tilted sections. The Congo-Zambezi divide was created in part upon the extremely smooth early-Cainozoic surface of Africa, the previous divide having been situated among mountains some scores of miles to the north (Fig. 85). A similar indefinite divide situated within a broad plain exists in Tanganyika, at Shinyanga, water finding its way almost impartially to Victoria Nyanza and the Nile in the north or to Lake Tanganyika and the Congo in the south.

Where cymatogeny affects country already of substantial relief, especially where the movement is a rejuvenation along previously established lines, great changes of drainage are not likely to be instituted. Thus cymatogenic watersheds rejuvenated at long geologic intervals often preserve near the crest remnants of several relatively ancient cycles of denudation. Numerous examples of Jurassic (Gondwana) and Cretaceous (post-Gondwana) planations (Chapter IX) flanking the African rift valleys have been cited by Dixey (1938). Other examples of these planations are on the highest parts of the Brazilian mountainland between Rio de Janeiro and Belo Horizonte; the summit and sub-summit levels of the Nilgiri Hills in Southern India; and the " Mt. Dale level " of Western Australia (Fig. 133). In favourable localities it is indeed possible to map within a few miles as many as four continental denudational cycles graded respectively to Jurassic, Cretaceous, early- and late-Cainozoic base levels.

b) *The nature and amount of cymatogenic deformation.* The maximum of vertical displacement governs the available relief that can be developed by ensuing dissection; and the breadth and steepness of the flanks govern the probability of certain landforms such as wall-like scarps or parallel stream gorges being produced there (Figs. 63, 64). Flat dissected arches have sometimes escaped observation until accurately measured by experienced topographers; other steep flanks have developed wall-like scarps impressive to all beholders. Important also is the rock composition and related "critical height", uniformly resistant terrains such as gneisses provide quite a different task for denudational agencies compared with, say, alternately strong and weak sedimentary beds.

c) *The action of post-tectonic denudational agencies.* Upon the flanks of a cymatogenic arch already established as a divide, one or other of two modes of dissection may develop. Where the relief is not great, and especially if the bedrock is weak, downstream tilting rejuvenates the rivers along their length, thus causing rapid incision between the crest and the foot of the arch. Lateral tributaries incise sympathetically, and with further branching of the drainage the whole of the arch becomes dissected by innumerable valleys large and small, all busily lowering their beds. After a short time, few traces of the originally arched topography may survive and those only upon the major ridges (Fig. 63).

In heterogeneous terrains where strong and weak formations alternate, the key to dissection may lie with the weak strata which are etched into valleys, possibly wide-bottomed, while the parent landscape is preserved for a longer time upon the ridge crests of resistant rock. The Schooley peneplane of the Appalachian region (p. 364) is an example of this.

Where the arching is stronger and the bedrock is uniformly resistant quite a different sequence of landforms may appear. Only very large rivers are able to cut down over the full length and breach through towards the crest of the arch. All smaller streams are retarded and processes of scarp-formation become relatively active on the flank of the arch beyond a certain critical relief (p. 153) that is defined by local denudational conditions in relation to resistance of the bedrock. A scarp then forms parallel to the trend of the arch (Fig. 64).

Later the scarp retreats parallel to itself, eating back as a wall into the higher part of the arch. These conditions are admirably fulfilled in the coastal belt of Rio de Janeiro where, following upon powerful Plio-Pleistocene warping of a seaward-plunging monocline, a Quaternary erosion scarp 3,000 feet high has been developed behind the Bay of Guanabara: other major

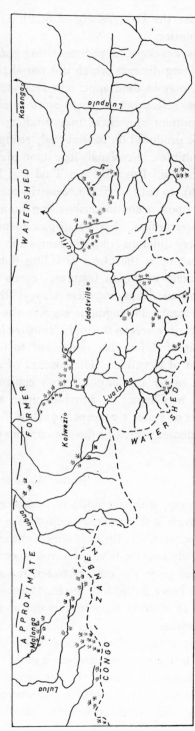

Fig. 85. Severance of former Zambezi River headwaters by uparching which produced the present very flat divide. Between the old and new divides, backtilted reaches have expanded into lakes that now drain northwards to the Congo River. Larger swampy areas farther to the north are due to rift valley faulting.

examples are the Drakensberg of South Africa and the Yunling scarp on the Chinese-Tibetan frontier.

Scarps, developed as pedimentation gnaws into the elevated sectors of a cymatogen from adjoining districts which did not share the uplift and which preserve the same base level, may in time appear to separate surfaces of two different ages which are nevertheless referable to a single continental cycle of planation (Fig. 57).

Intermittent movement may produce multi-stepped scarps; but stepped scarps can also be produced on continuously rising arches which exceed the critical height by several multiples. Erosional steps upon major scarps, such as were described upon the Rocky Mountain Front by van Tuyl and Lovering (1936), and commented upon by Rich (1936), do not therefore necessarily record intermittent uplift, but could have been produced upon a continuously-rising mountain front upon which denudation acted without interruption. Vertical displacement on the Front Range is great and the aspect is steep, very different from the gentle upbowing which created so indecisive a physiographic feature as the Great Dividing Range of Queensland, but it is by no means unique among mountain features. Steep upwarping and faulting characterise parts of the Andean flanks and here also youthful steps are sometimes apparent on the mountain front. Photographs suggest also minor berms at places along the youthful Yunling scarp, whereon the mid-Cainozoic landscape of Central China is upcast through 12,000 feet of differential movement to form the high plateau of Tibet surpassing 15,000 feet of elevation. The concept of critical relief, and the inevitability of scarp formation under the physical laws controlling running water and mass movement developed in Chapter V, provides upon sufficiently tilted landsurfaces the physical vindication of Penck's concept (1953) of " piedmont treppen " or stepped benchlands on rising domes, which he developed from field observation.

BASIN WARPING AND FILLING

Downwarping, with formation of basins, affords exceptionally interesting results, not least of which is that river, swamp or lake deposits may accumulate towards the nadir of the depression, e.g. the sudd region of the Nile or the area about Lake Chad. Certain ancient reedy swamps have given rise to coal, and in Yallourn, Victoria, where the coals still contain 50-70 per cent. of water, the seams are 150-200 feet thick but increase to 700 feet in bores drilled into the East Gippsland syncline farther east. At basin margins lacustrine or riverine material cuts out and windblown deposits appear under suitable climatic regimes.

About a basin-plain successive denudational surfaces may extend singly or as flights of terraces. Each landscape cycle thus appears in corresponding degradational and aggradational phases. Under repeated subsidence the highest of the erosional surfaces is normally the oldest, and corresponds to the lowest of the unconformities in the basin-fill. Such occurrences afford valuable opportunity for dating of erosional

PLATE 8

Three cyclic erosion surfaces occurring in close proximity in the Leichardt-Gilbert area, northwestern Queensland. A-B-C is the mid-Mesozoic (Gondwana) surface which (A-B) is resurrected over considerable areas; B-C is the same surface as an unconformity between Precambrian mica schists below and mottled siliceous Mesozoic siltstones above; D is the lateritised early Cainozoic planation; and E is part of a rapidly extending late Cainozoic-Quaternary surface.

C. R. Twidale.

surfaces, and matching of cyclic denudational landscapes with unconformities in neighbouring regions is one of the most important methods of geomorphic research (Chapter VIII).

Where a basin has been long in existence, and been accentuated intermittently by renewed onset of tectonic forces, the engirdling planed landsurfaces are successively tilted towards the interior so that they cross one another before passing beneath the ensuing sediments of the basin. Such crossings not infrequently take place along a narrow zone or hinge line, where distinctions between the various surfaces may be exceedingly difficult to draw. Thus four cyclic landsurfaces, the sub-Karroo, the Gondwana, the post-Gondwana and the African (Chapter IX), that are separated vertically from one another by hundreds of feet in the eastern highlands of Rhodesia converge towards Bulawayo, and west of that city pass independently beneath the several series of Kalahari deposits. Anywhere along a line from Bulawayo to Hartley the relations between these various cycles are difficult to disentangle as the surfaces converge and cross, giving often very flat country indeed.

Marked also is the frequency with which certain zones have acted as hinges. The Sudan is a zone on the north side of which depression has repeatedly occurred, simultaneously with uplift upon the southern side, so that sequences of continental and marine rocks to the north, covering the period from the Palæozoic to the present day are matched to the south by a suite of erosional bevels whose fashioning supplied much of the detritus for the sediments.

The term " basining " is often used in a relative sense, for essentially similar topographical results accrue from circumferential upwarping as from sinking of the centre. Thus, though the Kalahari has acquired the form of a shallow dish, the lowest portion now stands nearly a thousand feet above its original elevation, the surrounding terrains having risen a maximum of three or four times this amount.

" Basins " are of many ages, and many stages of infill. Victoria Nyanza, nowhere more than 273 feet deep, occupies a relatively recent depression upon the face of Africa (Fig. 83). Only in the north-eastern, Kavirondo sector, which was the earliest to form, is infill extensive, as seen in the Nzegi swamps. The Congo Basin is a little older, its lowest part being occupied by the Pliocene Busira beds. Lake Eyre, in Australia, affords a superb example of intra-continental depression to below sea-level. Little inundation of the lake occurs now, despite occasional floodings of the great tributary river systems which drain an area of half-a-million square miles; but immense accumulation took place in the basin during former times. Existing lakes Eyre, Gregory, Blanche, Callabonna and Frome are, indeed, but the shrunken remnants of an ancestral Lake Dieri which occupied in Pleistocene time, according to David (1950), an area of at least 40,000 square miles. The rivers of this vast drainage basin " rise in regions of low rainfall—10-15 inches per annum—and as they are directed towards the most arid area in the continent, with an annual rainfall of less than 7 inches and an annual evaporation equivalent to about 110 inches, it is not surprising that they are all

o

ephemeral ". As an example of the desperate conditions, " the Todd, Hale, Plenty, Hay, Field and Mulligan [Rivers] all disappear in the Simpson Desert, partly through percolation ". Yet when heavy rains do fall the flood waters " spread to an amazing extent over the alluvial plains, so that adjoining streams merge into one great sheet of water. If the flood waters are high enough they may be diverted into unusual courses causing the water of tributary creeks to back upstream and even flow over low divides. The Cooper and Diamantina have been known to spread for upwards of 50 miles, and it has been stated that in full flood Cooper's Creek in South Australia may be 90 miles wide . . . the delta formed by this river in Lake Eyre is said to be one of the largest in the world " (David 1950) (Fig. 86).

All the rivers have braided courses and tried out many braids during deposition. These are easily identified in the flat country because one *rises* towards them. Rivers deploy on both sides of low hills to join up again beyond; and so flat is the country that distributaries from one system often overflow into another system. Two branches of the Cooper below Windorah, after diverging by 20 miles, reunite after a separation of 100 miles along the course.

Astonishing are the " incised braids " in Lawn Hill Creek and Widdallion Creek about the Barkly Tableland where the streams flow strongly, dividing and subdividing in well-dissected country. Whitehouse (1941) opined that these have certainly been superimposed from earlier braided courses developed upon a plain, possibly of laterite. The reticulate regime has certainly been in operation a very long time; with changes, conceivably throughout the Cainozoic and Quaternary eras.

Gradients of streams correspond in a general way with the attitudes of gently-dipping bedrock strata, and the whole provides optimum run-off in response to periodic flooding and is the depositional equivalent of pediplains in denudational landscapes. These reticulate drainages produce vast inland deltas. That of the Warrego on the border of Queensland and New South Wales is, for instance, larger in area than the deltas of any of the world's great rivers except the Ganges.

The interior of Australia has stood at lower elevation than the regions to east and west, indeed, ever since the mid-Mesozoic for there are three systems of accumulation (a) the Cretaceous marine and terrestrial deposits, overlain in some parts by early-Cainozoic (Eyrian) beds. Both of these are truncated by a planed surface of Miocene age which is duricrusted (Plate 8) and stands on marginal tablelands above (b) an older series of alluvia, red in colour and Mio-Pliocene in age. These continue extensively from western Queensland into all the adjacent States and are well displayed along the upper Diamantina River. (c) Lastly accumulated grey, post-Pliocene alluvia, dated by Pleistocene mammalian bones and leading up to the modern vast inland deltas.

Where basin plains such as these have been much aggraded, quite exceptional floods may rapidly undermine and incorporate huge volumes of earlier alluvia converting the waters to sludge that after violent onrush is rapidly deposited over lower areas as a single thick layer of mud. The historic "Deluge" of the Tigris-Euphrates depression was probably of this type.

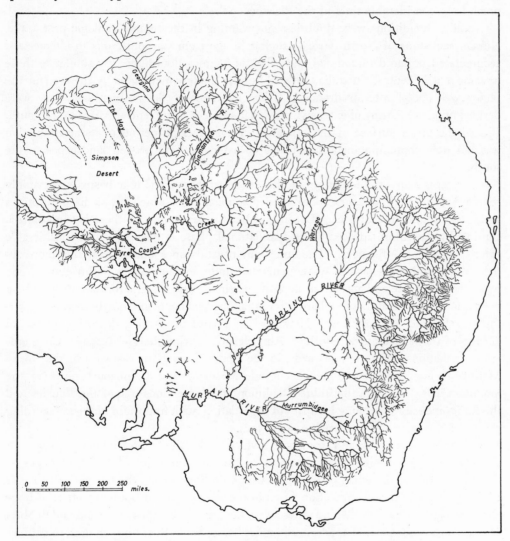

FIG. 86. The drainage system of eastern Australia. In addition to the Murray-Darling system which traverses a large alluviated basin, several independent, centripetal systems lead to shallow or dry lakes where the waters are evaporated *e.g.* Lake Eyre.

The Sudan also is a vast plain of deposition. Andrew (1948) assigns as reason: " the general slope of the land is very gentle and the rainfall is insufficient to produce persistent run-off which escapes from the area *via* the Nile ". The *sudd* region of the Upper Nile is a filled basin which earlier may have had an internal drainage system.

" There is as yet no evidence to show whether flow at any stage failed entirely through the Sabaloka Gorge, but it seems probable that the White Nile Basin had no outlet north for a considerable time in the Pleistocene ".

Similar conditions were doubtless not wanting in the remote geologic past. The Nubian sandstone of North Africa, ranging in age from Carboniferous to Cretaceous, accumulated under denudational and climatic regimes doubtless very similar to those now current in central Australia, with additional shallow incursions by the sea (for the region was not of interior drainage). The materials of the Nubian sandstone were derived upon the cutting of extensive erosional surfaces over Central Africa to the south. Indeed the upper surface of the sandstone at any specific period of its accumulation was not only contemporaneous, but also co-extensive with eroded landscapes to the south.

Any cessation or fluctuation in the erosional phase about a basin is inevitably reflected elsewhere in the corresponding depositional phase which shows disconformities and interruptions of sequence. Lensing of beds is common, and there is sometimes a continually flattening surface. The denudational phase is governed to a considerable extent by tectonic influences. The upheaving of landscapes almost invariably increases the amount and coarseness of waste generated under erosion and is faithfully recorded by an increased rate and amount of deposit. Coarse conglomeratic formations have long been quoted as indicators of violent differential displacements in a nearby region. Thus the gravel plains of Canterbury, New Zealand record the tearing down by rivers and glaciers of the ranges of the Southern Alps elevated during the Pleistocene. Conglomeratic formations, thinning eastwards, in the Prairie formations eastward of the Rocky Mountains are direct consequences of late-Mesozoic and Cainozoic uplifts in the mountain belt. Tectonically induced submontane depressions east of the Rockies and the Andes indeed record long histories of aggradation, with important hiatuses recording phases of exposure and erosion (pp. 373, 522).

Together, tectonics and transport (which links the complementary phases of denudation and deposition) govern most of the characteristics of basin-fill deposits. For an example of the effect of transport we quote Bowman on the Chapare River east of the Andes: " At and above San Antonio the river is full of boulders, often of huge size. At Santa Rosa, less than 20 miles away, the bars are composed of sand and pebbles of 8, 10, and 12 inches in diameter. Six miles below Santa Rosa one can discern pebbles only in patches upon the upstream sides of the bars, and fifteen miles farther downstream, or forty miles by river from the edge of the existing upland, it is impossible to find any pebbles whatever—the bars are wholly of sand ".

Even sands vary widely not only in grain-size, but also in composition according to the source of supply and manner of transport. Arenaceous deposits of the Palæozoic and Mesozoic differ markedly on either side of the cordilleran axis of North America. Those on west are greywackes, dirty with admixed volcanic debris, while those on the east are clean, well-washed silica sands from the shield area of the mid-continent.

A transition from one type to the other occurs in some places. In the latitude of Yellowstone, for instance, several of the early-Cainozoic formations of the Great Plains region, ranging from the Colorado shale to the Fort Union, become andesitic in the west and are known collectively as the Livingstone formation.

An interesting viewpoint of recent years concerning thin but persistent conglomerates resting on bedrock is that they represent pediment veneers. Stockes (1950) has applied this view to three thin but widespread conglomerates of Mesozoic age in the Western United States (the Shinarump, Buckhorn and Dakota) regarding them as the tools fashioning the surface below and contemporaneous with it. He quotes the following characteristics: (a) wide areal extent, (b) exceptional thinness, (c) fluvial origin, (d) scarcity of fossils, (e) pebbles of only durable rock types, (f) erosional unconformity at base but gradation with overlying deposits. Finer-grained sediments on the other hand accumulate normally in regions remote from highlands of strong relief and freshwater limestones may indicate a virtual absence of terrigenous waste from circumscribing regions of wide planation.

Nor should shallow epicontinental marine basins be overlooked. Hudson's Bay affords a modern example where a shield area of low relief has sunk shallowly beneath the sea. The amount of sediment supplied annually to it is not large and its flat shores probably advance but slowly to fill it up. But during the geologic past North America has frequently been flooded by such seas in which, with continued subsidence, considerable stratigraphic thicknesses have been laid down.

Subsiding basins upon the continental shelves are often the sites of great deltas with enmeshed channels (Lena River) or vast swamps. Most of the modern swampy Mississippi delta is, for instance, covered by water.

Mixed types of basins sometimes occur. In China, on the lower course of the Yangtze Kiang between Shasi and Hankow, " regional subsidence has caused ponding with the formation of large areas of standing water (Fig. 87). The consequent silting-up has furnished the broad expanse of fine sediment upon which local meander-swing is easy. At intervals downstream rocky barriers, half submerged under the plain, act as constrictions on the swing of the meander belt. Such nodes exist at Hankow and Nanking and at other points where the river abuts areas of extensive bedrock exposure " (Barbour 1935). Delayed junctions are common on alluvia and Barbour records " Near Shasi where the Yangtze and the Han cease to hug the foothills, they are within 30 miles of one another, but their junction lies nearly 300 miles further down the Yangtze ". " Undercutting on the outer side of the meander bends makes annual inroads through caving in of the banks, and below Shasi are places where the banks are retreating at a rate of 30 metres per year. No one stretch of its course is so prone to flooding that it is safe to infer that subsidence is taking place today at a greater rate there than elsewhere."

But this subsidence is recent and forms only part of a greater sagging represented by the great alluvial plain of China extending northward across the unfilled Gulfs of Pohai and Liao-tung to the lowland of Manchukuo, where its western boundary lies along

the downwarped foothills of the Great Khingan.   Beyond Harbin it is virtually continuous
with the broad plain of the lower Amur River.   Even at the western edge the Great
Plain of China does not rise to 500 feet above sea-level (Fig. 88).

The boundary of this vast basin is the downwarped flank of the Central Asiatic
plateau, of late-Pliocene or Pleistocene age, which extends from near Indo-China
(Hunan and the Yaoshan in Kwangsi) to northern Manchukuo.   The eastern limit of the
basin may be sought far out in the Yellow and East China Seas, perhaps indeed in Korea,
Japan and Formosa where these are reached by the continental shelf.   This vast
depression is now partly filled with the delta plains of the great rivers that debouch from

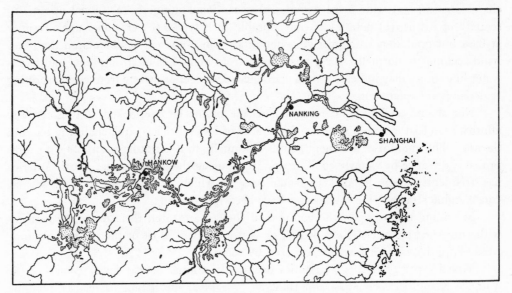

FIG. 87. Ponding and drainage diversion in a subsiding region along the
lower Yangtze-Kiang, near Hankow, China.

the western and southern mountains.   The instability of river courses upon aggrading
surfaces of alluvia is nowhere better exemplified than here: the notorious change of
course by the Hoang Ho in 1852 from the southern to the northern side of the Shantung
Peninsula is known to every schoolboy.

Upon the main downcast block are regions of accentuated subsidence.   That along
the Yangtze above Hankow has already been noted.   The largest covers all of Hopei,
the western part of Shantung, the greater part of Honan and the northern part of Anwhei.
Part of this, the Gulf of Pohai, is not yet filled in.   On the other hand, sundry horsts
that escaped much of the general abasement are now lapped about by the rising tide of
alluvium, so that they protrude like islands above a sea.   Shantung Peninsula, united to
the mainland by the plain, has the lower reaches of its valleys invaded, and even some
of its lower divides are overtopped by the alluvium so that certain of its hilltops are now
isolated.

Study of the modern Lake Eyre and East China Basins and their deposits assists in the interpretation of numerous other basins active in subsidence and filling during

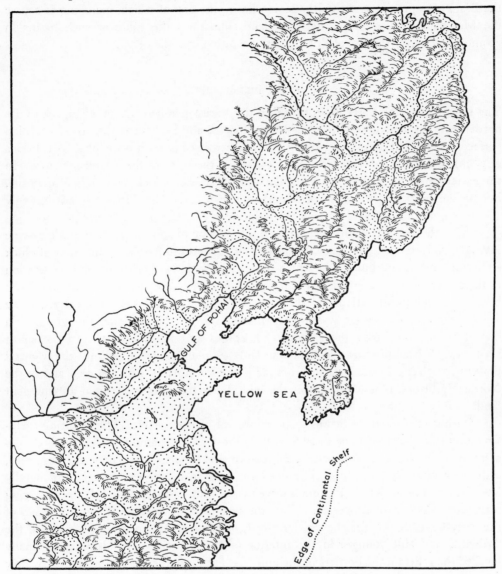

FIG. 88. The subsided basin of China, the Yellow Sea and the
Manchurian Plain.

late-Mesozoic and Cainozoic time. Many of these have experienced repeated subsidence at widely spaced intervals of time, so that the aspect of the given region has varied from shallow sea, lake, or swamp to delta plain, the record of these different environments being plainly preserved in the changing types of sedimentation. Repeated or inter-mittent depression is evidenced in the three famous basins of France; the Paris Basin, the Basin of Aquitaine and the Rhodanian Basin, the first of which, including of course the Mesozoic terrains of southern England, illustrates the value of such basins in geomorphology, so that we shall follow its evolution in some detail.

THE PARIS BASIN

The basement of the Paris Basin is within the Variscan zone of Europe (Fig. 89). Its borders are battlemented with ancient fault blocks, and its floor is the post-Hercynian surface, usually cut across the folded Palæozoic rocks but with occasional local basins of pebbly Permian and Triassic rocks localised in the ruins of the Variscan chains. In the eastern part the outcrops are regularly the Triassic (mainly continental) deposits, but on the border of the Central Massif by the Morvan the Triassic is not strongly developed, and this is so also along the Armorican Massif and the Cotentin.

From the late Trias, the area showed a tendency to subside. The Liassic marine invasion, only moderately deep at any one time, permitted an accumulation of thick alternating marls and limestones which indicate pulsations of elevation and denudation in the surrounding framework of the basin. Along the Ardenne (p. 392) and the Ruhr border tectonic perturbations are shown by the facies and the detrital minerals. The rest of the eastern border was widely planed during the Jurassic, though the sea flowed at one time over the sites of the Vosges and Black Forest. In the south also seas of Mediterranean connection laid sediments over much of the Central Plateau (p. 383). In the west the Jurassic is thick compared with the east, and in the Normandy littoral Liassic beds form the base, lying transgressively upon an emergent land.

During the late Jurassic was a short interval of emergence. The resulting early-Cretaceous landsurface is of considerable interest as an example of the discordances associated with halts in the subsidence of continental basins. It is a polygenetic surface, elaborated progressively and of different local dates in neighbouring regions, generally later in age the farther it is from the centre of the basin: conversely the covering formations show marked overlap. Thus the surface is of Valanginian age in the axis of the early-Cretaceous gulf, Hauterivian north of Ornain, Albian on the borders of the Ardenne, and still younger in the interior of that massif. The denudation finally levelled the relief on the borders of the gulf. At each stage as the sea crept more widely over the surrounding landscape, the drowned surface was covered by sediments derived by continued erosion of the peripheral regions, and the successive zones of fossilisation, littoral wear and subaerial planation were carried progressively outwards towards the margins of the tectonic basin with each subsidence.

The corresponding sediments reveal, for each stage, several different facies: marine or lacustrine, brackish water or continental, in beds from one to ten metres or

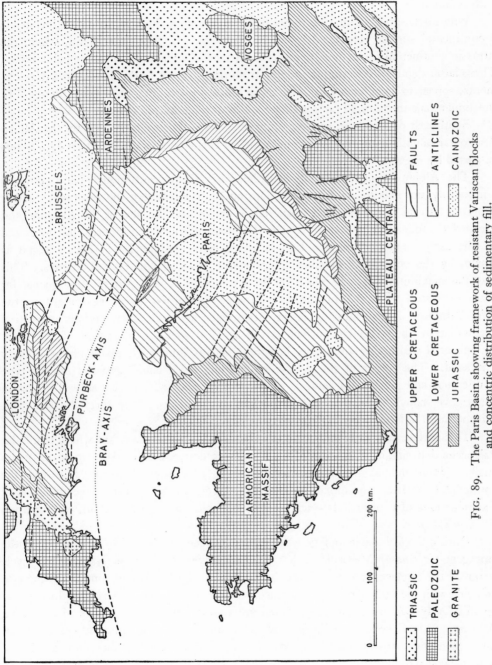

FIG. 89. The Paris Basin showing framework of resistant Variscan blocks and concentric distribution of sedimentary fill.

so in thickness, succeeding one another as each small gulf was formed and then filled with sediment.

Where transgressive marine deposits cover the floor directly the unconformity is a continental surface retouched by marine erosion. On the other hand, where the Jurassic continental formations persist the surface of subaerial erosion remains intact. These latter deposits, covering the region from the Ardenne to Paris in limited developments, appear to have been laid down as an alluvial plain in front of the Ardenne. In the Boulonnais they are 50 metres thick, and indicate a humid climate.

South-east of Argonne, sands resting on a very flat surface planed by the Albian Sea contain a notable proportion (20 per cent.) of aeolian grains derived from dune-sands re-sorted by the sea.

The Albian transgression flooded the Paris Basin continuously and covered temporarily the massifs on the east. During the Cenomanian the sea made further progress. From the Armorican borderlands, it covered the site of the Ardenne and invaded Flanders and Brabant. By the Turonian it covered northern Holland : and by the early Senonian the two transgressions converged finally in the Ardenne as shown by the occurrence of silica in the white chalk of the Hautes Fagnes. This was the maximum : by the close of the Cretaceous a new general emergence, far more extensive than that of the late Jurassic, permitted the development of the infra-Cainozoic landsurface of latest Cretaceous age. A characteristic terrestrial accumulation upon this landsurface is the *argile à silex*, an alteration of the chalk by subaerial weathering to a fine, impure, siliceous mud with many grains of very fine sand. The colour of the decalcified product is chocolate and the normal type is unctuous and plastic, but some is rigid. The *argile à silex* affects several modes of occurrence, chiefly as sheets and in pockets and fissures. The former are ancient (Paleocene), the latter recent (Pliocene).

This surface was early subjected to subsidence in the Paris Basin where lenticular Paleocene deposits, of which the Montian is the oldest, are discordant upon the white chalk. Upon the surrounding older masses (*e.g.* Central Plateau), however, the continental surface continued to develop through the Eocene, receiving local accumulations of continental facies the first of which is the Sparnacian, resting upon the *argile à silex*.

During the Cainozoic, polygenetic erosion surfaces continued to develop upon the emergent terrains of Mesozoic rocks. In successive stages the early-Cainozoic cycle removed the Cretaceous cover about the borders of the basin, and sometimes came to coincide with the early-Cretaceous surface. Various facets of different ages thus appear on this (early-Cainozoic) surface. Small gulfs occupied the lower parts of the basin. All through the Eocene and Oligocene was a very complex sedimentation with considerable variations in the extent of the several stages and also in their facies and thickness. The palæogeographic inter-relations of the various phases are fascinating to follow. As the seas waxed and waned, denudational landscapes, alluvial and littoral plains, lakes, estuaries and lagoons marched and counter-marched across the region, leaving their appropriate records behind them. Marine transgressional series, ranging from Palæocene to Oligocene, are: Montian, Thanetian, Cuisien, Lutetian, Bartonian and Stampian. Inter-digitating lagoonal or continental facies established by retreats of the sea are: Sparnacian, Argile de Laon, Calcaire grossier supérieur, Calcaire de Champigny et Gypse, Meulières, and the Calcaire de Beauce.

Capturing a mid-Eocene moment amid these kaleidoscopic changes, we should see in the Sparnacian a broad littoral plain growing progressively into the Thanetian gulf where the sea was shrinking. About its margin were broad delta flats, dominantly sandy and pebbly but with muds and vegetation along the unstable courses of the rivers, like the Camargue at the present day but more extensive. The balance of the level of groundwater, according to Tricart (1949) governed the cementation of the sands and grits; and much iron oxide in the mud is thought to denote a humid climate.

The fluctuating conditions are largely the result of an unstable tectonic background. Tilting is evident, the southern border being elevated and the northern depressed; and posthumous folds were developed in Mesozoic rocks overlying Variscan structures in the south of the basin where marine incursions were, in consequence, limited.

In the Sannoisian the sedimentation acquired new characters which presage the final emergence of the basin. Except for the Stampian the marine formations give place to Sannoisian lacustrine deposits, and the surrounding country is planed with a descent in the direction of Paris from the Plateau Central, the Plateau de Langres, and the Southern Vosges. Silicification under deep weathering (meulièrisation) appears to the east in Lorraine where the planed landscape was largely inherited from the late Cretaceous.

Earth movements were recurrent through the late Cainozoic and Quaternary. On the whole, movements were short and sharp, with culminations in the Oligo-Miocene (Alpine), late-Miocene and late-Pliocene, and were separated by prolonged tranquil periods, so that a polycyclic scenery has developed across the strata of the basin and the peripheral regions. The fresh reliefs, newly created in successive stages, do not advance progressively to senility. They are interrupted and elaborately complex, being formed of elements diverse in age and fashioning. Landscapes are polygenic and polymorphic, sometimes with flexed facets. This is the complex structure that was worked over by erosion during the later Cainozoic.

Deformations fall into two categories (Tricart 1949): (a) flexures and faults; (b) undulations. The flexures are produced generally in the same direction as the dip, of which they constitute an accentuation. The most important coincide with the limits of the blocks where the sedimentation is different and the rhythm of subsidence dissimilar. Some are very long, and are related to one another as with the flexures in the Valley of the Meuse. They coincide with the ancient margins of the Albian Sea and the Eocene Lakes. Faults are generally curved, with a wide radius. An important fault is rarely isolated, it is accompanied by a series of small breaks. Also the faults are usually associated with the flexures. Sometimes faults pass into flexures.

Different regions show different tectonic styles. One of the best-known contrasts is in Lorraine, where in the country of Triassic red beds the deformations are weak, but on the borders of the Triassic cuvette the tectonic accidents are obvious and strong, and often clearly posthumous. Thus towards the west the Lorraine tectonic type disappears in the region of the Meuse which forms a hinge of prime importance operative since it first formed the margin of the Triassic cuvette. It halted the Albian transgression, and also the Cainozoic Stampian Sea developed by subsidence in the west.

The Plateau of Langres, in turn, has behaved in an elevated, semi-rigid manner, the subjacent gneiss has a thin cover of sediments in which appears a close succession of anticlines and synclines. Faults have the same orientation as the borders of the region.

Along the border of the Ardenne a marginal line of flexure occurs in proximity to the rigid mass. Along this line the stages of sedimentation and erosion follow rapidly, while the thickness of the cover damped out tectonic movements and permitted a difference of behaviour between the cover and the basement. There is also considerable divergence between the Jurassic structures and the much less accentuated dips of the Cretaceous.

The Basin of Aquitaine, comprising broadly the greater part of the Basin of the Garonne and two major parts of Dordogne, compares closely with the Paris Basin (Abrard 1949).

The Jurassic outcrop follows straight along the border of the Central Massif and occupies the broad depression of Northern Aquitaine. It often lies upon Trias which interposes between it and the crystalline rocks. The Cretaceous transgression did not begin until the Cenomanian, deposits of which rest directly upon the late Jurassic. There is thus a prolonged lacuna representing an emergence corresponding to the late-Jurassic emergence of the Paris Basin, which was, however, much shorter.

The early-Cainozoic sea reached the west and south of the basin in a gulf largely open to the Atlantic: in the Ypresian and Lutetian (a widespread stage) there was a connection to the Mediterranean. The Pyrenean movements (Eocene) then excluded the Bartonian towards the west, and the gulf, thus reduced to a fraction of its former area, was occupied by the lagoonal and continental formations which assumed a wide extension in the Oligocene, as the molasse sheets spread northward of the Pyrenean mountain front.

At the beginning of the Neogene a new gulf appeared in the Bordelais, but though important in the Vindobonian stage it did not surpass the eastern limit attained by the Bartonian. The molasse continued to be shed as before during the beginning of the Miocene, but it is in the Pliocene that the demolition of the Western Pyrenees appears to have attained its greatest intensity following a rejuvenation of relief (p. 515). Great sheets of conglomerates, sands and gravels were then formed to the exclusion of marine facies. The last detrital formation of the Pyrenean province is the sand (2-20 metres thick) of the Landes, Quaternary at most places but near Bayonne extending back into the Pliocene. Elsewhere are alluvia and terrace deposits.

The third of the great basins of France covers the Valley of the Rhône and adjacent regions. Rhaetic and Jurassic formations are present up to the late mid-Jurassic when the sea retired and a lacustrine and lagoonal regime was established, contemporaneously with the emergence of the Parisian and Aquitanian basins. Beginning with the Aptian, the sea returned and established a direct communication with the Paris Basin to the north, and this remained until the beginning of the Senonian. Following an interval during which bauxite was formed, the sea returned only slowly till the later Miocene when a rapid regression enabled valleys to be incised deeply. The Pliocene saw a rapid transgression of the sea as a narrow fiord to within 20 km. of Lyons, but intermittent uplift, the effects of which are recorded in fluviatile and marine terraces has since excluded it.

The basic tectonic similarities of the three basins of France, as recorded in their respective sedimentary series, are complicated by considerable local variations, such as have been already noted in the great basin of China.

Basin fills of one epoch are often partly removed in another, nevertheless, cumulative thicknesses may be quite astonishing. Thus between the Altai and the Uskuk Mountains in the heart of Asia (Fig. 75), lower-Cretaceous, Oligocene, Miocene, Pliocene and Pleistocene maximal fill totals 10,000 feet in thickness.

But the continental basin *par excellence* of all known geologic history remains the great Karroo-Gondwana Basin of the southern hemisphere (Chapter II) transcending the boundaries of the present continents, containing thicknesses of infill which attain a maximum of 20,000 feet and persisting as an entity over the whole time-span from the Carboniferous to the Jurassic period. Much research remains to be done upon its facies changes, the source areas of its sediments, and its intra-tectonic movements that could well be the subject of international collaboration following upon the Gondwana Symposium of the XIXth International Geological Congress. The palæogeographic vision so obtained would be unique.

FOSSIL LANDSCAPES

By burial beneath accumulating deposits, continental or marine, a topography may be removed from study and remain entombed for even geologically long periods of time. Subsequent removal of the cover, sedimentary or volcanic, revealing an ancient, buried landsurface anew to the elements of destruction affords an important canon in landscape development. Resurrected or fossil landscapes are known from most periods of earth history, and though they may or may not crop out over large superficial areas, they are always highly significant in the elucidation of the landscape history. Restoration of such surfaces is, however, often difficult because of imperfect resurrection, destruction by later erosion, or deformation by subsequent earth movements.

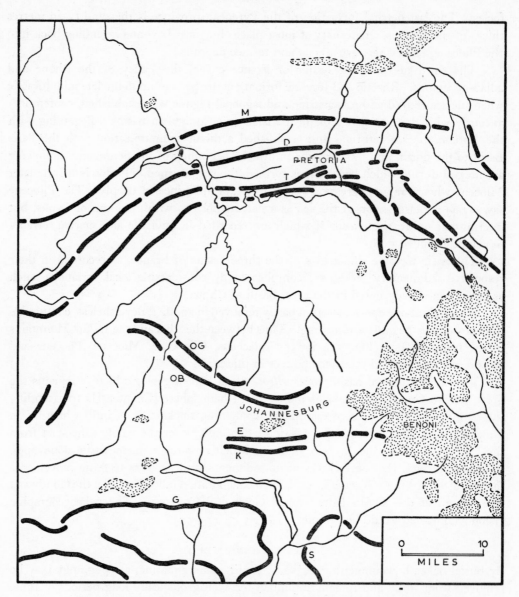

FIG. 90. Superposed drainage and fossil topography in the Southern Transvaal. Remaining areas of covering beds stippled, resurrected ridges of pre-Karroo landscape in heavy lines. (M = Magaliesberg, D = Daspoort Ridge, T = Timeball Hill Ridge, OG = Orange Grove Escarpment, OB = Observatory Ridge, E = Elsburg Ridge, K = Klipriversberg, G = Gatsrand, S = Suikerbosrand). The stream courses bear a wholly discordant relation to the ridges which they traverse and even cross more than once. *after J. H. Wellington.*

Fossil surfaces are frequently independent of the hydrography and subjacent structure. But independence of hydrography and structure (superposed drainage) (Fig. 90) is not *per se* a conclusive argument for fossil surfaces in the absence of outliers of cover, as hydrography may in any case become independent of structure in the very late stages of a cycle of erosion.

Buried topographies may be of all kinds of relief from smoothly planed to markedly uneven. As an example of the latter, hills of older rock protrude in places through the Nubian sandstone of North Africa; and the sub-Karroo surface, over-ridden by the Dwyka ice-sheets of Carboniferous age, in South Africa was rugged in some areas and smooth in others. Sub-glacial terrains of the Pleistocene ice sheets, now lying buried beneath a mantle of till and outwash are occasionally important (Horberg 1950) (Fig. 91).

PERICONTINENTAL DEPOSITION

The margins of continents have afforded remarkable sites of cymatogenic tilting with repeated uplift upon the landward and depression upon the seaward side of axes trending closely parallel with present coasts. Corresponding with the polycyclic denudational history of the lands is therefore a polycyclic depositional record embodied in the offshore sediments (Fig. 212). While these generally remain beneath the sea, upon certain recently uplifted coasts they have been exposed in coastal plains where they afford primary data to the geomorphologist (Chapters IX-XII), for whereas successive erosional cycles upon the lands destroy the traces of their predecessors, sedimentational effects are generally cumulative.

Offshore disconformities correspond with phases of low erosive activity in the coastlands; and unconformities correspond with tectonic interruptions, altering the attitude of previously deposited beds and usually provoking an abundant supply of fresh debris. The bulk of sediment in a series affords an approximation to rates of erosion upon neighbouring lands; and the nature of the sediment reflects both the composition of the source material and the nature of the transport. Minor structures—bedding, current bedding, intraformational folds and slumps and a host of other details afford additional data for interpretation. Maximum quantities of detritus have been deposited in the great deltas. A description of the Yangtze delta by Barbour (1935) is perhaps typical of many.

" That the area of the delta proper has been sinking over a prolonged period cannot be doubted. At Shanghai well-borings strike conglomerate and beach deposits 300 metres below ground-level. This indicates an original land relief of the order of 700 metres, almost half of which has since been forfeited by subsidence. . . . A study of the most carefully kept well-log is instructive. The column seems to fall into several blocks. Below the top-dressing of alluvium comes a layer of beach material underlain by the upper fine marine series which passes down into sand, with coarse sand and gravel again at about 85 metres. Below —130 metres the material again becomes

10 5 0   10   20   30   40 MILES

FIG. 91. Pleistocene topography of Illinois, now buried beneath deposits
of the Ice Age. *after L. Horberg.*

fine, remaining so with only two minor coarse horizons to a depth of 240 metres after which it is beach material to the bottom."

" The continued subaerial denudation of the hardrock hinterland since the beginning of the Tertiary shows that the sinking of the delta region was balanced by a bowing up of the mountain area. But if these movements were not always smooth, continuous and perfectly synchronised, it is in the neighbourhood of the Nanking Hills that the resultant irregularities might be expected to have left their record."

The period of sinking is uncertain, but " the sinking of the Yellow River delta at Tientsin has only lowered early-Pleistocene freshwater fossiliferous deposits to a depth of 17 metres below sea-level in an area where bedrock is probably more than 300 metres below the surface ". China has, indeed, only continental Cainozoic accumulations, their marine equivalents having sunk in the China Sea. The east coast of Australia, also a monocline, is likewise devoid of marine Cainozoic rocks.

Such results of differential movements, hinging about the shoreline, are widespread. If the hinge axis is upon the landward side the coastline will be one of subsidence, as in China and eastern Australia, but if the hinge axis be sited seaward of the current shoreline, an uplifted coastal plain appears and fringes the continental area, as along the eastern United States of America. Upon such coastal plains the sedimentational record of past cycles is exposed to study. Fortunately, many of the world's coasts bear either narrow uplifted selvedges or even broad coastal plains upon which are exposed sequences of late-Mesozoic or Cainozoic rocks, which afford by correlation, therefore, a means of dating the denudational episodes apparent in related coastal hinterlands (Chapter VIII).

P

THE AGES OF LANDSURFACES

Methods of Dating. The Ages of Continental Landsurfaces. The Pattern of World Landscapes. Some Doubts Allayed. Mapping of Cyclic Landsurfaces. Landform Analysis from Topographic Maps. The World's Denudational Cycles.

METHODS OF DATING

Most landscapes are reticent of their ages. As erosional forms they are products of destructive forces, and evidence for dating is more likely to be obliterated than preserved. Yet dating of the world's cyclic landscapes is one of the chief tasks before us, and the guiding principles must be established before we proceed further.

Landsurfaces have been dated from covering deposits with fossils (including human artefacts); elevation above sea-level; correlation with adjacent, already dated, surfaces; correlation with episodes of erosion or deposition off-shore; and stage of development in the cycle of erosion. All these methods are valid; but results by the different methods have often been at variance, and sometimes different parts of a single long-existing surface have failed to give concordant ages even under the criteria of a single method.

As an example, and using the method of dating by superficial deposits the ages of which can be satisfactorily determined, an ancient landscape of low relief may acquire a thin cover, partly detrital and partly residual, of perhaps Cretaceous deposits. The original landscape must therefore have been of Cretaceous or pre-Cretaceous age. In course of time, the region not being invaded from outside by valley incisions or other features of fresh continental erosion cycles, the landscape continues to develop by pedimentation or local planations which partly remove the cover and erode off a few inches or feet of bedrock. Upon the area so replaned, Eocene deposits may accumulate, and so from time to time other remodelled patches may acquire still more youthfu l formations, all resting partly upon bedrock (Fig. 92). Of what age is the planation as a whole?

At no time subsequent to the Cretaceous does the entire landscape depart materially from the originally planed condition; the net alteration in the landscape produced for instance by one pediment cutting shallowly across another may be small indeed and quite irregular, yet its parts are manifestly of several different local ages, as defined by the various superficial deposits. Unquestionably, the planed floor of bedrock under discussion is at one point Cretaceous, at another Eocene, at another (say) Pliocene, and at yet another Pleistocene, so that the subjacent bedrock surface is a compound

Cretaceous-Eocene-Pliocene-Pleistocene surface. The several " local " ages adduced from the relevant deposits are genuine yet the concept of dating to which they lead is confusing applied to the landscape as a whole.

To derive the fundamental age of such a compound landscape we must argue as follows. The landscape, viewed as a whole, was planed first in Cretaceous time. From the planed aspect then achieved, it has never since materially departed. What we see now is essentially a Cretaceous planation that has since undergone minor modification only. Its fundamental age, by which it should be compared with other planed surfaces, is Cretaceous; and so we shall regard it. *The oldest deposits known to exist upon a cyclic surface are significant in establishing its age for comparison with other surfaces.*

A further problem is that an erosion cycle, generated at the coast during one geological period, may require until another period to extend into the far interior of a continent by the processes of river-incision, scarp retreat and pedimentation. Its

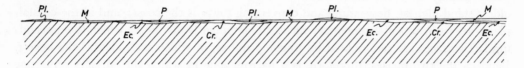

FIG. 92.   Remodelled denudational landsurface bearing superficial deposits of several different ages—Cretaceous, Eocene, Miocene, Pliocene and Pleistocene. Each part may be dated from the deposits resting upon it, but the original planation was older than the oldest depositional series, *viz.* Cretaceous.

" local " age in widely sundered districts, as computed from fossils in covering beds for example, might range from almost the date of inception of the cycle until the land forms have been utterly destroyed by some succeeding cycle. The argument is very like that for homotaxis rather than synchroneity between fossil assemblages; but just as palæontologists have found in practice that the time required for faunal dispersal is short compared with the great spans of geologic time that species remain in existence, so also in comparative studies of cyclic landsurfaces older than the Quaternary the time span required for their expansion seldom seems significant. For comparative studies the time taken for cyclic landsurfaces to spread may seemingly be neglected. Certainly no great error introduced by this practice has yet come to my notice.

Cahen (1954) has conceived three datings for cyclic landsurfaces (a) *local age* as established for any point on the surface, (b) *initial age*, which refers to the commencement of the cycle at the coast, and (c) the *terminal age* when the features of the cycle are destroyed by an ensuing cycle. At the coast the initial age of one cycle is the terminal age of its predecessor, but in continental interiors relicts of ancient cycles may survive locally for such long periods in polycyclic landscapes that the terminal age there has little significance. Indeed several distinct cycles could all have the same terminal age if they are obliterated simultaneously by a fresh cycle.

Coasts afford the most satisfactory regions for dating continental landscape cycles. Many of the world's coasts are monoclinal in structure and so many examples are known of cyclic landsurfaces passing seaward as unconformities beneath a mantle of coastal plain sediments, not infrequently fossiliferous (p. 197). Successive datings for surfaces thus readily established may be compared with local data from continental interiors where datable formations of continental sedimentation rest in basin plains.

Each sedimentary series rests upon an *older* surface, erosional or depositional, and is itself the debris of a synchronous denudational surface, with which its upper limit is contemporaneous and sometimes coterminous. Many examples will be cited in Chapters IX-XII.

THE AGES OF CONTINENTAL LANDSURFACES

About the margins of Central and Southern Africa very clear monoclines are developed which display upon the landward side a series of successive planations, of which the oldest stand highest, descending and converging towards the coast; and in the coastal-plains are sequences of sedimentary rocks, predominantly marine, in which the descending landsurfaces are represented by unconformities, of which the oldest is the lowest. Between the two phases, therefore, is a narrow zone in which the surfaces cross one another. Similar structures are known along other coasts such as Eastern Brazil (p. 317) and the eastern United States (p. 364).

Further crossings are known about the margins of long-enduring continental basins that have acted as foci for deposition (*e.g.* Kalahari; Gobi).

Matching of the denudational and aggradational phenomena (both marine and continental) in Africa has yielded the following chronology (King and King 1959) (Fig. 78) (see also p. 248).

 a) the " Gondwana " landsurface, found only on the highest divides, equates with the bedrock surface beneath the earliest Cretaceous sediments (mid- to late-Jurassic in East Africa). The Gondwana cyclic landsurface is therefore Jurassic in age and because it underlies the earliest marine rock system of the east coast, and ante-dates the present outlines of Africa. In terms of Chapter II it is to be interpreted as part of the original landscape of Gondwanaland existing before that supercontinent fragmented during the late Mesozoic.

 b) the " post-Gondwana " landsurface, also found only on divide areas where it makes valleys or rolling terrains below the levels of the Gondwana tabletops, passes beneath the Cenomanian or Senonian overlap. (The former date is general in North Africa, the latter in South Africa). Denudation during this cycle supplied the early- to mid-Cretaceous marginal sediments.

 c) the fundamental planation of the African plateau standing commonly around 4,000 feet warps down marginally to pass beneath Miocene (Burdigalian) strata of the coastal plain. The cycle was current over Africa from the late Cretaceous until the mid-Cainozoic. As the latter is the age of deposits known to lie upon it in many places it is often called the mid-Tertiary surface, but in deference to its long term of currency we shall in this text refer to it as the " early-Cainozoic " or " African " cyclic surface. It supplied the late-Cretaceous and early-Cainozoic sediments of both the coastal margins and interior basins. It is sometimes armoured with duricrust (*cf.* Uganda).

d) a cycle which transgresses the late-Cretaceous and early-Cainozoic sediments, supplied detritus for the early-Miocene beds, and forms the floor of later Cainozoic formations, represents a cyclic denudation current at least during Miocene time. On land it forms an incompletely planed or undulating landscape that now covers perhaps a greater area in Africa than any other cyclic surface.

e) a second late-Cainozoic denudation that shed fresh sandy or clayey debris on the coastal plain appears to have been of shorter duration and probably terminated shortly before the end of the Pliocene period. In the African interior it may not be readily distinguishable from the preceding denudational cycle but its depositional phases are distinct (Chapter IX). It commonly bears the best preserved pediments, perhaps in erosional basins.

f) following major rejuvenation of the coastal monoclines during the Plio-Pleistocene deep gorges widely gashed the coastal hinterland of Africa and advanced at nickpoints far up some of the major rivers (on the Cunene to Rua Cana Falls) (Fig. 119). This erosion supplied the beach and dune sands of the littoral.

Datings for these six cyclic denudations are confirmed by continental deposits of the interior, and *the chronology is basic for virtually the whole of the African continent* (Chapter IX). Established for an entire continent, it may well serve as standard for the whole globe (Chapters IX-XII).

The Pattern of World Landscapes

Each of the several cyclic landscapes has a characteristic physiognomy that may be recognised by an experienced observer even in widely sundered districts. Where confusion has been introduced by local factors, reference to earlier or later surfaces will often make the identification clear. We cite these characteristics for Africa, the continent wherein cyclic landsurfaces are best displayed, and have been most studied (Chapter IX).

Unless they have been downwarped and buried, remnants of the Gondwana landscape appear only upon the highest terrains such as the Nyika Plateau of Malawi or in high Basutoland. Large or small, the remnants almost all record a pristine smooth planation, but because of their long exposure to weathering since Mesozoic time they are nowadays commonly etched by a minor secondary relief. One point should perhaps be emphasised: these are not fossil landsurfaces that have been buried for a prolonged span of geologic time and then undergone resurrection, but are landsurfaces which have, according to all the geological indications, been continuously exposed to the elements since the date of their essential planation. Vertical lowering under erosion has been insignificant upon their higher parts during the time interval between their planation and the present day. Sometimes they may coincide with older, resurrected topographies: for instance the Gondwana landscape often approximates to the resurrected sub-Stormberg and sub-Karroo surfaces of Rhodesia and the Transvaal. These two earlier surfaces are unquestionably of Gondwanaland origin, so what is more likely than that the surface which occasionally strips them at similar level also originated in that ancient super-continent?

Lastly, these archaic landscapes have in many continents been locally dimpled to receive patches of continental, or more rarely marine, deposits. In almost every instance these begin with beds of late-Jurassic or early-Cretaceous age; and the sequel will indeed show many places in different parts of the world where the oldest landscapes now visible have survived from late-Mesozoic time. These landscapes ante-date the disruption of both Gondwana and Laurasia and are older therefore than the present continental outlines.

" Post-Gondwana " cyclic lineaments are usually present as systems of valley heads dissecting the Gondwana cyclic plateaus, for example the broad-floored valleys of high Basutoland traversed by the route from Sani Pass to Mokhotlong (Frontispiece). Sometimes they make minor plateaus below the Gondwana level, as the Vipya plateau which stands below Nyika in Malawi. Over North Africa, Gondwana base levels persisted into post-Gondwana time and so Cretaceous post-Gondwana denudation merely continued to plane the Jurassic lowland to greater smoothness.

The post-Gondwana cycle was initiated presumably not by uplift of the continent but by roughing out of the new coasts at the dismemberment of Gondwanaland (Fig. 12). Betrunking of the rivers was sufficient to cause rejuvenation without uplift about Central and Southern Africa; but in the north, which had been peripheral in Gondwanaland, Gondwana and post-Gondwana cycles are not distinct and there is a single mid- or late-Cretaceous planation.

The " African " cyclic planation, current during the long time interval between late-Cretaceous and mid-Cainozoic, attained an unique perfection of bevelling that renders it generally recognisable at sight. Sometimes it still bears a thick duricrust, a soil profile of extreme maturity, relict from early Cainozoic time (e.g. in Uganda, and even the Natal coastal belt (R. R. Maud and B. E. Beater). To the geomorphologist it forms a datum widespread through the interior plateau to which other cyclic surfaces, earlier or later, may be referred.

Where there are no remnants of the older cyclic surfaces the early-Cainozoic surface makes very smooth crest lines upon the ridges (e.g. in the highveld) or occasionally broad, extremely smooth plateaus. The early-Cainozoic planation was thus the fundamental landsurface from which nearly all existing African (and world) scenery has subsequently been carved (Plate 7).

Where cymatogeny occurred during the late or at the close of the Cainozoic era the manner of crustal deformation is often rendered strikingly evident by the attitudes assumed by this planation.

Incised below the early-Cainozoic planation are broad valley plains and rolling topographies that now make up most of the scenery of Africa. In many areas two cycles are evident and of these the upper is always by far the more extensive. It was carved during the Miocene period. The lower is often confined to the vicinity of trunk river valleys or local basins. These are the late-Cainozoic cycles 1 and 2, of varied topography. The second late-Cainozoic landscape usually exhibits the finest pediments and this is often true in other continents also. The early-Cainozoic and first late-Cainozoic cyclic landscapes were similarly affected by post-Miocene crustal deformations, and now often appear associated in similar attitudes, *e.g.* tilted together, with the second late-Cainozoic phase in basins excavated below them. Elsewhere there may be little difference of elevation between the late-Cainozoic landscapes 1 and 2.

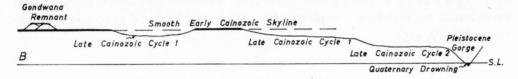

FIG. 93. The pattern of world cyclic landscapes (denudational) expressed in diagrammatic profile.

About the close of the Cainozoic era violent cymatogenic upwarp of the Cainozoic landsurfaces afforded opportunity for deep gorge-cutting by the main river systems. Hence the most recent group of landforms creates a strong, youthful relief such as characterises the marginal regions of East and South Africa (Plates 6, 7) and zones alongside the rift valley system. In such regions it is commonplace to find the strongly arched Cainozoic planations perched high on watersheds above the gorges, *e.g.* the highlands of Zambia and Rhodesia on either side of the middle Zambesi gorges.* In some areas piedmont treppen have developed on the flanks of cymatogenic arches, *e.g.* Natal (King and King 1959), and considerable minor retouching of the older landsurfaces has locally occurred. This is less apparent in Africa than in some other continents

---

* In certain mountainous regions such as the Andes or New Zealand, late Cainozoic planations were hurled to great heights and nearly all the scenery consists of profound Quaternary valley-systems. The incision was well advanced before the onset of Pleistocene glaciation, and indeed modification of the pre-existing valleys by the glaciers was often less than has hitherto been accepted.

In these, or similar, regions sheets of gravel from the canyon-cutting are spread over adjacent Pliocene landscapes, and buckshot gravels, sometimes covering hundreds of square miles (as about Marton, New Zealand) are locally the most characteristic of Pleistocene deposits. Alongside extreme deformations gravel piedmonts such as the Canterbury Plains or the Indo-Gangetic plain may appear.

Not enough attention has been devoted to the topographic effects of Plio-Pleistocene cymatogeny, and to the terrains resulting from stream incision into these initial landforms. Most of the world's more rugged tracts are derived from them, not as is commonly stated from the Alpine orogeny of mid-Cainozoic time.

where the Quaternary landscapes are the most extensive and varied with a multitude of minor details such as river terraces, moraines, erg dunes, and so forth. These are of special interest to geographers as constituting the *present* surface of the globe; but they are too detailed and recent for protracted discussion in a text concerned to demonstrate the surface history of the globe in geological terms.

The *pattern* of cyclic landscapes in Africa may be expressed in diagrammatic profile (Fig. 93). A better device is the " morphocyclic " curve invented by Mescherikov (1963) in which elevation of a cyclic landsurface is plotted against absolute geologic time-scale (Fig. 158).

Once these profiles are established for Africa the same pattern becomes evident in other continents (Chapters IX-XII) with modifications suited to greater or lesser uplift, or other local factors. The wide planations of the early-Cainozoic and the deep incisions of the Plio-Pleistocene are most readily identified and the other cyclic surfaces are related simply to them. Even if the dates of deformation differ somewhat from place to place owing to heterogeneity of the crust and differential (shear) movements in the subcrust, the pattern and sequence of landforms will be found to remain the same everywhere (p. 425).

Some Doubts Allayed

The great ages assigned to certain of the landscapes discussed in this chapter may raise doubts in the minds of sundry colleagues whose lives are cast in relatively youthful regions. Are such ages for planed landscapes real? Can a planed surface survive without burial from the Cretaceous and still be a Cretaceous surface? Is such a surface not so altered by erosion in the interim as no longer to be an original Cretaceous surface?

The chapter began by noting that even well planed surfaces may be modified locally from time to time so as to produce insignificant changes of surface forms, as by the shallow cross-cutting of one pediment by another. In this sense planed surfaces *are* occasionally modified, lowered by a few inches or feet without departing at any time from the planed condition. The reality of such modifications is already brought out by the several " local " ages of superficial deposits sometimes found resting upon an ancient surface. But are such modifications significant when viewed upon the continental scale? The surface planed in the Cretaceous is still planed and may still bear local examples of Cretaceous surface deposits. Consider the vast extent of planed surfaces in several continents armoured with surficial residual substances—bauxite, terra rossa, calcrete, silcrete, laterite, duricrust, caliche and so forth. How much have these surfaces been lowered since the deposit first attained significant thickness? Inspection of these deposits soon provides an answer, they have been lowered scarcely if at all since they originally attained significant thickness.

Once a surface has been planed really flat in a pediplanation cycle why should it alter significantly thereafter? What agency is competent to lower in any marked degree a widespread surface of planation for which the top of cyclic scarps alone provides the current base level? From inspection in six continents the author believes that the landscapes of the world described in succeeding chapters provide their own answers, emphatically, that a widespread surface of planation, not subjected to new tectonic deformations or invading erosion cycles, survives in an essentially unaltered state for an indefinite period of geological time.

Geologists have often averred that sedimentation is prolonged and erosion cycles are of relatively short duration. On the continents at any rate the reverse now appears often to be true.

The great ages herein assigned to certain planed landscapes assist in the understanding of many related phenomena. Duricrusting, for example, is seen to be a process long in operation and its effect should cumulatively be evident upon landscapes of at least Cainozoic age. This is so. Quaternary cycles have only minor incrustations. Many authors have declared that duricrusting is now in progress only to a slight extent (Walther; Woolnough 1927); others that most duricrust is fossil and assignable to an epoch when the climate was either wetter or drier and the processes more active. But with the great ages of many of the world's planed landscapes there is no need for an acceleration of the duricrusting processes beyond their present activity nor for any extensive change of climatic regimen—though the possibility of such is by no means excluded.

MAPPING OF CYCLIC LANDSURFACES

Key method in the study of polycyclic landsurfaces is field mapping. The ordinary methods of land survey suffice to delineate quantitatively the distribution, elevation, attitude and nature of those fundamental landscape units the cyclic denudational surfaces. Each such surface begins at a valley floor or at the crest of a scarp or rise, and ceases at a succeeding scarp or declivity where the next cycle takes over. Suitable symbols can be used to depict such adjuncts as superficial accumulations, resurrected surfaces, and so forth. The data provided by such maps are valuable to engineers, soil conservationists and others as well as to geomorphologists. There is no substitute for such morphological maps, even though useful data may be gleaned from the ordinary topographic sheets.

A few countries have issued morphological maps, France, Belgium, U.S.S.R., while in Africa individuals have provided maps for Angola (Jessen), Malawi (Dixey; Lister), Rhodesia and parts of the Republic of South Africa (King); but an ever-increasing number of such maps for all territories is necessary. As the number of morphological maps increases, and landscapes are accurately dated, so the erosional histories of the lands can be compared more widely, ultimately with accuracy even upon world-wide correlations. The present text offers (Fig. 119) a provisional morphological map, in terms of the cyclic units above specified, for the entire African continent.

Landform Analysis from Topographic Maps

Patently, there is no real substitute for field work, in which the distribution and altitude of landsurfaces may be meticulously observed, small irregularities and superficial deposits examined, the existing agencies of erosion studied, and where the investigator may soak himself in his problems, and map and record his data at first hand.

Nonetheless, supplementary methods need to be used in the laboratory to gain knowledge of very large or unfamiliar areas. Nearly all such methods stem from map reading or analysis of survey data, and their accuracy is limited by the accuracy of the original surveys or hindered by the restraints of draughtsmanship. Even the 50 feet contours which are usually the best available sink much of the essential detail. Important data slip through the finest statistical net, but maps do permit a synthetic view of the facts, where quantitative aspects can be emphasised and are themselves conducive of general hypotheses. They also permit a rigorous demonstration of a case that may be put forward, a method of demonstration that may be varied to suit the nature of the country and the nature, more or less refined, of the researches. Maps of 1:50,000 scale are generally satisfactory for local studies, while 1:500,000 or 1:1,000,000 scales are indispensable for studies covering a large country.

Geological maps are generally no less necessary for adequate researches than are topographical maps. But frequently these maps show only the " solid geology ", and ignore the river terrace, glacial and other superficial deposits that are of importance to the geomorphologist.

Graphical methods which are particularly useful in regions of polycyclic relief deal generally with one or other of two aspects: either stream profiles, or planed land surfaces.

Attention has been directed to river profiles by many authors, who have recognised the concave curve of water erosion in the longitudinal profile as fundamental. Not only does the profile flatten from source to mouth, but there is also a flattening of the curve below each important junction. This effect has been observed in trough experiments also (Lewis 1945). The actual curve of even a simple stream profile is a function of several variables of which length, fall, volume, amount and comminution of load are the most important. Local bedrock and tectonic history introduce in practice a further set of variables. Yet several mathematical formulae have been put forward (Steinberg 1875; Jones 1924; Green 1936; Lewis 1945) to cover the profiles of graded reaches along various streams. Mathematical expressions can be obtained to fit a graded reach very closely: but as Jones has shown, more than one expression may be satisfactory, and when extrapolation is attempted in order to adduce the former sea-level to which the reach in question was graded conflicting results may be obtained. For the Towy River, cited by Jones, allowing a distance of 56 miles to the sea, the extrapolative values were 259 feet and 416 feet above the sea respectively. Austin Miller (1939) using curves with an improved fit on the Towy profile obtained extrapolative values of 362 and 553 feet.

Further mathematical treatments have appeared in the United States of recent years (Horton 1945; Leopold and Maddock 1952); and Baulig (1936) has adopted another approach, plotting the longitudinal and terrace profiles from maps or other data, and supplementing them with cross-profiles taken at suitable intervals, to determine graphically the probable positions of former, higher profiles (Fig. 72). For such purposes, only streams which have a present flood-plain are deemed suitable. Experience has shown that such restored profiles are rarely accurate within 10 metres: hence only the main levels separated by not less than 40-50 metres can be distinguished with certainty.

Quite a literature has grown up concerning the interpretation of landscape history from river terraces and partial plains. Briefly, valley-plain terraces, in order to be of use, must be " paired " on both sides of the valley, also they must be cut into solid rock and not built of alluvium. It is further necessary to demonstrate that the river has not been revived by capture of additional waters upstream and that the terraces are not due to slow cutting through a barrier downstream before they can be deemed of cyclic, and tectonic, significance. Quinn (1957) has attributed paired terraces in Texas to Pleistocene climatic variation.

Paired terraces join in mid-valley above the nickpoint marking the head of the valley-floor sunk below them, and above this point the river flows in the valley appropriate to an older cycle. Thus, where the profile of a river is composite, height above the valley floor is no criterion of terrace age. Each terrace in turn merges upstream into a part of the present valley-floor, and the valley-floor may show the effects of several cycles or partial cycles.

Limiting considerations are:
a) restored tributary profiles should be accordant with the main restored profile, and the profiles within a river system should constitute one harmonic whole.
b) successive profiles are mutually dependent in any section of the same valley, and upper profiles, being more mature, should be less steep, in each section, than the lower.
c) if one level has been distorted, all former levels will also have been affected.
d) wide erosion surfaces truncating the region offer measurable limits to any deformation affecting the valleys between them.
e) at or near the shoreline, correlation may be established between the restored profiles and erosional features of the coast.

A comparative study of the river profiles of Southern England, conducted in the field by Wooldridge and Kirkaldy (1936) has exposed a significant correspondence in denudational activity in a large number of streams over a wide area, and up to a height exceeding 200 feet. The elevations of nickpoints given by these authors when corrected to sea-level, may compare also with suggested former sea-levels for Jersey and Guernsey given by Hanson-Lowe (1938). But as an example of what may be deduced from river-profiles Baulig's study (1928) of the Central Plateau of France is surely outstanding.

For the determination of planed landsurfaces, topographic sections, either single or multiple, may be constructed from contoured maps. Superposition of profiles, or the construction of composite (projected or " zonal ") profiles in which are added details of elevated points right and left of an actual section line, soon focus attention on any planed remnants or significant accordance of summit levels. Equally spaced sections are not always desirable and better results may sometimes be obtained by siting sections along, or at right angles to, ridge crests. Several complicated models have been made from multiple, closely-spaced sections, but these offer little advantage over a complete model, except that geological details can be painted on the faces of sections.

Better use can usually be made of a contoured map by considering it areally, when the distribution of cyclic facets becomes plain even on preliminary inspection. To supplement this, several quantitative methods have been employed. Baulig has plotted the frequency curves for equally spaced spot heights in Brittany and in Leon, and deduced therefrom the presence of bevels at specific elevations. Other investigators have measured by planimeter the area between each pair of consecutive contours and plotted the result as percentages of the total area (hypsometric curves). Difficulties are sometimes encountered with sloping surfaces, and the method fails to detect or include bevelled spurs and small remnants.

In order to bring out the essential form of dissected surfaces generalised contours may be employed, smoothing out the deflections caused by the excavation of later valleys and depressions. The accuracy with which this can be done depends primarily upon the proportion of surviving ancient surface in the landscape and the distribution of the residuals.

The methods employed by Maze (1944) are here of value. A transparent grid is placed over the map, and the maximum height determined for, and entered upon, each square of the grid. A grid of one-thousand-yard squares upon a 1:50,000 map is usually satisfactory. The success of the method depends on the fact that cyclic bevels may be lowered by later erosion but not raised (except locally where deposition is in progress) and therefore the superior heights are chiefly significant. Where a surface is imperfectly bevelled, slight over-emphasis on minor irregularities is introduced, but such errors are seldom serious.

The figures on the grid may be used to construct " high point " profiles representing a strip of country of any desired width (measured in thousands of yards if a grid of that scale is used). Composite " high point " profiles of this kind afford maximum opportunity for the detection of planed uplands and bring out very clearly any regional slope in the sectional azimuth.

Accepting the spot heights of the grid, generalised contours can be drawn to render the original forms of bevelled surfaces, but this can only be done where reasonably large portions of the surfaces remain. Conclusions also need checking back on to the original topographic sheet.

Still more recent is the application of statistical analysis (Strahler 1950). Statistical analysis is essentially the method of the bulk sample, and is admirable for the study of complex phenomena and processes into which enter a large number of variables. As yet few geomorphic topics provide data suited directly to statistical or computer treatment, and methods may have to be adapted to the new field of enquiry, so that too facile results should not be expected. The net result must be, however, a greater precision in geomorphic thinking.

THE WORLD'S DENUDATIONAL CYCLES

In studying the world's scenery we find that mountains have hitherto attracted a disproportionate amount of geomorphologists' attention. Their histories are often complex and involve tectonic and denudational maxima that are often specialised in application. Hence it is to the great plains and plateaus (using the term without structural connotation) that we shall first turn for enlightenment regarding the chief trends of global geomorphology.

The monotonous aspect of the great erosional plains, their seeming lack of useful data, and some misunderstanding of their essential nature, modes of origin and ages have, however, discouraged the study to an unfortunate degree, and it is only in relatively recent years that much research has been directed to the study of the world's plainlands. Quite naturally these researches have been concentrated in Africa, the continent almost devoid of folded mountain ranges, but renowned for the extent and perfection of its bevelled erosional surfaces.

With Africa, therefore, our survey of the world's plainlands begins, but the reader should be aware that the objective is not merely to afford a description and history of African landscape but to adduce from this region a natural scheme which may be found, with suitable modifications, in any continent: that is, a global plan.

The basic premises are already before us: (a) the development of continental landscapes by pediplanation; (b) that pediplanation acts cyclically in conjunction with intermittent earth movement; (c) that the number of continental denudational cycles since the mid-Mesozoic is small; (d) that essential synchroneity for the major denudational cycles is demonstrable in different theatres of study, and (e) that a wide range of local variations amid minor landforms is possible in conjunction with local tectonics, heterogeneity of bedrock, climatic changes and so forth.

In search of data we now explore the scenery of the plainlands.

PART C

THE SCENERY OF THE PLAINLANDS

CHAPTER IX

THE GEOMORPHOLOGY OF AFRICA

The Cyclic Episodes of African Geomorphology. The Face of Modern Africa. The Geomorphology of Africa. The Carboniferous-Permian (pre-Karroo) Landsurface and the Triassic (intra-Karroo) Landsurface. Post-Karroo Land Movements. The Jurassic " Gondwana " Planation and the Cretaceous " post-Gondwana " Cycle of Erosion. Cainozoic Cyclic Landsurfaces in Southern Africa. The Kalahari. Dating of the Cainozoic Landscape Cycles. Cainozoic Events in Congo Republic. Cainozoic Landsurfaces of Central and East Africa. Cainozoic Denudation in Abyssinia and Arabia. The Sudan, Nigeria and the Guinea Highlands. The Sahara. The Plio-Pleistocene Cymatogeny and ensuing Landforms of Southern Africa. The Rift Valley System of Central Africa. Quaternary Events in Congo Republic. Cymatogeny and ensuing Denudation in East Africa. Cymatogeny in Syrabia. Quaternary Events in North Africa. The West African Coastal Monocline. Conclusion.

THE CYCLIC EPISODES OF AFRICAN GEOMORPHOLOGY

The pioneer student of African geomorphology has been Frank Dixey who, in a long series of papers published between 1938 and 1958, classified the multitudinous land-forms of Central and Southern Africa into a relatively simple system of denudational cycles that are developed uniformly throughout the greater part of the continent. Moreover he dated the cycles correctly even in his first publication (1938) by reference to fossiliferous covering deposits; but these are unfortunately rare over most of South and East Africa so that the planed landsurfaces tended instead to be correlated upon a basis of relative altitude above sea-level. The " mid-Tertiary " landscape for instance was widely identified as a planed surface around 4,000 feet elevation, and the " late-Tertiary " as around 2,000 feet. Correlation by elevation, however, proved inadequate and numerous errors resulted from its employment. As will appear in the sequel, elevation of the African continent has been much less uniform than the early investigators realised and over long distances the smooth surfaces of planation rise and fall due to tectonic movement almost imperceptibly through hundreds and even thousands of feet (cymatogeny). Miscorrelations of surfaces inevitably resulted.

Further confusion was introduced by other investigators, Beetz (1933), Jessen (1936) and King (1946) who all began at the irreproachable datum of sea-level and carried their investigations inland from the coast, across the series of denudational terraces that rise step-like through the marginal lands to the high interior plateau (4,000-5,000 feet). All three independently arrived at the conclusion that the plateau, which Dixey had

Q 241

dated as mid-Tertiary, was really Mesozoic (Jurassic or Cretaceous) in age. None of these investigators appreciated at that time the immensity of the marginal outwarping (nearly 5,000 feet) that had affected the coastlands of Africa as late as the end of the Cainozoic era. Dixey was right and they were wrong.

Dixey's later publications showed from the attitudes of cyclic landsurfaces what deformations had affected the face of Africa during its geomorphic development, and independently King (1961) has advanced the hypothesis of cymatogeny under which cyclic landsurfaces are thrown into great waves.

After twenty years experience, trained investigators can now recognise the several cyclic denudation cycles upon their inherent physical characteristics whatever their elevation and attitude, and map them with confidence over vast areas. It is becoming difficult, almost, to recall the days when observers worked in isolated areas hundreds and even thousands of miles apart, always in uncertainty as to how their work would correlate, each with the other.

Now, in 1958, all major problems of dating and correlation seem to be resolved, and the outline of geomorphology for the whole African continent that follows can be stated with full confidence in its essential correctness (Fig. 119). Little appreciated as yet outside of Africa, the researches of the past twenty years have nevertheless laid the foundation for deciphering the history of continental landscapes all over the globe, a thesis that will become firmly established through succeeding chapters of this book.

The face of Africa is a polygenetic and complex thing developed over a vast interval of geologic time, with successive local phases of denudation or sedimentation that have developed in response to the attitudes of the surface assumed periodically after disturbing land movements. Commonly, elevated areas become eroded and relatively depressed areas serve as sedimentary basins, and by combining the historical records preserved in these contrasting environments the geomorphic aspect of Africa at any given period may be reasonably determined. Naturally, the more ancient landforms are less perfectly preserved in the modern landscape than those of younger cycles; but frequently an ancient planation is clearly demonstrable in small plateaus or summit accordances though all its original detail has been destroyed. Many such survivals are quite remarkably authentic. The Rhodesian watershed plateau for instance terminates at an abrupt scarp some distance north of Salisbury; fifty miles away to the north-east however, atop a steep hill called Shoshi is an unmistakable remnant of the same plateau at the same height (4,720 feet) and measuring only two acres in extent. Geomorphologists mapping the cyclic landsurfaces of Africa have long learned to trust these small remnants and even to follow them through quite a range of altitude where surfaces have subsequently been deformed.

Best preserved are remnants that have stood not upon the elevated country but in depressions where they have been buried for long intervals of time beneath covering formations that have recently been stripped to reveal the resurrected topography more or less in its pristine state. Many such fossil topographies survive in Africa, some from very ancient times; but the first that is significant in the modern landscape is a late-Palæozoic denudational topography that has been identified locally at intervals from the Cape to the Equator, beyond which it is represented by a sandy piedmont aggradational phase.

a) Known as the " pre-Karroo surface ", this landscape of late-Carboniferous time was heavily glaciated in the south (Chapter II) where it lies as striated pavements upon a landscape of moderate relief beneath a mantle of Dwyka tillite. Where the tillite has recently been removed from above harder rocks the ancient topography is often re-exposed with surprising fidelity (p. 253) (Fig. 94) over wide areas. Farther north beyond the reach of the Dwyka ice sheets and their deposits of ground moraine, the late-Carboniferous topography continued to be exposed to the weather during early-Permian time and the first deposits to overlap upon it belong to the Ecca series and its correlatives. This condition prevails over much of Africa between the Transvaal and the Sudan. The nature

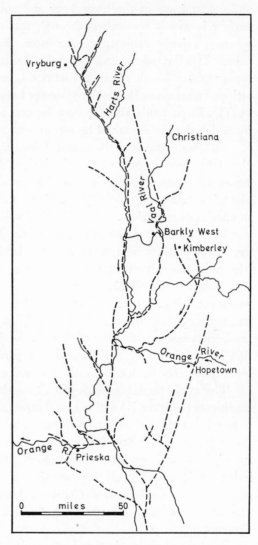

FIG. 94.

Showing the close approximation between the valleys of pre-Karroo and present-day erosion surfaces in the northern Cape Province. This is a remarkable instance of faithful resurrection over a wide area. *after A. L. du Toit.*

and age of the " pre-Karroo " topography thus change progressively from south to north, but so marked in African stratigraphy is the change from the denudation that had prevailed for a long time previously, to the widespread continental-type deposition of the Karroo system, that little attempt has been made to analyse the late-Palæozoic denudation cycle in the several African territories. The sense of its uniformity is strong, and its known local differences have not been emphasised.

b) Very widely through Africa the Triassic period embodied a phase of denudation, or at least an interruption of Karroo sedimentation, that occasions the conception of an intra-Karroo desert landscape (Chapter II) now often buried beneath the fluvial and eolian sands of the Stormberg and equivalant series. In a resurrected state this surface is widely recognised through the Transvaal, Rhodesia and the Congo region whence Triassic sediments have been denuded in late-Cainozoic and Quaternary time. This Triassic surface generally displays far less relief than the earlier pre-Karroo topography. North of the Equator this surface is scarcely recognised, though small stripped plateaus of Permo-Triassic age have been identified in the Atlas Region (Dresch 1941). In part this absence may be due to a lack of continental Triassic formations by which the surface could be recognised.

c) Over Jurassic Africa, and following the late-Triassic sedimentation, smooth planation unaccompanied by significant deposition was almost ubiquitous. This smoothness was achieved because land movement between the Triassic and Jurassic planations had been only slight, and the Jurassic planation was therefore accomplished in close approximation to the Triassic levels, both denudational and aggradational.

Two very important attributes of the Jurassic cyclic planation are: (i) it affords the oldest cyclic remnants in modern landscapes that have evidently survived from Mesozoic time without necessarily undergoing burial and resurrection. As such it is identified as summit planations and accordances upon the highest parts of African watersheds (Fig. 93). Details of the original smooth planation are generally marred by weathering during the one-hundred million odd years of its survival, but its existence has been remarked by many workers in the African territories. Alternatively, in regions that have persistently failed to rise, as parts of the Congo-Kalahari region, the same landsurface lies buried beneath a cover of early-Cretaceous continental sediments. (ii) The cycle (and landscape) is older than the present configuration of southern continents (Chapter II) and is flexed down at the eastern and western margins of Africa to pass below the early-Cretaceous formations that are the first marine deposits related to the Atlantic and Indian Oceans, and a similar relationship exists along the coasts of Brazil, India and certain of the coasts of Australia. A similar Jurassic landsurface may indeed be identified in all these continents (Table IX). Furthermore, this cyclic land-scape was the landscape of Gondwanaland before that super-continent fragmented, and hence derives its name—the " Gondwana landsurface ", of Jurassic or early-Cretaceous age.

Little has been conjectured concerning the drainage pattern of this ancient, smooth landsurface. Under the aridity or semi-aridity that prevailed over most of Gondwana-land during Jurassic time, much of the drainage was doubtless directed centripetally towards interior basins, themselves standing within a few hundreds of feet of sea-level—as the basins of Lakes Eyre, Frome and Torrens in South Australia do at the present day.

d) When Gondwanaland disrupted during the early-Cretaceous period, new coasts such as the eastern and western coasts of Africa were created by monoclinal flexing (Fig. 77) and the betrunked rivers became tributary to the base-levels of the new oceans (p. 62). In so doing they initiated a fresh cycle of erosion, the " post-Gondwana cycle " of early- to late-Cretaceous age, that began the dissection of the earlier " Gondwana " planation, incising it with a system of broad open valleys in general a few hundreds of feet deep. This is the condition in Southern Africa.

In North Africa, where there was no disruption and no new coasts were created because of its originally peripheral position in Gondwanaland, the pediplanation and deposition of the Jurassic continued without interruption into the Cretaceous period resulting in an unicyclic surface of low relief. Ultimately this subsided shallowly beneath an epi-continental sea that stretched during the late Cretaceous from the Mediterranean to the Gulf of Guinea. To the east, in Sudan and Egypt, the long-accumulated piedmont deposits of the Nubian sandstone were also partly overflowed by the late-Cretaceous sea. Over North and West Africa, therefore, there is generally no distinction between Gondwana and post-Gondwana landscape cycles of Jurassic and Cretaceous age respectively, only a mid-Cretaceous landscape of extreme planation.

e) Simultaneously with and following widespread incursions of the late-Cretaceous sea, continental uplift with outward flexing of the eastern and western margins initiated a fresh cycle of erosion that was to prevail (with minor interruptions in the extreme north of the continent where the peripheral tremors of the Alpine orogeny were felt) throughout the early-Cainozoic era until the close of the Oligocene period. Except for basins such as the Kalahari or the Congo, where detritus accumulated from surrounding areas undergoing erosion, almost the whole of the continent was reduced to a denudational plain of extraordinary smoothness. This " African " cyclic landsurface still contributes to the wide prospects and rectilinear skylines of parts of the African interior including the South African highveld, the watershed regions of Rhodesia and the Serengeti Plains of Tanganyika. Over most of Africa relief was reduced to an almost incredible minimum.

This extraordinarily smooth planation affords the datum that is most sought by geomorphologists concerned with mapping and dating the cyclic facets of the continental landscape. Above it stand, on the highest parts of the country, rare smoothly-crested relics of the Gondwana landscape, possibly with later post-Gondwana dissection; below it lie the broadly countersunk valleys of late-Cainozoic cycles and the deep canyons of late-Pliocene and Quaternary rejuvenations.

The continental basins of early-Cainozoic time were aggraded with detritus, generally fine-grained, shed from neighbouring regions. Thus in the Kalahari accumulated a three-hundred feet thickness of marls capped, as the supply of waste failed, by calcrete up to fifty feet thick. In the Congo Basin an equivalent formation is the *grès polymorphe*, likewise calcreted at the top. These broad basins of sedimentation also contributed to the extraordinarily smooth aspect of Africa before the mid-Cainozoic.

Where the " African " cyclic landsurface (denudational or aggradational) bears covering deposits, the oldest of these, continental or marine, are early-Miocene (Burdigalian) in age.

f) Moderate cymatogenic uplift, first at the end of the Oligocene and later about the end of the Miocene, created fresh base levels to which the major rivers and valleys were soon graded at elevations below that of the early-Cainozoic pediplain. The broad valley forms of these cycles have now advanced to the heads of the main river systems so that they have destroyed most of the early-Cainozoic landscape. Most of the South African highveld, for instance, consists of open, widely spaced valleys from a few feet to three-hundred feet in depth between interfluves bearing the smooth skyline of the early-Cainozoic planation. The combination of the shallow late-Cainozoic valleys, often miles in width, with the even-crested, early-Cainozoic interfluves engenders the gently rolling topography generally associated with the interior plateau of Africa. On first acquaintance it may appear to be a single cyclic surface in late maturity, but it is truly two-cycle with a small vertical interval separating the two respective base

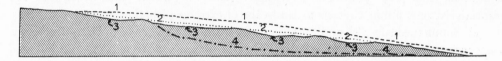

FIG. 95. Plio-Pleistocene monoclinal warping of the early- and late-Cainozoic landsurfaces in Natal from near sea-level at the coast to 6,000 feet near the Drakensberg. 1. Early Cainozoic surface. 2. First late Cainozoic surface. 3. Second late Cainozoic surface. 4. Quaternary valley incision. Diagrammatic section. West-east from Giant's Castle to Durban. *after L. C. King and L. A. King.*

levels upon a regional scale. Throughout the Cainozoic era, therefore, the aspect of Africa departed only locally and exceptionally from a smooth landscape of vast dimensions.

Locally, one, two or three late-Cainozoic cycles may be detectable in the landscape, depending upon either the nature of late-Cainozoic land-movements or the splitting of nickpoints by structural controls existing in the bedrock. This condition is especially well displayed in the marginal regions below the Great Escarpment of South Africa.

g) Towards the end of the Pliocene the monotonous Cainozoic landscape was subjected to powerful uplift and warping, the action of which is possibly not exhausted even at the present day. The continental interior was elevated as a plateau, generally to about 4,000 feet, across which ran axes of still greater uplift such as the continental divide, a curious feature worth tracing out upon a map (Fig. 82). Other axes cracked open at the crest as the rift valley system of Central Africa. The eastern and western margins of the continent were tilted violently outward so that the early- and late-Cainozoic landsurfaces now rise from sea-level at the coast in places to 2,000 or more feet at 20-30 miles inland, *e.g.* in Natal (Figs. 95, 96).

Erosional response was immediate; all the major rivers carved great gorges through

the coastal hinterlands and sometimes well into the interior plateau. Certain of the
nickpoints are still marked by great waterfalls such as Aughrabies on the Orange River,

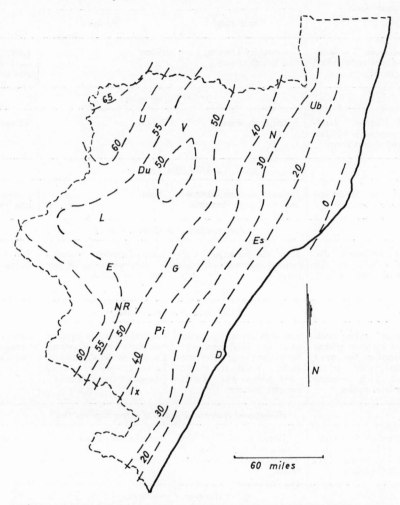

FIG. 96. Deformation of the planed early-Cainozoic ("African") cyclic
landsurface by the Plio-Pleistocene rejuvenation of the originally jurassic
Natal Monocline. Elevations in hundreds of feet. D = Durham, Du =
Dundee, E = Estcourt, Es = Eshowe, G = Greytown, Ix = Ixopo,
L = Ladysmith, N = Nongoma, NR = Nottingham Road, Pi = Pieter-
maritzburg, U = Utrecht, Ub = Ubombo, V = Vryheid. *after L. C.
King and L. A. King.*

and Rua Cana on the Cunene, and Kebra Baça on the Zambezi. Nowhere has the
Quaternary cycle advanced to the stage where the landscape is planed by it, though
two or three sub-stages in the down-cutting are sometimes denoted by river terraces.
These perhaps record stages in the general uplift, but insufficient research has been

TABLE VII

CYCLIC EPISODES OF AFRICAN GEOMORPHOLOGY (South and Central), WITH TECTONIC INTERLUDES.

Denudational	Depositional		Age
	Continental	Marine	
(a) " pre-Karroo " landscape of moderate relief, partly glacial	Covered by Dwyka, Ecca and Beaufort series	None	Late Carboniferous and Permian
Mild Epeirogenesis			
(b) " intra-Karroo " landscape generally of low relief and desert form	Stormberg series	None	Triassic
Mild Epeirogenesis			
(c) "Gondwana" landscape of extreme planation	Jurassic deposits known only in Congo Republic	None	Jurassic (and late Triassic)
Fragmentation of Gondwanaland			
(d) " post-Gondwana " dissection usually in the vicinity of upwarps	Série de Kwango : Cretaceous sediments of Nyasa rift.	Late - Jurassic — early-Cretaceous series of east and west coasts.	Early Cretaceous
Mid-Cretaceous Disturbances			
(e) " African " cyclic landscape of extreme planation forming the most perfectly planed surface of Africa, much dissected now by later cycles	Late-Cretaceous dinosaur bed of Bushmanland ; early-Cainozoic Botletle beds, Kalahari marls, *Grès polymorphe*. Chief calcrete horizon	Littoral Senonian strata of east coast with succeeding Eocene in Moçambique. Late-Cretaceous and Eocene strata of Angola	Late Cretaceous— mid-Cainozoic
Widespread epeirogenic uplift of a few hundred feet			
(f i) Broad valley-floor pediplains widespread into early - Cainozoic, " African " surface	" Plateau sands " of the Kalahari-Congo region, Minor laterites and calcretes	Burdigalian marine series	Miocene
Moderate Cymatogeny			
(f ii) Second phase of late-Cainozoic valley planation. Coastal plains	Pipe sandstone of mid-Zambezi valley	Sands unconformably overlying Burdigalian and transected by coastal plain of East Africa	Pliocene
Strong Cymatogeny			
(g) Deep gorge-cutting in eastern and western coastal hinterlands. Locally multiphase	Widespread Kalahari sands (two phase). Cavern deposits	Red " Berea " and other coastal sands	Quaternary
Minor Differential movement			
(h) Coastal drowning	Recent alluvia	Recent dune sands	

done to determine whether they can be correlated over long distances or are of local significance only.

Within the central depression of the Kalahari eolian sands spread widely at this time under the influence of a very dry climate.

h) With recent drowning of the river mouths and the construction of minor shoreline features the final fashioning of the modern landscape was accomplished.

THE FACE OF MODERN AFRICA

By the end of the Cainozoic era most of Africa had been reduced to a rolling lowland of broad late-Cainozoic valley-plains between occasional, smoothly bevelled ridge crests of

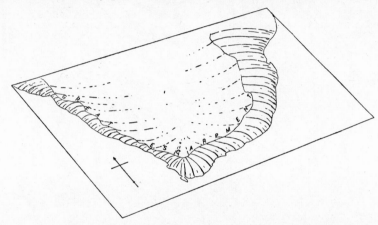

FIG. 97. Idealised block diagram to illustrate Plio-Pleistocene cymatogeny about the Great Escarpment of Southern Africa.

the early-Cainozoic planation. In relative depressions such as the Kalahari and parts of the Sudan widespread sands and muds of inland deltas made even flatter landscapes; and over the whole, duricrusts were widespread showing that modification of the landscape was proceeding with extreme slowness. The average elevation was low, perhaps between 1,000 and 1,500 feet above sea-level in the interior of the continent.

This tectonic quiescence was rudely shattered before the conclusion of the Cainozoic era when cymatogeny elevated the interior plateau to heights of 4,000 to 5,000 feet above sea-level and tilted the eastern and western marginal regions violently towards the Indian and Atlantic Ocean Basins respectively. As the coastal hinterlands were strongly uptilted, so the offshore continental shelf was correspondingly depressed. Where the hingeline lay closely along the previous shore little change of coastal outline occurred, but where the hingeline lay seaward extensive coastal plains were added to the geographical outline of the continent. Maximum upwarping occurred not towards the centre of the continent but along a rim parallel to the coast and distant commonly 200 miles or more from it (Fig. 97). There the maximum uplift often exceeded 6,000 feet whence the planed landscapes declined in elevation to 3,000 feet or even less in the basins of the interior. The super-elevated plateau rim makes an orographic boundary of the first magnitude surmounted by high mountains on which are still preserved relicts of the Mesozoic Gondwana and post-Gondwana erosion cycles, *e.g.* Basutoland; but even so it often fails to make the continental divide, *e.g.* in Zambia and Rhodesia, for it is breached by the valleys of major rivers such as the Limpopo and the Zambesi.

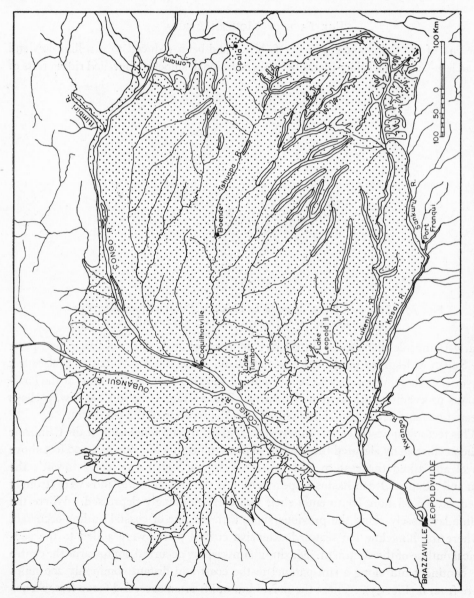

Fig. 98. Quaternary deposition in the Congo Cuvette following basin formation towards the close of the Cainozoic era.

On a lesser scale the cymatogenic movements created numerous axial upwarps that separate broad dimples in the surface. The former now often function as watersheds (Congo-Zambezi divide) (Fig. 85) the latter as foci of centripetal drainage, either lakes or swamps (Lake Chad, Victoria Nyanza) (Fig. 83). Certain of these deformations followed earlier movements in the same sense so that older elevations were re-emphasised while already established basins became subjected to renewed deposition; but the movements also followed new lines, creating fresh watersheds with the Cainozoic planations arching smoothly over them and no relicts of older divides (*e.g.* the present Congo-Zambezi divide, the former site of which lay farther to the north by the Kundelungu Mountains), and fresh basins such as that which occupies the middle course of the River Congo (Fig. 98). Very prominent along the crests of violently uparched axes in Central Africa are the rift valleys created contemporaneously with the uplifts from late Miocene until the present day. Several of the rifts follow lines of earlier, repeated uplift, and there were indeed extensive rift valley systems during the Cretaceous period (Malawi) and following the deposition of the Karroo system (mid-Zambezi).

FIG. 99. "High Africa, Low Africa and the Atlas".

The face of modern Africa thus derives mainly from deformations of the Cainozoic landscape (dominantly two-cycle) produced by Plio-Pleistocene cymatogeny.

Regional elevation was greatest in the south and east, progressively less towards the north and west except for the Atlas region which, like the rest of the Alpine belt, was greatly elevated. Thus arises the geographical division into "High Africa, Low Africa and the Atlas" (Fig. 99)*. Briefly, therefore, South and East Africa are characterised by the highest interior plateaus, greatest scarps, most deeply incised river valleys and the presence of rifts. On the highest elevations also they preserve the best remnants of continuously-exposed Mesozoic landscapes available in Africa. The region is, and has been, dominated by active denudation, and a continental sedimentational

* Readers unfamiliar with African geography may find great assistance in A. K. Lobeck's block diagram and description published by the Columbia University Press. Similar diagrams are available for all continents except Antarctica.

record is furnished only by the Kalahari region extended into the southern Congo Republic.

Low Africa occupies the region from the Congo Basin to the Atlas Mountains, and from the Atlantic coast to the Nile. It too has its uparched regions such as the Ubangi-Shari watershed or the domes of Ahaggar, Tibesti and the Nubia-Arabian massif; but basins and regions of late-Mesozoic and Cainozoic sedimentation are more widespread and important (Congo, Upper Niger, Chad and the Middle Nile) including the dune-sand *erg* deserts of the Sahara.

THE GEOMORPHOLOGY OF AFRICA

The geomorphology of Africa may be stated either geographically, region by region in space, or historically chapter by chapter in time. The latter method, applying to the entire continent, doubtless leads to suppression of much interesting local detail; but as the object of this book is not to produce a compendium upon African topography but a scientific geomorphology that may be compared with the geomorphologies of other continents the main outlines must be kept clear and these are episodic in time. As to the detail, naturally upon a landmass of heterogeneous composition local structural controls cause local deviations from strict rule but these are insignificant in the overall plan of Africa. Even the law of gravity does not hold true for very small particles!

We therefore treat the subject chronologically, as stated in the foregoing Table VII. In so doing it will be convenient to group the several landscape cycles in pairs that commonly occur together *viz* : (a) Carboniferous and Triassic cyclic landsurfaces associated with developments of strata of the Karroo system; (b) Jurassic and Cretaceous landscapes of the Gondwana planation and its subsequent post-Gondwana dissection following the disruption of Gondwanaland; (c) the early-Cainozoic (" African ") planation and its late-Cainozoic valley-floor dissection; and (d) following the violent Plio-Pleistocene cymatogeny, the Quaternary canyon cutting and scarp retreat. Concurrently at each stage the corresponding aggradational landforms will receive consideration.

THE CARBONIFEROUS-PERMIAN (PRE-KARROO) LANDSURFACE AND THE TRIASSIC (INTRA-KARROO) LANDSURFACE

Both these cyclic landsurfaces are reported only in the fossil state having been buried for a great lapse of time beneath strata of the Karroo (and equivalent) rock systems. They are, therefore, associated with developments of those strata and are revealed once more in the modern landscape where the covering strata, which still lie subhorizontally, have been stripped away by recent denudation. The pre-Karroo surface seems generally to have been of moderate relief, so that on resurrection the tops of its hills and ridges sometimes protrude from enveloping strata which wrap around the flanks and floor the valleys. The resurrected Triassic landscape on the other hand seems generally to have been much smoother, and is judged from the quality of its overlying sediments to have been a desert.

In South Africa, to as far north as the Witwatersrand, the pre-Karroo landsurface is everywhere a product of severe continental glaciation (Chapter II). In the extreme south the ice-sheets discharged into water, but elsewhere typical polished and striated pavements were developed upon the bedrock which later, as the ice melted away, sustained a cover of ground moraine several hundreds of feet thick except towards late Carboniferous highlands where the moraine thinned away to nothing. In succeeding geological periods several more thousands of feet of Karroo strata were added (Chapter II).

Much of the pre-Karroo topography has been resurrected along the Vaal-Harts river valleys between Prieska and Vryburg where du Toit was enabled (Fig. 94) to reconstruct the main drainage lines of late-Carboniferous time and show that the modern river courses follow these to a remarkable extent considering their superposed nature. The reason for this fidelity in exhumation rests in the relative weakness of the Karroo cover as compared with the bedrock, so that once the ancient topography begins to be revealed, the rivers tend to migrate laterally against the weaker rocks of the cover. West of the Vaal River the Campbell Rand scarp, the Kaap limestone plateau, the Kuruman Hills and the Langeberg are all largely resurrected pre-Karroo features and in the Kalahari much of that same landscape is preserved beneath the Dwyka tillite and later sediments of the Kalahari Basin that are penetrated by boreholes.

The extent of resurrected pre-Karroo topography through Namaqualand and South-West Africa has not yet been assessed but several features belonging to this cycle have been identified. The prominent scarp of Neint Nababeep, for instance, still has Dwyka tillite banked against it, and parts of the country around the Karas Mountains have had the Dwyka cover stripped from them in recent times. The ancestral Windhoek highlands formed a gathering ground from which ice radiated in Carboniferous time (du Toit 1954).

In the goldfields of the Orange Free State borehole prospecting has enabled a contour map to be made of the sub-Karroo surface which there shows 2,500 feet of glaciated relief. Eastward through Basutoland and Natal the Karroo cover is too thick to penetrate and the pre-Karroo landsurface is identified again only along the Natal coastal monocline where it presents the usual glaciated form with a relief of several hundreds of feet.

The most comprehensive studies of the pre-Karroo landsurface have been made by Wellington (1937) where it is favourably exposed over the Southern Transvaal. There the Karroo cover thins away under Cainozoic denudation: much of the relief is pre-Karroo and ridges like the Witwatersrand, Suikerbosrand, and the ridges towards Klerksdorp and Pretoria are all in part resurrected pre-Karroo features. Originally they were strongly controlled by structure and trend generally from east to west, with ridges sited upon tough quartzites and valleys aligned along beds of shale or other weak rocks. The existing drainage pattern of the region developed independently upon the uniform Karroo cover and was directed north and south from the continental divide that lies along the line of the Witwatersrand. The disharmony between the resurrected ancient ridges and the drainage pattern is starkly displayed by the many curious *poorts* (watergaps) by which even small streams cross and recross the ridges (Fig. 90).

The Dwyka tillite, many hundreds of feet thick in the south, thins away until it disappears north of Pretoria and the succeeding Ecca series lies upon a gently rolling, non-glaciated landscape of early-Permian age. In swampy hollows of this surface the coal beds of South Africa accumulated. The physiography of these times is well described by du Toit (1954). This is the form in which the pre-Karroo landscape is known generally through Central Africa and Malagasy. Locally in Rhodesia and Zambia, Angola and Congo Republic tillite and varved shales of glacial origin have been identified (Bond 1952; Mouta 1954; Cahen 1954): they pertain not to continental ice-sheets, however, but to minor mountain and valley glaciation. More typical is the manner in which the Karroo rocks of the Wankie or Eastern Transvaal coalfields rest upon a diversified landscape of normal subaerial denudation. Greater relief is indicated in the Luangwa Valley of Zambia where the post-tillitic shales and sandstones were laid down in deep valley-bottoms, and in the Ruhuhu coalfield east of Lake Nyasa where the high ridges are parts of a sub-Karroo surface passing beneath the sub-horizontal coal-bearing strata (Dixey).

The distribution through the territories of Central Africa of rock series correlated with the lower Karroo indicates that the pre-Karroo landsurface in the forms described extended almost to the Equator.

Over North Africa a slightly older landscape is preserved beneath the extensive Carboniferous sandstones that build plateaus (Tassili) about Ahaggar. This infra-Tassilian surface is described by Dresch* as very even, but inselbergs stood up on exceptionally hard quartzites and granites. As the cover was transgressive, the surface is not quite of the same age everywhere and it was also warped slightly before burial. As the sandstones resist erosion better than the basement schists, gneisses and granites, which weather very deeply, pediments about the tassili belong usually to younger denudation cycles and do not represent the stripped infra-tassili surface.

Later Palæozoic landscapes of North Africa were largely aggradational forming vast, sandy piedmonts that stretched northwards from the denudational landscape in the south. Continental sandstones of Carboniferous age, passing northwards into partly or wholly marine sandstones as the Tethys geosyncline was approached, extend from Egypt to Mauretania and make many plateaus through the Sudan and the Sahara. The cyclic phases by which these have been built up have, in the absence of reliable fossils, not yet been identified but it is possible that there was much less deposition during the Permian than in the Carboniferous period. Two denudational cycles may

* Private communication.

thus be represented, one below the Carboniferous strata and one above. The latter is sometimes referred to, by analogy with Europe, as the post-Hercynian cycle and it occupied much of Permian and Triassic time.

About the middle of the Triassic period local movements, of which the most notable were the rise of the Cape Mountains and rift faulting near Lake Tanganyika, caused an interruption of Karroo sedimentation over South and East Africa. Then a phase of erosion succeeded for a short time over wide tracts. Well before the end of the period, however, accumulation of detritus was resumed in beds of the Stormberg series indicative of an arid environment and finally by huge outpourings of basaltic lava (Chapter II). Transgressive relations are shown by both stages across the Triassic landscape which seems generally to have been relatively smooth, or with isolated hills and ridges in Rhodesia and about Rehoboth in South-West Africa.

About Basutoland the Triassic erosion shows only by a sedimentary hiatus, with very slight unconformity, below the Red Beds and Cave sandstone. Because the sandstone, which is partly loessic in nature, is relatively resistant and stands in cliffs the underlying Triassic surface is rarely stripped and makes no resurrected feature in the modern landscape. But through the Transvaal and Rhodesia the equivalent Bushveld and Forest sandstones are friable, permitting small areas of Triassic landscape to be locally re-exposed as about Springbok Flats and over small areas from west of Bulawayo towards Salisbury. Continental denudation of Triassic age, followed by Stormberg transgression, is widespread also in eastern and southern districts of the Congo Republic and is continued into the Lunda district of Angola.

Superposition of river courses from the Stormberg cover on to the Triassic or later landscape has resulted in many curious poorts through resurrected hills in Rhodesia where by small detours the rivers could have avoided the hills altogether. Through Low Africa Triassic rocks are virtually unknown and no likelihood exists of Triassic landscapes being preserved to the present day throughout that vast region. Red continental sandstones of the period in the Atlas region, however, record an aggradational phase.

Though the resurrected pre-Karroo and intra-Karroo landscapes are of restricted distribution in the present aspect of Africa their geomorphic importance is very large, affording vital glimpses into more ancient landscapes than are normally available for study. They throw light, moreover, on the development of later cyclic landscapes.

POST-KARROO LAND MOVEMENTS

According to Dixey (1956) early post-Karroo disturbances in Southern and Central Africa were of considerable magnitude, and many of the present highlands such as parts of the Congo-Zambezi watershed and the North Nyasa area, themselves subsequently rejuvenated, are but reduced remnants of formerly much greater highlands. This is important, for most of the later repeated rejuvenation of watersheds (and lagging behind of the major relative depressions) follows the pattern of the early-Jurassic tectonism. The marginal rim of Africa began to appear at this time and the Kalahari-Congo basin began to function as a receptacle for continental detritus from surrounding plainlands.

Certain of the major post-Karroo boundary faults were of large throw and Dixey quotes a minimum of 15,000 feet upon the Mwanza fault of the lower Shiré, and 18,000 feet upon the Cholo fault. Erosion of considerable thicknesses of Karroo rocks may have gone on *pari-passu* with dislocation.

The strongest dislocations occurred during the Liassic but doubtless some of the movements continued well into the Jurassic. Most of the movements seem to have been local in effect, and this may explain the occurrence in the Congo and East Africa of Jurassic continental deposits shed from the upcast sectors. The perfect bevelling of the Gondwana landsurface that became characteristic of Africa during Jurassic time obliterated the post-Karroo fault scarps of the Nyasa, Luangwa and Zambezi troughs before the deposition of the Cretaceous sediments.

North of the Equator, over the Sudan and Sahara, little evidence is forthcoming of land movement during the Jurassic period. The diastrophic history here is possibly very different from that of South Africa.

THE JURASSIC " GONDWANA " PLANATION AND THE CRETACEOUS " POST-GONDWANA " CYCLE OF EROSION

The face of Gondwanaland lay exposed to denudation for the entire Jurassic period by the end of which time most of the proto-continent was reduced, under a prevailingly arid climate, to a state of extreme planation. Rarely in the African sector did continental sediments accrue to render an accumulative phase of the cycle, the chief exception being the Lualaba series of the Congo Republic. The recent discovery of fossil fish in this series, allied to Jurassic marine fish of East Africa, attests the low stand of Central Africa at this period. Because much of the Jurassic landscape was denudational, and because most of Central and Southern Africa has remained dry land ever since, the principal drainages must have originated in the Jurassic landscape. Despite subsequent repeated deformations of considerable magnitude many of the ancient river courses remain in the modern landscape.

By the early-Cretaceous period the ancestral proto-continent had fragmented and from the new monoclinal east and west coasts defining the African continent for the first time (Chapter II) rivers and scarps worked inland to dissect the broad plains inherited from the Gondwana landscape cycle. The effects, as they survive in present-day landscapes, are variable according to the available relief and distance from the sea. In some regions the later cycle is expressed merely as valley heads, more or less broad, incised into a plateau of Gondwana age, elsewhere a fresh planation is substituted at lower level and no trace of the earlier Gondwana surface remains. This was so amid the weak Karroo sediments downfaulted along the Limpopo and Zambezi troughs, wherein friable sediments, possibly of early-Cretaceous age, now often represented only by a thin spread of residual gravels, accumulated to thicknesses of as much as 3,000 feet.

Occasionally the two cycles operated at more or less the same level and the observer may find detailed discrimination between them difficult or impossible. This is so over North Africa where the two are represented in a single broad landscape now being exhumed from beneath a cover of Cretaceous rocks. That many of these rocks are marine shows that the compound Gondwana and post-Gondwana landscape stood in its time at low level (*cf.* the Jurassic deposits of Central Africa.)

But in South Africa, nearer to the centre of the Gondwana supercontinent, the land stood higher so that when the outline of Africa was created the rivers were betrunked and rejuvenated. In this way may have originated the greater distinction in levels between the Gondwana and post-Gondwana cyclic landscapes in the south.

Dixey's (1938) original dating of the Gondwana planation as Jurassic remains unchallenged; but there is less certainty concerning the age of the post-Gondwana incision which seems to some extent to have depended upon local earth-movements that were not contemporaneous throughout Africa. Around South-east Africa the coastal plain sediments lying upon the downwarped Gondwana surface, and supplied by post-Gondwana denudation, are early-Cretaceous; and the currency of the post-Gondwana cycle was terminated by mid-Cretaceous movements. The mid-Cretaceous hiatus, corresponding in the coastal sequence with culmination of the post-Gondwana cycle upon the land, is followed by late-Cretaceous (Senonian) sediments of a later cycle. This history is consistent through Moçambique and Zululand, and a corresponding history is revealed in the coastal belt of Angola (Jessen 1936). Moreover, inland on the farm Kangnas in Namaqualand sediments containing *late*-Cretaceous dinosaur bones lie in a shallow head valley dissecting a remnant of the Gondwana surface. The post-Gondwana cycle was therefore current from the end of the Jurassic until the middle of the Cretaceous period.

Though contrasted in appearance, the Gondwana landscape being a smooth planation with the post-Gondwana incised as valley-forms into it, the landforms of the two cycles are generally associated in the field, both standing as summit features on relict highlands rising abruptly above the level of the early-Cainozoic pediplain. In actual area these cyclic landscapes constitute an infinitesimal portion of the scenery of Africa, but the surviving remnants are readily identifiable, consistent in appearance and occurrence, and widely spaced through the southern lobe of the continent. In North Africa, as has been explained, they coalesce into a single planed landscape of early- to mid-Cretaceous age. The land movements ending the Gondwana cycle are sometimes represented by faulting of early-Cretaceous age, often of considerable magnitude. The Worcester fault of the Cape Ranges, 300 miles long, has a displacement exceeding 10,000 feet. Local faulting also occurred at the close of the post-Gondwana

R

cycle (mid-Cretaceous). Throw upon the Empangeni fault in Zululand was probably of the order of 10,000 to 12,000 feet. The fault brings the Stromberg basalt down beside the Archean granite, and after erosion the Senonian marine beds were laid smoothly across both formations.

Because the landforms of the two cycles are closely associated in the field they are hereinafter discussed together.

Following upon the vast outpourings of Rhaetic basalts over the country from the Cape Mountains to Victoria Falls, southern Africa began the Jurassic period as a waste of lava. Across this terrain Jurassic denudation planed the Gondwana landsurface. Residuals of this planation, with its later post-Gondwana dissection, now survive along the crest of the Great Escarpment that separates the interior plateau from the marginal regions. The highest and best preserved remnants have been identified between 10,000 and 11,000 feet above sea-level and declining southward across the high mountain ridges of Basutoland (Plate 4; Fig. 100). The ridges are flat-crested, with indecisive drainage forming a tundra, boggy in summer, frozen in winter. Nowadays, the ancient plateau of Basutoland is carved into pieces by gorges, 3,000 feet deep, of the Orange River system operating in the early-Cainozoic cycle appropriate to the neighbouring highveld planation. The valley heads, however, are openly incised about 1,000-1,500 feet below the Gondwana summit and here represent typically the post-Gondwana cycle (Frontispiece).

Surrounding the mountain kernel of Basutoland is a rugged country of bold, castellated scarps bounding tablelands of Cave sandstone such as the Platberg behind Harrismith. With rolling table-tops they stand, as in Herschel, abruptly above the broad Cainozoic highveld. Similar features occur in other districts and upon other geologic formations. While structure undoubtedly plays its part in the production of these tablelands some may well represent an extramontane phase of post-Gondwana (Cretaceous) planation as described by du Toit (1910). Such remnants, standing between the Gondwana surface and the " African " cycle of the highveld, have been recorded over a great distance along the Great Escarpment from the Stormberg to the Zambezi Valley by Dixey, du Toit, Stockley, King and others. Though the elevations cited vary between 6,000 and 8,000 feet the remnants appear morphologically consistent whether attributable to a single cycle or to multiple partial planations. Displayed in the Wakkerstroom—Dullstroom—Mount Anderson highlands and along the frontier between Rhodesia and Moçambique, these interstages are probably related to the axial uplift of the Gondwana surface along the line of the Great Escarpment in Cretaceous time. They probably illustrate a Cretaceous cymatogen.

Along the eastern highlands of Rhodesia the Gondwana cycle is encountered as small relict plateaus upon the highest country: Inyangani (8,517 feet), Nuza and the Chimanimani Mountains (7,992 feet).* In all these situations it is dissected above

* Much of what was mapped here in 1946 as " Gondwana " (King 1951) is now known to be violently upwarped " African " surface.

7,000 feet by shallow valleys assignable to the post-Gondwana cycle. Along the water-shed of Rhodesia morphologically similar Gondwana remnants bevel the Umvukwes (5,450 feet), Hunyani, Manesi and Mhlaba Hills. The sides of all these hills rise abruptly from the surrounding early-Cainozoic planation of the watershed.

Facets of Triassic (intra-Karroo) planation may also be present. In Thabas Induna, a flat-topped hill of Triassic sediments and lavas resting upon Archean basement

BASUTOLAND

SHOWING REMNANTS OF
MESOZOIC EROSION SURFACES

FIG. 100. Basutoland, showing together remnants of the Jurassic ("Gondwana") and Cretaceous ("post-Gondwana") summit bevels.

rocks (Fig. 101) that rises from the early-Cainozoic ("African") plain of the watershed near Bulawayo, all three cycles are clearly distinguishable. The Triassic landscape is recorded on the hillside, as the surface of unconformity at the base of the sediments; the flat crest transecting the lavas preserves the Jurassic planation; while the surrounding plain belongs to the early-Cainozoic cycle. When these three surfaces converge west-wards distinction between them becomes very difficult in the absence of outcrops of Karroo or younger covering beds, and the country presents an extraordinarily smooth polycyclic planation (e.g. at Leighwoods).

In the Republic of South Africa similar convergence of the African and Gondwana cycles is probably responsible for much of the very smooth country east of the Vaal

River valley, as between Bloemfontein and Kimberley. Eastward from this line the surfaces diverge towards Basutoland where they are separated by a vertical interval of more than 4,000 feet, westwards the surfaces diverge again across the Kaap Plateau (African cycle) to the Kuruman Hills and the Langeberg the crestlines of which may signify the Gondwana cycle. Beyond, in the Kalahari, the surfaces cross and the Gondwana (or a post-Gondwana modification) passes below the early-Cainozoic, Kalahari

Fig. 101. Relations between cyclic landsurfaces in Thabas Induna near Bulawayo, Rhodesia.

marls, the calcrete horizon at the top of which represents an aggradational culmination of the African cycle (Fig. 102).

Westward and southwestward of the Kalahari Basin the compound Gondwana and post-Gondwana landscape emerges from beneath the marls, as upon the face of the Weissrand near Mariental (p. 261), and with westward acclination is projected above the early-Cainozoic landforms to the crest of the western Great Escarpment. There it has been identified upon Kamiesberg as the ridge crest bevel sloping eastward (though the internal drainage of the Berg passes through deeply cut valleys westward towards

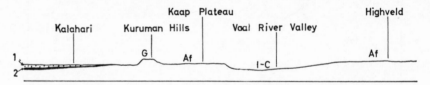

Fig. 102. Relationship of cyclic landsurfaces in section ESE-WNW from the highveld of South Africa to the Kalahari. G = Gondwana, Af = African, l-C = late-Cainozoic. 1. Kalahari sand, 2. mid-Cainozoic calcrete overlying Kalahari marls (early Cainozoic).

the coastal lowland). Around Springbok a little farther north, the hills again bear Gondwana summits sloping eastward, where also the massed hills break down into isolated clumps, e.g. Naib Hills (Fig. 110), still bearing the same summit level. Certain of these hills carry open valley heads that are not distinguishable morphologically from valleys grading down into the African pediplain. But at Kangnas a borehole in one of the valley heads passed through deposits containing late-Cretaceous dinosaur bones, thus proving conclusively the post-Gondwana allegiance of the valley-head and confirming the Gondwana age of the summit planation upon the hills.

The same morphological pattern of small plateaus and bevelled ridge crests continues at intervals to the east. Aggenysberg (3,700 feet) near Pofadder is matched by other bevelled Gondwana residuals on the north of the Orange River, forming links ultimately with the Langeberg and Prieska district to the east, thus closing the southern end of the Kalahari Basin and joining with the morphology of the eastern region.

Another residual of the Gondwana cycle in the Cape Province stands above the Nuweveld Escarpment near Beaufort West, and the upper elevations of the southern mountains may retain elements referable to the Mesozoic denudation cycles such as the small plateau remnant (? post-Gondwana) near the summit of Swartberg Pass. Like Basutoland, these mountain chains afford morphologic evidence of powerful uplift in the earliest Cretaceous. Additionally in the Cape, faulting with 10,000 feet of vertical throw created deep east-west valleys that received Cretaceous gravel infill (Enon conglomerate).

North of the Orange River, through South-West Africa, upwarped highlands with Gondwana summit bevels overlook the Great Escarpment. Thus upon the Naukluft Mountains (Mabbutt 1955) a summit plateau at 6,250 feet carries silcrete and is traversed by shallow valleys of an *eastward* drainage. As the whole stands well above the early-Cainozoic planation of the Bullspoort Flats (p. 273) and correlates morphologically with Kamiesberg to the south and the Khomas mountainland to the north the plateau and perched valleys may without hesitation be referred to the Gondwana and post-Gondwana cycles respectively. The highest elevation in this region (Gansberg 2,332 metres) carries a cap of Stormberg rocks, so the summit planation is Gondwana, with the Triassic unconformity below.*

The zone of elevated country along the Great Escarpment is separated from the Kalahari by the Quaternary canyon of the Great Fish River, tributary to the Orange. The zone of crossing between the realms of repeated denudation and repeated aggradation has thus been largely cut away. But pebbles of Nama facies from the western mountains occurring in the early-Cainozoic gravels of the Weissrand near Mariental show that at that epoch the Fish River Valley did not exist.

Near Windhoek an east-west axis of uparching transverse to the Great Escarpment has generated the Khomas highlands in a series of distinct heaves corresponding with the initiation of the several continental denudational cycles which therefore appear as summit bevels upon steeply dipping quartzites in the south and granitic inselberg topography in the north of the arch respectively (Gevers 1942). Two distinct bevels are apparent : the upper, smooth skyline of the Khomas highlands is of the Gondwana cycle, while the broad valley-heads incised into it are post-Gondwana. Only the Auas Mountains rise above the Gondwana surface. Because of the Khomas uparching, and perhaps also because of a former Karroo cover, the drainage of the highlands is transverse to the strike and the rivers all pass the rough quartzite ridges in deep poorts or watergaps.

Upon Erongo (7,628 feet) where the granitic massif rises precipitously above the early-Cainozoic planation at its foot to a cap of Triassic sediments and lavas, the

* Dr H. Martin, private communication.

Triassic cycle lies beneath the sediments, and the summit plateau with valley forms is a compound of the Gondwana and post-Gondwana cycles. Farther to the north, too, on the Waterberg tableland a caprock of Triassic (Etjo) sandstone covers the Triassic unconformity while the structurally controlled summit plateau may be deemed Gondwana.

The Benguella highlands of Angola stand in similar relationship to the Great Escarpment as do the Khomas highlands. Here Jessen (1936) has described three partial cycles standing above the level of the early-Cainozoic interior plateau (his peneplain IV). The highest of these at 2,450 metres constitutes the Gondwana planation, the two lower surfaces that decline from 2,000 metres to 1,600 metres towards the south merge in that direction into a single post-Gondwana surface. This post-Gondwana surface is far more extensive in Angola than the Gondwana which occurs

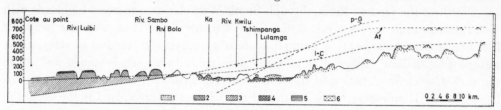

FIG. 103. Relations between cyclic landsurfaces and coastal sedimentary series near Mayumbe, Congo Republic. 1. Sands, 2. Plio-Pleistocene, 3. Younger Cainozoic, 4. Marine Cretaceous and Eocene, 5. Grits, 6. Precambrian basement. *after L. Cahen.*

only as isolated remnants above a wide rolling post-Gondwana landscape. This increase in relative importance of the later cycle at the expense of the former is characteristic also of the Congo Republic and perhaps implies lesser available relief in these regions during the early Cretaceous than existed in the Republic of South Africa.

In the coastal monocline of Angola and the lower Congo the Gondwana landsurface is flexed down to pass beneath the earliest coastal plain sediments, which are lagoonal and continental Aptian and marine Albian-Cenomanian in age (Carvalho 1961). The post-Gondwana surface, somewhat less flexed, passes over these formations into the unconformity below the late-Cretaceous and Eocene sequence (*e.g.* near Mayumbe, Fig. 103).

Likewise in the east, upon the coastal monocline of Moçambique and Zululand, the Gondwana surface is bent down below the Neocomian marine series which results from post-Gondwana erosion upon the land (Fig. 78). The termination of that cycle is represented in the unconformity beneath the prominent Senonian overlap. The denudation cycles of the interior are thus satisfactorily dated in the coastlands on both sides of the continent.

In the Congo Republic Gondwana and post-Gondwana surfaces often amalgamate in a single extensive smooth planation with silicified gravels and sometimes, as at Mount Binza, a lateritic mantle. From Katanga to near Lake Albert the surface is cut across ancient rocks and direct means for dating it do not exist; but in Kwango and part of

Kasai it is cut across the Jurassic, aggradational Lualaba series, and it contributed its detritus to the formation of the late-Cretaceous Kwango series (Fig. 104). Farther west it is overlain by the early-Cainozoic series of the *grès polymorphe* (p. 245), which facts collectively assign to it a late-Cretaceous age (Fig. 105).

Most of the occurrences are in the eastern Congo towards the rift valley. Remnants of the post-Gondwana (and here and there Gondwana) landsurfaces are thus distributed

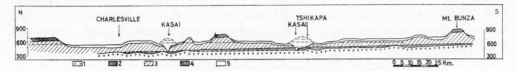

FIG. 104. Depositional cycles in the region of Charlesville Congo Republic. 1. Basement, 2. Lualaba Series (Jurassic), 3. Kwango series (Cretaceous), 4. *Grès polymorphe* and *sables ocres* (early and late Cainozoic respectively), 5. gravels and sands (Plio-Pleistocene). *after L. Cahen.*

alongside Lakes Kivu and Tanganyika to elevations of 8,000 feet. But they are speedily succeeded to both east and west by inferior landsurfaces of the early- and late-Cainozoic cycles. In the Katanga region uparching is said to carry the surface from 1,100 metres in the west to nearly 1,900 metres in the rifted zone: the later African cyclic surface is likewise super-elevated. On the Kibara Mountains, for instance, the post-Gondwana residuals of Lumbele and Kilongwe dominate from heights of about 70 metres the very regular early-Cainozoic surface at approximately 1,800 metres. The Kundelungu

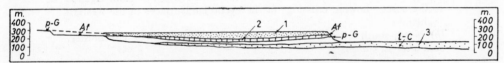

FIG. 105. Schematic profile from the Congo-Zambezi divide (left) towards the Congo Basin showing relations between the cyclic denudational landsurfaces of the south and the aggradational landsurfaces (disconformities) of the basin. 1. *Sables ocres*, 2. *Grès polymorphe*, 3. *Sables plio-pleistocene*. *after L. Cahen and J. Lepersonne.*

Plateau likewise has fragments of post-Gondwana surface at its highest points and in the east is sometimes covered by several metres of *grès polymorphe*. The most southerly remnants are found along the Solwezi-Mwinilunga border road at 1,700 metres.

In the north-eastern Congo (Lepersonne 1956) the Cretaceous surface stands between 1,700 and 1,900 metres with vestiges of a higher surface (? Gondwana) at 2,000-2,200 metres. These are matched in Western Uganda (Pallister 1954) by morphologically similar surfaces at 1,650 metres or more and 1,420 metres respectively. All the surfaces are separated by scarps. The post-Gondwana surface hereabout frequently bears strongly indurated laterites 20-60 metres thick. Over the northern Congo Republic it slopes from southeast to northwest at 5 metres per kilometre, which is definitely more than the slope of the later " African " surface. It passes, indeed, below the *grès poly-morphe* of the Congo Basin to reappear at Thysville, 60 miles south of Leopoldville where the surfaces rise again towards the western mountains along the Great Escarpment (Fig. 106). Towards Stanley Pool the post-Gondwana surface, together with the African surface, is abruptly truncated by a fault with 350 metres upthrow towards the west. In the north-eastern Congo there are river captures of several ages corresponding in parts with the tilting of surfaces imposed near the rift valley. The oldest drainage pattern is indicated by senile river profiles associated with the Cretaceous surface. This has been disrupted by earth movements initiating the African, late-Cainozoic and Congo Basin cycles of erosion (Lepersonne 1956).

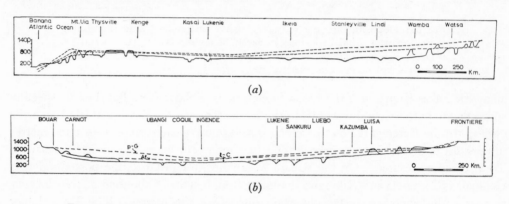

FIG. 106. (*a*) East-west section across the northern Congo from Uganda to the coast showing crossings of the cyclic landsurfaces in the western highlands.
(*b*) North-south section from Bouar to the Congo-Rhodesian border. *both after L. Cahen.*

The denudational landscapes of Cretaceous age (with exiguous Jurassic relics) are thus found upon an elevated rim of the country about the main hydrographic basin of the Congo River. In late-Mesozoic time detritus from the rim was deposited within the basin, affording aggradational landscapes in counter-part with the cyclic denudation of the rim. The Jurassic Lualaba series, predominantly continental in type, thus cor-responds with the Gondwana cyclic denudation. Contemporaneous with the planing of the post-Gondwana highlands was the widespread deposition of the Kwango series of vari-coloured mudstones and soft grits 900-1,000 metres thick which now covers vast areas in the southern and western Congo Republic. Size and wear of pebbles indicates that they travelled from sources in the southeast and the surface slopes at 1·55-1·70 metres per kilometre to the northwest. In Kasai the series rests upon an apparently planed Gondwana surface and includes at the base fragments of silcrete and compact red argillite indicating a dry climate with wind action. Fossils include fish that are almost certainly marine and derived from the Atlantic Ocean at least 300 kilometres away, thus demonstrating how low the region stood during the late-Mesozoic era. The top of the Kwango series is truncated by late-Cretaceous denudation forming a surface which now slopes at 0·70 metres per kilometre from south to north.

Followed eastward into Zambia the post-Gondwana surface alone is present. Thus only the post-Gondwana cycle is present (at 5,400 feet) upon the extensive Abercorn plateau and the Muchinga Mountains forming the Zambian watershed and the chain of minor remnants linking them. But the Gondwana bevel reappears and becomes of increasing importance and elevation towards Lake Nyasa.

The highest planation upon the elevated country both west and east of Lake Nyasa belongs to the Gondwana cycle. On the Nyika plateau this surface, exceeding 7,000 feet in height, cuts across the boundary faults of Karroo rocks and, along its deeply dissected sides where it drops into the ancestral Nyasa and Luangwa troughs, early-Cretaceous rocks overlie it. The same cycle is found, ascending at places above 10,000 feet, upon the Mafingi Mountains of the Livingstone Group about the head of Lake Nyasa. In all these districts the Gondwana surface is bordered by a more extensive plateau of post-Gondwana (Cretaceous) age (Dixey 1938). Similar Gondwana landscapes exist upon the Namuli Mountains of Moçambique above a post-Gondwana landscape that extends into southern districts of Malawi (Mlanje, Zomba, Vipya, Dedza and the Marambola ridge near the Shiré-Zambezi confluence) (Lister 1966). In all localities the Cretaceous (post-Gondwana) elements of the landscape stand at abruptly scarped margins thousands of feet above the neighbouring plains of Cainozoic age. Thereby they demonstrate the magnitude of arching that took place along the site of the Nyasa rift in late-Cretaceous time.

From the Livingstone Mountains remnants of the Gondwana and post-Gondwana cycles continue with decreasing altitude north-eastwards into Tanganyika along the Iringa arch and Uluguru Mountains. At the Ruaha the summits are at 6,000 feet but upon the eastern flank of the arch the Gondwana surface descends until it passes below the Mesozoic rocks of the coastal belt. According to Willis the low plateaus of the coastal hinterland represent the Gondwana surface from which upper Jurassic strata have been stripped. In similar manner the post-Gondwana surface is deemed to pass beneath the late-Cretaceous rocks of the coastal belt. Aitken has also demonstrated that Jurassic rocks near Tendaguru were slightly folded before the Cretaceous was laid down. This disturbance thus corresponds with initiation of the post-Gondwana cycle in South Africa.

In the far interior of Tanganyika small plateaus preserving fragments of Gondwana planation have been recorded upon Mbeya Mountain (where they have been strongly upwarped and tilted in the angle between the Rukwa and Fufu rift scarps), Sumbawanga, Katjaswa, Sege, and upon the top of the Kungwe Mountains overlooking Lake Tanganyika. Further remnants standing above the Serengeti Plains on the border between Tanganyika and Kenya lead northward through a country of high ridges (flat on top at 7,000-8,000 feet) to the upwarped districts of Kenya west of the rift valley.

The same belt of elevated, ancient terrain, following the north-north-eastward grain of Africa and paralleling the Iringa arch, crosses the rift valley north-west of Nairobi to the Aberdare Range crowned with rift valley volcanics above the combined, and crossing, arches. Thence remnants of the surface decline across Central Kenya to 8,000 feet upon the Matthews Range near Maralal. Features belonging to a post-Gondwana cycle have also been reported from this region. Both cycles are represented also towards the Uganda frontier, the Gondwana upon Cherangani (9,000 feet) and the post-Gondwana at about 6,200 feet upon the Kitale plateau. The latter cycle indeed persists the whole length of the Uganda-Kenya frontier into the Sudan (Dixey 1948) where it swings westward towards the Nile.

Through Somalia, eastern Kenya and Tanganyika the Mesozoic cycles make the unconformity beneath the Jurassic rocks of the low country reaching far inland from the coast and supply the debris making the rocks themselves. Across these sediments all the later erosion cycles are cut (p. 288). " The unconformity is excellently exposed at many localities, . . . The frequent variation in altitude can be explained by tectonic deformation." Thus behind Mombasa, eleven miles from the sea, in an old quarry, a relatively smooth Gondwana surface showing no signs of Jurassic weathering underlies Bathonian shallow water limestones and is cut across Duruma (Karroo) sandstones. The seaward dip is here unusually large, 8°, though the height above sea-level is less than 100 feet. More irregular relations near the main road are said to be faulted, and a small outcrop of Cretaceous at Mtapanga, north of Mombasa dips *inland* at 10°. But such disturbed relations are unusual.

In the Somali Republic " continuous deposition took place from upper-Jurassic into lower-Cretaceous times in many coastal areas [but] . . . over much of what is now the plateau [early Cretaceous] emergence caused erosion and removal of . . . Jurassic rocks."*

Dixey (1946) has assembled the relevant data for Abyssinia, Eritrea and the Yemen which constitute an uniform assemblage of tablelands through which the Red Sea rift has gashed a passage. The tablelands bear little relation to the modern rift though it is indeed possible that, like Lake Nyasa and other parts of the rift valley system, they may have been profoundly influenced by ancestral, late-Mesozoic rifting. The Afar lowland, for instance, though bordered by great scarps passing out of the rift valley and splaying out to north and east, was nevertheless in existence early in the Cretaceous period. The tablelands, which stand about 10,000 feet with isolated peaks reaching nearly 14,000 feet, are composed of basic lavas of supposedly Cretaceous age resting upon a clear erosion surface at 6,000-8,000 feet. In central Abyssinia this end-Jurassic erosion surface is largely cut across rocks of the basement complex and is highly irregular, but in part it truncates evenly sediments of mid- or late-Jurassic age that were folded and faulted before the end of the period. " During the early-Cretaceous (Neocomian) the sea extended across the Afar lowlands to the very foot of the Abyssinian

* J. W. Pallister.   Private communication.

plateau, near the point where it is surmounted by the Jurassic sediments. Hence . . . to allow time for the erosion of the peneplain as well as for the great uplift . . . the peneplain must have reached its final development here at the very end of the Jurassic." The very different nature of the Jurassic landsurface upon the basement rocks and upon the weak sediments respectively is indeed a testimony to the short time available for its fashioning.

Uplift of the Jurassic landscape on the Abyssinian and Yemeni plateaus was without marked folding or faulting, and early-Cretaceous erosion rapidly carved out broad post-Gondwana valleys and lowlands in the weak Jurassic strata before the voluminous outpouring of Cretaceous basalt. Phonolitic lavas were also extruded over the Mesozoic landscape beneath the Athi Plains in Kenya.

In the Yemen a similar surface lies buried beneath Cretaceous lavas, but along the watershed in Arabia the Asir and Hejaz crystalline plateaus preserve the surface without burial. These are matched along the opposite side of the Red Sea by similar residuals carved across granite at 6,000-7,000 feet from Eritrea into Nubia. As far as can be judged from literature, most of the older topography in both these regions belongs to a Cretaceous cycle and may perhaps be classed as post-Gondwana.

Across North Africa and Arabia the Gondwana landsurface flexed downward during the Cretaceous period and became the floor upon which were laid continental deposits (the Nubian series in the east and the *continental intercalaire* in the west) to a thickness of hundreds of feet. These early-Cretaceous accumulations, making a belt 1,000 miles wide, correspond to post-Gondwana cyclic denudation upon lands upwarped to the south (Fig. 107). Though the base is usually depositional and may even be banked against the flanks of inselbergs as in the Sudan, some sections show it passing down locally by weathered gradation into underlying granite. The Nubian sandstones are false-bedded but are not dune-sands. With accompanying ferruginous shales they represent a shallow freshwater deposition, though there are local intercalations of Cretaceous marine rocks of Tethyan shelf facies. The upper surface of both Nubian series and *continental intercalaire* represent the aggradational phase of the post-Gondwana cycle.

Legoux (1939) writes of the *continental intercalaire* in West Africa that it " expresses in fact the prolonged deposition erosion and renewed deposition of the products of subaerial denudation over much of the interior. There is evidence that the beds were once more extensive ". Monod and Cailleux (1949) argued from the shapes of the sand grains that the formation was laid down in water (it contains *Ceratodus* and crocodilian remains, with Cenomanian dinosaurs in Tunisia) but that the abundant eolian grains (excluding those from the Cambro-Ordovician) imply wind action upon the surrounding country prior to and during deposition. In the Cretaceous and Eocene marine beds that follow, eolian grains are rare.

The early-Cretaceous, continental facies is overlain, with few breaks, from the Atlantic to the Persian Gulf by late-Cretaceous marine limestones and marls of a wide

Tethyan transgression that during the Senonian stage extended up the Nile Valley to latitude 23° N. where there is a transition to Nubian facies with marine fossils (Sandford 1937). South of the marine belt therefore the Nubian facies may have continued to accumulate beyond the end of the Mesozoic. In West Africa the late-Cretaceous marine transgression advanced from both the north and the south (Fig. 108). " Stages of overlap have been traced into the interior of the continent over the Saharan *hamada*, the Niger and Nile Basins, as well as along the Benue and the Congo " (Sandford).

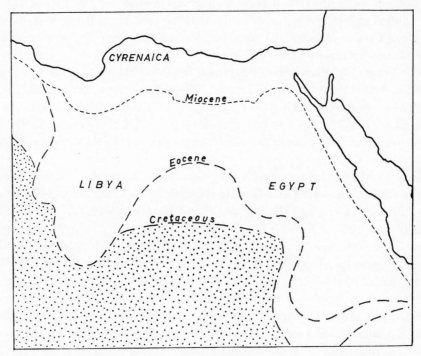

FIG. 107. Showing the distribution of marine Cretaceous and Cainozoic formations over Egypt and Libya. Cretaceous continental area stippled. *after K. S. Sandford.*

Despite the immense smother of Cretaceous rocks in North and West Africa, certain ancient terrains were upwarped at the time so that remnants of Gondwana planation survive upon them and the Cretaceous deposits are wrapped about their flanks in Ahaggar and Tibesti (Menchikoff 1957). The former even bears three distinct stages of planation (Butler 1922) that are all deeply weathered and may perhaps be identified as pre-Carboniferous, Gondwana, and post-Gondwana. The first descends upon the flanks of the dome beneath Palæozoic strata forming the engirdling tablelands or Tassili, while the Gondwana cycle in part bevels these and passes also beneath the *continental intercalaire* of neighbouring depressions from which it is seldom resurrected. Post-Gondwana denudation of the highlands supplied the material of the *continental intercalaire* and afforded an early-Cretaceous scene in which degradation and aggradation proceeded side by side as they do today in many parts of North Africa.

Though the Cretaceous marine deposits are typically limestone (for little terrigenous waste was supplied to the wide epicontinental sea), about the ancient domes, (*e.g.* Adrar das Iforas of the Ahaggar group) girdles of sandstones, conglomerates and clays with wood and reptilian fossils represent a piedmont phase like the *continental intercalaire*.

In the far west, the Anti-Atlas, a Variscan chain, had shed Permo-Triassic sediment northward into the Atlas region but itself remained exposed to erosion apparently

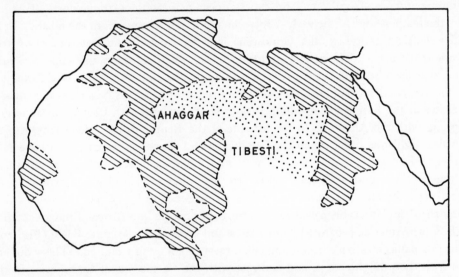

FIG. 108. The maximum Cretaceous marine transgression across North Africa (ruled), with the *continental intercalaire* (stippled).

continuously until the mid-Cretaceous when red, continental sandstones wrapped around its flanks, fossilising a dissected post-Gondwana cycle of strongly structural landforms. During the long interval from Permian to mid-Cretaceous the swell was apparently intermittently rejuvenated.

The Atlas on the north affords a far more detailed record of events, with marine transgressions of the Tethyan shelf to date them. Pre-Triassic, pre-Jurassic and pre-Cretaceous planed surfaces are all in a state of exhumation in the present landscape: the summit plateaus of rhyolite exceed 12,000 feet while the middle plateaus belong to the stripped later cycles. Exhumation has been much aided by arching, first during the middle Eocene and later at the close of the Cainozoic.

In Senegal and Upper Gambia, Lamotte and Rougerie (1955) identified certain relict plateaus of the Chaine de Nimba, between 1,300 and 1,600 metres as "Gondwana", antedating the disruption of that supercontinent; and Michel (1962) considers that this cyclic surface is marked down to pass beneath Maastrichtian sediments of the basin of the Lower Senegal. The Gondwana (or post-Gondwana) landscape has been recorded also by Dresch upon the quartzitic summits (2,000 feet) of the Atacora Range in North Dahomey. He noted extensive alteration of the surface under weathering.

On the younger granites of the Nigerian plateau, south of Jos, flat-topped hills preserve the Gondwana planation at 5,800 feet with a slope to the north. Between these bevels and the early-Cainozoic surface (here upwarped to 4,000 feet) are valleys attributable to the post-Gondwana cycle. These valleys contain the fluvio-volcanic series consisting of decomposed basalts with comparatively thin tin-bearing sands and clays. The series is bevelled by the early-Cainozoic cycle and bears laterite. Both the Gondwana and post-Gondwana landscapes appear again in the extreme north of Nigeria where the feather-edge of the early-Cretaceous sediments enters from the north. In the frontier districts, therefore, the Gondwana is a resurrected landscape emerging from beneath these beds. The post-Gondwana cycle which transects the same formation is itself fossilised beneath the late-Cretaceous and Cainozoic formations of Sokoto.

The rise southward of both the Mesozoic landsurfaces across Nigeria is very marked but ceases at the Benue Valley which is floored at low level with Cretaceous sediments beginning with the Albian. On the far side of the Benue, in the Cameroons, rise the Adamawa highlands upon which the Gondwana and post-Gondwana cycles have again been recognised at high elevation. The Benue Valley is thus a Cretaceous rift valley, like the northern end of Lake Nyasa. Its profundity, however, is remarkable; the Cretaceous sediments are said on geophysical evidence to be 15,000-30,000 feet thick (Dixey 1956), and it has been evaluated as the continuation into Africa of the great rift by which South America separated from Africa and created the Atlantic Basin (Fig. 109). As such its flanks may have been monoclinal rather than cleanly faulted. The sediments agree with those of the coast, and contrast with the Cretaceous of the interior in that the lower group is marine, the upper terrestrial. The later Cretaceous and Cainozoic rocks show nothing more than gentle folding, but gigantic anticlines of simple form affect the early-Cretaceous series. " In some cases the basement appears in the core of an anticline, in others it does not emerge but cross-sections show that it cannot be deeply buried. The anticlines have flank dips up to 45°, well defined culmination and long regular pitching ends. An individual anticline has a length of 50 miles, and the structural uplift from syncline to anticlinal crest is up to 15,000 feet " (Lees 1952). Such huge simple folding in a laterally protected situation can surely be due only to vertical laminar displacements. " Farther south-west, below the junction of the Benue and Niger Rivers conditions become more complex and faulting more important ". This is just the region where the vertical structures within the Benue Rift are crossed by the Niger Rift of slightly younger age.

In the Cameroons the Gondwana surface, which has been identified by J. Pugh (1954) and by J. Dresch,* has been differentially uparched for 250 miles along a north-east-south-west axis and now stands at elevations between 3,000 and 6,000 feet (which

* Private communication.

is attained upon the Mambila plateau where the basement rocks are at their highest elevation). The axis is crowned with volcanics, many of them quite recent, but Pugh * reports that the oldest volcanics are " indistinguishable in hand specimens from the fluvio-volcanic series of the Jos Plateau "; also that arching of the Gondwana surface was begun before the advent of the African cycle of Cainozoic planation. " Between

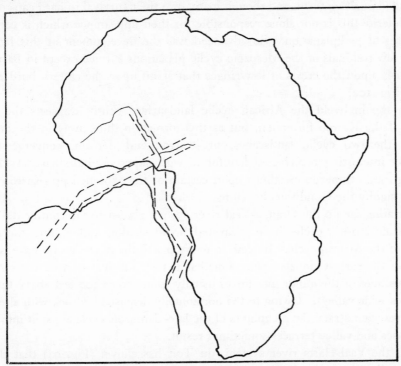

FIG. 109.   Continuation of the South America-African rift into Africa as Cretaceous rifts of the Benue and Niger valley systems. Also an east-west rift valley 100 miles long and containing 20,000 feet of supposed Cretaceous and Cainozoic beds lies just south of lat. 4° N. in British Guiana and is apparently collinear with the Benue Rift. Another possibility is figured, that the rift turns down into the Amazon Valley, the drainage of which must have been reversed in direction during the Cretaceous period (p. 321). Both possibilities may, of course, exist together.

the Bamenda highlands and the Benue River isolated basement relicts go up to nearly 6,000 feet, again suggesting the ' rise to the rift ' you put forward in the case of the Jos Plateau " (J. Pugh*). Geze has reported a Cretaceous surface in the Cameroon highlands which may be modified Gondwana.

CAINOZOIC CYCLIC LANDSURFACES IN SOUTHERN AFRICA

The " African " or early-Cainozoic cyclic planation is fully expressed in both its denudational and aggradational forms in Southern Africa, the former upon the highveld

* Private communication.

and the latter in the Kalahari Basin. The highveld of the Republic of South Africa is an immense smooth plateau standing between 3,000 and 5,500 feet above sea level. These great elevated plains that in places possess an horizon like the sea are wholly denudational in origin and consist of coalescing pediments or locally convex, senile interfluves that have been converted from pediments. Where residual hills remain they are typically of steep-sided *inselberg* form, and though many owe their survival to hard caps of sandstone or dolerite this is not alone responsible for their appearance which is controlled by processes of pediplanation. So advanced was the development of this landscape cycle that few residuals of the Mesozoic cyclic planations survive except in Basutoland or exiguously upon the crests of low ridges that stand upon the eastern border of the Kalahari (Fig. 102).

Upon the highveld the African cyclic landsurface gently transects the several members of the Karroo formation, but as this formation thins away in the Southern Transvaal the two cyclic landscapes, pre-Karroo and African, converge to give exceedingly interesting resurrected landforms with superposed drainage (Wellington 1937) (Fig. 90). Subeven crestlines upon certain of the exhumed pre-Karroo ridges, moreover, signify the Gondwana bevelling.

Penetrating far up the Orange-Vaal river system almost to the continental divide, late-Cainozoic erosion cycles have excavated broad shallow valleys into the smooth planation of the African cycle. Indeed, in many places the newer cycles have removed so much of the early-Cainozoic planation that it now survives only as the extremely smooth crestlines of the minor interfluves usually from 100 to 300 feet above the floors of the miles-wide valleys. Owing to the horizontally disposed bedrock with alternating weak and resistant strata, the nickpoints of the late-Cainozoic cycle are split into several minor phases and valley terraces sometimes result.

Along the Vaal-Harts river system, du Toit has shown (Fig. 94) that the late-Cainozoic valley excavation has largely followed the resurrected pre-Karroo topography because the rivers, on encountering the hard uneven surface of the underlying pre-Karroo rocks, have migrated laterally in the relatively weak Karroo shales and tillites until they came to occupy, in part, the axes of the ancient valleys.

West of the Vaal river valley the gently undulating surface of the Kaap Plateau, compounded of early- and late-Cainozoic cyclic features is not regularly pedimented, but as the surface is of dolomite or shale the irregularity is due largely to underground drainage. Reported occurrences of Dwyka tillite in sinkholes and the smooth flanks of the western hills resembling ice-worn topography suggest some resurrection of pre-Karroo topography, but scarcely any of this is demonstrable in the present plateau landscape. The Gondwana planation was evidently higher and passed over at about the summit level of the Kuruman Hills and Langeberg (Fig. 102).

East of the Vaal River the broad, shallow tributary valleys correspond cyclically with incision of the Kuruman River and its affluents into the aggradational early-Cainozoic plain of the Kalahari upon the west.

In the south the plateau swings to the southwest between the lower Orange River and the Great Escarpment. There the African cycle makes the smooth plain of Bushmanland reaching as far west as Calvinia. The Neint Nababeep plateau is part of this landscape, the general elevation of which is 3,200 feet. The surface is broadly pedimented, and is extensively calcreted where it approaches the Kalahari in the north. The surface is in some places covered with sands which lie in flat beds rather than in dunes: where dunes occur the sand has usually been redistributed in later geologic time. This is characteristic not only in Namaqualand: the late-Cainozoic " Plateau Sands " of the Kalahari do not lie within the late-Cainozoic valleys, the sands of which are disposed as dunes of presumed Pleistocene age. This is in accord with similar evidence northward as far as the Congo Republic where Cahen and Lepersonne (1951) record that the Plateau Sands " do not extend into the valley plains limiting the mid-Tertiary African surface ".

Late-Cainozoic dissection by tributaries of the Orange River has taken place in two stages developed at 2,600 feet and 2,000 feet respectively above sea-level. The extremely broad, shallow valleys of the earlier of these cycles, e.g. Koa Valley, exhibit superb pediments. Most of the pedimented country around Springbok, too, is of this cycle, which is probably Miocene in age.

The later (? Pliocene) stage is less broad in dissection, its pediments are steeper and often show braided rill channels and it is often expressed as straths or shoulders above the deep Quaternary incision of the lower Orange gorge (p. 296). As this stage occurs well within the Orange Valley (sensu lato) its landforms bear the hallmark of extreme aridity, as north of Vioolsdrift.

Through South-West Africa the smooth planation of the African cycle, armoured with calcrete, passes upon both sides of the Fish River valley (which includes all the cycles appropriate to a tributary of the lower Orange) and finally closes round its head south of Rehoboth. Thence the huge calcreted plain cuts across the Dwyka formation north of Stampriet and along an uparched axis towards Gobabis. At 25 miles north of Stampriet, however, the rolling surface of the late-Cainozoic cycle is developed at lower level across Stormberg basalts; the African surface then extends towards the Kharubeam Hills, the first ridge of the highlands towards Windhoek. From their base pediments sweep out into the African plain while the crest is superbly truncated by a Mesozoic bevel.

In the Bullspoort Flats at the base of the upwarped Naukluft Mountains the altitude of the African surface is 4,920 feet, which corresponds with the average slope south-eastwards of the Kalahari calcrete surface (Mabbutt 1955). The calcrete itself is admirably exposed capping the Weissrand near Mariental. This scarp displays the aggradational phase of the African cycle which was current in the Kalahari. Resting upon Dwyka and Ecca formations are early-Cainozoic gravels and sands capped by grey-white cherty or sandy limestone 100 feet thick. The clastics are marginal to the Kalahari marls which were laid in the central part of the desert basin during the early-Cainozoic.

S

The Kalahari rivers (Auob, Elephant and Nossob) are incised into the early-Cainozoic sediments by the usual two late-Cainozoic cycles, following uparchings along the Khomas axis. Now usually dry and with few tributaries, the valleys have steep sides in which the mid-Cainozoic calcrete makes minor cliffs beneath the later Kala har sands.

At two places, from Okahandja westwards alongside the Swakop River and from Bullspoort Flats westwards down the Tsondap, the African cyclic planation arches over the crest of the Great Escarpment into the Namib. Remnants may continue far towards the coast before flexing down monoclinally. In the south, along the Lüderitz littoral, a surface lying below early Miocene marine beds may be regarded as representing the African cycle, and continental beds of this age containing vertebrate fossils were reported in the Namib of South-West Africa by Kaiser. In the coastal belt, the Namib plain of the late-Cainozoic cycle flexes down beneath Pliocene sands.

North of Windhoek the featureless plains of Hereroland carry the early-Cainozoic calcreted cycle northward to Ovamboland where it becomes dissected by broad valley floors of the first stage, late-Cainozoic cycle, down to Etosha Pan and the Cunene River.* In similar form the early-Cainozoic planation is continued eastward from 5,000 feet at the foot of the Mossamedes highlands in Angola, becoming progressively more dissected to the east by the broad tributary valleys of the Zambezi River. Upon the broad, flat interfluves it passes beneath " Plateau Sands ". Two stages of late-Cainozoic planation are also present.

On latitude 12° S. the Lunda swell carries the African cycle upon granite far to the east where it forms the watershed between the Congo and Zambezi River systems.

THE KALAHARI

From east, south and west the clear datum of the early-Cainozoic African planation declines towards the Kalahari, a central region which failed to rise significantly when the Great Escarpment was elevated by several thousands of feet. This deformation has been repeated in several stages, always in the same sense; so that drainage has always been directed into the Kalahari which has served as receptacle for the sedimentary detritus—clays, sands and locally even gravels—that were shed from the surrounding denudational plains. This was especially so during the early-Cainozoic when the Kalahari must have resembled closely the present riverine plains of eastern Australia (p. 358). To this day the panlands of the central Kalahari approximate to the early-Cainozoic cyclic landscape.

The deposits of the early-Cainozoic are marls and sandstones capped everywhere by a limestone sheet that was partly of fluviatile origin and partly of chemical

* But north of Etosha Pan and near Grootfontein Cainozoic beds similar to those of the Kalahari fill basins in Karroo strata to depths of nearly 1000 feet (Dr H. Martin, private communication).

precipitation under a dry climate. The thickness of the entire formation is variable, depending upon irregularity of the floor and locale, but is commonly 300 feet and may exceed 1000 feet. Marls frequently compose the oldest part of the sequence, with sandstones generally cropping out beneath the bluffs of hard limestone exposed along the sides of major valleys such as the Kuruman near van Zyl's Rus *. Unfortunately the flat terrain limits the finding of illuminating sections away from the incised valley sides, but borings have proved useful. Drusy chalcedonic depositions are often diagnostic of this series.

The limestones are widespread. In the southwest from Mariental to Gordonia and thence far up the Molopo River they define a tableland 250 miles long by 50 miles wide, and outside the Kalahari they cover the early-Cainozoic denudational landscape also in the vicinity of Mafeking, though they disappear before Koster. They form, indeed, the main stratigraphic marker over this region, accumulated after the supply of clastic debris to the basin had become insignificant. The age, which has still to be accurately defined by fossils, is probably late Eocene to Oligocene, corresponding with the almost perfect planation of the " African " cycle across adjoining regions such as the highveld of the Republic of South Africa.

The lowest level of the surface limestone, at Abiquas Puts and about the confluence of the Molopo, Nossob and Kuruman Rivers, is 2,800 feet, where the thickness of the limestone itself is about 300 feet. Westwards the limestones rise rapidly to 3,500 feet at Aroab and more gently to nearly 5,000 feet where the plain abuts against the Naukluft Mountains. Eastwards and northwards this main horizon of calcreted limestones appears to be continuous beneath the Kalahari sandveld to the Gamagara Flats and thence to the Kaap Plateau by which it is linked to the equivalent denudational plateau of the highveld.

The drainage pattern of the Kalahari clearly follows the deformation of the mid-Cainozoic limestone plain (an end product of the early-Cainozoic geomorphic cycle); but the rivers may have been sited upon similar lines even earlier as shown by river gravels in the limestone (calcrete) deposits along the present drainage lines, where also the limestones are thicker and commonly slope towards the axes of the valleys. There are even semi-continuous fluviatile deposits *below* the limestones along present drainage lines.

Borings in Bechuanaland have revealed a succeeding, thinner sequence of clastics topped off with a newer, less massive limestone phase. These deposits correspond with the late-Cainozoic " Plateau Sands " of the Congo region, and were derived by cutting of the broad valley floors that shallowly dissect the African cyclic surface of the interior plateau. These sands seem not to have been recorded from the western Kalahari, but

* But dune-sands, partly re-deposited along deeply-cut channels, are known grading upwards into the marls alongside the Nossob River south-eastwards of the Khomas axis. The buried river system accords with the present in the headwater region, but differs lower down (Dr H. Martin, private communication).

at numerous places a later, minor, limestone phase is present. Near the confluence of the Molopo and Nossob rivers the younger limestone is formed secondarily from the older limestone and is converted almost into puddingstone by fragments of green or brown sandstone and marl that seem to have been laid in ephemeral lakes and sun-cracked into polygons that were then swept down by floodwaters. Followed upstream along the Nossob the puddingstone facies, 6 feet thick upon the older limestone, contains worn quartz pebbles that must have travelled from a distant source in the north or west. North of Eindepaal the quantity of gravel increases and the upper calcrete becomes a conglomerate with pebbles up to 2 inches in diameter shed from the Khomas highlands.

During late-Cainozoic time the rivers tributary to the Orange all became incised nearly to their heads, and the lower course of the Molopo (now dry) carries terraces accordant with the 2,600 and 2,800 feet stages of the Orange River Valley. The rivers of the northern Kalahari tributary to the Zambezi, however, were little incised at that time.

" During the late-Tertiary desiccation set in over a vast region in more than one phase, that culminated in the spreading during the early-Pleistocene of the Kalahari sand, blotting out drainages " (du Toit 1954). East of the Nossob River these sands form long, linear dunes. They are the latest series of deposits with the Kalahari Basin.

DATING OF THE CAINOZOIC LANDSCAPE CYCLES IN SOUTHERN AFRICA

Fossils from the Kalahari deposits are inadequate for dating the African cycle in its aggradational phase; but fortunately, both the early- and late-Cainozoic landscapes are downwarped on both the eastern and western coastal margins where they are trans-formed into unconformities in the coastal plain stratigraphy before passing below sea-level (Figs. 78, 103).

Along the whole eastern seaboard of Africa denudation in the early stages of the African cyclic planation provided the detritus for the late-Cretaceous rocks sometimes succeeded by Eocene, but by the end of the Eocene and Oligocene the smooth landscape provided little or no detritus and rock series of that age are missing. An hiatus in the offshore sedimentation therefore records the culmination of the African cycle on land. Sedimentation was resumed with coarse sandstones during the Burdigalian (early Miocene), and rocks of this series crop out at intervals from Arabia to Cape Agulhas. These sediments reflect uplift of adjacent lands by small amount and sedimentation does not usually continue through the middle and upper stages of the Miocene period. Marly limestones appear where only fine detritus reached the sea, and related conti-nental Miocene deposits sometimes help to define the shoreline, as near Magude in Moçambique. After this second hiatus new sands, Pliocene according to their fossil fauna (Cox 1930), record fresh uplift and erosion.

According to these data the African planation was current in East Africa from the

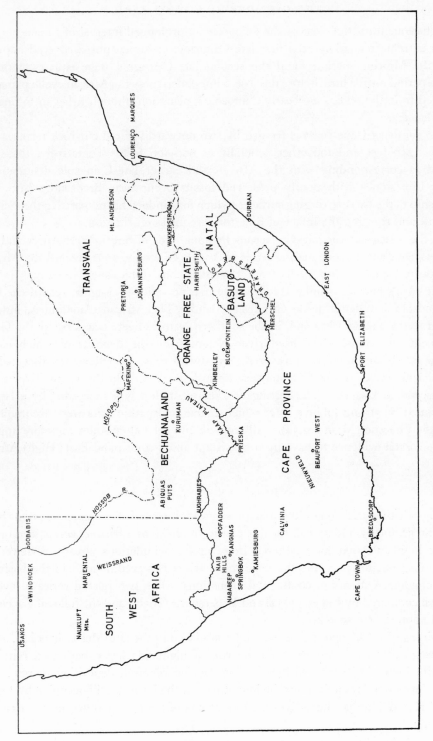

FIG. 110. Locality map of Southern Africa.

ate-Cretaceous until the close of the Oligocene, a prolonged interval of time according with its extreme planation; the first late-Cainozoic erosional phase covered approximately the Miocene period; and the second late-Cainozoic stage equates with the Pliocene period until a little before its close. For conciseness the African cyclic planation is referred to in the text as an " early Cainozoic " planation, though it began to operate before that era.

The southern Cape coast is fringed by two outwardly-tilted cut-rock terraces one at 1,000-1,250 feet and the other generally at 600-800 feet. Tentatively, these are regarded as corresponding with the African and earlier late-Cainozoic denudational cycles. Limestones with poorly preserved fossils occur near Bredasdorp but their relationship to the two converging surfaces (which may indeed have crossed in the vicinity of the lowland fronting the inface of limestone) requires elucidation.

On the west coast the late-Cretaceous Pomona Beds of South-West Africa and the late-Cretaceous and Eocene marine series of Angola (Carvalho 1961) record the African cycle nearby; and marine fossils from Bogenfels, now established as early Miocene (du Toit 1954), and the similar transgressive marine series of Angola, record the first late-Cainozoic denudation cycle on adjacent land. The African planation is, indeed, apparent in the Tinkas Flats and, in the southern Namib, Beetz traces below the Great Escarpment an extensive fossilised river system from the deposits of which early-Miocene vertebrate fauna was recovered. Westward these planations are dissected by late-Cainozoic cycles descending stepwise towards the sea. Up the Khan River these cycles ascend to Usakos. The Burdigalian sedimentation was succeeded by a lapsus accompanied by strong folding, after which coarse feldspathic grits were accumulated during the Pliocene (Mouta 1954). All tectonic and related episodes therefore appear from the coastal evidence to have been consistent about South and East (High) Africa.

CAINOZOIC EVENTS IN CONGO REPUBLIC

For Cainozoic time the Congo Republic presents a full record of geomorphic events both degradational and aggradational, for it is cast in the form of a basin encompassed on all sides by highlands that have suffered those cyclic denudations already reviewed in neighbouring territories, while the resulting detritus has accumulated in the basin as a corresponding sequence of continental formations. The two related series of events have been compared by Cahen (1954) and Lepersonne (1956), and the following account is based upon their researches.

Basining of the Congo region was well established in the late-Mesozoic era (p. 263), and subsequently from time to time the rim of highlands has experienced renewed uplift with increasing tilt towards the basin causing renewed deposition therein. At present, deposition lags a little for the lowest part of the basin is still occupied by Lakes Leopold II and Tumba, themselves mere remnants of a formerly much more extensive water body.

In the south the highland rim bears the African planation, with small post-Gondwana residuals, upon the Congo-Zambezi watershed; but along all the northward flowing rivers the smooth planation soon gives way to post-African valley forms of late-Cainozoic cycles. By latitude 7° S. the African planation survives only as scattered plateau remnants above an uneven late-Cainozoic landscape at 1,000 metres above sea level, as to the north and north-west of Lake Upemba.

In Katanga many complexities have been introduced by earth movements in proximity to the rift valley but the cyclic landsurfaces are nonetheless clear, and are sometimes accompanied by the relative depositional phases. The African surface stands at 1,100-1,250 metres west of the faulted zone and at 1,450-1,800 metres in the east. It appears as the upper surface of the *grès polymorphe* (*q.v.*), an early-Cainozoic depositional series equivalent to the Kalahari marls, and is overlain by a thin lateritic gravel covered by ochreous, Plateau Sands of the late-Cainozoic.* The post-African group of surfaces is represented at 1,200-1,300 metres around Elizabethville. The eastward part of the Kundelungu plateau likewise shows the *grès polymorphe* and the Plateau Sands with a slope to the east. Corresponding erosion surfaces appear again east of the plateau where they also slope to the east. They are bevelled by more recent surfaces in the centre and west. A very large part of the Kundelungu plateau is thus a Pleistocene surface though the basic age of the plateau itself is probably post-Gondwana *i.e.* the surface below the *grès polymorphe*. On the Bia and Kibara Mountains the African surface is regularly established at about 1,800 metres, but it is dominated by residuals of the Gondwana and post-Gondwana cycles.

Between the Lualaba (River) and the western rift zone the African planation, rising eastwards from 1,200-2,000 metres, predominates over a wide area. Its eastern margins are commanded by post-Gondwana residuals that tower along the edge of the rift, while its western sectors are nibbled by valleys of the post-African denudation cycle that, west of the Lualaba, appears as flat watersheds between the Quaternary valleys and above the depositional plains of the middle Congo (Fig. 98).

Conditions are very similar in the north-eastern Congo Republic, the post-Gondwana, African and post-African cycles (Lepersonne 1956) being present in typical forms. The first is found only towards the rift (Fig. 106). The African surface stands between 1,200 and 1,450 metres with gentle inclination from Irumu towards the north, becoming extensively dissected by the post-African cycle (900-1,000 metres) around Watsa. There the African planation is reduced to a number of winding laterite-capped ridges 1,400-1,500 metres in altitude that may be followed westward in other residuals to within 50 km. of Stanleyville. Towards the rift the African planation rises to 1,800 metres and makes an extensive upland. Within the Lake Albert rift early-Miocene fossiliferous beds prove the prior dislocation of the African surface; and there may have been as

---

* Originally the *grès polymorphe* may have been a calcrete like that of the Kalahari, but it has subsequently been silicified (possibly from the Plateau Sands above) under a climate with wetter summers.

much as 2,000 metres of late-Cainozoic deposition before the Pleistocene Kaiso beds were laid down.

Across the Congo-Nile divide into the Sudan, Andrew has noted the African planation upon low ridges armoured with ferricrete only 5-25 metres above features of the late-Cainozoic cycle at an elevation of 1,000 metres.

The late-Cainozoic landscape of north-eastern Congo Republic is generally irregular, appearing as very large valleys incised into the African planation. They stand between 800 and 1,100 metres above sea-level and there is a group of partial cycles rather than a single definitive cyclic surface. Thus a particularly well developed older phase making a regular planation stands in the Ituri catchment between 1,200 and 1,250 metres.* The late-Cainozoic surface carries a mantle, sometimes 20 metres thick, of red sands capped locally by eluvial quartz and zones of lateritic ironstone. Along the route from Irumu to Stanleyville the planation rises steadily towards the west, maintaining its characteristics to within 50 km. of Stanleyville. Thence it sinks progressively to an altitude of 500 metres. In addition to broad warping, faulting has also affected features of the late-Cainozoic cycles.

Lepersonne (1956) has shown that the hydrographic system of north-eastern Congo Republic includes river captures of different ages corresponding to the several denudational surfaces. He evaluates the several sections of the river courses as follows: (a) senile sections in equilibrium with the Cretaceous landsurface oriented from south-east to north-west; (b) sections responsible for forming the African landsurface, rejuvenated and oriented from north-west to south-west; (c) fragments responsible for cutting the first post-African surface, rejuvenated and oriented from north-north-east to south-south-west or north to south; (d) sections in equilibrium with the second post-African cycle oriented from north-east to south-west or from east to west; and (e) sections rejuvenated in accordance with the Congo Basin. This analysis shows that an ancestral drainage towards the Congo River was partly interrupted at the beginning of the Miocene period, and that certain river courses related to the late-Cainozoic surface before the beginning of the Quaternary again partly traverse the rift valley south of Lake Edward.

Upon the swell between the Congo and Oubangi Rivers is a group of irregular, late-Cainozoic surfaces (600-800 metres) with laterite coverings. Most of the geomorphic events in this region are comparatively recent, remnants of the African and first post-African cycles being reduced to inselbergs, now in a state of decay, and much of the second post-African cyclic surface is cut away by river terraces. Superficial formations seem scarcely anywhere to be older than Quaternary.

The western highland rim of the Congo Basin again bears residuals of the standard denudation cycles, all tilted eastward from the crest towards the basin and westwards on the opposite aspect towards the coast. Post-Gondwana and African cycles make the smooth summits on which the rivers rise in swamps; but the post-African cycle is the most extensive. Glimpses of both the post-Gondwana and African cycles have

* In many parts of Congo Republic, post-African surfaces are polycyclic.

been reported from near Thysville whence the rise westward begins (Fig. 106), and the latter is known to be faulted in the vicinity of Leopoldville.

Within the Congo Basin and especially in the provinces of Kwango and Kasai (Cahen and Lepersonne 1952), and in neighbouring Angola (Mouta 1954), the denudational cycles of the highland rim transpose to aggradational landscapes upon widespread accumulations of continental detritus. The Kwango series equivalent to the post-Gondwana cycle (p. 246) is the first of these depositional series; the second, which equates with the African denudation cycle, is the *grès polymorphe*. This series includes a large number of silicified rock types. It rests upon a remarkably smooth plain that transgresses both basement and Mesozoic covering rocks up to a late-Cretaceous age and which represents therefore the post-Gondwana cycle. The post-Gondwana surface, however, was deformed and the *grès polymorphe* was laid in the synclinals, its deposition corresponding to erosion of the elevated parts of the same surface. The principal synclinals are in Kwango and Lomami but conversely the lower Congo, Kasai and Katanga are areas where the deposits were originally less thick or have since suffered erosion. The top of the series is defined by a new and remarkably smooth surface which like its predecessor passes across the *grès polymorphe* and older terrains alike; this represents the culmination of the African cycle in both denudational and depositional phases.

The beds of the *grès polymorphe* are generally silicified with a chalcedonic cement. The bulk of the series may be of eolian origin but fluviatile and lacustrine horizons are indicated by limestones and freshwater marls subsequently opalized and chalcedonised. The fossils *Cypris*, with *Physa*, *Planorbis* and *Chara* are found in these beds at widespread localities, and show an early-Cainozoic age. Breccias and edge wise conglomerate appear where sediments were cracked in ephemeral lakes under desiccation but the top of the series is of eolian sandstones showing desert conditions. Erosion and silicification towards the top of the series correlate with the calcrete cap of the Kalahari marls to the south. Both duricrusts extend laterally also on to the pediplaned surfaces of surrounding ancient rocks showing that the duricrusting is not a function solely of the depositional series but implies prolonged exposure to the weather with little erosion or deposition of material. Duricrusting was widespread also at the close of the earlier, Kwango sedimentation, before the unsilicified base of the *grès polymorphe* was laid upon it.

As the *grès polymorphe* corresponds with the African denudation cycle, so the Plateau Sands or *Serie des Sables Ocres* correspond with the late-Cainozoic cycle. The series rests upon the smooth upper surface of the *grès polymorphe* or overlaps beyond it upon the African denudational landscape. It consists of yellow, unstratified sands, reddish and commonly conglomeratic towards the base. The matte surface of the grains proclaims that the final agent of transportation was certainly wind. Fossils are unknown. The Plateau Sands are, however, incised by valley plains of the latest Cainozoic cycles. Thus over the vast area in the west between the Kasai and Kwango

Rivers the late-Cainozoic erosional cycles form a narrow strip on both banks of the rivers. Upon the interfluves the early-Cainozoic depositional cycle (*grès polymorphe*) covers the earlier, post-Gondwana topography, and is itself overlain at the African cyclic truncation by Plateau Sands. This type of topography is general between lats. 6° S and 12° S.

CAINOZOIC LANDSURFACES OF CENTRAL AND EAST AFRICA

In the Central Transvaal planation by the African cycle appears upon the Pietersburg Plateau, but most of that region displays late-Cainozoic pediplanation in at least two distinct cycles. To the west the surfaces decline and disappear beneath the deposits of the Kalahari, eastwards they are cut away below the Transvaal Drakensberg by the end-Cainozoic landscape of the Lowveld.

Similar topographic relations exist along the watershed region of Rhodesia.* From the Umvukwes south to Umvuma and thence past Bulawayo into Bechuanaland the wide and monotonous plain of the African cycle makes the smooth watershed, into which elements of the Triassic and Gondwana cycles also enter locally, rendering by their combined planation at common level some of the flattest denudational country on earth, for instance at Leighwoods. Surface ironstone, and sometimes chalcedonic sands, are widespread.

Westwards of Bulawayo (which itself stands in a shallow post-African valley-head) the African surface bevels flatly across the Stormberg formations which dip more strongly westward than the present landsurface. There is thus a crossing of the Triassic and African planations.

Eastwards from Salisbury, the African planation rises (with but a single breach by later erosion) from 4,800 feet to the summits of the frontier highlands where it stands at a maximum of 6,900 feet below Inyangani and a more usual elevation of 5,500 feet. This is a region of mighty upwarp already discussed under cymatogeny (p. 197).

Both east and west, late-Cainozoic valley-heads bite into the narrow watershed plateau and widen downstream into broad pediplains at lower level (Fig. 101). The late-Cainozoic landscapes are polycyclic, with the several phases separated by clear scarps in the Sabi River catchment (Fig. 73). Together they constitute the dominant aspect of Rhodesia, covering the whole eastern (denudational) sector apart from the watershed and the narrow range of eastern highlands (above) and the deep Quaternary valleys of the Zambezi and Limpopo (below). Wide, sweeping pediments (sometimes occupying the whole landscape from the base of residual hills to the very river banks) make up most of the scenery, with bornhardts clustered (as in Angola) towards the inner margin where each successive subcycle is demolishing its predecessor. Along the

---

* In referring to Rhodesian surfaces the reader should note the change of views on the ages of surfaces mentioned at the beginning of the chapter. What was earlier referred to as a " Primitive " surface is now taken to be " Gondwana ", and what was mapped as " Gondwana " is now deemed to be "African".

line of the Filabuzi-Shabani-Mashaba road the pediplain reaches its finest development with a relief of only a couple of hundred feet for many miles.

The late-Cainozoic surfaces stand generally between 3,000 and 5,000 feet above sea-level, continuing eastward through the Zambezi and Sabi gaps in the eastern highlands (p. 298) into Moçambique where a corresponding pediplain is extensive at 2,500 feet. At the Amatolas scarp the surface breaks away again to a younger stage at lower level. Both African and post-African surfaces decline ultimately below the broad depositional coastal plain of Moçambique which seldom rises above 500 feet.

The early-Cainozoic planation in Zambia, though it bears no direct evidence of dating, is morphologically continuous with that surface in all neighbouring territories. Its elevation is usually about 4,500 feet. The largest area of it surviving in the present landscape lies in the north-west, around Mwinilunga, whence the surface (above 4,500 feet and with post-Gondwana residuals at 5,000 feet) extends westward a few miles beyond the border into Angola and eastward and northward into the Congo Republic. From the same point also a southward-sloping tongue, 100 miles wide, passes near Makokoni. The African cyclic surface is thus preserved on the Congo-Zambezi-Kafue watersheds. Away from the divides the surface has been destroyed by post-African, late-Cainozoic valley heads so that in the Copper Belt of Zambia only detached plateaus 20-40 miles in breadth, remain of it.

Large expanses of the African landsurface are present also for 500 miles along a line passing from north-east to south-west through Lusaka. Thus the Kalomo-Lusaka ridge, broken through in an antecedent course by the Kafue River, exhibits the surface with a slow rise north-westward to 4,000 feet at Lusaka where with great monotony the surface stretches eastward for 100 miles. Further residuals appear, indeed, still at 4,000 feet, beyond the lower Luangwa along the ridge leading to Fort Jameson. On the Muchinga Mountains the surface, averaging 30 miles in width, rises from 4,600 feet near Serenje to 4,800 feet on the Tanganyika border, and bears several prominent post-Gondwana remnants (*e.g.* Abercorn plateau). West of the Muchinga Mountains minor plateau remnants of the African cycle between the late-Cainozoic valleys of the rivers link the occurrences near Abercorn with those in the Copper Belt.

On the eastern side of the Luangwa Valley most of the border country between Zambia and Malawi presents extensive developments of the African planation the elevation varying from 3,500-5,000 feet due to later warping. The belt of African cyclic planation is about 60 miles wide and is studded with large remnants of the post-Gondwana, and even Gondwana, cycles which tower above it as great plateaus on the western flank of the Nyasa rift. In southern Malawi east of the Nyasa-Shiré rift, the African surface is tilted eastwards from the Shiré highlands to the foot of Mlanje Mountain which rears its " post-Gondwana " head 7,000 feet above the African planation at its foot. Thence the early-Cainozoic landscape extends far beyond the borders of Moçambique, especially in the province of Niassa where it stands mostly around 3,000 feet.

Late-Cainozoic landsurfaces are extremely widespread in Zambia occupying the vast basins of the Zambezi, Kafue, Chambezi and Luangwa Rivers. They have been called " valley-floor peneplains ", but individual planations (which are splendidly pedimented) may be 50 miles or more across and hundreds of miles long. Because

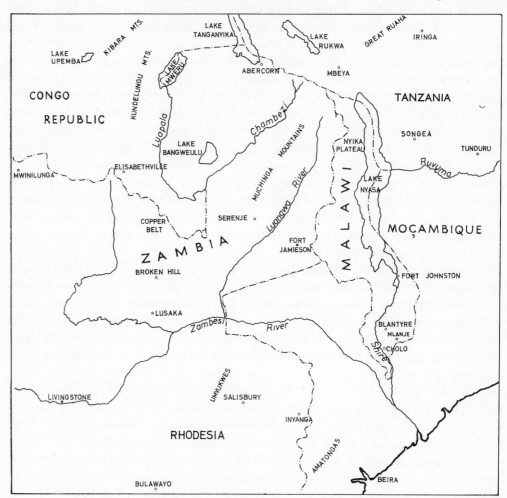

FIG. 111. Locality map of Central Africa.

the post-African cycle is incomplete the surface is undulating and assumes different forms depending in part upon the resistance of the underlying rocks. The depth of the pediplains, which are all related to the drainage pattern, below residuals of the African surface is between 500 and 1,000 feet; and their altitude lies between 3,000 and 3,500 feet, though it is somewhat affected by later warping.

Following the middle course of the Zambezi River, itself belonging to the second late-Cainozoic cycle, the first late-Cainozoic landscape forms a bench about 30 miles wide on the northern side of the river between the Lusaka-Kalamo ridge of the African planation and the Pliocene gorge extending upstream to Victoria Falls. The bench is by no means continuous along its length, however, having been dissected at least 1,000 feet by the Pliocene rejuvenation of the Zambezi drainage.

In the vicinity of Victoria Falls the broad late-Cainozoic floor of the Zambezi valley is covered with silicified (Pipe) sandstone, fossiliferous chalcedony and related deposits that are older than the red Kalahari sand resting upon them but younger than the sands and calcretes resting upon the African planation. Analogous deposits are widespread throughout Zambia, Angola and Congo Republic, and represent a very late Cainozoic arid phase of intense silification preceding the Pleistocene spread of the Kalahari sand. In some places silicification also affected deposits resting on the early-Cainozoic planation.

The late-Cainozoic landscape in the Chambezi and Luapula catchments tributary to the Congo River, does not differ in aspect from that of the Zambezi-Kafue-Luangwa affluents but stands higher, usually around 4,300 feet. This region has been more strongly uplifted in association with rift valley movements, the differential nature of which is shown by the dimple of Lake Bangweulu on the divide between the two rivers.

In Malawi the post-African cycle occurs as valley-floors incised into the African planation and descending westwards into Zambia, and also as a belt 10 miles wide between the Quaternary erosion along the lake shores and the older cyclic plateaus to the west. The latter occurrence is prolonged southwards in the late-Cainozoic Shiré Valley system from Lake Malombe to Matope whence a Quaternary cycle becomes dominant along the river. Rifting, however, has complicated the pattern, and Cretaceous rocks are abundant on the valley-floor, as happens also in the Luangwa Valley (Fig. 80).

Throughout East Africa (Uganda, Kenya, Tanganyika) the same pattern of landscape cycles is persistent; most of the present topography consists of undulating late-Cainozoic landscapes incised below the level of an early-Cainozoic planation of extraordinary smoothness. Both these suites of cyclic landforms are affected equally in the vertical sense by " rift valley " and associated earth movements that culminated towards the close of the Cainozoic era.

Thus the central plateau of Tanganyika between the eastern and western rift valleys is an immense pedimented landscape of the late-Cainozoic cycles surmounted by scattered or grouped residuals rising to the common bevel of the early-Cainozoic planation. This bevel stands usually from 200-500 feet above the plain (e.g. about Tabora) but may exceptionally rise superior to 1,500 feet. This is the typical landscape association of Central Africa, and here it extends across the Shinyanga upwarp to Victoria Nyanza. The same topography is let down east of the Fufu scarp to form the floor of the Great Ruaha Valley; but the Iringa arch, warped and faulted, that bounds the valley on the south-east bears the African planation almost entire with Gondwana residuals standing above it. Eastward of the arch to Liwale the African planation is dominant at 2,500 feet. Thence in the coast belt, where the Gondwana surface descends beneath the Jura-Cretaceous rocks of the coastal plain, the African surface is cut across the *cuestas* of Cretaceous strata, the subsequent lowlands of which belong to the late-Cainozoic cycle. This type of country continues far past the frontier into northern Moçambique.

Along the coastal plain the converging African and post-African plains of the hinterland pass in many places beneath appropriate series of early-Miocene and Pliocene sediments with abundant marine fossils, thus demonstrating the form of the coastal monocline through Tanganyika and Kenya. Notable, however, are local axial deformations according with the north-eastward grain of the country. Thus the tableland at Lindi is an arch 700 feet high declining north-eastward and the differentially depressed sector inland is covered to unknown depth by alluvial deposits of the Lukuledi River, which itself escapes by an antecedent gorge through the tableland, which is made of Cainozoic strata distinct from the plateau of Cretaceous strata to the west. Locally also coastal sedimentary sequences may be missing, as at Mombasa Island where Pliocene formation lies upon late Jurassic without intervention of the usual Cretaceous and Miocene series.

In Northern Tanganyika the Masai Steppe is likewise assessed by Stockley as part of the African planation that is again continued eastward across Cretaceous strata.

The drainage of eastern Tanganyika was originally directed north-eastwards from the northern end of Lake Nyasa in accordance with the grain of the country. The Ruvu, for instance, probably had the Luwegu and the Mbarangandu as head-waters. These were captured by the Rufiji from the coastal belt which then further extended itself to capture the upper reaches of the Great Ruaha. These captures were probably effected at the time of the African planation. Late-Cainozoic uplift and arching, followed by Quaternary rift faulting, both in a north-easterly direction, have both failed to alter the pattern, and the modern Ruaha crosses the belts of upraised country in antecedent gorges.

The Serengeti Plains in the extreme north of Tanganyika express the early-Cainozoic denudation cycle somewhat below 5,000 feet. Thence, bounded on the east and south-east by rifting, the African planation extends northwards over a width of 40-80 miles into Kenya, and carries towards the northern extremity a number of Gondwana remnants at over 6,500 feet. Extensive (Kapitian) phonolite lavas cover the surface east of Nairobi. The same belt of elevated country passes through the whole of western Kenya to Kitale (where it is bounded on the east by the Elgeyo Escarpment) and thence along the Uganda border into the southern Sudan. Standing upon the western flank of the rift valley the African landsurface has been cast up to great heights, even 10,000 feet locally along the escarpment. Westwards it declines towards Victoria

Nyanza, becoming progressively more dissected by two late-Cainozoic denudation cycles as it does so. Ultimately, in the vicinity of the lake little of the early-Cainozoic landsurface remains, but it is known to pass, on Rusinga Island, beneath deposits with early-Miocene vertebrate fossils. This is an important occurrence for dating the surface.

Many groups of hills bear the African planation about the southern end of Lake Rudolf, whence it passes to the eastern side of the rift valley. There the planation stands generally above 5,000 feet with prominent Gondwana relicts but the surface flattens out eastwards into the El Barta and Il Bonyeki plains around 4,000 feet and continues thus to the Matthews Range of early-Cainozoic bevelling and Gondwana residuals. Eastward of a line through this range only outliers of the African surface survive, buried beneath Cainozoic lavas on the Merti Plateau and Merille Hills. Extensive survivals occur around Nanyuki and Machakos, and between Mt. Kilimanjaro and Mombasa a chain of residuals reaches down from the interior plateau to the warped and faulted coastal region. At Fundi Isa, north of Mombasa, Miocene marine formations overlie the surface.

First Pulfrey (1960) and then Saggerson and Baker (1965) have compiled contoured maps showing the present attitude of the early-Cainozoic surface in Kenya. It is arched and domed towards the rift valley, with a transverse furrow towards Kavirondo Gulf (Fig. 112). In the east, it descends below sea-level and is covered by younger formations east of long. 39° E. At lat. 2° N., however, the axis of flexure swings from north-south to east-west and passes on that azimuth into Somalia. Deformation occurred in two stages, one post-Miocene, the other post-Pliocene. The latter was much the stronger.

Virtually the whole of the Northern Frontier District of Kenya is a great plain of late-Cainozoic erosion ascending westwards to 2,500 feet. Out of it the great volcano, piles of Marsabit and the Huri Hills rise to 3,000 feet above their bases. About Waju and Garissa, and elsewhere to the west, the plain, which Pulfrey now dates as mid-Pliocene, is cut across sediments and basalt flows thought to be contemporaneous with the Miocene beds of Turkana west of Lake Rudolf and the lake deposits intercalated with lavas near Nairobi. (Lavas and pyroclastic sediments of middle- and late-Cainozoic age are, indeed, widespread in Kenya). The early-Cainozoic planation is not encountered again until near the Abyssinian frontier at Gurar and in the broad 3,000 feet plateau between el Wak and Derkali, equivalent to the Abyssinian plateau which slopes eastwards at 16 feet per mile. As all three planations are cut across Jurassic strata, the Gondwana surface is here fossilised below them all. In the unconformity along the Derkali-Takabba scarp, the surface was markedly uneven.

The late-Cainozoic landscape occupies most of Turkana also, between Lake Rudolf and the Uganda scarp which is bevelled around 4,000 feet by the early-Cainozoic planation. This African cycle is widespread upon interfluves in Uganda generally, but everywhere gives way to the late-Cainozoic cycle in the valleys. The landscape in

Buganda is typical. It is a well-dissected tableland with a majority of main interfluves flatly bevelled and capped with laterite standing at scarps 400 feet above the valley floors which themselves bear a later duricrust. In eastern Uganda volcanic effusions are extensively associated with the Cainozoic landsurfaces (Trendall 1959). Mammalian fossils entombed in ash beds show that local dissection of the early-Cainozoic surface had begun even before the Miocene period (Bishop 1958).

As the present attitude of Cainozoic landsurfaces in Kenya was dominated by their proximity to the rift valley, so these surfaces in Uganda are disposed centripetally towards the compound dimple of Victoria Nyanza-Lake Kioga (Fig. 83). Thus where the late-Cainozoic surface is shallowly overflowed by the waters of the Nyanza, flat-topped residuals of the earlier, mid-Tertiary surface (the Sese Islands) occur far out in it.

Lepersonne (1956) has correlated the cyclic landsurfaces of north-eastern Congo Republic with those of western Uganda and southern Sudan, and confirmed the unity of these regions from a study of the hydrography which shows major changes during both the early-Miocene and at the end of the Pleistocene. His dating of the highest residual landscapes as Gondwana and post-Gondwana (p. 263) has since been challenged by Ruhe who regarded them as upwarped " African " landsurface, which is the view of Hepworth also (1964).

Most of Somaliland is a late-Cainozoic plateau, both degradational and aggradational, whereon elements of the early Cainozoic cycle have not been distinguished though denudation has been operative continuously since the Eocene (Pallister 1963).

As an adjunct to East Africa the island of Malagasy shows a similar suite of erosion bevels (Dixey 1960). Following Gondwana and post-Gondwana episodes of denudation with accompanying marine deposition in basins along the western side of the island (the mirror-image of conditions upon the East African coast), early-Cainozoic planation carved a landscape of low relief over the eastern crystalline and western (Karroo sedimentary) districts alike. The surface, equivalent to the African cyclic planation, was armoured with laterite. Residuals of the Gondwana planation survived locally south of Tananarive and much of the detritus was shed westward to accumulate as Cretaceous marine strata.

Following uplift about the mid-Cainozoic the original plain was moderately dissected and converted to a rolling landscape. The detritus was shed westward to accumulate as a Miocene (Burdigalian and Aquitanian) series transgressive upon the Cretaceous along the shores of the Moçambique Channel. Further mild movement and erosion produced a Pliocene series. At the close of the Cainozoic the island was violently uplifted with a strong tilt to the west. Deep gorges have been cut from east and west into the elevated Cainozoic plains and reaching far back into the crystalline upland. In all respects Malagasy has behaved as a miniature Africa and as the mirror image of the coastal hinterland of East Africa.

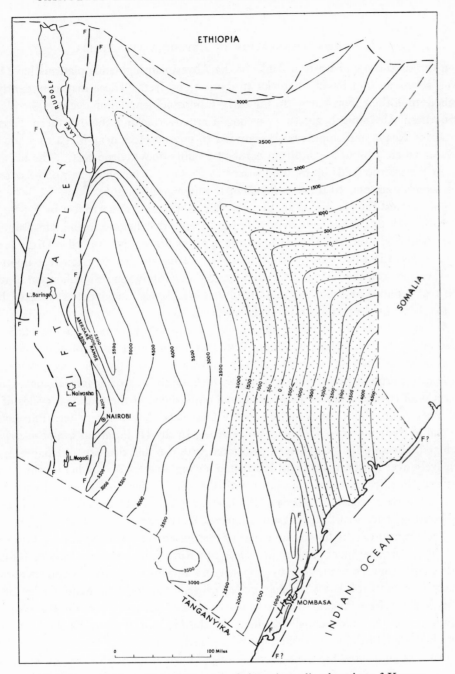

FIG. 112. Deformation of the early Cainozoic cyclic planation of Kenya in post-Miocene and Plio-Pleistocene times. Contours in feet; area of Quaternary sediments stippled. Major faults marked F, lesser fault shown by breaks in contours. *after E. P. Saggerson and B. H. Baker.*

T

Cainozoic Denudation in Abyssinia and Arabia

Upon the southern and western flanks of the Abyssinian highlands plateaus have been carved across ancient basement rocks at about 4,000 feet. These may confidently be ascribed upon their morphology to the early-Cainozoic denudation cycle. The plateau in Southern Abyssinia begins at a strong scarp overlooking the Northern Frontier District of Kenya and slopes south-eastward from 4,000 feet near Mega to 3,400 feet at Gurar where residuals exhibit an earlier bevelling above 5,000 feet. The northern limit of the plateau leads up by bold scarps to Cretaceous bevelling at 7,000-8,000 feet upon which were poured the lava floods of the highlands (p. 266).

On the west the plateau, at about 3,000 feet, is dissected to 2,250 feet by flat-floored valleys of both the White and Blue Nile catchments that belong to the late-Cainozoic cycle. And northwards of the high plateau as far as the Egyptian border Dixey (1946) has identified the early-Cainozoic cycle in an upland surface at 3,400 feet upon the watershed between the Nile and the Red Sea. Post-Gondwana residuals upon it attain 5,000 feet. Late-Cainozoic surfaces stand at lower levels, and basic lavas have been extensively erupted upon all three cyclic surfaces.

A large part of the Arabian interior is inadequately known for interpretation of landscape cycles, but western Saudi Arabia is an uplifted zone of the compound early- and late-Cainozoic landscape, cut across Archean and Palæozoic rocks, that slopes to the east. Through Nefud tabular reliefs ensue upon the Palæozoic formations. Cainozoic rocks of eastern Arabia (the depositional equivalents of the erosional cycles of the west) were gently folded and faulted in the Oligocene, late Miocene and Pliocene by marginal movements of the Tethyan orogenesis. In the Hadhramaut *schuppen-struktur* developed, and step faults in Yemen associated with the Red Sea rift. At Bahrein, and extensively over northern Iraq and Kurdistan a conglomerate occurs before the Asmari limestone (Burdigalian) that correlates with the similar deposit found at intervals all down the eastern coast of Africa. During the Pliocene the whole of Arabia and neighbouring states was emergent and subjected to erosion.

The Transjordan highlands are a part of the Syrian plateau that has been upwarped along the eastern margin of the Jordan—Dead Sea Rift. This plateau is built of unfolded Jurassic and Cretaceous rocks resting upon more ancient rock systems and most of its surface belongs to the late-Cainozoic cycles of denudation. The eastern edge of the Syrian platform from Aleppo to Bahrein is straight and scarped above the Iraqi lowland by faulting or steep monoclinal warping. In the lowland north of Baghdad, indeed, the undulating late-Cainozoic landscape reigns once more.

From Sinai a late-Oligocene surface warps down from 900 metres on crystalline rocks to 400 metres, on Cretaceous, in the Negev (Quennell 1958). It is surmounted by remnants of a late-Eocene (Egma) plateau also warped down from 1650 metres and rising again to pass over the highlands of Judea. Several late-Cainozoic, low-level cycles are distinguished by Quennell, and the main warping appears to be late in the history (see p. 307).

The coastal hinterlands through Israel and Lebanon have been much affected by mid-Cainozoic folding and late-Cainozoic block-folding and faulting with the production of local depressions and foci of deposition. " The folds are broad, with relatively flat anticlinal crests and steep asymmetric limbs, similar to [coffin folds] of the Jura. The folding mechanism is not one of tangential compression but rather differential vertical upwards movements " (Mitchell 1959). Already in the Miocene period the Jordan-Orontes depression was extensively floored by sediments of continental type; and Picard (1943) visualised the late-Cainozoic landscape of the Middle East as consisting of marine gulfs and continental basins in which detrital accumulations attained enormous thickness, pointing to " an immense and continuous erosion (on a particularly huge scale in the big basin of Egypt and Iraq) " that could only be maintained by continued sinking of basins and rising of interfluves.

THE SUDAN, NIGERIA AND THE GUINEA HIGHLANDS

Interpreted broadly, the Sudan is a vast tract stretching from the Nile Basin to the Atlantic Highlands of West Africa, south of the Sahara. Depositional plains are of vast extent because the northward drainage, except for the Nile and Upper Niger Rivers, is endoreic and the rainfall is insufficient to produce persistent run-off over the gently sloping ground. Slight warping has generated the basins of Bahr-el-Ghazal, Chad and Upper Niger separated by broad flat watersheds. Detritus from the southern watersheds has partly filled the depressions and caused huge swamps that vary in size with the seasons.

The territory of the Sudan (*i.e.* east of long. 22° E.) is a country of low watersheds separating the northerly slopes of the north-west desert from the southerly slopes of southern Darfur and Kordofan and also the Blue and White Nile Basins. In the desert the Nubian sandstone makes flat *hamada* plateaus extending into Libya. Though the relief is usually small, 600 feet appears near Umm Keddada. Towards the east, inliers of a pre-Nubian inselberg landscape increase in importance until a (presumably) Gondwana landscape is cut by the superposed course of the Nile through the Sabaloka gorge below Khartoum.

Following deposition of the Cretaceous Nubian sandstone, denudation prevailed during the Eocene and much of the Oligocene periods and culminated in the African planation with lateritic ironstone encrusting the surface. A local Oligocene freshwater lake is, however, recorded by outliers of Hudi cherts about 50 feet thick that occur widely scattered between lat. 15° and 20° N. These beds are transected by the late-Cainozoic surface which passes thence between *jebels* of Nubian sandstone.

African and post-African cyclic landscapes are only slightly separated in some areas (*e.g.* Yambio) and widely separated in others (*e.g.* Aloma Plateau) (Andrew 1949).

The former cycle extended over most of the Sudan though now preserved only as scattered fragments in some districts; the latter is well planed only south of 9° N., and may include more than one stage. Pliocene depression between Kosti, Juba and Malakal in the upper Nile is indicated by the Umm Ruwaba series of unconsolidated sands and clayey sands, which are older than the Kordofan sands.

In Nigeria the smooth African planation surrounds the Jos highlands and extends from Bauchi north-west to Gusau, in which direction it truncates Eocene rocks. It slopes gently northward and is separated from the cyclic landsurfaces above and below by scarps. Where dissected about Kano, therefore, it makes small tablelands. Within the highlands it bevels the Fluvio-Volcanic series, developing thereon a laterite sheet of considerable thickness and extent (Grove 1952). Pugh (1954) has also noted African cyclic planation uniformly about 2,000 feet elevation along the eastern frontier highlands and has inferred that the " rise to the rift " took place earlier than the African cycle, which accords well with the super-elevation of the Gondwana surface on the Adamawa highlands and the occurrence of Cretaceous rocks within the Benue rift (p. 270). The same African landsurface extends far to the east of the highlands along the watershed between the Oubangi River and Lake Chad.

Post-African landscapes, usually well pedimented and studded with inselbergs, are much more extensive spreading from Kano and Sokoto far across the neighbouring (formerly French) territories of West Africa and Equatorial Africa. Two distinct cyclic surfaces are developed, and there are also in Oubangi two sets of grits described by Babet and tentatively correlated by Dresch (1953) with the *grès polymorphe* and Plateau sands of the Congo Republic. Quite extraordinary is the extent of depositional landsurfaces in the Western Sudan. Through Northern Dahomey, Northern Nigeria and Cameroon the African cycle, carried upon Cretaceous and Eocene sediments, is itself fossilised (Mio-Pliocene) by grits, conglomerates and muds of the *continental terminal* which themselves build up the late-Cainozoic landscapes. With degradation and aggradation alternating and prevailing locally from time to time the Cainozoic landsurfaces were subjected to constant retouching, provoked in some instances (according to Dresch) by earth movements of considerable magnitude and changes of climatic regimen. Towards the south, " between 13th and 9th parallels, the cover of Cainozoic muds and sands is less thick and more vigorously attacked. Where it is protected by a duricrust immense horizontal plains appear (Upper Volta) giving the impression of structural plains. The valleys and flat depressions incised into the plains are overlooked by steep slopes crowned and protected by one or two cornices. In Upper Dahomey (Djoujou) the ancient surface of aggradation survives only in a state of corniced buttes. Little by little the crystalline basement is involved; but the aspect of the plain does not sensibly differ. The major rivers are superposed through the cover on to the crystallines ". Here and there, sometimes along the interfluves, the shield rocks make solitary or grouped *inselbergs* " disposed strangely upon an infinite flatness ". Some of this topography has been fossilised and resurrected more than once.

Locally post-African landscapes have also been basined and have received an alluvial cover (Chad, 800 feet above sea level, is but the largest of many extensive swamps), and alluviation continues along the major river courses. About lat. 13° N., after alluviation of the upper Niger and Chad Basins was practically complete, increased aridity caused the growth of a gigantic dune complex the dead front of which bars the Macina between Nara and Lake Bebo (*erg* du Ouagadou), the Niger to the north of Timbuktu (*ergs* of Guidigri and Manga), and the dead *erg* of Kanem which bars the Chad.

The same cyclic surfaces make the flat major divides such as the Benue-Chad divide and the Oubangi-Shari upland. A northward extension builds the domed Darfur upland dotted with inselbergs some of which are 10,000 feet in height. These late-Cainozoic landscapes bear unconsolidated, rarely stratified laterites described as partly lacustrine and partly terrestrial in origin. Nowhere are they forming at present; instead they are " undergoing erosion, rearrangement and gradual removal ".

In Dahomey and Ghana, the oldest and highest denudation cycle is of early-Cainozoic age. The surface is strongly duricrusted and all the economically important bauxite deposits occur on it. It appears around the Atacora Mountains at 1,600 feet, and Dixey and Willbourn cite it at 1,400-1,700 feet in the Konkori and Cambaga highlands. They find it well developed also upon the southern and eastern rims of the Voltaian Basin at 1,700-2,500 feet (Mampong), descending upon the coastal monocline to about 1,000 feet at 30-40 miles from the shore. Dissected remnants of a post-African cycle " rise inland from 150-200 feet above sea level on the coast to 550-1,000 feet at the foot of the south-western rim of the Voltaian Basin ". In the Upper Volta area north of Ghana duricrusted residuals of a late-Cainozoic cycle stand above the youngest surface at Lac de Bam, with the early-Cainozoic summit bevel upon the Birrimian Ranges (*c.* 2,000 feet) behind. The late-Cainozoic surface was typically pedimented, sometimes about inselbergs (Brammer). The interior of Dahomey, too, is mostly late-Cainozoic pedimented landscape with numerous flat-topped residuals of the early-Cainozoic planation.

Between Guinea and the Ivory Coast granitic and gneissose highlands attain 3,000 feet above the sea at only 150 miles from the shore. They represent a warped divide from which the upper Niger and Senegal rivers flow inland. Though some of the greatest eminences may belong to the Gondwana cycle, the principal surface, at 2,000 feet, appears to be the African planation with deep lateritic mantle (Lamotte and Rougerie 1955). Open incision of valley heads in a post-African cycle renders a rolling landscape as far as the eye can see. They also carry a laterite. On the Atlantic aspect lower plains step down from this as phases of the late-Cainozoic denudation, and are themselves gashed by deep gorges of the Quaternary rejuvenation.

The whole of the Guinea coast is thus a monocline of repeated displacement upon which the Cainozoic erosion surfaces converge seaward to pass beneath corresponding marine sequences in the coastal plain. In the coastlands of Ghana the Amisian series of conglomerates (with plant fossils) suggests an initiation of the flexure during late-Jurassic or early-Cretaceous time. Planation of the interior during early stages of the African cycle shed late-Cretaceous, and sometimes Eocene, sands, clays and limestones into the coast belt (Nigeria, Ivory Coast), and the culmination of the cyclic planation on land is represented as an Oligocene hiatus in the coastal sequence. Neogene sediments likewise represent the post-African cycle.

Through the low country of Senegal such monoclinal structure is again apparent (Michel 1962). In the hinterland two cyclic denudations have been described, one Eocene the other Pliocene; these are warped down into an appropriate marine sequence in the lower Senegal basin. Upon the Mauretanian upland and into Rio de Oro is a pediplain of granite and gneiss at 1,000 feet with monadnocks rising to 1,500 feet. Tentatively this may be accepted as the late-Cainozoic landscape.

THE SAHARA

From the Atlantic Ocean to the Nile, and from the Mediterranean at Libya 1,500 miles south to the Sudan, the Saharan region is essentially homogeneous in its geomorphology. Apart from the great domes of Ahaggar and Tibesti and the Anti-Atlas in the west, wherein ancient rocks are exposed, the region consists of immense tablelands of almost flat-lying sediments strewn with pebbles (the *hamadas*, of which there are four groups developed upon Cretaceous, Oligocene, late-Miocene or late-Pliocene strata respectively) or equally vast depressions partly or wholly filled with enormous inland deltas or the *erg* sand-dune deserts. This has been the aspect of the Sahara throughout much of Cainozoic time. Although the Sahara is extremely arid and (unlike the Sudan) lacks an integrated drainage system, its geomorphic forms, apart from the *ergs*, are due almost entirely to stream and sheet-flood action upon warped structures.

The geomorphology of the Sahara differs in two important respects from that of Africa already reviewed. Firstly much of the Sahara was overflowed by the sea during the Cretaceous period, leaving a legacy of marine strata that has exercised ever since a profound effect upon its topography. Indeed, though the sea withdrew from about half the inundated area shortly after the close of the Cretaceous period, leaving for a time relict Eocene waterbodies in which accumulated the valuable Eocene phosphatic limestones, it relinquished the remainder in the north only progressively through Cainozoic and Recent time (Fig. 107). Secondly, timings of tectonic events over the Saharan region differ from those in the Sudan (which are purely African continental) in that they are related to the tectonics of the Tethyan geosyncline. Eocene and Oligocene deformation, for instance, though unknown in Central and Southern Africa, are progressively more important northward in the Sahara.

The Cretaceous sea shrank rapidly towards the north (Perret 1935) leaving Eocene relicts that persisted for a time, especially in the Nile Valley, central Libya, Niger Valley, Sokoto and the interior of Senegal. The African cycle of erosion then planed off parts of the marine beds on the topographic highs and deposited the detritus by water action in the depressions, thus producing a complicated assemblage of planations graded to a variety of local base levels. The plains so produced afforded by the early Miocene the most extensive system of *hamadas* from which rise residuals (Joly 1962). The pediments and fans are encrusted with ferricrete and are often strewn with pebbles. Eocene and Oligocene earth movements produced lake basins in which accumulated limestones, gypseous marls and pebbles supplied by new partial cycles of erosion on neighbouring regions, but the aspect of the whole polycyclic region was not vastly different from what it had been soon after the Cretaceous. The history is, indeed, better deciphered in some of the more unstable regions like the rejuvenated Hercynian massifs of Anti-Atlas and Ougarta (Birot and Joly 1952) where the extensively planed landsurface beneath the fine-grained Miocene sediments rides up to elevations of 2,000 metres. Farther to the east the relief increases.

FIG. 113. Hamada or flat stony desert upon Mesozoic and Cainozoic sedimentary series, Mahjez, Morocco. *from a photograph.*

The Anti-Atlas was strongly upwarped during the middle-Miocene period, following which the stream pattern was established and superposed on to the Hercynian basement, and valley plains were excavated. In the late Miocene also, red conglomerates, sandstones and marls sometimes built up in depressions almost level with the Oligocene surface. These Miocene *hamadas* were very smooth, for when the climate became wetter during the Pliocene, lakes stretched over the northern part of the Sahara from the extreme west to Ghardaia. They even penetrated into the subsequent lowlands of the Atlas chain.

The late-Pliocene (Villafranchian) sandstones, marls and limestones have fossilised the ridge and valley landforms of the Ougarta chain* and stretched southward into Spanish West Africa. Nowadays they form the youngest *hamadas* of all.

The Miocene sea still covered parts of Egypt, Cyrenaica and Dergardaia in the interior of Algeria. Its deposits lie unconformably upon an eroded surface of older rocks and form a plateau rising gradually southward to heights of over 600 feet. The combination of marine conditions in the north with uplift providing detritus from the south implies a northward tilt of the African landsurface during the mid-Cainozoic (Ball 1939).

* J. Dresch.   Private communication.

Elsewhere marine Miocene formations are absent from the block of North Africa, though they appear in the exotic Atlas Mountains.

The Atlas, indeed, on account of its tectonic instability preserves a very complete record of cyclic episodes related to the deposition of sedimentary series changing from continental in the south to marine in the north (Tell Atlas). The several stages of cyclic landscape development are typically displayed in the *meseta* of central Morocco, where tabular Cretaceous and Eocene formations have been stripped from upwarpings such as the Djebilet (Dresch 1941) to reveal the irregular surface of the post-Hercynian massif. Deposits and surfaces of the Miocene and Villafranchian *hamada* stages are likewise well developed throughout the length of the Atlas.

THE PLIO-PLEISTOCENE CYMATOGENY
AND THE ENSUING LANDFORMS OF SOUTHERN AFRICA

Towards the end of the Cainozoic era the face of Africa consisted of broadly pedimented, undulating landscapes sometimes rising to smoothly bevelled interfluves inherited from an early-Cainozoic planation. Upon the major divides stood, as tabular highlands, the last vestiges of Mesozoic cyclic landforms, (apart from those buried where the surface dimpled and formed a focus for accumulation of detritus from surrounding regions as inland deltas). Away from the residual highlands the relief generally was of the order of a few hundreds of feet and the elevation above sea level rarely more than 2,000 feet. The aspect was unmistakably that of Africa with the divides, basins and most of the rivers in the same places, but it was a very subdued replica of the continent that stands so starkly forth at the present day.

For as the Cainozoic era drew to a close the surface began to heave in broad undulations, mostly along old-established lines. The previous divides were uparched again and the former depressions lagged and were deepened (Fig. 76). At maxima of local displacement rift valleys were generated in Central Africa; but the continent as a whole was uplifted most in the south and least along the Mediterranean shores. Everywhere the relief was accentuated, and across the tilted and corrugated landsurface drainage patterns were ponded or rejuvenated (Fig. 83). Though antecedent courses were maintained by the major rivers, many large captures of drainage were effected. Gorges have since been cut, river terraces have been carved, but so recent has been the deformation that the fresh cycles of erosion induced have not yet had time to produce even a partial planation except upon low-standing areas of weak rock. As denudation proceeded *pari-passu* with deformation the Quaternary landforms are often multiphase, especially upon the flanks of the cymatogenic arches (p. 206). Ruhe (1954), for instance, described five phases of Quaternary erosion on the western side of the Lake Albert rift. Three phases are widely known under a variety of circumstances and may indicate tectonic control of each phase, but this is not proved. The name Congo cycle is sometimes used to cover these Quaternary phases of landscape development because both degradation and aggradation were characteristically displayed at that time in the Middle Congo region, while deep gorge-cutting took place in the lower reaches.

Further complication amid Quaternary landforms has been induced by climatic fluctuation embracing arid and pluvial episodes associated with the Ice Age. The size and energy of waterbodies and extent of deserts have varied greatly, causing local alternations of degradation and aggradation in the landscape. Studies of such landforms have been greatly facilitated by the use as index fossils of the stone age implements so liberally strewn over the face of Africa by Palæolithic man. Stone Age man witnessed, indeed, many of the landscape changes described hereunder, including the retreat of Victoria Falls by at least five miles, and the generation of parts of the East African rift valley.

Most spectacular of all the cymatogenic deformations was the uplifting around the southern lobe of Africa, from Equatorial Africa to the Cape and thence to Moçambique, of the rim of highlands about the Great Escarpment. This feature had been begun by the monoclinal flexing that formed the outline of southern Africa early in the Cretaceous period; but it was re-elevated at the close of the Cainozoic era by 4,000-5,000 feet along a line somewhat inland of the maximum of previous upwarping and made into a much more prominent feature. Major rivers like the Zambezi, the Orange and the Cuanza maintained antecedent courses through the rising barrier but the mighty Congo is said to have changed its exit. These rivers all have waterfalls marking the head of the Quaternary cycle, and the Congo in particular makes its way to Matadi through a series of rocky gorges. Most other river systems fail to breach the barrier. Hence arises the fact that so few rivers drain so huge an area, and that some of them rise almost within a couple of hundred miles of the opposite side of the continent (Fig. 82). The intracontinental divides between them, on the contrary, are often insignificant, and sometimes, being developed by warping of the early-Cainozoic planed landsurface, so flat that water may flow either way across them according to the incidence of rainfall.

From the Great Escarpment the marginal lands were tilted with increasing declivity seaward so that over the last 50-70 miles the African and post-African landsurfaces may plunge 2,000-3,000 feet to meet the coast (Figs. 95, 97). Steepening of the landsurfaces as they approach the coast has been recorded in the desert Namib behind Walvis Bay, and is clearly displayed in Natal where the African planation descends from 5,000 feet at Mooi River and Qudeni to the sea at an average rate of 100 feet per mile (King and King 1959). Into these flexed landscapes the short rivers flowing directly from the escarpment to the sea have incised gorges with a profundity of 1,000-3,000 feet. In the starkly arid terrains of the west coast (South-West Africa and Angola) these are vastly impressive but even on the more benign eastern aspect the Valley of a Thousand Hills behind Durban and the Tugela Valley (3,000 feet deep) equally attest the power of erosion into the monocline. The north-south frontier range of the Lebombo expresses the monocline perfectly in the eastward dip of its basalts and rhyolites. The range, which locally bears a late-Cainozoic summit bevel, is transected by the poorts of no less than 13 rivers maintained across it as the monocline steepened (Fig. 114). In weaker rocks behind the range the drainage has opened out the extensive plain of the Lowveld which in the eastern Transvaal extends to the foot of the Drakensberg. North of the Limpopo River the arch of the Natal-Eastern Transvaal monocline is matched by the eastern highlands of Rhodesia whereon the African planation attains nearly 7,000 feet. An arch was previously in existence there and had indeed been largely cut away along its eastern half by Cainozoic erosion which produced the great scarp of the frontier mountains, but cymatogeny rejuvenated the topography and the streams of the Sabi River catchment, operating profoundly in several stages, excavated the Rhodesian lowveld west of the frontier mountain chain.

Gravity anomalies along the Lebombo indicate that stability upon the monocline is still far from being achieved (Fig. 243).

Across Zululand, Moçambique, East Africa and Somalia extensive coastal plains were cut by the sea and furnished with Pleistocene limestone and sand deposits (*e.g.* Bluff Sandstone of Durban, and the Bamburi reef limestones north of Mombasa).

Crosswarping upon the coastal monocline is demonstrated by rise and fall of coastal terraces upon both western and eastern aspects (Thompson 1941); and along the escarpment culminations of summit levels sometimes indicate crosswarps, *e.g.* the Benguella highlands where the Lunda axis meets the escarpment. In Tanganyika strong north-easterly archings even supersede the simple, coastal monocline to some extent. The transition takes place about the Moçambique border (*e.g.* at Lindi, p. 286).

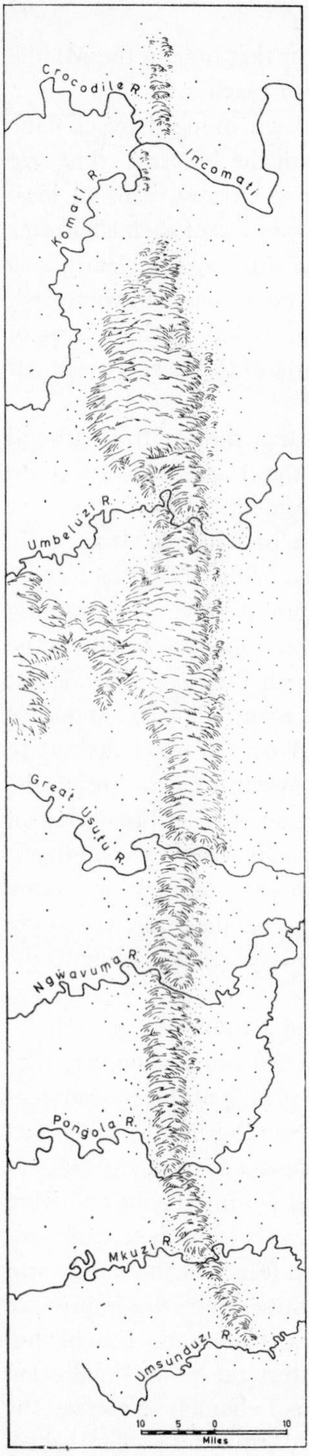

FIG. 114.

Watergaps (poorts) through the Lebombo Range, South Africa, where thirteen successive rivers have maintained antecedent courses across resistant rhyolites raised by Plio-Pleistocene tilting.

Over the Kalahari Basin from the Orange River northwards through adjoining parts of South-West Africa and the Transvaal into Angola, Zambia and Rhodesia, the characteristic Quaternary activity was the spread of an almost uninterrupted mantle of red to grey Kalahari sand that rests unconformably upon all older formations, even upon the late-Cainozoic Plateau and Pipe sandstones and the surface limestones of the Kalahari, as at Victoria Falls (Maufe). Its lateral boundary is often sharply defined by erosion and a formerly greater distribution, especially towards the east, is attested by outliers as at Umvuma and Lydiate in Rhodesia, the Makapan Caves in the Transvaal, and even across the Moçambique border near the Limpopo River (Bosazza).*

Though variation in colour is well known, most fresh exposures are red due to coating of the grains by hematite. The sand is fine and uniform and is often distributed in long *seif* dunes trending from north-west to south-east, that in Rhodesia and Zambia are often well timbered. Occasionally in the west, the base of the sand can be seen overlying flat floors of the preceding late-Cainozoic " puddingstone " phase of calcrete (p. 276). The thickness is commonly 50 feet or less, but local thicknesses of over 200 feet have been proved. Distribution by wind has never been doubted, and its age (early- to mid-Pleistocene) shows that a period of extreme aridity prevailed in South Africa at the time of heaviest glaciation in high latitudes.

Not all Pleistocene deposits of the Kalahari are arid. The northern Kalahari is, indeed, currently a region of rivers and swamps, for warping between Ghanzi and Bulawayo impounded the Okavango River which has thereby spread a huge inland delta just south of the Caprivi Strip. The waters of this major river are in consequence largely evaporated and only a small proportion reaches the Zambezi *via* the Linyanti River.

Following the spread of Kalahari sand the principal activity of late-Pleistocene time over southern Africa was the deposition of high-level gravels and the cutting of river terraces. The terraces of the Vaal River in particular have been studied for the evidence they supply of occupation by early man. A middle- to late-Pleistocene age is indicated for the terrace gravels by the included vertebrate fossils. Comparable deposits and faunas have been recorded from Victoria Falls, and many other localities to beyond the Equator.

Similar Quaternary incision follows the Kafue River for scores of miles into Zambia. In Zambia the chief result of cymatogeny is seen in enhancement of the great arch which forms the north-easterly trending watershed, and which may be said to continue beyond the northern end of Lake Nyasa as the Iringa Arch of Tanganyika. Effects north of this fall under the rift valley system in southern Congo Republic. Thus, downstream from Kapalala, the Luapula (River) becomes increasingly incised into the late-Cainozoic landsurface producing a definite escarpment which has in places

* V. L. Bosazza. Private communication.

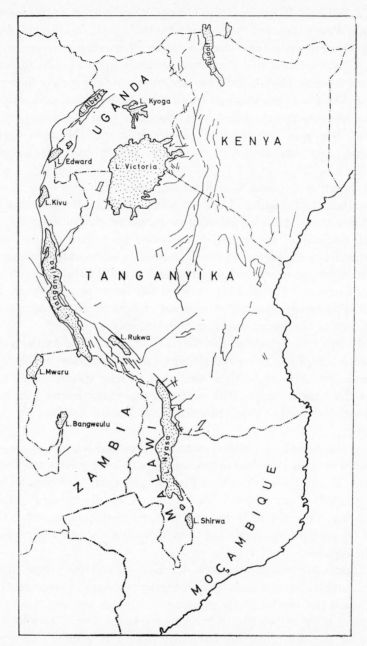

Fig. 115. The Rift Valley system of Central Africa. Faults of both
eastern and western systems demarcate the principal rift valleys,
but the main topographic effects lie in the huge cymatogenic arches
and basins with tilted landsurfaces leading from one to the other.

retreated many miles from the river. The valley ultimately widens to 80 miles before it reaches Lake Mweru which is surrounded by this Congo cyclic surface (p. 296).

THE RIFT VALLEY SYSTEM OF CENTRAL AFRICA

The rift valley system dominates Central Africa (Fig. 115): not the rift valleys themselves which are minor features, but the huge cymatogenic arches and basins with the warped and tilted landsurfaces leading from one to the other, which indeed often occur where no rift valleys are present. The rifts are merely cracks at the crests of some arches where the elasticity of the rigid uppercrust has failed. All later authorities have emphasised this point. Few details of the rifts appear, therefore, in this text, for this interesting subject the reader should consult Willis (1936), Dixey (1956B) and Mohr (1963) with the references that they give. While it is usual for the crest to subside under tension like a keystone, where unbalanced forces have operated segments of country have sometimes been forced violently upward. Mbeya Mountain, in the angle between the Rukwa and Fufu scarps (Fig. 118), is an uptilted corner of the Central Tanganyika Plateau; and Ruwenzori is a whole mountain range whereon the late-Cainozoic surface, that to the east stands at 5,000 feet. has been upcast to 14,000 feet as a result, apparently, of a wrench with the eastern component moving south (Fig. 116). Parts of the mountain outline are defined by fault-scarps and other parts by steep warps, now converted into erosion scarps.

Closely along the flanks of both eastern and western rifts crowd remnants of the older erosion cycles, Gondwana and post-Gondwana, showing that the end-Cainozoic cymatogeny follows closely along axes of elevation already long-established (Fig. 119). The topography that is upwarped towards the rift is in almost every instance a compound of African and post-African cycles and the tilted flanks of the arch are commonly scored by rejuvenated courses of streams draining away from the crests of the scarps. In Kenya the up-arching took place in two, almost equal, stages: one post-Miocene, the other post-Pliocene (Saggerson and Baker 1964), and evidence accumulates that this was so also in the Albert rift of the Congo-Uganda border region. Rarely are antecedent courses maintained across the arches: there are on the contrary many examples of betrunked drainages.

The fault scarps are often so new as to have suffered little or no erosion and certain grids (e.g. Sikes's) of intersecting faults render assemblages of earth blocks that look as though they were jumbled only a few centuries ago. Even faults of middle Pleistocene date, ranging up to 5,000 feet in height, are often remarkably fresh.

Within the rifts, deposits of fluctuating Pleistocene lakes afford a fascinatingly detailed history of rift valley development, accompanied by a wealth of stone tools that provide the necessary basis for correlation amid rapidly changing environments.

Quaternary volcanism is endemic along great lengths of the rifts.

FIG. 116.

The fault-pattern of Ruwenzori. The mountain block has *risen* by a maximum of 9,000 feet through *tensional* activity on this pattern coupled with slight right-handed wrench movement. Rift valley deposits stippled. *Interpretation by W. Q. Kennedy and P. E. Matthews.*

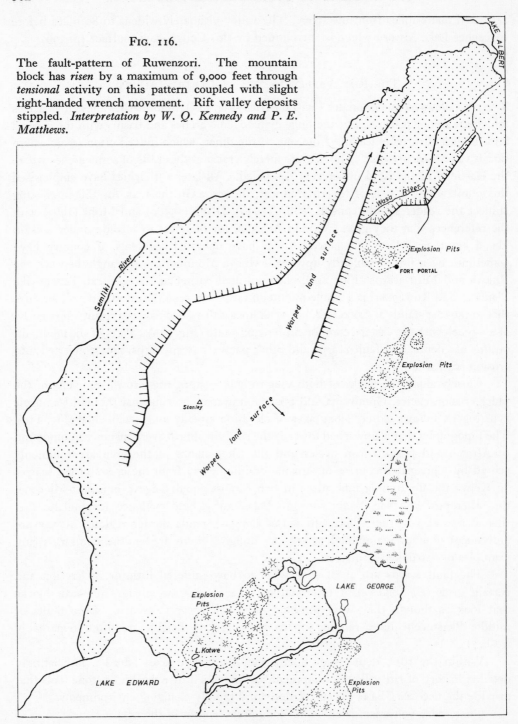

Even Malagasy has a rift valley where vertical faults with 1,000 feet of throw have formed the Alaotra Lake depression in the middle of the crystalline plateau. The basin probably formed during the Pliocene, and is nearly filled with detritus.

QUATERNARY EVENTS IN CONGO REPUBLIC

In Katanga, Lakes Upemba and Mweru occupy depressions caused by rift valley displacements and there are two local landsurfaces of Pleistocene age in the vicinity of Elizabethville, including the valley of the Lufira. Multiphase planation in the south-western Congo Republic is apparently linked with tilting of the rivers from the Lunda Axis (Chapter VII). The axis dies out near Mualango for the streams follow an apparently primitive eastward direction, but to the west the drainage is wholly to north and south away from the axis. Along the rivers of the Congo drainage, between the post-African landsurface and the sub-Recent river terraces, exist a number of minor intermediate planations: three or four of them in the headwaters of some of the larger rivers, e.g. Lulua and Kasai, and a group of six or seven imperfect surfaces in the middle and lower courses of the principal rivers. All these partial planations are closely allied, and to some extent they interdigitate with Plio-Pleistocene sands. The interval between successive surfaces is usually of the order of 20-30 metres and does not surpass 50-60 metres. " The number and regularity of these planations is very great in weak sub-horizontal beds ". The successive phases destroy in turn all the preceding planations of the same geomorphic cycle. Base level for the group is probably the lowest point of the primitive Congo Basin a little to the north of Coquilhatville. For the terrace phases it is Stanley Pool. Here, like Ruhe's five Quaternary stages associated with warping in the north-eastern Congo, appears to be an instance of multiplicity of minor geomorphic phases when upheaval on a cymatogen is large; river planations appear to split as well as scarps (Chapter VII).

Along the Lualaba (the Upper Congo River), the Congo denudation cycle extends to Kasongo being marked by rapids between there and Kongolo.

The Congo Basin is a vast centre of Quaternary deposition the margins of which extend along the northern bank of the Kasai and Sankuru Rivers, and past Katako Kombe, Opala, Isangi, Aketi, Budjala, Ouesso to Gamboma (Fig. 98). Within this entire basin deposition is ubiquitous; but towards the rim, especially in the south, the rivers have eroded their valleys in Recent time and only the interfluves bear the sub-Recent sediments. The stratigraphy varies locally. Thus the Busira beds comprising many metres of argillaceous and yellow sands covering a vast area around Coquilhatville are fluvio-lacustrine. (They rest upon several metres of laterite). The Yangambi series around Stanleyville, though essentially contemporaneous, was partly eolian. Thirty-five metres thick it is succeeded by further series before the Stanleyville sands with artefacts of a Levallois culture.

The oldest beds in the modern Congo Basin (including the Yangambi) probably correlate with the Kaiso series of the Lake Albert depression, containing Villafranchian vertebrate fossils.

The valley incision of the Lower Congo, below the 500 metre contour, belongs to a Congo (post-cymatogenic) erosion cycle, but seaward of Boma the erosional cycle changes to a depositional one.   Also, narrow zones of a similar erosion cycle fringe the shores of Lakes Tanganyika and Mweru, widening for a short distance up the valleys of incoming streams.

CYMATOGENY AND ENSUING DENUDATIONS IN EAST AFRICA

The present rift valley structures of East Africa generally run transversely to the pre-existing topography which they have modified profoundly (Teale and Harvey 1933).   The pre-rift oceanic divide (Fig. 117) passed on a relatively simple line from the north end of Lake Nyasa to the line of the Gregory Rift in Kenya.   Drainage passed eastward to the Indian Ocean, and westward to the River Congo.   As a direct result of rifting two large dischargeless basins were created, the Rukwa Basin and the East African Rift Valley Basin.   The waters of each of these relatively dry areas are led to shallow lakes where they are evaporated.

Between the eastern and western branches of the rift valley system, the broad and shallow Victoria Nyanza Basin (the largest lake in Africa does not exceed 273 feet depth) expanded across the former headwaters of the Ituri-Congo hydrographic system which was also severed by arching of the country just east of the Lake Albert-Lake Edward rift (Fig. 83).   The severed drainage pattern of western Uganda is now largely back-tilted to Lake Victoria, which finds a new, though devious, outlet northward to Lake Albert and the Nile.   Lake Kioga is a similarly downwarped area.   These drainage changes have wrought many small-scale changes of topography.

Except in the northwest, little of Tanganyika falls within these changes.   Instead, the cymatogeny largely followed a pre-existing north-easterly grain in the country (Teale and Harvey 1933) thereby enhancing old axes of elevation such as the Iringa Arch and the Lindi Plateau.   Even the major faults follow the same line; six of them in succession: the Lindi, Pugu, Ruvu, Fall, Ngorongoro, and Kilosa scarps mostly bounding earth-blocks tilted to the west (Fig. 118).

The displacements failed to alter the river courses, and the Ruaha crosses the belts of upraised country in antecedent gorges.   Youthful canyons, incised into the elevated blocks (e.g. Iringa highlands) correspond to the incision of the antecedent gorges.   In the fault-angle depressions of the belted country, directed north-eastward to meet the coastlands successively en échelon, sediments were deposited.   Along the Great Ruaha alluviation extends, at a width of 25-40 miles, for 225 miles, overlooked by the Fufu rift scarp in the west.   East of the Iringa arch where the buried post-African plain descends nearly to sea level, the Kilombero lowlands make a wide plain at 1,000 feet above sea level.   The country is still swampy against the scarp in the west, showing how recent some of the earth movement has been. Inland from the Lindi Plateau a third depression is occupied to unknown depth by alluvial deposits of the Lukusedi which escapes through the tableland in an antecedent gorge.

In Uganda the Congo denudation cycle extends great distances up the rivers that flow into Lakes Victoria and Kioga (100 miles up the Katonga). All the streams between lat. 2° N. and Lake Kioga exhibit the cycle even when they are mere swamps incised

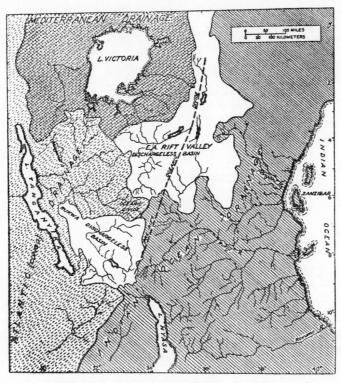

FIG. 117. Distribution of drainage in Tanganyika following Quaternary
cymatogeny and rifting. *after E. O. Teale.*

below the level of the late-Cainozoic surface. In the south-west, Lake George occupies a shallow depression below the late-Cainozoic surface and is occupied by Pleistocene deposits like those of the rift valley Lakes Albert and Edward. Similar rejuvenations and denudations attend the rift valley in Kenya, together with much Pleistocene infill within the rift valley itself. Additionally, deep incision of rivers flowing towards the coast testifies the rapid and considerable warping that occurred in that region. The head of the Quaternary cycle now reaches to Lugard's Falls on the Galana River, to Grand Falls on the Tana, to beyond Habaswein on the Dera, while on the Abyssinian border the Dana River is incised 1,500 feet below the plateau of the African cycle. The Ganale Dorya in Abyssinia is even more deeply incised at Verme Falls, east of Negelli.

U

Where the rift system bifurcates to form the Red Sea and the Gulf of Aden (with earlier movement in the late Eocene and in the Miocene (Mohr 1963)), uplift has been very great with the planed surface truncating the Basement Complex rising to

FIG. 118. Physiographic diagram of Tanganyika showing extensive correspondence of Quaternary faulting with pre-existing north-easterly grain of the country. *after E. O. Teale and E. Harvey.*

10,000 feet near Lake Margherita in the south. The walls of both rifts are deeply gashed by the canyons of short streams descending to these waters. Across the Arabian plateau, too, the headwater valleys have been deeply incised following rift valley movements, and some of the detritus of the Nefud desert has been supplied following this rejuvenation. Comparable topographic effects follow the rift valley system into Syria, where also late-Cainozoic lacustrine and alluvial deposits lie east of the upwarped zone, *e.g.* Homs, Damascus.

The Red Sea rift has not only opened by cymatogeny, the sides have actually drifted apart. Along its centre is a zone of *positive* gravity anomalies showing the introduction of heavy material from below as the rift widened. The movement has caused the Dead Sea rift to develop left lateral wrench displacement (107 km. during early Miocene, 62 km. during early Pliocene and 45 km. since middle Pleistocene) (see p. 291; Fig. 81).

CYMATOGENY IN SYRABIA

As in Africa the Jordan rift conforms to older lineaments, but not perfectly for the graben does not follow consistently any major tectonic line, indeed the Paran Range, approaching the graben at right angles, protrudes straight into it. The structural contour map of Israel by Bentor and Vroman (1954) shows the whole region between the rift valley and the Mediterranean broken by folding and faulting which began in the Cretaceous and has continued intermittently. Already in the Miocene (*cf*. Red Sea) a deep depression with terrestrial sediments existed along the line of rifting, but major rift faulting has occurred since the Miocene, and faults were still active in quite recent time. According to Picard (1943) the most active epoch was the Plio-Pleistocene when arose the Galilean, Judean-Samarian and Negev upwarp zones extending into northern Sinai and Egypt. In accentuated form were uplifted the Lebanon, Hermon and Anti-Lebanon massifs, with buckling of the sediments in adjacent basins. In contrast, the Akaba graben descended to a depth of 2,000 metres, and the Jordan and Red Sea rifts were widened and deepened. Both Dubertret and Quennell (1958) describe transcurrent movement upon the Dead Sea rift with the eastern side moving north.

Quaternary deposition has been mainly of fluvio-lacustrine series in the depressions with some spread of aeolian sands. Terraces, both erosional and depositional, occur in the coastlands from 30-380 metres above sea level.

Lower Egypt, as the " gift of the Nile ", is largely of Recent alluvial construction and the gravel terraces of the river, the Kordofan dune sands and the clays of the Sudan plain are all dated to about the Pleistocene-Recent boundary. The line of the middle river however, follows a warping, associated with the Red Sea rift, that created a hollow running northward from the Sudan. Local deposition within the hollow produced sands and gypseous clays with the remains of large Pliocene vertebrates.

QUATERNARY EVENTS IN NORTH AFRICA

The latest tectonic movements over the vast terrain of North Africa warped the late-Pliocene landsurface creating fresh rises and depressions. Upon the elevated country a recrudescence of erosion incised valleys with Pleistocene terraces and rockfans not only in the mountains but also across the *hamadas* which, stepped one above another, overlook the basins and valley-floors from various heights.   Near the Anti-Atlas the " Villafranchian " *hamada* itself stands sometimes from 250 to 400 metres above the valley bottoms, thus affording a measure of Quaternary river activity in the Sahara (Joly 1962).   According to French geologists (Birot, Capot-Rey and Dresch 1955), the present elevation of the Ahaggar and Tibesti massifs is attributable to the same late-Pliocene tectonic cycle.   The deeply entrenched radial drainage and annular depression indeed point to recent domal uplift, but the presence of older relict denudations towards the summits proves that such movement must have been a repetition of former displacements.   The Nile valley represents a Quaternary incision into the late-Cainozoic desert surface which stretches away to either side.   Steep scarps mark the transition at Luxor and even as far downstream as Cairo.

Quaternary dissection of the Cainozoic plateaus upon Nubian Sandstone is widespread and much is due to waterwork.   Broad pediments have been formed in the first Quaternary cycle near Omdurman and Wadi-Halfa.

Certain remarkable depressions in North Africa (some of them below sea level, *e.g.* Qattara, and the Tunisian Chotts) doubtless owe their initiation to tectonic movements, but their sides have in some instances become scarped and have since retreated considerably.   Other depressions such as the Tanezrouft are immense plains floored with sand and gravel, some are swampy (Chad and Upper Niger), while yet others are now occupied by the great sand-dune deserts (*ergs*).   All these accumulations are Quaternary in age.

Late-Cainozoic and Recent volcanic rocks are sporadic throughout more than two-thirds of North Africa.   In Egypt and the Sudan are three groups (Sandford 1937).   The middle group, of trachyte and phonolite, has by circumdenudation afforded the startling volcanic necks which pierce the air like spikes (Ahaggar); the last is a fresh basalt group building great cones (Emi Kusi) and invading ravines in the mountains.

The Western African Coastal Monocline

From the heights of the West African divide the Cainozoic denudation cycles descend by flexure to pass beneath corresponding marine sediments of the coastal plain between Lagos and Abidjan.   The structure is familiar as that of a coastal monocline (p. 246) of end-Cainozoic age.   Since this flexure, the major rivers (Niger, Volta) have excavated great lowlands with several phases of partial planation far into the interior, much of the resulting Quaternary debris being accumulated in the relevant deltas: but the coastal monocline originated much earlier.   Cretaceous sediments, both marine and continental, attain thicknesses of 15,000 feet in some sections thereby indicating a total flexing since the Jurassic of possibly 35,000 feet (Dixey 1956).   West of Abidjan, through Sierra Leone, Guinea and Liberia however, short steep rivers have cut ravines into a crystalline hinterland which reaches the coast in cliffs (Tricart 1957).

The axis of zero movement in the monoclinal tilting here passes seaward of the present shore, and land waste is shed directly into the sea (*cf*. Natal and Zululand on the Natal Monocline). The monocline continues into Senegal (Michel 1962) where, below the level of the late-Pliocene surface, the river is bordered by Quaternary terraces. Powerful incision also marks the head-streams on the inland side of the divide, the abundant waste produced being carried to the basin of the upper Niger and into the lower Senegal.

Conclusion

Research over the past twenty years has shown amid the immense variety of landforms in Africa, a relatively simple system of landscape cycles that has operated with essential uniformity over the whole continent, following a corresponding number of tectonic episodes that have also been essentially alike over most of the continent. These results are now embodied in a map * (Fig. 119).

Of local departures from conformity, both in the effects of local structure and bedrock, and in tectonic differences of timing due to the proximity of North Africa to the Alpine system we are also well aware. They are minor variations that do not negate the overall continental plan.

It is now, indeed, possible to express the landscape features of any given area in a relatively simple formula that can be readily understood by any worker familiar with the typical cyclic scheme: The expression 18S 20E: 2E, 4L (2), 4Q (d) would thus be read that within the area bounded by the 18th and 19th parallels south and the 20th and 21st meridians east, two-tenths of the landscape consisted of the early-Cainozoic planation, four-tenths of the late-Cainozoic undulating landscape in two sub-stages, while four-tenths was of Quaternary depositional origin. Patterns of landscape thus established in the mind can be readily correlated on a continent-wide basis. Further, the way is open for similar treatment of landscape in other continents, and perhaps intercontinental comparisons with the derivation of common formulae for all.

In no other continent, however, has geomorphic research advanced to the stage where the topography throughout can be so described in terms of erosion cycles as has been done for Africa.

Though we shall seek to ascertain whether landscapes of the other continents are similarly systematic, and, if so, whether the systems of the several continents differ among themselves or all conform to a single global plan governed primarily by tectonic episodes, our treatment of the other continental landscapes may be more severely limited where fewer data upon erosion cycles are available. In such regions the treatment must be less ordered and more open to error. Such error can be corrected for the future by the interest of researchers in those regions.

---

* The present map is upon too small a scale for depiction of detail. It is hoped to publish a map upon the scale of 1:5 million in the near future.

CHAPTER X

CYCLIC LANDSURFACES IN THE REMAINDER OF GONDWANALAND

South America. Denudational Cycles in Brazil. Red Sands, Earths and Dusts in Brazil. The Succession of Alternating Denudational and Aggradational Landscapes. The Carboniferous Glaciated Landscape and The Triassic Desert. "Gondwana" and "post-Gondwana" Cyclic Denudation in South America. The Sul-Americana and later Cainozoic Landscape Cycles. Cymatogeny and Quaternary Landscape Development in Brazil. Summary of Southern Uruguay. Quaternary of the Argentine. Antarctic Contribution. Palæozoic and Mesozoic Landsurfaces of India. Cainozoic Landsurfaces of India and Ceylon. Post-Cainozoic Deformation and Drainage in Peninsular India. Australia: the Continent. The Permo-Carboniferous Glaciated Landscape. "Gondwana" and "post-Gondwana" Landscapes in Australia. The Great "Australian" Denudation Cycle. Late Cainozoic Landscapes in Australia. The Kosciusko Cymatogeny and subsequent changes of Landscape. Conclusion.

SOUTH AMERICA

The continent of South America presents a gigantic cordillera (Fig. 173) flanked upon the east by a trough that has been well-nigh filled by Cainozoic and Recent sediments shed from the uplifted ranges. In some sections the cordillera possesses a dissected summit plain, which in the Bolivian Plateau has been uplifted to the astonishing altitude of 15,000 feet; while the trough is remarkable for the breadth of its depositional surfaces. Yet neither of these shall now detain us,* and our search for erosional plains of great age shall be prosecuted upon the stable plateau areas of the Guianas, Brazil and Patagonia.

Like their counterparts in Africa, the first and second of these regions have escaped invasion by the sea since the Palæozoic (Weeks 1948), while Patagonia has experienced only brief transgression in the late-Cretaceous—Palaeocene and late-Cainozoic (la Plata). Landsurfaces in these regions may therefore have survived from remote antiquity, perhaps from "Gondwana" time. There is a further point of resemblance: for, as the West African plateau received in Cretaceous times a cover of continental and marine sedimentary rocks, so the chief post-Palæozoic deposits upon the Brazilian Highlands are the widespread, fresh-water, late-Cretaceous formations such as the Cayua, Bauru and Urucuia series, passing northward into a marine facies which extends almost to the mouth of the Amazon. There is some doubt as to the exact age of the Cayua series,

---

* See Chapters XIV and XV.

PLATE 9

The broad tableland of the "Sul-Americana" (early Cainozoic) cycle of erosion in the eastern highlands of Brazil. View north near Senador Murão, Minas Gerais.

Lester King.

[KING: *Morphology* . . . to face p. 311

it may be Jurassic or lower-Cretaceous, consequently the " pre-Cretaceous " or " Gond-wana " surface may pass locally at the base of the Bauru (Senonian) or at the base of the Cayua series. This, too, is matched in Africa (p. 245) by convergence of the Jurassic " Gondwana " planation and the early-Cretaceous " post-Gondwana " dissection of South Africa into a single planed Cretaceous phase in Congo Republic.

Brazilian geologists are, moreover, agreed that the principal dislocations of their country are pre-Mesozoic, and the Mesozoic and Cainozoic formations are there conti-nental. Cainozoic deposits generally rest in simple attitude upon relatively ancient formations. Stratigraphic comparison with the great plateau of Central Africa is very close for both the Mesozoic (Chapter II) and Cainozoic sequences (King 1956).

DENUDATIONAL CYCLES IN BRAZIL

As has been done with landforms in Africa (Chapter IX), the multitudinous landforms of Brazil may be classified under a relatively small number of denudational and depositional cycles that have developed under the dominant agencies of scarp retreat and pedimentation. The landforms of successive cycles, standing at different levels and separated by erosional scarps, have been mapped with facility (King 1956). A traveller in Brazil, indeed, soon learns to recognise the horizon-wide planations of early-Cainozoic age (Plate 9) and to use them as a datum to which the features of older and younger cycles can be referred. They represent, indeed, a " master surface " from which most of the existing landscape of Brazil has subsequently been carved. Though later polycyclic stream incision has almost everywhere carved valleys into this surface, reducing it locally to a dissected upland or even to a mere set of accordant skylines, nevertheless this dissected upland remains recognisable almost anywhere from the Parana hydrographic basin to Ceara. This vast planation, which accords with deposi-tional surfaces in the Andean foothills and below the pampas of the Argentine, is termed the " *Sul-Americana* " planation.

Older planations, " Gondwana " and " post-Gondwana " stand above the Sul-Americana cyclic landforms in the mountainland south of Belo Horizonte (Fig. 122). Inversely, along the watersheds trending northwards towards the Rivers Amazon and Tocantins the early-Cainozoic planation trensects Cretaceous rocks that themselves lie upon the older (Gondwana) planations, so that the two major denudation cycles have here crossed and appear in inverted sequence (*cf.* Fig. 123).

Later cyclic erosion has excavated broad valley-floors and maturelands into the Sul-Americana planation in all the main drainage basins, so that early- and late-Cainozoic cycles are nowadays coextensive and much of the upland scenery of Brazil exhibits early-Cainozoic plateaus or accordant ridge crests standing 100 metres or more above undulating country, itself often dicyclic, of the late-Cainozoic (*Velhas*) cycle.

Later still, and following pronounced Plio-Pleistocene cymatogeny, youthful gorges have been incised along most of the larger rivers (Jequitinhonha, Paraguaçu).

Repeated land movement, and structural elements encountered in the streambeds, have caused numerous substages of this (*Paraguaçu*) cycle to develop stepwise in some localities, and two or three of these are usually evident in the river profiles of eastern Brazil.*

Pronounced drowning of river mouths, to which Brazil owes its many excellent harbours (Salvador, Vitoria, Rio de Janeiro, Santos), is a manifestation of recent cymatogeny along coastal monoclines. Inland the rocky river beds rise steeply with rapids and waterfalls (Rio Itabuna, Rio das Contas).

RED SANDS, EARTHS AND DUSTS IN BRAZIL

Repeated reference will be made to formations of red sand and sandstone widely distributed over the interior of Brazil, and to similar sands of the coastlands termed *barreiras*. Indeed, the enormous development of detrital sands, vermilion to pink in colour and with pebble bands towards the base, recurring at intervals in the geological column from early-Mesozoic until Recent time may well give rise to astonishment.

Lithologically, the several red sands and earths are practically identical whatever their geological age, which suggests that there was *one original source*, the earliest or Botucatu sandstone, that has been broken down and redistributed from time to time and place to place. This concept is the more feasible because the bulk of all the sandstones is of eolian distribution. Apparently, when the parent source was broken down under erosion, the sands and clays were spread out in seasonally dry river beds and piedmonts whence they migrated once more, under the influence of wind, over the surrounding country to form new series.

The table of formations (p. 317) shows that each successive cycle of denudation was followed by a phase of red sand accumulation. There is not just one final phase that covers all previously-planed landscapes impartially, whatever their ages; each successive planation bears its separate and appropriate mantle. Whether there have been successive epochs of limited duration when conditions were favourable to the supply and accumulation of red sands (*e.g.* by climatic oscillation), or whether the climatic conditions have been uniformly favourable but the sands could not accumulate until the erosive vigour of each successive erosion cycle had been blunted and a flat terrain was developed locally for deposition to occur upon, remains a moot point. On the latter view, when sand accumulated sufficiently over the pediments it would dispel by absorption the normal flow of surface water and accentuate the apparent aridity. The interior of Brazil may thus have been persistently arid or semi-arid, with episodic invasions of sand from the beginning of the Mesozoic until Recent time.

While the climatic factors may have remained uniformly favourable to the accumulation of red sands and earths, the development of fresh erosion bevels is controlled by

* A corresponding set of cyclic denudational landscapes has been recorded from north-eastern Brazil by J. Demangeot (1959, 1961).

tectonic movements. Thus the apparent alternation of denudational and aggradational phases in Brazil over the past 150 million years may well be a function of intermittent tectonic activity (*q.v.*).

The older (Mesozoic) series (Botucatu, Cayua, Bauru and Urucuia) are all well authenticated in literature, but surprisingly little attention has been directed to the various younger series which rest upon the several Cainozoic plateaus and even upon the valley-floors of the major rivers. The extreme rarity of fossils in the older series, and their virtual absence from the younger series (apart from caves), induces much chronological uncertainty and some of the datings given below should be regarded as provisional.

Several distinct series are recognised:

a) the Triassic *Botucatu* series is well known in the state of São Paulo (de Oliveira and Leonardos 1943) where it consists of red, pink or yellow sandstones with pronounced cross-bedding and well rounded grains indicative of accumulation under conditions of extreme aridity. Some horizons are finer grained and more typically loessic. Frequently very thick, the series underlies the basaltic lavas (Rhaetic) where these are present. Where the lavas are absent the series may be transected by the Gondwana landsurface.

b) the *Uberaba* series of Triangulo Miniero and the *Cayua* red sands of São Paulo both contain tuffaceous material and rest in places upon the Rhaetic basalts which would suggest an eo-Jurassic age. Elsewhere they may post-date the smooth Gondwana surface, which would make them early Cretaceous. Both series are unfossiliferous. They are less widespread than the next series.

c) the *Bauru* and *Urucuia* series are probably both phases of a late-Cretaceous phase of eolation. At the base are washes of rolled quartz pebbles lying in shallow valleys of the post-Gondwana cycle. There is a break in the middle of the Bauru series and the upper division carries dinosaur remains thought to be of Senonian age.

In Minas Gerais the Urucuia sandstones differ from the Botucatu in possessing perfect stratification instead of cross-bedding, by concretions and in certain petrographical characteristics; but in São Paulo the Bauru series may be lithologically identical with the Botucatu, upon which it lies in districts where the São Bento (Rhaetic) lavas were removed by denudation in the Gondwana and post-Gondwana cycles. The maximum measured thickness of the Bauru is 310 metres, on the Serrados Agudos in north-western São Paulo; and the greatest elevation of the beds above sea level is between 900 and 1,000 metres, on the Serra Mata da Corda where they overlie the smooth Gondwana summit plane and occupy head valleys of the post-Gondwana cycle on the flanks of the range. These sands appear to have been long stabilised and are well consolidated, some at 2 km. south of São Gotardo being silcreted.

The occurrence of proved Cretaceous continental sands, often in loose or semi-coherent condition, upon so many high watersheds and covering so vast an area of the interior (Fig. 120) is proof positive that Brazil has evolved throughout the Cainozoic era by pediplanation, involving scarp retreat and pedimentation. There has been only insignificant lowering of the highest parts of the interior. Peneplanation by lowering

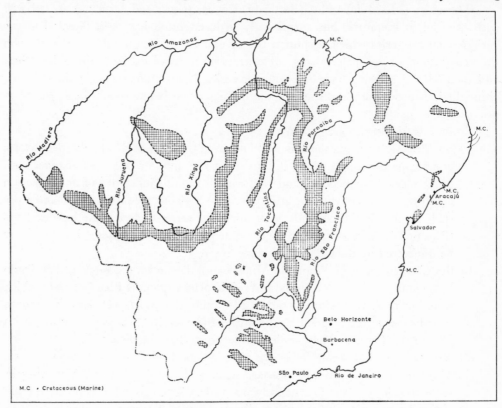

FIG. 120.   The wide distribution of Cretaceous continental sandstones upon watersheds in Brazil.

of interfluves in the Davisian sense is totally inadmissible as a mode of development among Brazilian landscapes.

    d) *the mid-Cainozoic sands.*   Upon the plateaus of the mid-Cainozoic (Sul-Americana) landscape about the Jequitinhonha Valley rests a series of red, yellow and white sands that accumulated in shallow lagoons and lakes (Morães Rego 1936).   Individual grains, however, afford evidence of wind travel.

    Other noteworthy arenaceous accumulations rest upon the same cyclic landsurface in western Minas Gerais.   Thus of two series of red sands in the vicinity of Lagoa Formosa the earlier rests upon the Sul-Americana surface only and its grains are coarse and rounded with a coating of iron oxide.   The younger series is finer and dustier and rests against the scarp leading down northward from the plateau.   It may be of Quaternary eolian origin.   Fifteen kilometres westward from Pirapora, at 600-700 metres altitude the Sul-Americana plateau bears deep, coarse red sand without internal evidence of age. To the south, the higher plateaus of the Serra Gerais and the Serra do Morro Vermelho are both capped by 100 metres of red sand that could well belong to the Cretaceous Urucuia formation and act as source for the arenites of the lower plateau. Beyond Jatoba Lake the mid-Cainozoic sands are thoroughly silicified into hard silcrete. Partly consolidated red sands continue westwards with a thickness that is usually between 50 and 100 metres beyond the Rio Paracatu. Shallow valleys and undrained hollows are common features of the sand country upon the Sul-Americana planation.

e) *the (late) Pliocene sands.* Sands similar in type to the sands just described, but unconsolidated, appear widely upon the lower planation (500-550 metres) of the Velhas erosion cycle towards the Rio Paracatu. These belong to a series younger than those (silcreted) upon the Sul-Americana plateau, and resemble very closely the Kalahari sands of South Africa (Plio-Pleistocene).

About Itu in São Paulo similar red, windblown sands and dusts lie extensively in valleys of the Velhas River cycle and upon the mid-Cainozoic (Sul-Americana) upland. The material seems to have been derived extensively from weathering of the Gondwana formations, both the sediments and the lavas. The former have supplied the sand and the latter most of the fine red dust.

Along the coastlands of north-eastern Brazil is the famous series of reddish " *barreiras* " sands resting upon the Velhas landsurface and subsequently cut into by late phases of the Paraguaçu erosion cycle. The age of the *barreiras* is nowhere fixed with precision, but the evidence from a number of states suggests a Pliocene age (*e.g.* plant fossils from Baia studied by Berry). The *barreiras* at Pinheiro near Sergipe, have been silicified to the stage where they form hard silcrete caps on hills rising above the valleys of the Paraguaçu erosion cycle. The *barreiras* are found as far south as Campos.

f) *the Pleistocene sands, earths and dusts.* The latest red accumulations, which are still accumulating in some regions of the *Planalto* of São Paulo, are red dusts and earths rather than sands, but sands are present in some localities where they appear to have been derived from earlier deposits of loose red sand. These materials are widespread over western Minas (Patos de Minas) and eastern São Paulo (Campos) where they nestle loess-like in sheltered hollows of the hillsides, or spread over the *planalto* mixed with the soil. The dusts are several metres thick and cover all the countryside as though of eolian distribution.

Over a large extent of the São Francisco valley between Pirapora and Joazeiro, Morães Rego (1936) has described incoherent sediments, muddy and sandy, with false bedding. Included are beds with eolian phenomena, and the whole he called the " *serie des Vasantes* ". The remains of mammals from this series indicate a Pleistocene age. Today the river trenches these beds though previously it deposited materials of the same facies over a wide alluvial plain. The laying down of the serie des Vasantes is doubtless a consequence of the tectonic rifting movements that subsequently to the Velhas erosion cycle lowered the floor of the valley far below the level of the adjacent plateaus (King 1956).

Also in the same reach of the Rio São Francisco, near its great eastward bend, are the surface limestones (calcretes) described by Branner (1911).

Strong confirmatory evidence relating to Pliocene and Pleistocene phases of red sand accumulation comes from the limestone caves of Central Minas. The cavern systems about Lagoa Santa and Pedro Leopoldo were excavated by ground-water solution acting for long ages below the plateau of the Sul-Americana cycle. This is the normal mode of origin for such cavern systems (Bretz 1942), and for the whole period of their formation, so far as can be ascertained, the cavern system was continuously filled with water. Later, when the rivers incised in the Velhas cycle of erosion, the water table fell in sympathy and innumerable subterranean caverns and galleries within the Bambui limestones were drained, some were opened to the atmosphere and the cave system dried out. Subsequently many of the caverns acquired, in whole or in part, an internal spelean sequence including, above a basal stalagmite, a deposit of red sand, usually cemented, in which are entombed abundant remains of late Pliocene or earliest Pleistocene mammals. This earlier red sand is covered by heavy stalagmite corresponding to the main period of ornamentation of the caverns. A second, younger red sand or cave earth overlies the main stalagmite, and carries a relatively recent fauna including *Equus* and man (Gorceix).

In the two distinct accumulations of red cave earths and sands referable to the late Pliocene and late Pleistocene respectively, we may recognise the two sand-spreads of similar ages that blanket the appropriate erosion surfaces in Western Minas and São Paulo.

The Succession of Alternating Denudational and Aggradational Landscapes

Since the mid-Palæozoic era the face of Brazil has been almost continuously land. Across the face of the country denudational and aggradational cycles have alternated in time and space, though frequently existing side by side at any given epoch, for denudation in one region may be the cause of deposition in another. The presence of fossils within the sedimentary members enables both sequences of landforms to be dated with tolerable accuracy enabling tabulation (Table VIII).

The earlier phase from Carboniferous to Triassic is dominantly sedimentational upon a sinking continental mass; the latter, from Jurassic to Recent, is dominantly denudational upon an intermittently rising landmass.

Remarkable indeed is the correspondence, episode for episode, between events and landforms in Brazil and those already recorded (Chapter IX) *from Africa.* Such correspondence, continuing into Recent times, can only be a result of similar tectonic activity *in the vertical sense* on opposite sides of the Atlantic Basin (King 1956A).

THE CARBONIFEROUS GLACIATED LANDSCAPE AND THE TRIASSIC DESERT

Withdrawal of the widespread Silurian seas left only small relicts—in Amazonas, Goiaz, and Parana. Elsewhere Brazil seems to have been land until late-Carboniferous time when continental glaciers spread over a landscape essentially of low relief. This landscape, as in Argentina (p. 41), they abraded, smoothed and polished until most of it

TABLE VIII

ALTERNATING EPISODES OF DENUDATION AND DEPOSITION IN EASTERN BRAZIL

Recent	Coastal sands, alluvia, surface limestones and red dusts of the interior.
Pleistocene	*Deep valley incision and retreat of major erosion scarps. " Paraguaçu " denudation cycle—two or three phase.*
Pliocene (probably late)	Barreiras and related series of red sands. Silcrete. Unfossiliferous.
Late Cainozoic	*Valley incision over Minas and São Paulo, with smooth planation over northern Baia by the " Velhas " cycle of erosion.*
Early Miocene	Sundry arenaceous deposits resting upon the Sul-Americana surface but in the absence of fossils difficult to date accurately. On the coast of Para, and probably offshore farther south, the lower Miocene rocks of the Pirabas formation.
Early Cainozoic	*Widespread smooth planation of the Sul-Americana cycle which forms the " master surface " from which erosion has subsequently carved most of the present Brazilian landscape.*
Late Cretaceous	Red sandstones and pebble beds of the Bauru and Urucuia series. In Sergipe, following renewed flexing, late Cretaceous marine rocks. Fossils in both continental and marine series.
Late Cretaceous	*Following elevation of the land, a " post-Gondwana " cycle of erosion cut valleys and minor plains into the pre-existing smooth Gondwana landscape.*
Early Cretaceous	In restricted localities, red sandstones of continental type. In Sergipe the Gondwana surface was flexed down below sea level and received a cover of early Cretaceous (Albian) marine sediments.
Jurassic	*Over most of Brazil was developed an erosional landscape of exceptionally smooth planation. This represents the " Gondwana " denudation cycle.*
Late Triassic	Botucatu series of red desert sandstones, followed by Rhaetic outpourings of basalt on a vast scale in the southern states.
Triassic	*An aggradational landscape under a desert regime: represented by the unconformity at the base of the Botucatu series. Few details known, but apparently of wide extent and low relief.*
Triassic-Carboniferous	A great sedimentational phase on a sinking landmass. Accumulation of Gondwana-type rocks beginning with tillite, then cold temperate types, finally warm temperate types. Plant and reptile fossils. No marine series.
Carboniferous-Devonian	*A landsurface of moderate to low relief: finally moulded under continental ice-sheets.*

consisted of bare rocky hummocks and irregular, undrained hollows. This ice-worn landscape may nowadays be inspected in the southern states of Brazil where it forms a selvedge about the outcrop of Gondwana-type rocks in the Parana hydrographic basin, *e.g.* about Itu and Indaiatuba in São Paulo, or at Lauro Muller in Santa Catarina where the relief was about 200 metres. Whether the Carboniferous landscape north and west of Abaete was heavily glaciated like that of São Paulo remains uncertain.

The importance of the glaciated Carboniferous terrain for correlation with Africa is very great.

Accumulation of the Gondwana-type sediments was followed by a short interval of denudation when a truly arid landscape was developed. Though the original extent of this Triassic desert is uncertain, it was widespread, and de Almeida opined that it was one of the largest desert areas recorded in post-Algonkian time. It correlates with the sub-Stormberg desert episode of Southern Africa.

The actual Triassic landsurface, marked in some regions by a thin and irregular band of silicified limestone, is preserved in the unconformity at the base of the Botucatu sandstone; for the desert speedily became a sandy desert with widespread red dunes and infrequent watercourses where stormwaters occasionally ran into temporary lakes before disappearing (Santana facies). In the type localities of São Paulo the maximum thickness of Botucatu does not exceed 250 metres. Only near the lower end of the Rio São Francisco does the continental type of Triassic deposit, with plant fossils, inter-digitate with marine facies containing abundant pelecypods.

During the Rhaetic, floods of plateau basalt overwhelmed the desert and indeed welled out sporadically far to the north where they came to lie on older rocks beyond the desert sands. These São Bento basalts correspond with the Drakensberg lava floods of Southern Africa.

Though of considerable stratigraphical importance, this resurrected Triassic desert has little significance in the modern landscape. On the whole, the Triassic formations appear to have been removed over wide areas by the Gondwana cycle before the Creta-ceous terrestrial deposits were laid down; but there remained a general concordance of attitude and form between the Triassic and Gondwana landscapes.

" Gondwana " and " post-Gondwana " Cyclic Denudations in South America *

After the emission of Rhaetic lavas, denudation prevailed over practically the whole of Brazil. Only locally did red sandstones (Uberaba series) accumulate. Prolonged throughout the Jurassic period, this Gondwana erosional phase reduced the landscape everywhere to an extraordinarily smooth plain which locally included already-razed fragments of Triassic (or sub-Botucatu) desert landscape.

At the dismemberment of Gondwanaland the plain was warped down below sea level along the east coast and in Sergipe at least received a cover of early-Cretaceous (Albian) marine sediments. This infra-Cretaceous landsurface, cut across granite and gneiss, has been described from north-eastern Brazil (Borborema) as undulating and ranging from 450 metres in the Moxoto Basin to 900 metres above Mimosa. The surface is deeply weathered and may bear up to 200 metres thickness of continental or lacustrine grits (Dresch 1957).

In the interior, the post-Gondwana cycle of erosion cut broad valleys into the earlier planation in Southern Brazil, but north of Sete Lagoas the two cyclic landscapes

* Data regarding the distribution of denudational cycles in Brazil are taken from the author's *Geomorfologia do Brasil Oriental* (King 1956) wherein fuller accounts are rendered.

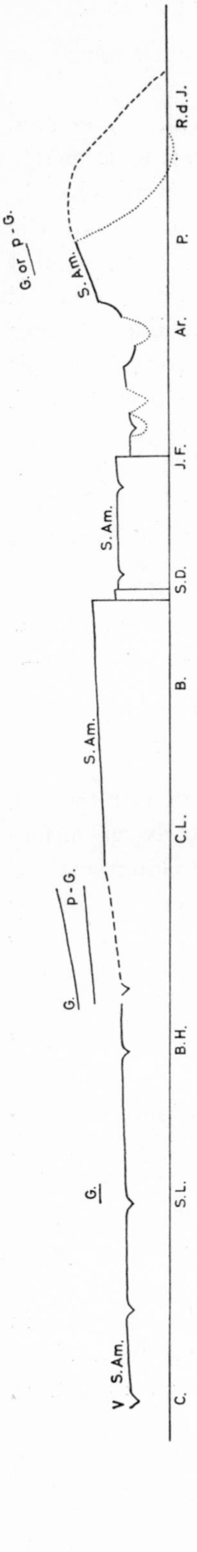

converge and the smooth Jurassic plain was superseded by a smooth Cretaceous plain which now lies buried beneath a widespread cover of late-Cretaceous continental red sands (*e.g.* Bauru series).

Relicts of the Gondwana landscape (Fig. 121) survive best in the smooth skylines (cut across Algonkian rocks) of the Serra do Curral, Serra do Ouro Fino, Serra da Maquina and Serra da Moeda of the mountainland south of Belo Horizonte (Fig. 122). There is no evidence that the mountainland, despite its rectangular outline, is encompassed by recent faults. Quite the contrary, its boundaries everywhere appear to be erosional in origin. Even the great south-east face of Caraça Mountain (1,700 metres high) appears to be solely a product of differential erosion between tough Itacolomi quartzites and a foreland of weak Minas schists, so that the issue of an elevated later surface does not arise.

Upon the high ridges the Gondwana surface has a rolling relief of up to 100 metres owing to later etching by the elements, but in the pristine Mesozoic state it must have been extremely smooth. Where cut across itabirites the surface bears a 10-metre-thick covering of *canga* or ferricrete which in many places is worked for iron ore. This mantle may be ochreous and pulverulent, but where cemented makes a caprock so strong that slopes of 60° are in places maintained below it, as where the road to Gandarela crosses the Serra da Maquina at 1,635 metres. In places the mantle is an aluminous residuum, but this is too contaminated by ferric oxide to be a bauxite.

The high ridges (1,400 metres and more) and the elevated post-Gondwana valleys incised into them slope from south to north more steeply than the valley forms of the younger denudation cycles that dissect them showing that differential movement operated between them.

The post-Gondwana upland is present as a high terrace, usually incompletely planed, and as small valleys and depressions in the earlier, Gondwana surface. About Itabirito its elevation is 1,200 metres, approximately 400 metres below the Gondwana summit bevel; west of the

FIG. 122. Generalised N-S section: Curvelo-Sete Lagoas-Belo Horizonte-Conselheiro Lafaiete-Barbacena-Santos Dumont-Juiz de Fora-Areal-Petropolis-Rio de Janeiro. G. = Gondwana, p-G. = post-Gondwana, S.Am. = Sul-Americana, V = valleys of Velhas cycle, valleys of Paraguaçu cycle dotted. Coastal monocline shown in broken line.

highway from Belo Horizonte to Rio de Janeiro the elevation is 1,100 metres with the Gondwana some 300 metres higher.

Through western Minas Gerais the Gondwana surface, with *canga*, is preserved at 1,400 metres upon the mountains west of Pocos de Caldas and at about 1,150 metres near São Gotardo. In both areas post-Gondwana valley excavation is again evident.

From all these mountainous regions the Gondwana and post-Gondwana cyclic landscapes decline northward and north-westward converging as they go, so that ultimately they coalesce into a smooth plain of early-Cretaceous age which, followed still farther, passes beneath an extensive cover of late-Cretaceous red continental sands (Fig. 120). As the late-Cretaceous sands are themselves truncated by the early-Cainozoic Sul-Americana planation a crossing of cyclic denudational surfaces takes place through central São Paulo and western Minas Gerais.

This crossing has been described (King 1956): "The Gondwana planation which at São Pedro stood 350 metres above the Sul-Americana cycle then passes below it. As the crossing takes place over a wide zone, part of the Sul-Americana landscape is a resurrected

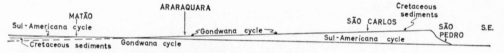

FIG. 123.   Crossing of the Gondwana and Sul-Americana planations in
the neighbourhood of Matão, São Paulo.

Gondwana surface. About Araraquara shallow Sul-Americana valleys often cut through the Cretaceous formation into the underlying basalt, revealing the Gondwana surface in the valley sides. It is also exposed in road cuts. But as both the Gondwana and Sul-Americana planations were very smooth, and the angle at which they cross is very small, it is often difficult to decide, even in the field, how much of the modern scenery in the zone of crossing is Sul-Americana and how much is resurrected Gondwana. At Matão, however, the transition to the Sul-Americana planation is complete and the countryside is bevelled far and wide by the Sul-Americana cycle alone, at 600 metres " (Fig. 123).

In the fossil state beneath late-Cretaceous sands the compound Gondwana-post-Gondwana plain may be identified west of the Rio São Francisco in Matto Grosso, and thence continuously far northward towards and beneath Amazonas, observing always a steady declination (Fig. 124). Sometimes the surface was lightly channelled before burial by the red sands, the channels being partly filled with well rounded quartz and sandstone pebbles usually derived from the Bambui series.

Beyond the Rio Amazonas Gondwana planation may perhaps be identified in lateritized summits truncating a horizontal or gently folded sandstone series at above 1,000 metres in the Guianas; and a planation surface at over 650 metres has been assigned (by McConnell*) to a late Cretaceous cycle. "The surface corresponds in altitude and other characteristics with the flat-topped hills and plateaus in the Estado Bolivar of eastern Venezuela" and is capped by residual hematites (cf. Brazil).

As the original slope of the Gondwana landscape in Brazil must have been dominantly westwards and north-westwards towards the proto-Pacific Ocean the eastward

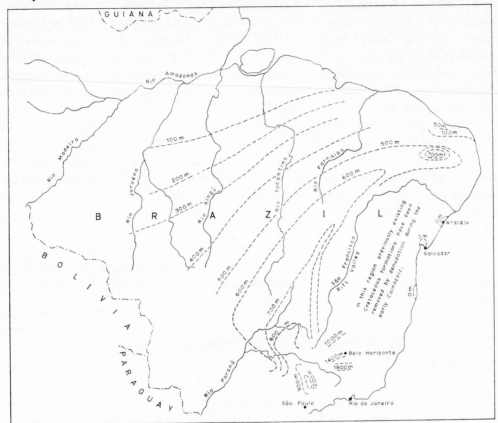

FIG. 124. Structural contours upon the base of the Cretaceous formations, showing the deformation of eastern Brazil since the late Cretaceous (mainly Quaternary).

course of the Amazon, and the basining of the Gondwana surface in Amazonas must post-date the rupture from West Africa (Fig. 109). Geophysical explorations have revealed, indeed, north-west to south-east Cretaceous faults in Maranhão with a throw of 500 metres to the south-west on a single fault, and graben-filling at the mouth of the Amazon (Marajo Island) begins with presumed Cretaceous marine beds (corals). Right through the Cainozoic era basining continued intermittently in the lower Amazon, yet the extent of country below 200 metres *widens* westwards. Right into the foothills

* Unpublished MS.

X

of the Andes, up the headwater rivers such as the Ucayali and the Maranon, the wide plains through which the rivers meander (*e.g.* Huallaga River) do not attain 200 metres in elevation. The hills here, such as the Contamana Mountains are faulted, and contrast sharply with the alluvial plain.

Through the ancient geological basin of the Rio Parana, Cretaceous continental beds (Bauru series) upon the watersheds bury the Gondwana or post-Gondwana landscape in a manner similar to that described for western Minas, Goiaz and Matto Grosso. In Rio Grande do Sul, south of the Serra Geral, a borehole has penetrated 1,000 feet of late sediments overlying basalts and affording data for scenic interpretation, though details are not available. In south-western Uruguay and the adjoining Argentinian province of Entre Rios also, dinosaur beds cover a Mesozoic landscape down to relatively low levels.

On the plateau of Patagonia, too, red dinosaur-bearing sands appear at Roca on the Rio Negro (lat. 39° S.) and again beyond 48° S., so that we may take a sub-Cretaceous unconformity in these regions, also, to represent the compound Gondwana and post-Gondwana denudation. About the forty-first parallel of latitude and east of the sub-Andean depression, stands a broad elevated plain ascending westwards and surmounted by mountain peaks at 1,000-1,200 metres, with local rises to 1,600 metres, which is almost as high as the cordillera of the Andes in the same latitude. Willis (1914) described the surface as a plain partly of pre-Cretaceous erosion cut across Archean rocks, and partly a surface of basic lava flows which rest upon the earlier bevel and descend into deep valleys previously scored across it. May these features perhaps represent post-Gondwana incision into an earlier Gondwana plateau?

THE SUL-AMERICANA AND LATER CAINOZOIC LANDSCAPE CYCLES

From the Amazon in the north to Patagonia in the south the smoothest cyclic bevelling apparent in South American landscapes is patently of early-Cainozoic age, and is analogous in extent, importance and age with the " African " denudation cycle of Chapter IX. We call it therefore the *Sul-Americana* landscape cycle. North of the Amazon River the early-Cainozoic surface is less clear. Nonetheless smooth surfaces of early Cainozoic planation capped with 20 feet or more of bauxite are widespread at elevations above 1,000 feet in all three Guianas, Venezuela and Colombia, where many curious river captures have taken place upon it. Northwards of an arch through Nassau Mountains a coastal monocline carries the surface and its bauxite below later sediments of the coastal plain.

More extensive is a well developed plain with inselbergs known as the " savannah surface " or " llanos " upon which is the curious Casiquiare Canal linking along an ancient drainage the Orinoco River with the Rio Negro tributary of the Amazon.

Bauxites and ferricretes cap outliers of this surface which, in the el Tigre oilfields of Venezuela, transects folded Miocene strata. Finally this, the most widespread planation north of the River Amazon, is dissected by Quaternary valley plains which become involved (with all their cyclic predecessors) at a rejuvenated coastal monocline.

In Brazil the dominant planation of the early-Cainozoic was dissected by a number of late-Cainozoic broad valley-incisions that have generally reduced the Sul-Americana plain to minor plateaus and smooth ridge crests upon the watersheds. At least two " post-Sul-Americana " late-Cainozoic cycles are known, but they are not universally present and only one stage usually appears. In eastern Brazil this has been called the " *Velhas* " cycle.

The broad *chapadas* between Senador Mourão and São Domingo do Arassuai typify the Sul-Americana landscape (Plate 9) and the same landscape in a dissected state extends for great distances upon the elevated country east of the São Francisco Rift Valley. Within and beyond the valley it makes a smooth planation that may

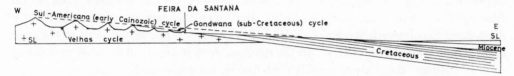

FIG. 125. Relations between cyclic erosional surfaces and coastal sedimentary series in the vicinity of Feira da Santana, Baia. The Sul-Americana landsurface may here be represented by an unconformity below the lower Paraguaçu series (presumed Miocene).

be recognised far westward beyond the Rio Paracatu, bearing in this region silcreted sands of presumed early-Cainozoic age. Southward as a dissected upland at 400-700 metres it covers most of the region between Rio Grande do Sul and São Paulo.

Combined locally with earlier Gondwana planation the Sul-Americana cycle renders the almost incredibly smooth plateau at an altitude of 900-1,000 metres about the focus of the Parana, Tocantins and São Francisco Rivers in the Triangulo Miniero about Uberaba and Uberlandia, extending thence into Matto Grosso and Goiaz (Ab 'Saber and Costa 1948). It frequently bears deposits of canga and in various hollows upon it accumulated local lake or swamp deposits such as are described by C. F. Hartt and L. J. de Morais about the headwaters region of the Jequitinhonha and Pardo Rivers. To these an Oligocene age has been provisionally assigned.

Nearly all the northward trending interfluves of the Amazon Basin are flat-topped by the Sul-Americana cycle truncating red, late-Cretaceous sands overlooking late-Cainozoic incised valleys of the rivers; and in the north-east of Brazil, (Piaui, Paraiba and Rio Grande do Norte) it has been identified forming a number of plateaus at 700-800 metres covered to a depth of scores of metres by continental red sands and muds of a series like but prior to the barreiras (Dresch 1957).

East of the Rio São Francisco the Sul-Americana planation is widespread and well preserved through eastern Minas, but is lost to later erosion over most of Baia (King

1956). The Serra Geral, rises abruptly above the planation as a series of residuals upon tough Algonkian quartzites, otherwise significant residuals are rare. A likely exception is the plateau north of Vitoria da Conquista that may also bear an older bevel.

Though the cyclic landsurfaces flex down monoclinally towards the east coast the Sul-Americana planation does not attain sea level before the shore is reached and hence no corresponding unconformity can be identified within a sequence of marine sediments. The surface must truncate Cretaceous beds, but even in Sergipe no Miocene sequence is known that could lie upon the Sul-Americana hiatus.* Only in the north of Brazil does the Miocene Pirabas formation of Para (Maury 1952) rest upon a presumed equivalent of the Sul-Americana cyclic denudational cycle.

The Velhas or late-Cainozoic landscape cycle is the most widespread of any in Brazil. From Guiana, where it bears bauxite deposits, the landscape, undulating between 200 and 500 metres, covers a wide territory on the northern flank of the Amazon Basin, and again on the southern interfluves, the cycle is extensive as broadly flat-topped *Serras* overlooking the lowlands from scarps. The lowest limit of the cycle again stands around 200 metres. In the north-eastern states it enters as an undulating country between the plateau massifs (Sul-Americana cycle) of Borborema and makes surrounding plains with an altitude of 450-550 metres (Moxito Plains). The distribution of these plains is chiefly upon the areas of weaker rocks. Dresch has compared these pediplains with the late-Cainozoic cyclic landsurface of Africa.

The table-topped type of country (*chapadas* and *taboleiros*) continues through the north-eastern states to Baia. The general aspect is of an undulating, splendidly pedimented landscape occasionally bearing island-mount residuals. In places the cycle is two stage; and not infrequently bears silcreted sands of Pliocene age. In Sergipe a marked south-eastward slope carries the surface below the *barreiras*, late-Pliocene coastal sands near Aracaju (*cf.* Fig. 126).

Southward through the maritime states of Brazil the late-Cainozoic surface has been progressively more strongly uplifted upon the coastal monocline to several hundreds of metres, and there the short river systems have carved a rugged younger terrain leaving little of the original Velhas landsurface through Espirito Santo and Rio de Janeiro.

Widely over the interior of Brazil the Velhas cycle has destroyed the Sul-Americana planation except upon the interfluves, and through Minas Gerais, São Paulo and the great Parana hydrographic basin it makes the broad valley systems incised by 100 metres or more, that ramify through the landscape. It has penetrated indeed to the heads of all the major hydrographic systems of Brazil—Amazon, São Francisco and Parana. At a few localities it is overlain by red sands of presumed Pliocene age as along the valley of the Paracatu. These are not silcreted like the red sands overlying the Sul-Americana

---

* A possible exception is in the region of Feira da Santana, Baia, where it may pass under the supposed Miocene of the lower Paraguaçu series (Fig. 125).

surface of the interfluve plateau above, *e.g.* near Lake Jatoba. Similarly unconsolidated sands and dust lie extensively in valleys of the Velhas cycle about Itu in São Paulo. Apparently the rivers diminished in volume during a dry episode and spread their loads out in the valley bottoms whence the material was blown out over the surrounding

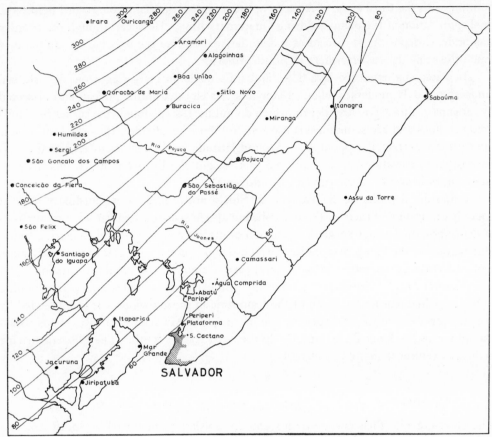

FIG. 126. South-eastward descent of the late Cainozoic (Velhas) land-surface below the *barreiras* series of coastal sands in the region of Salvador, Baia. Elevations in metres. *after geologists of the National Council for Petroleum*

countryside. At the coasts, too, the reddish barreiras sands overlie the Velhas landsurface.

In southern Brazil from São Paulo to the plateau of eastern Santa Catarina, cut across crystalline basement and Permian sediments, the same combination of early-Cainozoic accordant ridge crests and late-Cainozoic valleys with about 100 metres of relief is standard between 800 and 950 metres elevation, and the same paired cycles continue, with southerly declination, into Uruguay (p. 332) where remnants of the Sul-Americana surface render a smooth plateau.

But in Argentina conditions are very different. There the smooth early-Cainozoic landsurface sank down and received a cover of mid-Miocene and later sediments upon the granite basement (Weeks 1948). The first late-Cainozoic phase of geomorphology is therefore depositional. An hiatus and a later Pliocene phase of deposition corresponding with the third stage of Andean uplift complete the Cainozoic record before the final aggradation of the pampas during Quaternary time. However, though the country was under a depositional instead of a denudational regime the tectonic episodes are of much the same date as elsewhere in South America.

In Patagonia extensive lava-flows and tuffs made an early-Cainozoic depositional landscape of only moderate relief. Later this was elevated into a plateau and dissected by canyons of 150-200 metres depth, which do not necessarily follow the earlier (pre-tuff) drainage lines and are sometimes transverse to the earlier divides, thus rendering some interesting resurrected topography. Around latitude 40° S. a series of erosional bevels rises between elevations of 300 and 700 metres, but the history is much obscured by late-Cainozoic and Quaternary volcanic effusions.

Cainozoic deposits of the Patagonian Shield are indeed of extraordinary interest not only on account of their wealth of fossils but also because of their varied environments of deposition, including repeated alternation of marine continental and lacustrine facies. Outstanding is the Patagonian molasse which was laid down with great uniformity upon a planed surface transecting Mesozoic and early-Cainozoic continental formations. Of late-Oligocene age, it formerly covered three-fifths of the area of Patagonia, corresponding to the principal marine incursion of the Cainozoic in those regions. It is succeeded by the Santacruceno series, and then by the marine, late-Miocene Entre Rios beds which extend far up the River Plate but only tip the coast farther south. The Pliocene marine beds are even more limited in extent.

CYMATOGENY AND QUATERNARY LANDSCAPE DEVELOPMENT IN BRAZIL

The effects of Plio-Pleistocene cymatogeny are not less pronounced in South America than in Africa. In typical form they appear as huge archings, coastal monoclines, basins and even as rift valleys, deforming the Cainozoic cyclic landsurfaces and, with subsequent erosion, provide most of the present relief.

At the northern edge of the continent Venezuela and parts of the Guianas were elevated so that their inherited denudational landscapes now stand high. In Amazonas and Para, however, two existing basins of sedimentation were deepened, the latter at the mouth of the river subsequently receiving (according to two boreholes put down on Marajo Island) the greater part of 4,000 metres of sediment. A number of Quaternary rejuvenations have also affected the Amazon Basin below 200 metres. Though progress and survey are well-nigh impossible in that great jungle-land, the river itself with its tributaries affords the necessary data: on the great waterways breaks in the evenness of flow (nickpoints) have been faithfully recorded and, when compared, show a systematic

PLATE 10

The broad tableland of the early Cainozoic cycle (right) abruptly truncated at the São Francisco rift valley (left), between Barrocão and Francisco Sa, Minas Gerais, Brazil.

Lester King.

break in the thalwegs as follows: on the south side of the trunk river Rios Juruena and São Manoel 100-150 metres, Tapajoz, Canuma and Tocantins 100 metres, and on the Xingu +100 metres; on the north side Rios Branco and Paduiry 100 metres, with 80 metres on the Rio Negro. These separate a planed upper stage from a medley of lesser depositional and denudational features below. The truly cyclic nature of these nickpoints is further attested by corresponding nicks in excess of 80 metres, along the thalwegs of independent river systems such as those of British Guiana.

An outstanding example of Plio-Pleistocene cymatogeny is provided in eastern Brazil where a huge arch of country, involving all the cyclic denudational surfaces of the Mesozoic and Cainozoic eras, rises steadily southward from the Amazon Basin to a rifted crest at the São Francisco valley (Plate 10) whence the surfaces decline again more steeply on a coastal monocline to the Atlantic (King 1956) (Fig. 127). Towards the crest the chief surface is the Sul-Americana, surmounted by the Serra Geral, a series of residual ranges upon tough Algonkian quartzites; but the rift at the crest of the Plio-Pleistocene arch lies some distance west of the belt of residual mountains. Between Portierinha and Monte Azul the ranges are continuous and strong, and still define the watershed: on the flanks of the ranges only remnants of the Sul-Americana chapada remain, to both east and west deep valleys of the Velhas cycle have destroyed most of it. In the neighbourhood of Grão Mogol, however, the ranges are less impressive and the chapada more extensive. Curiously, the mountains here no longer form the watershed but are breached by the gorges of rivers which rise in the west at the edge of the São Francisco rift and flow *eastwards*. The chapada between the Serra Geral and the rift has been back-tilted for more than 50 km. and its drainage reversed (Fig. 128). Now broad-floored valleys of the Velhas cycle reach almost to the crest of the rift scarp along the Riberãos Ticororo and Congonhas. About the Jequitinhonha Valley only lines and groups of residual hills make the Serra Geral and the Sul-Americana and Velhas cycles meet from opposite sides of the range. The quartzite ranges of the Serra Geral continue northward only a few kilometres beyond the border of Baia. The up-warped Sul-Americana chapada, at 1,100 metres, then makes the watershed. But here again the axis is frequently broken through by valleys of the Velhas cycle, and this state continues northward through most of Baia. By Morro do Chapeu, however, the line of highest country (a long ridge bevelled at 1,100 metres in the Sul-Americana cycle) stands *west* of the watershed where active tributaries of the São Francisco drainage have cut right through the crest of the upwarp into the wide expanse of the Velhas cycle to the east. West of the high ridge the *taboleiro* of the Velhas cycle still rises westward, however, towards the main ridge fault, which postdates that cycle (Fig. 128).

In the attitude of the Cainozoic erosional surfaces may be recognised the typical cymatogenic " rise to the rift " of the African plateau, of a similar age and in a similar environment.

The São Francisco rift has not yet been adequately explored, and many even of its major scarps remain to be mapped (Fig. 127). Its dimensions, with a general width

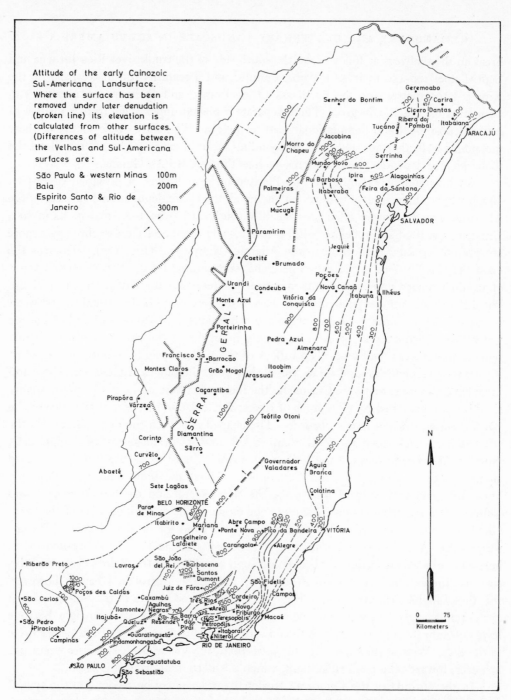

FIG. 127.   Quaternary deformation of eastern Brazil involving a huge cymatogenic arch broken at the crest by the São Francisco rift valley, and farther south by the Paraiba rift valley.   The coastal monocline swings from south-south-west through Baia and Espirito Santo to south-west beyond Cabo Frio, thus forcing up the elevated knot of country about Teresopolis.   Lost beneath the sea, south of Rio de Janeiro, the axis returns to the continent south of Florianopolis (*cf.* Figs. 122, 124).

exceeding 50 km. and a depth of several hundreds of metres, are closely comparable with those of East African rifts and may express a fundamental physical magnitude for the failure of normal crustal materials. The scarps are fresh and rectilinear, in conformity with extreme youth. Subsidiary rifts occur at some points, one of the largest leading up to Paramirium in Baia (Fig. 127).

The floor of the rift is formed by landscapes of the Sul-Americana and Velhas cycles, but for a great distance north of Montes Claros these are overlain by Pleistocene and later alluvia of the Rio Verde Grande and the Rio Gorutuba. The absence of such deposits from the trench of the São Francisco valley between Joazeiro and the sea, whereas they are present in the valleys of the Vasu Barris (30 km. wide) and Itapicuru at comparable altitudes in northern Baia suggests that the present lower course of the Rio São Francisco is quite new. It has, indeed, abundance of waterfalls and gorges.

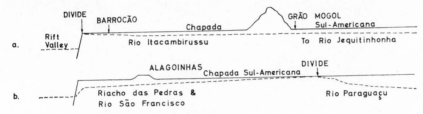

FIG. 128. Contrasted changes of divide associated with cymatogenic arching and rift valley faulting in Brazil. Sections from west to east through (a) Grão Mogol, (b) Alagoinhas.

Confirmation of differential movement on the seaward side of the axis is provided by a borehole at the edge of the Paraiba delta. It passed through 3,000 metres of youthful sediments.*

About Cabo Frio the strike of the great arch swings more westerly and the resultant stresses have forced up part of the country to the highest point in Brazil, the Pico de Bandiera (cf. Mt. Kosciuscko, p. 357). At the same time the seaward limb steepens abruptly so that a cross-section from Curvelo to Rio de Janeiro is exceedingly asymmetric (Fig. 122). This steep monoclinal warping, combined with the elevation of tectonic gneisses along this axis, makes the renowned coast of the Serra do Mar, and the spectacular mountainland of Rio de Janeiro state (Plate 11). The Quaternary scarp, 1,000 metres high, has now retreated under erosion behind the head of Guanabara Bay. It is crossed on the ascent to Petropolis and is one of the finest in existence. A similar scarp stands between Santos and São Paulo. No evidence of Recent faulting is anywhere associated with the seaward face of the Serra do Mar, the features of which must be wholly ascribed to erosion acting upon a steep monocline of tough, massive, tectonic gneisses.

So close is the axis of the monocline to the coast of this region that headwaters of the Rio Tiete rising only 10 km. from the sea, flow north-westward away from it

* Dr. H. Martin.   Private Communication.

several hundred kilometres to join the Rio Parana, and reach the sea only at La Plata nearly 4,000 kilometres away (Fig. 129).

Here also the crest of the cymatogen has cracked open along the Paraiba graben (Fig. 130), of which the Paraiba River flowing into the sea near Campos has taken advantage to capture some of the former headwaters of the Tiete making a curiously

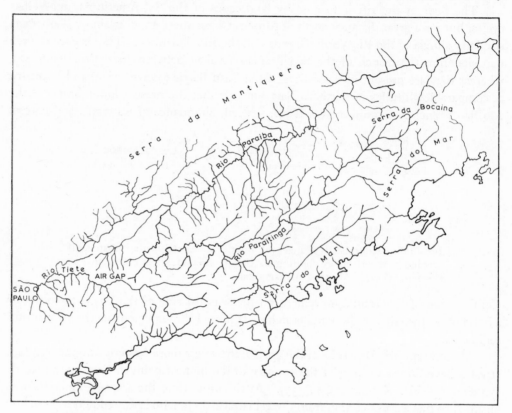

FIG. 129. Capture of former headwaters of the Rio Tiete following generation of the Paraiba graben. Modern, and former, headwaters of the Tiete rise only 10 km. from the steep coast of São Paulo state but flow nearly 4,000 km. to the sea *via* la Plata.

hooked system perched above the shoreline mountains (Fig. 129). The northern flank of the graben is the splendid face of the Serra da Mantiquera on which the cyclic erosion surfaces have been uptilted to nearly 3,000 metres. At Itatiaya the summits bear the imprint of Pleistocene glaciation.

For a space the axis of the monocline passes out to sea, but it re-enters the continent just south of Florianopolis where the Serra do Mar standing at 1,850 metres dies away or is replaced by a number of small ridges, and the Rhaetic lavas warp down to the coast near Torres. South of this point begin the coastal lagoons and the low flats of the Rio

PLATE 11

Clustered bornhardts of the Quaternary landscape cycle in Espirito Santo, Brazil.

Lester King.

Jacui where Miocene and Plio-Pleistocene sediments are known overlying granite along part of Lagoa dos Patos. Late Cainozoic faulting appears here. In Santa Catarina, Putzer has observed widespread block faultings, tensional in type and in part associated with intrusion of the Rhaetic lavas. Displacements are of the order of 100-200 metres, and the directions of several of the major faults are parallel with others in the fractured belt of Rio de Janeiro. These features suggest that the monocline originated during the Mesozoic and was greatly rejuvenated (with some fracturing) during the mid-Cainozoic and again in the Plio-Pleistocene (*cf.* Natal Monocline of South Africa). The scarp of the lavas (Serra Geral) does not correspond with the watershed, being to the west, but generally through Parana, Santa Catarina and Uruguay it has retreated about

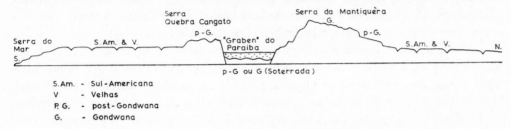

S.Am. - Sul-Americana
V   - Velhas
P. G. - post-Gondwana
G.   - Gondwana

FIG. 130. Section from south to north across the Paraiba graben showing cyclic denudational landsurfaces.

200 miles from the coast—which compares with 150-200 miles for the Drakensberg in in the same period of time.

All regions of Brazil affected by the mighty arching of Plio-Pleistocene and Recent time, wherein also the rivers have short courses to the sea, have been profoundly dissected by deep valley systems. But where the rivers take longer, circuitous routes, the late dissection is not yet apparent. Thus a large area of Baia is affected but relatively little of Minas Gerais, and virtually none of São Paulo outside the magnificently scarped coast. Almost everywhere this Quaternary (Paraguaçu) cycle is represented by two phases of which the former is recorded by terraces standing above the present graded and ungraded valley-floors. Waterfalls on the major rivers also serve to demarcate the sub-stages which are consistently displayed from Sergipe southwards to the Rio Riberão in São Paulo.

In addition, minor complications and splitting of nickpoints are introduced by local differences of rock hardness and structure. The resulting detailed landforms are transient and are merely symptoms of youthfulness in the cycle.

SUMMARY OF SOUTHERN URUGUAY

Apart from the northern districts, most of Uruguay consists of gently rolling landscape at no great height (50-150 metres) above sea level. Away from hilly areas upon ancient rocks (*e.g.* Cerra dos Minos) which bear no summit or flank bevels, the accordance and smoothness of many of the ridge crests, especially in the divide region about Tala, north of Montevideo, are reminiscent of the early Cainozoic planation. Incised valley heads are very broad and shallow, but lower down incision is more marked and recent.

Several series of depositional formations are associated with the landscapes of Uruguay and assist, with enclosed fossils, in dating the topographic facets of the landscape. Towards the River Uruguay, and within a graben crossing from east to west north of Montevideo, are continental sediments of late Cretaceous age resting upon a surface that was described (J. Caorsi and Goni 1958) as representing an erosional phase current throughout Jurassic and early Cretaceous time (*cf.* Brazil and North Africa). Marked mid-Cretaceous earth movement is indicated by the thickness of the sediments (2,000 metres) in some parts of the graben (Cuenca de Santa Luzia).

The Cainozoic truncation of the Cretaceous rocks left them ferruginized (in places with a complete lateritic profile) both upon the ridges and in the broad valley heads, where occur also the *calizas* of Queguay, which are silicified calcretes with *Planorbis* like the *grès polymorphe* of Africa. Accumulated when clastic debris was unavoidable in the senile landscape, the calizas are regarded as of Oligocene age by Caorsi and Goni.

Also within the shallow valley heads of this region occur examples of the Fray Bentos calcareous (eolian) clays. Post-dating the calizas of Queguay and antedating the fossiliferous sands of the Pliocene marine Camacho transgression, they are provisionally regarded by Uruguayan geologists as late-Miocene in age. They attest the existence of the first late-Cainozoic erosional and depositional cycle.

Resting upon an horizon of Fray Bentos in a depression along the Rio Urugua y the Camacho Pliocene marine sands of the second late-Cainozoic cycle are in turn overlain by the widespread eolian Pampeano sands and dusts with abundant vertebrate fossils and terrestrial mollusca.

The small relief of Uruguay renders differentiation of cyclic denudational surfaces difficult, but aggradational phases illustrate that several episodes have occurred during Cainozoic time.

QUATERNARY OF THE ARGENTINE

A very different Quaternary history is recorded from the Argentine. Over the pampas of Central Argentina are extensive Pleistocene and Quaternary formations that imply a regime of great tectonic stability. Through north-western Argentina and Paraguay stands the Gran Chaco, a region of immense swamps and infilling by detritus brought in by rivers from the recently uplifted Andes in the west. This part of the sub-Andean depression doubtless subsided gently in sympathy with uprise of the mountain chains to the west.

To the north-east, around Corumba, are the Pantanals, a further area of immense marshes occupying a tectonic depression about the head of the Paraguay River. These regions form a " negative reaction " to the cymatogenic upheaval of the Andes on the west, coupled perhaps with tilting of the open country of the Brazilian Shield on the east.

ANTARCTIC CONTRIBUTION

To analyse the topography of Antarctica is difficult; a huge ice-cap and unusual exploratory hardships have combined to preserve most of the Antarctic from the prying eyes of geologists. But a start has been made, and the usual cyclic and tectonic episodes are being recognised (King 1966).

The pre-Karroo surface, for instance, finds equivalence in the ancient surface beneath the Buckeye Tillite (and transecting the Devonian) of the Horlick Mountains (Long 1962); and this, or a somewhat later, surface has been recorded in the Mt. Markham region (Gunn and Walcott 1962) and farther north as the " Kukri Peneplain ".

Upon the TransAntarctic Mountains, extending over 2,000 miles from the Horlicks to Cape Adare, a gently uneven crestline is apparent for great distances rising and falling gently as a measure of unequal uplift. This appears to be the older late-Cainozoic cyclic landscape that has been typically (and greatly) arched towards the end of the Cainozoic time.

In several regions the normal crestline of the mountain wall is surmounted by still higher massifs (*e.g.* Royal Society Range) that sometimes preserve, amid undoubted structural plateaus such as Mt. Markham which conforms to the outcrop of the thick " Peneplain Sill " of dolerite, summit accordances and bevels of presumably an early-Cainozoic planation. These may be seen upon the Horlick and Queen Maud Mountains, and perhaps upon the Dominion Range at the head of the Beardmore Glacier. Both the cyclic planations dip towards the Polar-Wilkes Depression (Fig. 182) and so disappear in turn beneath the ice and snow of the Polar Plateau (10,000 feet).

The front of the TransAntarctic Mountains is the deeply dissected face of a mighty, end-Cainozoic monocline (King 1966). It is not due to modern faulting, as was surmised by David and Priestley (1914) who termed it "the Antarctic Horst"; for portions of the monocline have been preserved, as near Cape Hallett where the ancestral summit planation is warped down eastwards at about 7° " so that the erosion surface passes beneath the coastal shield volcanoes and the Ross Sea " (Harrington *et al.* 1965).

Two similar surfaces have also been identified in the Vestfold Hills, Princess Elizabeth Land; where warping is demonstrated upon a single surface falling from 125 metres at Edward VIII Gulf to 30 metres at Mawson, and also upon a similar surface at heights ranging from 1,000 to 2,600 metres in the Prince Charles Mountains " whereas around the Amery Ice Shelf similar flat-topped exposures have summits only 60 to 200 metres above sea-level " (McLeod 1965).

The presence first of late-Oliogocene to early-Miocene, and later of presumed

Pliocene marine beds upon the western side of the Weddell Sea and dipping towards that basin (p. 469), suggests that the usual Cainozoic cycles of denudation were developed upon the region of the Graham Land Plateau, and that these have subsequently been tilted towards the south east.   These datings are important.

The tectonic movements in all these regions were virtually completed before the onset of glaciation (*cf.* Wales, the Alps, New Zealand and British Columbia) thus fitting the global scheme of Plio-Pleistocene cymatogeny.

PALÆOZOIC AND MESOZOIC LANDSURFACES OF INDIA

The presence of Gondwana rock sequences in India implies the existence there of the associated Carboniferous glaciated terrain on which these rocks lie, and although a great part of the Indian glacials was waterlaid in peripheral lakes the usual striated pavements upon older rocks underlie many of the southern exposures.

A Triassic hiatus between the Panchet and Mahadevi series corresponds to the sub-Stormberg phase of erosion in South Africa and the sub-Botucatu of Brazil, while the red and buff sandstones of the Pachmari stage that follows indicate that the climate was dry in India also.

The Gondwana history included effusion of the Rajmahal basalts after which the country, still forming part of the ancestral Gondwanaland, lay exposed to erosion for a large part of the Jurassic and Cretaceous periods and the usual " Gondwana " cyclic landsurface was planed.   From Cutch into the Himalaya the Tethys Sea extended, and the sediments shed from the old land are now found as fossiliferous marine rocks in those areas.   By the end of the period a marine facies also crept down the eastern flank of India.   But on the subcontinent itself, wherever denudation was not dominant, continental type sedimentation (Jabalpore) produced an aggradational landscape. Jurassic sediments also appear in faulted basins on the opposed aspects of India and Ceylon.

While the original slope upon the Gondwana landscape was probably from south to north, subsequent tilting in the same direction has been repetitive so that remnants of the Gondwana planation now survive at elevations of 8,760 and 8,800 feet upon the Nilgiri and Cardamom Hills respectively in the extreme south of the peninsula.   Near Ootacamund imperfect bevelling around 6,500 feet suggests a post-Gondwana cycle of landscape development there, and some of the higher levels upon the Eastern Ghats, which are residual mountains, may approximate to this cycle.

In Ceylon, too, a gneissic plateau, the Horton Plains at 7,000 feet, is carved upon exceptionally hard rocks.   There are also lower surfaces at 6,000 feet or more (Kularathnam 1952).   Though some authors have claimed that the great escarpments that bound the high plateau are due to recent faulting, direct evidence of such faulting has not yet been forthcoming (Cooray 1956) and the mighty rock faces are seemingly true erosion scarps. The summit and subsummit topographies, therefore, probably correlate with Gondwana and post-Gondwana cyclic landscapes of the Nilgiri Hills in India.

Much of Bombay and the Central Provinces is underlain by the Deccan Traps, a series of late-Cretaceous and Eocene basaltic lava-flows that attain a thickness of 10,000 feet and originally covered an area of 400,000 square miles. The flows are horizontal except near Bombay where the dip is about 5° seaward. Beneath the flows is the Lameta series of estuarine and fluviatile formation seldom 100 feet thick but of wide distribution. The lower part consists of cherty or siliceous limestones, of which Fermor has demonstrated that many " have resulted from the calcification of the underlying Archean gneisses and schists " (Wadia 1937). All stages of alteration may be seen and the change affects all the various kinds of underlying rocks. Quite clearly these basal formations represent the ancient calcreted Gondwana or post-Gondwana landsurface.

Little evidence is available to show whether independent Gondwana and post-Gondwana landscapes existed in Central India or whether a single phase of " remodelled " Gondwana planation survived through the Cretaceous period; but an incursion of the Tethys covering the Salt Range, Western Sind and Baluchistan sent an arm up the ancestral Narbada Valley where it left Cenomanian (Bagh Beds) far in the interior. The deposits are usually situated upon the flanks of inliers of Precambrian rocks through the later Deccan traps (*cf.* Adrar das Iforas in West Africa), and reach almost 1,500 feet above modern sea level. These Bagh Beds perhaps represent a post-Gondwana depositional phase resting upon an inherited Gondwana surface. Certainly the Mesozoic landscapes now stand, in the fossil state, at low elevations in Madras and the Central Provinces.

Northward of the outcrops of the Deccan Trap evidences of Mesozoic cyclic landsurfaces are difficult to find, and perhaps they do not exist. Exiguous remnants may survive upon the tops of the Vindhyan Range and the Aravalli Hills, but they seem not to have been recorded in literature.

CAINOZOIC LANDSURFACES OF INDIA AND CEYLON

Outside the main valleys most of Peninsular India is a plateau between 1,500 and 2,000 feet above sea level. Part of this plateau bevels the Deccan traps, of late-Cretaceous and Eocene age, so the erosion cycles responsible for the plateau are Cainozoic. Most of the plateau is an undulating surface that compares morphologically with the late-Cainozoic cycle of other continents, but accordance of the higher parts of the landscape suggests strongly that the essential planation, *e.g.* in the Central Provinces, was achieved by a previous cycle, of early-Cainozoic age. Radhakrishna's description (1952) of the Mysore plateau compares: " A study of the profiles indicates that the original plateau is everywhere deeply dissected. If the tops of the low mounds and elevations as indicated in the profiles are connected together the line would roughly indicate the level of the old plateau. Remnants of this old plateau can be made out by the presence of isolated flat-topped hills and mounds capped by laterites, or by bold hills formed of granite or steeply dipping ferruginous quartzite. The old plateau would thus represent an almost level surface with cappings of laterite here and there. Above this level would stand out some ranges, the resistant remnants of an ancient landsurface in the course of peneplanation. The average height of the old plateau is roughly 3,000 feet and the surface is seen to slope gently towards the east ".

" The dissection of the old plateau appears to have gone on at a rapid pace along the 12th and 14th parallels where much of the old plateau surface has been removed. In these regions a new plateau surface has been formed nearly 800-1,000 feet below the surface of the old plateau. . . . The profile drawn along the 13th parallel still retains more the character of the old plateau ".

Unfortunately, analysis of the denudational cycles on a subcontinental scale remains to be done; but the laterites of India are divided into " high-level laterites " above 600 metres and " low-level laterites " in depressions and upon the coastal lowlands to east and west. The second of these groups is much less massive and mostly of detrital (as contrasted with residual) origin, " being formed by the products of mechanical disintegration of the high-level laterite " (Wadia 1937). Primarily, therefore, the laterite is the regolith of an older planed surface, which it may still identify, despite local variations of laterite age. In these respects it agrees with similar deposits upon the early-Cainozoic landsurface of Australia, and the presumed early-Cainozoic planation of India may by analogy be termed the " Indian " landscape cycle.

Further indication of the dual-cycle nature of the plateau topography is afforded by the corresponding Cainozoic rocks cropping out along the east coast. These fall into two main series respectively Eocene to Miocene and Pliocene in age. Outcrops of the latter (Cuddalore sandstone) appear at intervals all along the coast from Orissa to the extremity of the peninsula. Rocks of the same age are also developed on the Malabar coast both north and south of Goa.

The Cainozoic cyclic landsurfaces did not escape differential movement. Long ago, Dunn wrote of uplifts in Chota Nagpur and Bihar amounting to 1,000 feet during the early-Cainozoic and a similar amount about the middle of the era; but Krishnan (1953) noted that along latitude 25° N. there was practically no corresponding movement, the region acting as a hinge zone. Periodically, too, changes of a negative character took place in the foredeep region of the Indo-Gangetic Plains wherein, with the region to the north, the whole Cainozoic sedimentary history of India is exhaustively recorded. While the deposits were received mainly from the rising chains of the Himalaya in the north, their relation to the sinking of the northern flank of the Peninsula is important and worthy of further study by deep drilling. Moreover, as the Cretaceous and Cainozoic formations of the coastal regions do not appear at excessive elevations, outward monoclinal tilting of the coastal hinterlands is indicated as for other fragmented coasts of Gondwanaland. Quite exceptionally, however, Krishnan (1953) writes of the Bombay coast as " a fault-scarp of probably Miocene age, the downfaulting being of the order of 6,000-7,000 feet ", and late-Cainozoic fault systems are cited from the Narbada-Tapti regions of the Deccan.

More than half the area of Ceylon is likewise a plateau mostly at 1,200-1,600 feet above sea level separated by a marked erosion scarp from coastal plains 5-20 miles wide. Adams (1929) correlated the Sinhalese plateau with the Deccan plateau of India which would make it of late-Cainozoic age agreeable to its morphology.

According to Wadia (1943) the Sinhalese plateau is surmounted near the central highlands by flat-topped hills, ridges and buttes (? 2,500 feet) which give an impression of a previously smooth topography from which the late-Cainozoic landscape may have been carved. If this is correct, these residuals then represent the early-Cainozoic " Indian " denudational cycle.

Post-Cainozoic Deformation and Drainage in Peninsular India

In elevation India is markedly asymmetric both from south to north and from east to west. Much of this asymmetry arises from deformation by tectonic movements, the last of which have operated to elevate the late-Cainozoic plateau of the interior (in Ceylon also) and warp the marginal coasts. This warping has lately affected all the river systems by rejuvenation and marked indeed are the nickpoints of Quaternary cycles that have advanced headward as waterfalls generally across half the breadth of the Peninsula (on the Godavari to the Province of Bombay). Examples are: Sivasamudram Falls (Mysore) 300 feet, Gokak Falls (Belgaum) 180 feet, Dhurandhar Falls (Jabalpore) 30 feet but of large volume, Gersoppa Falls (Northern Kanaza) 850 feet, and Yenna Falls (Mahableshwar Hills) 600 feet. Cainozoic warpings caused several changes of drainage patterns. The River Cauvery, for instance, rises upon the *western* flank of the Western Ghats and flows east through the highest part of the Range (Fig. 131). Its course is senile almost from the beginning, but after crossing the early-Cainozoic plateau of Mysore, it passes into an antecedent gorge through differentially uplifted hills. Conversely, the Sharavati River of the west has captured a perched headwater system formerly belonging to the east.

Nearly all the major rivers of the Peninsula rise amid the Western Ghats only a few score miles from the Arabian Sea and yet make their way across the entire breadth of the Peninsula to the east coast. Only the Narbada and Tapti flow in the opposite direction.

Plio-Pleistocene negative differential movement is of course profound in the Punjab depression north of which the Salt Range makes a line of flat-topped cliffs extending from the Jhelum westwards for a long distance beyond the Indus. The prominent

Y

level plateau top of the Salt Range slopes gently northwards to merge into the high Potwar plains (Wadia) which represent a filled Cainozoic trough between the Salt Range and the Rawalpindi foothills. Considerable uneven warping is indicated here for Plio-Pleistocene time.

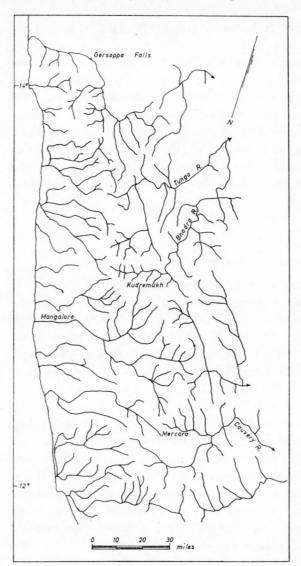

0   10   20   30
miles

AUSTRALIA: THE CONTINENT

The Palæozoic unity of Australia with Gondwanaland has been amply demonstrated (Chapter II). This relationship persisted until the Cretaceous period when most of the continent appears to have been of low relief and the east central region was inundated by the (Roma) sea. Over the site of eastern Australia, however, rose the bevelled stumps of late-Palæozoic mountain chains.

Australian geologists have insisted (David 1932; Bryan 1944) that land extended eastward far beyond the present coast, and even beyond the line of the Great Barrier Reef over what is now the Tasman Sea. Modern

FIG. 131.

Drainage pattern in the west of Peninsular India, showing river captures.

geophysical exploration reveals no trace of this land now upon the sea-floor; instead it appears (with the aid of continental drift) in the New Guinea-New Caledonia-New Zealand orogenic belt (Chapter XIV) which includes just those marine Mesozoic and Cainozoic formations that are missing from the eastern aspect of continental Australia.

Aside from evidence in the east, the date of separation of Australia from the parent Gondwanaland may be fixed from Western Australia, in which state Triassic rocks are absent but marine Jurassic, Cretaceous and Cainozoic formations all occur marginally. Conditions thus resemble those along the eastern coasts of India and Africa which rifted during the mid-Mesozoic.

Australia " contains no high mountains; the Mesozoic and Cainozoic strata which in other continents and in the girdling Pacific island arcs have been severely folded and upfaulted to form Alpine mountain-systems, are here typically horizontal. Highlands, indeed, there are but they are for the most part uplifted and dissected peneplains, and none of them attains any great height; it is estimated that less than half the continent has an altitude of more than 1,000 feet and that about 5 per cent exceeds 2,000 feet, while the highest point is only 7,308 feet above the sea " (David 1950).

The vast expanse of almost horizontal Mesozoic sandstones crossing the central region from north to south shows that great plains have existed there continuously since the mid-Mesozoic. Doubtless, though such proof through marine strata is lacking, almost the whole of the Australian interior has been of similar planed aspect throughout the last hundred million years.

Modern Australia is divided into three physiographic regions: the Western Plateau, the East-Central Lowland, and the Eastern Highlands (Fig. 132) of which the first-named occupies more than half the total area and constitutes a typical stable shield with vast erosional plains bevelled across Precambrian granites and gneisses. The low east-central region from the Gulf of Carpentaria to the Great Australian Bight seems largely to have been induced in earliest Cretaceous time when the region was spanned by a shallow sea for its entire length. Later, after the seas retreated, the region was occupied by extensive lakes (e.g. Lake Winton) and in Cainozoic time warping induced a further series of depressions, e.g. Lake Eyre, that have become foci of centripetal drainage systems. Aridity has rendered much of this region only sparsely habitable, and indeed the Simpson Desert occupies a prominent position east of the railway line between Oodnadatta and Alice Springs. The eastern highlands trend more or less parallel to the seaboard, coming closest to it in Queensland where the belt is narrow and retreating from it with a broadening to 400 miles or so through New South Wales. In Victoria the belt turns east-west. The rugged island of Tasmania may be regarded as part of the belt that has been separated by tectonic movement at Bass Strait.

Plateaus form the major physical features of the continent. These are chiefly the result of broad, cymatogenic uplift acting upon planed Cainozoic landscapes but the varied scenery of the eastern highlands belt has prompted certain authorities such as Süssmilch (1928, 1937) and Stanley (1927), to postulate extensive faulting of Pliocene to Recent date in the uplift of this region. Sharply divergent opinion has been expressed by Bryan (1928, 1930), by Craft (1933, 1933A) and by Maze (1944) who regard the numerous scarps of the eastern region as predominantly erosional in type. Reviews by Cotton (1949) and by King (1959) note only the Cullarin scarp near Canberra as tectonic, with possibly certain of the scarps in the neighbourhood of Mt. Kosciusko described by

David. In the modern view the numerous scarps of the eastern region are erosional in origin, and recent faulting is negligible in Australia (*cf.* Antarctica p. 333).

Two other of Craft's conclusions are in full agreement with the account we have already given of landscape development in Africa and South America. He has recognised the antiquity of denudation in eastern New South Wales by regarding it as following immediately upon post-Mesozoic or even pre-Mesozoic updomings; and he has related

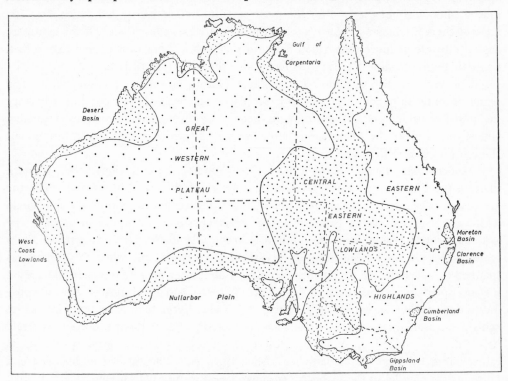

FIG. 132. The three physiographic regions of Australia.

the rejuvenation of the valleys of coastal rivers in New South Wales to seaward tilting of a compound surface that, at the end of the Cainozoic, already sloped in that direction.

THE PERMO-CARBONIFEROUS GLACIATED LANDSCAPE

The landscape moulded by late-Palæozoic ice-sheets is now being resurrected in all the states of Australia except perhaps Queensland. Many extensive glaciated pavements in a fine state of preservation have been described, as at Bacchus Marsh, Victoria. On the whole the landscape was undulating or subdued but mountainous terrain existed in parts of the eastern states (p. 45). On the north a fringe of lakes existed with occasionally glacial debris delivered into the sea, perhaps by icebergs.

The Triassic phase of denudation prevalent in Gondwanaland, too, affected almost the whole of Australia apart from the east coast where marine formations appear.

There is no evidence, however, of a desert environment such as afflicted the remainder of Gondwanaland, the glacial episode was too recent in Australia (p. 58).

GONDWANA AND POST-GONDWANA LANDSCAPES IN AUSTRALIA

The primary datum in Australian geomorphology is the early-Cainozoic, "Great Australian" planation (p. 345), that reduced the continent almost everywhere to an extremity of low relief. Nevertheless, in a few places residuals stand above this datum, and certain of these are bevelled by a yet older surface accepted by workers in Australia as of Mesozoic age. "In the Great Western Plateau and the Eastern Highland belt great numbers of isolated hills, plateau remnants great and small and residual mountain ranges rise above the Miocene surface. In view of the length of time during which sedimentation was proceeding in the great continental depression now forming the Great Artesian Basin, and of the fine grain of most of the deposits in this and other basins of Cretaceous deposition, we may assume that most of the land-area was in closing Mesozoic time in a state of peneplanation. The monadnocks upon the Miocene surface are usually regarded as remnants of this peneplain, which was uplifted to a varying extent probably during the late-Cretaceous Maryborough diastrophism" (David 1950). The remnants are too exiguous in themselves to give a coherent picture of the landscape of Mesozoic Australia, but their historic importance is out of all proportion to their present area, as we may legitimately believe them to be fragments of a truly Mesozoic "Gondwana" landscape. Widely over the central lowland, also, a surface of unconformity beneath flat-lying Jurassic and Cretaceous formations may be regarded as a Gondwana surface in the fossil state * (Plate 8).

In Western Australia Clarke and others (1948) describe an early-Mesozoic land-surface in the Irwin River Basin, and further work in the Carnarvon Basin reveals, according to Fairbridge, additional Mesozoic surfaces that may perhaps collectively be termed "Gondwana". Some of these pass beneath the Cretaceous sediments of the basin. Without resurrection, a possible Gondwana surface is present upon the South Esk Tableland and the Rawlinson Range standing some 300 feet above the surrounding plateau level, and east of the state boundary, almost in the centre of the continent, the smooth crestlines of the Everard and Macdonnell Ranges together with the transverse drainage lines may have been inherited from a Gondwana cycle of planation. It is

---

* Upon the Western Australian plateau, one of the most stable regions of the globe, even earlier erosional surfaces have been resurrected. Thus Hills (1945) records : " In the Pilbara, Murchison, Kimberley, Northern Territory and parts of South Australia there are broad tracts of Archean rocks which had been planed to a smooth landsurface prior to the deposition of the Proterozoic (Nullagine) sediments, which surface is now still undisturbed or only gently warped over large areas. Owing to the difference of rock hardness, the thin and relatively soft Proterozoic sediments are often stripped off by erosion exposing the tattered remnants of an ancient Precambrian peneplain ". This Precambrian planation was primarily responsible for laying bare many of the originally deep-seated ore-deposits of the Archean rock systems.

No folding of any consequence has involved the plateau since the Precambrian, while " the late Palæozoic sediments of the Desert Basin are still so unconsolidated and porous as to be an important source of artesian water, and Palæozoic coals there are still somewhat hydrous " (David 1932). Geographically it has been a great plain ever since the late Palæozoic.

more probable, however, that the former summit planation of these central ranges belongs to the early-Cainozoic cycle. No earlier bevels have been recorded from the Musgrave Ranges, though Mt. Woodruffe rises to nearly 5,200 feet.

In Swanland numerous Gondwana remnants survive as the " Mount Dale level " (Jutson 1934), and along the Darling scarp two Mesozoic landsurfaces are warped down to pass below sea level, the first beneath late-Jurassic or early-Cretaceous plant-bearing sediments at Bullsbrook and in the Brewery Bore No. 2 at Perth, and the second below late-Cretaceous and early-Cainozoic rocks of the coastal plain. These probably correspond to Gondwana and post-Gondwana cycles respectively, and indicate that the ancestral Darling Scarp, though repeatedly rejuvenated by later warping and perhaps faulting to attain its modern form, functioned as a coastal monocline at the fragmentation of Gondwanaland (Fig. 133).

About the Gawler Ranges in South Australia where Permian tillite was reworked by a Cretaceous sea (thus giving rise to an earlier belief in Cretaceous glaciation), Parkin recorded that " the pre-Cretaceous physiography was apparently one of very marked relief with mountain ranges in the Maree, Coward Springs and Mt. Dutton area and many isolated peaks in the south and west. For example, the bore at Lake Phillipson penetrated over 3,000 feet of sediments, whereas basement rock outcrops only 12 miles distant ".

Somewhere to the eastward of the central Australian ranges the Gondwana surface flexes broadly downward beneath the Cretaceous and early-Cainozoic formations of the central lowland and is lost from view until it reappears in Queensland where Whitehouse (1941) and Twidale (1956) have noted the surface in the fossil and partly resurrected state forming the planed floor upon which the widespread early-Cretaceous sediments were laid down. These sediments have themselves been smoothly transected by the early-Cainozoic planation and dissected by late-Cainozoic or Quaternary valley systems sufficiently deep to pass through the Gondwana unconformity beneath the Cretaceous sediments. The Gondwana planation thus appears in section along valley sides or ringing about flat-topped residual hills of sandstone (Plate 8). This relation is typical over many thousands of square miles. As Twidale indicates, dating of the " Gondwana " surface does not refer to an " instant " of geological time. It was prepared, in Queensland, over a long interval and even where covered by early-Cretaceous strata it may have existed in a planed state for an indefinite period previously. In this it resembles the Jura-Cretaceous combined Gondwana and post-Gondwana cycles of Congo Republic, Brazil and other areas that were very stable during the mid-Mesozoic. The Gondwana surface was bevelled across diverse rock systems frequently of high dip.

Twidale records the mid-Mesozoic erosional plain in and about the Isa Highlands, upon the Gregory Range and as plateaus and plains throughout the Einasleigh Uplands. " The frequency with which a return has been made to the pre-middle Mesozoic surface, which appears to be a fundamental datum, is remarkable and the persistence of relief as a whole through geological times is one of the most noteworthy features of the

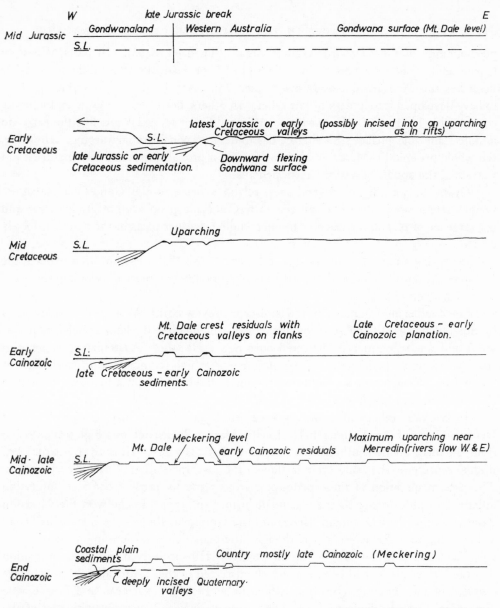

FIG. 133.   Physiographic evolution of the southwestern districts of Western Australia. Following early Cretaceous fragmentation of Gondwanaland, valleys were incised into the previously-existing Gondwana surface (Mt. Dale level) and the debris was shed down the coastal monocline to accumulate in the coastal plain region.   Mid-Cretaceous, marked uparching near the coast, perhaps extending eastward for a great distance as almost uniform uplift, was succeeded by late Cretaceous and early Cainozoic planation which shed appropriate sediments offshore.   About the middle of the Cainozoic era gentle, and slightly uneven elevation induced incision of broad shallow valleys (Meckering level) and in the east the surface was submerged to receive sediments (Norseman and Nullarbor). Strong end-Cainozoic upwarping (possibly with some faulting near the coast) along axes 20-50 miles inland from the coastal plain and through Merredin, caused changes of drainage and initiated the present denudational regime.

physiography of the Leichardt-Gilbert Area " (Twidale 1956A).   In parts of eastern Queensland, also, it is known in a " stripped " or resurrected condition.   Twidale describes the widespread Gondwana surface " in many localities the surface appears to have developed into a plain of low relief.   In others, however, there was undoubtedly considerable local relief.   In most areas this is difficult to assess for, like the early- to middle-Cainozoic surface, this surface has undergone considerable warping.   However, the whole pre-middle-Mesozoic surface of erosion probably attained late maturity and warranted the application of the term peneplain ".

Owing to warping of several ages, relations between the Gondwana planation, various stratigraphic deposits and the early-Cainozoic plain are not always clear and convergence of planations, such as has been noted in other parts of the world, is locally evident.

Excepting a moiety in the south-west, New South Wales has not been beneath the sea since Mesozoic time and the present topography has been developing since the Cretaceous period at least.

Small tableland fragments in the landscape of New South Wales have been ascribed by Süssmilch (1937) to a Cretaceous peneplain which suffered a late- or epi-Cretaceous uplift and was subsequently dissected by a new cycle (the " Australian ") which also attained extreme planation.   These fragments which compare with residuals of " Gondwana " landscape surmounting the main divide of Victoria may be assigned to the same ancient cycle of erosion.

In Victoria relicts of a once-planed Mesozoic surface survive upon resistant Devonian lavas of the Warburton-Healesville-Marysville district, as a high prolongation from the main divide south-eastwards towards Mt. Baw Baw (Hills 1934, 1940).   Mt. Buffalo represents the same cycle farther to the east upon other resistant rock masses. The present elevation of these plateaus is from 3,500 to nearly 6,000 feet, indicating differential uplift during their subsequent history (p. 353).   In the west the Macedon Range, composed of Devonian dacite, and the Grampian Ranges are quoted by David as belonging to a Cretaceous cycle, though little planation is evident upon them.

The Cretaceous age assigned to the bevels by Hills is derived from the observation that the former plains had been extensively dissected in the " Australian " cycle before eruption of the Older Basaltic lavas which lie at Berwick, Narracan and Pascoe Vale upon pipe clays of Oligocene age.   The age so derived is consonant with that of the similar small plateau remnants in similar situations in other states; but it should be pointed out that at the Morwell monocline, where the elevated plateaus of the divide sink beneath the sedimentary series of the east Gippsland syncline (Fig. 134), the Mt. Baw Baw planation could correspond with either of the unconformities beneath the Jurassic or the possibly Cretaceous series respectively.   Subsidence of the Murray Basin on the opposite side of the divide likewise began in the Jurassic, so that a similar age for the summit plateaus seems not yet precluded.

The survival of mid- and late-Mesozoic landscapes in Australia, though exiguously in so vast an area, is well established upon the work of many authors. The landscape seems generally to have been well planed, to be locally of either Jurassic (Gondwana) or Cretaceous (post-Gondwana) age, and may with confidence be compared with Gondwana and post-Gondwana cyclic landsurfaces still surviving in Africa and in India.

THE GREAT "AUSTRALIAN" DENUDATION CYCLE

In all the states of Australia geologists have described remnants of a formerly continent-wide, extraordinarily smooth, early-Cainozoic landscape that was heavily lateritised (Woolnough 1927). Though not universal, the armour of duricrust sometimes aids in

FIG. 134. Attitude of cyclic denudational landsurfaces and sedimentary formations upon the Mount Morwell monocline. Mesozoic landsurface of Mt. Baw-Baw and infra-Jurassic unconformity in broken line, early Cainozoic "Australian" pediplain and unconformity below Miocene in (heavy line), late Cainozoic cycle and sub-Pliocene surface (light line), Plio-Pleistocene valleys (thin broken line).

identification of this early-Cainozoic plain. For Queensland, D. Hill has suggested that the main duricrust is Miocene in age, and this may be general for Australia. Younger duricrusts have, however, been developed also upon late-Cainozoic denudational surfaces, so that care must be exercised in correlation if confusion is to be avoided.

Local evidence survives that in its pristine state the early-Cainozoic landsurface was a pediplain and so effectively did the processes of pediplanation operate that only a few, steep-sided residuals remain. Elsewhere evidence of such processes is lacking and the mode of development under erosion is uncertain.

Concomitantly, during the early-Cainozoic, deposition was widespread upon the central lowland (Eyrian series); and there the form of landscape may well have resembled the present alluvial plains of the Murray Basin (p. 359).

Near Coolgardie also (Balme and Churchill 1959), about 400 feet of late-Eocene or early-Oligocene continental sediments with brown coal of the "Nothofagus flora" record a depositional phase of the cycle in Western Australia.

The early-Cainozoic landscape has everywhere been attacked by later cyclic denudation to the extent that late Cainozoic landscapes now dominate the Australian scene; but sufficient relics survive to show that uplift of the early-Cainozoic or

" Australian " surface has been differential. Now local occurrences appear at elevations from below sea level up to 6,000 feet (David 1950; King 1959). Most of this deformation was accomplished after dissection by the late-Cainozoic cycles (p. 356) (Fig. 135).

The vast undulating plateau of Western Australia standing approximately 1,500 feet above the sea consists mainly of wide, shallow valley-forms of the late-Cainozoic cycles; but the ruler-straight profiles of the interfluves preserve extensively the smooth bevelling of the early-Cainozoic planation. Along the railway these interfluve crests with their cappings of duricrust descend from west (1,600 feet) to east (1,100 feet), with a renewed rise towards Kalgoorlie. Around Zanthus the landscape becomes noticeably flatter, the late-Cainozoic dissection being reduced to minor proportions and the earlier planation being better preserved. A little farther east it sinks gently below the Miocene limestones of the Nullarbor Plain which, being depositional and little

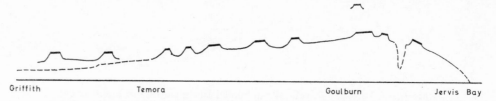

Griffith   Temora   Goulburn   Jervis Bay

FIG. 135. Section through New South Wales from Griffith to the coast near Jervis Bay showing the attitude of the cyclic denudational surfaces: Gondwana (projected), early Cainozoic (heavy line), late Cainozoic (light line) and Quaternary (broken line).

dissected by surface drainage (the limestone is cavernous and the arid region is without flowing rivers) is so extremely flat that the railway runs for 330 miles without a single curve. Here in the Eucla Basin, Singleton (1954) has distinguished two series of limestones, the Wilson's Bluff limestones believed to be of late-Eocene and Oligocene age thus corresponding as a depositional phase to the widespread early-Cainozoic planation upon the surrounding lands, and the early-Miocene Nullarbor limestone that records still wider deposition upon both aspects of the early-Cainozoic cycle. About Koonalda Cave, Crespin has reported still younger limestones that correlate with lower Pliocene of the Adelaide area and may correspond with a second phase of late-Cainozoic denudation over the mainland.

Residuals upon the early-Cainozoic surface of Western Australia are extremely rare, forming isolated or grouped hills and hummocks with an increase to hill ranges eastward toward the boundary fence. Some of the largest (e.g. South Esk Tablelands) bear an earlier (Gondwana) bevel.

E. de C. Clarke has considered that the original divide of the plateau, resulting from uplift, trended as a broad arch first northwards along a line parallel with the Darling scarp and thence, from the latitude of Geraldton, to the north-east. Stronger deformation is indicated in the regions of North Kimberley and Pilbara, though this decreases steadily towards the interior.

In South and Central Australia, exceptional hilly tracts are limited to the ancient, dissected strike-ridges of the Macdonnell and Musgrave Ranges in the heart of the continent, and the Flinders and Mt. Lofty Ranges, a series of horsts, in the south. The smooth crestlines of the Macdonnell and Musgrave Ranges, thought to belong to the early Cainozoic cycle upwarped near an ancient divide, are broken by vales occupied by sediment (with duricrust) of supposed Cainozoic age. The rest of the region consists of plains, in which two levels are prominent, one generally above and one below 500 feet. The upper is the " Australian " landsurface which enters without alteration across crystalline terrains from Western Australia. These plains slope gently eastward and south-eastward until they are encroached upon at low scarps by a younger cycle. The " Australian " cycle passes also across the Cretaceous and Eocene rocks of the Central lowland; but here a younger cycle is dominant and the " Australian " pediplain, heavily lateritised, truncates the flat-topped hills which rise sharply from the younger plain, *e.g.* near Oodnadatta. In the southern part of the state the early-Cainozoic planation makes the smooth tablelands bevelled across Cretaceous and Eocene sediments as well as ancient rocks in the vicinity of Woomera; and near Ooldea a similar surface appears to pass below the Miocene limestones (*cf.* Zanthus) but relations are much obscured by sand dunes. Around the head of Spencer Gulf numerous tablelands of pre-Miocene planation stand at 500-1,000 feet above clean fault-scarps of Pleistocene rifting (Fig. 136).

In the Northern Territory the same " Australian " cyclic planation makes the striking summit bevel of the Barkly Tableland (Whitehouse 1940A), on which feature it is carried into western Queensland. Except upon the elevated block of Arnhem Land, however, the surface has not been greatly uplifted in North Australia (David 1950).

About the coast of south-western Australia marine deposition coeval with the early-Cainozoic planation upon the land is represented (Singleton 1954) by beds believed to be upper Eocene and Oligocene penetrated by deep bores in the Perth Basin, by the Plantagenet Beds (that may be of the same age instead of Miocene as previously reported (Singleton)), the Wilson's Bluff limestone (p. 346) and, in South Australia, interdigitating lignitiferous and marine facies with pollen flora and impoverished marine fauna respectively. The Murray Basin, which began to subside in the Jurassic, also has Eocene (marine) beds followed by an Oligocene hiatus to represent the early-Cainozoic planation.

Passing from South Australia into Victoria the early-Cainozoic denudational surface emerges by upwarping from beneath Miocene marine beds as between Narracoorte and Mt. Arapiles (Fig. 137). Both the beds and the surface are transected by a late Cainozoic surface rising eastwards. Upon the Dundas Plateau the " Australian " cyclic surface is arched to nearly 1,000 feet above the sea, and near Casterton, at 500 feet, it truncates Jurassic and Cretaceous beds (Kenley 1954).

Thence eastwards it crops out at intervals along the Victorian Divide rising until in the Bogong high plains (Hills 1934) it attains an elevation of over 5,000 feet from which it descends northwards towards the Murray Basin and southwards towards the

East Gippsland depression (Fig. 134). Near the divide it is surmounted by Cretaceous or Gondwana residuals, and Hills describes the early-Cainozoic cycle as an upland topography of hills and valleys leading to flat land away from the divide. Later, when the Older Basalts were poured out, converting the gravels of the stream-beds into deep leads, they were confined to the valley-floors up country, but spread much more widely as sheets upon the lower lands.

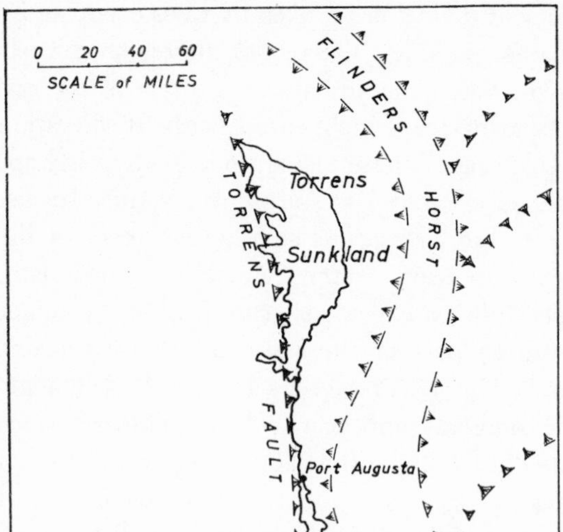

At Beaumaris on Port Phillip the surface descended, as a result of dislocations, beneath a shallow incursion of the Miocene sea.

Most of the " Australian " surface of Victoria has been lost to later cycles of erosion. Some of it has descended under tectonic influences to low level where it has been blanketed by marine or paludal formations (*q.v.*). Nevertheless, it was upon the " Australian " cyclic surface in early-Cainozoic time that the main divides and stream courses of the state were first clearly established, following differential movements in the Murray Basin to the north and Bass Strait to the south (Hills 1940).

Tasmania, then part of the mainland, also bore a lateritised and bauxitised planation that at Ouse in the Derwent Valley and south of Launceston descends (partly by mid-Cainozoic faulting) below sediments with supposedly Miocene plant fossils.

The centre of the island is a high plateau sloping gently from 3,100 feet in the north to 2,000 feet in the south. It bears monadnocks and ranges and

FIG. 136. Horsts and sunklands of South Australia due to Pleistocene rifting. *after C. Fenner*.

a newer cycle is incised into it by 500 feet. According to Fairbridge (1949A) the plateau was carved in late-Mesozoic and early-Cainozoic time, and was " faulted and considerably elevated in mid- and late-Tertiary and even Pleistocene time, when basalts erupted and flowed down over an already well-dissected and youthful landscape". The imprint of Pleistocene glaciation, however, lies heavily upon the Tasmanian plateau, and details of the earlier topography have been widely obliterated.

In New South Wales the early-Cainozoic planation, many details of which have been given by Craft (1928-33), makes prominent tablelands along the Divide (David 1950). These stand usually at elevations of 2,000-4,000 feet due to later warping (Fig. 138). Griffith Taylor (1911) has noted a seaward inclination of the surface, *e.g.* upon the Blue Mountains; westward it declines more gently and passes ultimately beneath sediments of the riverine plains. Lateritic ironstone is endemic upon the surface (Woolnough), attaining with the subjacent weathered zone a local thickness of 50 feet (*e.g.* Blackheath).

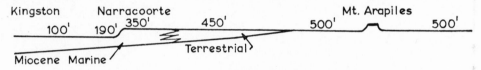

FIG. 137.   Relations between denudational landsurfaces and Miocene sediments (marine and continental), near Mt. Arapiles, Victoria. Early Cainozoic landsurface (heavy line), late Cainozoic surface (light line).

As in Victoria, flows of older basalt spilled out locally upon the planed landscape before it was dissected by late-Cainozoic cycles, making characteristic topography about Crookwell, south of Blayney and elsewhere.

While differential movements elevated the Australian cyclic planation along the belt of eastern highlands, in the Murravian Gulf the same surface was carried down below sea level to receive a cover of Miocene, and later, sediments. The same movement seems to have altered the courses of certain of the rivers, *e.g.* Darling (David 1932).

Much of Queensland had been covered by Cretaceous seas and swamps, and the accumulations of that period are still almost horizontally disposed, except near the coast at Maryborough where, in a restricted area of late-Cretaceous orogeny, Cretaceous strata are folded with the Jurassic and Triassic.

In consequence, early Cainozoic denudational and depositional landscapes developed side by side over western Queensland with an increasing dominance of denudational landforms towards the middle of the era producing the very smooth "Australian" cyclic landsurface planed across Eocene, Cretaceous and pre-Palæozoic rocks, accordingly as these had been affected by the broad warpings. Indeed from west to east the surface is developed across the three major physiographic divisions of Australia; the shield (Mt. Isa Highlands), the central lowlands (the Artesian Basin), and the eastern (Einasleigh) uplands (Twidale 1956A).

The early-Cainozoic planation, in part at least pedimented, is veneered with laterite, and residuals of this veneer surmount the principal divides. Clearly, when the laterite accumulated the divide was not in existence. On the Alice Tableland the laterite sheet,

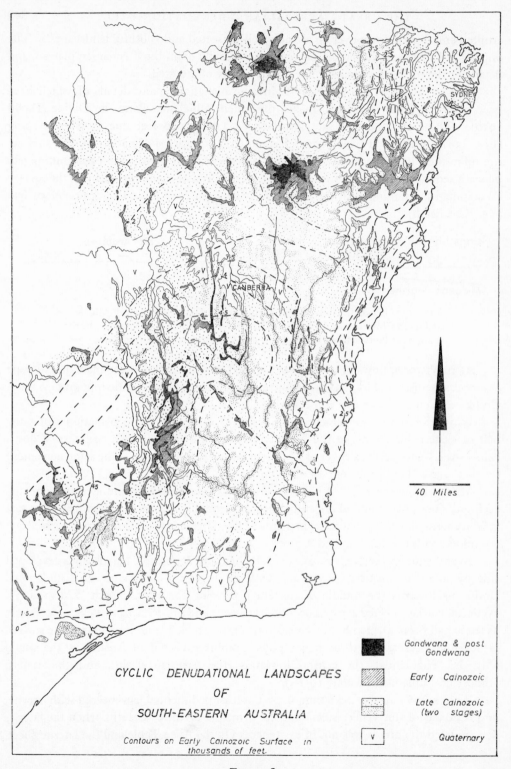

CYCLIC DENUDATIONAL LANDSCAPES
OF
SOUTH-EASTERN AUSTRALIA

Contours on Early Cainozoic Surface in
thousands of feet.

Gondwana & post
Gondwana

Early Cainozoic

Late Cainozoic
(two stages)

Quaternary

FIG. 138.

virtually unbroken, covers an area of over 20,000 square miles, and illustrates very clearly the pristine condition of the great plain. The youngest fossiliferous rocks from which duricrust has been derived have been placed by Hill in the Oligocene, and cannot be older than Eocene.

Mid-Cainozoic warping induced a late-Cainozoic dissection that, over vast areas in the basins of the Georgina, Thompson and Cooper Rivers has reduced the ancient plain to innumerable accordant mesas, each bearing an appropriate cap of laterite, *e.g.* around Boulia. Occasionally nothing is left but a scattering of " gibbers " upon a few divides, and the vast " Downs " and older alluvial plains of western Queensland have been developed by the destruction of the early-Cainozoic plain.

The early-Cainozoic planation survives also on the upwarped Great Dividing Range of eastern Queensland where, as in New South Wales, it forms numerous table-lands armoured with laterite and, as near Toowoomba, capped by Older Basalts.

Seldom does any marked topographic feature separate the interior drainage from that external to the Gulf of Carpentaria. The headwaters of the Diamantina are separated from the gullies of the northern drainage only by a plain a mile or two wide standing at 700 feet. Here again gentle warping initiated the divide and the Donors Plateau ranging in elevation from 350 feet in the south to 100 feet in the north demonstrates the fall of the surface towards the Gulf of Carpentaria.

Many of the drainage patterns originated upon the warped plain of the " Australian " cycle, and the Warrego drainage to the Darling has been quoted as an example of this. Some of the gorges of the Gregory River through strike-ridges of Precambrian rocks, and certain reaches of the Leichhardt, also probably originated by incision from the former " Australian " landsurface, though no laterite remains locally to prove its presence.

LATE-CAINOZOIC LANDSCAPES IN AUSTRALIA

Uplift and warping during the mid-Cainozoic initiated fresh cycles of erosion throughout Australia. These cycles have since destroyed most of the smooth, early-Cainozoic plain and substituted a varied topography of moderate or low relief with residual hill-ranges between broadly open valleys, that is still the most characteristic scenery of Australia. This topography is often two-cycle, the earlier late-Cainozoic cycle appearing in eastern Australia as wide plains, the later as broad valley-floors. In numerous localities outflows of Newer Basalts rest upon either, or both, of these cyclic surfaces *e.g.* Mittagong, Nimmitabel.

Two large regions, the Murray Basin and the Eucla Basin sank below sea level and in them accumulated Miocene deposits ranging from coaly formations at the base through three hundred or more feet of marine limestone to alluvial mud. Minor subsidences in a few localities such as Port Phillip and East Gippsland also received local marine Miocene deposits. Generally in Australia the earliest deposition following the mid-Cainozoic disturbance is mid-Miocene but both the Janjukian of Bass Strait and the corresponding marine deposit of the Northwest Basin are early Miocene in age, the latter corresponding to stage " e " of the Indonesian chronology (Singleton 1954).

Most of the Rolling Downs country of Western Queensland, developed with gentle convex slopes and with broad, braided river channels sometimes miles in width, is of the late-Cainozoic cycle upon weak Cretaceous rocks. Its elevation ranges from 50 feet near the Gulf of Carpentaria to 700 feet near the inland divide whence it declines again very gently towards Lake Eyre. Upstanding parts of the plain bear a lateritic crust less thick than that of the early-Cainozoic planation. Whitehouse (1940) has regarded the two laterites as of different ages. Twidale (1956) records several superficial deposits of grit and sand that appear to be a part of the plain and " it is believed that there was no interval between the deposition of the sands and silts but merely a change in conditions of deposition ". The sands, and the plain, of Western Queensland thus probably range in age through late-Cainozoic time (mostly Pliocene). Thin extensive superficial silts contain Pleistocene vertebrate fossils, and Twidale remarks that the plain has been subjected to Pleistocene epeirogenic movement.

Continued westward into Northern Territory the late-Cainozoic cyclic landscape occupies most of the huge endoreic basin about Tennant Creek, and in the small drainage systems of the north, tributary to the Timor and Arafura Seas, a cycle younger than the " Australian " is again apparent, as north of the Barkly Tableland.

Over most of the Georgina, Thompson and Barcoo catchments destruction of the laterite-capped early-Cainozoic plain is nearly complete and often nothing is left of the duricrust but gibbers upon a few divides. Thence the late-Cainozoic landscape spreads far and wide across adjacent parts of Queensland, New South Wales and South Australia as undulating country traversed by braided river courses occupying partly alluviated valleys often miles in width. The drainage systems are choked with two sets of alluvia, an older red, and a younger grey. The former are often extensively eroded, as also in the Flinders River Basin, and may belong with the late-Cainozoic or Pliocene cycles of erosion and deposition, which is suggested by their occurrence between the lateritic residuals of the Australian cycle and the sand dunes of the Arunta Desert, the last generated probably in Quaternary time.

Pliocene beds, representing late-Cainozoic aggradational landscapes, have been penetrated by boreholes in the Murravian Basin whence the sea had largely withdrawn at the end of the Miocene period. Comparable sandy formations sometimes ferruginised or silcreted crop out locally about the margins of the basin, e.g. at Tittybong and Boort, or appear upon structural highs within it, e.g. at Ivanhoe.

From the vast interior basins the late-Cainozoic denudational landsurfaces rise steadily eastward to the summit of the Great Divide whereon they have been elevated by Plio-Pleistocene cymatogeny (p. 356). Throughout this rise they maintain a diversified appearance with occasional residuals of smooth early-Cainozoic planation upon the highest country (Fig. 138), and the same compound landscape, now dissected by deep Quaternary valleys, descends from the Divide towards the sea. In this form it appears consistently (though occasionally with two instead of one denudation cycle) along the maritime slope of Queensland and New South Wales from Cape York Peninsula to Cape Howe. In Queensland, Bryan (1928) has remarked that the rivers do not reach the sea by the most direct routes " but only after long and tortuous passages in which it is notable that the longest sections of the streams are in well marked valleys . . . parallel with the coastline which the rivers are trying to reach ". This pattern, largely structurally controlled, is inherited from the late-Cainozoic cycle and has been little modified since by the strong, though apparently irregular, Quaternary tilting towards the modern coast.

Behind Sydney the surface stands low in the Cumberland Basin (Fig. 139), but thence it rises rapidly to the crest of the Blue Mountains (3,500 feet) near Katoomba and on to the 4,400 feet Jenolan Plateau of the early-Cainozoic cycle beyond.

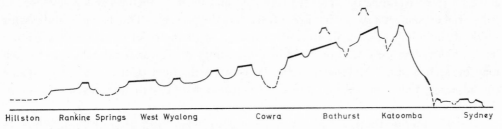

Hillston   Rankine Springs   West Wyalong   Cowra   Bathurst   Katoomba   Sydney

FIG. 139. Attitudes of cyclic denudational landsurfaces westward from Sydney. Gondwana (projected), early Cainozoic (heavy line), late Cainozoic (light line), Quaternary (broken line). Elevation at Katoomba, 3,500 feet. Compare with Figs. 135, 138.

Craft (1933) has followed the distribution of Cainozoic cyclic landsurfaces far to the south through the Shoalhaven catchment, showing very clearly the current steep rise of all these surfaces from the coast towards the Divide. His " Monaro Peneplain " about Cooma and Adaminaby represents the first late-Cainozoic cycle in full maturity (Plate 12). Minor, though broad, valley incision into this represents the second late-Cainozoic cycle. Amid the late-Cainozoic cycles developed the structurally controlled drainage pattern of the coastal hinterland in New South Wales, and the curious course of the upper Snowy River began to evolve.

Where the Divide turns westward through Victoria the late-Cainozoic surfaces have been upcast mightily and, following 4,000–5,000 feet of Quaternary valley incision, now survive only exiguously as undulating ridge crests. Westward where the Divide is lower the late-Cainozoic cycle extends unbroken across the watershed until at the border with South Australia it appears as valleys, 200–300 feet deep within the early-Cainozoic Dundas Plateau (p. 348).

Towards Mt. Arapiles, a depositional plain on Miocene strata presents a smooth horizon up to 500 feet above the sea (Fig. 137), and near Balmoral duricrust of late-Cainozoic age is well developed. A rather similar history is indicated for Tasmania where

z

Miocene lake beds resting upon down-faulted early-Cainozoic planation are transected and partly built over by the (probably Pliocene) Brickenden terrace.

" Newer " basalts have locally been extruded upon both phases of late-Cainozoic landscape seaward of the Great Divide through Queensland, New South Wales and Victoria, for example at 2,000 feet in the upper valleys of the Pliocene Yass-Canberra plain. Auriferous gravels buried by lava have since been mined as " deep leads ".

Southern Victoria experienced the same Miocene depression of the early-Cainozoic plain that affected the whole of the southern coast of Western and South Australia and formed the Murravian Gulf, and only the South Gippsland Highlands, Wilson's Promontory, the Mornington Peninsula and the Otway Ranges projected as islands above this shallow sea.

General uplift, accompanied by local warpings, supervened at the close of the early-Pliocene (post-Kalimnan). The sea retreated and most of Victoria was re-exposed to sub-aerial erosion, at a somewhat lower level than the present. The fluviatile and marine sands of the middle-Cainozoic were then carved, with the older terrain, into a mature land. The valleys were later overlaid by outpourings of Newer Basalt (Pliocene) which may be seen around Melbourne. In the western districts (Colac) wide lava plains spread across the country, the outposts of volcanic activity extending even into South Australia.

In the interior the sea had vacated the Murravian Gulf after the mid-Miocene and absence of late-Miocene deposits implies that surrounding planation was advanced in the first late-Cainozoic cycle. Weak crustal movement allowed early-Pliocene marine (Kalimnan) deposition in New South Wales and Victoria, as reported from boreholes (Gloe 1947) and this is followed in some boreholes by estuarine and terrestrial late-Pliocene (Werrikooian) deposits like the opalised and ferruginised sands of Tittybong.

In South Australia also a younger, planed surface stands below the Australian pediplain. The new cycle seems to have been initiated by late-Miocene uplift so that great rivers flowed southward through Central Australia to the sea. It truncates Eocene, and probably also Oligocene strata in the interior of the state, but presumed Pliocene deposits seem to be contemporary with it.

The new plains, post-Miocene in age, mainly erosional but depositional upon the emerged Miocene strata of the Mallee and the limestones of the Nullarbor plains extending into Western Australia, make the most widespread cyclic landscape in South Australia. The surface has been partly silicified, as at the opal fields of Coober Pedy. Remnants of the earlier " Australian " cyclic surface often form accordant, flat-topped, steep-sided " tent-hills " capped with silcrete, as in the same locality (Fenner 1931), and serve to demonstrate the pediplaned origin of much of the late-Cainozoic landsurface. The highest of the " tent-hills " stand about 200 feet above the lower plain, as near the boundary with the Northern Territory (Madigan 1936).

While the principal interfluves throughout most of Western Australia bear the smooth crestline of the early-Cainozoic " Australian " cycle, almost the whole of that gently undulating granitic plateau was fashioned subsequently into extremely broad valleys with a general depth of 100-300 feet. While several partial bevels are known, the best developed is the " Meckering Level " at 800 feet along valleys incised into the Darling Plateau of the west. These changes testify uplift of the duricrusted early-Cainozoic planation, but downward movement also carried the planation below Miocene sea level at Norseman (120 miles from the present coast) and in the Nullarbor region. Both these localities now stand 800-1,000 feet above sea level. The present elevation of the Plateau, commonly 1,200-1,500 feet, was achieved in two stages of uplift, one late-Miocene and the other late-Pliocene (Kosciusko). These uplifts were not uniform. Jutson (1934) records " very gentle folds or warps, broken occasionally by fault-scarps ". Slight irregularity of uplift may have caused the subdivision of the plateau into areas of exterior drainage and interior drainage into different centra; and the alluvial plains of some of the interior river basins may also be due as much to back-tilting as to the local abundance of waste in the dry climate. Indeed, over a great part of the plateau there are scarcely any flowing rivers or modern river channels, but evidences of a greater precipitation and runoff during Cainozoic time are not lacking.

Two late-Cainozoic cycles of planation and valley cutting respectively appear in many parts of Australia. Where a single (post-mid-Miocene) cycle is apparent now, it has sometimes manifestly destroyed an earlier, perhaps Miocene, version. Almost everywhere great plains, both erosional and depositional, formed the scenery of Australia from early-Mesozoic time until the close of the Cainozoic era. Such changes as occurred in its morphology were induced by comparatively gentle warping that altered the sites of deposition slightly, admitted or excluded the sea here or there for a while, but seemingly did not create relief amounting to more than a few hundreds of feet. A more violent change, of cymatogenic type, ushered in the Quaternary regime.

THE KOSCIUSKO CYMATOGENY AND SUBSEQUENT CHANGES OF LANDSCAPE

The crown of Australian scenery, Mt. Kosciusko, is borne upon a dissected tableland of the Gondwana cycle (Craft, King 1959) which stands at 6,000-7,000 feet surmounting the 5,000-5,500 feet plateau of the early-Cainozoic cycle that itself reaches (Fig. 138) from the Federal Capital Territory south-westward to the Snowy Mountains. It is not a region of mountain peaks but of long even-crested ridges separating steepwalled valleys that plumb a profundity of 3,000 feet. This tableland represents the culmination of the Quaternary " Kosciusko " cymatogenic movements along a rising arch from Cape Howe, between the conflicting monoclines of New South Wales and Victoria (Fig. 138); but the presence of the Gondwana tableland implies that the region functioned as a watershed at least through Cainozoic time.

Upon the Australian mainland the late-Pliocene and Pleistocene " Kosciusko " movements did not involve any significant folding or crumpling of rock masses. Even the extensive faulting formerly invoked amid the eastern highlands by Süssmilch (1931, 1937) (p. 339) is now largely discounted by Australian authors and the only extensive recently-faulted features are the fresh rift and horst scarps of the Spencer and St. Vincent Gulfs in South Australia (Fig. 136) with probably the Cullarin scarp near Canberra. Instead, following the work of Taylor (1923) and Craft (1928-33) in particular, the principal dislocation even of the eastern highlands is recognised (Cotton 1949; King 1959) as by strong warping, arching and tilting that involved all the Cainozoic landsurfaces, carrying them from near sea level at the coast to maxima of 4,000 and 5,000 feet upon the Great Divide (Fig. 138) beyond which they descend regularly towards the riverine plains of the interior. These plains now fill with alluvia the broad depressions created by the cymatogenesis (Plate 13).

Out of the polycyclic Cainozoic lowlands the Kosciusko movements created the modern relief of Australia wherein Quaternary denudation has carved deep gorges through the highlands (e.g. Cox's—Wollondilly Rivers, Abercrombie River) and spread out the resulting waste in interior basins (Murray River, Lake Eyre), or upon the continental shelf.

Owing to previous planation and the relatively short time since uplift the crest of the divide is often quite smooth and an observer may pass over it in places without recognising it as a divide at all. David (1950) even records a number of basins of centripetal drainage at the very crest. Moreover, the two major Cainozoic planations sometimes converge towards the crest indicating that it was in existence, locally at least, before the Kosciusko cymatogeny.

Unfortunately, despite the steep inclination of the Cainozoic planations in the coastal hinterland of eastern Australia, e.g. from 2,000 feet at Sassafras to 600 feet behind Tomerong, N.S.W., the axis of no relative movement on the coastal flexure lies seaward of the present coast so that, as in eastern Brazil, the planations are not brought down to sea level before the coast is reached and the corresponding sedimentary record is lost to view in the submerged continental shelf.

On Cape York Peninsula the crest of the divide stands at 1,000 feet or less but behind Cairns it soars swiftly and upon the Atherton Tableland the early-Cainozoic planation exceeds 5,000 feet with the late-Cainozoic cycle at 3,000 feet. But these elevations are not maintained and, according to David, in the hinterland of Rockhampton the Pliocene plains and valley systems stand at small elevation. The line of the divide has here been forced to the west by younger cycles acting from the coast, so that windgaps now appear at the heads of certain of the westward-flowing rivers (Wearne and Woolnough 1911).

Through the New England Ranges the late-Cainozoic landscape stands at 5,500 feet, on the Blue Mountains—Jenolan highland at 3,000-4,000 feet. The two mountainlands are separated by the Bassilis geocol, where the amount of uplift was only 2,000 feet. A second geocol at Lake George (also 2,000 feet) (Fig. 138) similarly separates the Blue Mountain from the Kosciusko highlands where the divide briefly exceeds 7,000 feet.

Through New South Wales and eastern Victoria the divide stands less than 100 miles from the coast towards which the downwarping is very steep. The coastal hinterland is thus deeply dissected by Quaternary gorges of the short coastal rivers, except in the Cumberland tectonic basin behind Sydney (Taylor 1923). Contours upon the early-Cainozoic surface show (Fig. 138) that the coastal monocline steepens from the south towards Sydney and the amount of uplift upon it decreases in the same direction. Hence the sea was enabled to cut the Bulli cliffs whereas southward beyond Woolongong a widening coastal plain becomes manifest as the flexure broadens (*cf.* Zululand).

At Cape Howe the coastal monocline abruptly changes direction to east-west through Victoria thereby creating a plunging fold that rises from the Cape almost directly to Mt. Kosciusko (p. 355) whereabout ancient granites and gneisses are elevated to 7,316 feet—the highest point in Australia.

Through eastern Victoria the summits of the divide remain above 5,000 feet and its flanks are deeply dissected by southward flowing rivers. Curiously, the crest of the tectonic arch seldom coincides with the water-parting which often lies 10 miles south of its highest points. The Mitta Mitta River, indeed, rises much farther than this to the south. Clearly the water-parting is older than, and the rivers are antecedent to, the cymatogenic arch. Westward the crest is brought down rapidly at the Kilmore geocol, beyond which it remains a low, and sometimes anomalous feature.

The descent of the early-Cainozoic surface upon the southern flank of the cymatogen through eastern Victoria, as recorded upon the crests of high ridges, is rapid from 4,000 to 1,500 feet when the monocline becomes so steep that it passes into the Yallourn fault which forms for many miles the northern margin of the East Gippsland synclinal lowland wherein intermittent drowning is recorded by sedimentary series, paludal and marine, aged successively: Jurassic, ?Cretaceous, Older Basalt, late-Oligocene (lignitiferous), Miocene and Pliocene, and ending with the Pleistocene Haunted Hills gravels. The "Australian" cyclic planation corresponds with the hiatus below the late-Oligocene (Yallournian) formation, and the coastal plain surface that transects the marine lower Pliocene (Kalimnan) may be correlated with the second late-Cainozoic stage of valley cutting that is well known in the middle course of the Snowy River catchment. In the lower courses of the river this partial planation is swallowed up in the much more profound valley excavation, in several stages, that followed Kosciusko uplift and elevation of the coastal plain.

According to these data the monocline has been repeatedly rejuvenated (Fig. 134) since mid-Mesozoic time.

From the arched divide upon the eastern highlands the Cainozoic denudational landsurfaces decline steadily westwards towards vast interior tectonic depressions wherein profound changes of drainage have been induced. The most northerly of these is the Gulf of Carpentaria, with the flat landscapes that encompass it. Even remnants of the " Australian " cyclic planation stand only a few tens of feet above sea level at the coast, and the very smooth late-Cainozoic surface is lower still. Even so, the general flatness of the country is enhanced by extensive thin sheets of silt containing Pleistocene vertebrate fossils. Across these terrains the rivers often spread widely under monsoonal influences (Whitehouse 1944). Even the Gulf, for all its size, is only 40 fathoms deep. David (1950) thinks that it began to sag during the late-Miocene, with subsidence extended by the Kosciusko movements.

South of the Barkly Tableland an independently subsided basin is partly occupied by the Polygonum Swamp.

The huge artesian basin of Western Queensland is drained by the Cooper and other rivers to Lake Eyre, below sea level in South Australia. The vast plains of the artesian basin, belonging to the late-Cainozoic cycle, are so flat that on the border just south of the Tropic of Capricorn a scarp of horizontal Ordovician sandstones 100 feet high is so prominent as to have merited the name of Toko Ranges. Across the landscape of the " Pliocene " cycle, the rivers, loaded with debris and adapted to carry rare floods, make the frequently braided and reticulate patterns (Cooper, Diamantina) which Madigan (1936) described as typical of Central Australia; " Though mighty rivers begin their long journey to Lake Eyre from 600 miles away, yet their courses are indefinite in South Australia for hundreds of miles and they have countless swamps and minor lakes to fill before their waters can reach Lake Eyre. The country north-east from Lake Eyre for 250 miles, to the Queensland and New South Wales borders, is a great alluvial plain, really the inland deltas of the Diamantina and Cooper ".

Lake Eyre, 38 feet below sea level and forming the focus of this vast endoreic drainage system, unquestionably occupies the site of one of the broad downwarpings resulting from the Kosciusko movements, and according to David, Lake Eyre was vastly more extended during Pleistocene time as an ancestral Lake Dieri.

The alluvia of the plain surrounding Lake Eyre are Quaternary in age. Of similar age are the dunes of the Arunta Desert to the north. The erosional surface on which the dunes have accumulated is that of the Pliocene or late-Cainozoic cycle. Dead dunes extend 120 miles east of the present living dunes, indicating, as for the Kalahari in Africa, more severe aridity during the recent past.

Other centripetal drainage systems leading to Lakes Gairdner, Torrens and Frome have been impounded north of the Gawler-Peterborough-Olary upwarp, created by Kosciusko movements. Like Lake Eyre they are level salty mudflats, covered by a thin sheet of water only after exceptional rains. The Olary arch is a broad, upwarped plateau at 1,000-2,000 feet upon which, according to Howchin, stream courses are " uncertain and anomalous, and may change direction from one flood time to another ".

A third interior depression is that of the Murray-Darling Basin covering nearly a quarter of a million square miles. Here again the drainage systems are choked with alluvia constituting vast inland deltas and causing reticulated drainage patterns (Fig. 86) in which many of the streams die away (*e.g.* Willandra Billabong) or end in shallow lakes. The delta of the Warrego has been described as " larger in area than the great deltas of the Nile, the Congo, the Indus, the Irrawaddy and the Mississippi ". In the north the abundant alluvia are due partly to the ready supply of debris from Cretaceous and early-Cainozoic beds and partly to the exceedingly low gradients of most of the streams; but, even in the south where Cretaceous formations are absent, abundant waste was supplied by canyon cutting in the eastern highlands and the alluvial plains of the Riverina extend without significant relief as far as the eye can see. Pleistocene mammalia have been fossilised in certain of the alluvia; but others are so recent as to be accumulating now. Between Kerang and Swan Hill in Victoria broad shallow lakes perhaps indicate a currently subsiding part of the basin; and Sprigg (1952) records that the South Australian section of the Murray River has its bed frequently 50 feet below sea level. This condition cannot be due solely to channel erosion in so sluggish a river, and continuing recent subsidence is indicated. The rim of the subsidence crosses the lower reaches where the river has eroded its bed successively through a veneer of lacustrine and other terrestrial sediments, through Tertiary oyster beds, marine calcareous sandstones and fluviatile sediments, and finally into granite bedrock.

Latterly, much of the southern region (Mallee) has been traversed by late-Pliocene and Recent sand-dunes. No streams now rise in the Victorian Mallee, and were it not for the great size of the Murray River and certain of its tributaries which rise in more humid regions, there would doubtless be no outflow at all from this region. Erosion by running water has thus produced relatively little modification of the original late-Cainozoic depositional plain.

Upon the hills to the west of Murray Bridge also, the early- and late-Cainozoic surfaces descend smoothly to pass from the Mt. Lofty ranges beneath the alluvial basin fill.

South and west of the Mallee, the extensive alluvia (in places 200 feet thick) of the Wimmera overlie the slightly-dissected marine deposits of the Murray Gulf. Fluviatile effects have been aggradational rather then degradational.

Apart from minor touches, mainly along the coast, the configuration of Victoria was completed in the Kosciusko orogeny, when the central highlands were elevated, with tilting of the torrent gravels upon their flanks; concurrently doming and block-faulting created the southern highlands, and the sea finally withdrew from the Murray Basin.

For Quaternary time it is only necessary to record erosion of the upwarped and upthrown blocks, the drowning of Bass Strait with the formation of modern Port Phillip and the Gippsland Lakes, and the accumulation of extensive coastal dunes.

Block-faulting within the Kosciusko diastrophic cycle finds expression in the Mt. Lofty and Flinders Ranges and the adjacent Yorke Peninsula, and the sunklands of Spencer and St. Vincent Gulfs (Fig. 136). The total movement on the faults is of the order of 3,000 feet. Remnants of the Miocene marine limestone remain upon several of the lower blocks: Port Willunga, Port Noarlunga, Myponga on the Para block behind Adelaide, and at a height of nearly a thousand feet at the head of the Hindmarsh River and near Mt. Mary. From the higher blocks the marine cover has been stripped under Pliocene erosion (Fenner) so that the summit topography is either an uneven late-Cainozoic landscape or a smooth crestline of the resurrected " Australian " cycle. Certain of the intermediate blocks, such as the Sturt Block and Belair Block, also bear the stripped " Australian " surface and aid interpretation of the scenic evolution of the ranges which is reminiscent of rift valley topography in other continents. Campana (1955), however, eschews the faulting hypothesis and believes that the Miocene inliers in the Hindmarsh and Myponga areas " are situated well below the general level of the pre-Miocene erosion surface and have been deposited in rejuvenated Permian glacial valleys ". Lower parts of the country northward of Spencer Gulf are widely strewn with red blown sand and dust like the Pleistocene eolianites of São Paulo (Brazil) or the Kalahari.

Over most of Western Australia the compound late-Cainozoic landscape was elevated a thousand feet or more by the Kosciusko movements which were not uniform but involved a maximal uparching near Merredin. This caused much back-tilting of the originally westward drainage with dismemberment of co-ordinated systems and the development of extensive salty flats whereon most of the precipitation is now evaporated.

From a divide upon the early-Cainozoic plain (1,600 feet) near Quairading, the late-Cainozoic cycle occupies progressively more of the landscape eastward until about Southern Cross it extends on every hand without visible relict of the older cycle. Before Kalgoorlie, however, early-Cainozoic bevelling is again evident upon ridge crests above 1,500 feet. In all this country of internal drainage there is no phase of river incision towards Quaternary base levels as in eastern Australia.

Differential movements referable to the Kosciusko tectonic cycle, however, raised the broad dome of North Kimberley, a region that is essentially a dissected erosional plateau, the numerous " ranges " on the map being merely the unconsumed plateau ridges between the valleys of the incised streams (Jutson 1934). The south-western face may be a fault scarp, but the eastern boundary is less definite and leads down by erosion scarps to the Ord Plateau. Many streams radiate from Mt. Hann, a monadnock 800 feet above the plateau at its base. On the north and west there appears to be a monoclinal outwarp towards the coast; for the early-Cainozoic plateau descends from about 1,500 feet around Mt. Cockburn to a couple of hundred feet near Joseph Bonaparte Gulf and the country is gashed by deep valleys with vertical cliffs of sandstone.

Updoming appears again in Arnhem Land where residuals of the early-Cainozoic planation make flat-topped hills above the " Pliocene " landscape. Towards the north

PLATE 13: Smooth surface and skyline of the broad alluviate

PLATE 12: Late mature landscape of the first late Cainozoic cycle near Boorowa N.S.W. Gently rolling in form it lacks the smooth planation of the Early Cainozoic landscape from which it was developed under erosion.

Lester King.

...ain of the Murray River basin, western New South Wales.

Lester King.

PLATE 14: Sub-skyline tor of the Late Cainozoic cyclic dissection in high Lozère, Central Plateau of France. The smooth early Cainozoic planation shows in the skyline through the trees.

Lester King.

coast the older surface descends until it is only some tens of feet above the sea (30 feet is reported at Darwin), and it descends below sea level in parts of that submerged and embayed coast.

All about Australia, indeed, one of the last movements has been a drowning of 150-200 feet, remarkably like that which has affected the African continent.

In Murchisonia the descent towards the coast is gradual but southward the change takes place suddenly at the Darling Scarp, below which marine Cretaceous beds appear at intervals (500 feet altitude at Gingin). Of this scarp, D. W. Johnson has expressed the opinion that it may have developed from a monoclinal fold of the coastal zone, with differential erosion upon rocks of different degrees of resistance. Prider (1945) also regards it as a scarp due to differential erosion. But Fairbridge (1951) has regarded it as a fault with a series of down-stepped blocks. Certainly there was marked rejuvenation upon the monocline following the Kosciusko movements. A suggested history for the Darling Scarp and its hinterland is sketched in Fig. 133. Repeated outward warping along a coastal monocline is indicated by the manner in which the elevated cyclic denudations of the plateau are successively carried, in inverted order, beneath sedimentary sequences: Jurassic or early-Cretaceous, late-Cretaceous and Eocene, Miocene, ? Pliocene and Recent of the low-lying Swan Coastal plain where they are recovered in boreholes. In places the warping has been steep or was assisted by faulting, *e.g.* where the early-Cainozoic plateau has been carried down beneath Miocene sediments of a borehole at Muchea. Near Bullsbrook in the same area spurs along the scarp appear bevelled at 15° as though the Gondwana surface was resurrected thereupon.

Persistently along the Darling Scarp at 200-250 feet is a narrow bench (Ridge Hill shelf) that is duricrusted and appears to have been tilted seaward. Northward of Bullsbrook this bench broadens rapidly and appears to make a cyclic surface below the Meckering level. It perhaps represents a Pliocene cycle.

The modern aspect of the Darling Scarp post-dates the Kosciusko diastrophism and there is also evidence of strong depression of the coastal plain with the Pleistocene formations going down to 100 feet below sea level at Perth and still more at Fremantle. But from the altitude of Proterozoic Cardup shales along the scarp at Armidale, and in 4,000 feet deep boreholes at Guildford and Midland Junction, Prider (1945) has surmised that the line of the Darling Scarp has been a critical zone defining the western limit of the Australian Shield from very early times and that modern displacements are mere rejuvenations.

A strong upwarp during the Kosciusko epoch seems to have occurred only a few miles behind the crest of the modern scarp, creating the present watershed there. Only the Avon River maintained an antecedent course, with modification, through to the coast.

Elevation of the Stirling Range and Leeuwin block in the south may also be assigned to the Kosciusko tectonics.

CONCLUSION

The facts reviewed in the last two chapters lead to a simple conclusion: that the late-Mesozoic to Recent morphologies of all the fragments of Gondwanaland are essentially identical (Table IX). All the southern continents (with India) have experienced similar types of tectonic displacement occurring at closely synchronous epochs. This points to fundamental subcrustal controls operating similarly over half the globe. Displacements are in the vertical sense and can, with the continents established in their present positions prior to the Cainozoic era, have no connection with continental drift—an activity characteristic of late-Palæozoic and early-Mesozoic time (p. 64).

During the longer time-intervals between the tectonic episodes, denudation carved a series of cyclic landscapes upon the continental scale. Each cyclic landscape acquired individual characteristics that largely reflect the time interval that was available for its development, coupled with the time available for subsequent cycles to indulge in its partial destruction. The characteristics are sufficiently marked for each major cycle to be recognisable not only over each of the southern continents individually but also from continent to continent.

The next two chapters will review the landforms of those parts of the northern continents that have likewise not undergone late-Mesozoic or Cainozoic orogenesis to ascertain whether these have likewise a common morphology and, if so, whether it agrees with, or differs from, the morphology of the southern continents. Unfortunately the author's acquaintance with the boreal continents has been less extensive and the review in consequence relies largely more on the published work of others.

CHAPTER XI

NORTH AMERICAN PLAINLANDS

Introduction. Denudation Chronology. Erosional Bevels in the
Appalachian Region. The Canadian Shield. The Great Plains.
Pleistocene Landscape of the Interior. The Central Lowland.
Pleistocene Glaciation. Greenland. Conclusion.

INTRODUCTION

Literature on the geomorphology of North America is voluminous, and covers all
parts of the country (Fenneman 1931, 1938; Thornbury 1965), yet there is lacking a
continent-wide synthesis of the various erosional and depositional cycles that have ranged
across its face since mid-Mesozoic time. Lacking a local guide we set out, therefore,
somewhat in the spirit of those pioneers who, a hundred and more years ago, pressed
westward on the physical exploration of this self-same continent, hoping for a peaceful
passage but prepared to defend themselves if assailed too smartly by the native occupants
of the territory.

The manner in which North American landscapes are reduced to the planed condition does not, in our view, depart significantly from that demonstrated for other
continents. American authors, while recognising the operation of pedimentation in
the less rainy states of the west and centre, have tended to regard this as a special mode
of landscape reduction operative under an arid climate. But as W. M. Davis (1930)
had begun to appreciate before his death, and as noted (p. 157), pediplanation was
operative in the east also, as is indicated by the presence in the Appalachian region
of at least three distinct erosion cycles separated one from another at scarp and terrace
edges, and spanning in age from early-Cainozoic to Quaternary time. Confirmatory is
the fact that the boundaries of cyclic surfaces in the Appalachians often do not agree
exactly with lithologic contacts: where each younger cycle is sufficiently advanced its
pediments transgress such contacts from the weaker on to the resistant strata.

DENUDATION CHRONOLOGY

The cordilleran belt is reserved for treatment in Chapters XIV and XV; the present
search for cyclic denudational landscapes is therefore prosecuted upon the eastern highlands and the Canadian Shield coupled with the record of deposition, both continental
and marine, from the central region. Notwithstanding, relations of many erosional
plains to fossiliferous strata are obscure or unknown so that precise dating of the former

363

has sometimes been in dispute. In three instances—Schooley, Ouachita and Arbuckle (Fenneman 1938) planed landsurfaces formerly deemed to pass below neighbouring Cretaceous strata (which would date them as " Laurasian ", equivalent to the Gondwana cycle) are now regarded as younger and transgressive to the Cretaceous formations. Even the great bevelling of the Canadian Shield is surprisingly reticent of its age. Part may be a resurrected surface of ancient vintage, emerging from beneath Cretaceous sediments in Alberta and Minnesota, which makes those parts " Laurasian "; but much of it was exposed to the elements as a lowland during early-Cainozoic time, when the existing smooth skylines originated (p. 232). Late-Cainozoic and modern cycles have since carved erosional features both prior to and after the continental glaciation of Pleistocene time.

Denudation chronology is well established in the Appalachian and Coastal Plain regions of the United States. In the mountains four erosional cycles of decreasing maturity—Schooley, Harrisburg, Somerville and Modern—have been reported (Johnson 1931).

The Schooley is a summit planation originally of great smoothness corresponding in position, preservation and appearance with the early-Cainozoic landscapes described from the southern continents; the Harrisburg and Somerville cycles are represented by minor plains and broad valley planations (often developed upon areas of weaker rocks) that in stage of development correspond with the late-Cainozoic landscapes of our earlier descriptions; while the Quaternary cycles differ considerably in development from the north, where they are incised only slightly below the Somerville terrace, to south where they gash deep ravines into the flanks of the Blue Ridge. These contrasts are clearly due to much greater Quaternary cymatogenic uplift in the south (p. 367).

In the coastal plain sequence of marine rocks noteworthy unconformities exist below the early Cretaceous, beneath the late-Cretaceous overlap, below the Eocene (locally near Asbury, N.J. and in parts of Virginia (Richards 1945)), below or within the lower Miocene (a major break), beneath the Pliocene and finally below the Quaternary sands that mantle much of the plain. All the deposits form wedges thickening seaward, each successive sedimentary surface dipping seaward less than its predecessor. Thus the sequence of tectonic events is unmistakably monoclinal, with repetitive steepening of the continental margin.

The repeated elevation of the land and cutting of stepwise cyclic landsurfaces is complementary to the thickening wedges of offshore sediment. In equating the denudational cycles with coastal unconformities we shall surely not err if we regard the Schooley cycle as having furnished the bulk of late-Cretaceous and Eocene rocks, with the planation itself (when little or no waste was supplied) corresponding with the hiatus below the Miocene deposits (Fig. 140). In the southern Appalachians, where the Schooley planation failed to subdue the Blue Ridge and Great Smokies, sedimentation did not cease and an Oligocene formation is identified beneath the coastal plain.

The Harrisburg and Somerville cycles then supplied the Miocene and Pliocene

series respectively, with the intervening tectonic uplift corresponding to the unconformity below the Pliocene. This latter series is often limited in thickness and distribution, because not much material was denuded (and that upon fine-grained weak
formations) during the Somerville cycle. Subsequently only Quaternary accumulations,
synchronous with the modern river cycle, are in evidence.

Reverting to the earlier major unconformities, infra-Cretaceous and intra-Cretaceous
in position, these imply the former existence upon adjacent Appalachian lands of
" Laurasian " and " post-Laurasian " cycles of erosion. The former of these under
the name of " Fall Zone Peneplane " has long been known in a resurrected condition
along the inner edge of the Coastal Plain all the way from southern New England to
Northern Texas. " One of the best places to see the Fall Zone Peneplain in something
approaching its pristine state is on top of the Palisades [where] . . . is a flat upland

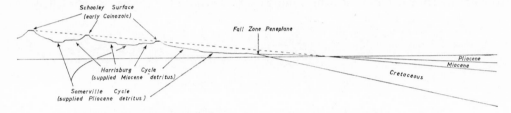

FIG. 140. Suggested relations between cyclic denudational surfaces
of the Central Appalachian region and coastal plain sedimentary series.
In the higher southern Appalachians small remnants of Cretaceous
surfaces may also survive.

surface sometimes a mile wide bevelling the structure most convincingly. [It] rises
northward from sea level at Staten Island, where it passes beneath the Cretaceous, at
a very even rate of 20 feet per mile " . . . " Profiles, well records, field observations,
and map study indicate that at the time of the burial the Fall Zone Peneplane was a
remarkably smooth surface " (Sharp 1958). In the central Appalachians no trace of
these cycles remains, the Schooley planation of the early-Cainozoic seems to have been
complete; but the Blue Ridge of the southern Appalachians appears still to retain
evidence of relict planation, possibly of Laurasian vintage (p. 367).

Earlier still, a resurrected sub-Triassic surface is known locally alongside the
northern Appalachians, and resurrected Palæozoic surfaces make small facets particularly
in areas surrounding the Canadian Shield (Sharp 1958).

The history of degradational and aggradational events in the eastern United States
is governed primarily by a series of monoclinal displacements. At all points this history
accords closely with that adduced upon coastal flexures for the several portions of
Gondwanaland (Table IX), and a primary corelation is therefore established between
Laurasia and Gondwana. The minor anachronisms at the end of the Cretaceous and
within the lower Miocene (below the Yorktown beds) may be attributed either to

heterogeneity of the earth's crust or to local variations of activity in the substratum responsible for the tectonics.

EROSIONAL BEVELS IN THE APPALACHIAN REGION

Long familiar to geomorphologists, Johnson's (1931) classic study of the Appalachian ranges westward of New York expounds the typical geomorphology of the region with prominent smooth skylines of the early-Cainozoic, Schooley cycle residual around 2,500 feet upon ridges of hard rock, in a landscape principally of late-Cainozoic Harrisburg and Somerville cycles expressed as terraces and valley-floors (Fig. 141). With the modern river beds these cycles stand generally below 1,000 feet. Across this terrain of open folds in Palæozoic strata the drainage is regionally superposed (Johnson 1931) from a former Cretaceous cover, with considerable subsequent adjustment to structure by river captures, leaving wind-gaps nicked into the ridges. Upon flat-lying

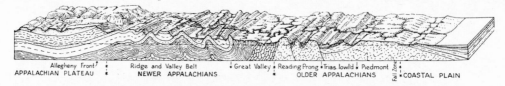

Allegheny Front ¦   Ridge and Valley Belt   ¦ Great Valley ¦ Reading Prong ¦Trias. lowld ¦ Piedmont ¦
APPALACHIAN PLATEAU ¦   NEWER APPALACHIANS   ¦   OLDER APPALACHIANS   ¦ ¦COASTAL PLAIN

FIG. 141. The Central Appalachians showing ridges of hard rock bevelled by the Schooley (early Cainozoic) cycle, and Harrisburg and Somerville (late Cainozoic) terrace stages. *after D. W. Johnson.*

strata of the west the Allegheny plateaus substitute for the ridge and valley topography where the rock series are folded.

The Appalachian ranges extend, however, for great distances to north and south, from the Long Range of Newfoundland to Central Alabama, and throughout this length of 1,750 miles the physical characteristics of the mountainland change very considerably owing to (a) heterogeneity of bedrock structures and (b) different measures of vertical uplift, especially during the Quaternary era.

According to American literature the even-crested ridges (Schooley) and broad valleys (Harrisburg) persist with a relief of 2,000 feet through the folded " Newer " Appalachians as far south as Alabama where the older surface stands between 3,000 and 4,000 feet above the sea. The eastern side of the belt is formed, in the younger cycle, by the Great Valley separating the ridge and valley topography from the stronger topographic contrasts of the Blue Ridge province. This is a new element in the landscape which begins with an elevation of 1,000 feet at the Potomac River and climbs for 200 miles south-westwards to 4,000 feet near Roanoke, south of which it builds a plateau 10-65 miles wide averaging 3,000 feet elevation, and overlooking the Great Valley on the west and the Piedmont province on the east. Both these lowlands are said to be carved in the Harrisburg cycle, so that unless there be complication by piedmont treppen (Chapter VII) the upland of the Blue Ridge is an unreduced contemporary of the

Schooley cycle. Indeed ver Steeg (1940) recorded that the northern Blue Ridge (Catoctin belt) was cut by water gaps like the Schooley plain of the Newer Appalachians and that the backbone of the province was a series of monadnocks upon the Schooley surface. In North Carolina Stose and Stose (1951) recorded, " At Blowing Rock and vicinity the Schooley Peneplane stands at 3,400-3,600 feet altitude, and throughout the Blue Ridge plateau in North Carolina the surrounding mountains rise to over 4,000 or 5,000 feet altitude, culminating in Mt. Mitchell 6,684 feet ". Further, "On the north side of the Blue Ridge Plateau, south-west of Salem, Virginia . . . North and South Forks of Roanoke River have attacked the higher level of the plateau and reduced it to lower levels ". The Stoses agreed with W. M. Davis, that two levels of the Schooley plain were here related to two drainage systems of different length; but this argument, formerly adduced in Africa, has had everywhere to be abandoned, and we shall not err if we regard the superior relics of erosion upon the Great Smokies as belonging to a pre-Schooley cycle, either Laurasian or post-Laurasian, standing now at accordant summit levels around 6,500 feet *.

In the extreme south the bounding scarps transgress the rock systems of the Blue Ridge province, and the Miocene (Harrisburg) cyclic landscapes of the Great Valley and the Piedmont unite and close the highlands. Within the Great Valley the Coosa River has cut to still lower levels in fresh cycles, leaving bauxite-capped relics of the Harrisburg cycle upon intermediate ridges.

The Piedmont province, an area of crystalline rocks between the Blue Ridge and the Atlantic coastal plain, is described by Eardley (1951): " It is a vast plain along the horizon but is maturely dissected to a local relief of a few hundred feet in places. Numerous hills and ridges rise as monadnocks 200-1,000 feet above the general plains surface and are more numerous near the Blue Ridge escarpment ". According to American authorities, the province, which increases from a few miles width in Pennsylvania to 170 miles in and southward of North Carolina, includes elements of both the Harrisburg and Somerville cycles. The Blue Ridge scarp developed erosionally (p. 207) upon an eastwardly tilted Schooley landscape as the Harrisburg cycle planed the adjacent Piedmont.

In the New England-Acadian region, extending from New York State to Newfoundland, smooth skylines of the Berkshire Hills, Green Mountains, Shickshock and Long Ranges, sometimes crowned with monadnocks, have been referred by American physiographers (Atwood 1940) to the Schooley cycle rising northward from 1,500 to above 2,000 feet. Most of the New England plateau is, however, an undulating surface of the Harrisburg cycle, somewhat modified by the later glaciation of Pleistocene time. The Somerville cycle has been recorded by Twenhofel and Maclintock (1940) as valley-bottoms between 700 and 1,100 feet upon the Newfoundland plateau. The composite

---

* According to Fenneman (1938), southward from the Roanoke Gap the Blue Ridge has 46 peaks and 41 miles of divide above 6,000 feet, also 288 more peaks and 300 more miles of divide above 5,000 feet. Perhaps both Laurasian and post-Laurasian cycles are here present ?

upland has been dissected by deep valleys of the Deerfield, Housatonic, Kennebec and Penobscot Rivers that were excavated in belts of weak rock shortly before the glaciation.

Through the Maritime Provinces of Canada (Goldthwait 1924) the Atlantic Upland (Harrisburg cycle) is strongly warped down from maxima of 1,200 feet on Cape Breton Island and 1,500-2,000 feet in Newfoundland to within 200 feet of sea level along the Atlantic coast and Gulf of Maine, thus illustrating the cymatogenic arching that had to be assumed in the southern Appalachians for the successive erosional surfaces to pass down beneath the appropriate sediments of the coastal plain. This arching mostly precedes cutting of the valleys that dissected the upland prior to glaciation. No monadnocks are known to reach the Schooley level in the Maritime Provinces.

The cymatogenic crest of the Appalachian region often stands westward of the folded Appalachians in a zone of elevated plateaus that may overlook the ridge and valley topography to the east at a bold scarp. From south to north these are the Cumberland, Allegheny, Laurentian and Labrador plateaus, the structure of the first pair being of unfolded or gently undulating Palæozoic formations and of the latter pair mostly Precambrian rocks. Owing to uneven uplift, summit levels on the plateaus range between 2,000 and 4,000 feet, and the Schooley planation has been identified by local researchers as the oldest and highest surface upon all of them. Composite late-Cainozoic cycles (*e.g.* Lexington, Coosa) make most of the existing plateau surfaces, and deep dissection in the Quaternary cycle is locally evident. The upland surfaces generally slope westwards upon the flank of the arch towards the central Mississippi lowlands, beyond which the late-Cainozoic landscapes have been identified upon the domed Ozark and Ouachita mountain areas.

According to Atwood (1940), tectonic history following the Schooley planation has involved: (a) rise of the entire Appalachian region as a single low arch or elongated dome. In the central portion the uplift was 1,000-3,000 feet, declining in all directions, (b) while the Harrisburg (Miocene) cycle was proceeding, a broad general arching, nowhere exceeding a few hundred feet, initiated the Somerville (Pliocene) cycle in which entrenched meanders are prominent on areas of weak rocks, (c) before extensive removal of material could take place renewed cymatogenic arching caused stream incision just prior to the Ice Age. This arching was low and broad in the central Appalachians, but reached a maximum of 2,000 feet in the southern Blue Ridge, and a further major rise in New England.

The several cyclic denudational surfaces converge eastwards towards the coastal plain, southward around the end of the Cumberland Plateau and westwards towards the interior depositional lowland where " widespread evidence of a mid-Tertiary erosion surface exists " (Thornbury 1965) followed by a Parker Strath (Harrisburg) cycle and a probable still later cyclic landscape before the onset of Pleistocene glacial deposition (Horberg 1946; 1950).

In seeking the major cyclic lineaments of the Appalachian region we have glossed over a number of minor developments (such as multiple straths) noted by Fenneman

(1938). These developments are familiar to experienced geologists elsewhere also, and do not invalidate the overall view that the major tectonic, denudational and depositional phases of Appalachian scenic development conform with the pattern established from other world theatres.

In the geomorphic history of the Ozarks Bretz (1965) cites three stages of planation prior to a trenchlike incision of valleys that must surely be of Quaternary age. But no age is given for any of the planations which are: (*a*) a probable ancestral planation suggested by summit altitudes of the Boston Mountains of northwestern Arkansas; (*b*) a later (Springfield) planation of which only a few flat-topped monadnocks remain. The radial stream pattern of the region was developed during this cycle, which from this fact and the small area of planation remaining may perhaps have been of early-Cainozoic (Schooley) fashioning; (*c*) the widespread " Ozark " planation followed uplift of the earlier Springfield landforms, and now makes much of the Ozark landscape. With a characteristic red soil, it was also the planation beneath which were evolved the cavern systems for which the district is famous. A late-Cainozoic age would appear to fit all these characteristics; the assigned ages are, however, no more than first guesses.

THE CANADIAN SHIELD

Quoting extensively from Cooke (1947): " The Canadian Shield is a peneplain, which was uplifted to its present position, it is estimated, in middle- or late-Pliocene time. During this uplift it was warped and faulted in places so that parts of it now stand much higher than others. Since its uplift the shield has been somewhat dissected by stream action, particularly in the more elevated parts; and the topography has been further modified by the ice of the glacial period. This . . . smoothed off the hills, filled the valleys with debris, and thus completely disorganised the pre-glacial drainage ".

" From almost any elevation the skyline appears monotonously level, regardless of the differing hardness of the underlying rocks. Only at long intervals does a low hill break this even line, some remnant that has escaped the prevailing peneplanation. Viewed more closely, however, the surface is rough, with low hills and ridges rising a few hundred feet above the valley levels. This dissection, in part at least, undoubtedly took place after the peneplain was uplifted, and streams could once more commence vigorous erosion."

" Warping during uplift gave the shield a saucer-like shape, with high edges sloping in general towards the central depression of Hudson Bay (Fig. 142). The rim of the saucer is broken in places by depressions, such as the low valley of Ungava Bay, and the relatively depressed area south of James Bay through Lake Temiskaming. The remaining higher parts of the rim may be briefly described. At Cape Wolstenholme at the south-west entrance to Hudson Strait, the plateau fronts on the strait in cliffs about 1,500 feet high, and slopes southward. Across Ungava Bay it attains its greatest elevation, between 5,000 and 6,000 feet. The dissected edges of this plateau facing the Atlantic, are known as the Torngat Mountains. Southward along the Labrador coast the

2A

elevations decrease but still are greater than 2,000 feet, between Hamilton Inlet and the Strait of Belle Isle."

" Turning west along the north shore of the Gulf and River St. Lawrence, the

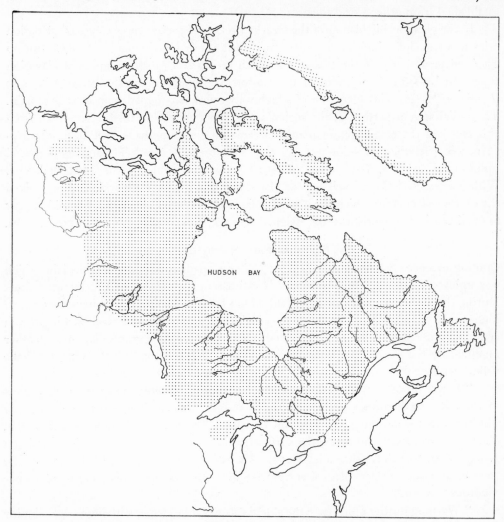

HUDSON BAY

Fig. 142. The area known to have been included by the Laurentian planation (early Cainozoic) of Canada. *after A. W. G. Wilson.*

edge of the plateau maintains its height nearly to Quebec, north of which it is still 1,800 feet above sea level. Farther west its elevation falls off gradually to about 800 feet, some distance west of Ottawa. From there to Lake Huron the shield ceases to rise as an abrupt wall above the surrounding plains, but passes without perceptible change of gradient beneath the horizontal Palæozoic beds that underlie these plains. Still farther west, north of Lakes Huron and Superior, the elevation of the plateau rises again to above 1,500 feet; and similar or higher elevations are maintained to the north-west as far as the Arctic Ocean."

" During and after the uplift streams cut and deepened their valleys, not only in the plateau surface, but in the upraised, rim-like edges. Later, when the ice came, these stream channels formed convenient conduits through which it could flow to the Atlantic and to the south. . . . The Great Lakes, as well as the large lakes of the North-west Territories, originated in large part through glacial action."

. . . " The debris of this great erosion [glacial] was in part carried completely off the shield, and in part scattered over its surface, choking old stream valleys and in some cases forming great ridges that extend for miles. As a result, the original well established drainage pattern is completely disorganised, so that only a few of the larger preglacial valleys can now be recognised. The effect has been to create a multitude of lakes, which spill at random across the lowest points in their rims. Many have more than one outlet, and where such lakes lie on a divide, they may drain to two entirely different river systems. In some parts of the north-west the number of lakes is so great that they constitute 25-35 per cent. of the total area."

" When the ice disappeared, a certain amount of elastic rebound took place, and the landsurface rose again. It did not, however, recover its former height. The Atlantic coast rose only some 250-350 feet, the north shore of the St. Lawrence 400-600 feet, and the east side of Hudson Bay apparently 600 feet or more. It is obvious, therefore, that the recovery was accompanied by some warping of the surface, but the rise was not sufficient to bring the Hudson Bay area above sea level, so that it has remained an inland sea."

This succint description* reveals a denudational history similar to that of the Appalachian region except that only one stage of dissection is recorded between the smooth summit planation and the incision of immediately pre-glacial valleys. But even the absence of a stage equivalent to the Somerville may be only illusory; any evidence is largely obscured by glacial debris. Drilling has indeed proved that some parts of the shield formerly regarded as " flat and featureless " are covered with debris to depths exceeding 400 feet, so the preglacial surface was more irregular than appears at first sight.

Additional information from Baffin Land and Labrador has been given by Bird (1959): " The high eastern rim of the Canadian Shield reaching 7,000 feet in the Penny Highlands of Baffin Land and over 6,000 feet in Labrador has been described as the dissected, upwarped (or upfaulted) edge of the main upland. Recent investigations in Baffin Land suggest, however, that a distinct, dissected, high-level surface is preserved at 6,000 feet in the Penny Highland. A high-level surface distinct from the main upland of northern Quebec may be preserved in the Torngat Mountains, but it is not certain as the main (2,000 feet) upland is not found on the west side of the Torngats ".

* For a subdivision of the shield area into physiographic provinces see H. S. Bostock (1964).

These relicts of an older plateau standing above the main, late-Cainozoic cyclic upland must surely represent the Schooley (early-Cainozoic) planation, though the possibility of their representing an older, exhumed topography cannot be excluded.

The late-Cainozoic upland, cut across many different formations, continues far north across the Arctic Archipelago to Ellesmere Land, where it finally gives way to the unconsolidated sediments of the Beaufort Series, possibly derived from its planation (Tozer and Thorsteinsson 1964). In the monocline of the Arctic Coastal Plain early Jurassic and early Cretaceous planations are known in the fossil state.

Incoming of Palæozoic rocks in Minnesota and Labrador has led to the suggestion that some parts of the shield surface are a resurrected Palæozoic feature, and Ambrose (1964) has found many examples of early Palæozoic topography to which the present drainage pattern often conforms remarkably well. But the extensive Palæozoic of the Hudson Bay region is truncated, and any area of resurrected topography there must be small. That these denudationally-weak formations have survived long exposure above sea level implies that they were never so greatly elevated as now, when from the evidence of raised beaches it is thought that the whole of the Arctic Archipelago has been elevated 500-1,000 feet in Quaternary time. Lignitiferous Cretaceous series in the Moose River Basin 50 miles south-west of James Bay fossilise a Cretaceous landscape there, and in the Rouyn district of Quebec, Cooke (1925) has recorded that " what appear to be remnants of the Cretaceous peneplain stand 500-500 feet above the remnants of the Pliocene plain ". Some doubt exists, however, whether the upper remnants should not be ascribed to the Schooley cycle.

Many planations have cut shallowly across the shield area since the late Precambrian but each has removed only a very thin shaving from its predecessor. As a direct result this region preserves more records of meteoritic infalls than any other on earth.

THE GREAT PLAINS

Measures of uplift have been much greater in the west, where the Cretaceous and Cainozoic formations of the Great Plains lead to the Rocky Mountains. Following late-Jurassic orogeny in the cordilleran belt, thick deposits of a Jurassic-Cretaceous marine transgression spread eastward across a subsiding Laurasian landscape to, and possibly beyond, Lake Winnipeg, though not as far as the south end of James Bay for the Jurassic and Cretaceous are there non-marine, with abundant plant fossils. " The Cretaceous period ended with a gentle uplift that caused the sea to retire from the Great Plains. The land remained low throughout most of Paleocene time, until the great thrust from the west that formed the Rocky Mountains. With the uplift of the Rockies, the western plains appear also to have been raised, and it may be presumed that the western edge of the shield was raised with them " (Cooke 1947).

There followed a long period when Paleocene, Eocene and Oligocene formations were laid down irregularly and with many breaks over the Great Plains province, ending with the early-Cainozoic landsurface that now forms the flat summits of the Cypress and Porcupine Hills and other mesas overtopping the prairie through south-eastern Alberta and south-western Saskatchewan. This ancient surface now slopes eastward from 6,300 feet on West Butte and 4,800 feet on Cypress Hills to 3,500 feet north of East End. To the east the main planation of the shield area also was achieved during this early-Cainozoic period, making it coeval with the Schooley surface.

The prairie surface of the Canadian Great Plains, standing generally around 3,000 feet, belongs to the late-Cainozoic denudation cycles of which two are sometimes manifest, separated locally by a scarp such as the Manitoba scarp 500-1,000 feet high. The earlier of the two cycles seems to have removed any formations younger than Paleocene over most of the region. Both degradational and aggradational processes swept in turn over the area so that gravels of many different ages were spread and removed from place to place. Of these, gravels capping the plateau in the Wood Mountain area of southern Saskatchewan have yielded Miocene vertebrate fauna. In places the gravels are cemented with lime and associated with sands. Other gravels are patently younger, but are still pre-glacial. Aggradational phases corresponding with both Harrisburg and Somerville cycles are therefore present.

All the larger drainage courses and many of the smaller ones are now incised below the plains level, in places by 200 or 300 feet; and north of 60° latitude the Mackenzie River and its tributaries are incised by 200-500 feet. Far north, Bostock (1936) presents evidence that implies a Miocene age for an extensive surface that may be part of the Arctic peneplain. This equates it with the pre-Ogallala surface (=Harrisburg) of the Canadian Great Plains.

In Montana, Wyoming and the states to the east, Cainozoic geomorphology of the Great Plains is intimately related to tectonic activity and ensuing denudations in the Rocky Mountain belt to the west (p. 497). The Rocky Mountain structures culminated during the Eocene and by the early-Oligocene aggradation set in over central Wyoming and the Great Plains. By the middle of the period it covered " all but the highest hills " and extended far to the east; and by the end of the period pediplanation of the hardrock areas and piedmont accumulation seem to have been complete in a single smooth vista (=Schooley) upon which the essential pattern of modern drainage was established.

Widespread deposition has continued intermittently across the Great Plains until at least the end of the Cainozoic but there are many unconformities and evidences of denudational surfaces through this same period. Fillman and Fenneman (1931) have both recorded an older buried surface (the Mountain Meadow surface) which is regarded as late-Oligocene or early Miocene and rises to cross the pre-Ogallala surface (q.v.) towards the Black Hills. In south-western Montana, too, a late Oligocene erosion surface is broken by Miocene movements and covered by Miocene (Deer Creek) beds before late-Miocene bevelling which precedes Pliocene block-faulting and deposition.

Among the Wyoming Rockies and basins are evidences of cognate denudation cycles (p. 536), and as these synchronise essentially with the Schooley and Harrisburg cycles of the east, a general continental programme of Cainozoic events begins to emerge from North America as from other continents.

The Kansas High Plains carry a mantle of fluviatile sediments (Ogallala formation) supplied by erosion of the Rocky Mountains in the west,* varying in thickness from 500 feet to zero, and ranging in age through the Pliocene. Westward these sediments wedge out upon the Sherman peneplain of Wyoming which corresponds with the major pedimented cycle along the Rocky Mountain front and the Ortiz pediment cycle of the southern mountain region.

The late-Cainozoic cyclic landscapes were thus both aggradational and, in pauses, degradational. As many as three interludes of non-deposition or even erosion thus appear locally in the Miocene. By the close of the era the Kansas landscape was a vast alluvial plain, coextensive with a pedimented surface in the Rocky Mountain region (Colorado) and merging in eastern Kansas with the erosion surface about the Flint Hills. This in turn graded eastward into the area of the Osage cuesta plains, and finally with the area buried by glacial drift that is so admirably described for Illinois by Horberg (1950) (Fig. 91).

During and since the Ice Age the High Plains have been slashed by major valleys of rivers rejuvenated following a cymatogenic upwarp of the Rocky Mountain belt (p. 535) which conferred an eastward tilt upon Kansas so that the surface now slopes from 4,000 feet in the west to between 700 and 1,000 feet in the east. Pedimentation has been recorded as active in widening these valleys. Farther west, in Colorado, three successive periods of incision and planation by the streams have produced three gravel-capped pedimented surfaces, cut on bedrock, with alternate incision and alluviation producing three, or perhaps four, alluvial stream terraces at lower elevation. Traced back into the mountains each of the alluvial terraces ends at an ancient glacier moraine (Condra, Reed and Gordon 1950).

The denudational landsurface beneath the Ogallala formation is carved across Cretaceous rocks in the west, and like the ground surface has a pronounced slope towards the east before breaking away at a crenulate and sometimes multiple scarp, initiated during the early Pleistocene, to the central continental lowlands.

A still earlier (Laurasian) landsurface lies buried, in central and eastern Kansas, Oklahoma and Arkansas, beneath early Cretaceous beds. It was a surface of moderate relief across which cobbles in the basal conglomerate show the drainage to have been south-westerly.

In Texas a comparable history is recorded (Frye and Leonard 1957): " At the beginning of the Neogene, an erosion surface existed throughout the Great Plains south of Nebraska. In central western Texas and adjacent New Mexico, the topographic relief was only a few hundred feet. However, south of Howard County remnants of

---

* Sediments in the eastern one-third of Kansas were, however, supplied from the east (Frye and Leonard 1952).

more resistant Cretaceous rocks stood several hundred feet above the general topography. It was on this surface that reduced stream competence started alluviation in the late-Miocene or early-Pliocene . . . and ultimately regional coalescence of the originally independent depositing systems to form an extensive integrated plain of alluviation. In the south . . . remnants of the higher upland on the Cretaceous and the thinness of the Pliocene Ogallala formations, effectively prevented the integration of the alluvial systems ". In the Llano Estacado ancient hills sometimes project through the Ogallala formation and, even in Kansas, Frye (1955) has recorded that the Flint Hills with their flint gravel cover derived from the west have survived from at least the early-Cainozoic, through three or four cycles of erosion and alluviation during the late-Cainozoic and three, or maybe four, more during the Pleistocene.

Though the delicate state of balance between phases of degradation and of aggradation has swung either way intermittently during the Cainozoic era, in the Great Plains region an early-Cainozoic levelling is clearly apparent. Late-Cainozoic levellings are less uniform though the final phase (Ogallala) was one of widespread aggradation.

Near the Edwards Plateau in the south, an infra-Cretaceous (Laurasian) surface is represented (Fig. 143).

FIG. 143. Section from the Llano Estacado (north) to Edwards Plateau (south) showing the infra-Cretaceous surface, late Cainozoic summit cycle, pedimented valley terrace of the first Pleistocene cycle, and a present tributary of the Pecos Valley.

PLEISTOCENE LANDSCAPE OF THE INTERIOR

The most interesting region for study of Pleistocene landscapes is almost exactly in the centre of the continent, through Nebraska, Kansas and Missouri. Here, almost in conjunction, appear (a) the glacial and peri-glacial deposits of four major ice sheets that advanced successively from the north over a landscape with 200 feet of mature relief etched into Pliocene sediments; (b) the fluviatile degradational and aggradational episodes of the Great Plains; (c) the denudational landscape of the Ozarks; and (d) the head of the alluvial deposits of the Mississippi embayment.

The graphic resume of the Nebraskan Pleistocene (Fig. 70) by Schultz, Luenging-hoener and Frankforter (1951) suitably illustrates the complexity of the tills, gravels, sands, silts, loesses and soils that have accumulated in association with the fluctuations of Nebraskan Pleistocene climate. Frye and Leonard (1952) have elucidated a comparable history for eastern Kansas that has already been discussed (p. 373).

The high plains of the west, extending a thousand miles from South Dakota to Texas had originally, at the end of the Cainozoic era, a smooth alluvial upper surface of the Ogallala formation, the latest member of the Great Plains sequence (so extensively fossiliferous that " fossil mammal remains are now known from almost every 10 feet of sediment from the base of the Oligocene to the Recent "). Though attended by the usual uncertainty as to the exact Plio-Pleistocene boundary (Colbert 1948), the original surface of the Ogallala closely approximates the end of the Cainozoic. Remnants of this flat prairie are preserved in western Nebraska by algal limestone or caliche layers of the Kimball stage. Where local ponding to produce the limestone was impossible the end-Cainozoic surface has been described as pedimented and gravel-veneered as in the big badlands of South Dakota.

During the Pleistocene (Frye 1946; Wright 1946) the major valleys were trenched in three or maybe four stages of downcutting with alternating stages of fill; the drainage pattern was extensively modified; basins and depressions were filled; and widespread eolian activity spread extensive blankets of loess and dune sand. Local faulting occurred, and the present varied topography was carved and built from the originally smooth high plains.

The Pliocene and early-Pleistocene cycles locally developed very advanced pediments such as the Ortiz pediment of Texas and New Mexico incised below the Santa Fe formation (=Ogallala) of the Llano de Albuquerque. Basalt flows cap part of the Ortiz pediment above the scarps of later multiple dissection to the Rio Grande 500 feet below Comparable are the pedimented valley-floors and depressions, up to 10 miles wide, that are sunk to 100 feet below the smooth Ogallala skylines about the Texan town of Midland. Within the Colorado plateaus, along the Little Colorado River, three Pleistocene stages of downcutting corresponding with the " canyon cycle " of the main Colorado River, have resulted in the Black Point, Wupatki and Little Colorado pediplains.

THE CENTRAL LOWLAND

From Hudson Bay and the Great Lakes, along the Mississippi River Basin to the Gulf of Mexico extends a north-south lowland wherein sedimentary accumulation has reigned throughout much of Cainozoic time. Long before, late in the early-Cretaceous period indeed, shallow Gulf seas and marshes extended north into Kansas and Iowa and west into Colorado and Montana, where ultimately they met the Rocky Mountain Cretaceous sea extending southward from the Arctic Ocean.* Late-Cretaceous uplift expelled the Gulf sea from the interior of the continent (only in Florida is the break between Cretaceous and Eocene not distinct); but it was back again as far north as the Ohio River by the Paleocene and has occupied an intermittently diminishing area with fluctuating shorelines ever since.

---

* Premonitary sinking of the central lowland began with the Permian basin of Texas—synchronously with premonitary subsidences leading to the East Africa-Madagascar rift of Jurassic time (p. 53) and the separation of eastern India and Western Australia (p. 51).

Murray (1947) has summarised the Cainozoic occurrences: " Twenty thousand feet or more of Tertiary and Quaternary sediments are present in the central Gulf region of southern United States. They comprise a large, seaward thickening, wedge-shaped sedimentary complex composed predominantly of deltaic deposits. Thin, relatively uniform and widespread, marine strata are present between the thick deltaic deposits and on the seaward edges of the deltaic masses . . . Landward, both marine and deltaic deposits are replaced by brackish-water and fluviatile sediments; seaward, the marine deposits are progressively of a deeper-water environment, the deltaic deposits are progressively more marine . . .".

Each successively younger rock series crops out nearer to the present coastline (Fig. 144) and dips less than its predecessor. The Paleocene, middle Eocene, upper Eocene and Oligocene groups each " contain important marine units "; the " lower Eocene, Miocene and Pliocene (?) are primarily deltaic units and constitute the thickest sedimentary accumulations in the eastern Gulf region ". (According to Guzman (1952), the " estimated total volume of certain Mesozoic and Cainozoic stratigraphic units in the Mexican Gulf Coastal Plain, excluding the Yucatan Peninsula, is of the order of 303,900 cubic miles ".)

The Pleistocene and Recent deposits, characteristically fluviatile gravels, sands, silts and clays, border or fill alluvial valleys.

Both the making of space for further deposits, and the derivation of fresh materials in great bulk, imply intermittent subsidence of the basin with renewed elevation of adjacent lands. As isostasy alone would be inadequate to furnish the required volumes of space and material, interruptions of sequence and fresh supplies of coarser debris necessarily imply activating tectonics; and these are, indeed, attested by the existence of anticlines and domal uplifts such as the Monroe-Sharkey uplift and the Wiggins Anticline in the Cainozoic rocks themselves.

The greatest break of sequence is above the Oligocene, which corresponds with the epoch at which the major planation (Schooley) of surrounding regions was everywhere tilted and uplifted for the first time. Between the marine Eocene and Oligocene is little or no break, corresponding to the period at which the planation was achieved.

Destruction of the uplifted summit plain by late Cainozoic denudation cycles supplied debris for the Miocene and Pliocene deposits of the lower Mississippi. Unfortunately, outcrops of the latter series are not known and borehole unconformities are as yet imprecise; but advance of the sea over the Gulf Coastal Plain during the Pliocene probably reflects the tectonic episode separating the two late-Cainozoic cycles (Harrisburg and Somerville) of the Appalachian region.

Quaternary cymatogeny has carried the base of the Quaternary formations to great depths in the delta region, thicknesses of 2,000 feet being attained in several depocentres and reaching 4,000 feet east of New Orleans. As noted elsewhere (p. 97) the sediments seem to be accumulating as fast as the area subsides.

The Cainozoic sedimentary history of the Central Lowland is thus in general

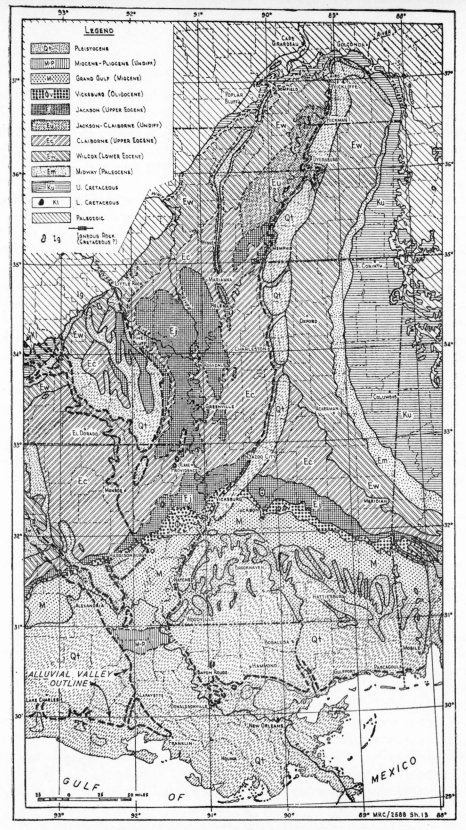

FIG. 144. Cainozoic deposits of the Mississippi basin, showing progressive
deltaic filling from the head and sides. *after E. G. Murray.*

agreement with the tectonic chronology adduced from neighbouring parts of the United States, providing a record of negative crustal movement complementary to the positive movements of encompassing denudational regions.

PLEISTOCENE GLACIATION

The effects of Pleistocene glaciation are widespread and important in North American scenery. Ice-worn terrains and till mantles record the passage of huge ice sheets, radiating from several centres, across the northern plateaus and the shield area; over-deepened valleys and summit arêtes attest abundance of mountain and valley glaciation amid the mountains of the west; and the heart of the continent preserves in its till and outwash plains a record of at least four major ice-front advances and retreats. Even in the far south-east, soil features record more lively action of frost at that time.

Much of the surface configuration, drainage patterns, lakes of all sizes and a host of other scenic phenomena are inexplicable without the hypothesis of Pleistocene glaciation, and this has received full acknowledgement in literature. Yet, admitting that the detail of landscape, north of latitude 40° N. at least, is owed almost wholly to glaciation, scarcely anywhere has glaciation destroyed the pre-glacial topography to the extent that it is unrecognisable. Valleys in the New England plateau, and elsewhere, have been modified and overdeepened, but deep valleys already existed there before refrigeration set in, and the plateau has undergone relatively slight modification from its original form. Have the outlines of Mt. Monadnock, for instance, been significantly redrawn by the moving ice? The major pre-glacial cyclic landscapes of even the Canadian Shield have been described above in quotation (Cooke 1947); they are still clear despite the glacial action; and the same can be said for the mountain systems of western Canada (Bostock 1948).

Even in the heart of the continent where the Cainozoic landscape lies concealed beneath the outwash, it is known and has been described from sub-surface studies by Horberg (1950). The glacial episode makes a fascinating study in itself; but this is already well served in literature, and the present text makes no original contribution to the subject.

GREENLAND

Greenland with its central ice-cap presents problems of its own. The sub-ice surface is basined, and geophysical probes have proved that though the rock-rim stands in some places nearly 10,000 feet above the sea, at its deepest near the centre of the landmass the sub-ice surface sinks below sea level. Part of this deformation is isostatic, due to the mass of contained ice (*cf.* Antarctica p. 65); but in part it may be attributed to Plio-Pleistocene cymatogeny. Prior to this deformation (and the Ice Age) the landsurface seems to have been " a lowland of erosion " homologous with the late-Cainozoic landscapes of America.

The littoral is generally of gneiss, comparable with the Laurentian (shield) gneiss of Canada, that also reaches 2,000 metres altitude in the northern part of the country where it makes, according to Koch (1923), a plain below the inland ice. Unless it be a resurrected ancient plain, this is surely the " lowland of erosion " of late-Cainozoic time. The gneissic basement is, however, overlain in the north by coastal sedimentary series of late-Jurassic and early-Cretaceous age (Koch) that presumably fossilise a true " Laurasian " landsurface. Near lat. 70° N. a further transgression, of late-Cretaceous age, partly marine but mostly " shallow water and estuarine " appears upon both eastern and western coasts of Greenland. There was, however, no connection across Greenland, and fossils from the west (Disko Bay) have been described as more akin to fossils from Montana than to fossils from East Greenland. Thus, a late-Mesozoic (? post-Laurasian) landsurface, which Wager described as " of subdued relief and near sea level ", is indicated for the region. Faulting was very active on both eastern and western coasts of Greenland during the Cretaceous, which is the period in which the sub-continent may have drifted from an original position in Laurasia (Fig. 166) to its present site.

The late-Cretaceous sedimentary series now ascends from sea level to 2,000 metres, and the overlying lower Eocene basalts, which extend for 1,200 miles between lat. 66° N. and 75° N., go up with a dip of 10° to 3,000 metres. Associated dyke swarms dip at 70°-80°, being intruded simultaneously with crustal flexing (Wager 1937). Here is a coastal monocline directly comparable with the Natal-Lebombo monocline of South Africa, though of Cretaceous-Eocene instead of Jurassic date. Wager and others have indicated the late-Eocene flexing as responsible for " the elevation of what is now the Coastal Mountain belt of East Greenland "; but the universality of early- and late-Cainozoic planation elsewhere may well persuade us that the coastal mountains produced by the Eocene monocline have long since disappeared and that the present youthful escarpment is due to renewed later, probably Plio-Pleistocene, arching like that responsible (p. 368) for the present elevation of the Appalachian belt. With this hypothesis the youthful dissection of the coastal belt on both sides of the sub-continent is in full accord.

CONCLUSION

This account of North American morphology, though incomplete in detail (which can be furnished by further field work), is sufficient to demonstrate that (a) pre-Cretaceous and intra-Cretaceous cyclic landscapes (Laurasian and post-Laurasian) existed at least in regions adjacent to rocks of that period; (b) (with Chapter XV) a smoothly planed early-Cainozoic landsurface was widespread, and possibly ubiquitous; (c) two late-Cainozoic denudational cycles are widespread in the present landscape, the earlier more so; and (d) following pronounced Plio-Pleistocene cymatogeny in some regions and epeirogeny in others, Pleistocene denudational cycles (both glacial and non-glacial) have operated to develop the modern topography, with aggradation prominent where land waste was superabundant.

This geomorphogeny tallies with that already adduced (Table IX) for the southern continents.

CHAPTER XII

CYCLIC LANDSURFACES IN EUROPE AND ASIA

Landscape Cycles of Western Europe. Geomorphology about the Central Plateau of France. Landscape Cycles of the Mediterranean Border and the Paris Basin. The Spanish Meseta. The Ardenne. The Bevelled Massifs of Central Europe. Blueprint for Britain. Geomorphic Outline in Scandinavia. European Russia. Lowlands of Western Asia. The Morphology of Inner Asia. Siberian Plateaus. Landsurfaces of Mongolia. Landscape Cycles in China. Conclusion.

LANDSCAPE CYCLES OF WESTERN EUROPE

Europe is the smallest of the continents and distances to the sea are nowhere great; consequently denudation under Quaternary cycles is dominant and opportunities for survival of the older cyclic landsurfaces are proportionately reduced. Moreover, first the Alpine storm of the mid-Cainozoic and then strong cymatogenic warping in the late-Cainozoic (p. 382) considerably affected the attitudes of cyclic landsurfaces and promoted extensive dissection that sometimes renders identification and correlation of the fragmentary relict landforms extremely difficult.

In Western Europe, the only part with which the author is acquainted, the earliest landscape widely available to study is a well-planed, late-Palæozoic (post-Variscan) surface analogous in many ways to the pre-Karroo landsurface of Africa. At first generally denudational, certain depressions upon it served as accumulative foci for Permian and Triassic red desert sandstones, which were themselves transected by a widespread mid-Mesozoic planation constituting the Laurasian cycle. Upon certain highlands remnants of this planation may still survive, but widespread Jurassic and Cretaceous seas covered large regions wherein landscapes of the Laurasian cycle are now revealed only in the resurrected state. A pre-Cenomanian ebbing of the sea caused a post-Laurasian denudational cycle, now found in localities scattered from Britain to Spain and Germany. The "Cenomanian overlap" concludes the landscape cycle evenly, but initiation of the cycle differs by locality from late Jurassic until well into the early Cretaceous.

Towards the close of the Cretaceous, withdrawal of the widespread "Chalk" seas left only landlocked basins (London, Paris, Aquitaine). Elsewhere new landscape cycles were generated that, continuing through the Eocene, permitted the development of a widespread early-Cainozoic landscape*. Morphologically, this early-Cainozoic

* "Eogene".

mainly late-Cretaceous and Eocene) surface is very important throughout Western, Europe. It was widely pediplaned, often with minor, characteristically steep-sided residuals (skyline tors) upon regions of suitably hard rock; and it now forms the original summit bevel of numerous plateaus and watersheds (Central Massif of France). From this fundamental surface most of the topography of Europe has subsequently been carved. In this respect it plays a role precisely analogous to early-Cainozoic landsurfaces in other continents. Superficial bauxite, silcrete and laterite (sometimes cited with a xerophytic fossil fauna as evidence of a dry climate) are consistent with a pedimented origin and prolonged development in France, though such features are absent in the meagre, more northerly, examples in the British Isles (p. 398). In one respect the early-Cainozoic landscape of Western Europe differs from others previously reviewed. Its terminal date, in France at least, is earliest- instead of late-Oligocene. This accords with local disturbance by the earlier (Pyrenean) phase of Alpine orogeny.

FIG. 145. Section showing the relation between skyline tors (relicts of an older denudation cycle) and sub-skyline tors (youthful features of a new cycle).

The high west-European plateaus bearing the early-Cainozoic bevel have everywhere been dissected by broad shallow valleys that now make up most of the plateau landscape. Standing also at considerable elevation, the newer cyclic landforms have in many instances obliterated the earlier planation and converted it to a rolling upland of low or moderate relief (Dartmoor). In suitable terrains secondary (sub-skyline) tors are sometimes etched by weathering along the valley sides (Fig. 145). These, in contrast with the residual skyline tors, are *youthful* features of a *new* cycle.

Sometimes the late-Cainozoic landscapes are polycyclic in two or three stages.

End-Cainozoic cymatogeny has elevated the late-Cainozoic landforms mightily upon the plateau regions of Central and Western Europe until now they often stand at thousands instead of scores of feet above sea level. The movements were, however, strongly differential (like the peri-Alpine movements before them), and the denudational surfaces were in places carried down into warped or faulted basins where they have been overlaid by younger deposits.

GEOMORPHOLOGY ABOUT THE CENTRAL PLATEAU OF FRANCE

As a region for study of the many cyclic landsurfaces the environs of the Central Plateau of France are unexcelled (Baulig 1928). The basic structure of the massif is a Hercynian pedestal across which planation was strong in a post-Hercynian landscape cycle. But feeble displacements at the end of the Permian created in Beaujolais local depressions, wherein accumulated gritty and arkosic continental Trias with marine intercalations of a shaly and marly facies. The post-Variscan surface was here very smooth, but has subsequently been much broken up by tectonic movements.

In the absence of Triassic beds, the Laurasian cycle terminating in the Jurassic is often difficult to distinguish from the earlier post-Variscan. Both were represented apparently by smooth planations, but where a planation is directly overlain by Jurassic rocks it may generally be deemed Laurasian. Fragments of the Laurasian surface are thus proved in the north and north-west of Limousin, by the presence of a Mesozoic cover. The surface dips outward and is truncated at a small angle by the Eogene surface. On the " Mountains " of Limousin also is a late mature surface, separated at scarps from the Eogene surface below, which may well be Laurasian.

Above the highest region of the Central Plateau, the Lozere, an extensive Laurasian surface appears to have been, at one time, completely mantled by Jurassic formations of constant facies. Outliers of the mantle are particularly abundant in the western sector towards Marvejols, and the deep weathering of the subjacent granite is also noteworthy. The Laurasian cycle holds, indeed, an important place in the history of Lozere. Though extensive, it has been faulted, and a double slope on the Plat de Lozere shows that it was affected by the Pyrenean movements.

In the lower southern country of the Causses, composed chiefly of Mesozoic rocks the Laurasian surface constitutes a notable part of the Plateau de la Viadene; and in the extreme south-west the same cycle again appears from beneath the cover of the Causses exhibiting a general slope towards the west and an abrupt convexity on the border of the Mediterranean.

From the heights of the Plateau Central the Laurasian surface is depressed into the tablelands of Languedoc and into the Rhône Valley trough. The transition is at the scarp of the Cevennes (constant in direction over hundreds of kilometres) and is dominantly, though not wholly, structural. Thus, while it is true that the orographic limits of the Plateau Central usually coincide with the contact of the older and younger rock systems there are numerous exceptions. At the elevation of the Causses the ancient landscape cycle sinks below a mantle of Jurassic limestones, and along the Saone the ancient terrains lie bordered by a zone of Mesozoic rocks which numerous faults have broken into tilted ridges alternating with granite humps. The moderately undulating plateaus of Languedoc reflect, according to the observations of Baulig, the presence of the Laurasian cycle at relatively low altitude, and the same cycle forms visibly the basement of the plateaus of Bas-Dauphine about the contact with the chains of the sub-alpine folds, Vercors and Chartreuse, and the southern Jura.

South and east of the Massif Central, the Laurasian surface is fossilised at lower elevations, often readily traceable through structural effects even where it is not visible. Occasionally, below the edges of the Massif, the contact of the Mesozoic cover with the Hercynian basement is not sedimentary but occurs on intermediate surfaces of sliding and over-riding.   These movements of horizontal translation antedate the vertical displacements of the border of the Massif, and may be Alpine (mid-Cainozoic in age).

The Vosges presents a history analogous with that of the Central Plateau.   There is Hercynian basement and a planation before the discordant deposition of the sub-horizontal Permian and Triassic.   On the highest summits (1,250-1,450 metres) appears a slightly arched profile—possibly to be correlated with the buried landscape on which rest the Permian-Triassic formations that appear on the eastern border of the Paris Basin.   The chain, indeed, sinks progressively towards the west to harmonise with the Basin, whereas on the east is an abrupt and fractured descent through the sub-Vosges to the Plain of Alsace.

The Cainozoic dislocations have affected profoundly the elevation of the Laurasian planations.   Thus from 1,000 metres in Lyonnais and Beaujolais it appears at 1,640 metres in the Forey and even higher in Lozere.   In the grabens, of course, it has been depressed, and its position can only be ascertained by boring through the later cover of Cainozoic rocks.   Thus in the Limagne, near Riom, 1,100 metres were penetrated without reaching the base, so that from this point to the plateau of the Puys a difference of level of quite 1,800 metres is indicated.   This is comparable with dislocations found in the Vosges crystallines and the adjacent graben of the Rhine.

As the post-Hercynian and several of the later surfaces have been buried and, after an interval of time, exhumed again, fossil erosion surfaces are important in the relief of the Massif, and their identification poses one of the principal problems facing the geomorphologist.   Sediments of determinable date are scarce in the central parts of the Massif and the sediments at the base of the cover are always poor in fossils, and they are very variable locally and similar for different epochs.

But the surface which makes the smooth skyline of the highest parts of the Massif Central (Lozere) above the tectonic scarps which front the valleys of the Rhône and Saone is the early-Cainozoic (Eogene) planation (Plate 14, between pp. 360-61) rendering a broad, monotonous plateau whereon deep valleys are rare, especially towards the divide.   Nowhere is this planation in its original position and though it must originally have been very nearly horizontal it is now greatly dislocated (Fig. 146) and more or less inclined.   Contiguous segments are sharply broken from one another by faults and not by flexures or folds.   Deformation dates not only from the Oligocene and Miocene periods but also from late-Pliocene time.

The early-Cainozoic surface represents the fundamental planation from which the scenery of the Massif Central has subsequently been carved.   There does not exist, *in the crystalline and metamorphic terrains*, a more recent smooth planation than that of the early-Cainozoic.

The early-Cainozoic cycle of denudation was terminated by dislocations of earliest Oligocene date, so that upon the surface and especially in the grabens or depressed blocks, were laid Oligocene sediments, continental and marine (Fig. 146).   Cainozoic fosses are numerous in and about the Central Plateau, where they constitute, amongst

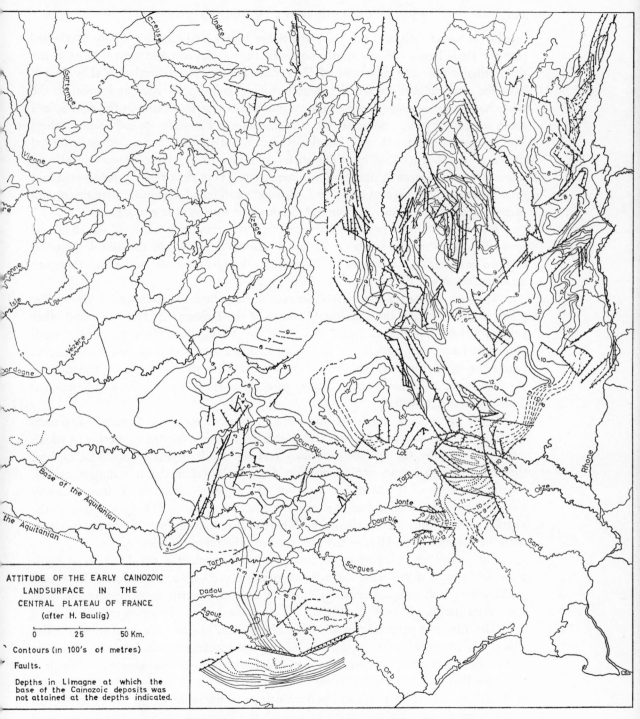

ATTITUDE OF THE EARLY CAINOZOIC
LANDSURFACE IN THE
CENTRAL PLATEAU OF FRANCE
(after H. Baulig)

0   25   50 Km.

Contours (in 100's of metres)

Faults.

Depths in Limagne at which the
base of the Cainozoic deposits was
not attained at the depths indicated.

FIG. 146. Deformation of the early Cainozoic (Eogene) surface on and about the
Central Plateau of France. *after H. Baulig.*

others, the upper valleys of the Loire and Allier Rivers, and continue thence northward into the Paris Basin. In the south, however, they strike east and west. Most of the dislocations follow the directions of Hercynian folding, but nevertheless they do not have the same amplitudes nor the same tectonic significance. Rare and feeble in the west, north-west and south-west they are numerous and important in the centre, and south and south-east. Some of the movements are Pyrenean (post-Eocene), others Alpine (post-Oligocene) in age. Local movements, both positive and negative, permitted the local development of multiple surfaces, either as terraces, or occasionally as unconformities separating phases of sedimentation. Very clear relationships sometimes exist between the emergent areas and adjacent localities of Cainozoic deposition, and many special features such as resurrected fault scarps have been elucidated.

About the Central Plateau in Cainozoic time was commonly a zone of varied littoral formations such as the sands of Perigord passing laterally into the lake limestones, molasse and marine limestones of Aquitaine. Early-Cainozoic landscapes therefore include elements of diverse type, origin and age.

Through Limousin the early-Cainozoic surface formed an exceptionally regular glacis which overlooks the consequent course of the Dronne, the Dordogne and other valleys. Minor elevations, domes and blunt cones rise above the exceptionally well-planed surface which rises in the south-east to 800 metres elevation, but in the central region the relief culminates in a large compact mass, essentially granulitic, constituting the plateaus of Millevaches and Gentioux carrying an earlier summit bevel (? Laurasian) which rises to 980 metres.

Earth movements, moderate to strong, have disturbed the surface. Pyrenean movements gave birth to folds and faults, striking from north-west to south-east which were truncated by the surface on which rest the sands of Perigord. The surface, therefore, though begun earlier, continued to evolve after the movements ceased. Beyond the edge of the Mesozoic outcrops, the Eogene surface approximates closely to the Laurasian emerging from beneath the Mesozoic rocks. The same is true in the vicinity of Berry and the Bourbonnais. There is also, indeed, some confusion in places with the Permian (post-Hercynian) surface about the region of Vienne.

The early-Cainozoic surface in Limousin has been tilted in the direction of Aquitaine, and similar disturbance extends also to the post-Oligocene terrains. These facts indicate a general subsidence of the basin of Aquitaine partly contemporaneous with the sedimentation and partly later than the completion of the Eogene surface.

The Limagne proper is an alluvial plain 40 km. in extent drained by the Allier River, and which lies between the two parallel escarpments which dominate Clermont and Riom on the west, Thiers on the east. Northward the alluvial sheets continue into the Paris Basin. They are Oligocene (Stampian) in age and serve to identify portions of the Eogene surface beneath and to demonstrate its fluviatile origin. They have great morphological interest also in connection with the Pyrenean faultings which dislocated the Eogene surface and created the fosses.

Important at the base of the Oligocene deposits are lenticles of bauxite representing an ancient duricrust upon the Eogene landsurface. The field relations are described by Baulig (1928). " The gneiss [bedrock] is reddened and altered . . . and arrives insensibly at an absolute transition to a sort of blood-red grit excessively hard and devoid of stratification. This grit, or bauxite, preserves the same characters for four or five metres. The upper part is then less compact and at the same time more quartzose, and passes insensibly again into very hard, blood-red shales, or into neutral quartzites and marls indistinguishable from the red argillaceous sandstones. Chemical analysis shows that the Oligocene bauxite is like the laterites of existing tropical countries. It is this formation . . . represents the same surface of the peneplain at the beginning of the Oligocene period ". On the Plateaus of Livradois also the lowest deposits upon the Eogene surface are, in places, silcretes and ferricretes. This early-Cainozoic surface survived upon more elevated tracts into the Oligocene existing contemporaneously with Oligocene deposition in the depressions. Of the Oligocene scenery Baulig has written: " The characters of Oligocene sedimentation in the Limagne attest the existence at the same epoch of a large surface of continental erosion developed across ancient rocks and in course of deformation and dislocation. It is this surface that forms once again the principal element in the topography. To the west of the Allier River it constitutes the foundation of the Puys and Mt. Dore . . . to the east of the river the planed summits of the Livradois and the Monts du Forez and at the same time the lower plateaus of the Chomette, etc."

" The basement surface surmounted by the Puys, Mt. Dore, etc., is identifiable with the surface at the base of the Oligocene in Limagne. The surface mounts gradually south-eastwards to 700-800 metres where it is concealed for a space by the later basalts of the Sioule chain . . . and finally surmounts 900 metres below the Puys of Louchadiere and Espinasse. The surface is senile and the drainage consequent. It is here faulted and the tectonic depression is occupied by Oligocene formations ". The surface is also widely exposed elsewhere. It appears at 1,000-1,100 metres west of the Dordogne where, also, it bears Oligocene deposits. Below the border of Cezallier it appears again at like elevation and descends thence, like the valleys and rivers, towards the west-south-west. Eastward from Cezallier, too, it descends, reaching 700-800 metres above the Allier River to the west of Langeac, and reappears east of the river in the form of a wide bench sloping gently to the north-north-east towards the " fosse de Paulhaguet ". In the Forez and Livradois are many such fosses, or Oligocene troughs occupied in consequent fashion by the principal rivers (Loire, Dore) but also their affluents flow ordinarily along the slopes of the inclined blocks in the long parallel valleys.

The systems of Oligocene fractures and faults reveal some remarkable conformities with pre-existing, Hercynian trendlines. Several of the major valleys, Rhône, Loire and Allier, coincide with Hercynian synclines as well as with troughs carrying Oligocene rocks.

The western and southern flanks of the Massif Central exhibit a comparable set of topographic features. The fundamental form of the Cantal was the early-Cainozoic surface, remarkably regular and free of dislocations. It presents only a regular descent to the Dordogne which thus marks a tectonic axis of depression. In a tectonic depression south-east from Aurillac the Oligocene argillaceous sands border all the valleys between 700 and 750 metres, but to the south-west, between the rivers Cere and Lot broad regular plateaus with a poor soil upon Archean rocks represent the Oligocene surface. In general the surfaces of the various plateaus descend westward from an elevation exceeding 800 metres to between 500 and 600 metres above the Causses de Quercy, which stand at 100-200 metres. The surface truncates the Jurassic in the east and the Cretaceous in the west; it bears ferricretes and passes beneath lower Oligocene deposits. "The surface at the base of the Oligocene on the crystalline terrains is thus continuous, despite important erosion, with the ferricreted surface of the Mesozoic terrains." Ultimately it plunges beneath the lower Oligocene beds of the Basin of Aquitaine.

In the Grandes Causses the Eogene surface is present forming the Plateau of Campuac (700-800 metres) near the River Lot. It slopes regularly to the south-west and in the Viadene truncates the older terrains in the north and the Mesozoic in the south. Along the Mediterranean border near Montpellier the Eocene, in contrast with formations both above and below, is continental in origin and formed an outwash plain to the denudational plain of the interior.

Summarising: a great part of central and southern France was smoothly planed during the Eocene before being disturbed by the Pyrenean movements. Apart from its earlier date of termination (end-Eocene instead of late-Oligocene) therefore, this planation, fundamental to the modern scenery and preserved either upon the highest parts of continuously emergent landscapes or beneath Cainozoic sediments in tectonic basins, corresponds with the similarly extreme, early-Cainozoic planation already described from other continents.

A correspondingly advanced cyclic planation, sometimes continued into the Oligocene period, is known from other plateau regions of Western Europe including the Spanish Meseta, Ardenne and Black Forest. Through Spessarts and Bohemia remnants may be traced as summit bevels even as far as Poland and the Ukraine.

Following uplift of the early-Cainozoic surface over the region of the Central Plateau the smooth planation was dissected by valleys that remain broad even to their heads in Lozere (Plate 14) where they now make most of the high plateau. Farther from the watershed a strong phase of Oligocene erosion effaced the relief due to faults and removed all trace of Mesozoic formations from the high country; but it is poorly developed across the crystalline rocks. Alpine (Miocene) dislocations revived the relief, and were succeeded by a newer phase of erosion which removed the traces of the Oligocene cycle over the areas of weak rocks and developed fault-line valleys in the crystalline rocks.

In the central region, unlike the Limousin where the cyclic landscapes follow one another regularly in succession, the ancient surfaces, strongly deformed, are frequently truncated by very recent surfaces of erosion.

Also, beginning in the late-Miocene, volcanism was manifest over an area of 300 by 250 km. upon the Central Plateau, following mainly the lines of dislocation. It is represented in the Puys, Mt. Dore, the Cantal, the eastern Velay and the Coiron, building domes and flowing as lava sheets down the valleys.

Detritus from the Massif was deposited about the Central Plateau first as Oligocene formations into which, following further tectonic disturbance, Miocene valleys were eroded in the Velay and on the borders of Limagne. South of the Central Plateau such valleys are 100 metres deep and 2 km. broad, incised into Archean basement as well as the Oligocene. The region had been folded into open anticlines and synclines by the Pyrenean tectonics, and now the durability of the granites preserves the older cyclic landforms while the weak resistance of the Permian and Cainozoic rocks facilitates erosion by the latest cycles well into the interior of the Massif.

Multiple late-Cainozoic erosional surfaces stand at inferior elevations about the flanks of the Central Plateau. The present elevations of the surfaces were produced by strong Plio-Pleistocene cymatogene displacements that affected the whole region about the Massif.

Within the Massif the corresponding valleys are deeply incised, with V-shaped cross-sections, except in weak rocks where the valleys are more widely flared out. Owing to tilting, nickpoints are not very clear on the rivers. On the Seine a nickpoint is recorded by Macar at 63 km. from the mouth near the 100 metre contour, and another may be present at 730 km. from the sea, about 275 metres altitude.

The existing drainage, just like the fossil valleys of the Pontian (late-Miocene), is essentially consequent upon the dislocations of the Oligocene surface.

Landscape Cycles of the Mediterranean Border and the Paris Basin

On the Mediterranean border the structure consists of several discordant sedimentary series lying on an invisible Hercynian basement. Late-Triassic, Jurassic and Cretaceous formations are all marine, but the Eocene is continental and important in the landscape north from Montpellier. The Oligocene, geosynclinal and more than 500 metres thick in the vicinity of Montpellier, rests with unconformity upon the folded Mesozoics. The Miocene exists only in tectonic depressions and makes smooth country.

The younger erosion surfaces are separated one from another at marked steps which run (largely) across the river systems, thus showing that, as we have demonstrated elsewhere, the surfaces have been developed from their predecessors by scarp retreat, though the scarps are often sited upon contacts between different types of rocks. The plains (plateaus) themselves are described by Baulig as certainly of continental planation (*e.g.* Grandes Causses), though carved in the vicinity of the sea. A reversal of movement at one stage drowned the valley of the lower Rhône, converting it into a gulf penetrating almost as far north as Lyons.   Within this gulf were deposited the blue Plaisancian marls, later covered by littoral and estuarine sands concluded by vast sheets of torrential gravels in the vicinity of the Alps.   Fossil Pliocene topography is sometimes revealed where these formations have later been removed.   The Rhône valley is not the true boundary of the Massif Central.   "The real structural limit is found to the east, coinciding with the great north-south Miocene synclinal which separates the Mesozoic plateaus of Languedoc from the folded chains of the Diois and Baronnies.   To the south-east, the boundary is better marked where the Mesozoic rocks sink below the Neogene along the line Remoulins-Nimes-Montpellier."   Alluvial terraces record the last phases of morphology of the peripheral regions (Paris Basin, Loire, Garonne and, less distinctly, Rhône Valley).

The relief of the Paris Basin is characterised by a profusion of structural and resurrected surfaces.   Notwithstanding, a smooth Oligocene landscape seems to be the fundamental form from which the present relief has been carved.   This Oligocene surface was deformed at the beginning of the Miocene, during which period the deformed surface was again remodelled, and reached the stage of an extensive meulièrised planation, e.g. Brie or Beauce before being profoundly affected by late-Miocene movements.   The meulières are interpreted by Tricart as alteration products of the chalk not in an arid but in a humid climate with descending groundwater.   The ferruginisation is a subsequent phenomenon, constituting in fact an alteration of a meulière previously formed and operative in a totally different (arid) climate, as shown by the presence of hematite.

The late-Miocene orogenic crisis governed the hydrographic network and hence the pattern of later erosion which excavated well into bedrock of differentially-elevated areas.   In these movements the borders of the Basin, e.g. the Morvan-Vosges axis, showed a tendency to rise, making a dome between the lakes of the plains of the Saone on the east and those of Lorraine to the north and of Paris to the north-west.   In Belgium the Miocene shows the characteristic regression of the sea, but the Pliocene is, on the contrary, again strongly transgressive even into the Ardenne, which must have been subsiding and received sediment from the elevated eastern part of the Paris Basin. Several captures occur with the incision of rivers such as the Moselle and Meurthe, adapted to deformations of the Oligo-Miocene surface.   Rivers formerly flowing from south to north thus tend to be diverted to east-west courses; the chief lines of the modern hydrography were thus fixed by the Mio-Pliocene dissections.   By the end of the Pliocene a great part of the topography of the Paris Basin had attained the stage of maturity, if not senility.   The chief traits of the topography were then already established.   The climate was apparently dry, residuals rose like inselbergs from a savannah, soil phenomena suggest a dry climate, and Tricart (1949) writes of fashioning by sheet flood.   Two or three late-Cainozoic sub-cycles are sometimes recognised.   These may stand locally as high as 400 metres where carried upwards by later movements.

In the Quaternary, with climatic change, came marked incision. The valleys of the rivers have been incised in stages, and areas of weak rocks excavated, leaving the Pliocene surface now upon the interfluves. With the slackening of orogenic activity during the Quaternary the structure of the Basin attained its modern form, and the topography its present aspect.

Formerly, the principal terrace levels of France and Belgium were attributed to variations of load and discharge consequent upon the Quaternary glaciations. But this explanation is now largely abandoned in favour of epeirogenic movements, for some of the terrace-levels have been deformed by local differential movements.

THE SPANISH MESETA

The meseta is an extensive upland consisting basically of an early-Cainozoic surface cutting across older Palæozoic and crystalline rocks but in one or two places transecting Mesozoic shales. The upcast block of the Sierra Guadarrama (exceeding 2,500 metres) divides it into Old Castile upon the north and New Castile in the south. The southern limit is the similarly elevated Sierra Morena, of Palæozoic granite.

On both Castilian plateaus the western portion is a compound early-Cainozoic surface standing around 1,100-1,200 metres and with plateau remnants up to 1,500 metres. It is much broken and warped. Two lower levels of planation, one late-Miocene and the other younger, are identified above the deep Quaternary valleys of the Douro, Tagus and Guadiana Rivers. Eocene rocks occur only in the Ebro trough south of the Pyrenees and in the region of the Betic Cordillera, which is also the only region where lower-Oligocene rocks occur. During the early-Cainozoic all the area of the Meseta underwent denudation. Only in the late-Oligocene do a few small brackish water deposits appear, with molluscs and mammal bones.

In the late Miocene, however, extensive basins sagged over the eastern portion of both parts of the meseta (Fig. 147), and the early-Cainozoic surface was buried beneath horizontal formations of gravel, sand, mudstone, limestone and gypsum. These deposits were supplied from surrounding regions by a late-Miocene cycle of denudation, but at no time were the basins closed off, and the rivers maintained exits to the sea.

A later cycle involved the Miocene formations also, which are today often left forming table-top topography above the undulating landforms of the Pliocene denudation cycle. On the older, westward terrain of harder Palæozoic rocks are residual ranges and subsequent valleys. Pediments are widespread landforms upon all terrains. Except above the Alpine depression of the Guadalquivir, Pliocene deposits are local and restricted to the coastal regions of both Spain and Portugal.

The violence of late-Cainozoic uplift is attested by the present elevation of the meseta (1,100-1,500 metres), by the deep youthful valleys by which the major rivers dissect it, by the abundance of Quaternary conglomerates and by the abrupt descent to the coast. The relatively low level of marine Cainozoic rocks in the coastal regions shows, moreover, that the elevation of the meseta has been accompanied by steep coastal warping.

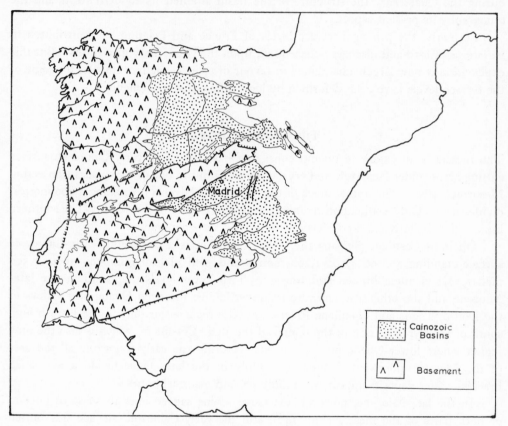

FIG. 147. Basins of late Cainozoic deposition upon the Spanish Meseta.

THE ARDENNE

In Belgium the Ardenne displays a history in most respects similar to that of the Central Plateau of France. The folded Palæozoic massif was truncated by a late-Palæozoic land-surface which began to be covered by water during the Triassic but during the Jurassic and early-Cretaceous it was emergent again, overlooking the sea of the Paris Basin on the west. Cenomanian rocks, however, spread over the western Ardenne, and the upper Cretaceous (Maastrichtian) covered the massif. After the post-Maastrichtian emergence the Sparnacian sands, gravels and muds of continental origin blanketed a great part of the region. The lower Lutetian (middle-Eocene) was equally extensive over all the region of Palæozoic rocks. Since then the Ardenne has been continuously land.

There are thus several fossilised landsurfaces (post-Hercynian, late-Jurassic and late-Cretaceous and pre-Oligocene) which Baulig (1926) has shown to be disposed along the northern and western flanks of the Ardenne in an arch with an axial plunge to the west (Fig. 148). With decreasing age the successive surfaces have lesser dips proving successive rejuvenations of the arched structure.

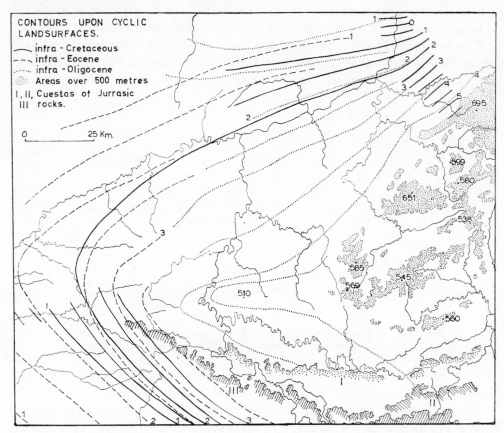

CONTOURS UPON CYCLIC
LANDSURFACES.
—— infra - Cretaceous
--- infra - Eocene
······ infra - Oligocene
▨ Areas over 500 metres
I, II, Cuestas of Jurrasic
III rocks.

0   25 Km.

FIG. 148. Arched and plunging fossil surfaces (sub-Cretaceous, sub-Eocene and sub-Oligocene) of the western Ardenne. *after H. Baulig.*

The Cainozoic history of the Ardenne is recorded in a number of cyclic denudations upon the higher country. The earliest of these, represented upon the Baraque Michel (678 metres) and Baraque de Fraiture (652 metres), is a smooth peaty moorland whereon the soil contains residual flints showing that it was developed not far below the level of the late-Cretaceous formations which to the north it transgresses. The original nature of this early-Cainozoic surface is difficult to specify owing to the amount of modification it has experienced under solifluction and related peri-glacial action, but it was certainly well planed and may originally have borne pediments. The surface slopes markedly northward as a result of later tilting, appearing upon the Hertogenwald

at only 550 metres.   Around Jalhay the surface bears silcrete, which is found also far
to the west upon the Crête du Condroz.

Late-Cainozoic cycles are three in number.   The first, of probable Miocene age,
attained a maximum planation level of about 400 metres whence it declines northward
to 340 metres across the Fammenian depression.   It is very widely distributed as a
ridge bevel through the northern Ardenne.   The surface is commonly deeply weathered
and hence the landscape has been thought to have developed under a humid climate.

The two later (Pliocene) planation levels do not show this weathering and have
been ascribed by Belgian geomorphologists (Macar, Alexandre and Pissart) to development under a semi-arid regime.   Upon the later of these two bevels, which reaches to

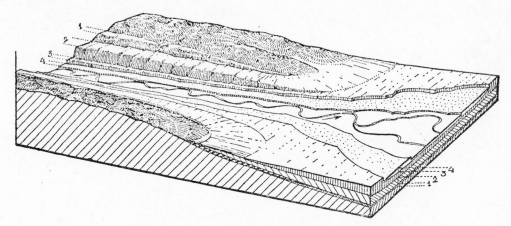

FIG. 149.   Diagrammatic expression of tilted and crossing denudational
surfaces as in the Netherlands.   *after K. Oestreich.*

the heads of even minor streams, developed the meander systems of the rivers that
subsequently became strikingly incised, *e.g.* Ourthe, Ambleve, Moselle.

The cymatogenic uplift which gave rise to these incisions occurred just prior to
the onset of European glaciation, that is, towards the end of the Pliocene.   The Quaternary valleys are deeply incised, but in their lower courses show a number of terraces
(Alexandre 1957) where the valleys have been widely opened out upon weak shales.
Abundant waste supplied by solifluction during the glacial epoch is thought to have
contributed to lateral erosion by the rivers.

Before leaving the Ardenne we may note that Macar (1955) has made a comparison
of levels of erosion in the Ardenne with those in the Appalachians.   He noted fewer
erosion levels in the Appalachians and attributed this to (a) absence of stratigraphic
formations of resistance intermediate between that of the prominent ridge makers and
the weak rocks of the lowlands;   (b) small epeirogenic movements in the Ardenne;
and (c) that major erosion surfaces in the Appalachians may be polycyclic.

Beyond the Rhine graben—a trough related to a Cretaceous arch but floored only with Cainozoic and later sediments, and upon which a strong sinking tendency has existed during the Quaternary (Fig. 150)—a chain of Variscan horsts and domes (Penck 1925) extends eastwards far across Central Europe. Upon all of these, from the Schwarzwald to Poland and the Balkans, Cainozoic erosional bevels are manifest; but though general similarities exist no comparative synthesis for the entire region seems to have been made.*

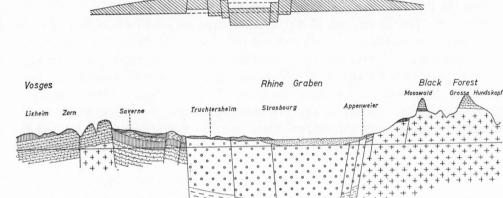

FIG. 150. Section from west to east across the Rhine graben.

According to data marshalled by Matchatschek (1955) the general history of the Variscan terrain is that already in the Permian the western massifs had been denuded and subsequently some had acquired a cover of red continental Permian and Triassic rocks. Beginning in the Jurassic, a sea from the north and west covered more and more of the area, but even during the late Cretaceous certain areas of the Harz and Thuringerwald, at least, remained unsubmerged as axial upwarps.

The sea then withdrew, and during the early-Cainozoic a landscape of low relief, partly lateritised, was characteristic upon the Harz, Erzgebirge and Sudeten. In the hollows of the landscape accumulated lignites, fine-grained river sediments, red earths and bog iron ore. Weak karst topography was developed upon limestone areas. Such a general lowland is known to pass below the middle-Oligocene marine transgression

* The author read extensively among the literature available to him but confesses to being quite unable without field work to correlate the local details of heights and surfaces recorded. Some of the statements in literature even seem suspect ; as for instance where Penck (1953), having carefully described five cyclic landsurfaces upon the Fichtelgebirge, finally insists that even the youngest of these ante-dates the Oligocene.

of north and middle Germany.   The rolling summit bevel of the Harz slopes to the north and north-west, and as marine Oligocene formations now stand at 650 metres in the Schonberg near Freiburg strongly differential movement is clearly involved.

The ancient landscape of low or stepped relief was disturbed, and in places faulted, by earth movements related to the Alpine orogeny (Chapter XV), and the landscape of Miocene times was therefore more diversified with local basins of brown coal deposition, lake beds and local basaltic outflows (Erzgebirge, Sudeten).   The fine grain of late-Miocene and early-Pliocene sandstones and the presence of freshwater limestones, however, postulate then a weak relief;   and there was considerable change of watersheds between the Rhine, Rhône and Danube about the Black Forest region.

The late-Miocene renewal of Alpine movements initiated fresh (Pliocene) cycles which largely erased the tectonically induced relief (about the upper Rhine the surface cuts across Miocene folds), and upon suitable terrains carved appropriate landscapes of low or moderate, sometimes dicyclic relief.   High standing Pliocene gravels show that many changes of river courses also occurred at this stage.   Through southern Poland (Jahn 1953;   Kondracki 1956) these late-Cainozoic planations, which are the oldest present, also slope northwards.   Only upon the mountainous Sudeten and the Lysogory Mountains near Kielce (Lencewiez 1933) is the early-Cainozoic surface recorded.

The Plio-Pleistocene deformation was very strong, leaving erosion to excavate the deep valleys and high reliefs that immediately preceded the onset of Pleistocene glaciation.

Over Northern Europe the imprint of glacial and peri-glacial activities is widespread. The North German-Polish Basin is filled with Quaternary deposits, but borings near Hamburg have revealed beneath them an irregular, late-Cainozoic surface, with steep-sided, broad-floored valleys 250 metres deep, cut into Cainozoic rocks.   This region seems often to have been submerged as the Central European massifs to the south were intermittently uplifted.   The " marine Eocene " seems thus to have been confined to the northern edge of the North German plain;   during the early-Oligocene period the sea advanced south as far as Magdeburg, and in the mid-Oligocene as far as Leipzig; but by the later-Oligocene it had retreated again and by the Miocene was restricted to the north-western sector of the plain.   This advance and retreat was probably due to hinging, elevated cyclic erosion surfaces to the south continuing to supply sediment which was deposited irrespective of the position of the shoreline;   a continental facies existing far south, for instance, of the Miocene coast.

BLUEPRINT FOR BRITAIN

Basic document for the study of geomorphology in Britain is the sketch map by Linton (1951) showing regionally by contours altitudes of the highest summits (Fig. 151). Admittedly provisional and indicatory only, this map nonetheless clearly demonstrates two things: (a) that summit altitudes in Britain represent in a general way a formerly existing summit topography of small relief; and (b) that this former topography has hinged along a north-south axis passing through East Anglia giving progressively more uplifted country towards the west (Wales) and a depressed area to the east (drowned beneath the North Sea).

No synthesis of British topography is possible without clear understanding of the differential movement involved. Previous attempts to systematise ancient erosional remnants were foredoomed to failure when their authors attempted to classify such remnants upon a basis of equality of height above sea level.

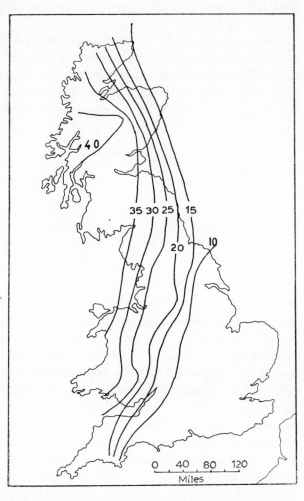

FIG. 151.

" Farthest east " altitudes of British hills and mountains demonstrating (a) the former existence of a summit topography of small relief (even though scarcely any of this topography remains today) and (b) that this former topography has hinged along a north-south axis passing through East Anglia, giving progressively more uplifted country towards the west (Wales) and a depressed area to the east (North Sea). Elevations in hundreds of feet. *after D. L. Linton.*

The age of the predicated ancestral landsurface is important for fixing the date of the main movement of tilting within the British region.   Linton, in common with the authors of the Memoir on Regional Geology for South Wales, unfortunately chose the pre-Cenomanian landsurface for the ancestral planation recorded in the summit elevations; but this stands confounded upon Linton's own diagram by the necessity to carry such ancient landsurface from 4,000 feet upon the Scottish Highlands down below sea level at the west coast to pass below the early-Cainozoic basaltic lavas of Mull and Antrim (Fig. 153).   For this neither the present topography nor the solid geology yield any warrant.

Patently the ancestral summit topography must be younger than the lavas and belong to a Cainozoic cycle of erosion which would pass over them.   This yields the concept of a parent landsurface of Cainozoic age from which the existing cyclic topography of Britain has been carved, partly during later-Cainozoic and partly during Quaternary time.   Is such a parent landsurface purely hypothetical, or do relics of it survive today in British landscape?

Search for remnants of a Cainozoic (and probably early-Cainozoic) planation in the British Isles is severely conditioned by the small area of those islands.   Few places are far from the sea and Quaternary erosion, fluvial and glacial, has taken heavy toll of whatever topography existed previously.   Only upon the highest terrains, represented in Linton's " contours ", are the remnants sought likely to be found.

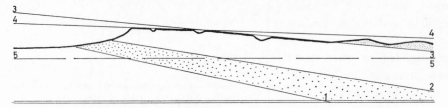

FIG. 152.   Successive denudational and depositional episodes of south-eastern England produced under successive tiltings.   1. Sub-Cenomanian surface, 2. Sub-Chalk surface, 3. Sub-Eocene surface, 4. Early Cainozoic surface, 5. Sea-level.

Beginning in the south-west, Dartmoor and Exmoor consist of broadly open valleys, standing generally between 1,500 and 2,000 feet above sea level, that morphologically resemble the first late-Cainozoic (Miocene) cyclic landscapes that we have recorded in other lands.   Between these valleys the highest interfluves occasionally present smooth profiles that rise like pediments towards *skyline tors*.   Anyone familiar with granitic plateaus elsewhere (*e.g.* Rhodesia) would immediately recognise a morphological analogy with the early-Cainozoic landscape of extreme pediplanation with its steep-sided residual koppies.   These tors are thus the final unconsumed remnants upon a surface of extremely advanced pediplanation and must carefully be distinguished (King 1958) from the *subskyline tors* which are developing now within the broad valleys as *youthful* features in a newer cycle of erosion.   The evidence on southern Dartmoor has been read by Orme (1964), who recognises four principal surfaces of which the oldest is " A tilted early-Tertiary peneplain at 1,620-1,520 feet."   Flanking this are two late Cainozoic surfaces at 1,000-875 feet and 820-730 feet respectively.   All were of subaerial origin and developed largely by scarp retreat.   At 700 feet appear the effects of an early Pleistocene* marine transgression.   To the east Waters (1960) has described " a particularly fine example of an upland plain which declines gently southward from 1,035 feet . . . to a little below 500 feet at the coast ".   The surface is composite and is present " over a large part of south-western England from Land's End to Shaftesbury"

* But for this dating contrast the views of Wooldridge and Linton (p. 402) on topography in southeast Britain.

truncating " virtually every major geological outcrop in Cornwall, Devon and Dorset ". The highest parts, upon Staple Hill, bear " clay-with-flints " (p. 401) (Fig. 155).

In Wales the Cainozoic landscape of the " high plateau " has been upwarped severely and not a great deal of it remains. The identifiable remnants (Brown 1957) are

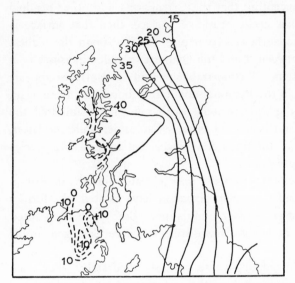

rolling and morphologically suggest the late-Cainozoic surface. Brown's " middle and low peneplains " may then be younger partial surfaces of non-cyclic significance upon a rising cymatogen (p. 207).

Fig. 153.

Erroneous correlation of the summit topography of Britain with the pre-Cenomanian surface beneath the lavas of Mull and Antrim. The summit topography should be dated as early Cainozoic and carried above the lavas. Elevations in hundreds of feet. *after D. L. Linton.*

In the Scottish Highlands Peach and Horne, Solch and others have described a " high plateau " which Linton (1951) shows to " rise westwards by some 600 feet in

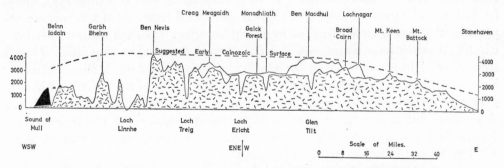

Fig. 154. Section from west to east through the Scottish Highlands to show cyclic erosion surfaces. *modified from D. L. Linton.*

rather less than 50 miles ". In doing so it ranges between 2,500 and 3,000 feet. " The gradient ", writes Linton, " may be partly original but it is at least as likely to be due to renewed eastward tilting ". This (Grampian) surface, together with a later and lower partial surface (Fig. 154), is incised by the deep valley systems of the Highlands, and may thus tentatively be regarded (Chapter VIII) as belonging to a late-Cainozoic cycle. Furthermore, certain monadnocks like Ben Nevis, Creag Meagaidh, and the Cairngorm Mountains rise abruptly above the main Grampian surface to elevations exceeding 4,000 feet (also greater in the west). Linton (1951) has regarded their summits as approximating to the pre-Cenomanian surface, but this we have shown (p. 397) they cannot be without doing violence to structural and stratigraphic relations at the west coast. Even the younger, "Grampian" surfaces of the Highlands should continue above the lavas of Mull. Accepting that the Cairngorms and other residual summits do represent a pre-Grampian cyclic erosional surface, then that surface is most probably the early-Cainozoic landsurface. Its nature, residual upon the highest country, with one major planation between it and the Quaternary valley incisions is at least consistent with this interpretation. A comparable pair of landsurfaces appears (at 2,000 and 1,300 feet respectively) in the Pennines about Ingleborough. Here again the upper one was in existence at the time regional earth movements initiated the present southward-flowing drainage and is quoted as early Cainozoic, while the latter, which is the most extensive surface of the upland, is succeeded by two later cycles within the valley system, both being pre-Glacial.

In sum, the meagre evidence available from the most elevated terrains of Britain suggests that two cycles of widespread Cainozoic planation have existed, the former possibly of extreme planation the latter broadly undulating. Both have been tilted eastward upon the flank of a broad monocline from Ireland where Cainozoic uplift exceeded 2,500 feet (Walsh 1966).

But no evidence has emerged for dating these surfaces accurately. For such evidence we must seek in the eastern region where the surfaces come to low level and may be related to unconformities within the late-Mesozoic and Cainozoic sequence. Distributed over the Chiltern Hills and North Downs, e.g. Box Hill (Fig. 155), and as far west as east Devon (Waters 1960) appear small local remnants of a former smooth planation that may often be identified by a residual surface deposit of " clay-with-flints " which in the strict sense corresponds to a duricrust developed upon the Chalk. Though approximating in places to an earlier sub-Eocene surface upon which characteristically lie the small dark flint gravels of the Reading Beds, the surface of the " clay-with-flints ", clearly represents a smooth cyclic landsurface of post-Middle Eocene age and long denudation that is the oldest continuously-exposed landscape of the region. It is fundamental also in that upon it arose the primitive radial drainage pattern of the Wealden Dome* (Wooldridge and Linton 1938).

Though this landsurface was later deformed and partly carried below sea level, in no place is it known bearing marine fossil deposit. Indeed, no Miocene series is known in Britain, though this is the formation which has been found normally to lie upon the smooth planation of early-Cainozoic time (p. 229). However, the Boxstones of Norfolk are rolled sandstone pebbles with enclosed Miocene fossils occurring in the Pliocene Crag, thus demonstrating an erosional phase (Mio-Pliocene) in which earlier Miocene

---

* The present pattern is quite different and derives from a much flatter surface developed under a Pliocene sea and later uplifted. A Wealden island remained, however, and upon this the older stream pattern has survived.

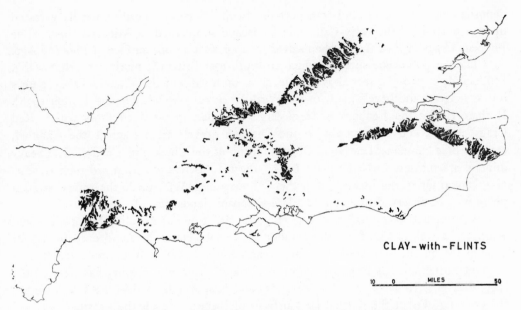

CLAY-with-FLINTS

FIG. 155. Area over which the " clay-with-flints ", a residual deposit corresponding to a duricrust, may occur. This defines the possible surviving remnants of an early Cainozoic landscape in south-eastern England. *after K. M. Clayton.*

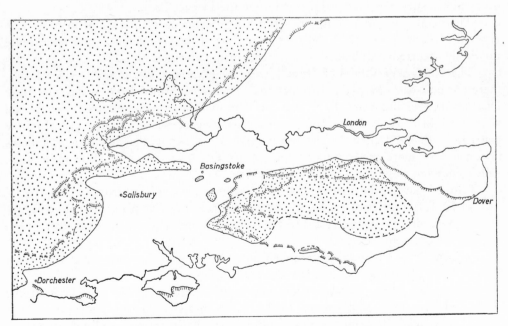

FIG. 156. Extent of the Pliocene sea over south-east Britain. Land area dotted. *after S. W. Wooldridge and D. L. Linton.*

2 C

deposits were broken up and transported.   Such Miocene deposits must have rested upon a portion of the early-Cainozoic landscape submerged in Miocene time.   The Pliocene Crags of East Anglia themselves lie upon at least one surface of Pliocene Age.

The early-Pliocene surface, which in south-east Britain is marine in origin, (Fig. 156) stands at 650-700 feet above sea level on both sides of the Thames Valley, passes into east Kent, and bevels many of the Wealden ridges (Wooldridge and Linton 1938). It there carries the Lenham Beds, of large, irregular, iron-stained flints with " Red Crag " fossils, and corresponds to the Diestian gravels which, across the Channel, cap low hills known as Les Noire Mottes on top of the Chalk near Calais.   The heavy mineral assemblage of the Lenham Beds indicates a derivation from old rock systems now known far to the west.   Upon the Chilterns near Whipsnade the wave-modified phase may be observed to pass into a late-Cainozoic landsurface.*

A later, 400 feet marine stage, with gravels at Shooter's Hill, Hampstead and Highgate is well known from the London Basin into Hampshire and even to the far west in Devon and Cornwall.   So far as can be ascertained it shows no trace of subsequent tilting and has been spoken of as eustatic.   But late warping has affected the east Midlands (Kellaway and Taylor 1953) and East Anglia, and in the Crags we see the crossing over of the warped landsurfaces of Britain towards the subsided basin of the North Sea.   The latest of the Crags, the Norwich Crag, contains at the base the earliest pebble tools (eoliths) and is believed to be part of the ancient Rhine Delta before subsidence of the coast near Cromer.   Some of the subsidence is very recent, Neolithic occupational sites now lying submerged upon the Dogger Bank.

The main phase of arching upon the British cymatogen thus seems to have been enacted towards the close of the Cainozoic though displacements in the same sense obviously occurred both before and after the main movement.

The chief river valleys of Britain, with their various Pleistocene terrace levels, therefore post-date the main deformation.   This is confirmed from Wales, the Lake District and Scotland where deep valley incisions following upon the maximum upheaval were accomplished only shortly before the onset of Pleistocene glaciation (p. 518).   In these districts, with the Cainozoic planations carried high upon the hills and mountains (1,500 feet or more), only minor benchings, often at confusing levels, appear upon valley sides and ridge crests at lower elevations.

Chronologically, the scenery of Britain seems to have evolved from

a) Partial stripping of a pre-Cenomanian surface of marine planation with development of a primitive, eastwardly directed drainage pattern superposed from the Cenomanian cover.

b) Locally, in the south-eastern counties at least, a sub-Eocene surface overstrewn by the Reading gravel beds and Thanet sands.

c) An important early-Cainozoic planation.   Rescue of this episode from the oblivion to which its almost total destruction under later erosion seems to have consigned it, removes much of the emphasis formerly placed upon the

* E. Brown, Private communication.

pre-Cenomanian resurrected surface as the fundamental planation from which the scenery and drainage patterns of Britain have been carved. Moreover, it accords with the wide extent of such a planation upon the mainland of Europe and in other continents. If this planation is represented approximately upon the highest summits of Scotland (p. 400), then

d) the Grampian main surface, and most of the British uplands belong to the first late-Cainozoic cycle. (? Miocene).

e) The lower partial surface of the Grampians and the elevated " basins " of that region represent the second late-Cainozoic phase contemporary with the earlier stages of cymatogenic uplift, (*cf.* Wales). Correlative surfaces in south-east England bear Pliocene marine formations that about the Thames Valley and along the south coast to Dorset maintain an elevation of 600-700 feet for over 100 miles. Yet equivalent formations (and the surface beneath them) are brought down in East Anglia to pass below the North Sea, and at Utrecht in Holland are 1,200 feet below sea level.

f) Following the late-Cainozoic cymatogenic uplift, just before

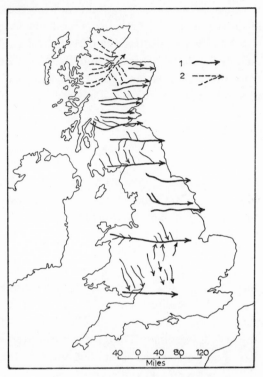

FIG. 157. Primitive drainage pattern of Britain. *after D. L. Linton.*

the onset of Pleistocene glaciation, were incised the deep valleys that now create the major reliefs of the western and Midland mountainlands. Though the impress of glacial excavation in the valleys is distinctive, " over the remainder of the area, it seems probable that the removal of weathered rock, and a mild scouring and rubbing down of prominences . . . is perhaps the sum-total of the effect of the . . . ice sheets of the past " (Hollingworth 1937). This conclusion upon the efficacy of Pleistocene glaciation in the Lake District accords with previously expressed opinion for North America (p. 379).

Study of drainage patterns reveals many changes throughout Britain, and a noteworthy series of papers upon this topic is by Linton.* The primitive drainage pattern is illustrated in Fig. 157.

* *Scottish Geog. Mag.*, Vols. 48, 49, 56, 65, 67, 70.

Despite the paucity of surviving evidence due to the small area available for study, the outline of Cainozoic geomorphology for Britain accords stage by stage with that of the European mainland (p. 388); and attempts have been made to correlate directly topographic facets upon opposite sides of the English Channel (Guilcher 1949; Macar 1936). According to W. B. R. King (1954) the Channel has had a tendency to subside along intermittent downwarps ever since the late-Palæozoic, whereas enclosing land areas have had a tendency to rise together.

The North Sea Basin apparently did not exist during the Jurassic for, according to Arkell, the deltaic Bajocian and Bathonian deposits of north-east Britain were derived from the Scandinavian Shield. It subsided intermittently during the late-Mesozoic, the Oligocene and the Plio-Pleistocene.

GEOMORPHIC OUTLINE IN SCANDINAVIA

The hemi-cymatogen of Britain has an analogue across the North Sea in Scandinavia, where also Cainozoic erosion surfaces, vastly upheaved behind the steep coast of Norway, incline south-eastwards through Sweden towards the Baltic Sea and Gulf of Bothnia, and through southern Norway towards the Skagerrak coast where a Cainozoic surface sinks beneath the sea.

Strøm (1948) has distinguished two principal upland surfaces in Norway of Miocene and Pliocene ages respectively. The younger is the *vidde* or high plain of southern Norway descending eastwards from about 1,100 metres to 700 metres. Coinciding in places with a resurrected sub-Cambrian surface, this is the latest planation that was uplifted differentially before the fiords were incised. In Finnmark it stands around 600 metres above sea level, but towards much of the western coast it descends to a plateau between 200 and 400 metres.

The upper, and older, planation stands around 1,800 metres as the Jostedalsbre area, and Strøm describes it as imperfectly planed and hilly in some places. Its dating as " Miocene (probably early) " is based on Alpine parallels, but this elevation certainly cannot be older or the surface would have been much more dissected in the highlands.

Overtopping the plateau level of the Jostedalsbre by about 1,100 metres are the Jotunheim Mountains. These relicts of an older topography possess a significant accordance of summit levels at a maximum of 2,400 metres, and photographs suggest a possible former planation of the region. If this is so, it would probably be the early-Cainozoic planation.

Marked throughout middle and northern Sweden and southern Norway are the parallel south-easterly courses of the rivers induced by tilting of a formerly planed landscape; but the shorter courses leading to the Norwegian fiords are less simply controlled. Many, indeed flow parallel to the coast for long distances before breaking through to the major inlets. While much control of drainage pattern is obviously exercised by Caledonian structures of the bedrock, there is a dearth of any indication from the drainage as to what the nature of the western aspect of the Scandinavian hemi-cymatogen may be. Is it faulted, or is it a steep monocline like Rio de Janeiro? Holtedahl has considered it to be faulted, Strøm (1960), bearing in mind that " the general shield-like ancient surface of Southern Norway [has its] maximum elevation far inside the coast, [regarded] the sea-land boundary zone [as] the steepest part of a great flexure with accompanying faults, as envisaged by Gerard de Geer. The western coast of South Norway is no coast of the Labrador type ".

Finland stands almost everywhere below 1,000 feet, and was extensively scoured by Pleistocene ice sheets. Yet despite these handicaps Tanner writes that the essential element in the morphology was a monotonous plain of subaerial erosion " dominated only by monadnocks and ascribed to the beginning of the Tertiary ". All older surfaces are fossil surfaces. The early-Cainozoic surface was later tectonically deformed, so that several younger cycles succeed at lower levels and have almost everywhere destroyed the fundamental early-Cainozoic surface; " but its former existence is a necessary postulate to understanding of the whole plan ".

In the Arctic, northern Spitzbergen exhibits above steep marginal cliffs a rolling abrasion plateau with prominent gipfels and occasional remnants of an earlier plateau (cf. the Alps p. 542). Truncating crystalline and folded Palæozoic rocks (and both under-lying and truncating sundry basalts which cover these) the surface, which from the manner in which it cuts "late faults and flexures in the east" (Harland 1961) is probably late-Cainozoic in age. It rises southward from 500 metres to beyond 1,000 metres about the Veteran Mountains of New Vriesland (de Geer 1923). Fragments survive locally even to 1,500 metres. The Chydenius Mountains appear as a residual north-south range. Farther south, between 77° and 78° N. latitude Spitzbergen is very mountain-ous and heavily glaciated. Here updoming of the main island is, on the data above, indicated to be Plio-Pleistocene in age, with possible continuance into Recent time indicated by raised beaches and strandflats around the coast.

The geomorphic history of Western Europe north of the Alps shows significant minor differences from that revealed in the continents reviewed hitherto. There is a greater multiplicity of local Cretaceous landsurfaces, the early-Cainozoic planation is often represented by both " sub-Eocene " and " sub-Oligocene " phases, and though two phases of late-Cainozoic partial planation are normal, a greater multiplicity of surfaces of this age is by no means uncommon. As each new phase of denudation was initiated by tectonic movement, an unusual activity related to various phases of Alpine orogenic development is manifest.

The initial and terminal dates of the several denudation cycles are also aberrant in the emerging global plan. Whereas the early-Cainozoic planation elsewhere had a terminal date at the end of the Oligocene so that the oldest sediments resting upon it are Burdigalian in age, in Europe the earliest deposits in this position are often mid-Oligocene.

The several basins of deposition—Paris, Vienna, Hesse, Hungary—afford depositional records that may be correlated with the erosional records of the uplands. The large amount of differential movement involved, however, introduces practical difficulties in the field.

EUROPEAN RUSSIA

The U.S.S.R. west of the Ural Mountains is of small relief, the country seldom exceeding 300 metres above sea level. Discrimination between cyclic facets in the landscape therefore presents difficulties in some regions. The northern marches are, furthermore, smothered beneath a mantle of Quaternary deposits, especially moraines and gravel terraces, that obscures the earlier record almost entirely. Near Lake Peipsi, however, a flat pre-glacial limestone plateau with incised, broadly-terraced valleys, and sloping westward from 200 down to 80 metres, appears to be of late-Cainozoic age

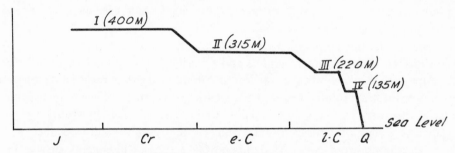

FIG. 158. Morphocyclic Curve (for the Southeast of the Russian Platform)
Vertical axis: Average elevation of surfaces.
Horizontal axis: Absolute time in million years. (? Overestimated, L.C.K.)
J Jurassic; *Cr* Cretaceous; *e-C* early-Cainozoic; *l-C* late-Cainozoic;
Q Quaternary. *after J. A. Mescheriakov.*

with the valleys probably Plio-Pleistocene. In Estonia, these valleys have been drowned at their mouths by 100 metres, and in Latvia where the valleys are incised 200-300 metres, drowning is 150-200 metres.

The general scheme of cyclic denudation for European Russia has been expressed in a " morphocyclic " diagram, wherein elevation is plotted against geologic time, by Mescheriakov (1963) (Fig. 158). Comprising late-Mesozoic, early-Cainozoic, two late-Cainozoic and Quaternary cycles of geomorphic development its form is arrestingly similar to the landscapes which it represents and to the emergent plan of world-wide cycles. The cyclic landsurfaces cut across all geologic formations successively.

The terraced western aspect of the Ural Mountains, likewise, has been assigned by Yerbikaya to cycles of : (a) early-Cainozic, (b) Miocene, (c) Pliocene and (d) five stages of Quaternary landscape development.

South of a line through Babaevo, Yaroslavl, Kazan, Kuibyshev, Aktyubinak,

European Russia is made up of a number of earth blocks standing at different elevations. These make minor structural complications in the cyclic landscape.

In the south-east, for a long distance, the Volga River marks the boundary between the Mesozoic and early-Cainozoic rocks and the lowstanding late-Cainozoic and Quaternary sediments that occupy an extensive area between the Black Sea and northward of the Caspian. Here four cyclic surfaces have been described by Mescheriakov (1961): a late-Pliocene surface between 120 and 160 metres elevation in the higher parts of the Volga Basin passing southward into a coastal plain aggradational surface; a late-Miocene to early-Pliocene surface at 500-600 metres upon the crest of the Stavropol massif and corresponding with surfaces at the coast and in the Ergenines Hills at 175-200 metres; an early-Cainozoic surface at 300-340 metres upon the Transvolga heights, with a corresponding marine depositional surface at 280-350 metres and a corresponding fossilized surface at depths of 500 to 600 metres below the most recent deposits of the Caspian plain; and a Mesozoic surface upon butte relicts (400-420 metres altitude) of the Transvolga uplands. These surfaces are not all due to one and the same agencies, and different agencies are responsible even for different parts of the same surface; they are polygenetic.

Beyond the Caspian Sea, in the Kirghiz Steppe, Cainozoic deposits are bevelled about 200 metres above sea level, but as the region (Ust Urt) is tributary only to inland seas, and has perhaps been disturbed tectonically, the value of this landscape for correlative purposes is diminished. The surface is certainly older than the scenery due to the Ice Age and overlooks on the north, at low scarps, the former glacial lakes of the ice-front. It would therefore appear to represent one of the late-Cainozoic cycles.

Here we enter Inner Asia, a vast region of endoreic drainages and local base levels wherein Plio-Pleistocene faultings have in places carried Cainozoic planations to great heights upon the crests of mountain ranges, and elsewhere depressed them into basins where they now lie hidden beneath notable thicknesses of Quaternary sediments.

LOWLANDS OF WESTERN ASIA

Western Siberia stands at low level. Along the railway between the Ural Mountains and the Irtysch River the aspect is of broad plains with an horizon like the sea, diversified by table-topped hills. This low-level landscape joins southward with the Aral-Caspian depression. Eastward of Tobolsk and southward of the railway the plains of the Baraba steppe rise into the rolling Kalunda steppe which continues right to the foot of the Altai. Between the rivers Ob and Yenesei the southern border of the plains lies north of the railway.

The plains of Western Siberia are formed from horizontally disposed Cainozoic and Quaternary sediments (*cf.* the Delta Plain of North China) which towards the Urals and eastward of Tomsk rest upon the upturned edges of Jurassic and Cretaceous rocks. There are also hills of older rocks, crystalline schists and eruptives of the Devonian and Carboniferous periods, crumpled in the Variscan orogeny across which both Mesozoic and Cainozoic formations are transgressive. " Near the Urals the Tertiary is mainly lower-Tertiary in table-tops and the Neogene rests unconformably upon its eroded surface. Eastward of the Tobol River the older Tertiary appears only in the bottoms of deep valleys and in boreholes. The Neogene is a continental formation, and in places the uppermost Oligocene also, so that the connection between the Arctic Ocean and the inland seas of the south was broken during the mid-Tertiary (Oligo-Miocene) " Obruchev (1926). The ancient Irtysch and Yenesei rivers built great deltas, denoted now by the broad zone of Miocene sandy, lignite-bearing strata cropping out along the northern foot of the mountains (Hausen 1922). Across these piedmonts the rivers prolonged their courses with the regression of the sea. Subsequent tilting of these formations is perhaps responsible for the north-east to south-west structural alignments of ridges and streams in the embayment of younger rocks south-west of Novosibirsk.

Northward of a line from Tyumen to Tomsk the Neogene appears only in the valleys of the Irtysch and Ob, being elsewhere mantled by Quaternary accumulations, alluvial in the south, glacial or marine in the north. There are two phases of Quaternary marine incursion, one at the beginning of the Quaternary and the other post-glacial.

More than 100 deep boreholes in Western Siberia penetrate the crystalline basement (Bogdanoff 1957). These show as much as 2,400 metres of Jurassic and Cretaceous cover thinning westward towards the Urals and with an upstanding mass of the folded basement and Palæozoic just east of the River Ob. The central part of the Palæozoic floor is almost horizontal, and there is no " direct connection between the Polar Urals and the Taimyr Peninsula. Between them lies a depression reaching a depth of 4,000-6,000 metres " (Nalivkin, 1960).

Another area standing at low elevation is found about the Aral Sea, with the Kirghiz Steppe in the north and Russian Turkestan in the south. Most of this region does not exceed 300 metres above sea level, though the eastern margins of the Kirghiz Steppe rise almost to 1,000 metres at the summits of some of the hill-ranges. Obruchev writes of the steppe as a homogeneous landscape of broad plains, valleys and basins surmounted by small and large hills distributed as ranges and in groups such as the mountains of Koktschetan, Karkaralinsk, Ulu-tau, Delegen and so forth. In the south is the low country of the Hunger-steppe below the 200 metres contour.

The geomorphology begins with a Cretaceous cycle of erosion which cut across a variety of marine Palæozoic formations and also the continental shales of the Rhaetic and Jurassic. Unconformably upon the Cretaceous planation rest Eocene sandstones and reddish Oligocene marls, laid down during a marine incursion which covered the Hunger-steppe without drowning the higher mountains.

The late-Cainozoic denudation which supervened developed a broad planation since extensively destroyed by Quaternary cycles.

The continent of Asia sustained greater assaults in the Variscan period of mountain building than any other. Much of it was remote from the sea and might be expected to escape ultimate planation over a long interval of time, so that even Suess believed that sundry of the Palæozoic mountain ranges of the interior still survived as such in the modern landscape. Yet evidence to the contrary is explicit, and many observers in different parts of the continent have found that by the early- and middle-Mesozoic all the Palæozoic relief had either been destroyed by erosion or smothered, following subsidence, beneath enveloping Jurassic sediments. W. A. Obruchev (1926) describes Siberia thus: " Except for the Verkhoyansk Mountains created at the close of the Trias, on all sides of the Neocomian Sea no high land could be seen. Everywhere appeared erosional plainlands of negligible relief such as the Kirghiz Steppe, Amurland and the Yenesei-Lena plateau, and at rather greater elevations the Altai, Dzungaria, Sayan, Transbaikalia, the ancient shield, and Sikhota Alin ". Similar conditions existed in Mongolia and China, and there can be little doubt that at the beginning of Cretaceous time virtually the whole of the vast continental interior had been reduced to a landscape of low relief—the Laurasian surface. Both the basins of Gobi and the Cainozoic mountain regions were formed later by warping and dislocation of this, or later, surfaces.

The early-Cretaceous was a time of extensive submergence, perhaps corresponding to the opening up of the Arctic Basin in the north (p. 614). The sea overflowed the lower Yenesei region, the Taimyr Peninsula and extended up the Lena as far as the lower Aldan and Vilyui tributaries. It covered the northern part of the Verkhoyansk Mountains and the Yana and Anadyr Basins while on the Pacific front the Amur expanded itself with the Bureya Lake into a vast expanse of water. In the interior were continental basins as numerous and broad as those of the middle-Jurassic. The lower-Cretaceous sediments are uniformly of shallow-water type with lagoonal and coal-bearing phases. Though the post-Laurasian cycle is widely depositional over Northern Asia, the centre of the continent may have undergone erosion during the same cycle.

An emergent phase followed in the late Cretaceous, with local elevations and subsidences. The sea retreated from many parts of the north coast and from the Aldan, Lena and Yana. The Anadyr Basin became a lake and also the Bureya Basin. Almost the whole of Asia remained emergent during the Paleocene, the land area being then at a maximum, and representing the early-Cainozoic denudational cycle over a vast area. But across the lowland east of the Urals an Eocene submergence began and the polar sea crept southwards across Western Siberia to the Caspian Sea and the Mediterranean. The Kirghiz Steppe was then reduced to an archipelago.

The subsequent history of Asian landscape has not progressed uniformly. Plateau-making and basining movements have been particularly strong: large areas have been uplifted into high-standing plateaus, e.g. Tunguska plateau, Inner Mongolia; others have sunk below sea levels of Cainozoic or Recent time, *e.g.* the delta plain of China, and the west Siberian plains (Fig. 159). The boundaries between the regions respectively elevated or depressed are normally abrupt and marked by steep scarps and plateau edges, carved into mountain fronts. At the close of the Oligocene for instance, the

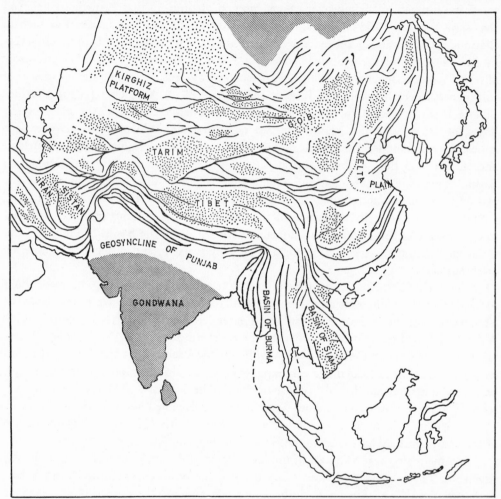

FIG. 159. General Structural Lines of Asia. Shields (ruled), mountain trends (lined), basins (stippled).

Turgai Strait and Kirghiz Steppe of the west were elevated and the through sea retreated to the north and south. In the east, however, sinkings were widespread, often with ridges and lake basins created by minor differential movement, *e.g.* about Tomsk, in the Amphitheatre of Irkutsk, and the grabens of Baikalia and Transbaikalia, the Lena and Yana valleys, the New Siberian Islands (then united with the mainland) and in the Amur and Ussuri areas.

Pronounced emergence characterized the close of the Miocene in Siberia, and to the subsequent river incision the interior of Siberia owes much of its youthful appearance. In the west renewed emergence occurred in the area of the Turgai Strait and Hunger-steppe, new horst-making arose along old fault-lines in the Altai, Tarbagati and Dzungaria with rising also of the ancient shield areas and the elimination of lakes.

Following the Miocene uplifts, virtually all Pliocene and Quaternary formations away from the eastern coast are continental in type, and the land-area was again of maximum extent. According to Obruchev (1926), Bering Strait did not exist and the Chukotsk Peninsula was united with Alaska. Not a little differential movement has occurred in Quaternary time. For Siberia, Obruchev assesses it at 100-400 metres of elevation in the north and 1,000 metres or more in the south. Quaternary submergence around the periphery is shown along the east coast by drowned harbours from Southern China to Bering Strait, in the north it is exhibited in the shallow shelf of the Polar Sea, and the Quaternary advance of the sea up the Yenesei and Lena valleys to lat. $67\frac{1}{4}°$ N and 63° N. respectively.

To the relative lateness of Quaternary uplifts is due a mixture of features in the river courses. The upper thalwegs are flat and the valleys broad, in the middle reaches are commonly rapids and waterfalls of advancing nickpoints, while the lower courses are mostly smooth, with minor nickpoints and appropriate terraces.

SIBERIAN PLATEAUS

Asia is so huge and its aspects so manifold that we can review it only part by part, (Fig. 160) beginning with the high plateaus of Central Siberia, which slice indifferently across Archean, Caledonian and Variscan terrains.

Obruchev (1926) describes the broad upland between the Yenesei and lower Lena rivers, which stands generally above 1,300 metres and is now deeply dissected and rugged, as reaching almost to the Polar Sea upon the Taimyr Peninsula and leading in the south to the Sayan Mountains and the boundaries of the Baikal high plateau. Great tracts he describes as having an accordance of summit levels or a rolling upper surface, *e.g.* Taimyr Peninsula, the Anabar massif and, in the southern part, the area between Sayan and Baikal which Suess designated " the Amphitheatre of Irkutsk ". The greatest heights about 1,500 metres are attained in the bevelled Syverma Mountains, about the sources of the rivers Kotui, Cheta and Kureika; and the morphology of the rolling dissected upland defines it as of late-Cainozoic cyclic age. Though it was originally uneven in form, much of its rise and fall as measured along ridge crests is due to warping at the time the plateau was uplifted (Plio-Pleistocene), and locally it has been downfaulted in rift valleys (*e.g.* middle Lena, Lake Baikal).

This Tunguska plateau, rising at sharp and perhaps monoclinal scarps overlooking the West Siberian lowland and the Yenesei Valley, is one of the most extensive dissected plateaus in the world. Basically it consists to lat. 58° N. of Permian trappean rocks, largely tuffaceous or effusive and lying horizontally or with gentle centripetal dip upon Silurian or Cambrian rocks which are themselves greatly intruded by dykes, sills and laccolites. Despite the tabular attitude of the rocks, the dominant summit-surface is by all accounts erosional in form.

The deeply sunken valley-floors of Pleistocene age are often wide, and partly of tectonic origin, *e.g.* the Lena with its tributaries the Vilyui and Aldan. There, following

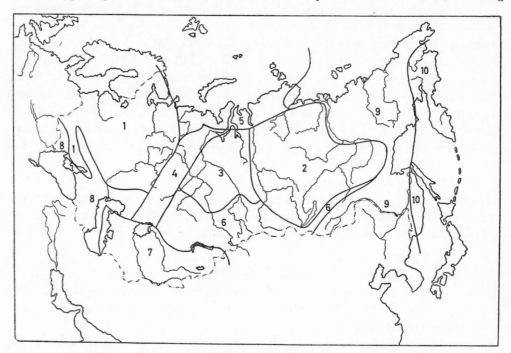

FIG. 160. Geological Regions of the U.S.S.R. 1. Russian Shield, 2. Siberian Shield, 3. West Siberian Lowlands, 4. Ural Mountains, 5. Western Arctic, Timan and Taimyr Peninsula, 6. Asiatic Palæozoic Mountain Systems, 7. Central Asia, 8. Tethyan Geosyncline, 9. Mesozoic Welt, 10. Pacific Geosyncline. *after D. V. Nalivkin.*

marine Triassic in the lower country of the Olenek and Lena valleys, are Jurassic accumulations, partly marine and partly continental, and marine Neocomian. The Cainozoic is continental. The eastern frame of this lowland is provided by an arc of Permian, lower- and middle-Triassic rocks which extends as the Verkhoyansk ranges almost from the Arctic Ocean to the Sea of Okhotsk. Dating from the late Triassic, this range was clearly an important feature of mid-Mesozoic geography to which the Jurassic sediments in the bend of the Lena are related. These sediments now stand, in the Lena graben, only 200 metres above sea level, amid high plateaus bevelled and strongly uplifted in later geologic time. The structure has been thought to resemble the rift systems of Africa and California which are extensions of the Mid-Oceanic Rift (p. 576).

In Southern Siberia, which Obruchev (1926) has described as an ancient erosional plain elevated and dissected by a labyrinth of deep valleys, the summit plane of the upwarped Sayan-Baikal-Aldan highlands transects Archean and early-Palæozoic rocks as an open mountainland of broad furrows and ridges at 1,300 metres (late-Cainozoic cycle) surmounted here and there by flat-topped or cone-shaped gipfels rising steeply to as much as 2,500 metres. These latter summits may tentatively be considered as representing an early- or middle-Cainozoic cyclic planation. In appearance and position as judged from photographs, they resemble such relicts in other parts of the world very well. Precisely similar morphology appears in the Tchuski mountains upon the Kolyma massif. Above deep valley incisions there appears the customary rolling summit bevel itself surmounted by an upper, originally smoother, bevel preserved upon hard granites. All this region was arched and broken along its length by fault scarps sometimes pairing to make rift valleys. Lake Baikal rift trends north-east but most of the scarps run more nearly east. Pleistocene and recent basalts, alkaline rocks and carbonatites also appear as with the African rifted cymatogens, and northward in the Vilyui downwarp diamantiferous kimberlites appear. The pattern of tectonic events and erosion cycles in southern Siberia conforms with the global pattern suggested in Chapter VIII.

Even in Southern Transbaikalia where bevelled mountain tops are absent over broad areas, there remain sufficient accordances of summit levels to demonstrate the former existence of a plain above which, among the high snowfields and Alpine forms, occur occasional rocky gipfels or gipfel groups. Of the Vitim plateau, standing about 2,000 metres, Krapotkin remarked that deposits of late-Cainozoic lakes occur in the depressions; and outwellings of Cainozoic basalt overlie the surface. These lavas lie upon the very ridges and gipfels of the Tunkinsk and Kitoisk mountains and upon the east Sayan. Small Quaternary volcanic cones stand locally above the great basaltic sheets.

Visiting the Aldan plateau Krapotkin noted long ago that, though constituting the Arctic-Pacific divide, it lacked a continuous dividing range and evidently was also a warped former erosional plain; curious river captures are also evident there.

In the upper Yenesei region, where the high plateau may be descried from the railway rising higher and higher towards the Sayan and Altai Mountains in the south, part of the plateau surface may be a resurrected sub-Devonian surface, and part, in common with the same plateau in Transbaikalia, may be resurrected sub-Cambrian, but in each instance the plateau corresponds to Cainozoic bevelling.

Along the Siberian-Mongolian frontier generally, the plateau of the far interior was shattered into pieces (Hausen 1922) by powerful mid- or late-Cainozoic block-faultings. In this phase were rejuvenated the Altai, Kunetsky, Alatau, Sayan, Tannu Ola, Khangai, Kentei, and Transbaikalian mountain ranges, upon some of which the Cainozoic planations ride above 3,000 metres upon the sites of earlier Precambrian and Palæozoic chains. Like the Pamir and Tien Shan to the south, on which the Cainozoic bevel approached 4,500 metres in elevation, the ranges display a flat-topped skyline, and all afford evidence of strongly differential movement. Profound faulting also created rift depressions. "They attain their greatest magnitude in the west where there is found the enormous hollow of Lake Baikal with depths down to 1741 metres Territorially they begin with the depression now occupied by Lake Kosogol in the Mongolian People's Republic. This is followed by depressions situated between Kosogol and Lake Baikal, infilled with thick Quaternary deposits. To the east of Baika, the depression branches . . . along the River Bargusin and . . . the Upper Angara, these continue as long and narrow depressions crossing the valleys of Vitim, Chara and Olekma."

"Similar depressions continue to the east of the Olekma River as far as the Dzhugdzhur Range, stretching along the shore of the Okhotsk Sea" (Nalivkin 1960).

In the east, the Great Khingan range is capped by Oligocene basalts lying upon a presumed early-Cainozoic plateau surface. Where the range is crossed by the Trans-Siberian railway the surface is " warped a few hundred feet higher and, extending over the crest, is represented in the summits of the long spurs which constitute the deeply-canyoned eastern slope. In Manchuria it sinks beneath the alluvium of the Sungari " (Willis 1907). According to Richthofen the range is more warped than faulted. Between the valleys of the south-eastward flowing rivers which are there encroaching headwards into it, the ancient surface continues eastwards for a considerable distance before being broken up in the newer cycle which develops into a plain at 800 metres before being itself dissected by the later Cainozoic cycles which in turn sink below the great alluvial plain of China. Similar relationships exist along the road from Peking to Mongolia. Thus Peking stands near the inner border of the alluvial plain. In the Western Hills appear the bedrock formations and the road climbs steeply to the Nan-kou Pass beyond which opens out the Kalgan Basin, a cyclic erosional landscape nearly 800 metres in elevation (Barbour 1929). Kalgan itself stands at the foot of another scarp, erosional in nature though possibly initiated as an obsequent fault-line scarp, and this leads by passes to the high interior plateau at about 1,500 metres above sea level. All the passes are cut through the Cretaceous Kalgan series, of acid porphyry lavas, resting on the eroded stumps of Yenshan (q.v.) mountains.

Farther to the south near the exit of the Yangtze Kiang from its gorges at Ichang the descent from the plateau to the plain is described by Willis as a warped erosional surface showing a continuous stratum of Carboniferous limestone from top to bottom of the slope. Differential movement carried the interior plateau higher here. The boundary scarp is identifiable south-westward indeed as far as Indo-China, while farther west is the still greater scarp of the Yunling leading upwards to the Alps of Sino Tibet. So the great plateaus of Inner Asia, upheaved in the Plio-Pleistocene, sink down to low levels on the east by powerful monoclines only locally aided by faulting.

Through the upcast Asiatic blocks, many transverse antecedent gorges were carved by the main rivers: Irtysch, Yenesei, Welenga, Vitim, Olekma and Amur. The youthful state of these gorges attests the recent date of the plateau upheavals. On the other hand the drainage pattern shows many deflections and captures of the headwaters of great rivers that have been induced by deformations of the late-Cainozoic surface. Maximum movement seems to have been in the late-Pliocene, for there are lacking thick sedimentary sequences such as should have accumulated if the modern mountains had been long in existence. In Turkestan, on the southern side of the Tien Shan, for comparison, where the mountain crests tower 5,000 metres above the flanking depressions, no record exists of deposition before the mid-Cainozoic, and Quaternary accumulations are especially thick. Of the work done by Soviet geomorphologists in the Siberian plateaus since the war very little has been available for study to the author, but the data given above, derived largely from maps, are surely sufficient to demonstrate therein the usual global pattern of cyclic denudational surfaces.

Beyond the block mountains separating Siberia and Mongolia operate the continental, local base-levels of the vast internal drainage systems of Central Asia, probably no less ancient in origin.

LANDSURFACES OF MONGOLIA

Berkey and Morris (1927) describe Mongolia as a vast tectonic depression, enclosed by bordering ranges. Earth movements were not uniform throughout, so that the eastern and southern provinces are warped while in the western province Cainozoic block-faulting of the Altai type controls the major relief. Thus the hills of the eastern and southern provinces are all residual plateaus developed from low, gentle upwarps (Fig. 75), e.g. the Chakhar Hills along the Kalgan-Urga caravan route; while the western and northern province contains many impressive fault-block ranges, such as the Khangai-Kentani group, the Khingan Chain, the Baikal-Yablonoi group, the Altai and the Tien Shan. All show marked summit planation, with strips of desert lowland and sedimentary basins between the long narrow fault-blocks that build the constituent ranges. Topographic changes are sometimes abrupt, e.g. at Tiger Canyon in Baga Bogdo where the twin peaks of the range can be seen 1,300 metres above the mouth of the canyon though only five kilometres away. The summit of Baga Bogdo, at 4,000 metres stands 2,300 metres above the level of Tsagan Nor. Most of this vast area (at least a million square miles) of internal drainage is divided into numerous independent basins of centripetal drainage called " gobis ". Mongolian streams are mostly consequent upon the slopes of the warped and faulted basins, and flow centripetally. The larger rivers each terminate in a lake, while the smaller streams, still less integrated, mostly die out in the gravels before reaching the centres of the desert hollows. Several of the larger rivers rise outside the desert of Gobi, but of them all only two escape from the region, the Huang Ho which enters the southern region in making its great loop about the desert of Ordos, and the Kerulen which escapes via Dalai Nor to the Argun-Amur river system. The central parts of these basins have been subjected to deposition, and in a region where warping has taken place at intervals throughout the entire history of basin-making, it may be very difficult to distinguish an original slope from a deformation; but never-theless the landscapes are almost wholly of erosional origin, with the surface transecting in one place granites, in another place folded slates and greywackes, in a third tilted sands and clays, and in others horizontally disposed strata of many kinds. Many local base levels are current over the plateau and there is no universal base-levelling with respect to sea level. Photographs and sketches by Berkey and Morris make clear the manner of erosion operating: since Mesozoic time scarp retreat and pedimentation under running water have been responsible for the carving of the landscape (Fig. 54). As the region is one of internal drainage, alluvial fans and bahadas cover the lower parts of the pediments. Additionally, wind has removed much finely triturated debris from the lower plains where it has been spread by the action of water.

Jurassic rocks within Mongolia are invariably non-marine and have been extensively folded; Cretaceous and subsequent formations lie with discordance upon them and have escaped deformation other than gentle warping into open basins. " The oldest

FIG. 161.   Fault Block at Tsetsenwan, Mongolia, showing gently arched erosional plane on summit. *after C. Berkey and F. K. Morris.*

basin sediments of lower Cretaceous age, rest upon a nearly smooth erosion surface which truncates the edges of the complex rocks of the floor." With this early-Cretaceous (Laurasian) bevel begins the history of Mongolian landscape; but one doubts whether it now survives anywhere except in the fossil state. Berkey and Morris were undecided whether it is still discernable as a skyline bevel upon the mountainous areas of Mongolia. They describe it at an altitude of 700 metres in the Chakai granite mountains of southern Mongolia, and at about 2,000 metres towards the Arctic divide near Urga. But despite its hydrographic importance this divide is here an inconspicuous warped ridge of the kind already familiar upon deformed early- or mid-Cainozoic landsurfaces. The Tola River, indeed, makes a westing of quite 80 km. in an open valley before abruptly turning northwards to join the Selenga drainage of Lake Baikal. Planation at the divide is much too extensive and well preserved to have survived from the Mesozoic.

Farther west the Khangai Range makes a prominent divide, yet across the Khangai Mountains at an elevation of 10,000 feet extends a summit bevel identical in appearance with the Mongolian bevel, and Berkey and Morris (1927) were exercised in judgment whether this was an upwarped portion of the general Mongolian surface (herein regarded as culminating in the Miocene) or was older (Fig. 162). They concluded that it was the same, quoting as evidence: (a) the comparable stage of development of the surfaces and of the monadnocks upon them; (b) the two surfaces are equally dissected; (c) much warping and faulting can be demonstrated in Mongolia and it is entirely competent for an ancient surface of planation to stand at very different elevations in different parts of the country; and (d) the Khangai upland, if older, should scarcely have survived during the long interval required for planation of the Mongolian landsurface. With this we agree; it all adds up to the early-Cainozoic bevel. But they regarded it as of Cretaceous age. Likewise, along the caravan route from Kalgan to Urga, some 550 km. from Kalgan, crumpled Jurassic shales, limestones and quartzites standing upon edge and intruded by granites were so perfectly truncated by erosion that for 40 km. along the route it is possible to drive a motor car almost anywhere in any direction. This

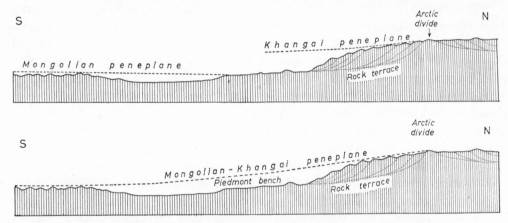

FIG. 162. Two interpretations by Berkey and Morris of relations between the Mongolian and Khangai planations. Warping of a single surface is the hypothesis accepted in this text.

" Mongolian " planation also they took to be Cretaceous, but again it bears the hall-marks of Cainozoic fashioning.

Berkey and Morris, having second thoughts later in their text, indeed envisage the possibility that the " Mongolian " surface "might have been completed in Cainozoic time, perhaps in the Miocene ".

Seeking clarity we return to the stratigraphy. The early-Cretaceous erosion plane was dimpled locally and received a mantle of continental sediments, all relatively thin, beginning with representatives of the lower Cretaceous. As the sites of depression shifted intermittently, various basins contain sequences beginning and ending at different times, and phases of deposition and erosion have alternated locally throughout most of Cainozoic time. The cumulative thickness of these formations may be consider-able, *e.g.* over 3,000 metres in the gobi between the Altai front and the Uskuk block where late-Cretaceous, Oligocene, Miocene, Pliocene and Pleistocene beds are present (*cf.* Kalahari), but nowhere are complete sequences present, the foci of maximum

2D

deposition having shifted from time to time as new centres of warping appeared. From time to time the areas of sediment have been partly replaned, together with exposed areas of bedrock, to form new erosional bevels of Cainozoic age. How much of these planed areas of older rocks are really resurrected remains uncertain. The planed sedimentary areas, widespread throughout Mongolia, and "separated by low ranges of maturely dissected hills composed of ancient complex rocks, whose upland is crowned by a well-developed erosion surface", are called "gobis". They are often, as proved by their relations with various Cainozoic sedimentary sequences, of different local ages—post-Oligocene, post-Miocene, or post-Pliocene—and there is doubt in how far they are multicyclic, or referable to different base levels and how far they represent the lateral extension, over a long period, of a single cycle originating in the mid-Cainozoic.

The absence of Miocene sediments over most of the area examined by the Central Asiatic Expeditions suggests, in particular, that this was a time of important planation. The uplands of the Gobi Desert most frequently appear upon Cretaceous, Eocene and Oligocene strata of the covering series, and as original depositional surfaces within these various formations are not equally well preserved, all must have been truncated during the late-Oligocene or Miocene, when the landscape must have been in extreme planation and incapable of supplying detritus. The landscape of Mongolia therefore, despite its endoreic drainage, idiocratic accumulations of detritus and lack of control by universal base level, nevertheless achieved its extreme planation almost simultaneously with early-Cainozoic planations elsewhere. The last phases of denudation upon hard rocks between the basins furnished thin Oligocene sediment, by the beginning of the Miocene no elevations at all survived.

A later phase of broad planation across sediments of the "gobis" leaves regions of harder rocks as bevelled interfluves. Near P'ang-Kiang this phase truncates Pliocene formations but elsewhere it appears contemporaneous with the laying down of sediments of this age. So is recognised a Pliocene landscape cycle in several centripetal basins.

Last of all are numerous hollows, basins and lowlands that have been eroded below the level of the Pliocene planation. Near P'ang-Kiang a younger lowland has been excavated from the weak strata during relatively recent time (Fig. 163). The topography of the lowland is plainly due to the action of running water, but as the lowland is a basin without exit, water cannot have been responsible for export of the vast amount of waste formed during the lowland excavation. Berkey and Morris regard wind as the exporting agent, as Ball did for the similar Qattara Depression of Egypt, but in both instances there is little evidence that wind exercised a significant abrading effect. Only the soft sandstones of the gobis are fluted and channelled by the windblast; on most rocks the slow disintegration under desert weathering outstrips any abrasive action by wind. The exposed surface of the open plains is moreover protected by a surfacing of pebbles (the desert armour) so that abrasion by wind is reduced to negligible proportions. Examples of the erosive action of wind upon rock are few, local and insignificant.

Throughout Mongolia, the depth of such lowlands rarely exceeds 400 feet. The sides of each hollow are typically gullied and dissected, occasionally into badlands, so that the retreat of the escarpment is mainly under the attack of running water. Only after the fine waste is spread out in the hollow and dried is the wind able to transport it. However these P'ang-Kiang hollows developed, they correspond in the denudational chronology with the deep Pleistocene valley excavations of coastal hinterlands controlled by universal base level.

The widespread planations of Mongolia, in order of decreasing age appear to be: early-Cretaceous planation, Miocene planation, late-Pliocene planation, Pleistocene and Recent flat-floored basins and desert hollows.

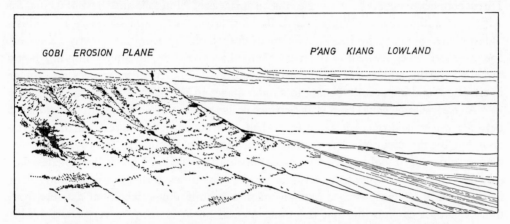

FIG. 163. Lowland incised below the level of the Gobi Erosion Plane (Pliocene cycle) at P'ang Kiang, Mongolia. The western scarp shown here is the normal transition between cyclic surfaces in water-eroded regions, but the P'ang Kiang lowland has no outlet. *after F. K. Morris.*

Berkey and Morris have remarked that " The axes of the Cainozoic mountains and lowlands agree very nearly with the strike of the folded Palæozoic sediments and with the structure lines of the ancient schists and gneisses. The general agreement is far more striking than the local divergences. The folding, thrusting and faulting that have made mountains, have followed much the same directions in successive revolutions since early Precambrian times, indicating an orderly constancy of control in the earth movements that, throughout the immensely long sequence of sedimentations, foldings and igneous intrusions, have welded together the continental elements that are now Asia ".

Occupying the heart of Asia, the province of Sin-Kiang is divided into northern and southern basins (Dzungaria and Tarim) by the east-west range of the Tien Shan. The northern is open on the west to the Kirghiz Steppe, but the southern is enclosed by the junction of the Tien Shan and Kuen Lun. On the east both are separated from the Mongolian Gobi only by relatively low, and probably warped, divides, and their scenic history is by all accounts similar to that of the Gobi (*q.v.*).

The latest history of Inner Asia is understandable only in terms of a fluctuating climatic regimen which altered the boundaries between the desert and the habitable regions from time to time right up to the present. Sir Aurel Stein showed the former presence of relatively highly-civilised settled communities in regions that are now scarcely habitable by nomads. To this day the boundaries of the desert are inconstant, a succession of rainy years extending the marginal grasslands into the desert, while a dry cycle expands the desert by many miles.

LANDSCAPE CYCLES IN CHINA

Direct connection exists between the erosion surfaces of Mongolia and those of China, for which our authorities are Willis (1907), Barbour (1929, 1935) and Lee (1939). Willis's oldest planed surface, the Pei-Tai peneplain, for which he suggested an early-Cainozoic age, may well be equivalent to the main Mongolian planation, an intervening link being provided by the appearance of the cycle in Ordos. The two occurrences are similar in situation, and apparently belong to similar stages in the history of Asiatic landscape.

An early-Cretaceous (Laurasian) surface is also present in China and the relationship between the two surfaces is clear at Kalgan (Barbour 1929) where " on the uneven floor left by the incomplete reduction of the Yenshan mountains (p. 507) there was poured out a formidable series of acid porphyry lavas ". This Kalgan series was slightly deformed and upon it rests the weak Nantienmen formation containing plant fossils of early-Cretaceous age. This formation is built almost wholly of detritus from the Kalgan series showing that the time interval between them is very short. This irregular early-Cretaceous surface is morphologically different from Willis's " very ancient and aged " Pei-Tai bevel which truncates certain of the higher mountain ranges (*e.g.* Wutai Shan where it is upwarped to 7,650 feet) and which appears similar to the smoothly planed early-Cainozoic landsurface of Mongolia and Siberia, itself locally broken up and truncating mountain ranges.

Indeed, the Kalgan series is itself truncated by the Pei-Tai planation as a " mature-land topography overlain by the Hanoorpa basalt which is deemed to be of late-Oligocene age ".

Upon the south-east China highlands, the late-Cainozoic upland surface of which now stands around 2,500-3,000 feet, unconsumed residuals at 4,000-5,000 feet represent the Pei-Tai or early-Cainozoic cycle (Barbour 1935); and stratigraphic evidence dates the initiation of the cycle there as late Cretaceous.

Early Cainozoic deposits for dating are, however, scarce in China apart from late-Oligocene basaltic lavas; but following local uplifts and faultings associated with the Himalayan orogeny, finely stratified and fossiliferous deposits collected in the bottoms of favourably situated depressions, with coarse river gravels in some areas.

All the later relief of China, like that of interior Asia, has been regenerated from the planed early-Cainozoic surface by flexing, dislocation, or by erosional dissection advancing from the coast and invading regions formerly of westward, interior drainage. So great have been some of the warpings that the ancient surface now ranges through a vertical elevation of at least 10,000 feet, from the mountain summits of the hinterland to beneath the alluvial deposits of the delta plain. Huang (1945) writes: " Here [a surface] lies quite flat, being only slightly uplifted above the level of the surrounding plain; there it is moderately tilted, the tilting sometimes reaching 20°. It is also common to see a peneplain ' climbing up ' a mountain from its foot way up to the top which might be 400-500 metres high ". As a result many different geological terrains compose the Chinese and neighbouring regions (Fig. 164).

The Tanghsien (or Tsinling) cycle, which follows the Pei-Tai was dated by Willis (1907) as " early- and middle-Tertiary " ; but Barbour (1929) has since referred it to an origin in the Miocene with a culmination in the Pliocene. It is represented by a landscape of late maturity with numerous and sometimes extensive monadnocks, and with rivers flowing in broad, open valleys. A residual relief of 1,000 feet may remain locally, but is generally less than 500 feet. The forms of the surface are smoothly rounded and there is much difference of aspect on various bedrock formations. Areas carrying this stage are widespread in Shansi and Hopeh, where it emerges from beneath the deposits of the great delta to an elevation of 400 feet or so in the valley bottoms about Tanghsien. Gravels and clays upon a warped Tanghsien surface in Shansi carry *Hipparion*. This Sanmen stage of lacustrine accumulation precedes the Fenho gorge-cutting (*q.v.*); and over the country of the lower Yangtze Kiang Pliocene beds rest extensively upon bedrock platforms which Barbour (1935) regards as the local expression of the Tanghsien cycle. In contrast with these low elevations due to downwarping, the cycle stands at 5,000 feet or more in the Wutai Shan and may be inspected far to the south-west where it is upwarped as the summit level of the Tsinling Shan, the mountains of the Han Valley and other ranges of the middle Yangtze region. Barbour (1929) described the mode of development of this landscape; " Though setting out with a combination of superimposed and consequent drainage, the Tanghsien cycle of erosion lasted long enough for the river system to become thoroughly adjusted to the underlying structure. Coincident with this adjustment the individual streams, after cutting down to local base levels, widened their valley-floors while weathering and erosion forced back the valley walls, carving into the upland surface until only patches of it were left along the line of local divides. Gradually the valley cross-profiles became those of mature streams in a maturely dissected mountain mass, with broad open bottoms and gently concave slopes."

" These landforms have since been considerably modified both positively and negatively by deposit and erosion, but they are clearly detectable in the general profiles of many of the main spurs and ridges. They are most obvious in the resistant terrains where later erosion has cut gorges in the bottom of the old Tanghsien valleys, leaving rock-cut terraces and platforms whose upper surfaces are accordant with the higher slopes of the valley."

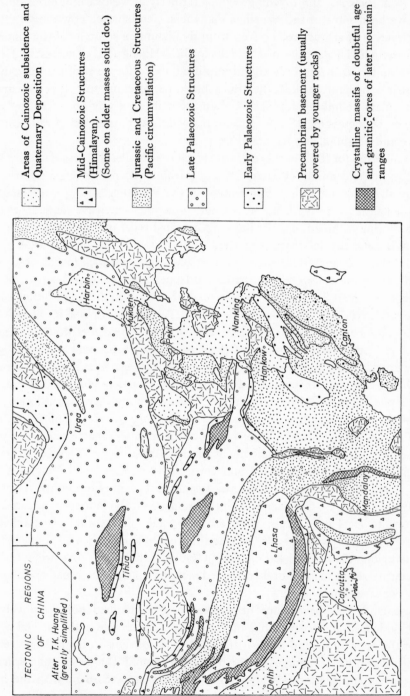

Areas of Cainozoic subsidence and
Quaternary Deposition

Mid-Cainozoic Structures
(Himalayan).
(Some on older masses solid dot.)

Jurassic and Cretaceous Structures
(Pacific circumvallation)

Late Palaeozoic Structures

Early Palaeozoic Structures

Precambrian basement (usually
covered by younger rocks)

Crystalline massifs of doubtful age
and granitic cores of later mountain
ranges

TECTONIC   REGIONS
OF   CHINA
After T.K. Huang
(greatly simplified)

Harbin

Mukden

Pekin

Nanking

Hankow

Canton

Urga

Mandalay

Lhasa

Tihua

Calcutta

Delhi

FIG. 164.   The tectonic regions of China. after T. K. Huang.

The main summit bevelling of the south-east China highlands at 2,500-3,000 feet has already (p. 420) been referred to the Tanghsien cycle; minor benchings at 1,000-1,500 feet perhaps indicate a Pliocene sub-cycle such as has been observed in many parts of the world, and corresponding locally with the Sanmen depositional phase.

The Fenho or Yangtze stage, late Pliocene to earliest Pleistocene, includes one of the most remarkable diastrophic episodes of which evidence remains in world landscapes during which the high plateaus of Asia were heaved up to their present exceptional elevations and the rivers incised their magnificent gorges. The typical features are warped and faulted older surfaces, basins, block-mountain ranges and subsided plateaus such as characterise the whole interior of Asia. Along the mountain bases Pliocene sediments of the lacustrine Sanmen stage are often folded in a remarkable way (Lee 1939), e.g. along the northern foot of the Nanshan and the western continuation of the Inshan.

As a typically flexed region, Willis (1907) cites the terrain of Central China between the Huang Ho and Yangtze-Kiang where the warped landsurface belonging to the Tanghsien stage exhibits differences in altitude of 12,000 feet. On the Tahua Shan, a northern branch of the Tsinling consisting of granite, the faces consist of " precipices, one of which exhibits a smooth plane, probably 2,500 feet in height, at a slope of 70° ". The summits, notwithstanding, are in some instances broad-topped as on the main range. " The Tsinling Shan rises from the valley of the Wei by a steep, warped surface and fault-scarp . . . Among the heights of the range we recognise a mature surface. . . . It extends beyond the Tsin-ling range, across the Han watershed to the middle Yangtze region, and is strongly warped." The major features to which the warping gives rise are: the Tsinling Shan on which the surface appears arched from north to south at 7,000-9,000 feet; the Han downwarp where it descends below the Quaternary deposits at 800 feet above sea level; the Kiulung Shan between the Han River and the Yangtze, where it rises again to 8,000-12,000 feet; and the present basin of Szechuan which is a region of continued subsidence and aggradation, as about Chungking. The basin is famous for its red, Cretaceous shales and sandstones, across which is bevelled the Tanghsien stage represented by opening out of the valley walls of the Yangtze about 2,000 feet above river level; and by the undissected planed surfaces on the upper Minchiang near Sungpan. Quite exceptionally the Fenho or Yangtze stage has here bevelled the weak basin sediments almost to a plain in the short time available. At the foot of the Yunling scarp were deposited gravels torn out of the western mountains. The alluvial apron is 40 miles wide towards Chengtu, but is probably only 200 feet thick. These stages were described by Lee (1939): Barbour (1935) thinks there is evidence of additional stages. At Chungking he gives the following sequence of events: (a) Yenshan folding; (b) planation (inferred from character of anticlinal crestlines and probable development of the Yangtze); (c) late-Oligocene uplift with warping and local faulting; (d) erosional reduction leading to planation of red beds and reduction of anticlinal cores to low ridges of only moderate relief (Tanghsien stage); (e) dissection in Yangtze stage; (f) deposition of Yaan and Chungking gravels and yellow loams on upper terraces; (g) rejuvenation to present day conditions.

Westward rears the immense tectonic scarp of the Yunling leading by still greater dislocations to the rarefied heights of Sikang and the Tibetan plateau at 12,000-15,000 feet with the mountain ranges sometimes exceeding 20,000 feet above sea level. The change here is in some ways analogous to that already noted for the Gobi (p. 415) where deformation of the landsurfaces in the eastern half was by open warping but in the western half by much stronger fault-block movements, *e.g.* Altai. The Yunnan Plateau rises from an altitude of about 8,000 feet in the Tali region in the south to over 15,000 feet near Atuntze and is, according to Barbour (1935), a portion of the Tanghsien landscape. Though so surprisingly elevated it carries remnants of an older planation, presumably early-Cainozoic in age, at elevations superior by 2,000-4,500 feet and above this again monadnocks soar to still greater heights—22,000 feet on Kakarpo, 20,000 feet on the Yulung Shan and the mountains east of Atuntze.

The response of the rivers to these large-scale dislocations in the late-Pliocene was immediate: basin plains formed within many of the depressions, *e.g.* Szechuan, captures have been numerous, and have probably affected even the upper Yangtze. Most of the antecedent rivers have cut gorges (*e.g.* the Yangtze gorges above Ichang) that are among the most profound and awe-inspiring canyons in the world. But the work they have accomplished in the highlands is small compared with the labour of denudation that lies before them for the rivers are long and only began their task in the Pleistocene; they are still prisoners of the tremendous canyon walls they themselves have carved to depths sometimes exceeding 4,000 feet.

In the Yunnan region of exceptional late-Cainozoic elevation appear the astonishing parallel gorges—thousands of feet deep—of the upper Salween, Mekong and Yangtze-Kiang rivers, flowing only 25 miles apart though their mouths are separated by thousands of miles (Fig 165). The gorges are incised into the Tanghsien cyclic surface, and are youthful; though their meridional trend is controlled by the strike of hairpin folds attributable to the Mesozoic Yenshan movements.

In the lower course of the Yangtze-Kiang two late subcycles are apparent in the landscape, the first is associated with the famous fossil primate occurrences of Choukoutien and the second is followed by deposition of the Malan loess.

The Pleistocene phase in North China was dominantly aggradational. It was the time of the early (Malan) loess deposits. From the wind-sorted dust brought down from the interior deserts, the blanket of loess spread far and wide over the rolling land of the Tanghsien cycle. Through Shansi, Shensi and Hupeh, it enveloped the lower hills as the alluvium of the delta partly buries the hills along its western margin now. In the apparent absence of satisfactory fossils, dating of the aggradational phase is not exact. Though it is not related directly to glacial features but to desert dust, there seems no argument against regarding it as of early- to mid-Pleistocene age. It was, moreover, succeeded by the Panchiao stage of erosion which is regarded as late Pleistocene. Modern cycles are predominantly erosional, " with periodic local deposition of alluvium and gravels each time the stream flow dwindles after the heavy rains " (Barbour 1929).

The stages of landscape evolution in China are clear and conform cyclically with the pattern established in other parts of the globe.

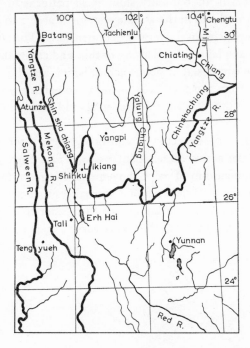

FIG. 165. Parallel gorges of the Salween, Mekong and Yangtze Kiang rivers which follow hairpin bends in structures of the Yenshan orogeny.

CONCLUSION

Through all continents the plainlands of the earth have revealed a history of denudational and depositional landscape cycles punctuated by briefer tectonic episodes that have created new states. This history, which is consistent from at least late-Mesozoic until Recent time was expressed succinctly (for Africa as standard) in Chapter VIII. We repeat it here: a Jurassic-early Cretaceous smooth planation (Gondwana or Laurasian), a Cretaceous partial planation (post-Gondwana or post-Laurasian) sometimes merging with the earlier phase; a prolonged early-Cainozoic cycle resulting in very smooth planation that forms the ancestral surface from which most of the world's scenery has subsequently been carved; one to three late-Cainozoic partial cycles, of which the earliest is the most extensive and to which most of the world's scenery belongs; and following powerful end-Cainozoic cymatogeny much valley incision and the glaciation of Quaternary time. Allowing for local variations, the basic pattern of cyclic landscapes is demonstrably the same in all quarters of the globe and argues a global control of tectonics which operates to regulate landscape by governing base levels. Tectonic movements may be in the same or opposite senses, when they promote complementary records of degradation or aggradation.

Future researches will undoubtedly show local patterns of landscape to be more complex than has been outlined in the simple statement above and will doubtless reveal numerous minor discrepancies in the temporal dimension. The author, who has studied landscape directly in many lands is well aware of this, and comments: " Though printed pictures (half-tone) are composed of dots, each of which may be imperfect, and though much may be missing from the total area owing to screening, a viewer comprehends a whole picture from the dots ". So the reader should endeavour to comprehend the picture here.

Complications are to be expected as consonant with heterogeneity of the earth's crust, and perhaps of the active upper mantle also. The function of the present text is not to provide a compendium of earth movements for given regions but to ascertain whether there has existed a pattern of major disturbances that can be truly acknowledged as global in its application. If the interest of the reader has been stimulated in this direction, the reviews of Chapters IX-XII have served their purpose.

PART D

THE SCENERY OF THE MOUNTAINLANDS

CHAPTER XIII

PALÆOZOIC MOUNTAIN CHAINS

Introduction. Palæozoic Mountain Systems of Laurasia : The Appalachian-Ural Welt. Caledonia-Greenland Welt. Laurasian Circumferential Welt. Palæozoic Mountain Systems of Gondwanaland. Old Mountains in New Scenery.

INTRODUCTION

The principles of crustal failure (Chapter IV) may well be illustrated by a consideration of the orogenic welts for Palæozoic time. Though since the time of Suess geologists have customarily referred Palæozoic orogenesis to two major " revolutions " called " Caledonian " and " Variscan " respectively, there is little support for this view in the Palæozoic ranges themselves. Even the often quoted correspondences on opposite sides of the North Atlantic fail signally to correspond in time, for the " Caledonian " phase of North America (Taconic) is post-Ordovician as against the dominant Erian phase (post-Silurian) of Europe. Likewise " Variscan " orogeny of the Appalachians is early-Permian whereas the chief phase in western Europe (Sudetic) is post-early Carboniferous.

The comparative table of Stille (1924) wherein orogenesis appears as intermittent throughout the Palæozoic (Table X) gives a much sounder temporal background of study. Eardley (1950) too, has shown a chronic state of stress intermittently relieved in the cordillera of western North America, and Gilluly (1949) also has applied the idea generally through the mobile welts of the earth.

While resultant tectonic forces must be expressed vertically to make the mountains and horizontally to form shear planes in mountain structures, associated tensional and compressional forces show no simple alternation in time. Thrust faults are currently active in California while normal faults are active only 100 miles away. World-wide epochs of alternating compression and tension are not demonstrable. These data and principles, conform also much better with our conception of crustal failure on engineering principles, as illustrated by the example of the demolished bridge (p. 127), though Umbgrove (1950) has once more stated a predilection for " relatively short periods characterized by folding of widely separated geosynclinal belts ". The two viewpoints may perhaps be reconciled. The planet is a structural entity and we shall rightly anticipate that major stresses may be relieved, and major orogenic events occur, with a broad simultaneity over its surface. But the planetary crust is a thing of infinite heterogeneity in detail, and we shall also anticipate that local deviations from orogenic similarity and simultaneity will be everywhere the rule. Moreover, as comparison of

Palæozioc structures shows (*cf.* Umbgrove 1947, Plates 1 and 2), the trendlines of both "Caledonian" and "Variscan" mountain ranges are usually parallel and often coincident, indicating that all the Palæozoic failures of the crust occurred in response to a single set of controlling telluric forces and thus represent one set of features, not two. That the Variscan foldings should be, particularly in Asia, more widespread than their Caledonian forerunners is to be expected if they represent the culminating phases of a single prolonged global state of orogenesis.

TABLE X

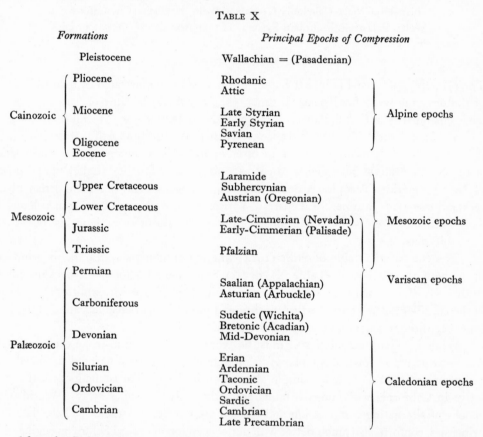

Formations		Principal Epochs of Compression	
	Pleistocene	Wallachian = (Pasadenian)	
Cainozoic	Pliocene	Rhodanic / Attic	
	Miocene	Late Styrian / Early Styrian / Savian	Alpine epochs
	Oligocene / Eocene	Pyrenean	
Mesozoic	Upper Cretaceous	Laramide / Subhercynian / Austrian (Oregonian)	
	Lower Cretaceous		Mesozoic epochs
	Jurassic	Late-Cimmerian (Nevadan) / Early-Cimmerian (Palisade)	
	Triassic	Pfalzian	
Palæozoic	Permian	Saalian (Appalachian) / Asturian (Arbuckle)	Variscan epochs
	Carboniferous	Sudetic (Wichita)	
	Devonian	Bretonic (Acadian) / Mid-Devonian	
	Silurian	Erian / Ardennian / Taconic	Caledonian epochs
	Ordovician	Ordovician / Sardic	
	Cambrian	Cambrian / Late Precambrian	

After the Palæozoic, or at latest the Triassic, a new set of crustal forces became operative, and the patterns of later mountain systems, except locally about the peripheries of Laurasia and Gondwana, often fail signally to coincide with the earlier trends (Chapter XIV).

Orogenic mountain chains have been ridged up during many periods of earth-history, but only those of late-Cainozoic-Quaternary date still survive topographically without rejuvenation. Most of the more ancient ranges have been obliterated at least once by denudation, and if they reappear now as mountains they do so by virtue of later earth-movements, generally of faulting or warping. The Altai Mountains of Central

Asia, for instance, preserve no vestige of the Palæozoic mountain chains. Those were wholly erased by erosion during late-Palæozoic and Mesozoic time, and the resulting plain, which may be inspected upon the present summits, was broken and re-elevated to great heights by Cainozoic faulting. Similar in most respects is the story of the bevelled ridges of the Appalachians, which after being levelled by planation during the Mesozoic and again in the mid-Cainozoic have been upwarped and redissected to their present form (Fig. 141).

Even where orogenic mountains have been planed out of existence, however, no difficulty arises concerning their detection for the cicatrice of orogenically contorted rock structures remains, like scar tissue in smooth flesh, for inspection in subsequent ages. Wherever the roots of ancient mountains are exposed in orogenic welts, the predominant structural planes are steeply inclined: usually as closely-packed repeated anticlines and synclines (isoclinal structure) in schists and associated rock types. From these cicatrices the pattern of Palæozoic mountain ranges, which occur in all continents but chiefly in those of the northern hemisphere, has been deciphered. The pattern of these ranges is interesting in that it departs materially from the pattern of orogenic ranges for post-Palæozoic time. Moreover, several of the orogenic structures continue without reduction obliquely to the continental margins where they terminate abruptly, giving rise to much conjecture as to their possible continuations (for continue they must) across the floors of adjacent oceans or in other continents. The Palæozoic mountain chains have been plotted in the restoration of Laurasia (Fig. 166) when the various severed ends at the present continental margins are found to join up in coherent fashion. No clearer proof could be found that through all the orogenic epochs of the Palæozoic era the northern continents were bound together in a single ovoid landmass, Laurasia, and that the present North Atlantic and Arctic ocean basins did not exist.

Not only do the chains fit spatially into a coherent pattern but the several orogenic episodes agree temporally along the several chains, as may be noted especially where chains of different ages cross one another. This happens in northern Norway and Karelia where the Appalachian-Ural belt (on a great circle) of Taconic and Saalian age is crossed by the British-Spitzbergen chain of Ardenne and Erian orogenic age. In the south-eastern United States appears the crossing of the (Saalian) Appalachian belt and the earlier Wichita-European zone (Sudetic). *Without such restoration the pattern of Palæozoic orogenesis must remain incomprehensible upon the global scale.*

No Palæozoic mountain systems survive in modern scenery: all have been obliterated by the gnawing tooth of erosion; but the toughened roots of the ancient chains have often guided, in part at least, later orogenic trends; and in some regions they have subsequently been re-elevated as horsts forming mountains of a newer kind (Germanotype) in the landscape (p. 458). In both rôles they are important in modern scenery: and we shall therefore review briefly the distribution in space and time of Palæozoic mountain welts in the two super-continents, Laurasia and Gondwanaland.

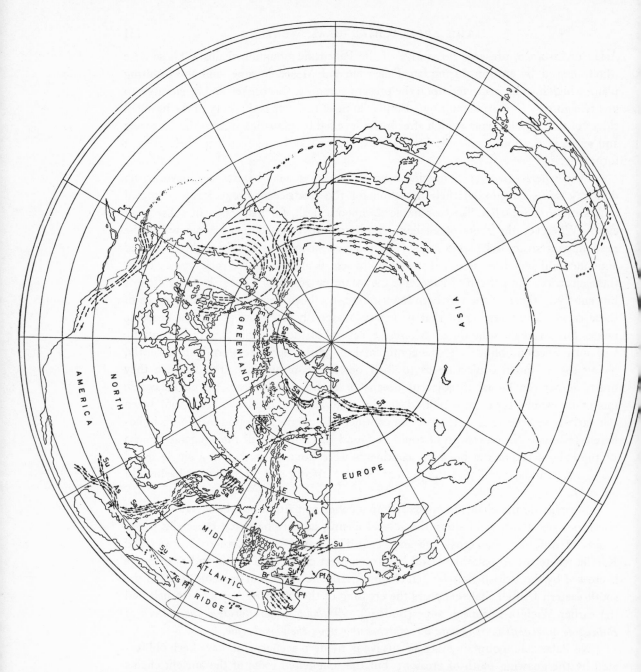

FIG. 166. Reassembly of Laurasia produced by rotating North America back towards Europe. The severed ends of Palæozoic orogenic welts then join between the New World and the Old. Circles follow older Palæozoic, dots younger Palæozoic, orogenic structures. Broken lines Mesozoic orogens. Projection, orthomorphic. T = Taconic, Ar = Ardenne, E = Erian, Br = Bretonnic, Su = Sudetic, As = Asturian, Sa = Saalian, Pf = Pfalzian, Tr = Triassic, J = Jurassic.

PALÆOZOIC MOUNTAIN SYSTEMS OF LAURASIA:
THE APPALACHIAN - URAL WELT

With the Laurasian reconstruction on a globe, this welt makes practically a great circle arc of almost 100°. Its two chief tectonic phases are the Taconic (post-Ordovician) and Saalian (Early-Permian) with a notable Devonian episode in mid-course through the Maritime Provinces of Canada and the North-eastern United States.

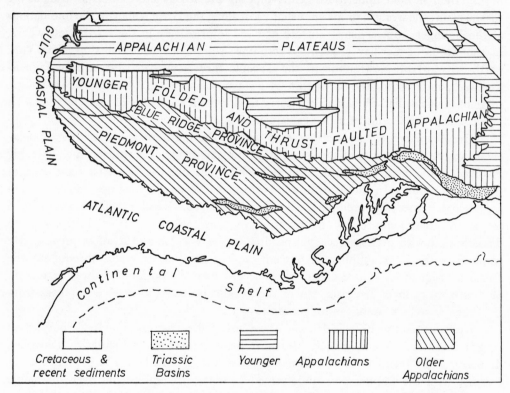

FIG. 167. Regions of Appalachian structure in the eastern United States of America.

For the American region it has been described in a voluminous literature (see Eardley 1962). In the south (Fig. 167) the rugged Blue Ridge stands boldly on the west and the lowland Piedmont on the east. Together they represent the Taconic (post-Ordovician) orogeny. Though the present boundary between the Blue Ridge and the Piedmont is a thrust (Martic and Brevard), some authorities have held that the Blue Ridge with its Precambrian rocks early rose as a median geanticline in the complex Appalachian welt separating, almost from the beginning of the Palæozoic, the profoundly metamorphosed and plutonically intruded Piedmont trough from the later developing (Saalian), less deformed and metamorphosed ridge-and-valley Appalachians, which are

2E

innocent also of plutonic intrusion. The Piedmont seldom rises above 1,000 feet. Its rocks are in part Precambrian but most of the crystalline schists are probably early-Palæozoic and there is little evidence that the Precambrian basement is extensively involved in the Palæozoic structures. Volcanic and batholithic rocks are important, the latter intruded in three phases, one Taconic and two Acadian. A belt of basic rocks with talc and soapstone may indicate the site of a Taconic peridotite belt (Hess 1937).

The eastern limits of the older welt (Blue Ridge and Piedmont) are concealed beyond the Fall Zone underneath gently-dipping Cretaceous and Cainozoic strata of the coastal plain; the western limits are usually lost along the Great Valley in the foundations of the Younger Appalachians, but are exposed impressively in the north-west where, in the words of Eardley (1962), " From the Adirondack Mountains in New York north-eastward of Newfoundland the Taconic thrusts pushed westward and north-westward, and override the flat or thin Ordovician sediments that blanket the crystalline rocks of the Canadian Shield. They carry thick trough sequences of more clastic facies into contact with the undeformed calcareous facies ".

The Acadian orogeny is also exemplified in the northern and Maritime Appalachians where it began in mid-Devonian and culminated in late-Devonian time. Notably involved is the great Catskill delta of red sandstones like the Old Red Sandstone of Northern Europe. In the Maritime Provinces of Canada all pre-Carboniferous rocks are much deformed, and even the Carboniferous is flexed. Eardley (1962) has contended for intermittent compressive deformation in these provinces from Proterozoic to Triassic time with perhaps orogenic maxima in the Taconic and Acadian phases. He emphasises the large number of unconformities and conglomerates throughout the Palæozoic sequence. These observations accord with the position of these regions in our reconstruction of Laurasia, where they would be likely to receive impulses from European as well as American orogenesis.

Westward of the Blue Ridge and the Great Valley rise the inner, Carboniferous Appalachians folded and etched into a trellised pattern by structurally controlled drainage. The thick series of sedimentary rocks represented here is geosynclinal in contrast with the thinner and undeformed stratigraphic equivalents over the stable area to the west, but the boundary is gradational into the Appalachian Plateau as where arborescent drainage patterns prevail, e.g. about Pittsburgh. The rocks of this zone are virtually free of volcanic and intrusive contamination.

The folding of the Carboniferous Appalachians (Saalian) which begins south of the Adirondack stable mass, is into open anticlines and synclines in places overturned to the north-west. But in the southern extension beyond Pennsylvania thrust sheets appear, stacked one upon another in imbricate fashion until in Tennessee nine sheets are overthrust, occupying the whole width of the zone. Only Palæozoic rocks are known to be involved in this overriding which is of mesodermal type (p. 134).

The source of sediments in the Carboniferous Appalachians may be found partly in the neighbouring zone of older Appalachians. But the source of sediments for these is clearly indicated by isopachs and lithological variation to have lain still farther to the east. Barrell, for instance, calculated that to supply the sediments of the Catskill delta alone would need a 10,000 feet plateau rising eastward to a drainage divide at the edge of the present continental shelf (Fig. 168). To this necessary, if unreal, hypothetical landmass was given the name "Appalachia". What happened to sediments shed eastward from Appalachia was ignored. Only a regrouping of northern lands so as to bring the then newly risen Caledonian mountain systems of north-western Europe nearer to America seems likely to provide an adequate answer. The accompanying reconstruction (Fig. 166) is conservative in so far as closing the North Atlantic gap is concerned, a closer fit can readily be made upon a globe if only slight distortion of existing continental outlines is permitted.

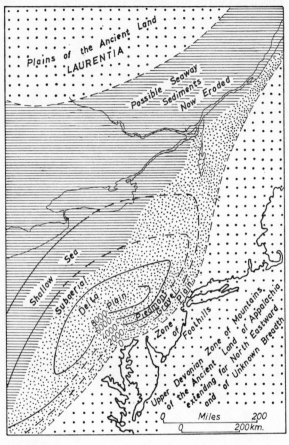

FIG. 168.

Source of sediments of the "Catskill Delta" showing derivation in a hypothetical landmass, "Appalachia" to the east. *after J. Barrell.*

Where they last appear upon the American continent, in Newfoundland, the Appalachian mountain structures are directed north-north-eastward into the ocean. They show no signs of abrupt termination and the welt must be deemed to have possessed a natural continuation (Fig. 169). Where is that continuation? Geophysical researches by Ewing have demonstrated not only that Appalachian topography does not continue across the North Atlantic Basin towards Europe; but also that there is no trace of Appalachian *structures* beneath the ocean bed; there is no change of constitution from the general basaltic floor of the basin where the line of welt is extrapolated. If a continuation fails even beneath the sea, where, we repeat, can the necessary continuation be?

According to the reconstruction of Laurasia, the continuation is to be found, in almost direct line, in the Taconic structures of the Kola Peninsula where Polkanov

(1937) has recorded a Caledonian folding, but as the Silurian lies almost horizontally (Stille 1948) such folding is almost certainly Taconic or older.   Polkanov and Holtedahl thought this zone extended across Kanin Peninsula into the Timan Range where it is possibly buried beneath younger Palæozoic formations.   These shelf facies are in turn

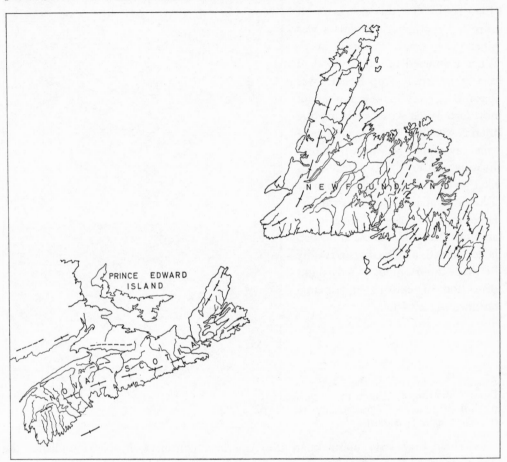

FIG. 169.   Palæozoic orogenic structures are directed north-eastwardly
in Newfoundland and show no sign of turning eastward towards Europe.

folded in the Saalian (Appalachian) phase (Umbgrove, 1950), the same as the main Ural geosyncline.

The Ural Mountain structures involve, besides the Angonkian undermass, a fairly complete Palæozoic sequence from the Cambrian to the Permian.   An upper Ordovician hiatus with metamorphism of the older rocks records the Taconic phase in the north (von Bubnoff 1952), and is followed by dolomites, grey and red shales with sandstone layers and massive limestones.   In the south, around the Ufa Plateau, the Silurian has more clastics and the whole of the period is spanned by volcanic effusions—spilites, diabases and tuffs which von Bubnoff relates to the sinking of the Ural geosyncline. The site of volcanism was transferred east of the Urals during the inundational Devonian phase when 6,000 metres of typically geosynclinal sediment accumulated. This volcanism appears to have been superficial and secondary for the rock types are sialic $\frac{1}{m}$ liparites and trachytes with dacites and andesites.

A very full Carboniferous sequence shows minor pulsations of the crust, with a pronounced erosional break in the southern mid-Carboniferous. The Permian sequence also is famous but this period also covered the Saalian and Pfalzian orogenesis that created the Ural Mountain structures, so that lower-Triassic conglomerates lie discordantly in the foreland.

The late-Palæozoic structures of the Urals (Bogdanoff 1957) are arranged in successive zones from west to east. The western autochthon is a sedimentary zone of Silurian to lower-Permian formations, sometimes carrying thrust sheets in advance of the next zone, which is of crystalline schists with four or five great anticlines revealing quartzitic cores. The third zone, which persists the length of the Ural, though it is somewhat narrow in the Central Ural is of dunite and peridotites, strongly serpentinised. Basic effusives, with contact metamorphosed sediments of bathyal nature, build the fourth zone, which is widest (with a double syncline) in the north but pinches out somewhat in the Central Urals. In the south it is represented by green schists. The fifth zone is of gneiss and granite representing the plutons intruded during later phases of the orogenesis; while the last zone, embracing the eastern ridges and foothills is of metamorphosed Palæozoic sediments which flatten progressively to the backland beneath the plain of Western Siberia.

Far north in the Arctic, amid Novaya Zemlya and the Pai Khoi Mountains, Taconic structures do not appear and orogenesis is wholly late-Palæozoic in age. Lower-Permian rocks are folded, and followed by molasse. Here, apparently, the Saalian phase appears on the same side of the older, Taconic line as in North America.

Away to the south-west, with quite a different strike, though of the same (Saalian) date, are the Palæozoic displacements of the Donetz Basin.

So, on our reconstruction, there is a single orogenic line of Appalachian orogeny from Alabama to Newfoundland thence across the sub-Arctic into the Ural Mountains as far as the Aral Sea. On the global reconstruction this is almost a great circle of over 100° arc. The Taconic phase may, after the Ural is met, continue rather west of Lake Baikal, but such continuation is independent of the tracing of Palæozoic orogenic zones across the Atlantic and Arctic Oceans. A Pfalzian late phase is also present, both in America and in the Urals.

Divergent opinions have been expressed concerning the dating and direction of folds in the Taimyr Peninsula and Severnaya Zemlya. Authors generally regard the folds as swinging northward from the mainland and through the islands. Archangelsky dissents (1937); Umbgrove delineates marked Caledonian as well as Variscan folds;

Stille (1948) thinks there are only Variscan (Saalian); Nalivkin (1960) considered " Timan and the region between Timan and Urals as a peculiar region of development of folded north-western branches of the Urals formed during the Hercynian orogenesis ". Under these circumstances the importance of the structure is difficult to assess, but it is not difficult to imagine that the main Ural folds, bent to the east through Novaya

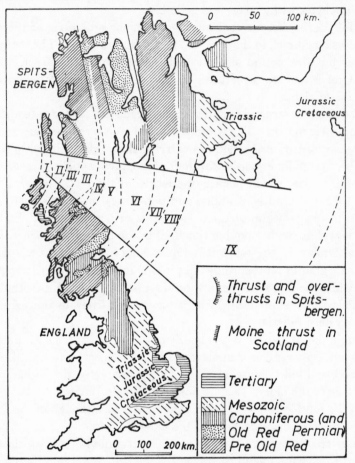

FIG. 170. Comparison of zones of Caledonian orogeny between Britain and Spitzbergen. *after E. Holtedahl.*

Zemlya and curving round the Kara Sea could pass through the islands of Severnaya Zemlya as they appear in the reconstruction.

CALEDONIA-GREENLAND WELT

From Scotland a lengthy chain of Caledonian folds that may possibly end in Angaraland stretches along most of the east coast of Greenland almost from the north-eastern corner of the island to beyond Scoresby Sound. Eardley (1962) cites the authority of Lauge Koch for regarding the structures as young Caledonian (Erian) " with characteristics similar to those of Norway and Great Britain". Westward thrusting of the beds indicates that the western flank of the orogen is present.

On the reconstruction, the fold-belt is continued almost directly with Spitzbergen which, from its present outlying position and the trend of its fold axes, may well have been detached from Eurasia and rotated slightly. The formations and structures of the island bear remarkable resemblance to those of both Greenland (Harland 1961) and Scotland (Umbgrove 1947) (Fig. 170), so that the western flank of the Caledonian geosyncline is again represented. The main phase of orogenesis is, of course, Erian with possibly weak Ardennic impulses.

From Spitzbergen the orogenic zone is continued by a short step into Norway where the eastern side of the geosyncline appears. abutting against the Fennoscandian Shield (Bailey 1929). Characteristic is the horizontal translation of plutonic masses for long distances from the north-west. Holtedahl (1939) has shown the symmetry of the Caledonian features of Finnmark with those of Scotland. Throughout the length of Norway the principal phase of orogenesis is again the Erian, with important earlier (Ardennic) phases, and a middle Devonian phase with strong horizontal displacement in both coastal Norway and Greenland. At the boreal extremity of Norway the maps of both Stille and Umbgrove indicate the trendlines swinging eastward towards the Kola Peninsula. But here an important distinction must be made. The trendlines extending east and west from Varanger Fiord are older and represent a Taconic phase which is nearly at right angles to the Erian trend, from which it is utterly distinct. The map in Bailey and Holtedahl (1936) shows this plainly, and shows the crossing here of the Appalachian-Ural welt with the Caledonian welt.

In Britain, classic area for study of the Caledonian orogeny, the full width of the geosyncline is present. The north-western foreland is represented by the Lewisian gneiss of the Hebrides, while the south-eastern front passes from Flamborough Head into South Wales. Many details are given by Bailey (1929). From Ireland, where the folds make their last appearance in Europe, is derived the name of the principal phase— Erian. A Taconic phase is recorded from the south-eastern margin by Stille and Umbgrove and is confirmed (Hess 1955) by the age of peridotites. Ardennic disturbances appear on a branch extending towards the Belgian coalfield.

From end to end, the visible length of this uniform orogenic belt is 4,000 miles. Its further continuation into the Atlantic region is overlain by Variscan structures, and is lost to view.

LAURASIAN CIRCUMFERENTIAL WELT

The main belt of Palæozoic orogenesis makes a girdle about Laurasia. The western aspect, along the cordillera of North America, has been the site of orogenic deformations from Precambrian time until the present day. This is understandable as it has always formed a peripheral segment of Laurasia opposed to the Pacific Basin so that essentially similar forces have operated upon it throughout much of geologic time. Palæozoic time was no exception, and mighty chains of mountains arose by orogenesis more than

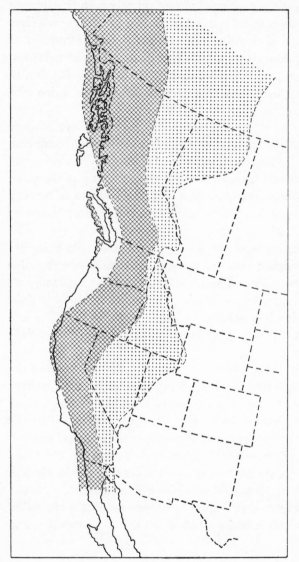

once during that era along the cordilleran welt (Eardley 1962; Gilluly 1963).

An extensive Mesozoic and Cainozoic cover, and abundant Jurassic plutons, now mask much of the Palæozoic history of the Cordilleran region, but the geosyncline is clearly extended along the whole western border of the continent (Fig. 171). Nevada, for instance, received more than 20,000 feet thickness of Palæozoic sediments.

Latterly, the southern half of the cordilleran trough was divided into eastern and western portions by a geanticline which began to rise before the end of the Devonian and grew intermittently until the Permian. Although the western trough received the greater thickness of sediment, both were of geosynclinal dimensions, the maximum

FIG. 171

Palæozoic cordilleran welt of North America. This welt was garlanded about the west coast by island arcs (blank). Volcanic rock assemblage (cross-hatched), eastern mainland assemblage (stippled).
After A. J. Eardley.

of sedimentation being in the Carboniferous. The sediments of these two portions are strongly contrasted. Those of the eastern trough are clean and derived from the stable landmass of the continental centre, the source rocks being plutonic basement or previous arenaceous sediments. Conversely, in every stratigraphic system of the western trough from Ordovician to Cretaceous, notable thicknesses of greywackes or pyroclastics accumulated (Kay 1948). Andesitic lavas are also abundant, especially in the Permian, Triassic and Jurassic. The western trough also underwent the stronger metamorphism, thick sequences of phyllite, argillite and various schists with pyroclastics being character-istic. Large bodies of intrusive rock are also distinctive. An impressive total of evidence indeed postulates a Palæozoic land or island arc with volcanoes along, or even beyond, the continental shelf, like the present-day island festoons of eastern Asia (Eardley 1962). Gilluly (1963) concludes that the missing borderland, which included crystalline sialic rocks in its composition, has since been carried under the continent by currents in the upper mantle (or perhaps overridden by westward drift of North America (p. 579, Fig. 236).

The chief orogenesis within the coastal geosyncline was late Permian or earliest Triassic, but the sedimentary history shows strong activity in the volcanic arc to the west intermittently throughout Palæozoic time. The arc was, however, always narrow.

The extreme south of North America is occupied by the profound subsidence of the Gulf Region, dating from mid-Jurassic time. This region is, however, well within the borders of the continent as defined by the mountain arcs of the Greater Antilles and stood as a highland for much of Palæozoic time, shedding north-westwards on to the continent the Carboniferous sediments that total 20,000 feet for the Ouachita system, 12,000 feet or more in the Marathon area and 10,000 feet in Coahuila. Through the southern United States, nevertheless, Palæozoic sequences are thinner than in the west and consist principally of limestone. Volcanic rock types are absent.

Two main orogenic systems are there apparent: the Wichita and Arbuckle system which embraces a number of allied, but not always similar, structures in the north; and the Ouachita and Marathon mountain systems in the south. The Wichita Mountains rise less than 2,500 feet above sea level and represent chiefly granite: the Arbuckle Mountains form an anticlinal arch with Precambrian granite rising centrally between flanks of tilted Palæozoic rocks representing a very full sequence (9,000 feet) up to the late-Pennsylvanian. Several other mountain uplifts extend westward into the Rocky Mountain belt where they are largely overlapped and obscured by later deposits and structures of the Permian basins of Texas and the marine transgressions of the Cretaceous, through both of which the various ranges now frequently protrude. Such are the Uncompahgre-San Luis, Brazos and Zuni mountains in Colorado and New Mexico. They curve towards a north-west strike as though to join the Palæozoic cordillera of the west.

The dominant phases of orogeny in this belt are Sudetic (Wichita) and Asturian (Arbuckle).

The Ouachita and Marathon systems which enter Mexico in the south as the mountain structures of Coahuila State resemble the Appalachians topographically, though they are less high. They represent a Permian folding and according to Eardley (1962) transect the Appalachian trend in the east and also the Wichita folds. The Coahuila part of the orogen was invaded by batholiths, but there is no proof that these were associated with the Permian folding. They may be related to Triassic or early-Jurassic events, though not as late as Nevadan (*q.v.*).

The eastern extensions of the Wichita and Marathon mountain systems are much obscured by later deposits and by the subsidence of the Gulf Region. Nevertheless, there is insufficient reason to believe, as has sometimes been stated, that these systems turn at a right angle into the Appalachian trend which is, in any case, of different orogenic age. Rather we are confronted with a system of orogenic folds which, when last visible, gave every indication of disappearing on a direct line into the ocean, like the Newfoundland Appalachians already discussed. Where, then, may the continuation of the Wichita and Marathon mountain systems be expected? According to our reconstruction (Fig. 166) the continuation should be through the Azores plateau into Western Europe.

The geology of the Azores Plateau includes continental rock types (p. 581), and its size and isostatic condition lead also to the opinion that it must consist of continental sialic material. Tolstoy and Ewing (1949) have stated: " The type of topography shown on the fathograms on the Azores Plateau obtained by the *Atlantis* was quite different from any noted on the rest of the Ridge. The surface of the plateau is characterised by a series of ridges, which the *Altair* expedition plotted as trending NW-SE (*i.e.* approximately at right angles to the trends noted in the Main Range farther south), and whose spacing is entirely different from that of the ridges forming the Main Range of the mid-Atlantic Ridge . . . the ridges on the Azores Plateau are separated by broad valleys." If Cretaceous and later deposits upon the Azores Plateau are thin (and whence may thick deposits be derived?), these ridges, disposed in two systems, may record the trends of Palæozoic orogeny.

The Palæozoic mountain systems of continental Europe are highly complicated (Kossmat *et al.*) and have formed the subject of an extensive literature from which we extract the salient facts of distribution in space and time. From south-western Britain to Brittany and again in Spain, extensive mountain chains strike east and south-eastward from the coastline, to which they are absolutely discordant in trend.

It is quite incredible that this broad belt of Palæozoic linear structures, which extends east-west from the Japanese islands across the entire breadth of Asia and of Europe should terminate abruptly and transversely at the Atlantic littoral, or even within the limits of the continental shelf, while still nearly a thousand miles wide from Ireland to southern Spain. Conversely, that such an orogenic zone should have sprung fully fledged into being, though no trace of it has ever been discovered upon the propinquent ocean bed is equally incredible. But our reconstruction of Laurasia affords an explanation: through the Azores Plateau the Palæozoic mountain systems of Western Europe may find continuation in the Wichita, Arbuckle and Marathon systems of the southern United States, with which they agree orogenically both in linear space and time. The corresponding episodes of orogenesis are: *Bretonnic*, strong in Western Europe but represented in the Southern United States only by the unconformity between the

Devonian Arkansas novaculite and the upper Mississippian clastics (Caney Shale) of the Ouachita; *Sudetic*, the principal phase of Europe, well exemplified in the Wichita structures; *Asturian*, also strong in Europe and represented, according to Stille and Umbgrove, in the Arbuckle movements of America; *Saalian*, of lesser importance in this welt; and sundry late-Permian earth-shudders that are strongest at the eastern and western extremities of the combined European-American welt (Coahuila-Marathon in America, Pfalzian phase which increases in strength eastwards through southern Europe).

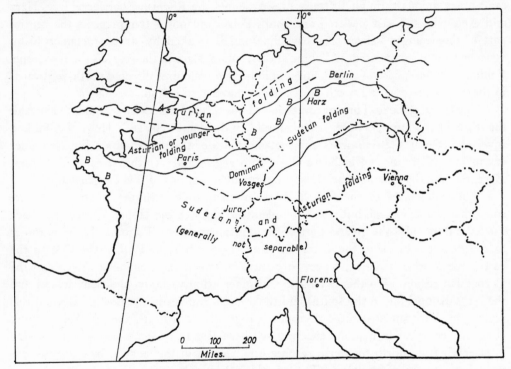

FIG. 172. Zones of late-Palæozoic folding in Europe. *after H. Stille.*

In Europe (Fig. 172) five east-west zones of Variscan orogeny, make most of the visible foundation structures. Through south-western Ireland, Cornwall, Brittany and the Central Plateau of France and the Schiefergebirge of the Rhineland appears the earliest phase of orogenesis—the late-Devonian, Bretonnic. The chief phase for Northern Europe, covering the region eastward from Britain and Normandy to Poland is, however, the Sudetic or post-lower Carboniferous phase. At this time were generated the main Variscan ranges and the northern secondary geosyncline which later received paralic sediments, including the main European coals, of the middle-Carboniferous or Westphalian. These in turn were crumpled by the Asturian orogenic impulses, *e.g.* in the Belgian coalfield, which preceded the late-Carboniferous or Stephanian, deposition.

Sudetic movements are apparent also on the flanks of the Central Plateau and in the southern Vosges.

From Western Europe, vestiges of the Palæozoic mountain chains continue eastward as a broad welt exhibiting five clearly marked tectonic zones. In the north is the "coal girdle" of the Westphalian zone comprising paralic sediments 6,000 metres thick with only small marine intercalations. Strong folding and overthrusting to the north belong to the Asturian phase.

The Rhenohercynian zone, of thick late-Devonian and early-Carboniferous sandstones, trends through Brittany, the Ardenne, the Rhenish Schiefergebirge, Harz and eventually the east Sudeten and south Polish uplands. It represents the central part of the younger Palæozoic geosyncline and is marked by strong metamorphism. Igneous action is expressed in diabase sheets: plutons are to the rear, in the next zone. Folding is intense, with overthrusting and imbricate structures directed north-westwards in the western region and north-eastwards in the eastern region.

The third, or Saxo-Thuringian, zone extends through the Schwarzwald, Odenwald, the Spessart, Thuringerwald, Frankenwald and Fichtelgebirge. Here the folding involves not only the sediments and metamorphics of the geosynclines, but also older crystallines of the floor which are sliced into sheets and overthrust as strike ridges. Here, too, are the abundant acidic and intermediate plutons of this orogenesis.

The boundaries of the fourth, Moldanubian, zone with the previous one are somewhat problematical, but it may be identified through the Upper Vosges and Black Forest and includes the greater part of the Bohemian mass. Tectonically, it continues to the Podolian block of the Ukraine (partly Precambrian). Within the welt to the east is the Moravian region, a great overthrust between the Bohemian massif and the Carpathian region. To this belong the Brunner eruptive body, the Schwarzawa and the Taya-Kuppel (all in the south) and the eastern Sudetes in the north. Beyond this region the Variscan structures disappear progressively beneath the blanket of more youthful geological formations covering southern Russia. Metamorphism, increasing in strength from north to south, reaches a maximum in this zone where gneisses are typical among the crystallines. Though older Palæozoic rocks appear in the heart of the Bohemian massif, Devonian and lower Carboniferous rocks are abundant in the Vosges and Black Forest. Massive plutons of early- and late-Carboniferous age follow Devonian gabbroidal intrusions. Metamorphic formations of the Moldanubian zone were overridden during the Cainozoic by Alpine structures, within which they appear as "inner horsts", *e.g.* Aar Massif.

The most southerly, fifth, zone corresponds with the Rhenohercynian zone of the north, and comprises unmetamorphosed Palæozoic formations from Cambrian to Permian in age. In Spain the chief dislocations are Asturian, following upon a weak Sudetan phase, Permian phases (Saalian) are weak in Western Europe (Pyrenees); but the end-Permian Pfalzian movements are widespread in the southern zone from Spain (where the Asturo-Cantabrian and Pyreneean mountain systems represent two distinct orogens (de Sitter)) and the Cevennes to Turkey. The zone is, however, greatly fragmented through Corsica, the Balkans, the islands of the Aegean Sea (Cyclades, Rhodes) and Turkey, with the principal orogenic phase in the east apparently the Sudetic.

Through Asia the Palæozoic mountain systems attained their most impressive development, the entire continent being spanned from east to west by a continuous tract of Palæozoic mountains that at its maximum breadth covers 1,500 miles north-south from Lake Baikal to the southern frontiers of Tibet. In China the east-west strike changed to a dominant north-east and south-west trend conforming more or less with the outline of the continent including the outlying islands from Formosa to Sakhalin. Whatever continent existed here before, the whole face of southern and eastern Asia was remade in the later-Palæozoic, when for a time central Asia appeared as a set of island festoons and archipelagoes from which rock debris was shed into late-Palæozoic geosynclines. With subsequent rejuvenations, the structural lineaments of that time still influence much of the topography of that vast region.

Curious is the manner in which the sheaves of ranges swept around and between several smaller nuclei (Tarim, Ordos) which remained relatively undisturbed amid the turmoil of the ranges (see p. 90). In Ordos and Indo-China the granite basement stands as a plateau, but elsewhere, as in the Tarim Basin, it subsided and was covered by marine Cretaceous or terrestrial Cainozoic and Quaternary rocks so that the presence of a resistant knot of the basement can only be surmised from the pattern of the encompassing ranges.

In Asia diastrophism was endemic throughout the Palæozoic era (Bogdanoff 1957). Cambrian foldings appear in an arcuate zone striking north-west in the Sayan Mountains and north-east in Transbaikalia, so enclosing the southern end of Lake Baikal. Taconic folds succeed to the south in the Altai and Tannu Ola and south-westward along the northern Tien Shan with granite intruding the belts of more powerful deformation. From Transbaikalia the structures follow the right bank of the Lena River, curving northwards about the Angara Shield towards the Arctic Ocean where they are last seen, still striking northwards, upon the New Siberian islands. Most of this zone, however, is heavily obscured and disrupted by a later Palæozoic geosyncline. Other early-Palæozoic deformations overwhelmed by later orogenesis appear in the Kuen Lun; and in south-east China were two early-Palæozoic mountain chains, striking south-east, with a late-Palæozoic trough between them into which were washed ill-sorted terrigenous delta deposits (Lee 1939). Even Japan is crossed by Variscan folds (Chugoku Range) appearing as a continuation of the Kuen Lun. Indo-China, too, has traces of early-Palæozoic orogeny, almost wholly obliterated by later crumplings; but most of this region seems to have behaved epeirogenically during the early-Palæozoic era.

According to literature,* the several late-Palæozoic impulses in Asia correspond closely with those of Europe. Strongest and most important in Central Asia is the

---

* See for instance, J. S. Lee (1939), T. K. Huang (1959).

Bretonnic which is found in the Kuen Lun and Nan Shan where powerful folding and metamorphism of a thick geosynclinal sequence (including greywackes derived from mountains to the north) was accompanied by the intrusion of large bodies of granite. Sudetic disturbance is indicated by a widespread unconformity. The southern boundary of the Kuen Lun is traced by Huang (1945) north of the Loktsung and Linzitang ranges (which involve marine Cretaceous) eastward to the Danbure Range where are red beds of probable Triassic or Cretaceous age. Farther eastward the line continues to the Bayen Kara whence it turns south-eastward, merging, according to Huang, with the Kam-Yunnan axis. The Tsinling, an independent system of ranges striking west-north-westward between the Kuenlun and the Nan Shan, is of late-Palæozoic age suggesting that a depression remained there after the Kuen Lun and Nan Shan were already lofty ranges. Late Carboniferous orogenic phases also occur in the Tien Shan and Nan Shan.

Through the provinces of Sikang and Yunnan, and into Assam, Burma and Siam, the Bretonnic and Sudetic diastrophic phases built great ranges striking north-west to the south-east or meridionally (Misch 1945). Their eroded stumps have guided the orientations of later ranges and the parallel courses of the present rivers of north-west Yunnan are old strike drainages. In all probability the Variscides of this region were later covered by Triassic and other sediments; but following Cainozoic movements erosion has removed these beds except in fault troughs and synclinals. To the north-west the sediments are better preserved.

Amid the Indonesian-Philippine island systems traces of Palæozoic orogeny are usually obscured by younger formations. In Sumatra and Java schists and granitic intrusions are elongated in the island axes, and some of the formations contain volcanic materials but the date of the formations and their metamorphism is not certainly Palæozoic and may well be Mesozoic. Traces of late Palæozoic orogenesis have been identified in Borneo.

Late-Palæozoic conglomerates of molasse type are widespread in Central Asia from the Tien Shan to the Kuen Lun and record several episodes of diastrophism. Eastward, in China, the Carboniferous formations constitute two very distinct series. In the north, between the main geosynclinal foldings, is a paralic sandstone-shale sequence with numerous coal beds and intercalated thin bitumenous limestones, some containing marine fossils. Lowland swamp and coastal plain environments are indicated. In the south through the provinces of Shensi, Szechuan and Hupeh, and farther east along the Yangtze-Kiang in Anhwei and Kiangsi is a vast single formation of marine fossiliferous limestone of open-water accumulation. The same formation continues widely across south-western China and Tibet to the Himalaya, Burma, Thailand and the Malay Peninsula. This sea remained over South-east Asia during much of the Permian and Triassic periods. Both facies are involved in the Permian and Triassic orogenic episodes that are widespread and characteristic in eastern Asia, where the late-Palæozoic diastrophic systems were maintained until the close of the Triassic.

This regional continuance of Palæozoic sedimentary and orogenic conditions well into the Mesozoic is important, for it links the purely Palæozoic orogenic systems of Europe and Central Asia with the circum-Pacific belt where orogenesis functioned less strongly during the Palæozoic but instead of then dying away it was intensified during the Mesozoic.

The last movements of the Palæozoic pattern in southern China occur at the end of the Triassic (Huaiyang and Nan-hsiang impulses). In the Permian and Triassic orogenic phases secondary folds and faults appear in the parageosynclinal troughs in addition to the main zones of crumpling.

The principal orogenic trends of eastern Asia are directed north-eastwards in accordance with a multiple (Palæocathaysian) geosyncline the history of which has been described by Lee (1939). Strong folds arranged *en echelon* pass along Honshu, Hokkaido and Sakhalin, and are paralleled by folds upon the Chinese mainland, Korea, Manchuria and through the Sikhota Alin (Yeliseyeva 1959) and Burein and Turana Mountains of the eastern U.S.S.R. to the Verkhoyansk Ranges. The oldest chain, the Chugoko Range of Japan, is Bretonnic like the Kuen Lun (Yamawaki), the youngest (Verkhoyansk) is late Triassic.

The trend of the Dzhugdzhur and Verkhoyansk ranges is northward, marginal to the Angara Shield, and continues from the Sea of Okhotsk to the Laptev Sea where occur vestiges of early- and late-Palæozoic folding and strong, exceptionally-dated, late-Triassic crumpling. All these structures then disappear beneath the sea. For their continuation, the reconstruction of Laurasia (Fig. 166) prompts an examination of Northern Greenland.

Through Northern Greenland, Ellesmere Land, Grinnel Land and Grant Land, and as far west as Melville Island, is a geosynclinal zone exhibiting marked orogenic impulses. Erian (late-Silurian) folding appears on Ellesmere Island and near Cape Rawson on the mainland of Greenland, recalling the western zone of the New Siberian Islands. The late-Palæozoic orogeny is dubious in the Greenland-Ellesmere Island sector; but Eardley (1962) remarks the possibility that unconformity between the Carboniferous and Devonian on Melville Island indicates a minor Bretonnic phase there. But the chief folding of this Arctic zone involves Triassic strata that thicken to geosynclinal proportions (Eardley 1962). Mesozoic folding occurs upon Greenland, Ellesmere Land, Axel Heiberg Land and Melville Island; the similarity with the contorted Triassic of the Verkhoyansk Ranges is very marked.

The stratigraphic and orogenic equivalences between the North Greenland and Verkhoyansk mountain belts affirm the identity of these two zones that is so clearly projected upon the reconstruction of Laurasia. At the same time, other late-Palæozoic mountain structures traverse from the lower Kolyma region eastward to Bering Strait, beyond which they link up with the Palæozoic cordillera of North America. Comparative details across the Bering Strait region have been discussed by Obruchev (1934), whose conclusion is that the two regions have been united since Proterozoic time, with the Tschuktschen Massif forming the undoubted continuation of the north-western and central part of Alaska. Palæozoic tectonic encirclement of Laurasia was thus complete. Significant differences of orogenesis appear later in the Jurassic, which is consistent with the rupture of Laurasia about that date.

Palæozoic Mountain Systems of Gondwanaland

The Gondwana super-continent also was engirdled by Palæozoic mountain chains, but there is less evidence of " intracontinental " welts like the Appalachian-Ural welt. In part this lack is due to the retarded state of geological exploration in the Antarctic continent which appears as the central " locking piece " of the reconstruction. If full information were available from this ice-clad continent, intracontinental Palæozoic welts might be demonstrable there also.

In South America vestiges of Palæozoic mountain chains appear at intervals in the foundations of the Andes (Fig. 173) (Stille 1941) which prompts a comparison with the Palæozoic cordilleras of western North America. But though the tectonics of these two mighty orogens both fronting the Pacific Ocean often compare spatially, precise dating of major tectonic episodes shows that these have seldom synchronised. *The two great cordilleras have behaved quite independently throughout post-Algonkian till Cretaceous time: a conclusion which is in harmony with their situations in Laurasia and Gondwana respectively.*

The principal tectonic phases of the Palæozoic in South America are:

a) the Cambro-Ordovician (possibly in part Taconic) which is believed to extend from Venezuela to Chile and thence through the Argentine Sierras to the Atlantic coast;

b) early-Permian movements (probably between the Asturian and Saalian phases of the northern hemisphere) which were strong along the Andes from Peru to southern Chile, but weaker progressively along the eastern branch;

c) Triassic corrugations which are powerful in an eastern branch through Argentina but are not certainly described from the Andes.

The northern end of the Andes frays out into three separate ranges, the easternmost of which passes with a north-east strike into Venezuela as the Sierra de Merida. The rocks of this Sierra afford positive evidence of late-Palæozoic orogenesis accompanied by granitoid intrusions. Palæozoic rocks are also said to have built in Colombia a series of folded ranges which persisted into Mesozoic time. Both early- and late-Palæozoic phases of diastrophism have been cited. Similar ranges existed in Ecuador, Peru and Bolivia according to Gerth (1932) and Steinmann (1929), and were still being eroded during the Triassic period, for strata of this age are missing. So the northern Andes provide consistent, if discontinuous, evidence of Palæozoic cordilleras probably little inferior, if at all, to the ranges that have twice occupied the region in later geologic time.

At about lat. 30° S., the Palæozoic ranges bifurcate (Fig. 173) one branch passing beneath the Andes of Chile to the Cordillera Costaneira and Tierra del Fuego; the other branch (much more fully studied, *e.g.* Picard 1948) turning eastwards into the Argentine. This eastern branch begins in the pre-Cordilleras of Mendoza, San Juan and La Rioga, and continues into the Sierra de Cordoba. The internal structures of these ranges are the result of Palæozoic movements supplemented by the intrusion of great masses of granite. For a space, the Palæozoic structures disappear beneath the Miocene pampas, but they reappear north of Bahia Blanca in the Sierras of Buenos Aires, disposed almost at right angles to the Atlantic coast.

Where is the continuation of this belt of multiple orogenesis heading into the Atlantic region to be sought? du Toit (1927, 1937) traced it in the Cape Ranges of South Africa, which on the Gondwana reconstruction (Fig. 17) become collinear with the Argentinian sierras. The general argument was strongly supported by a mass of detail (crossing of fold axes, lateral variation in rock series, and so forth, the linear gradations and differences being quite as important as the correspondences in proving the former continuity). But the two regions are mirror images: the Cape foreland was to the north, the pre-Andean foreland lay to the west and south-west.

A second bundle of fold axes forming the Cedarberg Ranges of the Cape strikes north-north-west, and this also may have a trans-Atlantic counterpart, though less clearly, in eastern Brazil.

The Cape orogenic welt is again truncated at the coast of south-east Africa, in the vicinity of Port Elizabeth. No continuation into the Antarctic continent is known, but a well defined welt involving early-Palæozoic formations has been identified along great lengths of the TransAntarctic Mountain scarp beneath the horizontally-lying Beacon formations. With the structures of similar age in Graham Land and the Ellsworth Mountains these orogenic vestiges form part of the Palæozoic fold girdle of Gondwanaland.

Palæozoic orogenesis is clearly expressed in New Zealand and in eastern Australia.

In the former, Macpherson (1946) has shown that the trends of the early-Palæozoic geosyncline, the late-Palæozoic—early-Mesozoic geosyncline and the Cretaceo-Cainozoic geosyncline are similar. In the North Island the directions are parallel to the Coromandel Peninsula and to the submarine ridges connecting New Zealand with Lord Howe and Norfolk Islands (Fig. 174). In the south the trends swing round to the south-east, but the graptolite bearing Ordovician beds, the Clinton River intrusive complex, the Otago schists and the major curve of the coast still remain parallel to one another.

The relationships of New Zealand are provocative. The islands are divorced from Australia, the nearest landmass, by 1,200 miles, yet the consensus of opinion among geologists is that they are continental in character, even to the extent of recurrent orogenic cycles. The Ordovician sequence of Preservation Inlet in the extreme south-west resembles that of Victoria very closely though it is only one-fifth as thick. And whence

Fig. 173.

Mountain ranges and structural elements of the Andean system. *after V. Oppenheim.*

Legend

 BASEMENT ZONES (PRE-OROGENIC)

A Guiana Shield

B Brazilian Shield

C Sierra de Tandil Land-mass

D Santa Marta and Guajira Land-mass

BASINS

I Llanos Basin

II Upper Amazon Basin

III Chaco-Pampas Basin

ANDEAN RANGES

1 Cordillera Patagonica

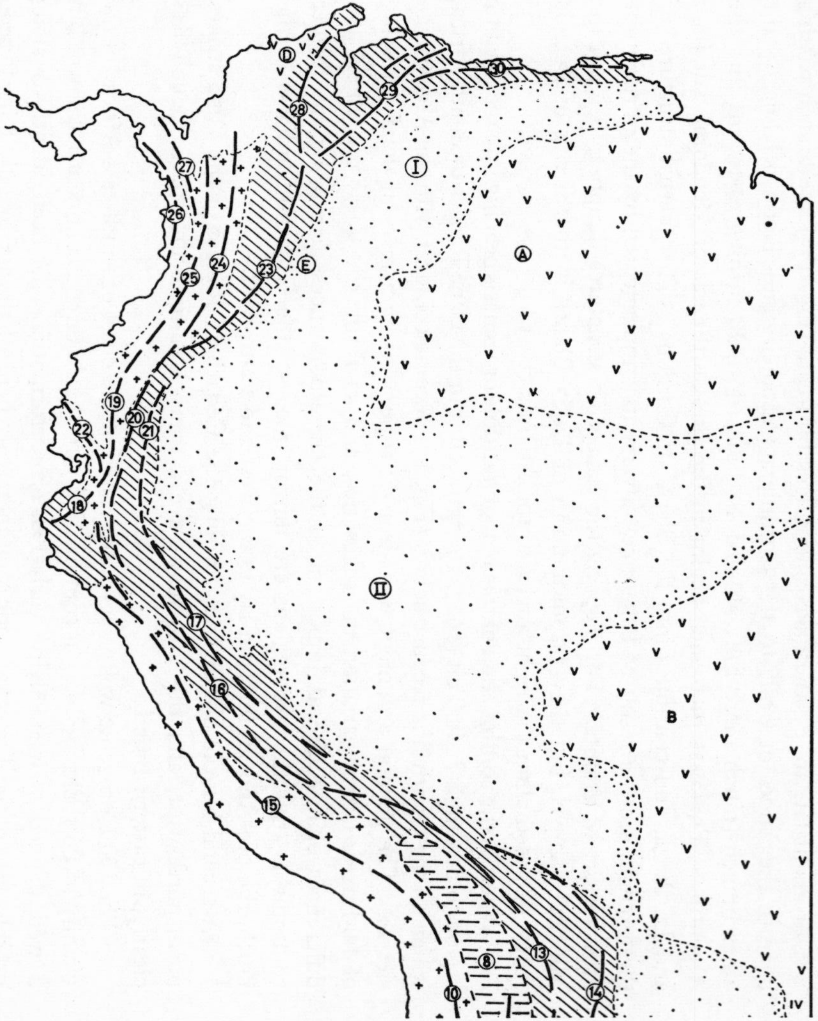

2 Cordillera Costanera of Chile

2A Cordillera Costanera (Ancient Element)

3 Patagonian Arches (Patagonides)

4 Cordillera Principal

5 Cordillera Frontal

6 Pre-Cordillera Argentina

7 Sierras Pampeanas

8 Puna and Puna de Atacama

9 Cordillera Central of Bolivia

10 Cordillera Occidental of Maritima

11 Cordillera Oriental of Argentina

12 Cordillera sub-Andina

13 Cordillera Real of Boliva

14 Cordillera Sub-Andina of Bolivia

15 Cordillera Occidental of Peru

16 Cordillera Central of Peru

17 Cordillera Oriental of Peru

18 Serrania de Amotape

19 Cordillera Occidental of Ecuador

20 Cordillera Oriental of Ecuador

21 Serrania de Cutuco

22 Serrania de Colonche

23 Cordillera Occidental of Colombia

24 Cordillera Central of Colombia

25 Cordillera Oriental of Colombia

26 Serrania de Perija

27 Serrania del Darien

28 Cordillera de la Costa of Colombia

29 Cordillera de Merida

30 Cordillera de la Costa of Venezuela

MESOZOIC BATHOLITHS

EASTERN GEOSYNCLINAL BELT

PUNA BLOCK

SIERRAS PAMPEANAS MASSIF

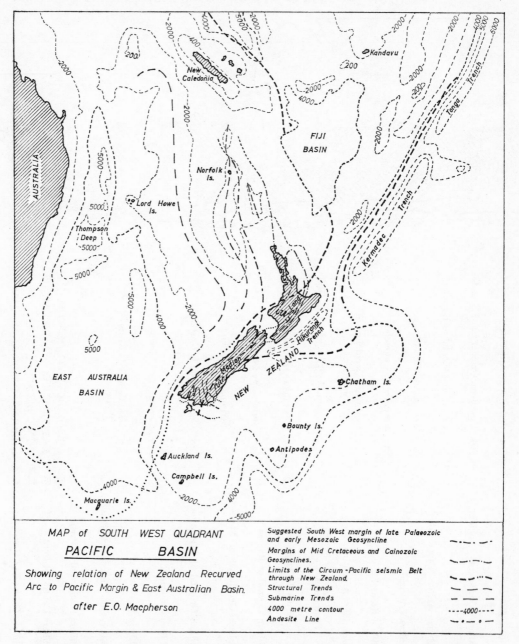

MAP of SOUTH WEST QUADRANT

PACIFIC   BASIN

Showing relation of New Zealand Recurved
Arc to Pacific Margin & East Australian Basin.

after E.O. Macpherson

Suggested South West margin of late Palaeozoic and early Mesozoic Geosyncline	—·—·—·—
Margins of Mid Cretaceous and Cainozoic Geosynclines.	— — —
Limits of the Circum-Pacific seismic Belt through New Zealand	— — —
Structural Trends	— —
Submarine Trends	— —
4000 metre contour	----4000----
Andesite Line	—·—·o—

FIG. 174. Orogenic relationships of New Zealand and submarine features of the South-western Pacific Basin.   The Palæozoic trend is from southwestern New Zealand to Lord Howe Island, the Mesozoic trend from Coromandel Peninsula (North Auckland) to Norfolk Island and New Caledonia.   The modern trend is from East Cape towards Kermadec, Tonga Ils. and Fiji.   *after E. O. Macpherson.*

came those colossal thicknesses of late-Palæozoic and Mesozoic greywacke and argillite that, before the locally overlying Cretaceo-Cainozoic strata accumulated, composed almost the whole of the major islands? Certainly not from within the present compass of the Dominion, and from the west if the absence of *marine* Hokonuian along the west coast of the South Island (as mentioned by Cotton) is accepted. " The west coast of

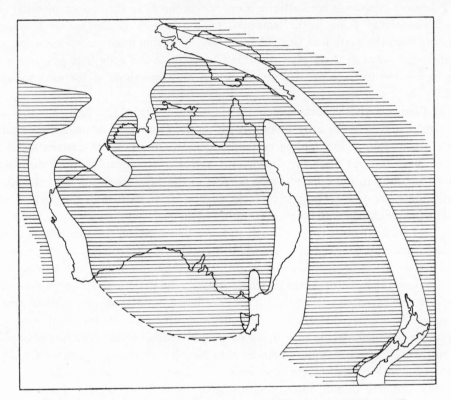

FIG. 175. Palæozoic geosynclines of Australasia (*after T. W. E. David*) showing a hypothetical landmass over the site of the Tasman Sea. Geological relations are better explained, however (p. 449), by a single geosyncline with New Zealand then apposed to south-eastern Australia.

the South Island, which was apparently not subjected to geosynclinal submergence and thick sedimentation in the Maitai and Hokonui periods is one of the few parts of the New Zealand region which might be expected to escape the folding paroxysm following that marine period ". Several of these problems are solved if it be conceded that New Zealand was formerly apposed to an Australian mainland, somewhat in the form of New Guinea at the present time. On the Australian side much evidence has been quoted (David 1950) of a " lost land " (called *Tasmantis*) which cannot have sunk beneath the Tasman Sea because Officer (1955) has demonstrated thereunder only the normal thickness of crust for an oceanic basin. Continental matter is absent except perhaps in the submarine ridges. Palæogeographic relations have been sketched by David (1950, Figs. 203-207) one of whose figures is reproduced here (Fig. 175). Clearly the whole matter would be simplified if the Tasman and Papuan geosynclines were regarded not as two but as a single feature lying off the east coast of Australia. I am not aware of any geologic evidence prohibitive of such a reconstruction (p. 453).

Palæozoic orogenesis in Australia is expressed chiefly in the eastern mountain belt from Tasmania to Cape York Peninsula, with a branch of the earlier movements extending from the south into Central Australia. " During none of the orogenic epochs was the whole area of deposition disturbed by folding and thus it is possible in one place or another to trace the deposits of one period into those of the next without a break."

In Tasmania and Victoria is a conformable passage from Cambrian to Ordovician and angular unconformities are unknown within the Ordovician sequence anywhere in the Commonwealth. But folding certainly occurred in the south-eastern states and western New Zealand after the Ordovician and was accompanied by " deep-seated plutonic injection in the orogenic zone parallel to the sub-meridional axes of folding " (David). Strikes of the Ordovician rocks at Preservation Inlet in the New Zealand Fiordland agree closely with those of Victoria and the beds have been intruded by granite on a grand scale (Benson 1933). Much stronger diastrophism followed the deposition of Silurian rocks, crumpling upon a wide belt occurring on a meridional strike through all the eastern states of Australia as far north as Rockhampton, and with a deflection to east-west into the heart of Australia where it made the structures still preserved in the Musgrave and Macdonnell Ranges. There are indeed, practically no Silurian rocks in Australia that are not disturbed by this *Bowning* orogeny. In the north was much associated volcanism, dacitic tuffs being particularly widespread. The intrusive phases are mostly concordant in type and confined to New South Wales; quartz-mica diorites are common rock types, but are accompanied by basic and ultrabasic masses in a belt 100 miles long and passing through Gundagai in New South Wales. These rocks are mainly altered to serpentine.

A middle-Devonian (Tabberabberan) orogeny was effective over much of New South Wales and Queensland ; but the principal phases of late-Palæozoic orogeny occurred both after the early Carboniferous and at the close of the Palæozoic era. The former structures are directed with a general north-north-westerly trend through eastern Victoria, New South Wales and Queensland. On the east they consist chiefly of broad folds or even domes and basins: only locally as at Ashford and Rockhampton are steep dips prevalent, with pressure coming from the east. On the west are two strong thrust-fault systems about 40 miles apart, the western beginning near Maitland. The full length of these fault systems is unknown, but they certainly continue parallel with the general strike of the Palæozoic structures for 150 miles.

The latter movements, heralded by extensive eruptions of rhyolite and basalt, are the most profound of the whole Palæozoic cycle (David 1950) affecting the geosyncline of eastern Australia through New South Wales and Queensland, and producing the north-west strikes that are still dominant there. The folding began with varying intensity according to locality and tended to the formation of anticlinoria rather than nappes. This is perhaps because the Carboniferous and Permian rocks involved had been laid down previously in pronounced basins so that their thickness varied locally. Associated fault-systems are large and extend along the general strike direction for at least 850 miles, with concomitant serpentine intrusions at Pine Mountain, Kilkwan and Rockhampton. Granitic intrusions also accompany the folding on a large scale in the New England and North Coast areas, together with minor massifs of monzonite and innumerable dykes and sills of differentiated rock types (minette, vogesite) where associated with the serpentine belt. All this varied igneous activity caused broad thermal metamorphic effects and produced a number of important metalliferous deposits.

Within the lakes and lagoonal hollows produced by this folding, coal measures accumulated during the late Permian. These final Permian formations were crumpled and thrust-faulted with the older rocks by renewed pressures from the east at the end of the Palæozoic era, when also masses of igneous magma stoped their way up into the folded strata. This was the end of the east Australian geosyncline that had persisted in one form or another virtually throughout the Palæozoic, and Australia entered the Mesozoic era with a splendid cordillera along its eastern margins.

Middle and late-Palæozoic sequences in New Zealand are mainly marginal geosynclinal, and have so far yielded insufficient evidence for a clear picture of late-Palæozoic orogenic phases to emerge.

The margins of Western Australia, like the east, show pronounced alternations of Permo-Carboniferous marine and terrestrial sedimentation, though coaly formations are relatively restricted. The belt has been called the Westralian geosyncline (Teichert) but some Australian authors (Fairbridge) have demurred that the dimensions and thicknesses of strata involved do not warrant the title. There was no accompanying volcanism or metamorphism, and folding at the end of the period was weak. Of importance for the reconstruction of Gondwana however, are comparisons with the marine and terrestrial Permian sequences of the eastern provinces of Peninsular India,[*] and the monoclinal flexures and normal faulting of both regions (cf. South-east Africa).

No Palæozoic rocks have been positively identified in Australian New Guinea, but in the backbone of the island, extensive metamorphic and plutonic rocks are believed to antedate Mesozoic strata. Thus Fisher (1944) has assigned the Kaindi series of the Morobe district, and its orogenic failure, to the Palæozoic. These indications hint a possibly Palæozoic orogenesis of considerable magnitude, involving also the D'Entrecasteaux and Louisiade Islands.

Beyond New Guinea the belt of Palæozoic orogeny may be expected to continue (see reconstruction of Gondwana) in the roots of the Himalayan mountain system and beneath Tibet, united now with the Palæozoic mountain systems of central Asia. The

* See data in Wadia (1937), Krishnan (1953) and Pascoe (1950).

evidence available from this region of difficult access is meagre and comes mostly from small inliers poking out from beneath the formations and structures of the later Himalayan geosyncline. Summarising the data : supposedly late-Cambrian movements are identified in the headwater region of the Ganges, with late-Palæozoic crumpling in the upper Indus and beyond the Tsangpo River. There is a suspicion that the movements are progressively younger towards the north. If so, then this system of Palæozoic folds is related to the older mass of peninsular India as the folds from Tibet to Lake Baikal are related to the Angara Shield and the two systems, mirroring each other, have come together in Tibet, thus explaining in some measure the extraordinary width of the late-Palæozoic fold belt in south-central Asia.

In the west the Iranian highlands, continuous with the high terrains of Afghanistan and Baluchistan on the east, constitute most of Persia and make a knot of high plateaus ($2\frac{1}{2}$ million sq. km. in area) between the curving Cainozoic mountain ranges of Zagros in the south-west, the mountains of Sind on the south-east and a separate northern line connecting Elburz, Meshed and the Hindu Kush. Structurally a part of Asia, the highlands appear to have escaped heavy Palæozoic orogeny, unless some of the abundant granitoid and syenitic rocks described by Stahl (1941) were intruded at that time. Umbgrove (1947) draws some east-west lines of Variscan folding, but gives no supporting details. On the whole, epicontinental flooding appears to have been more typical of Palæozoic activity in this region than orogenesis.

The Turkish promontory of Asia is more informative. The eastern part of that country, formerly Armenia, is built upon pre-Devonian gneisses and schists with a north-east strike (Oswald) strongly in contrast with later, easterly-directed dislocations that run into the mountain systems of Iran (p. 487). The eastern Taurus, too, is built of pre-Devonian schists of various types, folded marbles and limestones, quartzites and gneisses, with serpentines, and occasionally granite or diorite. These rocks are now disposed in horsts: in Djelu-Dagh they attain 5,320 metres above the sea. Similar strikes and structures occur locally over so wide an area as to suggest that most of eastern Turkey is underlain by an older Palæozoic, possibly Erian, fold-mountain system, with later folding towards the end of the Carboniferous.

The geological history recorded from western Turkey by Philippson (1918) is quite different. The orogenic phases occurred (a) between the Devonian and the Carboniferous and (b) at the close of the Palæozoic. Heissleitnen (1952) has assigned the ultramafic igneous belt of Jugoslavia and Greece to Palæozoic orogenesis, considering these rocks to appear in younger rocks only by tectonic emplacement.

In how far the Palæozoic fold-girdle of Gondwana is sunken beneath the Mediterranean is quite unknown, but the circumferential welt picks up again in Tunis, and Palæozoic mountain building is amply expressed within the later chains of the Atlas. Appearing first along the coast at Bone, Kabylie and the Rif, the ruins of denuded Palæozoic mountain structures underlie the region of the Tell Atlas and to the south compose the plateau of the Chotts between the Tell and Saharan Atlas. The Saharan

Atlas itself is but gently folded above a foundation of denuded Palæozoic structures, so that the late-Palæozoic mountain welt of North Africa constituted a zone of at least 250 miles in width directed west-south-westward from Tunis to the Atlantic seaboard. Here the ancient fold structures, somewhat confused by a converging system of fold-axes belonging to the Asturian phase and striking north-west from Ahaggar into Mauretania, are transected by the coast and lost beneath the Atlantic Ocean. Where may their continuation be sought? Surely through the basement of the Canary Islands and perhaps on part of the Azores submarine plateau (Fig. 166) whereon stand a number of paralle east-west ridges, to the other side of the Atlantic, in the Sierra de Merida of Venezuela. If this connection is valid, as suggested by our reconstruction, encirclement of Gondwana by late-Palæozoic orogenesis is almost complete.

Of no lesser interest in our reconstruction however, are the older Palæozoic plications that have affected West Africa. In the heart of the Sahara, just south of the Great Erg or sand sea, appear the strong, tabular mountains of the Touareg built of horizontal Devonian grits standing abruptly upon a platform of Archean and Silurian fold-systems (Lemoine 1914). The folds, at variance with the Atlas and late-Palæozoic folds to the north and north-west, strike almost meridionally and extend far to the south, the Silurian formations involved being rendered schistose and plutonically injected by acid magmas. The phase of folding is clearly post-Silurian or Erian; but at Tendouf and Taoudeni, to the north-west and west respectively, Lemoine records foldings prior to the Silurian, that is, of Taconic date.

On the borders of Dahomey and Togoland (Atakora Mountains), and extending with a south-south-westerly strike into Ghana, is a further welt wherein strongly deformed rocks of outstandingly quartzitic composition belong to the Akwapimian system. The fold structures, which are again of approximately Taconic date, attain the coast in the neighbourhood of Accra (Junner 1940) and afford yet another outstanding example of a Palæozoic mountain system transected and vanished at a modern coast. Where, once more we enquire, is the former continuation of this chain in the modern world? Remarkably similar rock types and structures strike parallel to the middle course of the Rio São Francisco in Brazil, and form the main watershed region or Serra Espinhaço. The orogenesis (pre-Silurian) is identical, and very similar rock systems both precede and succeed the tectonic episode to which we refer. Indeed, the more the similarities, not only of rock systems but also their expression in the present landscape, are examined the more remarkable they appear. The aspect of the Atakora Range in Dahomey for instance, is synphotographic with that of the Serra Geral in Baia.

Tabulating briefly, the following correspondences between Ghana and north-eastern Brazil indicate the close union of these two regions throughout a vast lapse of geologic time. See Table XI overleaf.

In Central and Southern Africa, north of the Cape Folded Belt, late-Palæozoic rocks of the Karroo system are never plicated but are disposed in broad basins upon a stable basement. There were thus no late-Palæozoic mountains.

TABLE XI

Ghana (see Junner 1940)	Brazil (see de Oliveira and Leonardos 1943)
Sekondian and Accraian Systems, respectively Carboniferous and mid-Devonian in age, found in restricted basins along the coast at Takoradi and Accra.	Late-Palæozoic basin of Rio Paranaiba in Piauhy.
Voltaian and Oti System of widespread, flat-bedded, clean-washed, fine-grained sediments Silurian in age.	*Bambui Series*, of widespread, flat-bedded lime-stones and fine-grained sediments of Silurian age.
Early-Palæozoic orogenesis :	Noted in text as collinear in the reconstruction of Gondwanaland.
Buem Formation. Variable clastics, including tillite, with lavas, agglomerates and tuffs, late Precambrian or early-Palæozoic.	*Lavras* Formation. Variable clastics including tillite. Volcanics. Late Precambrian or early-Palæozoic.
Akwapimian Formation. Characteristic quartz-ites building mountains with shales, phyllites, schists and silicified limestones.	*Itacolomi* Series. Characteristic quartzites building mountains, with shales phyllites and schists.
Tarkwaian Quartzites, phyllites, grits.	Upper. Quartzites and phyllites.
Upper Birrimian. Metamorphosed lavas, pyro-clastic rocks, subordinate greywacke, phyllite and schist.	Middle. Basic volcanics and pyroclastics, dolomite, phyllite, talc rocks.
Lower Birrimian. Phyllites, schists, tuffs, grey-wackes.	Lower. Phyllites (graphitic and sericitic), quartzites.
Archean.	*Archean.*

(In the Brazil column, the rows Upper, Middle, Lower are bracketed as: Minas Series*)*

Old Mountains in New Scenery

All Palæozoic mountain systems have long since been obliterated by denudation which has reduced the once-magnificent ranges to plains, perhaps with shallow valleys weakly etched below gentle rises which stand upon the more durable formations. Vanished, too, are most of the flatly-disposed nappe structures of the higher levels of fold-mountains: only contorted bedrock structures now testify to the previous existence of mountains, and the steep dips upon these, whether of sediments, schist or gneiss, attest the presence of deeper levels of mountain-building now exposed at the surface of the earth.

If this were all that is to be said concerning denuded mountain chains they would afford little interest to modern topographers, but the stumps of ancient mountains erased from the landscape by denudation, are sometimes re-elevated by fresh tectonic forces into new highlands.

Disregarding those sites where renewed subsidence after a first orogenic cycle has created a fresh geosyncline, which in due course has produced entirely new fold mountain structures (as about the Pacific margins), ancient and indurated mountain chains, denuded to lowlands, are not infrequently re-elevated by the application of vertical forces into either arched cymatogens or assemblages of block-mountains, the boundaries of which are defined by steeply-dipping earth fractures. Apparently, rock systems already tightly plicated and consolidated into a rigid foundation seldom crumple again in the same manner. They yield either by laminar flow over a broad zone or by brittle fracture. The new structures may be quite independent of the old fold axes which they transect at any angle. The summits of such highlands often exhibit erosional summit planes either broadly warped or sharply dislocated as in the Rocky and Bighorn Mountains of Wyoming.

Classic examples of ancient fold ranges rejuvenated as horst massifs in the scenery of late geological periods are provided by the Palæozoic mountain systems of Europe. On a geological map of France, for instance, two principal older regions are prominent: the Armorican massif of Brittany and the Central Plateau. The latter, below the volcanic relief recently superimposed, is composed of granitic and gneissic rocks, mica schists and lesser Carboniferous sediments. In the Armorican massif Palæozoic rocks occupy an important place bordering the ridges of granite and crystalline phyllites (Abrard 1948). Both of these massifs behaved as welts during the Palæozoic, and were then folded, consolidated and rigidified, but have since behaved as horsts or bastions. The Ardenne and the Vosges are two smaller massifs of the same type, the latter constituting with the Black Forest a single Palæozoic massif that has subsequently been split into two parts by the Miocene graben of the Rhine, which is analogous in situation with the Limagne in the Central Massif of France. The Vosges also forms a prolongation of the Central Plateau from its north-eastern portion, the Morvan. The folds in the middle section have the same north-eastward trend, and between the two is the smaller massif of the Serre near Dole.

There is also a chain of grabens: Rhône-Saone, upper Rhine, lower Hesse, Oslo and Lake Mjosa grabens, which follow the direction of Mesozoic Saxonian foldings instead of the original Palæozoic strikes, in which lack of respect for fundamental lineaments they vie with the fractured borders of the horsts themselves.

CHAPTER XIV

THE MOUNTAIN RANGES OF MESOZOIC
AND CAINOZOIC TIME *

Distribution of Mesozoic and Cainozoic Mountain Ranges. The Circum-
vallation of Gondwanaland. The South American Cordillera. The
Mountains of West Antarctica. The Structure of New Zealand. New
Caledonia. New Guinea. The Himalaya. The Mountains of Iran.
Gondwana Circumvallation in the Eastern Mediterranean Region. The
Atlas Mountains. The Circumvallation of Laurasia. The Cordillera, Rocky
Mountains and Coast Ranges of North America. The Circumvallation in
Eastern Asia. South-East Asia. The Yunnan-Karakoram Mountain
Belt and the Tibetan Plateau. The Circumvallation in Europe.
Conclusion.

DISTRIBUTION OF MESOZOIC AND CAINOZOIC MOUNTAIN RANGES

Late-Mesozoic and Cainozoic orogenic systems engirdle the two primeval continents,
Gondwana and Laurasia, and are therefore disposed globally in a large figure eight.
Along the mid-section the two opposed systems are sometimes welded back to back as
in the Himalaya-Tibet, sometimes with a median mass interposed, as the plateau of
Iran between the Elburz (northern) and Zagros (southern) mountain systems or the
Hungarian Basin between the Carpathians and the Dinaric Alps.

Each of the orogenic girdles stands upon older orogenic foundations, and the
stumps of Palæozoic welts appear within the Alps, Himalaya, East Asiatic island arcs,
Andes, Atlas and New Guinea. Even older systems may locally be disclosed, as for
instance the crumpled, Precambrian Belt series of the North American Cordillera,
but these are mostly buried beneath the younger geosynclinal series.

The two great cinctures (Figs. 176, 177) are each so long that mountain-making
has not been synchronous throughout their length. Even general earth stresses may be
resolved by failure at different points successively as well as simultaneously, owing to
crustal heterogeneity, to the quasi-independence and wide sundering of continents
achieved during the late Mesozoic (Chapter II), and to their subsequent differences of
aspect and structural detail. Thus though major orogenic phases such as the Laramide
towards the end of the Cretaceous or the Alpine movements at the close of the Oligocene
are continuous over thousands of miles, there are also numerous minor phases of local

* Modern mountain chains, of Quaternary age, are referred for consideration to the next chapter,
but readers interested to follow the Cainozoic orogenic history of a given region into Quaternary time may
do so conveniently as regional descriptions follow in the same order.

importance, and the general tectonic picture is of intermittent local activity with something going on somewhere most of the time, punctuated by a few *tuttis* when great lengths of the girdles were involved simultaneously.

Between the various orogenic phases, planation of elevated mountain ranges often reached an advanced stage, *e.g.* the late-Cretaceous planation that obliterated the Hokonui fold mountain system (earliest Cretaceous) of New Zealand.

On the whole, the Triassic was a period of quiescence, the late Jurassic one of strong activity about the Pacific margin, the early-Cretaceous period provided a static interval, while the late Cretaceous was a time of general activity which was not repeated until the mid Cainozoic when powerful dislocations afflicted the mid-section from the Alps to the Himalaya. By the end of the Cainozoic era denudation had erased the mountains of mid-Cainozoic time; but many of the welts were then re-elevated with little rock deformation as broad (cymatogenic) arches (Chapter XV), and movement of this kind has been sustained locally into recent time.

From time to time secondary flanking geosynclines were generated alongside the elevated tracts. The late-Jurassic rise of the North American Sierra Nevada, for instance, was accompanied by subsidence of both the Rocky Mountain geosyncline to the east and the Coast Range geosyncline to the west. Each of these has pursued its subsequent evolution semi-independently.

Special and profound geographical changes accompanied the Mesozoic circumvallations when Gondwana and Laurasia rifted into the present continental blocks. Thus major rivers that had previously flowed into the proto-Pacific were shut off by the newly-risen mountain chains and diverted to the newly-born Atlantic and Indian Oceans (Chapter XVII). At present the drainage to the Pacific Ocean is one fourth that draining into the Atlantic, though the latter ocean is half its size. The diversions may even include one or two reversals, chief of which is the Amazon, an ancient Gondwana waterway which presumably had drained part of Africa as well as South America *to the west*.

The Circumvallation of Gondwanaland

All peripheral segments of Gondwanaland are bordered by mountain structures of Mesozoic and Cainozoic age, commonly re-elevated during late-Cainozoic and Quaternary time to provide the present mountainlands there.

The Andes, commanding the entire western aspect of South America, curve at the southern extremity eastward through Tierra del Fuego into the islands of the Scotia arc (p. 593) and recurve thence once more into Graham Land, where allied ranges build the territory of West Antarctica to King Edward VII Land. After a gap the circumvallation picks up again through New Zealand, New Caledonia and New Guinea, all with related structures; but it is lost in Indonesia, the structures of which belong to Asia. It re-appears at the mountain syntaxis of Assam, and is sustained thence to the west as the Himalayan arc bordering the Indian sector of Gondwanaland, and continuing through Baluchistan, Mekran, the Zagros chains into Kurdistan and the Taurus of Asia Minor.   Through the mountains of Greece and the Dinaric Alps the girdle has been torn from Gondwanaland and welded on to Europe (p. 488), though its structures remain directed towards Gondwanaland.

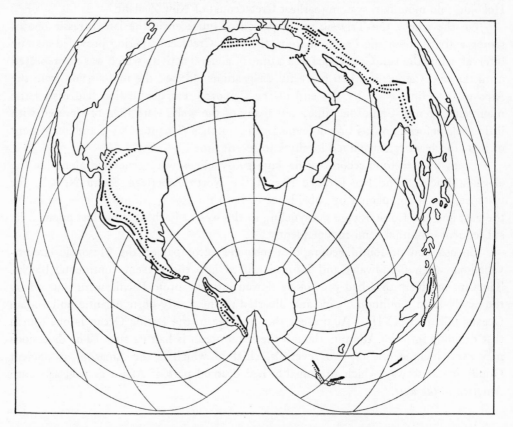

FIG. 176.   The circumvallation of Gondwanaland during Mesozoic (heavy line) and Cainozoic (dotted) time.   *modified after A. Holmes* (1929).

The structures are recovered to Africa at the shores of Tunis (Figs. 188, 189) and continue to the Moroccan Atlas where they are lost in the continental shelf.   They could not continue to exist away from continental basement upon the bed of the Atlantic Ocean, and soundings indeed prove this absence, but Mesozoic and Cainozoic mountain structures may again be picked up in Trinidad, Margarita Island and the Venezuelan Andes to complete the circumvallation.

The gaps in this great ring between each continent and the next are clearly due to separation of the several portions of Gondwanaland after its disruption (Fig. 176).   In its original state the ring must have been complete.

The cordillera (Fig. 173) make a double range, a western range of marine Mesozoic and later volcanic rocks with an elongated batholithic core, and an eastern chain of folded sedimentary, often Palæozoic, rocks like those of the shield to the east and occasionally with a core of basement granites and schists.   Thus in continental section from west to east may appear: stumps, perhaps Variscan, of older Pacific coast mountains;

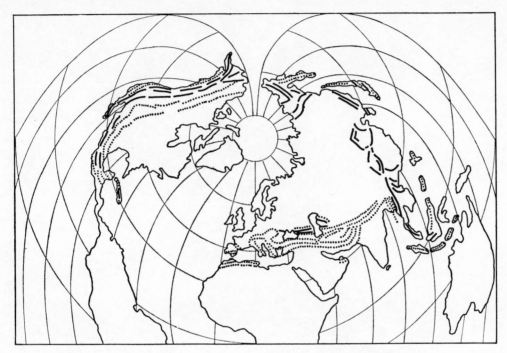

FIG. 177.   The circumvallation of Laurasia during Mesozoic (heavy line) and Cainozoic (dotted) time.   *modified after A. Holmes* (1929).

the western cordillera, crowned with volcanoes; the sedimentary and generally non-volcanic eastern cordillera, with front ranges to the east; the sub-Andean depression, filled with Cainozoic and Quaternary alluvia; and the old land of the Gondwana Shield.

Some eastward thrust towards the old land is shown by the westerly inclination of fold axes and thrust faults, and the eastern face of the ranges is often abrupt, as above the Gran Chaco.   In the plateau country of Peru the Andean folds are fairly open, becoming tighter with more overthrusts as the axis of the western ranges is approached, and this condition is fairly general.   Except in Venezuela and Colombia, where " between Mutiscua and Pamplona the crystalline rocks are pushed eastwards over the Cretaceous ", *nappes de charriage* are not known in the Andes; and only occasionally do inliers of the older rocks make large masses.   Largest is the Sierra Pampeanas of

Argentina, and in the north the Macarena swell and the Sierra da Santa Marta bordering the Caribbean Sea.

Except for the activity in the eastern ranges of Ecuador and the latent forces of the Central Cordillera of Colombia, volcanism is restricted to the western ranges facing the

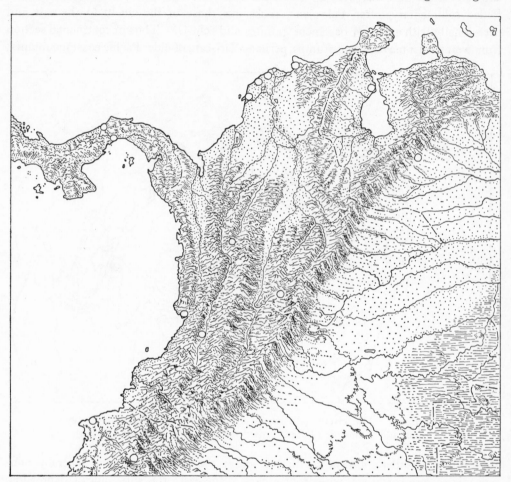

FIG. 178. Fraying out of the northern chains of the Andean mountain system. *after G.-H. Smith.*

Pacific. Andesites predominate; basaltic lavas appear only in isolated cones, mainly amid the southern ranges.

The double chains of the Andes fray out at the northern end (Fig. 178) so that through Colombia the volcanic cordillera swings north-west to join with the Cainozoic volcanic terrains of Panama. The eastern chain bifurcates, the Cordillera Real of Ecuador continuing into Colombia as the Cordillera Central with the Cordillera Oriental of Colombia branching off from it as a separate range at lat. 2° N. The Cordillera

Oriental, after sending a branch into the Guajira Peninsula, swings eastward through the Cordillera de Merida of Venezuela to a supposed insertion with the Antilles near Carupano.*

Through Ecuador the zone of the Andes is narrow, in places less than 100 km. wide; but the inter-Andean plateau rises majestically for some 3,000 metres above the Coastal and Oriente plains and above this plateau soar Ecuador's two rows of volcanic peaks, surmounting the Cordilleras Occidental and Real respectively. Chimborazo (6,310 metres) is the highest of the former, and Cotopaxi (5,943 metres) of the latter. Volcanic activity has almost ceased in the western range, but five of the major peaks on the Cordillera Real have been active in historic times. Upon the plateau which is largely built of tuffs and lavas, several independent basins such as the Quito Basin contain Miocene or Pliocene sediments several hundreds of metres thick and greatly folded. These sediments correspond with those on the Altiplano of Bolivia, farther to the south, where the sub-parallel Andean chains diverge for a space and enclose a high plateau basin, lacking outflow beyond the ranges.

Minor ranges rise from the Oriente plains, east of the Andean front. The Sierra de Cutucu, a continuation of the Cordillera del Condor and Cordillera Oriental of Peru, is heavily injected by igneous material, and extremely faulted and broken along its western edge where the synclinal depression separating it from the Cordillera Real is occupied by the Rio Upano (Oppenheim 1950).

The front ranges of the Andes in Bolivia, where the mountains are at their widest, and reach farthest east, have been studied by Mather (1922). They compare closely in appearance with the front ranges of the Rockies. The ranges to north and south of the Sierra de Charagua, which is the most easterly, lie successively *en echelon* a few miles behind one another. All have cuestas and hogbacks of Cretaceous sandstone on their eastern flanks, forms reminiscent of the Dakota sandstone of the United States, and these are frequently followed by early-Cainozoic terrestrial beds with flattening dip. But the fronts of the ranges themselves are usually steep, sometimes precipitous where faulted. The summits are often level (Sierra de Florida), sometimes serrate but accordant (Sierra de Limon) at 1,600 or 2,000 metres. All are traversed by narrow antecedent gorges (Chapter XV) even of streams which rise just behind the front ranges themselves. Noteworthy are the gorges of the Sierra de Aguarage. Subsequent tributaries have etched out the lowland separating the front ranges from the eastern Cordillera. About lat. 19° S. stands the divide between the Rio Grande, which is eventually tributary to the Amazon, and the Rio Philcomayo, which contributes to the Paraguay and Rio Plata. This point is almost opposite the most westerly visible extension of the Gondwana basement before it sinks beneath the sub-Andean depression.

The sub-Andean sierras of north-western Argentina continue the Bolivian sierras to the south at elevations rarely exceeding 1,000 metres. These sierras, which are

---

* Lees (1952) however, finds no support for bending of the east-west Northern structures of Trinidad into the Antillean arc, instead they seem to disappear into the ocean.

2 G

separated by a depression on the east from the accumulations of the Chaco, have a nucleus of Precambrian rocks showing their affinity with the shield, and also Mesozoic and Cainozoic rocks which link their later history with the Andean episodes.

The main line of the Andes continues majestically through north-western Argentina with the Puna de Atacama dotted with giant salars. But south of Copiapo the zone narrows and despite the climb it is crossed in less than an hour by aeroplane from Santiago to Mendoza. From Aconcagua (23,081 feet), the highest point in the western hemisphere, the ranges decline until beyond Lake Nahuel Huapi the typical Andean structure involving geosynclinal Mesozoic rocks is lost, though mountainous terrain continues with different components as the Cordillera Patagonica. This cordillera was subjected to various movements of different intensities. There is a zone of Palæozoic folding which is found as far south as Magellanes, and south of the Gulf of Penas is a huge granodioritic batholith associated with late-Cretaceous orogeny; but the region has also experienced to some extent the Cainozoic phases of Andean mountain-making. Suess regarded the oldest members of the batholith as equivalent to the North American (Nevadan) granodiorite, but many members are present, of various ages, even into Graham Land.

Contemporaneously with the mid- and late-Cretaceous movements that initiated the Andean orogenesis in the north, the discrete elements of the Patagonian region between the Gulfs of San Matias and San Jorge were welded together. The same structures continue from beneath the mesetas and terraces of volcanic rocks into the relief of the continental shelf.

Four distinct tectonic stages have marked the evolution of the Andean cordilleras. The earliest movements occurred in the late-Cretaceous,* following the accumulation of Cretaceous (Aptian-Senonian) limestones with succeeding gypsiferous sandstones and shales that are regularly found in the Andes, especially upon the flanks of the ranges. These movements were effective chiefly in the north where the geosynclinal seaways were finally excluded from the region, in the south (Magellanes) there was uninterrupted deposition. At this time the dominant folds and faults of the system were initiated and received their first impulses, and movement probably began upon the fractures that later became the great overthrusts of the region. Volcanic activity was already widespread and had, indeed, appeared as lava flows with beds of tuff and breccia through all but the later part of the Mesozoic era.

The date of thrusting in Venezuela is end-Cretaceous (Laramide), agreeing with the tectonics of the Rocky Mountains and the Antilles but differing significantly from the earlier folding of the rest of the Andean welt. The Central and Western Cordilleras played a relatively passive rôle during the Laramide orogeny. These facts suggest that the present geographic relations of the Americas, following upon the disruption of

---

* According to Arkell (1956) Jurassic orogenesis did not occur in South America (a marked contrast with North America); notwithstanding minor movements were not altogether absent from the cordilleran zone during that period.

Laurasia and Gondwana were assumed late in the Cretaceous period. Following the Laramide disturbance large-scale breaking down under faulting allowed deep subsidence of several areas in Venezuela, and Cainozoic beds over 10,000 feet thick are known. Continued independence from the Andean tectonics, and conformity with the Antillean region is there displayed by early- or pre-Pliocene orogeny, short but violent, in the Maturin Basin " which folded and faulted the older beds and led to a general transgression of Pliocene brackish water sediments ".

There is no evidence of widespread marine submergence, and certainly no marine geosynclinal environment, over the site of the Andes later than the Mesozoic; but deposition of fluviatile and shallow-water lacustrine facies was resumed on an irregular landsurface, and early-Cainozoic formations are widespread. There are very thick red beds of this age in both the western cordillera (McLaughlin 1924) and in the upper Ucayali River to the east. In the Altiplano, too, are flysch-like early-Cainozoic deposits of enormous thickness. All these deposits were closely folded in the Oligocene and again in the Miocene.

The second set of Andean movements reached a climax in the early Oligocene, when the Cainozoic sediments also were involved and the eastern Cordillera came into being. The volcanic unrest which still persists amid the present Andes began at that time with mudflows and explosive outbursts on the western ranges, blanketing the country with tuff.

Further strong movements of the third Andean phase, renewing the folding and faulting chiefly along old lines, occurred in the Miocene. They were accompanied by great igneous activity, and the main phase of Andean intrusion. These rocks now make up a large proportion of the western foothills of the Andes. Following these events, nearly the whole Andean landscape was reduced by erosion to a partly-bevelled mature-land (Puna surface) with hill residuals and plateaus from 1,000-1,500 feet higher in some localities. Upon the Puna surface appear local deposits of river and lake environment, containing abundant late-Pliocene mammalian fossils characteristic of low altitude. Of the magnificent ranges of today, nothing existed towards the close of the Cainozoic era.

The fourth Andean elevation is of early-Pleistocene date and consisted of a violent cymatogenic uparching of the ranges as a whole accompanied by extensive block-faulting which is not in harmony with earlier structural axes. This created the modern Andes, which are discussed in Chapter XV.

Oppenheim (1948) has regarded the Cainozoic Andean structure as the final stage in development of a late-Mesozoic island arc, of igneous composition, separated from the mainland by a geosynclinal depression and bordered on the oceanic side by a deep trough. This structure appeared at the Cretaceous, or first, stage of Andean orogenesis; since when the western outline of the continent has not changed much. Gradually by the beginning of the Cainozoic era, the connections were made between the partly volcanic islands until a more or less continuous outer mountain rampart existed, and the geosyncline was filled up with sediments, partly sands derived from the mainland, partly limestones of thalassic origin. By the early Oligocene the burthen was complete and in two great successive heaves the eastern sedimentary line of the Andes came into being before the mid-Cainozoic, and the whole structure was welded together. These mountains, perhaps not so impressive as the modern ranges, were reduced under erosion to a hill-dotted terrain by the end of the Pliocene.

The coast ranges of Peru and Chile appearing as isolated ridges in the north increase in strength southward until they form long, continuous ranges separated from the Andean chains by the Tarapaca and Atacama deserts, world-famous source of nitrates. The coast ranges appear to be remnants of a geanticline, for Archean rock basement crops out locally with Mesozoic rocks lying autochthonously upon it to the east. Where the coast ranges are absent, as between Paracas, lat. 14° S., and Cabo Tablas at 32° S. near Valparaiso, the Mesozoic rocks reach the sea. The grain is slightly oblique to later Andean structures and to the coast, causing both geologic and physiographic complexity.

Cretaceous and Cainozoic sediments composing the coastal belt of Ecuador are of shallow water deposition. As the Cainozoic alone is about 700 metres thick a slow continuous subsidence is indicated for the coastal region throughout most of Cainozoic time. Numerous igneous intrusions accompany the Cretaceous and early-Cainozoic beds of the coastal belt, and appear to be associated with the second or main episode of Andean orogeny; but in Colombia similar rocks are related to the intense late-Cretaceous diastrophism when the western cordillera rose for the first time.

From lat. 25° S., to the Chilean islands at 41° S., extends a coastal chain, the Cordillera Costanera, composed of ancient, possibly shield-type rocks elevated by the Andean movements. Most of Tierra del Fuego also is composed of Archean rocks like the Chilean Coast Ranges, with granodiorite corresponding perhaps with the Andean batholith. There are few andesites. With the coastal outcrops of Palæozoic and older rocks to the north the exposures of the Cordillera Costanera are of great importance in defining the boundaries of primitive Gondwanaland right to the western coast of South America.

The Mountains of West Antarctica

The Andean orogenic welt emerging from Tierra del Fuego is apparently linked through the recurved Scotia arc of islands (p. 609) with the Graham Land sector of West Antarctica so that the structures of the two continents confront each other across Drake Strait almost as mirror images. In the south, Fairbridge (1952) distinguishes two tectonic zones: firstly, the cordilleran belt of the Scotia arc and western Graham Land comprising a multiple chain of folds each differing somewhat from the others and built of folded Palæozoic and Mesozoic geosynclinal sediments (especially the flysch-greywacke-spilite lava suite) intruded by extensive granodioritic and gabbroidal rocks of Andean character (Adie 1962). Mudstones and grits, with limestones, resting upon granite in Alexander I Island display a northern neritic shelf-facies (late Jurassic to early Cretaceous) and tend to be thrust eastward in nappes by Cretaceous earth movements. The Mesozoic igneous assemblage of this zone is identical with the Mesozoic " Porphyry Formation " of Patagonia and Tierra del Fuego, and Recent volcanoes with basaltic, andesitic and dacitic lavas are also a feature along the northern aspect of this zone.

Behind the volcanic fold rampart stand the tablelands of Fairbridge's second zone found in eastern Graham Land and Hearst Land where neritic late-Mesozoic and Cainozoic sediments are scarcely folded but are locally faulted and cut by plateau basalts. Senonian marine fossils from Snow Hill not only indicate a warm climate but are of Indo-Pacific, not Atlantic, affinity (Reed 1949) (p. 616). Eocene-Oligocene floras, preserved in 500 feet of continental conglomerates and sandstones are of southern temperate type including *Notofagus* and *Araucaria*, as are the mollusca of the late Oligocene to early Miocene.

The region of James Ross Island is smothered in basaltic flows and palagonite tuffs which, being of aqueous accumulation, sometimes contain Oligocene beech leaves. Similar volcanics with identical leaves appear also upon the western coast from Cape Melville to Boyd Strait, and great sheets of presumably related dolerite cut the granodiorites of the axial range. Despite the abundant volcanic effusions mid-Cainozoic diastrophism seems to have been slight in the Graham Land region for dips are only $7°$-$10°$ towards the Weddell Sea.

The latest deposit of the Weddell Sea region, the " Pecten Conglomerate ", duplicates the Cape Fairweather beds of Patagonia and is deemed to be of late-Pliocene age. The elevation of the Graham Land plateau by warping and faulting may thus be dated as Plio-Pleistocene. The eastern scarp of the plateau is straight and relatively little dissected opposite the Larsen Ice Shelf.

In latitude $78°$ S. the sharply peaked Ellsworth Mountains " are composed of a thick sequence of deformed sedimentary rocks ". Orogeny has deformed these strata, which are of early-Palæozoic age, into asymmetic and even recumbent folds with production of a metamorphic facies (Cradock, Anderson and Webers 1965). Quite different are the rock series (basement complex and overlying volcanic series) of the Jones Mountains, inland from the Eights Coast. Potassium-argon age determinations for these rocks range from late-Palæozoic to late-Mesozoic, with late-Cainozoic for the overlying olivine basalt (Cradock, Bastien and Rutford 1965).

In Marie Byrd Land, Wade found 15,000 feet of highly contorted sediments matching the greywacke-shale sequence of the Graham Land geosyncline. Intrusive into these in the cores of the Rockefeller and Edsel Ford Ranges are granodiorites and other igneous rock types resembling those of Graham Land and the Andes. Intrusion apparently occurred before folding was complete, though after the rocks were regionally metamorphosed, for contacts are sharp. Much later came Recent volcanic activity, basaltic flows together with cinder cones and small craters aligned along the axis of the Raymond Forsdick Range. Southward of the strike of the Edsel Ford Range, in King Edward VII Land, the rocks are considered by Stewart to match the shield facies of

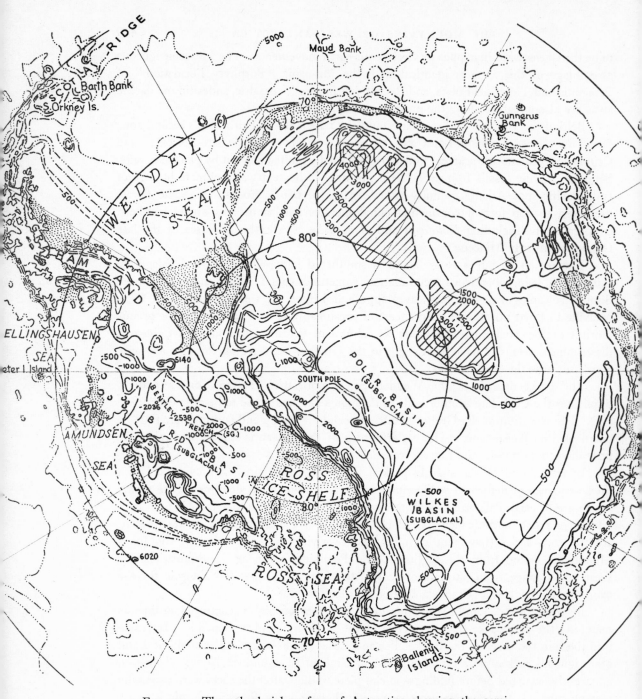

Fig. 179. The sub-glacial surface of Antarctica showing the semi-circular shield area and the outlying masses of Graham Land and Marie Byrd Land. The form of the bedrock surface shows intense cymatogenic deformation which is of immediately pre-glacial (end Cainozoic) age (King 1966). *Redrawn from inset Map of Antarctica, Geog. Review.*

South Victoria Land on the opposite side of the Ross Sea. Both granite and two specimens of Beacon Sandstone type have been recorded. Fairbridge therefore concluded that the meeting of the Palæozoic-Mesozoic fold belts with the shield lies within West Antarctica. A portion of the fold-girdle is here detached from the body of Antarctica (Fig. 179) and is displaced eastward along a transcurrent fault, marked by the Bentley Trench, passing from the Ross Barrier to the Bellingshausen Sea.

From West Antarctica a gap of 2,500 miles, produced by drifting apart of continental masses, ensues before the Gondwana circumvallation is again encountered in New Zealand.

THE STRUCTURE OF NEW ZEALAND

The girdle of Mesozoic greywackes and argillites, highly contorted and locally overlain by substantial thicknesses of Cainozoic sediments with volcanics, form the foundation of the islands, where MacPherson's (1945) splendid analysis affords the basis of modern tectonic discussion carried forward by Lillie (1951), Wellman (1956) and Kingma (1959). According to MacPherson the major islands of the Dominion stand at the convergence of three submarine ridges, two of them extending north-westward beneath the Tasman Sea and the third southward towards Macquarie Island (Fig. 174). The whole structure makes " a recurved arc with maximum convexities directed towards the western Pacific margin on the north-east and the East Australian Basin on the south-west " (Fig. 180). Transverse faults and earthquake shocks of shallow and intermediate depth are related to regions of maximum curvature, and volcanism is confined to the concave portions of the arc.

Following a preliminary phase in the middle Jurassic when large recumbent folds were formed; the orogenic maximum occurred at the dawn of the Cretaceous when, in the post-Hokonui (Rangitata) orogeny, practically all earlier formations embracing a vast thickness of late-Palæozoic, Triassic and Jurassic greywackes and argillites was isoclinally folded throughout the length and breadth of both islands; later a third phase of folding and faulting accompanied strong uplift, and the Alpine fault began to grow. Schist formation was prominent in the South Island during the orogenic phases, and garnet, biotite and amphibole porphyroblasts grew in isograds during the static phases between (Grindley 1963a). This contorted mass has subsequently operated as foundation to both islands. Younger formations (Cretaceous and Cainozoic) rest upon it, always with marked unconformity so that Cotton (1916) expressed the relation between pre-Cretaceous and later rocks as of " older mass and cover ". Benson (1936) has stressed the occurrence of a " Cretaceous peneplain " between the series.

Through most of the Cainozoic era the axial portions of both North and South Islands have exercised a geanticlinal rôle, with flanking geosynclines to east and west. The eastern geosyncline extends from the Bay of Plenty to Otago. The oldest sediments, occurring in Hawkes Bay, are Aptian and apparently of restricted distribution. The widespread cover begins with the late-Senonian group which may exceed 10,000 feet

FIG. 180. The recurved structural arc of New Zealand with major fault systems. *after J. T. Kingma.*

thickness in Hawkes Bay. Altogether, with the overlying Cainozoic, a section of over 25,000 feet of sediment was built up in the eastern geosyncline. Southward the sediments thin progressively through Marlborough and Canterbury to Otago. Sedimentation was frequently interrupted and recurrent mobility was a feature of this heterogeneous geosyncline.

Macpherson is positive that this geosyncline does not continue north-eastward beyond East Cape to the Kermadec region but swings north-westward from Lake Waikaremoana to Whakatane to be parallel with the North Auckland Peninsula, where similar lithologic groups appear in the Cretaceous. This contention is supported by the submarine contours which show a sea-floor ridge extending thence to Norfolk Island and pointing in the direction of New Caledonia and New Guinea (Fig. 174). North-eastward of Lake Waikaremoana, where the deflection of strike is most marked, occurs the Taitai overthrust whereon Aptian sediments are carried eastward for 40 miles across Santonian formations along a front of 100 miles.

The western geosyncline between North Auckland and Rangitikei is multiple, consisting probably of five folds of which the most easterly appears to be the oldest and primary. " The secondary folds are defined by greywacke basement folds with terrestrial Eocene and younger marine sediments enveloping these basement cores " (Macpherson). In south-eastern Taranaki where the Cainozoic sediments are much thicker gravimetric observations have revealed " high basement folds with thin crestal sections and thick adjacent synclinal sections ". Though the fold-axes may have been pre-determined to some extent by earlier trends of the post-Hokonui orogeny, all are described by Macpherson as " late-Cretaceous and Tertiary basement folds developed on a subdued mature land of lower- and middle-Mesozoic rocks ". Diastrophism was continued throughout the Cainozoic, as shown by discordances in the late-Cretaceous and Cainozoic formations that envelope the basement folds (Fig. 181).

The arcuate structure of the North Island has pronounced volcanic associations.

The reversed arc of the South Island (Fig. 180) is best expressed in the swinging strike of the late-Palæozoic and Mesozoic rocks, including the Otago schists, which form the axis of the arc. Late-Cretaceous and Cainozoic geosynclines again appear on either side of this axis. The eastern geosyncline through Canterbury and north-eastern Otago exhibits successively younger formations within the concavity of the arc towards the east and north-east; while discordances within the sequence indicate growth of the structure by recurrent orogenic impulses since late-Cretaceous time. Much volcanism appears within the arc. Speight regarded it as recurrent from the Triassic until Recent time.

The western geosyncline has been described for Westland by Gage (1949). The sediments accumulated from late-Cretaceous until mid-Oligocene within a narrow furrow that subsequently rose intermittently until now it forms the anticlinal Paparoa Range. As this developed, a new furrow sank immediately east of it to receive early-Miocene to Recent sediment. Both furrows were far too narrow to rank as independent geosynclines, though the term may be applied to the region as a whole. In Southland the western geosyncline is represented by sediments of the Clifden area. The boundary of the structure may be taken where Mesozoic rocks of the Nuggets group are overfolded and overridden to the south-west by the Otago schists.

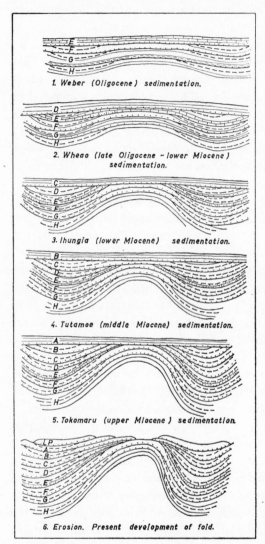

1. Weber (Oligocene) sedimentation.

2. Wheao (late Oligocene - lower Miocene) sedimentation.

3. Ihungia (lower Miocene) sedimentation.

4. Tutamoe (middle Miocene) sedimentation.

5. Tokomaru (upper Miocene) sedimentation.

6. Erosion. Present development of fold.

Recurving of the New Zealand arc is apparently responsible for the *Alpine Fault*, which defines the western slope of the Southern Alps and has been traced from Fiordland to Cook Strait (Wellman 1956; Suggate 1963). Transcurrent movement along the fault is estimated at 200-300 miles with the western side moving northward so that the ancient and schistose rocks of North-west Nelson have been divorced from their relatives in Fiordland. Though the Alpine Fault probably originated in the late Jurassic and early Cretaceous periods, at the time the New Zealand compound arc was formed, it is still active at the present day for glacial beds not more than 100,000 years old have been overthrust along it by schist in the Mount Brown area. Wellman and Willett also describe youthful river courses near Jackson Bay as

FIG. 181

Progressive growth of basement folds, arches and depressions during the Cainozoic era in the eastern New Zealand geosyncline (Hawkes Bay). *after* E. O. Macpherson.

displaced 0·8 miles by lateral movement along the Fault which they compare with Kennedy's description of the Great Glen Fault of Scotland. Vertical displacement upon the Alpine Fault since middle-Pliocene time amounts to 10,000 feet, thereby providing the magnificent western aspect of the Southern Alps.

The Cainozoic geosynclines of New Zealand have been mildly heterogeneous in their activity. Their history involves recurrent brief tectonic impulses, usually upon already established lines, so that certain areas continued to be depressed as synclines while others were intermittently raised. The bedrock is crumpled by purely vertical movement (presumably laminar) into sharp-crested anticlines which persist and are steepened from stage to stage, sometimes to 7,000 or 8,000 feet above the troughs of adjacent synclines. The crests are sometimes exposed, sometimes buried by sediments to be revealed at shallow depths by gravimeter, in a structure very similar to the folding of Cretaceous beds within the Benue Rift of Africa (p. 270). The basement relief increased progressively from late-Cretaceous time, and mainly from post Oligocene to late Pliocene (Fig. 181).

While discordances and overlaps to the number of ten or eleven, may be pronounced and obvious about the crests and on the flanks of the domes and anticlines, " In adjoining synclinal areas disconformity, blended unconformities, mild erosion intervals, or no obvious sedimentary break are observed ". Classification* of the Paleocene to Pleistocene deposits into seven series with twenty-three stages is itself a reflection of the disturbed state of sedimentation over this interval of time.

Thus New Zealand developed as a result of sustained, essentially vertical displacements. The sedimentational phases were pronounced when the whole geanticline subsided, and the ridges of the previous orogenic impulse were buried; sedimentational breaks over structural highs and changes of lithology follow the orogenic impulses. Sedimentation and orogenesis, interacted over a long period, and each apparently contributed to the other (Fig. 181).

The late-Cretaceous and Cainozoic diastrophic history of New Zealand thus begins with sinking of the subdued mid- or late-Cretaceous landscape on either side of a median land ridge to form the eastern and western geosynclines. The early sediments are fine-grained, light coloured and sometimes chemically precipitated. Only in the Hawk's Crag and Kaitangata breccias, 3,000 feet thick, are violent impulses recorded. Persistent quiet accumulation of fine-grained sediments, spreading ever wider, continued till the close of the Oligocene, interrupted only by gentle deformations in latest-Cretaceous, Eocene and intra-Oligocene epochs. Though slight, these impulses decided the location of major folds throughout the Cainozoic and by the mid-Oligocene the major structural plan of New Zealand was established, being confirmed by the stronger dislocations of the post-Oligocene orogeny.

Subsequently to the Oligocene, " the median land, ancestral New Zealand, began to grow by a succession of orogenies " becoming ever more clearly defined and progressively elevated to the hilly and mountainous country that is New Zealand today. In the Neogene also the sediments have darker hues, terrigenous materials increased and though sedimentational records indicate expanding seas the spread of waters is not, as formerly, over a widespread lowland but is controlled by the outlines of rising ranges. In the Pliocene the sea area attained its maximum and the median land was narrow in its central and northern extent.

* By the New Zealand Geological Survey.

The intensity of successive orogenic phases, three in the Miocene and three in the Pliocene increased, however, until folding was superseded in the late-Pliocene and Pleistocene by heavy block-faulting of the " Kaikoura diastrophism " which broke up much of the Cainozoic structure, (throws on certain of the faults breaking Pliocene strata exceed 5,000 feet in many places), and though the faults are often associated with

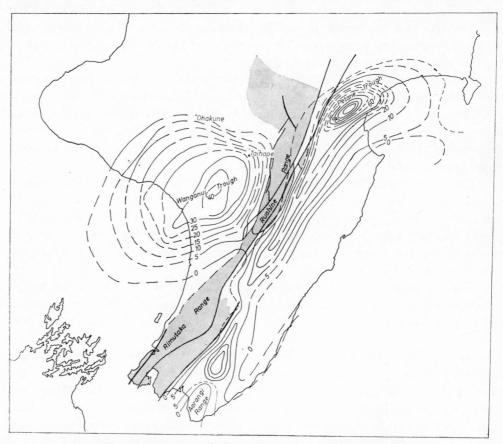

FIG. 182. New Zealand : the Wanganui and Petane troughs containing 4,000 and 10,000 feet thicknesses of Pleistocene sediments respectively (contours in 100's of feet) with the Ruahine Range raised simultaneously between them by " lemon pip " tectonics (Fig. 46). *after J. T. Kingma.*

folds the development and appearance of the region were thereafter radically altered. Most remarkable was the manner in which the Cainozoic geanticlinal sank in its middle section beneath the compound Wanganui-Petane depression within which maxima of 4,000 and 10,000 feet of Nukumaruan (Pleistocene) sediments were laid. At the same time the Rimutaka-Ruahine horst rose as a piercement structure (Kingma 1959) so that the difference of elevation between the Pliocene floor of the Wanganui depression and the eroded crest of the ranges is 20,000 feet (Fig. 182). The older rocks of the horst have a density greater than that of the adjacent late sediments and the structure therefore cannot be due to levity. Kingma has shown that the eastern side is bounded by vertical faults, the western by reversed faults dipping beneath the mass at 70-80°. The mass therefore wedges downwards and must have been forced up (but without imbalance that could be revealed by isostatic anomaly) by local "lemon pip" compression associated with the sinking geosynclinal floors on either side (Fig. 46).

It is to the Kaikoura diastrophism, that New Zealand owes most of its present rugged physiography (p. 523). Marked gravity anomalies and recurrent earthquakes suggest that pronounced differential movement is likely to continue.

NEW CALEDONIA

The Lord Howe submarine ridge is thought to have Palæozoic foundations like those of the western South Island of New Zealand. New Caledonia has in addition volcanic rocks that have been compared by Avias with late-Devonian and early-Carboniferous series of New South Wales and which also, according to the same authority, resemble the green, red and purple Tuapeka greywackes and Te Anau slates of New Zealand. But the most striking correspondences are in the late-Palæozoic-Mesozoic greywacke-argillite series that forms the backbone of the island structure. These flysch series can be divided into shelf and geosynclinal facies comparable with the Hokonui and Alpine facies in New Zealand. Though there are slight differences of age in the Triassic series, the general homology between the two island realms is beyond doubt. Marine Trias is absent, however, from Australia which experienced prior uplift, so that the two realms stand related as though the intervening part of the Tasman Sea had not been in existence during the Triassic period. Indeed, the sources for some east Australian late-Palæozoic and Triassic sediments appears to have lain east of the continent, and not in a volcanic island arc. On the hypothesis of continental drift, with Australia receding westward from the New Zealand-New Caledonia line during the Cretaceous period the Tasman and Papuan geosynclines of David become one (p. 543) (Fig. 175).

As in New Zealand, there is no break between Cretaceous and Eocene formations of New Caledonia; but thereafter differences in the Cainozoic stratigraphy multiply, notably with the abundance of Oligocene serpentinites and peridotites in New Caledonia and a paucity there of strata younger than Miocene.

Like Cyprus (Troodos Massif p. 17) New Caledonia has masses of ultrabasic mantle type rock that has " ridden over the adjoining continental crust instead of gliding beneath it " (Holmes 1964).

Macpherson has summed up the geotectonic affinities of New Caledonia by visualising it as a marginal part of a former Australasian continent that was practically continuous along the New Zealand-New Caledonia-New Guinea line until late-Cretaceous time. This concept, with which we agree, receives interpretation later (p. 649).

NEW GUINEA

The Mesozoic circumvallation appears again in the Louisiade and d'Entrecasteau archipelagoes and extends through the mountain backbone of New Guinea to Obi and the Soela Islands in the west.   Although mountains, often exceeding 10,000 feet, make a continuous divide throughout central and northern New Guinea, they do not belong to a single chain but form " a complex system of ranges of restricted length separated in places by broad upland valleys " (David 1950).   The cores of the ranges are occupied by large tracts of metamorphic rocks with minor igneous intrusions that are believed to be older than Mesozoic.

Palæozoic fossils have been found only in West Irian.   Triassic rocks are unknown in New Guinea, Obi and the Soela Islands; but the Jurassic is represented and, as in New Zealand and New Caledonia, earth movement inhibited deposition of the earliest

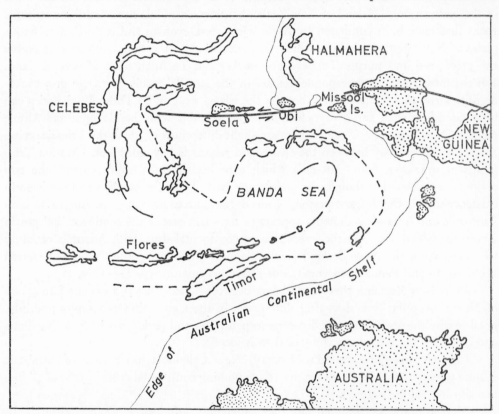

FIG. 183.   Relationship of New Guinea, Obi and Soela Islands with Gondwana geology (stippled) to the recurved Celebes arc of south-eastern Asia the geology of which is Laurasian.   Heavy line is the left lateral Sorong Fault Zone, deemed by some authorities to involve 300 miles of relative displacement.

Cretaceous. This is not so in the Indonesian geosyncline covering northern Celebes and Halmahera and calls in question the structural relations of Obi and Soela Islands. Deeply though these project into the recurved double arc of Indonesia, almost to Celebes, their geology, involving an inferred late-Palæozoic orogeny but no late-Triassic folding (David 1950), nevertheless assigns them to New Guinea (Fig. 183). The question arises whether this salient of the Gondwana mountain rim is not, indeed, the cause of the recurving of the Celebes arc. By contrast, the linking of the *Cainozoic* structures of the Vogelkop with the east Asiatic island arcs through Halmahera (Glaessner 1950) affords a clear indication that the New Guinea-Australia landmass assumed its position relative to the margin of south-east Asia at some date between the Triassic and the early Cainozoic. Even the known lower-Cretaceous faunas of New Guinea and New Caledonia, Glaessner observes, resemble those of Australia and New Zealand rather than those of Borneo and Sumatra, though all are related to the Indian faunas of that epoch. The Cainozoic marine faunas of New Guinea and the associated islands, on the contrary, exhibit remarkable correspondence with those of Indonesia. These datings and distributions are in accord with the chronology for the break up of Gondwanaland and the flight of the several fragments established in Chapter II. They may be compared with the datings which show, in similar manner, that South America assumed its present position with respect to the Antilles and North America also after the beginning and before the end of the Cretaceous period (p. 466). The extensive intrusions of serpentine in Celebes are late Jurassic or Cretaceous in age.

The Aptian sea returned to New Guinea as to New Caledonia and New Zealand and likewise sediments continued to accumulate locally until late in the Senonian epoch, the total Mesozoic thickness in Australian New Guinea being 16,000 feet. Cainozoic deposition followed until the mid-Oligocene when the coast and offshore region shallowed with much folding.

The principal Cainozoic eugeosyncline lies upon the northern flank of New Guinea whence it is directed through the Solomon and New Hebrides island arcs where any former continuation towards New Zealand (Macpherson 1946) is dislocated by trans-current faulting in the direction of Fiji (Fig. 240). A southern geosyncline is present only in the south-east near Port Moresby, where Eocene green tuffs, shales, and bands of sandstone with overlying Oligocene are invaded by serpentinites and gabbros providing a close correlation with New Caledonia. Some of the ultrabasic rocks have been described as " tectonically emplaced fragments of the peridotite mantle " (Krause 1965). On the Solomon Islands 95 *per cent* of the ultrabasics are harzburgites in a discontinuous belt 380 miles long. The area of New Guinea west of the Gulf of Papua, where Cainozoic rocks are not known, is generally regarded, however, as part of the Australian landmass.

In eastern New Guinea the twin geosynclines were maintained to north and south of the central ranges until the end of the Pliocene. Marine Miocene formations attain, indeed, a maximum thickness of 15,000 feet with pyroclastics and basaltic and andesitic lava flows on the southern flank of the Central ranges between Langimar Valley and

Rigo area.   Conformable Pliocene rocks, locally exceeding 6,000 feet in thickness, occupy disconnected basins; and Cainozoic sedimentation was terminated by powerful cymatogeny that produced before the Pleistocene period the great modern mountain ranges with their deeply incised valleys (Chapter XV).

Westward of New Guinea and Soela Islands, the fold-girdle of Gondwanaland is broken again; all the orogenic structures of Indonesia and most of Burma belong to the fold-girdle of Laurasia.   This corresponds with an absence of continental Gondwana

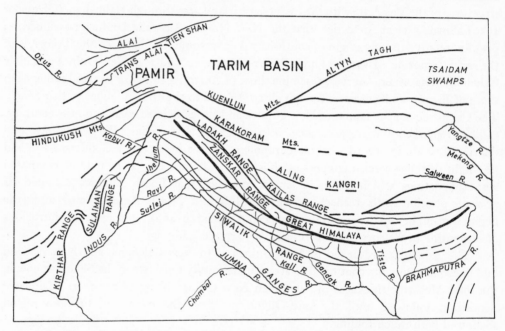

FIG. 184.   The wide zone of east-west mountain chains extending from India into Central Asia.   *after M. S. Krishnan.*

massifs from this region—the next remnant of that fractured landmass appears as India. In the Himalaya, therefore, must be sought the continuation of the Gondwana circumvallation.

THE HIMALAYA

The Himalaya forms the southern rampart of a wide zone of east-west mountain chains extending northward into Central Asia (Fig. 184).   Most of these mountains belong to Laurasia, but the Himalaya is structurally related to the foreland of India.   Thus, over a great distance, the fold-girdles of Laurasia and Gondwana here lie " back to back ", the line of differentiation between them being along the " crystalline zone " of the Tsangpo Valley.   The eastern extremity of the Himalayan arc in Assam with its south-eastwardly directed structures is matched across the Brahmaputra valley by the north-westwardly structures of the Patkai Range along the borders of Burma.   There

is also much evident similarity in the dates at which the reversed structures were achieved.
The region where the ranges meet is virtually inaccessible, but Lees's visual impression
from flying over it was that " The Naga (Patkai front) structures strike into the Himalayan
front and are overridden by it. There seemed no indication of a swing of strike from
one system into the other but rather that the Himalayas were dominant and were thrust
over their weaker neighbour ". The country between the Himalayan and Burmese
mountain arcs has been "sliced by cross-faults into blocks that have been pushed
southwards *en echelon* ". These relationships suggest a prolongation of the Gondwana
Shield north-eastward from the Rajmahal Hills, to the Shillong Plateau (5,000 feet)
and the Mikir Hills beyond (Lees 1952). The Plateau, which was peneplaned, consists of granite overlain by Cretaceous rocks ; and its attitude suggests that similar
rigid basement underlies the whole of the Brahmaputra alluvial valley between the two
great mountain systems. In the opposite direction, towards the Bay of Bengal, the
same basement, covered by an almost complete sequence of late-Mesozoic and Cainozoic
rocks, flexes steeply downwards from 5,000 feet above, to 20,000 or possibly even 30,000
feet below, sea level. There is much evidence that all these relationships came into
existence during the Cretaceous Period when Peninsular India is thought to have
assumed its present position with Asia.

The Patkai mountain arc that is convex towards India reverses its curvature in
the Arakan Yoma where not opposed by the Indian massif, and Krishnan has remarked
that the Andaman Sea took shape towards the end of the Cretaceous, which is also the
date of ultrabasic intrusions along the mountain arc.

In Burma (Krishnan 1953), the geology of the Shan States shows them to be a
part of the Yunnan-Indo China province of Laurasia; and that their proximity to
India was achieved only in post-Cretaceous times, as indicated by differences between
the Gondwana-type Cretaceous rocks of Assam and the Tethyan-type rocks of the
same age in Burma whose faunal affinities lie with Sind and Baluchistan. All these
observations are consistent with the hypothesis of the drift of India northwards from
Gondwana at that period, and that its eastward margin lies approximately along the
Burma-Assam frontier.

Throughout the 1,500 miles from Assam to Kashmir the curving trends of the
Himalaya are controlled by the shape of the Gondwanaland massif. Ultimately north-
west, the trend apparently ends at Nanga Parbat (26,620 feet), one of the highest peaks
of the central axis; but geological survey shows that the strikes make a hairpin bend
about that mountain first to the south and then south-west so that the structures, even
of individual fold-axes, continue unbroken about the Nanga Parbat focus into a new
trend directed through the Hissar Range towards Baluchistan. Thus it happens that
the geological structures of the Northwest Frontier Province mirror those of Kashmir
(Fig. 84). " The inflexion moreover is not confined to the central ranges only, but it
affects some 300 miles depth of the mountains from the Punjab piedmont to the Pamir
Plateau, which itself shares the same flexure " (Wadia 1937B). Upon the western limb

2 H

of the inflexion the " back-to-back " relation is again manifest. Argand records that towards Ferghana, and in Hazara also, thrusts carry Cretaceous and Eocene limestones to the north whereas in the Hissar range the normal southward Himalayan thrust is apparent. The cause of the inflexion was apparently the moulding of the contents of the Tethyan geosyncline in their southward creep about a tongue-like rise of the Gondwana massif—(the Punjab wedge). High interest therefore attaches to the discovery of typical Gondwana-type beds, including tillites, in the Kashmir Himalaya, while Gondwana beds low in the sequence are also found normally to succeed the metamorphic Daling series in the Darjeeling district. These and other factors suggest that the crystalline core of the Central Himalaya, which extends eastwards to Assam, represents the frontal part of Gondwanaland (Peninsular India) that was folded and caught in the nappe zone during the Himalayan orogenesis. Though the granites are probably of different ages, many of them are certainly Cainozoic (Krishnan 1953). No such crystalline core occurs in the Alps, from which the Himalaya differs also in that the most intense folding and overthrusting occurred away from the axis of the geosyncline (here the Tibetan zone).

The stratigraphy of the Himalaya is Tethyan, corresponding in facies with the southern part of that geosyncline the deeper zone of which is involved with the tectonic movements of Laurasia (p. 512). In Spiti and Kashmir sequences of marine sediments range, except for local or occasional breaks in the Palæozoic, from Cambrian to Eocene in age. The Permian and Mesozoic formations are similar to those of the Karakoram (p. 512), the marine Trias especially being 8,000 feet thick, and representing in the two regions deposition in a zone nearly 1,000 miles wide. The Jurassic is more variable lithologically, and thinner, representing a period of localised unrest synchronous with the Indosinian movements (p. 505) of Laurasia. The lower-Cretaceous deposits likewise indicate a shallowing in the southern Himalayan region contemporaneous with the Yenshan movements (p. 505) of the Karakoram. In the northern Himalaya the sea continued to deposit hemipelagic limestones and shales until the Cenomanian, when a thick, dominantly clastic, flysch series succeeded. Contemporaneous with the flysch are the Dras volcanics, greenstones, andesitic lava-flows and tuffites several thousands of feet thick; and their accompanying intrusions of gabbro and peridotite indicate the initial buckling of this region. In the Burmese arc also numerous occurrences of ultra-basic rocks, some associated with jadeite or steatite, are of similar late-Cretaceous age; but the only peridotites in the Baluchistan arc, those by Hindu Bagh near Quetta, are less certainly dated. Rather later than these intrusions, bridging into the Eocene, vast effusions of plateau basalt flooded the Deccan region of the Peninsula (Chapter X).

The Cainozoic history of the Himalaya reveals alternating episodes of deposition and orogenesis. Thus the Paleocene is marine throughout the Himalaya, but flysch is dominant by the middle Eocene in the northern Himalaya, and the upper-Eocene-Oligocene is there gypsiferous. Orogeny then broke up the Tethyan geosyncline into shallow basins (though Baluchistan and Burma remained connected for inter-change of fossils by the Indian Ocean) in which accumulated the Murree system of brackish water sandstones along the southern side of the ranges.

In the middle Miocene intense orogeny created the major structures of the Himalaya, including the great Tethyan nappes that occupy the upper valley of the

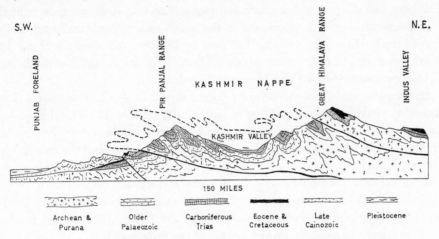

FIG. 185. Typical section through the Kashmir Himalaya showing southwardly directed overfolding. *after D. N. Wadia.*

Tsangpo and the Kailas ranges. Along the line of the Tsangpo developed the crystalline axial zone of many granites, some of which (Nanga Parbat, p. 114) are certainly of secondary origin. South of this zone the main fold-ranges of the Himalaya were built of crystalline rocks, granites gneisses and schists, with unfossiliferous sediments sometimes of very great age* all thrust to the southward sometimes in great recumbent folds (Fig. 185). In descending section through the Simla Himalaya, which is perhaps

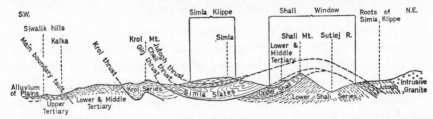

FIG. 186. Overthrust sheets of the Himalaya near Simla. *after W. D. West.*

typical (Fig. 186), are the Jutogh, Chail, Giri and Krol thrusts the last of which carries the ancient rocks forward over the lower- and middle-Cainozoic formations; while through eastern Nepal, Lombard (1953) has demonstrated in section from Mt. Everest to the Ganges Valley several great thrusts separating groups of nappes. The violence of the movements was such that there remain no unbroken structures suitable for the accumulation of petroleum in the whole Himalayan region.

* Some have been compared with the Dharwar and Purana formations of Peninsular India.

The Baluchistan and Burmese arcs suffered less, their sediments, though folded, being comparatively mildly thrust over the borders of the Indian massif, *e.g.* Naga Hills. Baluchistan was the more affected because two wedges of the massif, near Quetta and Dera Ismail Khan respectively, distort the smoothness of the arc. But the ranges, which display two distinct sedimentary and tectonic zones, Mesozoic geosynclinal and flysch in the north-west and calcareous in the south-east, spread out south of Quetta and west of the Kirthar Range where they pass into eastern and southern Iran. In this region are basic and ultrabasic intrusives. Throughout are foothills of both Murree (Oligo-Miocene) and Siwalik (Mio-Pleistocene) sediments.

Following the mid-Miocene orogeny coarse fluviatile deposits were laid down to a thickness of several thousands of feet in sinking depressions all along the foothills of the Himalaya to form the Siwalik system. Some of the depressions were new, but others had already been long established. The Potwar geosyncline between the Salt Range and the Hazara Himalaya, for instance, contains a 25,000 feet conformable sequence epitomising the whole Cainozoic and Pleistocene history of north-western India and geophysical surveys by Crookshank (1952) reveal that the basement rocks " exposed in Bikanir and Jodhpur dip very gradually below the Indus alluvium and reach their greatest depth, over 30,000 feet, on the margin of the Suleiman Range. . . . The basement does not seem to have buckled up into anticlines and synclines at all ". Even within the mountains local basins contain equivalent deposits (*e.g.* Skiu and Dapsang formations) but they are thin by comparison.

Towards the end of the Pliocene period the Cainozoic Himalayan chains had been demolished under erosion and their debris redistributed along the old mountain front. The stage was then set for the stupendous appearance of the modern Himalaya (p. 527).

THE MOUNTAINS OF IRAN

The double garland of Tethyan folds is admirably displayed in Iran for while the northern (Laurasian) chains extend from the Hindu Kush through the Ala Dagh into the Elburz and curve about the southern end of the Caspian Sea, the southern chains from Baluchistan swing far away to the south along the Mekran to link up with the Zagros Mountains east of the Mesopotamian depression. Between these two orogenic welts most of Iran and western Afghanistan has behaved as a rigid median mass, little or unaffected by late-Mesozoic and Cainozoic orogenesis. A corresponding median mass covers most of western Turkey, and a third such body in rather different situation crosses the southern Caspian region from Azerbaijan to Turkmen (Mitchell 1959).

The structure of the southern chains has been reported upon by de Bockh, Lees and Richardson (1929) who describe the section from south-west to north-east: " in the south-west is the Arabian foreland; then comes a very broad folded (and in the north-eastern parts sheared) zone, which varies in width from 100-200 miles; then comes the napped zone which is followed by the Median Mass. The hinder part of the napped

zone in the environs of Hamadan and Isfahan, passes over gently into the median mass ".
As with so many Cainozoic ranges (*e.g.* Himalaya) the immediate foreland is depressed
along a recent geosyncline, in this instance the alluvial valley of Mesopotamia and the
Persian Gulf.

Apart from the Cambrian, Palæozoic and early-Mesozoic rocks are of sparse distribution in the Zagros Mountains, and over the median mass; but at the end of the Jurassic
the Iranian geosyncline was formed, and in it strata ranging in age from lower Cretaceous
to Pliocene accumulated subsequently.   Simultaneously with the generation of the trough
the Cretaceous transgressed over the foreland and the median mass.   Strong pre-Gosau
movements such as are typical in the Alps, are absent from the Iranian geosyncline,
though occurring in the foreland at Oman.   The only Cretaceous movement of importance is pre-Maastrichtian and probably Senonian.   The timing of events therein is
indeed, more closely related to events associated with the break-up of nearby Gondwanaland.   There is a break of sequence also between Cretaceous and Eocene, and another
at the base of the Miocene which was accompanied by changes of great magnitude,
then a loading with Mio-Pliocene deposits up to 15,000 feet in thickness, followed by
late-Pliocene folding and elevation of the area to make a plateau 3,000-5,000 feet above
sea level, with finally some faulting around the synclines.

The folded structures of the Iranian mountains, much studied in the search for
oil, are accomplished in thick sequences often of weakly-consolidated sediments such
as the Cretaceous-Eocene flysch or the Mio-Pliocene Fars and Bakhtiari formations.
The latter group, only 800 feet thick upon the foreland where it begins with the Asmari
limestone, increases to 13,000 feet in the autochthonous folded zone.   The intensity
of folding increases eastward, but varies greatly along the strike.   Bockh *et al.* (1929)
have described the forward zone: " The most south-westerly ranges are often covered
by a great thickness of Upper Fars and Bakhtiari.   Then follows a zone in which the
Middle and Upper Fars and Bakhtiari have been strongly eroded, and in which a peneplane was formed towards the end of the Pliocene.   Then follows a zone in which the
pre-Miocene rocks are widely exposed ".   Eastwards as the intensity of folding increases,
fold-faults develop, and in place of regular anticlines small-scale thrusting appears,
as in the Swiss Jura.   Lees (1952) has cited this zone as an illustration of foreland
folding induced by movements in the basement.   " The anticlines of this zone have
truly majestic proportions " the structural uplift from syncline to anticlinal crest
sometimes attaining 25,000 feet.   While thick Miocene salt-beds are responsible for
the complicated " lower Fars tectonics " so often quoted in text books (Fig. 187),
these are on a small scale compared with the major fold pattern.

The nappe structures* of the more strongly folded eastern zone extend from
Kermanshah to the Zindon Range in a belt approximately 100 miles wide.   The nappes
which have been identified are: (a) an Eocene flysch nappe known only in the Zindon
Range and farther east; (b) a nappe which includes normal Palæozoic rocks with

* Mitchell (1959) lays much less emphasis upon nappe structures than de Borch *et al.* (1929).

Cretaceous and Cainozoic beds; (c) a Radiolarite nappe with basic and ultrabasic igneous rocks; (d) a nappe constituted of Cretaceous limestones with some Eocene rocks. " It is not everywhere a separate unit but only a big imbric of the Radiolarite nappe " and (e) " a nappe containing Palæozoic phyllites and older, strongly schistose igneous rocks, with transgressive Cretaceous ". The general direction of thrust is to the south-east, and typical klippen occur related to several of the nappes, e.g. in the Zindon Range.

Special interest attaches to the Radiolarite nappe for it contains rocks of the serpentine-ophiolite kindred, peridotites, harzburgites and gabbro-like rocks with pillow-lavas and tuffites, similar to those of the Pyrenees, Apennines, Dinaric Alps and of the Balkan Peninsula and Asia Minor. The farthest east that these are known is in

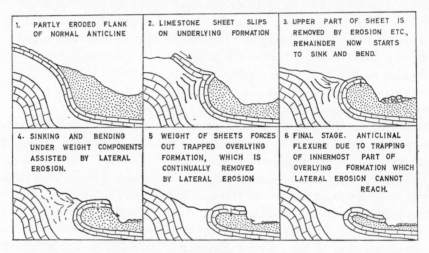

FIG. 187. Development of folds in limestones with weak mudstones typical of the Fars series in south-western Iran. *after J. V. Harrison and N. L. Falcon.*

the Zindon Range. The age of this peridotite belt appears to be Cretaceous, for pebbles of similar rocks are found in late-Cretaceous and Eocene conglomerates of the autochthonous folded zone.

Bordering the median mass of Iran, and extending indeed from Central Turkey* to Pakistan is a cicatrice zone in which plutonism and vulcanism is exclusive (Mitchell 1959). Throughout the zone magmatism preceded the orogenic maximum, whereas eruptives are syn- or post-orogenic: in Iran especially thermal springs accompany this zone.

In Oman is found an outlier of the Iranian fold system which has characteristics of its own. In these ranges pre-Gosau movements are strongly exemplified, and the Maastrichtian is highly unconformable upon older sequences. Ultrabasic rocks were

* (Where it separates the northerly and southerly directed folds respectively).

here intruded at this epoch. The zone of intense folding corresponds to the zone of deep-sea geosynclinal sediments including radiolarites. Sedimentation continued through the Eocene, locally even into the Miocene. Subsequently gentle folding and general elevation raised the ranges to nearly 10,000 feet. The present form of the ranges is therefore of late-Cainozoic age; but these movements are of lesser magnitude than those of the pre-Gosau (Cretaceous) phase.

The Oman ranges possibly extend into the submarine ridge that is a continuation of the Kirthar Ranges of Sind (Krishnan 1953).

Through Kurdistan the mountain ranges of southern Iran link by syntaxis with the Cainozoic arc (Anti-Taurus and Taurus) of Turkey, which is multi-convex towards the south. Folding was most widespread and severe during the Oligocene, but later phases were strong after the Miocene and Pliocene (Wallachian) periods respectively. Deformation, metamorphism and development of the ophiolite suite are all greater in the Taurus than in the Iranides. Nevertheless nappes, large-scale thrusts and recumbent folds are not characteristic structures (Mitchell 1959).

GONDWANA CIRCUMVALLATION IN THE EASTERN MEDITERRANEAN REGION

Between Turkey and Tunis the marginal mountain girdle suddenly disappears from Gondwana: instead appears the extensive landlocked basin of the eastern Mediterranean with no trace of submerged mountain ranges upon its floor. From Gaza to the Gulf of Gabes the shore of North Africa is formed by gentle descent of the Gondwana shieldmass into a subsided basin; the mountain girdle is missing from its appropriate position.

But this absence is not altogether real. The Taurus arc of Turkey, striking north-westward, is met in syntaxis along longitude 30° E. by the eastern extremity of the Dinaric arc which stretches south-eastwards from the Vipava-Postojna-Sava line, past Trieste, and broadening steadily through Jugoslavia ultimately covers most of Greece (Pindus Mts.) whence it curves on a wide zone through Crete and the Cyclades to enter western Turkey on a north-eastward strike. The circumvallation west of Turkey and Cyprus has thus become divorced from Gondwana and attached to Europe, or at least to the line of crystalline massifs such as the Rhodope Mountains of Bulgaria and the Pelagonian massif of western Macedonia.

Suess long ago remarked that the south-westwardly directed structures of the Dinaric Alps were opposed to the northerly directed thrusts of the Alpine-Carpathian arc. The direction of movement is foreign to Europe (Laurasia) and is appropriate to the Gondwana circumvallation. The boundary between the Alpine and Dinaric systems lies along the " Insubric Line " of crushing and mylonitisation on the southern side of the Alps and after a northward dislocation along the great Judicaria tear-fault it is continued eastwards as the " Pusteria Line ". de Sitter (1956) regarded it as a fundamental structure. " It certainly penetrates very deeply into the earth's crust, and has given access for granites and probably for basic rocks (Ivrea zone) . . . large vertical movements have taken place along its plane."

Several authors considering the relationships of the Dinaric structures have attempted to restore the older order of things before these structures became divorced from Gondwana and welded on to Laurasia. We present (Figs. 188, 189) the solution of Carey (1955) in which the Dinaric arc precisely bridges the gap between Turkey and Tunis and provides the necessary link between Taurus and the Atlas Mountains.

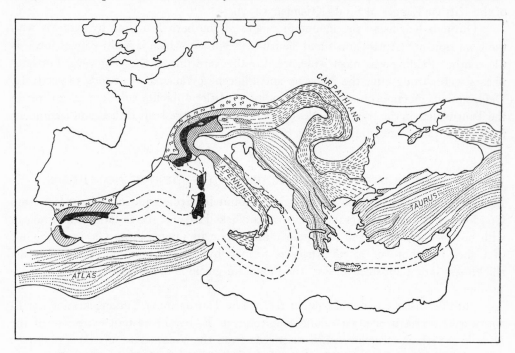

FIG. 188. Analysis of mountain structures about the Mediterranean basin in which the Gondwana circumvallation through Turkey is continued through Greece and Jugoslavia to junction with the Alpine system along the east-west " Insubric Line ". The fold girdle is absent from Africa east of Tunis. *after S. W. Carey.*

The reader would do well to consult also the geodynamic analysis by Glangeaud (1957).

Whether this curious attachment of the Dinaric structures to Europe, with all its resulting incongruities, is the result of a freakish northward subcrustal convection current, or whether it was due to a former northward movement of Africa followed by a southerly withdrawal is entirely speculative. What does seem certain is that the attachment to Europe must have come about during the Cretaceous, at the time of continental disruption, whereas the main orogenic crumpling did not culminate until the Oligocene. This follows from the general arrangement of fold zones with the youngest folds (of Mesozoic limestones and flysch), along the Dalmatian coast. The coastal hinterland is a summit-bevelled karstic terrain of high limestone blocks through High Croatia, West Bosnia, Hercegovina and Montenegro into Albania.   Behind this is a greywacke-schist zone, partly built of younger Palæozoic rocks, that extends through the hill country of Croatia, East Bosnia and West Serbia to the basin of the White Drina.   Serpentine belts appear in this zone.   In rear of the schist zone, through south-western Serbia and Macedonia appears the root zone of schists, marbles and orthogneisses.   According to Kossmat, the same orogenic zone is displayed in the crystalline rocks of Olympus.

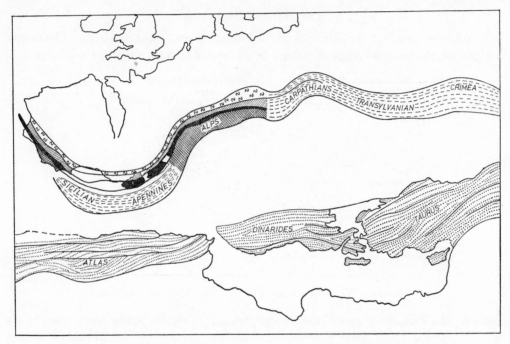

FIG. 189.   The original relation of the Gondwana and Laurasian circumvallations in the Mediterranean region.   *according to S. W. Carey.*

Tectonic disturbance was early in the root zone; for Thrace apparently occupied an elevated position throughout the Mesozoic, the Pelagonian massif was not covered by the Gosau transgression, and about the River Drina on the borders of Bosnia and Serbia the older block massifs are cloaked by unfolded Cretaceous flysch and even Miocene sediments.   To be noted here, though, are occurrences of mid-Cainozoic andesites and trachytes.

Following the main epoch of folding which involved the Cretaceous and Eocene flysch of the Balkans, a denudational landsurface was developed even by the early Miocene period.   This was elevated unevenly but apparently without severe dislocation until the mid-Miocene when fault-angle depressions and troughs dropped segments of it below the general level.   Many of these depressions were occupied by late-Miocene sediments either marine as along the Sava, or fresh-water as in the basin of Jajce which occupies a dislocated zone through the high plateaus of West Bosnia. Other depressions are occupied by Pliocene sediments. Differential movement was, indeed, widespread through the Balkans in late-Cainozoic and Recent time, and even the terraces associated with the lower course of the Drina River can be seen descending beneath the Pannonian Basin. The final arching of the high plateaus, *e.g.* in Hercegovina is usually dated as Pliocene by Balkan geomorphologists.

THE ATLAS MOUNTAINS

The Atlas ranges afford the only example of Cainozoic orogenesis in Africa. The ranges are double, the Saharan Atlas of Algeria being separated from the more northerly Tell

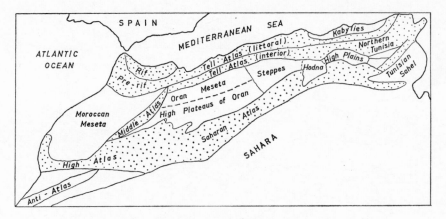

FIG. 190. Tectonic elements of the Atlas Mountains region.

Atlas by the Variscan horsts of the Chotts plateau. A similar subdivision exists in the west where the High Atlas is separated from the pre-Rif by the Moroccan meseta (Fig. 190). The folds, naturally, are directed to the south, and while the Tell Atlas includes the most deformed structures of the geosynclinal zone the Saharan Atlas corresponds tectonically with a shelf facies like the Jura Mountains of Europe, and indeed a comparison between the types of folding has been drawn by Joleaud (1922).

The littoral Tell and inland Tell (Caire *et al.* 1953; Caire 1954, 1957) (Fig. 191) form a double chain separated by the great sub-littoral plain, a Miocene basin but now mostly constituting a geanticlinal. The littoral Tell is built from a Tethyan assemblage, principally Jurassic and Cretaceous sediments in which unrest is indicated by hiatuses in the Jura and conglomerates in the Cretaceous. After a lacuna in the lower Eocene indicative of orogenesis, there is upper Eocene flysch and the Oligocene is of alluvial and lagoonal facies. Intermittently along the coast are fragments of Variscan massifs (Rif, Kabylies and near Bone) from which the nappes of the Rif and Tell flowed southward scores of kilometres during the early Miocene.

In the inland, or Tell Atlas proper, is a great development of Trias lying probably

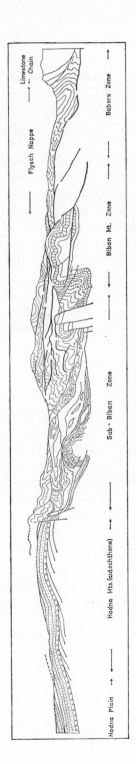

FIG. 191.   Structure of the Biban region of the Saharan Atlas.   *after L. Caire.*

upon gneiss.   The sediments of Jurassic and Cretaceous age are exclusively bathyal, and there is marine Eocene and lower Oligocene.   Clearly a geosynclinal axis lay here, where also is the maximum development of Cainozoic crumpling.   The first phase of orogenesis (Pyrenean) is marked by a thick Lutetian conglomerate.   There are no nappes comparable with those of the interior of the Alps, but a strongly imbricate system akin to the structure of the Apennines and the Pyrenees.   The mid-Cainozoic orogenic phase is of Dinaric type.

The forces which crumpled the Atlas were primarily directed from north to south, but the presence of older Variscan structures at an angle in the basement caused a deflection of the resulting fold chains to west-south-west instead of east to west.

After the orogeny Miocene marine and continental deposits were laid in depressions both north and south of the inland Tell with communications through gaps in the range, and these were followed by Pliocene formations. But the area was markedly unquiet and these were all later strongly folded, and even associated with diapirs of gypseous, salty, Triassic clays.   In the western Tell, late-Cainozoic uplifts have alternated with phases of subsidence, though Algeria remained emergent through most of the Neogene.   Late-Cainozoic movements extended eastward, however, into Cyrenaica and even lower Egypt.   Glangeaud (1953) has established a correlation in structure and evolution between the chains of Tell and Rif.

South of the Rif-Tell chains both the plateau of the Chotts and the Moroccan meseta remained as relatively stable massifs upon Variscan basements (Fig. 190).   Then rises the High Atlas, and to the south again are the regular folds of the Saharan Atlas, somewhat complicated by a chaplet of domes and diapirs of Triassic salt, progressively more intruded to the east.   The Anti-Atlas continues the chain to the Atlantic.   Both the High Atlas and the Saharan Atlas have virgations striking north-eastward and joining with the line of the Tell: these are the Middle Atlas and Tunisian Dorsale respectively.

In the High Atlas, where Hercynian folds are not al-ways easy to distinguish from the Atlas folds (Dresch 1941), a Precambrian granitic basement is exposed in the massif of Tifnout, the high Ourika and the high Zat.   The formations primarily involved in the Cainozoic folding are continental Triassic with marine and non-marine Cretaceous and Eocene.   Jurassic formations are seldom present and the Cretaceous lies upon a surface of subaerial denudation. According to Dresch, movements ranging from 300-500 metres had engendered an Appalachian type of relief in the Cretaceous and Eocene rocks before the Oligo-Miocene orogeny.   There was indeed much minor movement with the creation of unconformities and overlaps in this region throughout the Mesozoic and Cainozoic eras.

The orogenesis of the High Atlas passed through many phases; but as deposits later than the Eocene are rare, except in depressions like the Haouz and the Sous where they are generally unfossiliferous, the detailed interpretation of local phases is difficult.   There is, however, an Oligocene to lower-Miocene piedmont group that is always much affected by the main Atlas movements; also a later Mio-Pliocene group of different facies, generally alluvial and conglomeratic and frequently encrusted at the surface; and a final set of formations and high terraces that are vaguely termed " Pliocene ".   All the later series are continental in origin except where the depression of the Sous, between the High Atlas and the Anti-Atlas opens out towards the Atlantic. The history is perhaps more easily deciphered south of the Anti-Atlas on the borders of the hamadas (Joly 1962).

Apart from the flexures of the Rif zone that have been thought by some authorities to recurve through Gibraltar into Spain, the Atlas structures continue with south-westerly strike inexorably towards the Atlantic coast south of Mogador where they become involved with the coastal monocline described by Bourcart (1938).   Any extension is concealed beneath the ocean, and only the volcanic Canary Islands (Cretaceous to Recent) stand upon the same line.   Where is the continuation of the mighty Gondwana circumvallation to be sought ?

If our studies so far have any validity, that continuation should exist in the mountain welt of Venezuela entering perhaps through Trinidad (p. 462) unless indeed (Fig. 176) they correspond to the structures about the Gulf of Maracaibo.   But direct comparison is not possible for any date later than the mid-Mesozoic after which the parent Gondwanaland is deemed to have separated into the modern continents. Indeed, Venezuelan tectonics are later dominated by the Laramide phase, like North America, whereas the tectonics of the Atlas are Alpine in concert with Southern Europe. It is the Variscan basement structures of these regions that need to be compared, a study that has not yet been made by any geologist.

The circumvallation around Gondwanaland is complete and proves the unity of that landmass prior to its Mesozoic disruption.

THE CIRCUMVALLATION OF LAURASIA

Unlike the circumvallation of Gondwana which is currently broken at several gaps covered by the ocean, the circumvallation of Laurasia, except for a single gap across the Atlantic, is still virtually complete (Fig. 177).

The cordilleras of western North America begin in the Greater Antilles and enter the mainland through Honduras and Guatemala with the most modern phases in Nicaragua. Thence they are continuous as a welt from Mexico to Alaska where they span the Bering Strait into Asia. The entire eastern aspect of Asia is festooned with ranges of Mesozoic to modern ages either as part of the mainland or as island arcs now separated from the mainland by subsided basins. This island arc and basin topography, much of it relatively recent, rounds the south-eastern corner of the continent in Indonesia and bends back into Burma as the Arakan Yoma and the Patkai Range. Unlike the Himalaya which apparently terminates in this region, the ranges of Laurasia are thought to make a hairpin bend into the mighty mountain systems north of the Tsangpo Valley which, being folded *northwards*, belong to the Laurasian circumvallation. Thence the Kailas Range is reached and the Hindu Kush, beyond which the range of Koh-i-Baba continues the welt west-south-westward across Afghanistan.

The mountain ranges of Northern Iran then continue the circumvallation round the southern end of the Caspian Sea and into Armenia and the Caucasus. It appears in the Crimea and in the Balkan Mountains south of the lower Danube, which it crosses at the Iron Gate into the Transylvanian Alps and Carpathian Mountains enfolding the great plain of Hungary. Westward, the much-studied European Alps continue the welt in a great curve to the Riviera shores of the Mediterranean beyond which its course has been much distorted. The last remnants of the circumvallation are seen in the Pyrenees and the Betic cordillera of Spain, the latter possibly recurving across the Strait of Gibraltar to link with the Rif structures of the Atlas. Unlike the older, Variscan mountain systems the Cainozoic mountains of Europe reveal only minor " severed ends " transected by Atlantic shores, and it is questionable whether actual ranges extended well beyond the outlines of Western Europe. If they did so, a continuation would have to be sought in the Azores Plateau and thence again in the Greater Antilles. But the structure of the Azores Plateau is unknown and there remains the possibility that the circumvallation of Laurasia was originally incomplete in this sector.

THE CORDILLERA, ROCKY MOUNTAINS AND COAST RANGES OF NORTH AMERICA

Eardley's (1962) magnificent synopsis gives a clear insight into this region. From Mexico to Alaska the western mountains of North America comprise three longitudinal divisions (Figs. 31, 192): centrally placed are the structures of the late-Jurassic Nevadan orogeny; on the east are the Rocky Mountains with Cretaceous strata crumpled in the Laramide orogeny; while the western belt of Coast Ranges may be ascribed chiefly to Cainozoic movements. Yet these are not altogether distinct, and earth movements have affected all the structural zones intermittently from the Jurassic period to the Recent.

Almost the entire centre of Mexico to the Sierra Madre del Sur is dominated by Nevadan orogenesis until the strike turns from south to south-east and the structures reach the Atlantic coast. Whether Nevadan structures pass into Costa Rica and Panama is problematical: the oldest visible series of rocks on the Isthmus is akin to the Cretaceous Andesitic series of the Antilles, and adjacent South America does not show any precise equivalent of the Nevadan Orogeny.   Rather the Nevadan welt may bend back, with later fold zones, into the Greater Antilles.   On the largest of these, the island of Cuba, slates and schists with serpentinised peridotites that crop out in the south-eastern extremity have been regarded by Eardley as conforming with the Nevadan orogeny, but this is the only area in the Antilles where this orogenic phase is manifest.   Major Antillean structure plunges eastward so that if the Nevadan structures continue in that direction they lie below the Cretaceous outcrops of Hispaniola and Puerto Rico and lurk in the submarine plateau of the Virgin Islands.

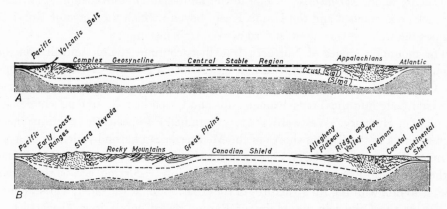

FIG. 192.   Structural elements of North America in east-west section:
(A) Palæozoic-early Mesozoic, (B) late Cainozoic.

The meseta of central Mexico is of folded rocks later broken and faulted like the Basin and Range province of the western United States, and the whole Nevadan welt where it crosses the international border extends in width from Baja California perhaps to the Pecos.   Northward, the unfolded Colorado Plateau (Fig. 193) constricts the welt for some distance but it waxes strongly again in Nevada and Utah where it embraces the full width of the high sierras and the Basin and Range Province.   Huge westwardly overturned folds, accompanied by gigantic thrusts such as the Mother Lode are present in the western Sierra Nevada and the rocks are widely altered through the lower grades of metamorphism.   These effects decrease in intensity eastward across the zone until the structures are obscured by Cainozoic lavas and dislocations.

At the borders of Oregon and Idaho the welt sinks gently until it is concealed beneath the basaltic lava-floods of Washington and Oregon, but it re-emerges beyond the Canadian frontier to form a whole complex of coastal and interior ranges described by Lord, Hage and Stewart (1947).   The batholithic coast ranges of British Columbia rise abruptly from the sea to elevations of 7,000-13,000 feet.   They are liberally indented by fiords, some of which are continued inland as deep, glaciated transverse valleys.

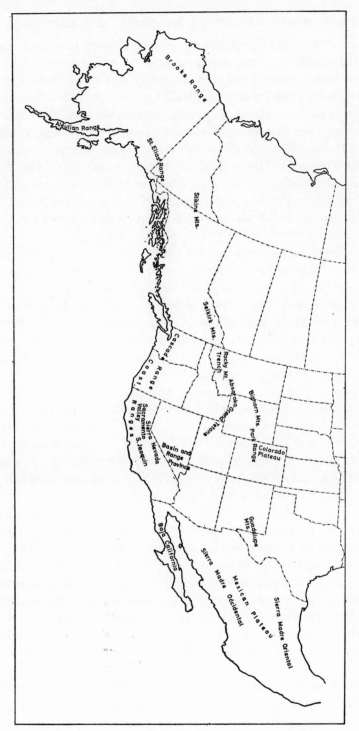

FIG. 193. Mountain Ranges of Western North America.

Also Nevadan is the " interior plateau ", standing between these ranges and the Rocky Mountain (Laramide) structures which continue the mountain section to Alberta in the east.   The dissected plateaus and scattered ranges, *e.g.* Yukon Plateau, Stikine Plateau, Selwyn Mts., Selkirk and Purcell Mts., make up a belt 200 miles wide, and are bevelled by an ancient erosional surface.   Finally, in the extreme north the Scolar Range of the Alaskan Copper River Plateau sinks below the lavas of the Wrangel volcanoes.

In plan the Nevadan welt shows two major arcuate structures with a linking cusp in the Klamath region, and the arc and cusp pattern is repeated on a smaller scale within both northern and southern sectors from Alaska to Mexico.   Peacock (1935) has demonstrated the pattern very clearly in the granodioritic batholiths of British Columbia and south-eastern Alaska, and as the batholiths are undeformed the pattern must have been decided by orogenic events prior to the intrusions.   Though there was some discordant fracturing during the late-Cretaceous, the pattern has survived undisturbed throughout the Cainozoic.   Peacock has compared it with the " linked " patterns of island arcs elsewhere in the circum-Pacific belt.   The geological histories of all sectors are broadly similar, and the Triassic and Jurassic sequences are both characterized by a liberal admixture of pyroclastics, predominantly augite andesite but ranging from rhyolite to basalt, deemed to have been derived from a geanticline crowned with volcanoes in the west.   General also are isoclinal folding, with steep north-easterly dips, and low-grade metamorphism of the involved sediments.

A plutonic cycle of decreasing basicity begins with peridotites (early serpentinised) then gabbros and diorites culminate in huge granodioritic batholiths; that of British Columbia extends from the Fraser River into Yukon Territory, a distance of more than 1,100 miles.   South of the Skeena River it measures 110 miles from east to west and in south-eastern Alaska the known width is from 35-60 miles.   In Southern California and Baja California the batholithic zone is again over 1,000 miles long and was formed as a score and more of separately stoped emplacements.

The onset of Nevadan orogeny was in the middle of the late Jurassic (Kimmeridgian) and folding appears to have been completed well before the end of the period.   Westward of the mountain system then created, a new trough developed and in this 20,000 feet of latest Jurassic sediments accumulated from both east and west, so that the orogeny seems to have been almost a catastrophic event (Anderson 1945).   A new volcanic zone and rejuvenated Pacific geosyncline was also established on the west of this trough. Batholithic intrusion came somewhat later and outlasted the Jurassic, being carried on into the early Cretaceous all along the belt from Alaska to Mexico.   From the contents of the trough were later built the Cascade and Coast Range systems of the United States.

Eastward of the Nevadan orogenic belt, the Rocky Mountain trough was deepened to receive a fresh sequence of Cretaceous sediments, often of heavy conglomerates from erosion of the Nevadan geanticline west, and sometimes overlying the margins of the older system, as in Mexico, but the eastern shelf facies is of muds and cleanly-washed sands

Pacific Coastal Ranges	Baja California and Mexico	Southern Arizona	Colorado and New Mexico	Wyoming	Utah	Eastern Idaho and Western Wyoming	South-West Montana
Gentle folding, late-Pleistocene and Recent	Colorado Delta	Erosion					Block-faulting continues into Recent
Mid-Pleistocene folding and faulting. End of coast geosyncline	Mid-Pleistocene folding and faulting						
Late-Pliocene thrusts; sedimentation	Thrusting and faulting in Mexico. Subsidence of Gulf of California	Plio-Pleistocene basaltic flows; faulting		Pliocene block-faulting			Pliocene; Third phase of block-faulting
Late-Miocene folding and faulting	Folding, faulting and sedimentation with volcanism	Local volcanism		Late-Miocene Brown's Park formation: Bear Mountain surface			Early- to mid-Miocene block-faulting; volcanism
Miocene sinking; thick sediments	Early-Miocene strong folding. Plutons in Mexico	Early-Miocene block-faulting		Early-Miocene Bishop Conglomerate: Gilbert Peak surface			
Reduction of sea, and small movements of land, mid Eocene to late Oligocene	Volcanism, emergence	Erosion, with minor volcanism and faulting	Late-Oligocene tensional faulting		Oligocene folding (Absarokan) volcanics		Mid- and late-Eocene erosion
Principal collapse	Deposition	Faulting	Principal thrusting	Major movement	Broadgate folds	Two stages of orogeny	Early-Eocene, late-Laramide movements
			Depression in Middle Park	Major movement	Conglomerate: folding	Paleocene thrusts	Beaverhead conglomerate. Paleocene, mid-Laramide movements
Slight disturbance	Slight disturbance	Thrusting, folding and uplift	Front Range began to rise		Latest-Cretaceous thrusting	Latest-Cretaceous early-Laramide movement	
Santa Lucian (mid-Cretaceous) orogeny	Laramide movements in Mexico. Marked disturbances						Dakota Conglomerate (mid-Cretaceous)
						Early-Cretaceous Conglomerate	Kootenay Conglomerate (early Cretaceous)

from the low continental centre (Fig. 192). The bulk of sediment (more than a million cubic miles) is so huge that Gilluly (1963) has sought explanation in a drainage system southwards from Canada and northwards from Mexico. Except at Absaroka volcanic ejectamenta are absent. Numerous unconformities attest local unrest during the Cretaceous (Table XII), but the climax came during the early Cainozoic (Paleocene and Eocene) as may be well seen along the Front Range (Russell 1951).

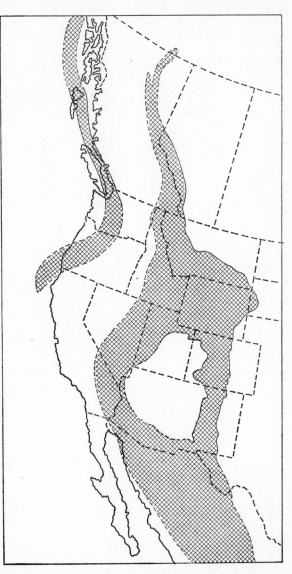

Under the Laramide orogeny (Fig. 194), the shelf zone deformed largely by thrusting and slicing. According to Lees (1952), the great thrust anticlines along the Rocky Mountain front in Dakota and Alberta are a consequence of fault-slices in the basement. The western part of the Rocky Mountain geosyncline where thick Palæozoic and Mesozoic sequences were involved, however, crumpled into folds; but this distinction should not be pushed too far. Deformation also extended westward into the Nevadan geanticlinal zone where outstanding thrusts were developed. Nor did failure

FIG. 194

Belts of the Laramide orogeny in the Rocky Mountains and the folded Upper Cretaceous trough of Oregon, Washington and British Columbia. *after A. J. Eardley.*

coincide with the ancient trend of thick Beltian (Proterozoic) sediments, so that Eardley (1962) has argued from the independence of isopachs and the pattern of deformation that the orogenic forces responsible were deep-seated.

Metamorphism is almost wholly absent from rocks affected by the Laramide disturbances, even from those carried forward in thrust sheets. The thrusts are generally low-angle and the sheets of rock involved are thin. Folds are frequently open, and isoclinal packets such as appeared in the Nevadan orogeny are unknown. Nor, with one exception (Idaho), does the Laramide possess associated batholiths of large dimensions. The plutons are mainly stocks, and even these are occasionally placed transversely to the main fold-axes, indicating a predominance of vertical over lateral forces in the crust.

Through the Cainozoic era tectonic activity continued intermittently and is typified by upwarping of ranges (*e.g.* Bighorn) and depression of basins (*e.g.* Wyoming). The maximum vertical height difference between the Bighorn Mountains and the bottom of their backdeep is 22,000 feet, which is comparable with the Palau Deep in the western Pacific Ocean.

Though sensibly continuous from Alaska into Mexico the Rocky Mountain geosyncline behaved with a great deal of local freedom so that the thicknesses of sediments and the times and manner of deformation vary considerably along its length (Table XII).

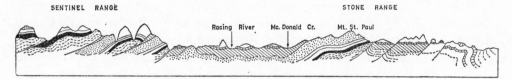

FIG. 195. Geological cross-section along the Alaska Highway, west of Fort Nelson, in north-eastern British Columbia. *after L. R. Laudon and B. J. Chronic.*

We note in passing, therefore, only a few items of special sedimentary or structural interest, leaving the reader who requires more adequate detail to seek it in Eardley (1962).

The Cretaceous on the north flank of the Brooks Range, Alaska is steeply inclined, though flat-lying in the Arctic tundra. Thicknesses here are: lower Cretaceous 10,000 feet and upper Cretaceous 15,000 feet, and Eardley has made the suggestion that some of this detritus was supplied from the north rather than the south. This could only mean a very different orientation of Arctic land and sea during Cretaceous time (p. 614).

The eastern foothills of the Canadian Rockies which between lat. 46° N. and 54° N. extend in a belt 5-25 miles wide, are thought to be built of small blocks bounded by reversed faults which merge downwards into " major low-angle thrusts " (Fig. 195). They are composed of easily erodible Cretaceous shales and bear a flight of erosional berms. Topographically, the foothills are more closely related to the Great Plains than to the mountains, though the great conglomerates of the Kootenay and Blairmore contain granite and granite porphyry pebbles indicating uplift and erosion of the Selkirk Range to the west by at least the earliest Cretaceous, and from that time every movement in the Rocky Mountain geosyncline or the earlier ranges to the west is recorded in the changing facies of deposition through Cretaceous and Paleocene time, the close of which saw the upheaval of the Canadian Rockies.

The Canadian Rockies are almost free of associated intrusions, but where the welt continues into Montana masses of quartz monzonite and diorite become conspicuous. The Idaho batholith is situated at the meeting point of two major arcs of the Nevadan system and its siting is therefore significant though the latest-Cretaceous or early-Cainozoic date associates it in part at least, with the Laramide orogeny. " It is strikingly discordant with Laramide structures locally, but overall a fairly close concordance prevails ". Some of its satellites are even as youthful as Miocene.

Southward of the Idaho batholith the Rocky Mountain system divides into two parts, the western is characterized by formations (including the Beltian) of geosynclinal thickness, the eastern by Mesozoic shelf facies. The two parts divide in Utah and Colorado to pass on opposite sides of the Colorado Plateau, south of which they are in syntaxis again and continue so into Mexico. Multiple orogenic impulses punctuate the succession from mid-Cretaceous to late Eocene giving rise to conglomerates which themselves partake of later deformation.

Structure in the cordilleran, or western, zone is dominated by great thrust faults. Displacement is generally to the east, but a few thrusts are directed to the west, especially in Montana. Rocky Mountain structures are more varied in the eastern branch. Through Wyoming and Central Montana asymmetrical domes, anticlines and basins, with monoclinal flexures and thrust faults are exemplified in the Bighorn Mountains, the Black Hills and the Wyoming Basin. The structures have been described as a " draping of the more flexible surficial sediments over faulted blocks below ". The sediments, thousands of feet thick, conceal the lesser folds, as beneath the Powder River Basin. The Ranges, *e.g.* Grand Tetons and Wind River Range, have crystalline cores and simple structures along the eastern side like the Bighorn and Black Hills arches. Early-, middle- and late-Laramide movements are widely known. All the ranges were in existence by the early Eocene except the Wind River—Teton Ranges (late Eocene) and the volcanic accretions of the Absaroka Range (latest Eocene).

Of especial interest is the terrain about the Uinta Mountains (a modern east-west arch 45 miles across). The flanking Uinta and Green River Basins each contain 25,000 feet of Mesozoic and Cainozoic sediments and the boundaries with the mountains are reversed faults dipping under the mountain arch down the flanks of which gravity slides have occurred.

Through Colorado the ranges increase in height and majesty, and the rampart of the Front Range, as seen by a traveller approaching across the Great Plains is very impressive. Behind the Front Range is a series of structural depressions, North Park, Middle Park and South Park, bounded on the west by the high continuous line of the Park Range, Gore Mountains and Sawatch Range. In front of the Colorado and New Mexico Rockies also a series of structural basins sagged during early-Cainozoic time. The Denver Basin was early, subsiding 5,000 feet during the Cretaceous and a further 1,500 feet during the Paleocene. The Raton Cainozoic Basin also sagged during the Laramide folding and its last deposits were Eocene. Through this basin broke the Spanish Peaks intrusives, towering in advance of the Rocky Mountain chains.

Extending into south-west Texas, the eastwardly-tilted block of the Guadalupe Mountains continues the line of the Rocky Mountain structures almost to Mexico, where it is continued by the Sierra Madre Oriental.

The Colorado Plateau, standing as a bastion of older rocks dividing the two branches of the Rocky Mountain system, has not entirely escaped deformation for several monoclines of Laramide age, *e.g.* Comb Ridge, East Kaibab and the Water-pocket which displace the strata vertically by 5,000-8,000 feet and extend for 75-125 miles, interrupt the uniformity of its flat-lying sediments. Its strong relief stems principally from deep dissection by the Colorado River system, and its starkness from the prevailing aridity (Glen Canyon). The margins of the Plateau are deeply bitten into by canyon systems (Bryce, Zion, Oak Creek and others). Volcanism adds variety with the laccolites of Henry Mountains, the cones of San Francisco Mountains (12,670 feet), Sunset and other craters. With Meteor Crater, Northern Arizona offers an almost unrivalled assemblage of scenic wonders. It is underlain by the same anomalous upper mantle that is known beneath the Sierra Nevada, the Basin and Range Province and the eastern Caribbean (p. 608).

Wrapping around the Colorado Plateau on the west, a narrow zone of parallel ranges extends the western Rocky Mountain system south-eastwards through Arizona into Northern Mexico. On the west this zone passes by gradation into the Sonoran Desert of the Basin and Range province. Laramide thrusting in the Arizona Rockies is directed north-eastward against the Colorado Plateau though some thrusts are directed in the opposite direction. Evidently this region, buttressed and sheltered between the folded Nevadan chains of the west and the Colorado Plateau on the east, escaped most of the warping into basins and domes that affected so much of the Rocky Mountain belt on the east.

Through Southern Arizona the Palæozoic and Mesozoic rock series were thin and so the Rocky Mountain structures consist largely of Precambrian rocks, but the same belt continued into Sonora as the Sierra Madre Occidental and the ranges to the west were active at least twice during Cretaceous time, crowding against the sediments of the Mexican geosyncline to the east and creating the Sierra Madre Oriental. The Laramide structures of the western region are much obscured by later movements, and by extensive blankets of Cainozoic lava.

The Mexican geosyncline developed during late-Jurassic and early-Cretaceous time as a series of broad basins extending partly over the Gulf area. Thus the parallel ranges of the Sierra Madre Oriental consist principally of strongly folded Cretaceous limestones. Notwithstanding the close, and even isoclinal, Laramide folding thrust-faults are few. Cainozoic block-faulting, however, has made a Mexican continuation of the Basin and Range structure of Arizona on the western side of the zone. The Sierra Madre Occidental, though dominantly a plateau of Cainozoic volcanic rocks, is not devoid of Laramide deformations, and accompanying plutons of granite thrust upward even through the blanket of early-Cainozoic volcanics.

In the Antilles, lower- and middle-Cretaceous rocks are absent from Cuba but the late Cretaceous has both clastics and limestones with abundant andesitic effusions throughout the Greater Antilles.   These trough sediments, including the volcanics, were intensely and even isoclinally folded and metamorphosed to phyllites or even locally into schists during the Laramide orogeny, which is general about the Caribbean. The southern framework of the Caribbean even received its extensive ultramafic intrusions at this time and in the Lesser Antilles were dioritic intrusions.   *These activities indicate for the first time a harmony of operation between North and South America.*

The Cainozoic history of the North American cordillera reveals many episodes of renewed dislocation, chiefly accomplished by faulting.   Two principal divisions may be recognised, the system of Rocky Mountain trenches extending from the northern border of British Columbia through Montana, Idaho and Utah into New Mexico, and farther south-westward, the block-faulted structures in the broad belt of the Basin and Range province reaching from southern Oregon to the down-dropped block of the Gulf of California and the upfaulted plateau of Western Mexico (Chihuahua).   The structures of both systems generally fail to conform with earlier Nevadan and Laramide structures.

The Rocky Mountain Trench seems to lie along the contact of the Nevadan and Laramide structures through British Columbia and Montana.   Parallel, but shorter trenches appear to the west amid the Nevadan batholiths and associated metamorphic rocks.   Cainozoic rocks, Eocene in the Okanagan Valley of British Columbia and the Flathead Valley of Montana, and Miocene near Cranbrook, B.C., appear within the trenches, serving to date them to some extent.

Southward, the Trench zone is continued along the western face of the Bitterroot Range, and the eastern aspects of the Ruby and Blacktail Ranges—all of them faulted. Through western Wyoming, cutting across Laramide structures, are the high-angle faults bounding the Teton and Hoback Ranges, with fill in the adjacent depressions enabling the history to be worked out (p. 536).   In Utah appears the high-angle faulting along the west front of the Wasatch Range; and from central Utah to beyond the Colorado Canyon in Arizona is a region of faulted plateaus (Coconino, Kaibab) in which appear faulted structures distinct from, and younger than, the well-known Laramide monoclines which characterize that region.   Vertical displacements on these younger faults range from a few feet to 5,000 feet.   Finally, extending through the Basin and Range Province from Santa Fe southwards to El Paso, the Rio Grande Depression, filled with Pleistocene gravels and cutting across the region of Ortiz Pediments, continues the graben line to Mexico.

The Basin and Range province is admirably discussed by Nolan (1943).   Here the typical aspect is of upstanding earth blocks bounded by deep-reaching faults* and frequently much dissected, standing above extensive bahadas and plains where alluvial and sheetwash deposits cover the relatively depressed blocks.   Though the faults generally head towards the downthrow, Nolan has adduced evidence that several of the

* Some are said to extend down to the basalt layer below.

blocks have been actively upthrust, so that a simple tensional hypothesis for the faulting does not seem adequate. Unfortunately, many of the faults are buried beneath alluvial sheets and the structural evidence is hidden. The first major phase of disruption fell within the late Miocene, the main uplifts, however, followed voluminous Pliocene eruptions (35,000 cubic miles of ignimbrites is quoted over the whole South-West.

Antillean Cainozoic deposits are widespread and usually flank or arch over the deformed Mesozoic rocks. Cuba had strong deforming movements in both the Eocene and Oligocene, to which rocks the lower-Miocene Guines limestone is unconformable. The rest of the Cainozoic is restricted, local and relatively undisturbed. Jamaica shared in some of the Oligocene movement; the remainder of the Antillean region, however, escaped, and Cainozoic diastrophism was limited generally to arching and subsidiary thrust-faulting. Jamaica for instance began to rise early in the Miocene as an east-west trending arch of large dimensions. Four terraces between 1,000 and 2,000 feet in the Karst country attest this Miocene and Pliocene arching, which is followed by a middle group of terraces between 200 and 400 feet. Warped planations are also present on the Puerto Rico-Virgin Islands block (p. 534).

Diastrophic climaxes of late-Miocene to early-Pliocene date were intense in Hispaniola and Venezuela, but are only weakly matched elsewhere.

The Pacific Geosyncline: The mountains reaching the shoreline of Washington, Oregon and California are entitled the *Coast Ranges*. They are separated from the cordilleran chains by the Great Valley of California and the Willamette-Puget depression, and their history is one of marked unrest during the Cainozoic and Quaternary. During Palæozoic time a volcanic archipelago or borderland had been festooned along the western seaboard of North America, but by the time of the Nevadan orogeny this borderland had been eroded down to its foundations of plutonic and metamorphic rock.

Immediately following the Nevadan orogeny a new Californian trough received 25,000 feet of latest Jurassic, and in places over 50,000 feet of Cretaceous, sediments. These colossal thicknesses indicate that the region in the west was a rugged orogenic and volcanic landmass, which was intermittently uplifted during minor orogenic phases in the end-Jurassic, mid-Cretaceous and mid-late-Cretaceous periods (Santa Lucian). Corresponding unconformities in the Californian trough decrease in intensity eastwards. Igneous activity continued at intervals through the Cretaceous period and Cainozoic era.

Cainozoic as well as Cretaceous folding is known from the Pacific Ranges of Alaska. Two lines of ranges appear here: an outer line from the Aleutian Range forming the coast as far as Yakutat Bay which is the site of numerous active volcanoes; and the Alaska-St. Elias Ranges with earlier volcanism, for large intrusive bodies of granite are found there. These are not Nevadan but probably early-Cainozoic, for certain of them cut the Cretaceous Cantwell formation. Great peaks are carved in these granites, including Mt. McKinley (20,300 feet) the highest point in North America.

Only in a narrow zone along the north-east coasts of Vancouver Island and on

Graham Island of the Queen Charlotte Archipelago (equivalent structurally to the Great Valley of California) are late-Cretaceous deposits found in the Columbia system. The structure there is granitic and fundamentally Nevadan in age. Nevertheless these deposits attain a thickness of 10,000 feet, and with similar deposits in Washington have been folded, though not intensely, in a late-Cretaceous orogenic phase probably equivalent to the Santa Lucian. Subsequent movements are chiefly of vertical displacement, with concomitant erosion. Cainozoic basins are few. Any continuation of the true Coast Range system of the United States must lie submerged in the continental shelf off British Columbia.

The Coast Ranges of Washington and Oregon are composed almost wholly of Cainozoic sediments, and Cainozoic volcanics lie upon the stumps of the Nevadan chain in the Cascade ranges crowned by Mts. Hood, Ranier and Shasta. Early-Cainozoic rocks are much better developed in the western than in the eastern parts of Oregon and Washington, but late-Cainozoic are more equally distributed.

Late-Oligocene disturbances producing only open folds were followed by the widespread effusion of the Columbia basalts, continuing westwards to the Astoria formation of the coast belt. Horizontal flows, mostly mid-Miocene in age, cover nearly 48,000 square miles and have intercalated pyroclastic and continental-type sediments. The lavas lie in a shallow basin, evidently a downwarp, which may have subsided as the lava was withdrawn from subjacent reservoirs. Eardley (1962) has contended for a Cainozoic volcanic archipelago offshore, as in Palæozoic and Mesozoic time, which interpretation fits well with formational isopachs and interfingering of sediments derived from the east. Pliocene rocks are scanty and rest unconformably upon the Miocene.

Geosynclinal orogenic conditions in one stage of development or another were chronic along the Pacific Coast of North America during Palæozoic and Mesozoic time, and the same is true right up to modern times when earthquakes like those of San Francisco, Santa Barbara and Bakersfield within living memory testify the continued activity of this zone peripheral to the Pacific Basin (a still active thrust in the Buena Vista oilfield on the west side of the Great Valley of California is growing at the rate of 7 feet per century interfering with power lines and oil wells in so doing.

The Coast Ranges of California preserve extensively the post-Nevadan, late-Jurassic and Cretaceous rock systems, largely in block-faulted basins. Both Cretaceous and Cainozoic formations thicken and thin rapidly and local dislocation plays a very important rôle throughout the history of this heterogeneous geosyncline. Great changes took place, for instance, in the Eocene and great thicknesses of sediment accumulated in relatively narrow basins, often striking at variance with the trend of the Mesozoic trough and showing marked local differences. Thus prominent folding across the general trend of the ranges produced the east-west deflection of the coastline and ranges of either side of Santa Barbara and may have aided in the development of the San Joaquin, Ventura, and Los Angeles Basins (Gilluly 1963). The sinking of these basins was very pronounced during the Paleocene and Eocene when 20,000 feet of strata may have accumulated in the Ventura Basin. Although the land area increased during the Oligocene and Miocene " the Santa Barbara trough continued strongly negative: and Miocene and Pliocene sediments accumulated 25,000-30,000 feet thick in the deepest part ".

" Over most of the central Coast Ranges the Miocene began with gentle sinking, and basins of the early-Cainozoic were first uniformly flooded and then overlapped. Early in the middle Miocene, the uniform and gentle sinking gave way to sharper down-warping, and great thicknesses of sediment accumulated locally. It is believed that the movement was caused by compression and that the interbasin areas rose at the same time as the basins sank. The heterogeneous pre-Cainozoic basement is believed to have precluded uniform folding throughout the Coast Ranges. . . . The crest of the Coalinga anticline, now composed of Franciscan series, stood above sea level throughout the Miocene " Eardley (1962).

Similar deposition continued in the same troughs during the Pliocene, especially in the Maricopa, Ventura and Los Angeles Basins where deposition continued through the lower-Pleistocene to combined thicknesses of 10,000-20,000 feet for these late periods. Near Ventura mid-Pleistocene events were catastrophic. The thickest known lower-Pleistocene columnar section (5,000 feet of mainly marine beds) was upturned to between 35° and 75° and, after an interval wherein denudation bevelled a late mature landsurface, it was overlain at an almost right-angled unconformity by 300 feet of upper Pleistocene fluviatile gravels (Putnam 1942; Bailey 1943).

THE CIRCUMVALLATION IN EASTERN ASIA

Across Bering Strait the Alaskan mountainland is matched by the equally rugged terrain of Eastern Siberia whence major depressions have created a series of marginal seas leaving the outer ranges of the circumvallation divorced from the mainland as a garland of island arcs. Under continental drift the reason is not far to seek, for with westward rotation of Laurasia during the Mesozoic the advancing American sector swept up and incorporated its Palæozoic island arcs whilst on the trailing edge eastern Asia produced tensional arcuate structures about initially Mesozoic foci of subsidence. Indeed, geologically the transition from America to Asia takes place not at Bering Strait but at Yakutat Bay, Alaska.

Hess has mapped the serpentine belts of the several orogenies that have afflicted the Pacific margin of Asia (Fig. 196) showing that they are progressively younger towards the ocean. Local foldings occur as early as Triassic, but the main orogenic climaxes are Indosinian (Liassic) and Yenshan (with phases dated provisionally as late-Jurassic, mid-Cretaceous and end-Cretaceous perhaps corresponding with the Nevadan, Oregonian and Laramide episodes of America).

The main Triassic ranges are the Verkhoyansk which strike across north-eastern Siberia from the Arctic Ocean to the Sea of Okhotsk in a zone broadening from 400 km. width in the north to 1,000 km. in the south, where much of the range is lost beneath the Sea of Okhotsk. It may be correlated, however, with the Ussuri region, Korea and some of the foldings about the Chinese nuclei. The youngest rocks involved in the folding are mid-Triassic and the ranges of this system were in existence by the late Triassic. Associated with the disruption were granodioritic intrusions upon a vast scale including, according to S. Obruchev, hundreds of massifs many kilometres long.

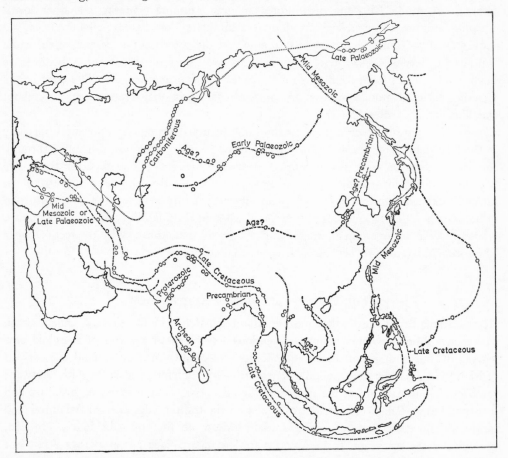

FIG. 196. Serpentine belts of Asia and their ages. *after H. H. Hess.*

Equivalent porphyritic tuffs, either wind-distributed or laid in the sea, are widespread.

Mid-Triassic orogeny is manifest again in Japan, Vietnam and Laos which owe much of their present form to this event which created the resistant masses of today (Fromaget 1937).

Liassic movements are manifest in the Sikhota Alin north of Vladivostock, and in Korea and Japan together with granodioritic batholiths of a later Nevadan phase. In all these regions, as in China, volcanic activity was intense and rhyolites, dacites and porphyries are characteristic of this petrographic province. According to S. Obruchev the Okhotsk-Tschaun ranges were also originally a Jurassic chain. Through southern China, Vietnam, and to a lesser extent Malaya and western Borneo, folding was intense and Liassic nappes were formed; but these tend to follow previous structures rather than a direction of their own. In the intramontane basins then accumulated the coal-bearing series of Kiangsi, Hunan and Kwangsi. Towards the lower Yangtze the folds are much weaker and in the upper Yangtze die out altogether so that in North China the Triassic and Jurassic are generally conformable wherever they are juxtaposed.

In the peninsula of Malacca and western Thailand, which was folded at the same time, great granite batholiths have, according to Argand (1922) " metamorphosed the lower-Mesozoic continental series ".

But it was during the latest-Jurassic and most of the Cretaceous period that recurrent " Yenshan " orogeny virtually remade eastern Asia (Huang 1959). Though a " meso-Cathaysian geosyncline " was in existence (Lee 1939) and Cretaceous rocks attain great puissance through Anadyr and Sakhalin, much of the force of the Yenshan orogeny was expended in more ancient terrains and affected vast areas of central Asia from the upper Amur of Manchukuo to as far west as Kashmir (p. 482). Over this vast area a wide variety of foundation and mantle folds was produced: in the Si Shan west of Peking broad anticlines and synclines are frequently associated with domes and basins, faults are common but overfolding and overthrusting are rare. On the other hand extensive overthrusts are found in the Tatsing Shan. In the Nanking hills, where previous multiple orogenesis had caused strong granitisation, folds are regular and open but often asymmetrical and incomplete, many faulted forms are present and there was syngenetic granitic intrusion occasionally of batholithic dimensions. Equally remarkable is a zone of " overthrusts and nothing but overthrusts " along the northern margin of the Red Basin of Szechuan where all three phases of Yenshan orogenesis are present.

Geosynclinal foldings extend through the Soviet Far East (e.g. Sikhota Alin), Korea, Japan and South China, with lavish granitic and granodioritic intrusions, porphyries, andesites and rhyolites as in eastern Shantung and the Great Khingan. In Fukien and Kwangtung so extensive was the granitisation of older rocks that the sedi-mentary rocks appear as roof pendants or as a thin mantle overlying a veritable network of batholiths. Conditions recall the granitisation in the Sierra Nevada but the date of intrusion is later—though whether mid- or late-Cretaceous has not yet been determined owing to the absence of Cretaceous deposits from south-eastern China. The extensive Mesozoic granites of Malaya also lack precise dating for the same reason.

The major fold structures of Japan parallel to the arcuate outline, with overthrusting to the south-east and dislocation along the " Fossa Magna ", date from the Mesozoic orogenies.

The Cainozoic history of eastern Asia is marked by intermittent tectonic activity with considerable development of Cainozoic sediments and, locally, volcanics. The

Cainozoic rocks of the Verkhoyansk-Kolyma region are partly marine, partly terrestrial: younger epeirogenic movements were shared by the folded Verkhoyansk and the Kolyma Table alike. In the region of Vladivostok the Cainozoic, mostly of continental facies, includes an abundance of eruptive rocks from basalt to rhyolite. The newer geosynclines lie east of the Mesozoic zones through the Anadyr depression and the Koryaken-Kamchatka chains which are curved as an arc *away from* the Pacific Basin. Sedimentation began upon Precambrian and Palæozoic rocks during the Cretaceous, but most of it is Cainozoic and totals 35,000 feet in thickness. The Oligocene is largely volcanic; Miocene granites are suspected; and there are ultramafic rocks believed to be partly Mesozoic and partly older Cainozoic in age.

The Cainozoic rocks of north-eastern and eastern Siberia are greatly folded (Bogdanoff 1957), and the strikes induced by different phases of diastrophism are often startlingly at variance with one another (Obruchev 1926). Thus in the coal basin of the lower Bureya River the early-Cainozoic is directed almost meridionally whereas the Miocene strikes almost equatorially; near Malyawkin the Miocene makes north-west striking folds while the Pliocene strikes nearly south-west. Folding is recorded as strongest in the Anadyr region and Sakhalin. In the former, post-Eocene plication was followed, especially in the late Cainozoic, by faulting: in the latter are three phases of folding, post-Eocene, post-lower Miocene and at the close of the Pliocene, of which the last is by far the most important.

Three orogenic phases are clear. On the west coast of Kamchatka the oldest phase is pre-Oligocene; pre-Miocene movements may also be indicated. The second phase is pre-Pliocene, accompanied by andesitic eruptions. The third is the post-Pliocene phase (p. 539). Southward, the Cainozoic geosyncline becomes double, the eastern branch of the Yellow Sea and Tunghai being separated by the geanticline of Sikhota Alin, North Korea and the Shantung Peninsula from the western branch including Manchukuo, the twin gulfs of Liaotung and Pohai and the great plain of China. The western, bounding geanticline is constituted by the mountain rampart of the Great Khingan, the Western Hills of Peking, the mountains of the Yangtze Gorges, the eastern margins of the Kweichow Plateau and possibly the Yao Shan in Kwangsi. Both eastern and western geosynclines are at present being filled by sediments of the lower Yangtze and Hwang Ho respectively; but sedimentation had already begun in the Cretaceous. The sea of Japan began to founder even earlier, during the Jurassic period.

Because so much of the circumvallation has subsided along the borders of Eastern Asia the episodes of Cainozoic orogenesis are locally difficult to decipher and correlate. An Oligocene phase, following upon earlier erosion, is apparent almost throughout. Lesser episodes during the late-Cainozoic are sporadic, but the entire region was greatly altered by movements ranging from simple arching to intense faulting and folding at the end of the era. Even islands at the very edge of the Pacific Basin such as Guam show intense late-Cainozoic folding and overthrust faulting.

In North China, Cainozoic movements produced broad gentle warps dominated by great faults (Huang 1959). The areas affected were Shantung, the Great Khingan, and the plateau of Shansi with perhaps the gorge district of the Yangtze. In southern China the Yenshan movements had left a rugged terrain with intermontane basins in which accumulated red Cainozoic sandstones and gypsiferous clay shales. During the Oligocene these deposits were crushed, folded and tilted while the older, intervening ranges were rejuvenated.

Volcanism in the Cainozoic welt is illustrated in Japan. Accompanying the late-Oligocene crustal movement that affected the entire group, lava and pyroclastic rocks accumulated over the greater part of north-eastern Japan and some areas of south-western Japan. In the vicinity of the Fossa Magna tholeiitic basalt and pyroxene andesite were followed by dacite tuff to a total thickness of 30,000 feet. These were intruded by stocks of quartz gabbro and granodiorite at the contacts of which metamorphic schists and amphibolites were formed. As at Waihi, New Zealand, and in California, these early-Cainozoic volcanics were hydrothermally altered and mineralised, including epithermal quartz-gold-silver ores.

During the Pliocene a second phase of volcanism set in that is not yet concluded. From Kamchatka, the Kurile Islands, Sakhalin and Japan most of the rocks erupted during this period were tholeiitic basalt, andesite, dacite and rhyolite. In central and northern Honshu, are some outstanding centres of tuff breccia, of andesitic composition and with associated ores of gold, cinnabar and stibnite. Only towards the end of the Pliocene period were the major traits of Japanese topography finally established.

South-East Asia

South-east Asia is here defined as the great semi-submerged platform bounded by the Philippines, Indonesia and Burma. Though the land areas are now relatively scattered, and are sometimes expressed only as island chains, the stratigraphy indicates a sensibly co-ordinated behaviour of the parts during Cainozoic and Recent time.

Borneo and the western parts of the archipelago reveal minor occurrences of Palæozoic rocks, with relatively more widespread Triassic marine rocks; but Malaya and Borneo were largely land, following orogeny during the Jurassic and Cretaceous. In the Philippines an assemblage of volcanic and sedimentary rocks of unknown age makes the foundation. Quartzose types of sediment are mainly in the west, as though derived from that direction. There are few limestones, indicating that the region was not then an archipelago, though volcanicity was early important there. While the time range of these foundation rocks may be considerable, the presence of ultramafic to intermediate plutonic intrusions suggests a correlation with the Trias-Jura circumpacific sequence and resemblances have been noted (Irving 1952) with the Jurassic of the North American cordilleran belt. The only proved Mesozoic rocks are Jurassic (in Mindoro) and Cretaceous (in central Cebu).

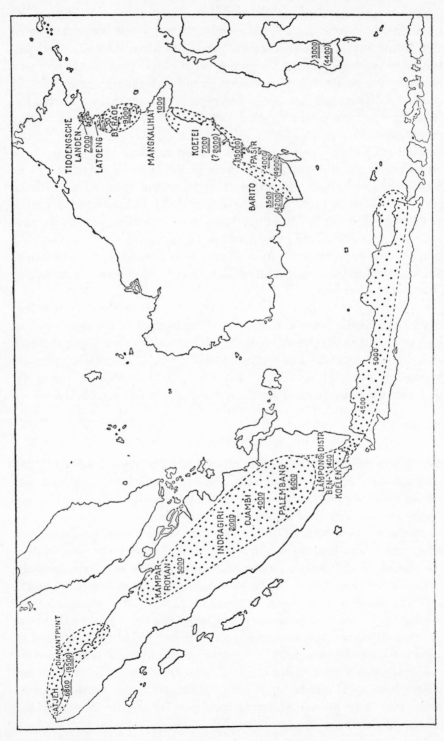

Fig. 197. Oil-bearing idiogeosynclines of Indonesia, with thicknesses of Cainozoic strata in metres. Where doubly underlined subsidence began in the Eocene, singly underlined in the Miocene. *after J. H. Umbgrove.*

Widespread diastrophism at or near the end of Cretaceous time caused a lack of deposition before mid-Eocene in Indonesia, but throughout the rest of Cainozoic time deposition there was fairly continuous, though crustal oscillations produced changes from marine to swampy conditions. Of particular interest are the oil-bearing idiogeosynclines of Sumatra (Fig. 197), East Borneo and South Celebes wherein vast thicknesses of marine and terrestrial sediments were rapidly built up (Umbgrove 1949). Batholiths are Mesozoic (Schwaner Mts., Bintan, Singapore), intra-Miocene (Java, Central Flores) and late-Cainozoic (Wetar, Lirang) (van Bemmelen 1949).

In the Philippines geosynclinal conditions do not appear until after the mid-Miocene orogenesis: the Eocene, predominantly calcareous, is a shallow-water marine deposit, and the lower-Oligocene is almost unknown. The late-Oligocene and early-Miocene, however, are widespread and their composition of coarse clastics grading into coal measure facies, with narrow seaways between high volcanic reliefs, shows that archipelagic conditions had by then been established.

Both the Philippines and the Timor-East Celebes belt underwent profound mid-Miocene orogenesis and even far west the mildly folded early-Miocene strata of Sumatra and Java are cut by granitic eruptives like those of Luzon. Following the orogenesis late-Cainozoic rocks accumulated to very great thickness in restricted localities. The Klondyke conglomerate alone is 10,000 feet thick in central Luzon.

Burma properly concludes the geologic province of South-East Asia with a tectonic history comparable with that of Sumatra and neighbouring parts of Malaya. Two major north-south geanticlines build the Tenasserim-Shan mountain line and the Arakan Yoma respectively. The former includes archean basement in its structures, the latter only Cretaceous and younger sediments and volcanics with intrusive serpentines of late-Cretaceous to Eocene age (Chibber 1934). Both the geanticlines have been land since they were established about the close of the Mesozoic era.

Between them through Cainozoic time extended a gulf that was filled with sediments from the intermittently arching geanticlines (indicated by numerous conglomerates), and by delta deposits from the north brought by the ancestral Irrawaddy River. This sinking trough, analogous with the similarly oil-bearing idiogeosynclines of Central Sumatra, experienced only minor folding during the early-Cainozoic but like them was powerfully affected by the end-Cainozoic diastrophism.

THE YUNNAN-KARAKORAM MOUNTAIN BELT AND THE TIBETAN PLATEAU

Through the Shan Plateau and neighbouring Yunnan, dominant fold structures are directed northwards towards Sikang. The date of folding is difficult to fix, but Eocene deposits 22,000-36,000 feet thick in Upper Burma, with a proportion of rock waste of crystalline schists and gneisses in the basal conglomerates, imply the presence of high late-Cretaceous mountains in this region; and in eastern Yunnan foundation folds of the Yenshan orogeny are situated above an already consolidated basement of crystallines or older folds (Misch 1945). This is the authentic circumvallation of Laurasia, passing almost at right angles across the arc of the Himalaya the eastern limit of which has not at present been accurately determined. Naturally, however, because the two regions have been in juxtaposition since the Cretaceous period both are affected similarly by Cainozoic earth movements. Both Yunnan and Sikang suffered strong Oligo-Miocene disturbance (mainly faulting) in sympathy with the Himalayan upheaval,* and Plio-Pleistocene rejuvenation of faulting and cymatogeny on a profound scale are salient features in this part of Asia (p. 541).

From Sikang the continuation of the circumvallation is accepted by most geologists as being through the Kailas Ranges north of the Tsangpo River where the rock folds are directed to the north towards Laurasia, in contrast with the Himalaya which is folded southward on to Gondwana. The full width of the orogenic welt is difficult to define for Cainozoic dislocations extend northward into the very heart of Asia, but for the present we shall limit it to the Kuen Lun, including thereby the Tibetan Plateau wholly within the orogenic girdle. Of its relation with the Yunnan arc, Huang (1945) was of opinion that the Karakoram and Yunnan arcs meet between the Salween and Mekong Rivers in a syntaxis.

In the Karakoram and Kailas Ranges, where the Permian and Mesozoic geosyncline had been filled up by the earliest Cretaceous, stupendous folds and perhaps also over-thrusts occurred after the Neocomian, and again at the end of the Cretaceous so that the folding belongs to the Yenshan phase. Involved in the folding were remnants of the Palæozoic (Variscan) chains " including the crystalline complex of Baltistan whose resistant granite masses constitute some of the loftiest peaks in the world including K2. Running north-west to south-east in Baltistan this complex splits up into two main branches towards the Tibetan border . . . one of them is the Ladak Range, the other is the Mustagh-Karakoram ". Folds in the Karakoram were rejuvenated by the Himalayan (Oligocene) cycle, (cf. Yunnan) and in Ferghana and the Hindu Kush there was unrest also in the Eocene.

Far into Central Asia the effects of Meso- and Cainozoic orogenesis are apparent (Huang 1959). In the western Kuen Lun, originally a Variscan range, four phases of Cainozoic rejuvenation have been recognised by de Terra. The first two are the most important and not only folded the Cainozoic deposits along the northern foot of the Kuen Lun but also overthrust them towards the Tarim Basin by Jurassic and even older rocks. Huang has called these " piedmont folds " because they occur on top of foundation folds in the Variscan or Yenshan orogenic cycles.

Even in the Tien Shan, Variscan folds that had been bevelled by late-Mesozoic time and lay beyond the zone of later orogenesis were block faulted and thrust about the end of the Cretaceous and again during the early and late Cainozoic. At the same time the Cretaceous and Cainozoic piedmont deposits, sometimes very thick, suffered plication with the axes of the folds parallel to the Tien Shan and movement away from

* But " the folding was not ' Himalayan ' " (Misch 1945).

both north and south sides of the range (p. 542). Similar secondary folding also appears in the Alai and Trans-Alai the Nan Shan and Tsinling Shan.

Less severe movements amounting to block-tilting appear in western Kansu.

We have accorded far less than justice to this, the greatest mountainland on earth; but its remoteness, sustained great elevation and severe climate have retarded geological exploration, and the same is true of its continuation through the Hindu Kush and the Koh-i-Baba of Afghanistan.

From Afghanistan the circumvallation continues through the Elburz and Caucasus ranges (Fig. 39) without complication (except that the ranges are folded to both north and south) to the Anatolian and Pontian Mountains of Turkey where movements were strong during the Cretaceous. The oppositely directed systems are separated by the east-west " Paphlagonian Scar ". The Crimea and the Soviet Carpathians may also be included in the folded zone. On the north is a foreland zone extending from the Dneiper-Donetz depression to Kara Kum in which folding is gentle, and the Neogene formations almost horizontal. The principal phase of folding in the mountain zone began in the late Triassic and terminated in the early Cretaceous (Cimmerian). Associated flysch deposits are very thick, there are many unconformities (Nalivkin 1960), and synorogenic intrusion and considerable slaty metamorphism appear. Alpine movements reshaped the major structures and added faults and thrusts. The main date of Cainozoic orogenesis is post mid-Miocene which is later than the main folding (late-Oligocene) of the Alps and Himalaya (von Stahl 1923). There were phases of lesser folding in the mid- and end-Cretaceous and again at the beginning of the Pliocene, when there was also much volcanic activity. Crystalline rocks make the highest ranges of the Central Caucasus reaching 4,480 metres between Mts. Elbruz and Kasbek, flanked by Palæozoic rocks in ranges rising north and south to 4,000 metres. Laterally, ridges of late-Jurassic and early-Cretaceous rocks pass into broad plateaus dissected by deep valleys. In the north particularly these are followed by Cainozoic rocks of which the Miocene shales attain 1,900 metres thickness.

The western extension has largely sunk below sea level in the basins of the Black Sea and the Sea of Marmara formed during the mid- and late Quaternary.

THE CIRCUMVALLATION IN EUROPE

Many texts have been devoted to the mountain systems of southern Europe * from the Balkan Mountains of Bulgaria, around the recurved Transylvanian-Carpathian arc enfolding the Hungarian Basin (an area of early-Cainozoic subsidence and transgression) to the Vienna Basin. Thence the system is magnificent through the Alps of Austria, Switzerland, France and Italy to the Ligurian Sea. The Alpine structures especially are so familiar as to form part of all but the most elementary courses in geology.†

* The Dinaric Mountain Systems of Greece and Yugoslavia have, however, already been assigned (p. 488) to the Gondwana circumvallation and are here regarded as foreign to Europe.

† Readers not familiar with Alpine structures may consult L. Kober *Bau und Entstehung der Alpen.* (Deuticke 1955); or R. Trumpy (1960) Palæotectonic Evolution of the Central and Western Alps. *Bull. Geol. Soc. Am.*, vol. 71, pp. 843-908. A modern summary is by Holmes (1965).

The famous nappe structures are directed northward, or at least on to the main mass of Europe in accordance with the rule of circumvallation; but we should note that the long-held theory of travel by crustal compression (" 250 km. of crustal shortening in the Alps ") is now abandoned (Gignoux 1948, 1950), and the nappes are conceived under gliding tectonics from higher levels into marginal troughs (cf. Trevisan (1950) for the Northern Apennines).   The transfer of lateral compression across the weak zone of the Swiss Plateau to fold the Jura above a plane of *decollement* leaving the basement unaffected presents insuperable mechanical difficulties.   Furthermore, whereas the Vosges-Black Forest-Bohemian massifs form the foreland to the Alpine movements, still farther north in the North German plain and Hanover Basin there is a broad zone with strong anticlines and complex structures of Cretaceous and Cainozoic rocks, making the belt still wider.   According to Lees (1952) all these structures seem best explained as an accommodation to steep folding and thrusting in the basement below. Fournier and Glangeaud have independently held the view that the crumplings are sited over earlier Variscan anticlines or synclines while Wegmann (1962) emphasises that " the folding is only one expression of a more complicated structure ".   The folding is superposed on several older anisotropies: an irregular basement, variable sediment thickness and earlier faulting.   Finally, deformation in the Jura was firstly of Eocene date (Pyrenean) which is older than either of the major Alpine orogenies; the wedge faulting was mainly pre-Miocene, and the final folding post-Pliocene.

The whole Cainozoic tectonic zone of Europe is seemingly far better explained under an hypothesis of vertical tectonics than by lateral crustal compression.   Chatterjee (1962) has even shown that the regional metamorphism of Mesozoic rocks found sandwiched between the Pennine nappes of the Simplon area took place " after the regional folding and thrusting movements died off . . . and owes its origin to the late plutonic actions ", though he still regards " dislocation metamorphism " as having paved the way for later " plutonic metamorphism ".   The Alpine system as a whole, however, does present some evidence of crustal compression that is not matched from most other mountain ranges (*e.g.* the Andes from which *nappes de charriage* are absent, and where, apart from local structures the mountain system is due to vertical forces).   We suggest that this evidence arises not from the orogenesis of Oligocene time but from the earlier divorce of much of the system from the Gondwana circumvallation (p. 488).   Further breakdown of the system occurred in the western Mediterranean, of course, during or after the Oligocene folding.   The main epoch of Alpine deformation was late Oligocene. After the first Alpine paroxysm at the end of the Oligocene, coarse Miocene waste or " molasse " was laid in a linear depression between the Jura and the Alps.   At the end of the Miocene, severe overthrusting of the second paroxysm affected the Helvetic nappes and Cretaceous rocks were thrust over the frontal " molasse ".   Nevertheless it was not until the close of the Pliocene that the Alps finally rose as the present lofty range of mountains (p. 542).

At the western extremity of the Alps the Apennines may be followed into Sicily, whence the continuation of the mountain system cannot be deciphered with any degree of assurance. The Atlas of North Africa belongs to Gondwanaland and direct continuation with the Laurasian belt of Sicily is not feasible. Instead, the curious double curvature of the Apennine arc probably indicates that it has been bent backward from alignment formerly directed towards Spain (*cf.* Dinaric " orocline "). In this regard the structure of Corsica is important. In the west of the island ancient crystalline massifs mark the ruins of a Variscan chain upon which autochthonous Mesozoic formations correspond in position with the Helvetic nappes. Behind (eastward) come the *schistes lustrés* corresponding with the Pennine nappes of the Great Alps, and finally Mesozoic non-metamorphosed nappes of Austro-Alpine type with slivers of crystalline rocks at the base. H. A. Brouwer, E. Raguin and R. Staub have considered that, with Sardinia, the island corresponds with part of the line of Alpine massifs in Savoy and Dauphine, and that this line passes from Sardinia, south of the Balearic Islands to be re-found, with the Pennine nappes, in the Sierra Nevada of southern Spain. Corsican folding, like that of Provence, was completed before the Oligocene and is therefore Pyrenean and not Alpine.

The separation of mountain structures through Provence (Chaine des Maures) on the one hand and the Apennines on the other is maintained westward in the Iberian Peninsula where the Pyrenees and the Betic Cordillera rise respectively to north and south of the central meseta.

The Pyrenees, from which alpinotype nappes are absent, stand upon a Variscan basement which is exposed in the Maladetta massif. North and south of this are Mesozoic terrains with red Trias like that of the Central Plateau of France and the Cenomanian flysch is transgressive over a landsurface of late-Jurassic and early-Cretaceous age that carries bauxite and lignite. The region was therefore marginal to the Tethyan geosyncline in which were laid the Alpine sediments. The present Pyrenean structures, rooted in place, date from the Eocene, and the present mountains from Plio-Pleistocene cymatogeny (p. 544), but de Sitter (1956) has drawn attention to the great age, in part, of the North Pyrenean fault-zone that was not only active during the mid-Cretaceous but was horizontally operative prior to the Trias, and may have been a facies boundary even as early as the Ordovician.

The Betic Cordillera represents the western extremity of the Alpine geosynclinal zone extending to the Gulf of Cadiz. Following Oligocene orogeny in which east Alpine and Pennine characteristics were developed with a crystalline core in the Sierra Nevada, a Miocene molasse developed along the foredeep of the Guadalquivir Valley.

CONCLUSION

The clear circumvallation of both Gondwana and Laurasia by Mesozoic-Cainozoic welts shows that when the location of these features was prescribed in late-Palæozoic to early-Mesozoic time *TWO* proto-continents were in existence. The concept of a single ancestral continent, Pangaea, by Wegener, recently revived by Carey (1958) can have had no validity at that time.

Moreover, circumvallation was certainly a long-established state about both Gondwana and Laurasia. Ranges at least as old as Palæozoic were almost everywhere involved, and fragments of Precambrian folded structures appear in many regions where the ancient terrains are accessible. Such a condition may to some extent explain the

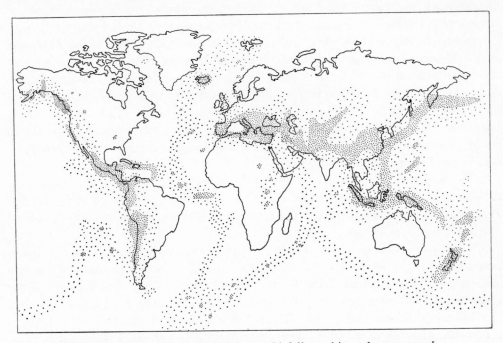

Fig. 198. Earthquake belts of the world follow: (a) modern mountain ranges, chiefly along the circumvallation of Laurasia and Gondwanaland, (b) the suboceanic ridges, and (c) African rift valleys. All are apparently zones of marked recent uplift.

rarity of Precambrian fossils (which must have lived abundantly in the proto-oceans) by excluding them from shallow epicontinental seas lacking connection with the ocean.

Circumvallation even survived the break up of both Gondwana and Laurasia, for Cainozoic orogenesis is restricted to the geosynclines already established in early-Mesozoic time and if new geosynclines have developed along the fresh continental outlines created about the Atlantic and Indian Oceans (p. 62), these have not yet reacted orogenically. *The pattern of modern mountain ranges is not circumferential about the modern continents, but in its fragmented state is still inherited from circumvallation of the proto-continents Gondwana and Laurasia.*

High seismicity and active volcanism are still endemic along both Gondwana and Laurasian girdles, especially where they front the Pacific Ocean (Fig. 198), and there seems no reason to believe that the ancient girdles, fragmented though they are, will cease to function orogenically in the future.

With due allowance for local differences due largely to heterogeneity of the earth's crust, orogenesis has followed a similar course about each girdle; but there are regional traits of chronology that may perhaps find explanation in sub-crustal phenomena. Thus the southward shift of the active belt as between Eocene folding (Pyrenees, Provence, Java) and the Oligo-Miocene activity of the Betic Cordillera-Apennine-Alpine belt may reflect a change in position of subcrustal controls, or alternatively crustal drift; as also the anachronism between the mid-Miocene folding in Philippines and Timor and the Pliocene movements of western Indonesia and Burma.

Important differences of orogenic chronology are manifest between Gondwana and Laurasia. Thus, seemingly, Jurassic orogeny was absent from Gondwana. There is none in South America (Arkell 1956), and there is apparently none in Antarctica. Between New Zealand and the island festoons of Asia there is, with the possible exception of New Guinea, no definitely Jurassic orogeny (Arkell), and the Himalaya was also exempt at this time.

Jurassic orogeny is, on the other hand, characteristic of the Laurasian girdle. The Nevadan orogeny of western North America, the Indonesian and earliest Yenshan diastrophism of eastern Asia, and movements in the Caucasus and Crimea all express Jurassic unrest along the Laurasian girdle. Both girdles participated, however, together with many other regions, in the cymatogeny occurring at the close of the Cainozoic era.

CHAPTER XV

MODERN MOUNTAIN RANGES

Modern Mountain Ranges. The Modern Andes. West Antarctic Ranges.
The New Zealand Ranges. New Guinea and the Solomon Islands. The
Modern Himalaya. From Asia into Europe. Cyclic Landsurfaces in the
Balkans. The Modern Atlas Mountains. The Mountains of Western
North America. The Far East during Quaternary Time. The Plateau of
Tibet-Sikang-Tsinghai. The Modern Alps. Conclusion. Summary.

MODERN MOUNTAIN RANGES

Under denudation continuing towards the close of the Cainozoic era all the mountain
ranges of late-Mesozoic and early-Cainozoic time were apparently reduced to plains,
or to maturelands seldom exceeding 1,000 feet of relief. This state was the prelude
to a series of mighty cymatogenic upheavals, some accompanied by fresh flanking depressions, that differentially displaced the rolling late-Cainozoic landscapes by vertical
measures sometimes of 10,000 feet or more. The resulting Quaternary mountains are
everywhere youthful, dissected by deep, narrow valleys the excavation of which can, in
many regions, be shown to ante-date the Pleistocene Ice-Age by only a very short
interval of time. This is so in the Andes, Wales, Switzerland, and New Zealand.

The date of maximum upheaval thus seems generally to be Plio-Pleistocene, but
in many regions uplift and depression are still continuing, as is proved by displacements
in historic time. Greatest uplift has taken place in the Himalaya, and here only seem
to be authenticated instances of lateral displacement under gravity where nappes have
crept forward into erosional gaps through the Siwalik (Pliocene) front ranges.

Quaternary mountain ranges as we see them are thus predominantly erosional in
form, carved from cymatogenic arches and fault-block uplifts, which often follow the
trendlines of earlier, Cainozoic mountain-making, but may also affect regions of Palæozoic
or even pre-Palæozoic orogenesis (e.g. Altai).

Quaternary cymatogenesis has affected not only the orogenic welts active in
Cainozoic time but also many of the shield areas that had remained relatively quiescent
during that era, uplifting them into plateaus that have since been deeply dissected by
rivers and streams. Though they are mainly discussed in Chapters IX to XII passing
references are made to some of these plateaus in this chapter.

Characteristically, Quaternary mountain ranges often preserve smooth skylines
derived from late-Cainozoic planation. These may permit quantitative estimates to
be made of the amount of vertical displacement involved.

518

The modern Andes were created by violent Pleistocene uparching, accompanied by extensive block-faulting which is not in harmony with earlier structural axes though often exercising considerable control of large river valleys such as the Magdalena and Cauca Valleys in Colombia, or the Huallaga Valley in Peru. Tectonic activity has, indeed, not ceased, and volcanic and seismic phenomena still find expression throughout the region.

The Quaternary tectonic forces seem to have operated vertically, with insufficient horizontal component to form nappes. The block-faulting is subordinate on the whole, to unbroken arching, but several huge blocks have been cited such as the Sierra Nevada de Santa Marta of Colombia and, beyond the Andes, the Sierra Pampeanas of Argentina. The eastern foot of the Cordillera Real through Ecuador and part of Colombia is defined by Oppenheim as " an extensive major fault bearing evidence of a widespread zone of fracturing and tectonic crushing. . . . Where exposed the fault appears to be of normal type, but with local thrusting to the east ".

On the Amazon slope profound canyons, some of them a mile and a half deep, have so cut back into the mountains as often to destroy all trace of the initial surface of the Andean upwarp, even where it is not faulted; but arching of the surface has been described in lat. 18° S. by Heald and Mather (1922) who reconstruct it from fragments rising from 3,000 feet at the margin of the eastern cordillera to 13,000 feet near Arani. Upon the front ranges of the Andes, e.g. Sierra de Charagua, it appears at 4,500-5,000 feet and " rises regularly by a few hundred feet upon each succeeding ridge until the crest is attained ", though at very few places are actual planed plateaus present. From the observations of Dresch (1959) the surface belongs to a late-Cainozoic cycle. On the Pacific slope where erosion is slower under a dry climate, the Andean front sometimes presents a gently arched surface with broad flat areas on the divides. It is upon the very heights of the Bolivian and Peruvian Andes, with their continuation into the Puna de Atacama of the north-western Argentine, however, that the " *Puna Altiplano* " is best displayed (Dollfus 1965). Bevelling structures and intrusives on both the eastern and western cordillera, this matureland makes broad meadows and uplands of moderate relief at elevations between 13,000 and 14,500 feet. Near Paso del Bombo, on the railway east of Lake Poopo, the Puna surface makes the divide separating the drainage eastwards to the Amazon from that to the high-level intramontane basin between the eastern and western cordillera.

Nowadays this basin is ringed with the " raised beaches and floored with the sediments of shrunken or extinct lakes (Titicaca, Poopo and the great relict *salars* of Bolivia) ". The deposits of these lakes and their tributary streams form an enormous lacustro-alluvial plain most of which stands at 11,000-13,000 feet above sea level and a thousand feet below the surrounding plateau. Minor relief is afforded by occasional piles of volcanic debris and lava flows, or by residual quartzite ridges. The basin was excavated following the Miocene orogenic movements and was completed during the Pliocene contemporaneously with the mammal-bearing sediments of Cochabamba and Tarija which also were laid in hollows excavated in bedrock.

To the north-west and north McLaughlin (1924) has demonstrated the Puna Altiplano upon both the Cordillera Central and Cordillera Oriental of Northern Peru, and to the south Bowman has noted a corresponding high, mature surface at the crest of the Western Cordillera upon the border between Chile and Bolivia. McLaughlin's descriptions of the Peruvian Cordillera in the departments of Junin and Lima reveal there " a central Plateau country [*Puna*] of low relief ranging from 13,000 feet to 14,500 feet, traversed here and there by a few broad rivers either in wide open valleys or more commonly in deep, precipitous canyons ". On the steep Pacific slope the rivers are torrents flowing directly to the ocean, the Rio Rimac which flows through Lima being an example. But the inland rivers (Marãnon, Mantaro) flow for long distances parallel to, and within, the ranges before breaking through the eastern cordillera to discharge into the Amazon. Along the continental divide a subdued range, 1,000-2,000 feet high, existed upon the Puna surface before the uplift and a similar subdued range possibly followed the line of the eastern Andes. The southern Andes, too, experienced a late episode of strong uplift to 6,000 feet of an earlier landscape of Pliocene age, but of marked relief. Eastward of Valparaiso and Santiago the crest of the Andean cymatogen is broken by a crestal rift valley 20-30 km. wide, 150 km. long at least and possibly mappable for 1,200 km. (Carter and Luis Aguirre 1965). The major graben, which is tensional, began to form before the Miocene, and " Most of the active volcanoes of Chile may be aligned along such features ". The cymatogenic uplift was followed by the excavation of canyons which now form the most striking features of the topography in the pampas as well as in the mountains.

Two, possibly three, marked pauses in the uplift of the Peruvian and Bolivian Andes are indicated by partial plains, valley terraces and rejuvenations which show equivalent stages of development and a remarkably ordered distribution over a large area. This is well brought out by a comparison of the surfaces recorded by Walker in Bolivia with those recorded by McLaughlin 800 miles away in Peru.

A thousand feet or so below the Puna surface in the high Andes is a broadly-developed terrain of wide valley-floors with monadnock ridges and occasional mountains 1,000-1,500 feet higher. It bevels the upturned sediments of the ranges, and carries in many parts a mantle of volcanics, mainly firm tuffs, perhaps 150 feet thick in the valleys and thinning out on the old slopes. Called the Valle stage it records prolonged stillstand. These volcanics have counterparts throughout the Andean region especially in the south.

On the western cordillera the great volcanic peaks may have begun to grow at this stage. In Peru, McLaughlin's Junin stage is described: " an early, rather slight, uplift, followed by a long period of quiescence, allowed the development of a series of broad valleys with flat gradients and gentle side slopes, some of which still exist in the broader interstream areas of the old topography. The broad pampa of Junin and similar high valleys were developed at this time." It is thus clearly an equivalent of the Valle stage.

"The next stage of uplift [Chacra stage] was more forceful and the streams rejuvenated by it deepened their valleys by 1,000-2,000 feet, but were again given time to reduce their side slopes [and widen their valley-floors] somewhat before the last powerful phase set the streams cutting the sharp gorges in which they are confined today."

Back in Bolivia the Chacra stage occurs as river terraces and bevelled spurs 500 feet below the Valle surface, and renewed erosion shows in the streambeds some 600-700 feet below the level of the Chacra stage. But there is a local difference. The streams did not carve simple canyons after the Chacra stage, but left evidences of an intermission in the spasmodic rising of the Andes in the form of an intermediate bevelling 400-500 feet below the Chacra surface and 150-200 feet above the present stream beds. In hard rocks the remnants of this " Piedmont " stage are slight, but where the valleys are floored with weak shales and then bedded sandstones the " pampas " of the region may be several miles wide, with the surface sloping always towards the axes of the valleys. No counterpart of this surface seems to have been described elsewhere.

The drainage of the Andes naturally shows a fine antecedent disregard of lithologic and structural controls. Yet one of the chief Amazonian headwaters, the Rio Marãnon, rises less than 100 miles from the west coast and flows north-west within the cordillera parallel to the coast for over 300 miles before turning eastward. In Bolivia the *altiplano* basin, produced possibly by block-faulting, has an internal drainage system, and stages of the conversion from the original through-going drainage to the present pattern may be followed with facility in the region of Uncia. South of lat. 38° S., where the Andes change from a mountain barrier and spread out as a number of parallel ranges which continue to Tierra del Fuego, the higher crest lies sometimes in the western, sometimes in the eastern ranges. Certain rivers rising in the extreme west of the mountain belt flow to the Atlantic, whereas seven others which rise in the *pampas* east of the cordillera flow through it to the Pacific. The summit accordances of this region at 2,000 metres show that all these curious courses must be, in part at least, antecedent.

Through Colombia and Ecuador Andean volcanism is mainly along the western edge of the Puna. The zone of most intense volcanic action lies west of the highest part of the pre-volcanic topography in the Maritime Andes of Southern Peru, where the bulk of lavas is enormous, seven or eight thousand feet thick and nearly a hundred miles wide (Bowman). Their passes are from 2,000-3,000 feet higher than the passes of the eastern Andes, and the zone of lofty mountains has been considerably broadened by the accumulation of volcanic material. The volcanic forces (which were intense here during the Mesozoic also) have been active through the late-Cainozoic and Quaternary, the latest effusions covering landscape features attributable to the Pleistocene glaciation.

Bowman describes the pre-volcanic topography as rugged: " the contact lines between lavas and buried surfaces in the deep Majes and Cotahusi valleys are in places excessively serrate ".

In the south, between lat. 34° S. and 51° S. the volcanoes are of Pliocene to Quaternary age and in some instances are distinctly post-glacial, with a tendency to an increased activity.

Eastward of the Andean front ranges the solid bedrock sinks rapidly out of sight beneath a cover, several hundreds of feet thick, of late-Cainozoic and Quaternary torrential conglomerates, sands and occasionally muds of several generations washed out of the Andean canyons. This is *the sub-Andean depression*, a trough continuous along the eastern front of the Andean chains through nearly 50° of latitude, from the mouth of the Orinoco River to Bahia Blanca (Fig. 173). At two points, (a) just north of the equator and (b) at Cochabamba, the trough is constricted where the Andes swing east and the Guiana and Brazilian massifs extend west. The sub-Andean depression may thus be considered as three linked basins: the Llanos Basin of Venezuela and Colombia, the basin of the upper Amazon, and the Chaco-Pampas Basin. The country stands from 1,200-2,000 feet above sea level towards the mountains, is often quite flat and poorly drained, with a few large rivers from the mountains passing through it to the eastern systems.

The upper Amazon Basin is wholly alluvial. The Oriente plains of Ecuador, east of the Galera Mountains which are of late-Cainozoic origin, display several large, north-south, anticlinal swells which diminish eastward towards the Brazilian Shield. The movements which gave rise to these may well be represented also in a number of partial erosional bevels along the eastern flank of the Cordillera Real.

The Bolivian Chaco reaching eastward to the Paraguay River, is mainly a sandy lowland with fixed dunes where wind action has been operative after the growth of an extensive piedmont. Nowhere are solid rocks revealed. Through the Argentine too is a great development of sub-Andean continental deposits of varying thickness. In the Andean border, sedimentation began in the late Cretaceous and in the Cainozoic continued on a vast scale, various diastrophic movements being shown by repeated basal sedimentation. Near the 40th parallel, south latitude, the depression was largely filled with late-Cainozoic tuffs (possibly the equivalents of those in the Valle stage of Andean erosion) before being topped with gravel fans and piedmonts.

West Antarctic Ranges

The great plateau of the southern Andes is matched in Antarctica by the mountain plateau of the Antarctic Peninsula. Beginning at 6,500 feet in the latitude of James Ross Island and rising to 7,000 feet beyond latitude 70° S., where it is surmounted by peaks ascending nearly to 11,000 feet, the plateau is generally of rolling or flat country from four to twenty miles wide which probably represents a late-Cainozoic erosional surface (p. 333).

Air photos suggest block-faulting in some parts, especially along the eastern descent to the Weddell Sea where islands at the edge of the Larsen Ice Shelf appear as down-dropped plateau segments about 1,000-1,600 feet above the sea. George VI Sound between Alexander I Island and the western aspect of the plateau also owes its origin to faulting, and the Douglas and LeMay Ranges are faulted. Alexander I Island, as a whole, has been tilted so that while the south sinks gently beneath an ice cover the north rides high as 10,000 feet mountains. Tilting has been repetitive since the Mesozoic, but the latest movements (with faulting) governing the present form are Plio-Pleistocene, only shortly preceding the Ice Age (Fig. 179) (King 1965).

Distantly, in the Sentinel Range, the plateau is surmounted by numerous gipfels some attaining to 16,000 feet in elevation (Mt. Tyree). Thence the continuation of the circumvallation is detached and displaced (Fig. 179); but on the other side of West Antarctica, in the southern Edsel Ford Mountains, is a suggestion of a similar plateau level around 5,000 feet surmounted by volcanoes.

THE NEW ZEALAND RANGES

New Zealand is a youthful terrain and visitors are often impressed by the steepness (and occasional instability) of its hillslopes. These features follow upon the extreme lateness of the " Kaikoura diastrophism ", a tectonic phase of broad warping accompanied by much profound faulting during late-Pleistocene and Recent epochs. The diastrophism is, indeed, still in progress, as is attested by warped Quaternary shorelines transverse to the grain of the country (King 1930; Cotton 1949) and by the numerous fault-line displacements that have occurred during the past century.

The dominant Kaikoura trend, as exhibited in the attitudes of Cainozoic strata, is to the north-east. In many places this differs from the strikes in Trias-Jura rocks of the fundamental New Zealand arc, but it perhaps indicates affinity with the directional tendency of the Kermadec-Tonga-Fiji megashears of similarly recent date.

Notwithstanding extremely active denudation, in part glacial, since the initiation of the Kaikoura movements, elevated regions of the median land frequently preserve traces of an advanced summit planation of Plio-Pleistocene age. According to Cotton (1957) it was formed "during an anorogenic interval between Pliocene and late-Pleistocene orogeny", but other authors have deemed it Pliocene (Stevens 1956).

From Fiordland, Benson (1936) has described remnants of the surface flexing strongly upwards from the sea to an inland elevation between 5,000 and 6,000 feet (Fig. 199). The quondam surface there truncated an infaulted belt of Miocene rocks near Lake Wakatipu.

Farther north the late-Cainozoic summit plain, described as the " Wainihinihi peneplain " by members of the Geological Survey in the first decade of the century, has been the subject of review by Wellman and Willett (1942) who, like Benson, have

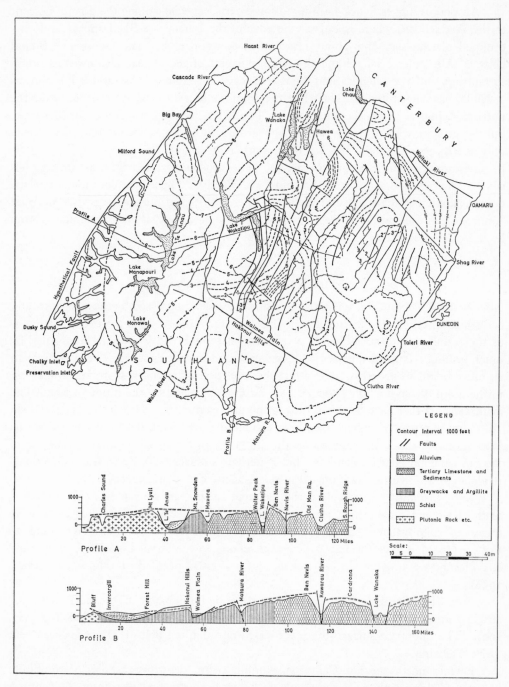

FIG. 199. The attitude of the late Cainozoic summit planation in Otago,
New Zealand. Contour interval 1,000 feet. *after W. N. Benson.*

restored the contours of the surface, this time to over 10,000 feet in the Mt. Cook region. Below 8,000 feet the contours are parallel to each other, to the Alpine fault and, broadly, to the West Coast: above 8,000 feet they are oval, showing doming about the highest ranges. Wellman and Willet by an incorrect stratigraphic reading allowed too short a time for the cutting of the plain before the onset of the Kaikoura diastrophism; but the subsequent researches of Gage (1949) at Ross have demonstrated that, as in the south, the whole of the Pliocene was available.

Remnants of the surface are generally thought to be absent from the northern end of South Island but the Puketeraki Hills closing the north end of the Canterbury Plains show notable evenness of crestline, and observation on an offshore flight from Christchurch to Wellington brings out a wonderfully even crestline for 50 miles upon the St. Arnaud Range. Even the knife-edged Kaikoura crestline gives a clear impression

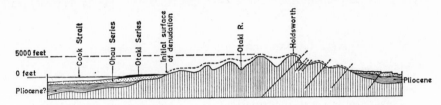

FIG. 200. Cross section of the Tararua Ranges, New Zealand showing how ridges and valleys follow details of the warped Pliocene landsurface. *after* G. L. Adkin.

from the east of a formerly-planed surface rising to a culmination about Mt. Tapuaenuku and thence declining northward once more. A complementary smooth descent northwards towards White Bluffs takes place upon the range west of the Awatere Valley. Though no significant areas of residual surface remain upon these mountains, a domal uplift complicated by faulting is perhaps indicated by the even crestlines, in accordance with the dextral transcurrent displacements (Fig. 180) postulated by Kingma (1959).

Across Cook Strait, above the steep hillslopes about Wellington, an ancestral upland (the Kaukau surface) is now known to have been strongly deformed. Like the later coastal terraces, it has been " tilted, strongly warped and broken by faults " (Cotton 1957). Even more remarkable are the " live anticlines " with topographic expression described from Western Wellington by Te Punga (1957).

Farther afield, Adkin (1949) has shown that the Tararua and Rimutaka Ranges forming the backbone of the North Island (Fig. 200) have been carved from an arched landsurface that rises to 5,000 feet with a plunge to north and south along the mountain axis. In section the warp shows a series of eight minor anticlinals which are themselves transected by a second set of at least six transverse anticlinals. To these lines the present divides, major and minor, conform, the drainage assuming a trellised pattern. Though, since the uplift, river erosion has converted what was once a rolling lowland into mountains, remnants of that lowland, hundreds of acres in extent, still survive on some of the higher country.   No remnants of any former Cainozoic cover are, however, known to exist, and the area may have been continuously emergent while the geosynclinal troughs to east and west were sinking (Fig. 182).

The arch is steeper on the east, where it is sharply bounded by the reversed Wairarapa fault which, to the northward, turns into the ranges and forms the precipitous eastern face of the Mitre-Holdsworth Ridge, highest in the Tararuas.

Conversely with elevation of the ancestral lowland upon the New Zealand ranges, the geosynclinal areas of Wanganui, Wairarapa and the Canterbury Plains have subsided during Quaternary time. Three thousand five hundred feet of presumed Quaternary deposits exist west of Banks Peninsula, the volcanic outpost of Canterbury.

The mountains of Eastern Australia are likewise denudational following upon strong arching of late-Cainozoic and earlier landsurfaces during early-Quaternary time (p. 355).

New Guinea and the Solomon Islands

The most widespread diastrophism of New Guinea occurred in late-Pliocene and early-Pleistocene time; but activity began in middle Miocene time depending on the locality. Uplift was considerable, and deformation is still proceeding (Krause 1965). The central highlands became a Pleistocene cymatogen standing 15,000 feet above the sea and through the northern ranges of New Guinea and the Bismarck Archipelago 5,000-7,000 feet of differential warping was accomplished. Folding was less important but at the end of the Pliocene, both sediments and basement were crumpled along the

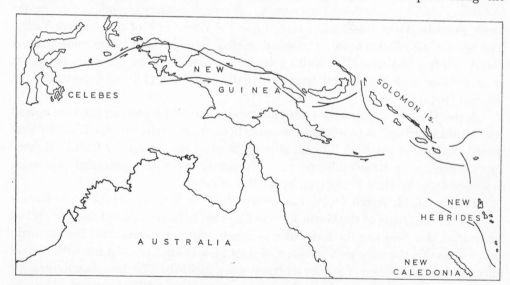

Fig. 201. Suggested megashear pattern of the New Guinea—Solomon Islands Region. *mainly after D. C. Krause.*

idiogeosynclines into a number of anticlines and synclines. In the rugged country of western New Guinea crystalline basement appears in the structural highs of the Kubor and Lai Anticlines and the Bismarck fault-zone (Rickwood 1955). Characteristically, the transcurrent Sorong Fault Zone (Fig. 201) with both left lateral and right lateral displacements and a " zone of fault breccia and mylonite that is several kilometres wide " was formed through West Irian. On the Solomon and New Hebrides Islands also, late Cainozoic beds were folded. Volcanism, too, was active and cones 7,000 feet high have been built.

South of the central ranges of New Guinea much Pleistocene debris was swept outwards from the mountains, accompanied locally by pyroclastic materials, as from the volcanoes Sisa, Bosavi, and Bivau. Pleistocene glaciation occurred in the Bismarck Range down to about 13,000 feet above sea level.

The frequency of earthquakes, particularly in the Torricelli and Bewani Mountain regions, together with much volcanism, indicates that in both New Guinea and the outlying islands diastrophism is still in progress.

Grover's (1958) structural analysis of the Solomon Islands (Fig. 202) shows numerous major east-west fold axes of post-Miocene date which " give way to block-faulting and shearing on a huge scale along the southern side of Guadalcanal and San Cristobal ". Upon Guadalcanal, indeed, the Miocene limestone is understood to ascend from near sea level in the northern coastlands to above 5,000 feet along the mountain axis. More youthful mudstones and conglomerates have also acquired a northerly tilt, and the coralline terraces of Honiara have also emerged since the Pliocene. On the south side of the island much Pliocene and Recent volcanism parallels the coast.

The islands of Malaita and San Cristobal are described as dominantly anticlinal in form, and a pattern of closed anticlines and synclines is seemingly widespread throughout the group, and may be typical of Quaternary diastrophism. Choiseul however (Coleman 1962), with basement of amphibolite schists, shows much displacement by faulting of a Lower Miocene and Pliocene sedimentary series into a jostle of earth-blocks.

Altogether the Solomon Islands constitute an earth block with sigmoidal axis, connected probably with New Britain and New Ireland but " quite separate from New Guinea, Australia and the New Hebrides " (Coleman 1965). A serpentine belt seems to separate the folded segment along the Pacific margin from the block faulted " Australian side ", Coleman assesses the thickness of this crustal block as " probably less than 15 km." Quaternary volcanism makes a belt on the Australian aspect where also shallow seismic shocks congregate (p. 646).

THE MODERN HIMALAYA

The vast recumbent structures of the Cainozoic Himalaya, with the fringe of thick Siwalik formations in frontal depressions, were thrown into convulsion again in the Plio-Pleistocene, and certain of the movements continue to this day. Then arose the

Siwalik foothills of the Himalayan system, a faulted and folded zone now carved by erosion into a maze of minor ranges. This " Nimadric " zone of the Himalaya has been controlled by pressures from the north, and Gill (1952) describes the structures in the Jhamat-Kushalgar district of western Potwar and the area between the Indus and Jhelum Rivers as passing from open folding in the south to closely spaced reversed faults enclosing severely compressed folds in the north where the foreland zone is terminated by the Himalayan boundary fault. He concluded, however, that the faults are not genetically related to the fold axes but are " fractures due to shearing stresses principally with a vertical orientation ". This brings the structures into accord with dominantly vertical Pleistocene movements elsewhere.

The Salt Range is an anticlinal bulge related to the Gondwana foreland. Its general trend parallels approximately the tectonic elements in the north, but axes of folds and faults may be oblique and are complicated by salt tectonics.

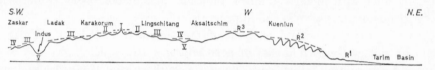

FIG. 203. Relations and attitudes of erosion surfaces in section across the mountain region from the Punjab to the Tarim Basin. *after H. de Terra.*

North of the Himalayan boundary fault, upheaval far exceeded even the mid-Cainozoic orogeny in violence. The old nappe structures were rejuvenated and new ones produced that rode forward far into the foreland. Wadia (1937B) and Krishnan (1953) afforded details of the completed Himalayan structures in several sections; and Heim wrote that " like huge floods the old Schistose Dalings east of the Tista have *been pushed towards the plain through the gaps eroded out in the Siwalik front wall.* Thus the shape of the thrust sheets depends on that of the Siwaliks rather than the contrary ". The Siwaliks (Pliocene) had been subjected to considerable erosion on their northern flanks before they were overrun by the creeping masses so that the movements belong well within Quaternary time. As such they are unique among modern mountains.

There is, of course, much evidence of very late vertical movement in the Himalaya. The Karewa series of Pleistocene lake and river deposits in the Kashmir Valley have been tilted to 40° and elevated to between 5,000 and 6,000 feet, and other fossiliferous Quaternary beds have been uplifted and dissected by 3,000 feet. There is even overthrusting of Pleistocene alluvial gravels by older Himalayan rocks.

There is lacking any general identification of a late-Cainozoic summit planation upon Himalayan ranges, though over a restricted area of the north-western Himalaya de Terra has reported broad-floored ancient valleys at 3,300-3,600 metres surmounted by older planed remnants about 4,000 metres and traces of an older feature 600 metres higher still. In any case the well-known antecedent drainage pattern in which three

great rivers Sutlej, Indus and Brahmaputra with their head tributaries rise upon the
northern flanks of the whole Himalayan system and traverse to the south side through
youthfully deep gorges attests not only the recent date at which the Himalaya has been
elevated but also a very different type of topography prior to the post-Pliocene tectonic
movements.

Geomorphic evidence suggests that the Karakoram, which as Hedin noted bears
a summit planation, and adjoining regions suffered broad arching and faulting during
this epoch (de Terra 1933) (Fig. 203).

With the creation of the modern Himalaya, a fresh set of depressions developed
in the Indo-Gangetic region (Fig. 204). Three major troughs are evident separated

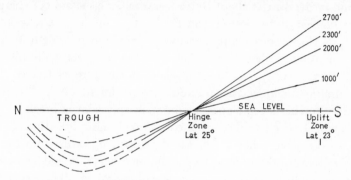

FIG. 204. Sinking of the Punjab depression concomitantly with uplift of
the Himalaya. *after M. S. Krishnan.*

by transverse ridge-like structures west of Delhi and east of Cooch-Behar. Within the
troughs Pleistocene alluvia are now from 6,000-15,000 feet thick; the accumulations
correspond more or less with a zone of negative gravity anomalies.

Volcanic activity is absent from the Himalaya; apparently the thickness of the
crust resulting from the conjunction of Laurasia and Gondwana is not favourable.

FROM ASIA INTO EUROPE

Westwards from the Himalaya to the Aegean Sea extends a broad belt of mountainous
country covering Afghanistan, Iran, Turkey and parts of neighbouring states. Both
northern and southern facies of the great Tethyan trough are represented as well as its
central zone, and the present mountains are extensively constructed upon the ruins of
earlier, Cainozoic orogenic chains (Chapter XIV). Great faults are known.

On the whole, Plio-Pleistocene tectonic activity was severe, even in regions little
affected by earlier movements, such as the Iranian Plateau (Schroeder 1944). There,
late-Cainozoic beds accumulated and the region became progressively more active with
increasing folding to the late-Pliocene (Wallachian) when the movements were severe,
though not alpinotype. In the general break-up and faulting, most of the area was

2 L

reworked into mountains some of which bear the smooth skylines of late-Cainozoic planation or deposition.

Along the margin of the Mesopotamia-Persian Gulf depression the Kuh-i-Ginas, Kuh-i-Siah and Kushk Kuh rise abruptly from the level coastal plain to heights of 5,000-8,000 feet. Pleistocene sediments overlying already folded and eroded Bakhtiari (Pliocene) formation on Kharag Island date the late folding and fracturing.

The Armenian highland, of even-crested ridges representing a late-Cainozoic cycle at 1,500-1,800 metres surmounted by snow-decked peaks to 4,000 metres, likewise suffered post-Miocene faulting and warping with volcanism and the formation of large lakes.

In Turkey, summit relics of Cainozoic planation are widespread. East of the Sea of Marmara and in the district about Bursa " several levels stand out sharply from one another. The highest and oldest (I), on the summit of the range, is hill country of subdued relief, its slopes consistently concave in profile, with wide trough-like valleys, the floors of which are at about 2,000 metres above sea level while the peaks rise to 2,500 metres " (Penck 1953). At lower levels a so-called upper terrace (II), " fringes the highest central mountainland as an undulating piedmont flat ". " It is bounded on the lower side by further steep slopes, giving a sharply convex break of gradient, and its edge has obviously been worked back considerably already. In some places these slopes belong to the steep relief which has developed upwards from the present-day sharply incised valleys on the mountain flanks; but in others they end below in undulating surfaces distinguished by a shallow valley-system of their own. These surfaces penetrate into the upper region as valleys and are preserved in broad fragments (III), on the intervalley divides of the north-western section of the mountains." " At the margin of the range, surface III reaches away on to the steeply tilted Neogene beds."

" The present day valleys, which give rise to the steep relief, form a fourth—the most recent—main level (IV), which is broken by terraces into a succession of several stages (intermediate levels)" (Penck 1953).

The ages suggested by Penck for these successive surfaces are: I, early Cainozoic, perhaps Oligocene; II, late Miocene; III, Levantine (Pliocene); with the deep valleys, IV, Quaternary; and these are supported by the stratigraphy and tectonics of the region. The Cainozoic rocks, mainly in the south (Cilicia) were basin-laid in semi-arid climates and include heavy conglomerates.

CYCLIC LANDSURFACES IN THE BALKANS

The passage of the Meso-Cainozoic circumvallation into Europe as the Dinaric arc has been recorded in Chapter XIV. Upon this arc, also, cymatogenic elevation was extreme following the close of the Cainozoic era and a late-Cainozoic surface is widespread through the Balkans uplifted to between 1,000 and 2,000 metres. Locally traces of a still older planation also survive, sometimes faulted into Miocene depressions; and thus rendering comparisons with Alpine geomorphology.

Most of the Balkan region falls within the Alpine orogenic zone involving Cretaceous and Eocene flysch that was folded into a mountainous terrain by the mid-Cainozoic era. No cyclic landsurfaces, therefore, can be older than Miocene in age. Many of the major uplands do indeed exhibit summit planation by what was evidently a mid-Cainozoic cycle, for the uplands are locally broken by faulting and in some of the troughs notable thicknesses of late-Miocene or Pliocene sedimentary rocks have accumulated. Notwithstanding these facts, existing regularity of summit planations indicates that the inherited topography was not a jumble of earth-blocks but was smooth with broad warpings. There was indeed a general late-Cainozoic denudational surface to which most of the present elevated plateaus should be referred. This late-Cainozoic landscape was widely, but not perfectly, planed, for above it numerous erosional relicts soar abruptly to the greatest mountain heights of the Balkan. For Greece this may be seen in the northern Peloponnese where a high surface of Miocene and early Pliocene age descends from 2,200 metres on Eurymanthos in the west to 1,000 metres upon Trapezone and allied massifs in Argolis to the east. A later, partial planation of Pliocene age stands at about 930 and 800 metres respectively. Both are deeply dissected by valleys of the Quaternary incision. Similar topography may be seen also near Delphi, where the smooth late-Cainozoic tributary valleys in a terrain of high relief (*e.g.* Mt. Parnassus) stand perched above rough deep incisions of the main rivers that post-date the cymatogenic uplift.

In the Istrian region of Jugo-Slavia the late-Cainozoic summit bevel is described as rising from about 800 metres on the Veitsberg Plateau to 1,100-1,300 metres towards Piuka Planina where the Sneznik overtops it to 1,796 metres. On the Velebit Range, which forms an orographic continuation of the coastal Karst to the south-east, a flattish summit relief again appears at 1,051-1,200 metres, and, as before, residual masses (*e.g.* Vaganski Mountain, 1,758 metres) surmount it. Still farther to the south-east, beyond the mountain cluster of Knin, the high plateau of West Bosnia and Hercegovina bears further relict peaks, some with traces of Quaternary glaciation (*e.g.* Dinara Planina (1,830 metres) and the Troglav (1,913 metres)). The general plateau level rises eastwards until upon the schist zone it stands at 1,600-1,800 metres above the sea, and in Hercegovina Machatschek (1938) actually quotes it as a wide plateau surface at 2,030 metres on the Lelja Planina, Treskavica (2,080 metres), Bjelasnica (2,067 metres), 2,230 metres in the Cvrsnica, and 2,120 metres on the Prenj Planina. The surface is generally described as undulating. Beyond the transverse depression, in which stands Trebinje, rear up the still higher mountainlands of Montenegro. The crestlines rise in elevation from west to east, and though deeply dissected by the valleys of the Tara and Piva Rivers the mountainland has not yet lost all trace of former late-Cainozoic planation, with monadnocks. In western Serbia the surface descends again to 1,100-1,200 metres. As a result of the downwarping, the plateau surface is locally strewn with late-Cainozoic gravels. Such gravel sheets indeed cross over the watershed region in Serbia between the rivers Lim and Vardar.

Some authors, pointing to the great elevations attained by the surface, have doubted that the flat summit relief of the Dinaric Karstlands was due to denudation related to earlier sea levels, and have sought explanations for planation at or near present elevations. But the deep incisions of the river valleys are themselves a proof of upheaval since the summit plain was cut, and detailed landforms within the valleys plainly show the upcast to have taken place in stages.

The nature of the summit planation is also important. River planation has been invoked under old principles; but the continued existence of steep-sided gipfels (inselbergs), and the widespread occurrence of surficial residual deposits (bauxites and their congeners) point strongly to pedimentation as the principal agency of late-Cainozoic denudation.

The present elevation of the late-Cainozoic compound landsurface may confidently be ascribed to Quaternary cymatogeny. Of special interest is the steep descent from the high plateau (well over 1,000 metres) to the floor of the Adriatic Sea. Step faulting has been described in some localities and assumed in others, but there is at least a possibility that the rapid descent of the late-Cainozoic surface to below Mediterranean level is accomplished largely by monoclinal warping, rather like the famous coastline of the Serra do Mar in Rio de Janeiro state, where, however, the open ocean has since performed a greater measure of coastal erosion than has been accomplished in the sheltered waters of the Adriatic.

The Quaternary denudation cycles are multiple and complicated by local factors such as extensive limestone terrains and underground drainage, split-nickpoints, and tectonic movements, but they fall broadly into two groups; the first group is expressed as numerous river terraces and upper valley plains commonly at elevations of 600-700 metres and sometimes associated with basins of soft late-Miocene and Pliocene sediments as along the Sava River. The high Karst surface of Postojna is also referred by Machatschek to this group; and perhaps a majority of the *poljes* or major depressions in the limestone country are assignable to this group, though freshwater Miocene and Pliocene sediments associated with some show them to be older.

This latter group includes terraces from 300 metres above sea level down to modern valley floors. Thus a flight of six terraces ranging from 60-330 metres has been recorded from the arcuate Velebit coast. Southward of the Velebit, Machatschek describes six similar terraces as fault steps associated with the coastal drowning that penetrated up the Krk Valley to Skradin. Of similar date with these longitudinal fractures is the arching of the Cretaceous limestone of the Poljica chain which caused the antecedent course of the Cetina River to the sea at Omis.

THE MODERN ATLAS MOUNTAINS

Throughout their entire extent, the existing aspect of the Atlas chains has been determined by Plio-Pleistocene or even Recent uplift followed by profound stream incision. Upon the highest parts of the ranges, Pliocene landsurfaces and deposits have been identified by many workers (Dresch 1941), with step-like pediments, partly structural, upon the flanks of the ranges.

Evident in the Rif and Tell is a late-Pliocene surface, gently bevelled and fossilised by lake conglomerates and limestones which are especially extensive also in the high plains of Constantina. Indeed, " a huge lake called Setif Lake used to cover both the Tell area, south of the Kabylies, and the Atlas area where only hard limestone islands protruded ". And in the high Atlas, Pliocene planation, quite distinct from resurrected earlier planations of the Triassic or Cretaceous, is evident upon the mountain crests at elevations between 500 and 2,000 metres (Dresch 1941). Even in the Anti-Atlas far to the west, the Pontian hamada has been upcast together with the post-Alpine folded relief (Appalachian type) that it covered.

Everywhere, although minor late-Cainozoic movements and denudation created local, prior, multicyclic reliefs, the main uplift creating the modern Atlas occurred at the Plio-Pleistocene. Later movements of lesser intensity are also evident from their topographic effects. The drainage pattern of the High Atlas, which is generally transverse to the folds and faults of the Alpine structure, also developed upon a late-Cainozoic landscape of low relief, though the rivers and streams are incised now in deep ravines that testify to the youth of the mountain chain. As one authority has written of both the High and the Tell Atlas: " the present mighty highlands are the result of Villafranchian tectonics ".

Even far south on the edge of the Sahara the domed centre of Jebel Saghro is a Pliocene plateau cut across granite and schist, and now elevated to 1,900 metres. Beneath flows of phonolite, early-Pliocene lake beds have been identified (de Sitter 1952).

THE MOUNTAINS OF WESTERN NORTH AMERICA

The Cainozoic tectonic activity with its creation of domes, anticlines, fault blocks and basins has been continued through Quaternary time, especially in the Coast Ranges, and Gilluly (1949) has considered Southern California to be currently a typical orogen. Geodetic surveys upon some of the most recent folds of the Los Angeles, Ventura and San Joaquin basins confirm that these are now growing. They are still scarcely modified by erosion, which is true also of certain fault scarps. Earthquake shocks accompany intermittent movement upon some of the fault lines.

" In the Ventura Basin, 5,000 feet of lower Pleistocene beds have been turned up so as to have dips of 30-90° bevelled by erosion and covered by about 300 feet of upper-Pleistocene fanglomerates. The fossil *Equus occidentalis* occurs both above and below the angular unconformity, apparently without change, and indicates that the structure was formed during a very short period of time " (Eardley 1962). Many records of folding and tilting in Pliocene and even Pleistocene strata also derive from the region of the St. Elias Range in Alaska.

Orogenic movements were climacteric at the close of the Pliocene and again in the mid-Pleistocene. Taliaferro has considered the former to be stronger in the western Coast Ranges, the latter in the eastern. He has pointed out also that where the granitic basement stood at shallow depths failure was by faulting, where the superincumbent sediments were thick (8,000-20,000 feet) folding and thrusting occurred. In addition to the thrusts, major transverse faults sometimes cut completely across the ranges.

The San Andreas Fault, at least 600 miles long, is a right lateral megashear along which recent shifts measurable in miles have been claimed through Southern California though near San Francisco, where 5 cm. per year is the present rate of displacement, 3,000 feet is the accepted recent shift. The movement cuts across late-Pliocene and mid-Pleistocene structures, but there was little volcanic activity in the Coast Ranges compared with the Cascades and Sierra Nevada. Some geologists have recently suggested that the San Andreas fault is very old and, like the Alpine fault of New Zealand, has a cumulative lateral shift of 200 or 300 miles, by which Baja California was moved north-north-west from the vicinity of Cape Jalisco and the Gulf of California was formed. The floor of the Gulf is of oceanic-type basalt.

As in New Zealand, profound geographical changes ensued upon the mid-Pleistocene orogeny. The Cainozoic depositional troughs were elevated, the Sierra Nevada, which had begun to rise before the Quaternary, was elevated to its full height by uplift and tilting to the west. Contrariwise, the Owens Valley and other blocks sank down. " In the Los Angeles Basin, stream-cut terraces and wave-cut surfaces are folded into anticlines and synclines whose relief is several hundred feet " (Gilluly 1963). At the coast, border segments of large size foundered into the continental shelf to be represented now by islands or by irregular submarine topography like that of the emergent Coast Ranges (Fig. 213). Indeed the present shoreline is clearly ephemeral; the submarine topography of ridges, basins, banks and seamounts comparable in size to features on the adjacent land could not more plainly express the view that the continental shelf here is part of the great orogenic zone to which the Coast Ranges belong (p. 551).

In Mexico, the Baucarit formation of basalts and conglomerates containing pebbles from the mid-Cainozoic granites was laid down during late-Pliocene and Quaternary time in the troughs of the earlier folds. The Baucarit has in turn been dislocated by normal and thrust faults, and gently warped like the contemporaneous deposits of California. R. E. King (1939) has assigned the main uplift of the Sierra Madre Plateau to this late phase of orogeny, making it coeval with formation of the Gulf of California. Denudation has gone on *pari passu* with tectonic movements, and even across the mid-Pleistocene displacements of California, numerous terraces have been cut.

The Central Cordillera of Guatemala carries a deeply weathered erosion surface recently uplifted to 2,000 metres but its age is uncertain.

At the southern end of the cordilleran belt even small islands of fold mountain structure exhibit summit planations. On Puerto Rico an " older peneplain rose from 1,600 feet about the Luquillo Mountains, to 3,000 feet between Adjuntas and Lares. On the adjacent Virgin Islands the same planation is found at 1,000 feet in St. John and there is a lower planation that descends from 600 feet above to 200 feet below sea level off Tortola. The older planation in Virgin Islands is of early-Eocene age. There are traces of an intermediate surface 500 feet below this older erosional plain; and the most extensive planed surface which is still later descends beneath mid-Cainozoic coastal plain sediments.

During the late Cainozoic and Pleistocene occurred an especial phase of high-angle faulting affecting both Nevadan and Laramide belts as well as the Coast Ranges. The faults are both concordant and discordant to the older structures and are manifested either as faulted mountain fronts (of which the Wasatch Range serves as an example for scores of others) or as a zone of elongated trench-making faults (*e.g.* Rocky Mountain Trench near Missoula) extending from New Mexico to British Columbia and possibly the Yukon. In Idaho and surrounding districts " tensional rifting by stresses related to those of the the the right-lateral, strike-slip, San Andreas fault system " has been claimed by Hamilton. In the south were generated the fault-blocks of the Basin and Range province (Nolan 1943) (p. 502), and the Pliocene Rio Grande trough filled near Albuquerque to depths of 5,000 to 9,000 feet with pebbly Santa Fe formation.

Major uplift of the Colorado Plateau to between 6,000 and 8,000 feet above the sea took place in two phases of which the first (late Miocene to early Pliocene) was accompanied by great volcanic outbursts about the periphery and intrusion of laccolites within the plateau area. The second phase, of much greater uplift, (late Pliocene to Recent) permitted the famous canyon to be cut and lesser volcanic cones to be built.

The thickness of crust, a normal 30 km. beneath the Great Basin, increases to 45 km. below the Colorado Plateau. Both Gilluly (1963) and Holmes (1964) explain this as due to transfer of relatively light material at the base of the crust: " erosion of the base of the crust in one place and addition to the crust in another ".

Drainage patterns, many of which were inherited from the early-Cainozoic cycle of denudation and basin fill, have in many instances not survived the recent movements but others have been maintained across the rising sectors as antecedent gorges such as the Shoshone through the northern end of the Bighorn Mountains, the North Platte which, after cutting through the mountains to escape from North Park, crosses both the Seminole and Laramie Hills before reaching the Great Plains, and (greatest of all) the Grand Canyon of the Colorado River.

Conversely, the continental divide in the upcast regions is often an insignificant topographic feature, or takes an anomalous and sometimes absurd route through the ranges and basins.

Throughout the mountain belt as a whole remnants of two (summit and sub-summit) earlier planations have been noted standing upon the highest country, from which they are often warped down into basins of Cainozoic deposition, *e.g.* from Bighorn Mountains into the Wyoming Basin or from the summits of the Sierra Nevada about Mt. Whitney (where two planations are visible) westwards down towards the San

Joaquin Valley where the final descent is accomplished by faulting in series *en echelon* to the valley.* The measure of differential warping often exceeds 5,000 feet and involves the continental divide.† Thus in Colorado where the railroad climbs to Rollins Pass (11,680 feet) by a spiral in the west and a double zig-zag in the east the crestline of the divide is still very even above 12,000 feet for miles on either side of the pass, and spurs and detached mountains carry the same bevel, descending below 10,000 feet in a few miles, far to the east.

Almost the whole of the elevated region of western United States is underlain by an earth layer with seismic velocity 7·9 or less which Thompson and Talwani (1964) regard as upper mantle (subcrust) rather than basal crust. This concept accords well with the evident continuation of the South-East Pacific Ridge structure beneath the North American continent (p. 579).

The higher and older surface is characteristically smoother and both are described for Wyoming by Bradley (1936) as originally pedimented and bearing conglomerates rather than the deep residual soils expectable upon a peneplain. Below these planations only deep valleys or river terraces of Quaternary dissection are manifest. The ages of these greatly warped surfaces are defined by reference to unconformities in adjacent sedimentary basins and though, bearing in mind the highly local nature of Cainozoic deformation in the mountainbelt, the two surfaces may not be of precisely the same ages throughout, there can be little doubt that they represent two phases of early- and late-Cainozoic planation respectively.

A typical study for dating was made by Bradley (1936) along the north flank of the Uinta Mountains:

" Long narrow remnants of four old erosion surfaces slope gently northward from the north flank of the Uinta Range and truncate the upturned edges of hard and soft beds. The Gilbert Peak erosion surface, which is the highest and oldest of these surfaces, once extended from the crest of the range at an altitude of about 13,000 feet to the centre of the Green River Basin. Because undisturbed remnants of this surface have gradients ranging from about 400 feet to the mile near the crest of the range to 55 feet to the mile 35 miles out in the basin, because island mounts of limestone rise rather abruptly from it, and because it apparently had a soil mantle but is covered in most places by conglomerate, this surface is interpreted as a piedmont formed in a semi-arid or arid climate. At the time the Gilbert Peak surface was cut the Green River Basin was filled to a greater depth than now with Eocene sedimentary rocks. The Gilbert Peak erosion surface truncated these rocks at very low angles and extended northwards across them as a continuous plain . . .

" The Bishop Conglomerate, which covers much of the Gilbert Peak surface, is coarse-grained and very poorly sorted and fills the deepest concavity in the profile of

---

* Personal communication, Dr. H. E. Wheeler.

† See, for instance, U.S.G.S. Topo. Sheet " Encampment ", or the Quadrangles " Saratoga " and " Savery ".

the pediment, where it is about 200 feet thick. The same streams that cut the Gilbert Peak pediment deposited the Bishop Conglomerate . . .

" No fossils have been found in the Bishop Conglomerate, but the Gilbert Peak surface truncates the latest-Eocene rocks and yet it is distinctly older than the Brown's Park formation (late Miocene or early Pliocene). Hence the Gilbert Peak surface and the Bishop Conglomerate are either Miocene or Oligocene . . .

" About 400-500 feet below the remnants of the Gilbert Peak surface these same streams later cut the less extensive Bear Mountain erosion surface. The characteristics of the Bear Mountain surface are so nearly identical with those of the Gilbert Peak surface that it is regarded as a pediment formed under arid conditions probably closely similar to those which prevailed while the Gilbert Peak surface was being cut. Correlated with the Bear Mountain surface are two large, rather smooth-floored valleys, the Brown's Park Valley and Summit Valley. These valleys are in the eastern part of the Uinta Range and are each roughly parallel to the range axis. The floor of the Brown's Park Valley descends beneath the Brown's Park formation which is of upper-Miocene or Pliocene age. As there is no indication that the deposition of the Brown's Park formation did not follow immediately the completion of the Bear Mountain surface, that surface is probably also of essentially this geologic age."

. . . " Along the Black's and Smith Forks of the Green River are remnants of two Pleistocene erosion surfaces. The older of these, the Tipperary surface, is about 150 feet below the Bear Mountain surface, and the younger, the Lyman surface, is about 50-75 feet below the Tipperary. Both, however, merge upstream with the present flood-plains."

The Gilbert Peak surface probably correlates with Blackwelder's Union Pass surface remnants of which survive at elevations of 8,500-9,500 feet on the Gros Ventre and Wind River ranges. A thousand feet below the Union Pass surface is the Black Rock surface. Both surfaces were pedimented, and the streams have been again rejuvenated and incised their beds 1,000 feet and more below the Black Rock surface. In other parts of the mountain belt, Beartooth and Bighorn Ranges, the Black Hills, and the Park Range in the south, only a single high-level planation is present. This is thought to represent the later of the two Cainozoic erosional cycles.

The ages assigned to the summit and sub-summit surfaces of the Wyoming Rockies by Bradley are confirmed by a number of additional deposits on the sub-summit surface. Quoted by Eardley are the Split Rock tuff in the Sweetwater Basin, the Miocene beds at the south end of the Wind River Range, the Camp Davis formation of Jackson Hole and the Hoback formation.

F. E. Matthes deciphered two parallel sequences of geomorphic cycles in the Kern River—Mt. Whitney and Yosemite areas respectively. The first is: Summit, sub-Summit, High Valley or Chagoopa and Canyon cycles; the second: " Eocene ", Broad Valley, Mountain Valley and Canyon cycles. The ages which he assigned, partly confirmed by Potassium—Argon datings on some of the basalt flows poured out upon the surfaces (Dalrymple 1963), are pre-Miocene, Miocene, Pliocene and Pleistocene in order. Despite the very great differential movements of the Rocky Mountain-Nevadan mountainland during Cainozoic time, therefore, the geomorphic history evidently synchronises with the Schooley and later cycles of the Appalachian region (p. 364). The Rocky Mountain Front therefore post-dates the Harrisburg cycle, and is carved into the flank of a post-Miocene upwarp as part of the development of the pedimented Pliocene landscape of the Great Plains while the resulting landwaste accumulated to the east as the Ogalalla Formation (p. 373).

In the Klamath region of Oregon an upland surface of uncertain age bevels both the Cascade and Coast Ranges with warping towards the Willamette-Puget depression. The upland was elevated and dissected by broad valleys during the late Cainozoic before further uplifts totalling 2,000 feet enabled the deep river valleys to be cut. These were later deepened and altered by glaciation. Summit bevels in the Coast Ranges were more severely affected during the Pliocene to mid-Pleistocene orogeny, being broken and jostled to different attitudes on the various fault blocks of that heterogeneous geosyncline.

Through British Columbia and the Canadian Rockies only one major high-level planation, presumably the later, is displayed (Bostock 1948). From the wide and shallow valleys of this upland the streams flow through narrow canyons to the floors of the huge flat-bottomed, steep-sided valleys enlarged by Pleistocene glaciers. Towards the coast the upland may be present at 3,000 feet rising rapidly inland to 7,000 feet and even beyond 10,000 feet on the St. Elias Mountains. Though the surface is somewhat irregular and is surmounted by major mountain massifs, the differences of elevation are due primarily to uneven uplift.

The Stikine Plateau and the Selkirk and Purcell Ranges all bear the former undulating summit planation, usually around 6,000 feet, and in the extreme north of the Canadian Rockies the Richardson Mountains are flat-crested at 4,000 feet. Even the Yukon Plateau and the Brooks Range of Northern Alaska overlooking the Arctic tundra bear extensive upland erosion surfaces, on the latter between 5,000 and 6,000 feet above sea level. Bostock (1948) shows it, indeed, to have been ubiquitous throughout the Canadian cordillera, cut across Mesozoic and Cainozoic sedimentary and volcanic rocks and the intrusive granites of the coastal batholith.

On the flanks of the Canadian Rockies through Alberta, an older cyclic erosion surface emerges from beneath a massive bed of earliest-Oligocene conglomerate. There is little suggestion of this, as an older bevel, upon the crests of the neighbouring peaks or ranges; but two cycles of planation have been recorded from the Yukon Plateau and Skeena Mountains amid the central plateaus; and in the far west where the regional summit planation culminates extensively at 8,000-10,000 feet upon the St. Elias Mountains, great blocky peaks rise precipitously as the Icefield Ranges as much as 8,000 feet higher. " The relatively smooth and rolling character of the upper parts of many of the great peaks, notably the summit area of Mt. Logan's mighty block, including four satellite peaks more than 18,000 feet high . . . suggest that formerly a surface of more even topography topped those ranges at a level 5,000-8,000 feet above that of the lesser peaks." If these relics truly indicate an early-Cainozoic planation then uplift of 8,000-9,000 feet is indicated for the region in mid-Cainozoic time, and a further 9,000-10,000 feet at the end of the Cainozoic era, subsequently to which profound valleys were excavated and filled with thousands of feet of Pleistocene ice. In the granite country of the Coastal Batholith the depth and steepness of the U-shaped valley sides is quite remarkable.

Towards the coast the undulating late-Cainozoic surface is rapidly warped down. On Vancouver Island " the mountains characteristically show remnants of a subdued, rolling surface that resembles the plateaus of the Interior system. . . . In the southern part of the island the plateau surface was peneplaned, with only a few rounded hills rising above it before it was uplifted some 1,500 feet. In the central part of the island the evenness is less marked, and the surface noted in the ranges is roughly 5,000 feet or more above the sea " (Bostock 1948). On Queen Charlotte Islands the surface stands between 2,000 and 3,000 feet.

THE FAR EAST DURING QUATERNARY TIME

The modern aspect of eastern Asia was largely created by strong Quaternary land movements that in general emphasised earlier lineaments. The Cainozoic geosyncline continued to subside and to receive sediment in vastly increased supply, building the great plain of China and the lowland of Manchukuo (Fig. 88). Thus late-Pliocene tilting caused lakes of the widespread Sanmen stage. Along the lower Yangtze, sedimentation has rather lagged behind subsidence causing the numerous lakes and abandoned river channels of that region (Fig. 87).

The island arcs in particular assumed their present form during the Quaternary. Thus Japan which during the late Miocene had occupied only half its present area expanded greatly during the late Pliocene and was strongly elevated in the Pleistocene when faulting was very active. Quaternary differential movements have been delineated on a map by Hatori et al. (1964). Both the Kitakami mountainland and Chugoku mountains show summit bevels and " staircase morphology ". Kaneko (1964) has emphasised the importance of Quaternary faulting (with wrench movements) in the topography of south Kanto district, which Matsuda thought was related to undulatory deformation of the underlying mantle at depths of 15-25 km.

Bevelled crestlines are not lacking upon many of the uplifted ranges of the mainland. The Anadyr and Kolyma ranges show a broad bevelling at 4,000-5,000 feet with occasionally a higher set of plateaus around 5,400 feet, some formed of basaltic outflows. The Sikhota Alin has Cainozoic basalts on both flanks, and in two places these basalts arch over the crest exceeding 6,000 feet as they do so. In these respects the Great Khingan which runs parallel 700 miles to the west is similar. Both these ranges show extensive bevels between 3,500 and 4,000 feet above sea level as also do the Burein and

Turana Mountains west of the lower Amur River. The rocks bevelled are of many different ages up to Cretaceous so the bevel is Cainozoic. Upon it lie the basalts, so the bevel has been much disturbed by Plio-Pleistocene movements.

In the Korean highlands a bevel standing at nearly 4,000 feet has flat-topped residuals in places at over 6,000 feet so that possibly early- and late-Cainozoic erosion cycles are represented. There are also traces of a later, Plio- or Pleistocene, cycle at 2,000-2,200 feet. Faults of Quaternary age appear also upon the older portions of the mainland such as Shantung.

In Indo-China, Pliocene planation bevels folded Miocene rocks and is itself overlain by a torrential conglomerate following powerful Pliocene dislocations which raised the broken fragments of the planed surface to irregular and unusual elevations. Thus while it stands at an average of 3,000-4,500 feet, in Tran Ninh it attains 4,000-5,000 feet in the zones of maximum elevation. Fanglomerates reach a thickness of 1,000 feet in this region west of Fan Si Pan.

A second cycle, which began in the southern Annam chain with fresh gravels and ended with a planed surface now at 2,000-3,000 feet elevation, seems to have been a partial cycle due to differential movement as it may have been formed at the same time that basins formed in Cambodia. These movements of de-levelling reached 2,000 feet magnitude in the middle of northern Indo-China and 3,000 feet in southern Annam. Fromaget writes of their date: " Entirely contained within the upper-Pliocene, these latest movements terminate the Indo-Chinese paroxysms of the Himalayan phase of plication ".

The early Pleistocene is remarkable for the deposition of loess and red muds upon the planed landscape of the Tran Ninh cycle, and thus ties up with the Malan loess of China. The fifth and last cycle, covering the mid- and late Quaternary is a phase of terrace cutting, especially on the coast of Tongking, in central and southern Annam and in Cambodia. In several ways, however, movements in Thailand and Cambodia reverse those of Annam, for depression is repeated instead of uplift.

Equally profound geographic changes affected the archipelago of South-East Asia, especially the western sector including Burma. Areas of moderate Plio-Pleistocene folding cover much of Burma, Sumatra, north Java, east Borneo and south Celebes where late-Cainozoic sediments thousands of metres thick were folded and elevated. Uplift was locally considerable. In the island of Ceram it amounted to almost 10,000 feet and on Timor unfolded Pleistocene limestones are at a height of more than 4,000 feet above present sea level. Pliocene folding affected Malaya, which is sliced by a left-lateral megashear, and parts of Sumatra, and in Burma sediments of the central geosyncline (p. 511) were thrown into anticlines and synclines, sometimes faulted, and the Pegu Yoma rose into existence.

Sub-recent geographic changes are indicated by the drowned river pattern that traverses the shallow bottom (depth 200 feet) between Sumatra, Java and Borneo (Fig. 13) which accounts for the curious disposition of species among river fish in the region. Elevated and tilted Pliocene planations are evident: thus in northern Luzon of the Philippines an extensive early-Pleistocene plain cut across Pliocene limestones has been uplifted 5,000-7,000 feet and numerous torrential streams have cut the uplifted block into many V-shaped canyons and knife-edged ridges (Dickerson 1941). Between Surabaja and Semarang on the northern aspect of Java, where an average of more than 2,000 metres of Cainozoic strata was denuded to near sea level, the plain was elevated between 100 and 200 metres and the rivers have incised their courses accordingly. In Atcheen, northern Sumatra, the amount of elevation appears to be about 1,000 metres and a rift valley is reported between longitudinal faults. Along the Burmese coastline, too, drowned landscapes and elevated coral reefs attest the importance of differential land movement during the Quaternary era.

Earth movements still continue abundantly throughout South-East Asia which is one of the most tectonically active regions of the globe.

THE PLATEAU OF TIBET-SIKANG-TSINGHAI

At the heart of Asia is a mighty plateau extending through 35° of longitude from the Pamir in the west to the Yunling scarp in the east. In maximum range north-south it extends from the Nan Shan to the borders of Burma. Not all of it belongs to the belt of Meso- or Cainozoic circumvallation, the northern parts are older, but the region is largely bounded by fold mountain ranges—the Kuen Lun and Nan Shan, the Kailas Ranges and the mountains of the Yunnan arc. Separate ranges traverse the plateau from west to east. They appear to be extensively block-faulted though the details remain to be explored.

Nearly the whole region exceeds 12,000 feet of elevation, and much of it is at 15,000 feet with mountain peaks and ranges rising above 20,000 feet. No other region on earth sustains over such an area so stupendous an elevation. Western Tibet, where the ranges are most numerous, is the most rugged region in the world and the mountain faces carved from slices of Shaksgam granite in the western Karakoram are without rival amid mountain scenery. Yet, due allowance being made for the difference of altitude, the region differs from neighbouring parts of Mongolia and China in degree rather than in kind. The landscape of interior basins and bounding ranges is of Mongolian type and appears to have been similar and composed of the same elements of structure and morphology until the great disruptions of late-Pliocene and Pleistocene time when its excessive altitude was achieved by arching and faulting.

Hydrologically the region falls into two clearly distinct parts: the western with independent basins of centripetal drainage, standing often above 15,000 feet, and each with the lowest part occupied by a lake rimmed with the ancient shorelines and alluvial fans of more humid times, e.g. Nam Tso; and a southern and eastern part drained by strong headwater rivers of the Brahmaputra, Salween, Mekong and Yangtze Kiang Rivers, all of which escape through profound antecedent gorges (p. 424).

With the Tibetan plateau is to be considered the Tien Shan. With a total length exceeding 1,200 miles and a breadth of nearly 200 miles the Tien Shan is one of the outstanding mountain systems of Asia, overlooking the basins of Dzungaria on the north and Tarim on the south. The best-known part of the range is Bogdo Ola east of Urumchi towering in 21,000 feet peaks above the Turfan lowland at 720 feet *below sea level*. Yet this stupendous chain, with cliffs 10,000 feet high, is no primary folded range but is now in its third existence as a mountain chain. Twice before, at least, it has been obliterated by erosion. Like so many of the ranges of Central Asia the first Tien Shan was a late-Palæozoic range that was planed by erosion during the early-Mesozoic. During the Jurassic the site was covered by Jurassic continental sediments that in their turn were crumpled isoclinally during the late Jurassic and then bevelled by an early-Cretaceous pediplain. This in turn received a cover of Cretaceous and Cainozoic formations with sundry hiatuses corresponding with local crustal movement. From this cover the chain has once more arisen, as a series of block-faulted ranges unaccompanied by volcanism. The faults are independent of the strikes of earlier folds.

Other vertical displacements by faulting exceeding 10,000 feet are known in Mongolia, *e.g.* Baga Bogdo which stands 7,000 feet above the 2,600 feet thick sedimentary fill of Tsagan Nor.

From Tibet into Europe the mountain garland—Hindu Kush, Elburz and Caucasus Ranges, and the Anatolian mountains of Turkey to the Bosphorus—is everywhere a product of uplift during Pliocene to Recent time, with high passes and deep valleys of Quaternary incision. Volcanic activity built huge cones of andesite or trachyte, with basalt, *e.g.* Mts. Ararat and Demavend, and sometimes dammed lakes at high levels.

On the northern border of Caucasus a complementary sunkland has received vast quantities of Quaternary sediment.

THE MODERN ALPS

Though the Alpine orogenic structures, produced at the end of the Oligocene and Miocene periods, are among the most familiar of geologic phenomena, it is less often realised that the present mountains owe little of their form and elevation directly to those structures. Instead, each of the Cainozoic orogenic phases was followed by an interval wherein denudation reduced most of the country to low relief; and it was these Pliocene lowlands, mightily uplifted at the close of the Cainozoic era, that formed the initial arched surface from which most of the Alpine peaks and valleys were carved. Except perhaps in Styria, little of the initial surface now remains: deep valleys had been incised into it even prior to the onset of Pleistocene glaciation, but accordances of ridge crests still permit recognition of the Alpine " gipfelflur " as a former entity.

The gipfelflur, which is independent of the folded structure and, within wide limits, of the nature of the bedrock, presents considerable undulations but is sensibly smooth and homogeneous when viewed over a large area. It is really a series of local partial planations upon which the " gipfels " stand as steep-sided residuals. " The calcareous pre-Alps, especially in the eastern part of the chain, deploy broad undulating surfaces which, truncating the folded beds, carry a cover of fluviatile gravels derived from the high crystalline massifs " (Baulig 1952).

For the Gurktaler Alps Spreitzer (1951) has given two interpretations of such polycyclic features, one involving uniform uplift, the other warping, of which the latter is the more convincing.

Penck (1953), to whom we owe a general account of the gipfelflur, has described its form as owing much to minor warping upon the main arch. " If one thinks of it as a surface which is tangential to the peaks and to the summits of the intervalley divides, that surface does not form a simple arch, including the whole mountain system from north to south; but it has in cross section the form of an arch compounded of undulations. In the region of each ridge zone, it swings up as a wave crest, and it sinks like a wave trough along each zone of longitudinal valleys ". Again, " The Alpine gipfelflur shows gentle curvature up and down, not only in its cross section but in its longitudinal section as well ". Transverse corrugations thus produce clumps of mountains on the rises, e.g. Bernese Alps, Todi group, Silvretta group, Bernina group. " In between, the gipfelflur sinks down, and most of the great transverse valleys, and the low gaps forming passes, are sunk in these areas of depression ". " *The course of the main Alpine valleys is on the whole independent of the structure of the folds and nappes*, and it is from these valleys that the complete disintegration of the whole mountain system into the well-known sea of peaks has taken its start." One is reminded of Adkin's report upon the Tararua Ranges, New Zealand (p. 525).

In the transitional zone between the Alps and the Karst the main plateau at 1,000 metres has been much broken up. About Lubuljana local authorities regard it as Pontian on the basis that it transgresses Sarmatian deposits but carries Pontian beds. This may be an older surface than the gipfelflur.

Broadly, two cyclic surfaces appear to be involved in the later history of the Alps, an older which passes above the gipfel summits and which in its development shed the Miocene molasse, and a younger which is the undulating surface from which the gipfels rise and which is apparently Pliocene in age. Both, of course, were involved in the Pleistocene upheaval. The folded and faulted Jura was likewise bevelled during the Pliocene, and renewed movement on old axes bent the summit bevels of the Jura again in the Pleistocene (Wegmann 1962).

Indeed, the Alpine foreland in general exhibits a bevelling which may locally cut across Neogene strata and forms the slightly uneven surface which underlies the Pleistocene outwash gravels. This is presumably the morphological equivalent of the gipfelflur.

In a few places folding and thrusting involving rocks as young as Pliocene has accompanied the cymatogeny. In the sub-Carpathians of Romania, where the pre-glacial Smeuret platform was carried up to over 1,000 metres, all the Pliocene beds are intensely folded (Popp 1933).

The Pyrenees, also, exhibit fragments of Miocene lowland now elevated and tilted outward from the axis of the chain where the " plate-forme d'Aston " reaches 1,800-1,900 metres altitude (de Sitter 1952). " On its broad back it carries mountain peaks, remodelled by Quaternary glaciers, that do not rise more than 600 or 700 metres above its level."

Finally, in southern Spain a "flat relief" appears between 2,000 and 3,150 metres upon the highest regions of the Sierra Nevada (Machatschek 1955) and from it gipfels rise to beyond 3,400 metres. This surface has been described as a Miocene surface coeval with laying down of the molasse, and subsequently upwarped. Widespread bevels between 1,000 and 1,100 metres are post-Miocene and well into the Pliocene. All are now greatly upheaved, and the same youthful cymatogeny has elevated the Pliocene strand formations to 450 metres near Lorca.

Throughout the European mountain welt Quaternary berms and river terraces (some of which are associated with interglacial episodes) are much in evidence.

CONCLUSION

In conclusion, therefore, modern mountains are everywhere the result not of orogenic periods of crustal crumpling, but of upheaval dominantly cymatogenic, beginning towards the close of the Cainozoic era, that elevated a rolling Pliocene lowland surmounted in places by relics of an earlier, smoother planation of approximately mid-Cainozoic age. From the domes and arches so created, Quaternary denudation (both subaerial and subglacial) has sculped the existing chains. Thus de Sitter, as long ago as 1952 wrote; "Modern tectonic theory, strongly influenced by the Alps, attempts to establish a causal connection between tangential compression (as expressed by folds, faults and nappes) on the one hand and a succeeding mountain uplift on the other. But Pliocene uplifts of virtually equal magnitude have taken place not only in the Alps, which were tremendously compressed from the Cretaceous to the Miocene, but also in the Pyrenees, strongly compressed but mainly without nappes in the Cretaceous and Eocene, the High Atlas, moderately compressed in the Eocene and Miocene, and the Anti-Atlas, not compressed since the pre-Cambrian. Vertical uplifts of this sort are better considered causally connected with contemporary phases . . . than with preceding phases ". We agree, and extend the concept to all the currently mountainous regions of the globe.

SUMMARY AND CORRELATIONS

The major tectonic and denudational episodes of late-Mesozoic to Recent mountainlands show similarities that imply a global control of timing and, to a lesser extent, of type of deformation. With greater variety of detail due to greater relative uplift, the cyclic landforms and the history of the mountainlands also agree with the global synthesis for the plainlands adduced for the southern hemisphere in Table IX; and surely a reasonable conclusion at which to arrive from a review of the landscape features of a single planet is that all these have been controlled, under erosion and deposition, by vertical tectonic activity originating within the mantle zone of the earth body.

PART E

THE OCEANIC BASINS

CHAPTER XVI

FORMS AND FEATURES OF OCEANIC BASINS

The Oceanic Basins. The Floors of the Oceans. Continental Shelves and Slopes. Submarine Canyons. Ages of Continental Shelves. Geomorphology of Continental Shelves. Shelves of the Continents. Seamounts and Guyots. Island Types. Island Arcs. The Great Suboceanic Ridges. Rock Constitution of Suboceanic Ridges. The Pattern of Suboceanic Ridges. The Importance of the Cretaceous Period.

The Oceanic Basins

The oceans are major elements of earth scenery, and the size and shapes of the oceanic basins, the nature of their bounding continents and included islands, their deeps and shoals, now command attention. The average depths of the great oceanic basins approximate closely (Table XIII) and the mean depths (which exclude the overdeep tectonic troughs and the submarine ridges) even more so.

TABLE XIII

Ocean	Area (millions sq. miles)	Average Depth feet	Average Depth (outside continental shelves
Whole Ocean	140	12,000	12,500
Pacific	64	14,000	14,200
Atlantic	32	12,900	13,100
Indian	28·5	12,900	13,100
Arctic	5·5	4,100	10,000
Minor Seas	10		

Ewing and his co-workers have shown by refraction shooting (1937, 1940) that beneath a veneer of bottom sediment the floors of all the major basins are of similar composition, approximating to basalt. The thickness of the basalt shell above the Mohorovičić discontinuity is usually between 5 and 10 km. (Fig. 205) and the similar depths of the oceanic floors are therefore a direct result of crustal isostasy. Judged upon volcanic effusions in oceanic islands the basalt is typically olivinic; but minor areas occur on all the ocean bottoms where a less basic, tholeiitic type is present.

Over vast regions the form of the oceanic floor is at present imperfectly known; but the wonderfully increased detail and accuracy of charts, following the invention of Sonar, gives hope that the details of the ocean floor may one day be as familiar as the topography of the lands.

THE FLOORS OF THE OCEANS

The relief of the sea bottom is of the same order as that of the lands (*i.e.* 10,000 metres) but is related inversely for whereas the greatest elevations of the lands are found along linear mountain ranges, the greatest depths of the ocean are found in long, narrow troughs or " deeps " All but three of these deeps are confined to the Pacific Basin, and all are marginally situated with respect to mountainous coasts or festoons of islands. They generally show a low rate of heat flow from the interior of the earth.

The rest of the open ocean floor resembles the face of the lands with hills and valley-depressions, basin plains, plateaus and ridges, and volcanic mountains; but many of the outlines are subdued, and topographic contrasts are less sharp.   Down to the greatest depths, the bottom profile is much more rugged than has been generally assumed, a large stretch of flat bottom being exceptional unless it represents abyssal

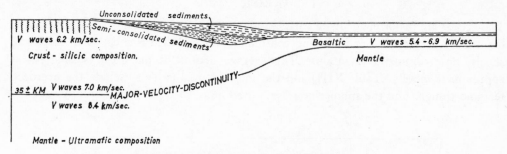

FIG. 205.   Nature of continental crust and oceanic crust on New Jersey
continental margin.   *after M. Ewing and F. Press.*

basins filled with sediment.   Hard bottom is of frequent occurrence especially in the Pacific and Indian Oceans, where lava flows are apparently extensive.   Doubtless much of the bottom relief has a permanence denied to subaerial relief which is subjected to active weathering and denudation.   Nevertheless, we must be chary of minimising the rôle of submarine erosion for the waters are not necessarily quiet at great depths: turbidity currents occur far out in the North Atlantic Basin, hundreds of miles from land (Ericson 1952), and global and tidal currents evidently possess velocity and power unsuspected until demonstrated by Pettersen where they stream from the ocean depths across the shallow continental shelves.

Most bottom relief is doubtless either tectonic or volcanic in origin.   Thus fault scarps over 3,000 feet high have been presumed, and parallel ridges and troughs in the Gulf of Aden have been interpreted as a system of faulted earth blocks.   Anticlinal and monoclinal ridges, fault scarps and volcanic accumulations may grow under the slower tempo of submarine denudation to greater potential heights than on the lands where destruction follows swiftly upon the initial displacements and occurs *pari passu* with all later tectonic or volcanic stages.

No features comparable with folded mountain ranges have been recorded from within the great oceanic basins. There is, indeed, no evidence from the deep ocean floors of the repeated cycles of erosion, accumulation, deep burial, metamorphism and uplift characteristic of continental orogens, and the evident conclusion is that these operations are dependent in part upon the existence of a continental raft that can sink deeply into the crustal substratum, and function partly by the direct energy of the sun manifested through subaerial denudation.

Wide plains of abyssal deposition are sometimes found in situations far from sediment-providing land. Certain of these sediments have accumulated without disturbance grain by grain. At shallower depths they are often composed, as oozes, of

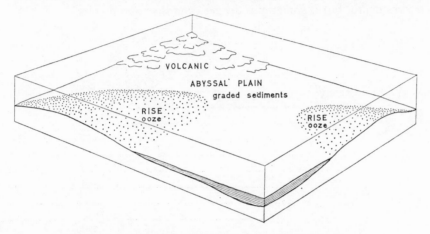

FIG. 206. Distribution of characteristic ocean floor sediments.

the tests of foraminifera and other organisms. At greater depths they are lutites, and below 2,400 fathoms, where all the carbonate has been dissolved out, they are red residual clays. Notwithstanding, over much of the ocean floor (amounting perhaps to 90 per cent. of the North Atlantic Basin) bottom sediment is disturbed and coarser grades are transported by turbidity currents, perhaps originating in slumps at higher levels hundreds of miles away (Ericson, Ewing and Heezen 1952). Material transported in the fluid state by these currents is nevertheless capable of sorting as the load is finally dropped. Indeed, Ewing and Heezen (1956) quote " an abyssal plain type of topography " and test cores " consisting of alternating layers of clay and well-sorted and frequently graded beds of sand or silt " as " two invariable evidences of turbidity current action ". Cores taken from small rises above the general level of the abyssal plains do not show these alternating layers (Fig. 206).

Studies by the seismic reflection method indicate that the total thickness of sediment in the open ocean basins ranges from nothing up to a few kilometres, though individual reflecting horizons may be continuous over distances of hundreds of miles.

CONTINENTAL SHELVES AND SLOPES

Ordinary maps do not reveal the true outlines of the continents. Broad marginal areas disappear beneath the oceanic waters as a gently sloping platform which may be as narrow as 4 miles or as wide as 150 miles, with exceptional areas (*e.g.* off Newfoundland, Falkland Islands) exceeding 200 miles. This platform makes the *continental shelf* (Fig. 207) and beyond it the gradient steepens to about 1:15 as the *continental slope* which leads down to greater depths, usually the main oceanic floor. Occasionally the continental slope is interrupted by a wide terrace, termed by Shepard (1948) the *continental borderland*. The break of slope at the outer edge of the continental shelf is commonly at 150 metres depth, but is sometimes deeper even than 400 metres.

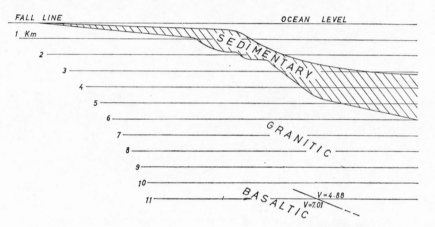

FIG. 207. Continental shelf and slope of the eastern United States, with crustal structure determined from seismic data. *after M. Ewing.*

Including the shallow epeiric seas such as Hudson Bay, the North Sea, the Yellow Sea and parts of the Arctic Ocean, altogether some 13 per cent. of the continental area, amounting to 10 million sq. miles, has been yielded to the oceans which overspill their basins. Echo-sounding has revealed the form of the continental shelves in great detail wherever such surveys have been carried out, and the reader may be interested to compare the old charts with the new in the offshore zones of, for instance, the United States. The surface of the shelf is less regular than was commonly supposed, and differs only slightly from that of the emergent coastal plains. In some areas the irregularities derive from drowning of formerly subaerial topography and a continuation of the Pliocene cyclic landsurface of the coastlands can nowadays be recognized in seismic profiles penetrating through the smooth depositional upper surface of later offshore sediments. Recent soundings also indicate a surprising number of areas where the shelf is almost bare of sediment (*e.g.* along the coast of California), and there are many instances where the outer shelves are composed of bare rock, cobbles or boulders.

Refraction shooting, too (Ewing *et al.* 1937), discloses that the blanket of Cainozoic sediment resting upon bedrock sometimes thins towards the outer edge of the shelf.

Though the continental shelves and borderlands occur within the geographical boundaries of the oceans and owe much of their form and extent to marine agencies, they are indubitably part of the continental, sialic crust and they behave tectonically in harmony with adjacent lands (Fig. 212). Several shelves (Norway, West Greenland, Antarctica and others) have a marked depression along the inner shelf area, thought to be related to crustal fractures formed in association with the uplift of adjacent lands.

The continental slope, constituting a major lineament of earth-relief, leads from the elevated stand of the continents down to the floors of the deep oceanic basins, involving a difference of level commonly 10,000 feet but locally attaining 30,000 feet. Fundamentally, the difference of level is isostatic and draws the distinction between the granitic material of the continents and the basaltic floors of the oceanic basins. The transition takes place without the development of significant gravity anomalies, though the continental slope is notably a seismic zone. Shepard (1948) has drawn attention to " Elongate trenches, extending below the average depth of the abyssal ocean floor . . . found at the base of about one-half of the continental slopes of the world ". Though less pronounced, these trenches resemble the deep troughs which occur marginally to certain island arcs of evidently recent uplift (*q.v.*). He has also remarked the general straightness of the outer edge of continental shelves, which is continuous even past the mouths of great rivers.

The average inclination of the continental slope about the Pacific Basin exceeds 5°, around the Atlantic and Indian Basins it averages about 3°. Normal angles of repose for fine-grained submarine sediments do not exceed 2°, so that these slopes, if depositional, must have been subsequently tilted. Slumping can, however, create steeper slopes in the same materials for a time, and is demonstrated in the western North Atlantic slope by core recoveries showing zones of brecciated clay. A further instance is known (Ewing and Heezen 1956) where " Miocene sediments of a small detached hill resting on Recent sediments gave further evidence of this phenomenon ". Turbidity currents, bottom currents and slumps are, indeed continuously removing sediments from the continental slope. Sometimes the slope is smooth, and sometimes it is irregular with hills and basins differing in level by as much as 2,000 feet from their surroundings. Exceptionally, " the shallow Gulf of Panama terminates in a steep, submarine cliff, descending for more than 3,000 metres " (Suess). Some shelves and slopes are interupted by wide terraces or borderlands which seem generally to be areas of irregular topography with hills rising to great heights and sometimes breaking surface as islands, partly volcanic (*e.g.* Canary Islands). There are also marked depressions partly filled with sediments. Some of the borderlands evidently correspond to geosynclines of past time. An area of sea-floor off California, for instance, described by Emery and Shepard (1945) possesses scarps that " in general parallel structural trends of the adjacent mainland or islands. The basins on the sea-floor also have their counterpart on land in such basins

as those of Ventura, Los Angeles, San Fernando, San Gabriel and San Bernardino."
This borderland is a portion of the North American continent that was shallowly
submerged in the Cretaceous, was land again during the early Cainozoic, sank once
more in the mid-Miocene, was broken and partly elevated at the beginning of the
Pliocene, and was perhaps re-sunk in still later times (Fig. 213).

Seaward from Florida, at depths between 200 and 1,200 metres, the Blake submarine
plateau constitutes another borderland.   Cores from the outer edge disclose Recent
globigerina ooze overlying Miocene chalk and clay, with fragments of Cretaceous
formations from the deeper parts of the slope (2,000-4,000 fathoms) (Ericson *et al.* 1952).

Upwarping of the Queensland coastal belt seems likewise to have been accompanied
by foundering of a borderland within " the Great Barrier Reef with its archipelago of
' horst ' islands of granite, slate, limestone, etc.   Nearly the whole of the eastern watershed of the old Divide to the east of Cairns was thereby sunk beneath the sea, leaving

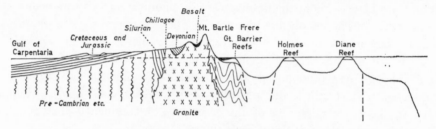

FIG. 208.   West-east section across northern Queensland showing
" sunkland " surmounted by reefs within the Coral Sea.   *after T. W. E.
David.*

merely the sources of the rivers perched high up on the top side of the fault scarp "
(Figs. 28, 208).   Interpretation of the neighbouring continental relief enabled Stanley
(1928) to date the down-flexed and faulted topography as late Pliocene.

Increasingly apparent is the close relationship between the tectonic behaviour of
uparched coastlands (Chapters VII and VIII) and the development of continental
shelves and slopes, and we shall return to this topic when considering the origin and
history of these shelves (Fig. 212).

Islands of the open ocean are sometimes bordered by insular shelves.   Most are
narrow, the chief exceptions, which may be 100 miles or more in width, being coral
islands where the building of the reefs has maintained a narrow range of depth.   The
insular shelf of New Zealand is now known to be traversed by submarine canyons, a
condition revealed also by recent marine survey about the Hawaiian Islands and even
around certain coral islands of the south-western Pacific.

SUBMARINE CANYONS

Along all the world's coasts, of whatever geological type, the face of the continental
slope is gashed by submarine canyons (Fig. 212), many of which (*e.g.* Monterey Canyon)

surpass in magnitude the largest canyons on the lands (Shepard 1948). During the past quarter-century sounding and dredging have provided copious data concerning the canyons of the continental shelf, and a thrilling account of deep diving by Frank Haymaker into the heads of offshore canyons along the Californian coast has been given by Shepard (1949).

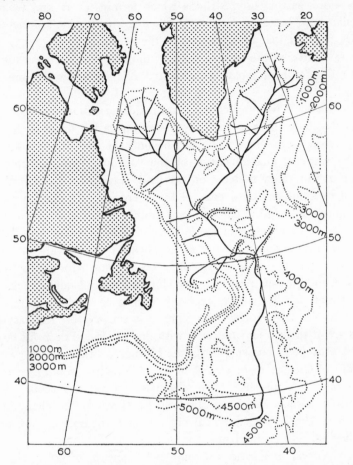

FIG. 209. Dendritic pattern of North Atlantic submarine canyons. *after*
M. Ewing and *B. C. Heezen*.

Submarine canyons (Johnson 1939; Kuenen 1953) are sometimes mere notches in the outer edge of the continental shelf, sometimes they traverse the whole width from the shore to the edge, and many of these canyons are collinear with major rivers, *e.g.* Hudson Canyon and the Congo Canyon. There is indeed an association of large canyons with large rivers, and conversely canyons are rare off desert areas. Certain canyons reach the shore off stream debouchures. Thus the head of Scripps Canyon, California, approaches to within 800 feet of the cliffed shoreline and corresponds to Callan Canyon on land, while its Sumner branch reaches towards Sumner Canyon on land. The head of the canyon has vertical walls in places, well stratified and consolidated Cretaceous, Eocene and Miocene formations with protruding concretions and overhanging resistant masses, more rarely Pliocene clay, and occasionally walls of alluvium and cobbles, *cf*. Hudson Canyon (Ericson, Ewing and Heezen 1952). Other canyon heads do not approach the shore, as that of the Indus which terminates 22 km. from land. Any former extension may, however, have been filled in with marine sediment. Still more remarkable are canyons that arise far out in the oceans. Dietz (1953), for instance, records three that arise on the eastern slope of the Honshu-Marianas submarine ridge one hundred miles south of Japan, as without " relation to any landmass or even to shallow water ".

Many canyons have winding courses and dendritic tributaries like normal stream patterns (Fig. 209), and there is normally a continuous fall towards the ocean basins with a fan of debris (sometimes trenched) beyond the foot of the continental slope. Altogether, the physical characteristics of the canyons reproduce to a remarkable degree the features of valley systems on the land, leaving little doubt that they have been excavated by some similar agency of linear erosion. Opinion nowadays assigns this rôle to submarine turbidity currents and mudflows active across, and beyond, the continental shelf. On both sides of the Hudson Canyon, for instance, the sequence of Recent sediments is undisturbed whereas flow within the canyon has been vigorous enough to move coarse gravel at depths of 2,300 fathoms. Jones (1938) has inferred similar agency in the geologic past from the slumped lower Ludlow rocks of Denbighshire where the materials flowed " in relatively narrow channels or gutters ".

Stetson has shown by bottom sampling that canyons off the east coast of the United States are at present slowly filling with fine mud, and deep fill possibly dating back to the Pleistocene is known from some borings. Other canyon floors are bare, cut into bedrock of Cretaceous or Cainozoic age. Repetitive soundings within the off-shore canyons of California show them alternately to fill and scour. The types of bottom deposit there have also been observed by Haymaker to change from time to time. The canyons thus appear to be currently evolving by both erosion and deposition rather like valley bottoms on the lands.

From their general similarities the submarine canyons of the world all appear to be of much the same age, and while the possibility cannot be excluded that some have been inherited and maintained from former geologic periods, the probability remains that most, if not all, are youthful and were developed, like canyons of the coastal hinterlands (Chapter VII), principally in Quaternary time (p. 560).

AGES OF CONTINENTAL SHELVES

Continental shelves border all types of coasts, elevated or depressed, fractured or faulted, concordant or discordant to the geologic structure of adjacent lands. That shelves are found on virtually all coasts is important. Generally the shelf is narrow along more recently folded coasts (*e.g.* western North and South America, and seaward of the island festoons of eastern Asia). Fractured or monoclinal coasts (*e.g.* Africa) normally have narrow to medium shelves, but where extensive drowning has occurred there may be a wide shelf or borderland (Queensland). The widest shelves are where the continental edges have sunk shallowly but broadly (*e.g.* the Arctic coast of Siberia, and the northern part of North America from the Grand Banks of Newfoundland into the drowned archipelago that reaches ultimately to Ellesmere Island, at nearly lat. 83° N.). On Pacific aspects island festoons may stand upon or beyond the edge of the shelf, but these festoons are not usual elsewhere.

That continental shelves are narrow along most of the coasts formed by Cainozoic fold belts, and along coasts subjected to strong outward tilting in late-Cainozoic time, indicates that the development of shelf width is related to tectonic movements of the continental margin quite as much as it is to processes of marine erosion and deposition.

The earliest marine rocks associated in coastal plains with the monoclinal coasts of Africa are late Jurassic (Somaliland-Tanzania), earliest Cretaceous or Neocomian (south-east Africa) and Albian (preceded by lagoonal Aptian) in Angola and West Africa. Prior to these dates these coasts did not exist, and there can have been no continental shelf. A similar Cretaceous initiation is indicated by the geology of coastlands in Australia, eastern South America and elsewhere. About the Atlantic and Indian Oceans therefore initiation of the continental shelf cannot antedate the mid-Mesozoic. Even upon regions where the sea had flowed in geosynclines during earlier geologic time, as along the eastern side of North America, coastal plain geology clearly indicates that conditions now ruling upon that seaboard were initiated about the beginning of Cretaceous time.

About the Pacific Ocean powerful Cainozoic diastrophism interfered with any pre-existing continental shelf and it is doubtful on available evidence whether the modern Pacific shelves can boast an ancestry much beyond the same Cretaceous period. Fresh shelf area may, of course, have been added at any subsequent epoch by sinking of land (*e.g.* the North Sea and the Java Sea during the Pleistocene period).

Recoveries from cores drilled into the continental shelf include representatives of all the major geologic epochs from earliest Cretaceous to Recent. As portions of the continental shelf may subside independently (Murray 1952), the pattern of sedimentation varies much from place to place. Nevertheless, Cretaceous rocks seem consistently to be recovered from the outer and lower parts of the shelf, with Cretaceous, Eocene or Miocene formations at the break of the slope between the continental shelf and slope (Fig. 212). Younger formations lie most thickly upon the inner and mid-sections of most shelves; but they do occur as gravels and sands upon the edges of both the North American and European shelves, also upon the extremity of the Agulhas Bank, South Africa, and along the eastern coast of Australia where, according to Fairbridge, " great slabs of beach rock have been dredged up from 70-75 fathoms ". Shallow-water fauna in these slabs suggest a Plio-Pleistocene age.

Fossiliferous samples dredged from the walls and floors of submarine canyons also belong to the Cretaceous and Cainozoic, with some Quaternary materials generally

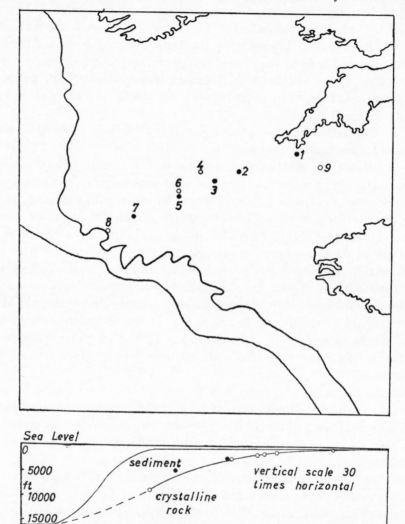

FIG. 210. Seismic soundings across the continental shelf off Land's End illustrating the thickness of sediment and attitude of the crystalline rock floor. *after C. G. Bullard and T. F. Gaskell.*

lying loosely upon the canyon floor.   No samples yet recovered are older than Cretaceous except perhaps a granite from Monterey Canyon and some fragments, possibly Trias-Jura, obtained from other Californian canyons by Emery and Shepard (1945).   By such observations Stetson (1936) has demonstrated that upon the Georges Bank the maximum thickness of Cainozoic beds is not greater than 1,500 feet, and the top of the Cretaceous, which forms the bulk of the Bank, is there submerged by only 1,450-1,800 feet.

Seismic traverses have provided useful data concerning distribution and thicknesses of sediment composing the continental shelf and slope. Thus beyond Land's End and the English Channel (Bullard 1941), the crystalline basement warps steadily downward to the level of the ocean floor beneath a cover of later sediments, which thickens westward

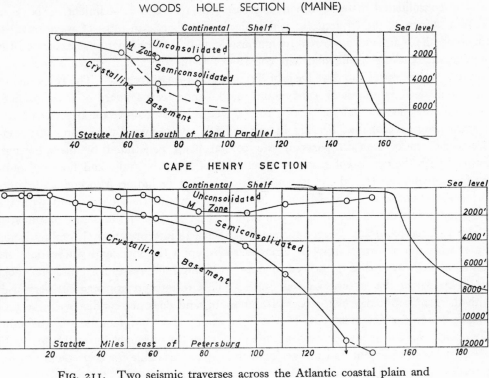

FIG. 211. Two seismic traverses across the Atlantic coastal plain and continental shelf of North America. *after M. Ewing, A. P. Crary and H. M. Rutherford.*

(Fig. 210). A complementary section is revealed by seismic traverses on the opposite side of the Atlantic (Fig. 211) where southward from Wood's Hole the crystalline basement is shown (Ewing *et al.* 1937, 1940) descending ever more steeply until it reaches a depth of 12,000 feet, or somewhat lower than the floor of the North Atlantic Basin. Such a simple monoclinal structure possibly exists in the basement beneath all continental shelves. But the seismic velocities alone are insufficient for interpretation of the basement as " crystalline ", for tightly consolidated Palæozoic or other formations may give comparable velocities. " Before the Cape Hatteras well was drilled a refraction seismic survey . . . had predicted basement at 8,200 feet on the strength of a medium of 18,000-20,000 ft./sec. velocity. This proved to be a Cretaceous limestone-dolomite formation " (Lees 1953).

Where the basement occurs beneath a cover of Cretaceous formations we may recognise the surface of unconformity as equivalent to the Gondwana (or Laurasian) denudation cycle on the lands; and the succeeding formations, and the unconformities between them, continue to record tectonic and denudational effects within adjacent coastal hinterlands until the present day.

Above the basement in the Wood's Hole section (Maine) is an ever-thickening wedge of semi-consolidated material which may safely be regarded as sediment. Above an horizon known as the M-zone, at which significant change in rates of wave-travel is apparent, the sediments appear to be unconsolidated. Miller (1937) has expressed the opinion that the unconsolidated lens consists of Cainozoic and Cretaceous rocks and that the " semi-consolidated wedge is of Triassic and Jurassic rocks." The thickness of unconsolidated material is at a maximum (4,000-5,000 feet) seaward of the shoreline; the semi-consolidated material attains 10,000 feet in hollows above the basement. But it seems more reasonable, bearing in mind the known seaward thickening of lower-Cretaceous rocks beneath parts of the coastal plain penetrated by deep borings, coupled with the consistent recovery of such rocks from the walls and floors of submarine canyons, to regard the unconsolidated lens as including Miocene and later-Cainozoic formations. The M-zone unconformity would then correspond with the Schooley peneplain of the Appalachian region (Fig. 141), and the semi-consolidated wedge to Cretaceous and Eocene formations. Such an interpretation also tallies much better with the known scarcity of Triassic rocks upon the mainland where they are continental in type and preserved mainly in faulted depressions. Jurassic rocks are unknown in the eastern United States. This re-interpretation agrees very well with the geomorphology of the coastal hinterland, and does not conflict with the case already made for fragmentation of the Laurasian super-continent during the mid-Mesozoic. All continental and submarine events are thus brought into harmony, with the volumes of sediment and the geologic time spans available for their accumulation according.

Further work by Ewing has indicated that the " semi-consolidated " formations extend beyond the feather-edge of continental basement and come to rest directly upon the basaltic layer which builds the lower parts of the continents and the ocean floors alike (Fig. 205). These sediments have thus been carried out by slumping and turbidity currents into the true oceanic basin. The same process has evidently continued into Quaternary time: " Positive evidence for transportation by turbidity currents is the distribution of the sands with respect to bottom topography. In the region of the Hudson Submarine Canyon sands and gravels have been found only in the canyon bed and not on the divides outside the canyon. This leads to the conclusion that the canyon has been the route of transportation, and that the agent has been some sort of flow under the influence of gravity, that is, turbidity current."

Outside the canyon " very fine sediment of abnormally high calcium carbonate content has been deposited intermittently in various deep basins of the North Atlantic. . . . Such fine grey relatively calcareous sediment, presumably of shallow-water origin, is exactly what a nearly exhausted turbidity current ought to deposit " (Ericson *et al.* 1952). Cores from depths below 3,000 fathoms show repeated sandy layers quite sharply marked off from calcareous muddy layers, and recalling many geosynclinal sequences such as the Trias-Jura greywacke-argillite system of New Zealand. Ewing is positive that sediment arrives far out in the ocean basins by sliding and turbidity in laden waters wherein turbulence develops. He notes a red colouring in sediments by Nova Scotia, far away to the north of the red Triassic lowland, showing, unless there be some curious source for the material undersea, transportation far from the source. Ewing also noted that the Caribbean (Antillean) trough is deeply filled with sediment at a considerable distance from land. The surface of demarcation between laden turbid bottom waters and overlying clear water is doubtless sharp, with little mixing, rather like the slowly heaving surface of a thick bank of cloud drifting in a general direction but with numerous local eddies and swirls evident to an aviator passing over the bank.

In the North Atlantic deposition by turbidity currents has decreased since the Wisconsin glacial epoch, as indicated by a decrease in the number of graded layers near the top of sediment cores. Sedimentation was exceptionally rapid during the glacial epochs: at present pelagic formations are accumulating over much of the material distributed by turbidity (Ericson *et al.*).

GEOMORPHOLOGY OF CONTINENTAL SHELVES

Structurally the shelves are part of the continents and their tectonics are intimately bound-up with the tectonics of coastal hinterlands (Chapters VII-IX). Fortunately, emerged coastal plains in several parts of the world permit study of the transition from one realm to the other. Thus the relationship between the major denudational cycles of the lands and the cycles of sedimentation with intervening unconformities of the coastal plains and continental shelves is already clear (p. 558), and we may elucidate the history of continental shelves about the Atlantic Ocean as follows. Consequent upon the Mesozoic disruption of Gondwanaland and Laurasia the new coastal outlines were downwarped monoclinally carrying with them the current denudational landscapes of those regions (the Gondwana/Laurasian surfaces) which became, with marine modification, the floor of accumulation for the earliest Cretaceous sediments (*e.g.* Fall Zone peneplain). On the neighbouring land the betrunked and tilted rivers were rejuvenated and, together possibly with strong scarp retreat, supplied sediment abundantly; hence the remarkable quantity and thickness of those Cretaceous sediments that constitute the bulk of the built shelf.

The minor movement on the lands closing the post-Gondwana landscape cycle is matched by mid- or late-Cretaceous unconformity in many coastal plain sequences, with Senonian overlap often following. Samples recovered by dredging and coring from submarine slopes, canyons, ridges and guyots belong more frequently to late-Cretaceous sequences, though this may not be significant of greater sedimentary volume.

Throughout the late-Cretaceous and Eocene periods the continents remained relatively stable and were reduced by the Oligocene to a state of extreme planation (Chapter VIII), when little land-waste was supplied to the coastal plain and shelf. Thus while Eocene rocks are not uncommon, especially towards the outer edges of shelves Oligocene accumulations are seldom recorded. Quiescence reigned also over the shelf areas, and this was the period when their essential reduction to the smooth state was accomplished. Lands and shelves alike apparently exhibited minimal relief during the mid-Cainozoic.

Late-Cainozoic displacements of the lands are paralleled by related basin subsidences upon the shelf areas, notably close offshore, so that much of the land waste supplied by rejuvenated erosion was not carried seaward and dumped over the shelf edge but accumulated as lenses upon the inner or mid-section of the shelf. Indeed, in isostatic response many shelf edges seem to have risen during the Pliocene and come within reach of wave-action. Late-Cainozoic accumulations on the shelf, beginning with the Miocene, occupy a minor rôle compared with the Cretaceous deposits.

The end of the Cainozoic era witnessed great upheavals of the land with pronounced outward tilting of many coastal hinterlands which have since been gashed by the canyons of rejuvenated river systems (p. 426). These events are duplicated upon adjacent continental shelves which, partaking of the outward tilting so evident upon the lands, have also had the delicate balance of submarine denudation disturbed. Slumps and turbidity currents were generated that, once channelled, have excavated during the Quaternary era the submarine canyons of the continental shelves and slopes. As a number of canyons with steep bottom gradients are widest in their middle reaches (e.g. Oceanographer, Bering) the similarity to deeply incised rivers on the flanks of uparchings, like the Grose River of New South Wales and the Tugela and Umgeni Rivers of Natal, is remarkable.

The geomorphic homology between coastland and shelf (Fig. 212) is thus complete for every stage since the mid-Mesozoic, and is rooted in an underlying tectonic unity. This extends to details such as the fault-block topography offshore as well as onshore in California (Shepard and Emery 1931), and the occasional continuity of axial uparchings of the lands across adjacent shelves.

Lightening of the shelf edge by canyon cutting, and perhaps further weighting of the inner shelf by sedimentation seem presently to have renewed a tendency for the shelf edge to rise, and hence develop by isostatic response the trench that Shepard (1948) has noted at the base of half the continental slopes of the world.

About the Pacific Basin submarine shelves and slopes tend to be steeper, perhaps in response to the more strongly uplifted girdle of highlands that surrounds that ocean.

Detailed history of the shelves may also show more local variation, with independent basins and ridges generated by tectonic movement (*cf.* Cumberland Basin on the coastal monocline of New South Wales). Emery and Shepard (1945) have demonstrated such submarine topography off the coast of California (Fig. 213). But despite the differences of structure along coastlines of Atlantic and Pacific types no fundamental differences are known in the shelf history. Thus Emery and Shepard dredged Cretaceous, Eocene and Miocene sedimentary rocks from the walls of La Jolla Canyon, with some Pliocene from part of the San Pedro sea valley. The canyons, they concluded, were Pleistocene in age. These are all features of Atlantic shelves also.

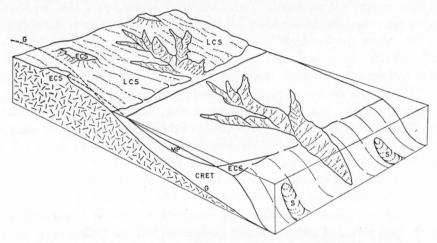

FIG. 212. Geomorphic homology between coastal hinterland and continental shelf. G = Gondwana landsurface (pre-Cretaceous), ECS = early-Cainozoic surface, LCS = late-Cainozoic surface, Cret = Cretaceous formations, MP = Miocene and Pliocene formations. Pleistocene dissection of the coastal hinterland correlates cyclically with submarine canyons, both following outward tilting of the continent towards the close of the Cainozoic era.

Although coastal hinterlands and shelf areas show remarkable geomorphic homologies throughout a long history, and although slumping and channelling operate by physical failure of materials to produce canyons below the sea equally with those on land, the notable question arises as to what marine agency was responsible for the levelling of the shelf in early-Cainozoic time, a levelling that was preserved, with minor modification, until the canyon cutting of Quaternary time? Briefly, the shelf is too wide, and towards the outer edge too deep, to have been controlled by normal wind-generated waves of the ocean surface (*cf.* Dietz 1952). There are few reliable data concerning emergence of the shelf caused by the swinging sea level of the Ice Age (Dietz and Menard 1951); but even allowing for quite unproven large eustatic withdrawals of the ocean, the period was too short to explain the essential levelling of the shelf, though it may account for many known minor features. Anyway, the

2 N

canyons were cut during Quaternary time into shelves that were already in existence prior to this date. Seemingly some other marine denudational agency is required.

For this we turn to researches by Pettersson, finely summarised by Carson (1953): " As the ocean water presses in toward [the Baltic Sea] it dips down and lets the fresh surface water roll out above it; and at that deep level where salt and fresh water come into contact there is a sharp layer of discontinuity, like the surface film between water and air. Each day Pettersson's instruments revealed a strong, pulsing movement of that deep layer—the pressing inward of great submarine waves, of moving mountains of water. The movement was strongest every twelfth hour of the day, and between the 12-hour intervals it subsided. Pettersson soon established a link between these submarine waves and the daily tides. . . . Some of the deep waves of the Gulmarfiord were giants nearly 100 feet high ".

Internal tide waves have also been recorded by J. L. Reid from each of three anchored hydrographic research vessels at 40, 160 and 320 miles off the Californian coast. " Waves of semi-diurnal period with amplitudes greater than 30 feet were found at the inshore station " but little at the outer station, " though there was considerable vertical fluctuation of isotherms ". The phase of the internal wave is the same as the surface tide wave at the coast, and the amplitude varied with the surface tide wave. Reid considered that the internal wave originated with the tide near the coast.

Surely, in the great internal tide waves that surge twice daily from the ocean depths over the shallow shelf areas under the influence of lunar instead of terrestrial gravity lies the agency responsible for levelling the continental margins and their development, during the long period of early-Cainozoic quiescence, into the basic form of the continental shelf. Internal tide waves, a truly marine agency unknown upon the lands, operating at all depths, may also be responsible for the ripple marks of various sizes revealed by photographs of the ocean bottom, as also superficially for some of the rises on which only coarse sediment remains or which are scoured free of sediment altogether. Thus Dietz (1952) presents photographs from 3,026 fathoms on a site 300 miles east-south-east from Bermuda showing " current scours on the up-current side of round nodular objects indicating currents strong enough to erode fine grained sediment ". But whether the agent is sediment-laden turbidity current from shoaler waters, or is a tide current remains uncertain in this instance.

Shelves of the Continents

Though the continental shelves are submerged beneath the oceans and are moulded by marine agencies, in composition and structure they belong with the neighbouring lands, to which they form indeed but a narrow fringe. We therefore describe them in continental, not oceanic, categories.

Africa:—The Mediterranean shelf north of the Atlas Mountains borders a flexed coast (Bourcart and Glangeaud 1954) and is relatively narrow, and so it remains, except for a broadening to 170 miles at the Gulf of Gabes, all the way to Palestine. The eastern shelf, beginning at Oman in Arabia is only 20 miles wide and along the steep-to coast of Hadhramaut is believed to be less than 10 miles: no details are available. The Red Sea has narrow shelves appropriate to its rifted formation. Towards Bab-el-Mandeb these broaden and unite, but the shelf is narrow again about Somaliland and down to Mombasa it is everywhere less than 10 miles wide and is reported in some places not to attain 2 miles. With the shelf off South-East Africa (4 miles wide at Sordwana Bay) it is one of the narrowest in the world, and is much gashed by submarine canyons. That of the Zambezi extends into the ocean basin as far as the abyssal plain southwest of Malagasy. Through southern Tanzania, and Moçambique the low coastal plain underlain by Cretaceous rocks is scores of miles in width and continues seaward as a shelf 40-80 miles broad. At Inharrime borings to the basement of volcanic rocks passed through 6,000 feet of coastal plain sediments, Cretaceous to Recent in age. Wide changes of the shoreline are recorded in this region by raised and submerged beach lines. From Natal to the eastern Cape Province the coastlands are again steep and rugged, and the shelf is correspondingly narrow, especially at Port St. Johns where the edge of the shelf is also deeper. The coastal hinterland and shelf are here monoclinal.

At the southern horn of Africa, however, the Agulhas Bank, 70-80 fathoms deep, broadens to 150 miles with bare rock proved by sounding near the southern tip. Crustal thickness on the outer Bank is only half normal, and between it and Port Elizabeth 400 miles away is only one-tenth. The Bank appears to be encompassed by the two monoclinal warps which define the east and west coasts respectively. Sand is the dominant deposit on the shelves of South Africa due to the steepness of the terrain and abundance of siliceous rock systems.

Most of the coast between the Cape of Good Hope and the Gulf of Guinea has a shelf of 20-100 miles in width, with an unusually steep inner margin along South-West Africa perhaps correlating with the tectonic movements which have steepened the seaward edge of the adjacent Namib desert. Again the shelf deposits are mainly sand, with mud near the mouth of the Congo River and off the bulge of the Niger Delta.

West of the Niger to Liberia the shelf is narrow (10-20 miles) and shallow, the depth being generally less than 50 fathoms. This peculiarity still lacks explanation. Beyond Liberia the shelf widens to 75 miles, swinging across the bight of drowned coast between Sierra Leone and the Gambia. The edge of the shelf is much straighter than the shoreline and swings about Capes Verde and Blanco with deflection but not protuberance. Between these capes the shelf again attains a width of 70 miles, the depth being somewhat greater than usual. From Cape Blanco to Tangier the shelf continues uniformly at about 80 miles width. There is a platform upon which the Canary Islands stand but this is at greater depth than the shelf, the edge of which does not descend below 100 fathoms. Curiously, where it crosses the ends of the Atlas ranges south of Mogador the shelf is ten times as wide as where it runs parallel with them along the Algerian coast.

The most remarkable feature of the African shelf, taken as a whole, is its narrowness, associated with strong monoclines upon the coastlands.   Exceptional indeed is a shelf more than 100 miles wide, while for long stretches the width is 10 miles or less.

South America:—The continental shelves of the Atlantic and Pacific aspects of South America are strongly contrasted.   On the eastern aspect of monoclinal derivation (*q.v.*) the shelf, from Venezuela to the Strait of le Maire in lat. 55° S., is generally broad. Along the western coast, rising steeply to Coast Ranges of late-Cainozoic age, the shelf is narrow and the descent to the ocean depths is abrupt.

From the mouth of the Orinoco River a shallow shelf nearly 100 miles broad continues to the Guianas and the Amazon where it increases to 150 miles width owing to an embayment of the coast.   The bottom sediments are described as mud inshore and sand in the outer zone with bare rock outcrops towards the edge.   To Cape San Roque the shelf, still very shallow, narrows progressively to 10 miles, a width that is maintained to Baia, with the coarser grades of bottom sediments distributed remote from land.   Between Baia and Cape Frio is the shallow protuberance of Royal Charlotte Bank, perhaps crowned with coral; and beyond Cape Frio the shelf off the steep coast of the Serra do Mar, a steep monocline, broadens to 100 miles and deepens, with a very irregular surface suggesting a drowned topography though the bottom deposits are mud. Beyond the River Plate, where monoclinal structure fails, the shelf widens spectacularly and south of Bahia Blanca it ranges between 200 and 350 miles in width.   Off Patagonia the surface of the shelf is uneven, with a relief of perhaps 50 fathoms; and in the extreme south shows a lack of grading in the sediments with coarse material that suggests glacial derivation.

The high, fiord-indented coast of southern Chile is bordered by a narrow shelf with a very irregular surface that is possibly attributable to glaciation.   By northern Chile and Peru the shelf is a little wider and the surface is more even, though just as deep.   Beyond the shelf edge are the Chilean and Peruvian oceanic troughs descending to more than 25,000 feet below sea level, and the whole region from the crest of the Andes to the oceanic deep is vastly tilted.   By Ecuador and Colombia, except for the Bay of Guayaquil, the shelf is almost non-existent as far as Panama.

Study of the marine fossil faunas of Pacific and Atlantic realms has led to the conclusion that a biologic link existed between North and South America during the late-Cretaceous period and that the isthmus of Panama emerged at the end of the Oligocene.   It was interrupted during the early Miocene, and was re-established for a while during the mid-Miocene.   A definitive emergence of the modern isthmus occurred during the Pliocene, as shown by the migration of North American mammals into Brazil and the Andes.

Antarctica:—The volume of information concerning the Antarctic shelves is increasing but still lacks both detail and cover.   Like other shelves in glaciated regions the bottom appears to be very irregular, and to be deeper than usual at the edge as though sinking of the the centre of the continent under the ice-cap had been isostatically compensated by a rise of the mountain rim with strong outward tilting of the marginal regions. Shelves appear to be narrow in the Indian Ocean sector, broad in the Atlantic and Pacific Sectors. South of Australia a marked depression lies along the inner margin of the Antarctic shelf.

Australia:—Between Brisbane and Cape Howe, where the dominant feature of the coastal region is a powerful, seawardly-directed monocline, the continental shelf averages only 25 miles wide, and beyond is an immediate and deep descent into the basin of the Tasman Sea.

Elsewhere the coasts of Australia are usually girt by a broad shelf. Tasmania is separated from the mainland only by the shallow Bass Strait, and the edge of the shelf passes round it and back towards the Australian Bight where is a broad crescentic shelf 100 miles wide with an outer edge at 70 fathoms. In Miocene time the sea included the Nullarbor limestone region also within the shelf area. Rounding Cape Leeuwin the shelf narrows considerably, and does not increase again beyond 40 miles until North-West Cape is passed. Thence the shelf steadily widens, underlying the Timor Sea and approaches within 50 miles of the island of Timor itself. The shelf is thus 200 miles across and carries a broad basin 30 fathoms deep opposite the opening of Queen's Channel. The cause of this basin is problematical though it may be connected with the formation of the nearer Indonesian island arcs. The Aroe Islands which stand upon the shelf edge opposite the Kei Islands, however, reveal clearly in their structure (Fairbridge 1951) their independence from the folds of the Indonesian chain. They form a low, limestone plateau of Pliocene, and probably Miocene, rocks, capping a broad swell, and detrital grains of quartz, feldspar and mica suggest that a granitic basement is not far off. North from Arnhem Land the shelf is continued to New Guinea, that island standing upon the shelf with the Bismarck Archipelago upon the farther side. The southern half of New Guinea, indeed, belongs geologically to the Australian continent, as has been proved by oil-well drilling. The granites there are of uncertain age, though Fairbridge suggests Precambrian. Together, the Arafura Sea and the Gulf of Carpentaria make one of the largest shelf seas in the world. Depressions across the Arafura shelf reveal the prior existence of a river system directed westward towards Tanimber.

Through Torres Strait the shelf is narrow at first but broadens out opposite Townsville whence for over a thousand miles the outer edge of the shelf (or borderland) serves as foundation for the Great Barrier Reef. The shelf makes an undulating terrace at about 200 feet depth (Bryan 1928), but though the shelf is often continuous with the Pliocene coastal plains there is no evidence of marked channels across it. On the other hand, the marked structural lineation of the land north-north-west is matched in the submarine topography by the valley-like depression known as the Capricorn Channel, by Whitsunday Passage and by groups of offshore islands. The width of the shelf about the southern end of the Great Barrier Reef is 200 miles, and a deep borehole on Wreck Island there passed 530 feet of Recent coral reef material, thence Cainozoic sediments to 1,795 feet where Palæozoic metamorphic rocks similar to those of the mainland were encountered.

North America*:—The northern extremity of America, including the " breccia " of Arctic Islands and Hudson Bay has been shallowly submerged and falls within the definition of the shelf. The coast of Labrador is, however, a fractured coast: the shelf there is in consequence only about 80 miles wide and has a channel along the inner margin. The Newfoundland Grand Banks, 250 miles wide and sometimes shoaling to 30 fathoms, form an extension of the shelf. The southern flank of the Banks is formed by a continuation of the St. Lawrence Gulf; the Cabot Trench, beneath which is a prism of sediments arranged in a sequence not unlike that reported (p. 577) for the submerged shelf off the north-east coast of the United States (Press and Beckmann 1954; Bentley and Worzel 1956), " thickens to almost 14,000 feet near the north-east margin where it is almost entirely truncated by basement rock ", indicating a structural location for this feature. In this vicinity occurred the Grand Banks earthquake of 1929 which severed the submarine cables successively by means of the submarine slumps and turbidity currents that continued 450 miles out on to the floor of the Atlantic Basin (Heezen and Ewing 1952).

The Gulf of Maine, where the outer edge is again shoaler than the mid-shelf, has an irregular surface plastered with Pleistocene glacial debris (Murray 1947).

South of Cape Cod the shelf is relatively flat with sandy bottom, and the outer edge at 60 fathoms is no longer raised above the inner shelf; and so it continues beyond Cape Hatteras where it ultimately attains a width of 70 miles. This rapidly narrows to Palm Beach, Florida where the shelf virtually disappears; the Bahamas Banks, however, constitute a North American borderland with many shallow shelves and islands. The western side of Florida has a wide shelf (150 miles), most of it less than 40 fathoms with a gentle slope out beyond the 100 fathom line, that apparently results from only gentle land movements in this region during later-Cainozoic time. By the Mississippi delta a great wedge of Cainozoic sediments builds the shelf (Murray 1952) which is less wide, though it broadens again along the Gulf of Mexico to 100 miles west of Yucatan. The eastern side of this peninsula, however, is virtually without shelf, perhaps for structural reasons, for a shelf 150 miles wide bulges out again off Honduras, contracting to 40 miles southward off Nicaragua and Costa Rica where the Atlantic aspect of North America ceases. The western shelf of Central America is very narrow for most of the distance from Panama to the head of the Gulf of California, with rock reported at several places near the edge. The western side of the Gulf has no shelf, deep water occurring right up to the land.

The continental shelf from California to Canada averages about 10 miles wide. Rock and coarse sediment frequently appear at the edge of the shelf, and the distribution of sand and mud on the bottom appears to be highly irregular. Offshore islands are a feature in some regions. The irregularities of this shelf are tectonically induced for it forms an integral part of the heterogeneous geosyncline of which the Coast Ranges form the elevated portion (Fig. 213). A detailed description by Emery and Shepard (1945)

* See Thornbury W. D. (1965).

also records ?Trias-Jura, Cretaceous, Eocene, Miocene and Pliocene (but not Oligocene) formations dredged from the walls of submarine canyons, which number 66 along this coast. Granite cobbles have also been recovered, and effusive andesite and basalt are found in many samples. The outer edge of the shelf is frequently abrupt, as steep as the Sierra Nevada scarp from 500 feet depth at the edge to —10,000 feet at the Pacific floor.

Along the coasts of Canada and Alaska the shelf is wider and the mixed bottom sediments show the effects of glaciation. The shelf north of the Aleutian Trench (Murray 1945) extends for 400 miles into the Bering Sea, and bears numerous islands and depressions. The bottom is chiefly covered with sand and as with the Arctic shelf north of Alaska bears little record of glaciation (Shepard 1948).

Europe and Asia:—About the Aegean Sea the continental shelf is generally narrow, but bulges serve as platforms from which rise the Cyclades and other islands. The Ionian Sea has no shelf, though most of the Adriatic is shelf with the extensive delta of the River Po built into the head. Sicily stands upon a shelf with prolongations towards Malta and Cape Bon, otherwise the rest of the Italian shelf is narrow, especially along the Ligurian coast. From Marseilles to Cartagena the shelf averages 40 miles in width; but the shelf elsewhere about the Iberian Peninsula does not exceed 30 miles and much is only 10, with a steep descent to a deep edge.

From Biarritz the shelf widens progressively across the Bay of Biscay, the edge trending north-west until off the Lizard it is 250 miles from land. The inner part is mostly smooth but the outer part is irregular. Thus the Irish shelf presents a series of banks upon the outer shelf, separated from the land by deeper water. Zones of bare rock and gravel appear south of Ireland. The same shelf edge continues beyond the Outer Hebrides to the Shetland Islands, whence it curves back towards the Skagerrak. Nearly all the North Sea is therefore a shelf sea and some of it was emergent, as late as Neolithic time. Thus from the Dogger Bank Pleistocene mammalian remains and human artefacts have been dredged in quantity. The course of the River Rhine, too, has been traced far out across the shelf. Regions to the south (Ardenne) and west (Britain), show in their topography tilting towards the North Sea Basin (Figs. 149, 157). The Baltic Sea is also a shelf area.

By contrast, the Norwegian shelf is narrow and passes rapidly down into deep water. It is scored by deep troughs both parallel and transverse to the coast. Some of the latter shoal towards the shelf edge and may well have been glacially excavated. Within the west Barents Sea the surface is irregular with troughs and banks perhaps engendered by deposition under floating ice, but the eastern 400 miles has flat bottom. Spitzbergen and Franz Joseph Land stand in the north upon broad platforms and their geologies are clearly continental. East of Novaya Zemlya the shallow shelf may correspond to a drowned part of the West Siberian plain, one of the flattest regions of the globe. With the shallow shelf seas (Kara Sea, Laptev Sea, East Siberian Sea) almost the whole of the Arctic border of Asia is shallow broad shelf continuous with low tundra shoreline. Beyond the shelf is a rapid drop to 2,500 fathoms, the general depth of the North Polar Basin.

The shelves of eastern Asia are generally narrow about the island festoons and broad along the submerged continental margins. Thus the shelf upon the western side of Kamchatka is much wider than that on the east and broadens steadily along the shores of the Sea of Okhotsk. All around the Sea of Japan, on the other hand, the shelves are narrow with a descent of 10,000 feet from the mountain tops of the Sikhota Alin to the sea floor. This has all the appearance of a tectonic basin. The shelf is continuous, however, from Korea to Japan closing the basin at the Strait of Tsushima.

Beyond Tsushima Strait to Formosa are two broad, epeiric seas, the Yellow Sea and the East China Sea, where the shelf is 750 miles wide. A large segment of continental Asia is here shallowly drowned; few details are available of these shelves, however.

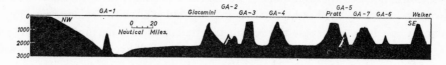

FIG. 214. Section north-west to south-east from the Aleutian Trench to Welker Seamount in the Gulf of Alaska. One seamount has been carried down by subsidence of the trench. *after H. W. Murray.*

The shelf off the south-east China highlands, an upwarped region, to Hainan is 150 miles wide, and the Gulf of Tongking falls also within the shelf area.

Off south-eastern Asia is a tremendous shelf reaching from the Gulf of Siam to the Strait of Macassar. Java and Sumatra stand upon the southern edge of the shelf and Borneo upon the eastern edge. Most of the sea is shoaler than 40 fathoms and the recent date of drowning is attested by the drowned channels of the river systems continued over the shelf (Fig. 13).

Malacca Strait is shallow shelf, also with drowned landscapes revealed by soundings, and a shelf 100 miles broad and dotted with islands continues past the Mergui Archipelago to beyond the mouths of the Irrawady River. The whole submarine topography here is highly irregular. North Burma has a shelf 30-50 miles wide that bourgeons off the Ganges delta to meet the shelf (20 miles wide) of the east coast of India. Though on the Malabar Coast the Western Ghats rise steeply from the coast, the shelf there is very flat and broadens progressively northward to Karachi with a maximum width off Bombay of over 150 miles. Both Indian rivers the Ganges and the Indus have developed extensive, submarine deltaic plains.

The steep coast of Makran is bordered by an appropriately narrow shelf. Patches of rock suggest that the tops of ranges may protrude through the shelf sediments. All the Persian Gulf is shelf. The head of the gulf has been filled in by the marshy delta plains of the lower Euphrates and Tigris Rivers.

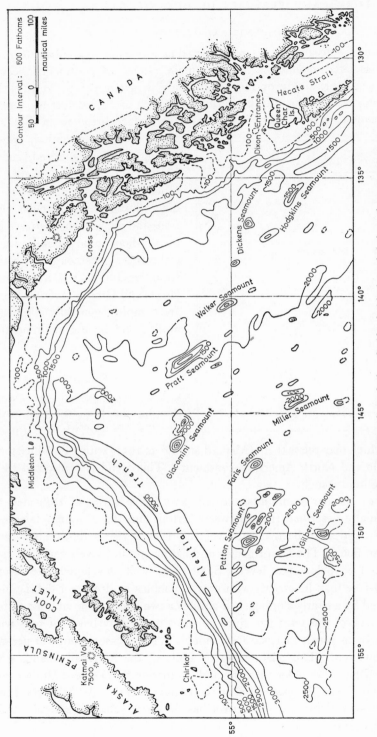

Fig. 215. Submarine topography of the Gulf of Alaska, showing the numerous seamounts some of which are elliptical and aligned parallel with the grain of western North America. The seamount province is transected by the younger Aleutian Trench. *after H. W. Murray.*

SEAMOUNTS AND GUYOTS

From many parts of the oceanic basins are reported elevations comparable in form and dimensions with isolated mountains and mountain ranges of continental scenery. Rising from the sea-floor, singly or more commonly in groups of 10 to 100, these *seamounts* frequently ascend abruptly by perhaps as much as 12,000 feet to summits, flat or irregular, standing a few hundred feet below the surface of the ocean (Fig. 214).

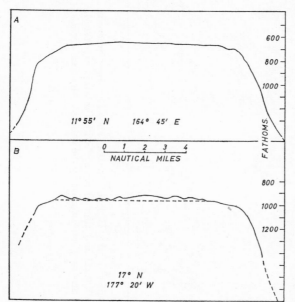

Some are simply conical, cratered on top, often magnetized, and are basaltic volcanic in origin, but others are less certain, as for instance the great semicircular elevations and depressions scattered over the sea-floor some 500 miles west of California. Seamounts described from the Gulf of Alaska by Murray (1941) and Gibson (1960) (Fig. 215) are complex, generally elliptical in outline and have a common trend

FIG. 216

Sections through typical guyots showing the truncated tops with shelving rim. *after H. H. Hess.*

north-westward which may relate them (Menard and Dietz 1951) with a Plio-Pleistocene orogenic belt upon the North American continent. This trend is transected by the more youthful Aleutian trench.

Certain oval or circular seamounts, termed *guyots* have curiously truncated tops (Fig. 216). Originally described from between Hawaii and the Marianas Islands by Hess (1946) " they appear to be truncated volcanic islands rising about 9,000-12,000 feet from the ocean floor. The flat or gently undulating summit levels generally range from 3,000-6,000 feet below sea level. Some, less well developed, are deeper. The flat upper surface may be strewn with gravel, cobbles or dead reef debris and is commonly bordered by a gently sloping shelf a mile or two wide. The summit surfaces are apparently not all of the same age since adjacent peaks may have flat tops which differ in elevation by as much as 1,000 feet, though in some cases groups of peaks do have the same elevation. The relationship to atolls of the Marshall Islands group indicate that the surfaces are older than the atoll formation." Derwent Hunter guyot in the Tasman Basin, bears *Acropora* coral at 196 fathoms depth. As " this coral could not have grown at such depth . . . the guyot has therefore subsided several hundred feet ". (Standard 1961).

Guyots are scattered over millions of square miles of the Pacific Basin, and are known also in the Atlantic and Indian oceanic basins. They differ greatly in size. One is only 2 miles wide, one near Eniwetok is 35 miles across the base and 9 miles at the top which is remarkably flat at 620 fathoms. The outer rim margin slopes at 2° - 3° to 70 fathoms lower, then breaks abruptly to 22° at the outer edge. This decreases gradually until tangential with the oceanic floor. Another guyot is 60 miles in basal diameter. There is no relation between the height of the guyot and the depth of the oceanic floor, nor other than locally is there any accordance of summit levels. Curiously consistent are records from the several oceans of Cretaceous rocks dredged from the summits of guyots with Eocene rocks from the flanks.

Island Types

Large islands standing upon sialic basements frequently exhibit a geology comparable with that of adjacent land masses. New Guinea is still joined to Australia beneath the shallow Arafura Sea, and Malagasy though more remote from Africa displays a geological history which is identical with that of eastern Tanganyika until at least the early-Cainozoic. New Zealand approaches identity with south-eastern Australia only in the Ordovician formations of the western South Island, but its later Palæozoic and Mesozoic formations supply the peripheral geosynclinal facies that is lacking from the Australian scene, so that the two regions are complementary. All such islands are patently continental fragments.

Conversely, small open-ocean islands devoid of sialic basement reveal no geosynclinal or continental sedimentary sequences and are built solely of volcanic accumulations that are almost invariably of basic composition. Typical is Mauritius (Walker and Nicolaysen 1954) where an early-Cainozoic volcanic series built a huge cone with numerous pyroclastic intercalations between massive flows of olivine basalt. Prolonged denudation reduced the cone to a few vestigial stumps, and then in later Cainozoic time two series of younger basalts built lava plains and minor cones beyond which the ancient stumps of the Older series still rise abruptly. All the basalts are basic, and " differentiation has produced accumulative picrite-basalts of the oceanite and ankaramite types ". Tholeiitic basalts are absent; and the only sedimentary deposits are coral reefs or local clastics derived from the basaltic parent rock.

Disposed singly or in archipelagoes (e.g. Tuamoto), islands of this class, without continental connection, are widely distributed about the oceanic basins. Neither they nor the continental islands pose any special genetic problems.

Island Arcs

A whole crop of such problems is raised, however, by the chains and festoons of islands which garland eastern Asia and of which further examples occur in the Antilles (p. 604) and Scotia (p. 609) Arcs.

These island arcs described by many authors (Umbgrove 1947; Hess 1948) possess a characteristic zonal structure first elucidated by Suess.   On the inner side of the arc is a volcanic zone, the typical effusions of which are andesitic.   Follows a zone of contorted Palæozoic or Mesozoic rocks which are sometimes covered by Cainozoic idiogeosynclinal deposits themselves also plicated.   An outer zone of Cainozoic limestones

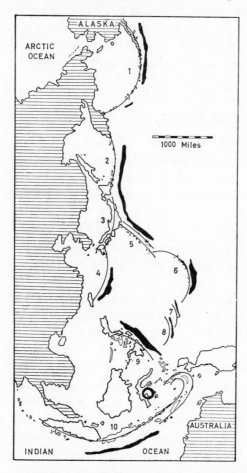

FIG. 217

Part of the north-western Pacific Ocean showing relation of island arcs and deep oceanic trenches.

1. Aleutian

2. Kurile

3. Japanese

4. Riu Kiu

5. Bonin

6. Marianas or Nero

7. Yap

8. Palau

9. Philippine

10. Indonesia

Circle, recurved arc of Celebes

concludes the visible zonation, but beyond the island front the sea floor descends abruptly to profound abysses wherein are recorded the deepest parts of the oceans (Fig. 217).   Within a given arc any zone may be suppressed.   The first to disappear is usually the cordillera; most persistent is the volcanic zone.   Arcs may be single (*e.g.* Marianas) or double (Indonesia) when the volcanic zone and cordillera are confined to the inner island festoon, but granitic batholiths may appear in either.

Umbgrove (1947) remarks that the batholithic granite of the inner arc is not derived by differentiation of tholeiitic magma but is due to migmatization of pre-existing crustal rocks by ascending emanations.   Indeed the rocks appear to become more acid with depth. This migmatization was especially active at those epochs when the Cainozoic formations were being folded, that is when the development of vertical laminar structures in the underlying formations provided especially favourable conditions for the ascent of volatiles perhaps accompanied by lightened activated materials from the lower crust.

The profound trenches in the ocean floor bordering the arcs (Fig. 217) are regarded as tectonic features (*gräben*) that, as recorded by a strong deficiency of gravity, are out of isostatic equilibrium. But the greatest deficiency of gravity, which often exceeds—100 and may exceed—150 milligals, is not always situated beneath the trench but is displaced towards or even beneath the island arc (Fig. 9). Thus while the negative anomaly is directly below the West Caroline Trench off the island of Yap, at Guam the main anomaly is under the western wall of the Marianas Trench and a secondary anomaly lies beneath the island itself (Fig. 218). Along the double arc of Indonesia the belt of negative gravity anomaly is situated beneath the outer festoon of islands. Similar changes of position of the gravity data relative to the positions of island arc and trench appear in the Antilles (p. 605). This disharmony between the negative strip and topographic detail is matched by a similar disharmony in Europe (Tanni 1942), where the negative strip of that continent runs in some places beneath the mountains (the Alps, the West Carpathians and the Caucasus) and elsewhere across the troughs of the sea (the Gulf of Taranto, the Black Sea). In the Carpathians also the negative strip follows the outer border of the mountains more than the lowland inside them. All these observations show that the gravity anomaly is sited not in the crust but in the subcrust. Earthquake epicentres lie mostly within this negative strip in both regions, Europe and eastern Asia.

The analogy with Europe is furthered by the volcanic arc of the western Mediterranean (Mts. Etna, Stromboli and Vesuvius) which lies within the negative strip. Volcanic rocks also appear within the inner parts of the Carpathians. These and similar facts from other parts of the world, together with the observed passage of certain island arcs into mountain systems on the lands (*e.g.* the passage of the Andaman-Nicobar island arc into the Arakan Yoma of Burma and of the Aleutian arc into the Alaska Peninsula) have led to close analogies being drawn between island arcs and mountain structures, and uncompromisingly assigns material of a *continental* affinity to the basal structure of island arcs, thus making them anomalous in an oceanic setting for the basins between the arcs and the mainland are floored by oceanic, not continental, material. Yet " no present day island arcs have developed over a geosyncline. Instead they seem to form on the ocean floor with little sedimentary cover though occasionally they may penetrate into continental slopes and shelves where a moderate thickness of sediment was present " (Hess 1955). The deep sea trenches associated with island arcs are narrow and deep. Geosynclines, judged from their contents were broad and of only shallow to moderate depth. To think of the youthful deep sea trenches as incipient geosynclines is surely an error. Thus is posed the query, how has typical

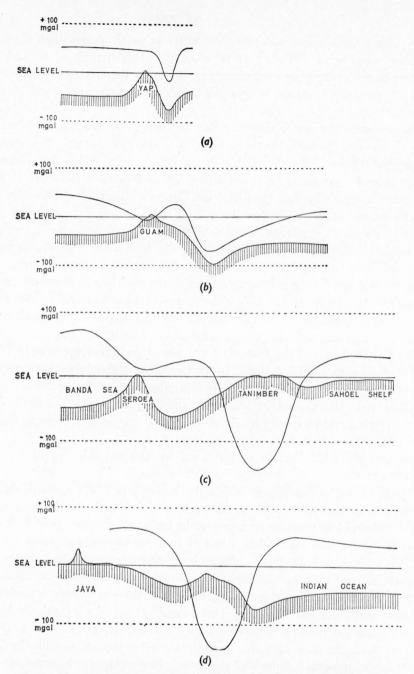

FIG. 218. Gravity anomalies in the island arcs of south-eastern Asia; (a) deficiency directly over the oceanic trench (Yap), (b) deficiency partly over the island (Guam), (c) deficiency over the outer islands in a double arc (Tanimber), (d) deficiency over the outer arc (submerged) (Java). *after F. Vening-Meinisz.*

continental matter become distributed within the oceanic basins even far beyond the limits of the continental shelves? Limited amounts of continentally-derived material carried towards the oceanic basins by turbidity currents are, of course, trapped within the deep trenches associated with island arcs; but this seems quantitatively inadequate.

In seeking a mode of origin for island arcs one asks first " What other geological phenomena are consistently arcuate in plan and perhaps also in depth? " The answer that instantly springs to mind is " The tensional shear plane " (p. 5), and this is now supported by Menard (1964) from a study of the trenches themselves. Only a perverse insistence upon crustal compression could have prevented geologists from accepting the analogy long ago. The entire pattern of East Asiatic island arcs is consistent with a westward withdrawal and rotation of Asia from a former position wherein the Indonesian arc was sited in the present curve of the Marianas arc (King 1958B) (Fig. 239). It is not beyond peradventure that such withdrawal could be effected in a thin rigid crust overlying a broad substral current, when the trenches might appear as crevasses do in the upper 150 feet of a glacier, above the zone of plastic flow. Dip-slip movements would doubtless be normal upon such shears, though analysis of earthquake records shows that strike-slip displacements also frequently occur.

In a similar east to west drift, America, which formerly had island arcs along its western aspect during Palæozoic and early-Mesozoic time, apparently united with them before the Cainozoic era. Only Alaska which was exempt from the rotation (Figs. 166, 236) has preserved its relation with the Aleutian arc (p. 614).

Explanation of the increasing depth of earthquake foci along shear planes dipping towards the continent (p. 5) is also more rational if those shear planes are tensional in successive media (Fig. 2).

The profound trenches that accompany the arcs not only may be interpreted as tensional in origin, but are so patently fresh and out of isostatic balance as to indicate that tension is active therein now, and such deep-reaching zones of potential fracture as must exist below them afford the most inviting routes for the rise of gas-levitated serpentine belts (Fig. 196), represented now by subjacent or alongside bodies of seismic velocity 7·2-7·5 km/sec. (p. 672). In their present forms all oceanic deeps are modern, as evidenced by (a) their departure from normal earthforms and their evident youth as topographic features, (b) the accompanying isostatic anomalies, (c) correlation with the latest strong Plio-Pleistocene-Recent tectonic movements. Their abnormally low rate of heat flow has already been remarked (p. 548).

THE GREAT SUBOCEANIC RIDGES

Paramount in the sea-floor topography charted with the aid of the echo-sounder are the great suboceanic ridges that span distances of many thousands of miles in the North and South Atlantic, the Arctic, Indian and the South Pacific oceans (Figs. 248-250). These elongated ridges are, in fact, major lineaments upon the earth's crust; they are greater than the largest continental mountain chains and are comparable in size rather with entire mountain systems such as the Cordillera of North America or the Alpine-Himalayan system of Eurasia. In most places the suboceanic ridges have the form of " a broad, gentle, more or less fractured arch " with crestal rift, volcanism, high seismicity and heat flow, *in short a typical cymatogen,* but there is no uniform pattern (Menard 1961a). Viewed on a globe " different sections . . . have quite different characteristics, which suggests that although the chain superficially appears to be one continuous and contemporary system, it may be a series of distinct, though very large, topographic units that overlap in space and time ". Nevertheless, though the origins of portions of the ridges and may probably have been independent, the modern behaviour of most ridges is alike and is governed by subcrustal activity (Chapter XIX).

Despite a paucity of accurate detail, the general trends and positions of the major ridges are known with sufficient geographical certainty to afford a basis for legitimate enquiry as to their patterns and origins. At a first approximation, these ridges are regarded as conforming in outline with the 4,000 metre isobath, but this measure probably makes them appear broader than they really are, a fact which should be borne in mind when the reconstructions (Figs. 222-226) are considered.

Certain of the ridges bifurcate or have side branches, single or multiple, others broaden locally into submarine plateaus and platforms; but the three major ridges in the three major oceans pursue on the whole long, slightly sinuous courses with relatively little irregularity. This form, and their remoteness from land, makes them appear true features of the oceanic basins. On the other hand, comparison successively of the Azores Plateau, Bahamas Plateau, Seychelles Ridge, Burdwood Bank and Agulhas Bank suggests relationship of some order with the continents. Indeed, unless the form and composition of the ridges prove entirely strange to geology, some of them must be deemed from the outset to possess many features akin to normal continental and insular landscapes (*e.g.* Azores Plateau (Tolstoy and Ewing 1949)).

For the mid-Atlantic and mid-Indian ridges, indeed, Ewing and Heezen have demonstrated that a median rift zone like the rift valleys of continental cymatogens is present in parts. Other regions, however, lack the rift, and-" Scripps soundings have not located a rift in the Pacific [Ridge], where earthquakes are equally common. Most surveys seem to show not one great rift but parallel ridges and troughs running lengthwise on the crest of oceanic rises " (Menard 1961a). Wherever the crestal rift strikes into the continental margins it joins with either rift valleys as in East Africa or with megashears of which the Alpine Fault of New Zealand and the San Andreas fault of California are examples. These correlations, datable on the lands, attest the modernity of the suboceanic rifts also.

Here and there the ridges are crowned by volcanoes (Iceland, St. Helena, Bouvet), by coral islands (Chagos), or more rarely by islands built of continental materials such as granite and schist (Seychelles, New Zealand) so that variety is evident in their composition. Though we shall emphasise the point again, it is important to realise, even at this stage, that this variety of type and composition probably reflects differences of behaviour and derivation in the geologic past. Thus ridges crowned with continenta islands (*e.g.* Malagasy and New Zealand) may, in behaviour as well as constitution, resemble continents more than they do the deep lying and apparently wholly volcanic ridges such as Carlsberg and Tuamotu. Two such contrasted types of ridge in relatively close proximity are Seychelles and Carlsberg, and it is exceedingly unlikely that these two ridges, very different in what is known of their constitution, possess at all similar geologic histories (p. 663).

Certain of the islands crowning submarine ridges show chapters of cyclic landscape evolution like those already adduced for continental areas. Malagasy not only shows as part of Africa in its bedrock series, but also exhibits, according to Dixey, a comparable suite of Cainozoic cyclic landforms; New Zealand shows a late Cainozoic summit planation. Even Iceland exhibits a summit planation (*e.g.* Esja Plateau northwest from Reykjavik) that has been thought possibly early Cainozoic in age, followed by long, high, level spurs (? late Cainozoic) above deep, pre-glacial valleys. These episodes, all pre-Pleistocene in age, are matched in Southern Greenland*. Einarsson calculated that the volume of material eroded in the third pre-Pleistocene cycle was 5 times the amount of Pleistocene erosion, that the ratio for the second cycle was 10 times that for the third, and that the least age possible for the plateau would be Miocene. Morphologically it could be compared with the early Cainozoic cycle of planation.

The mid-Atlantic Ridge, generally over 500 miles wide and rising to 1,000 fathoms, pursues a course midway between the opposed coasts of the Americas and Eur-Africa (Fig. 248) from Iceland and Jan Mayen in the north to beyond Bouvet Island in the south. Seismic evidence suggests, indeed, some continuation of the feature across the Arctic Ocean Basin to the mouth of the River Lena in Siberia (Emery 1949, map; Ewing and Ewing 1960) but this continuation is scarcely in the form of a ridge for the sea-floor as a whole becomes shallower.† Through more than 120° of latitude the Ridge preserves a striking parallelism with the shores of either side of the Atlantic; its slopes are locally terraced and partly buried under thick sediments (Tolstoy 1951) even as the opposed seaward slopes of the continents are terraced and partly buried. Though the mean sediment thickness is about the same, (100 to 200 metres) on both the North and South Atlantic sectors of the ridge, sediment tends to lie in pockets and to leave the crest bare in the north whereas it is draped over the southern sector as a blanket of uniform thickness. Seismic refraction measurements (Ewing and Ewing 1960) indicate semi-basaltic layers with wave velocities of 5·6 and 7·4 km./sec. respectively beneath the sediments. South of the Azores the basaltic crust has been deemed to thicken and project down into the mantle but another interpretation is preferred later (p. 664).

The most detailed description of the Ridge is that for lat. 30° N. (Tolstoy and Ewing

* T. Einarsson, Personal communication.
† Continuation is not through the Lomonosov Ridge which is aseismic and has no crestal rift.

2 0

1949; Tolstoy 1951) where it rises from a flat sea-bottom plain at 2,900 fathoms, "The central backbone of the ridge, or Main Range, which is shoaler than 1,600 fathoms, consists of a series of parallel ranges . . . several of these rise to less than 800 fathoms. Their trend follows roughly that of the Main Range. . . . The flanks, between the 1,600- and 2,500-fathom isobaths consist of a series of smooth shelves (bearing thick sediments), each from 1-50 nautical miles or more in width". This zone is from 200-300 miles wide. The centre zone is marked along its axis by a trench morphologically and seismically like surficial rift valleys. A large subjacent magnetic anomally 1000 km. wide along the axial zone has been taken by Heirtzler and le Pichon (1965) to indicate "a volcanic body . . . at, or very near to, the sea floor." Such a feature is apparently characteristic "of the entire mid-ocean ridge system ".

In the South Atlantic the Ridge is remarkable for two side branches or subsidiary ridges, one extending north-eastwards to Africa (Walvis Ridge), the other north-westwards towards South America. Of these, the Walvis Ridge is much the more prominent, shoaling even more than the main axial ridge of the South Atlantic. It is surely of continental affinity like the Malagasy Ridge.

So far as can be ascertained, no significant differences exist in the nature of the sea-floor to either side of the mid-Atlantic Ridge.

The Indian Ocean, on the other hand, is partly divided into contrasted eastern and western portions by the mid-Indian Ridge (Fig. 249) (Fairbridge 1948; King 1950). On the west are several large suboceanic ridges and many islands, on the east the sea-floor is much more even and the only islands are the microcosmic Cocos-Keeling and Christmas Island. The western part resembles the Atlantic floor, the eastern resembles the Pacific floor. The only shoaler portions of the eastern Indian Ocean are the relatively high subsidiary ridge projecting eastwards in lat. 30° S. towards Cape Leeuwin, West Australia, and a small horse-shoe shaped elevation in 15° S. 88° E. which also shoals to above 1,000 fathoms.

The mid-Indian Ridge, as interpreted by Heezen and Tharp (1965), springs from the Gulf of Aden as the Carlsberg Ridge, of low elevation above the adjacent sea bed but complete with axial rift. Wiseman and Sewell (1937) regarded this ridge as of mid- or late-Cainozoic age (p. 585). It is crossed by the profound Owen fracture zone (Fig. 228) and Vema Trench but is continuous to Rodriguez where, beyond another powerful fracture zone (aligned east-west), the Ridge bifurcates. One half passes southwestward where it is mightily sheared (left lateral) west of the Crozet Plateaus to swing round into continuity with the mid-Atlantic Ridge (Figs. 219, 228). The other half swings southeastward to be fractured near the islands of Amsterdam and St. Paul before passing south of Australia to join with the East Pacific Ridge to the south of New Zealand (Fig. 228). Everywhere the mid-Indian Ridge carries a crestal rift (paired rifts on either side of a shallow central ridge to the south of Australia and New Zealand), and by its seismicity indicates a modern elevation.

Additionally to the principal Ridge appear several independent Ridges and Plateaus built in part of continental type rocks (p. 615). They all stand high and are old in contrast with much of the mid-Indian Ridge.

The Pacific Ocean has a single trans-oceanic ridge of huge dimensions but relatively smooth relief spanning from North America to Victoria Land in the Antarctic (p. 633). In this great length it has only two major sinuousities, each of which is linked with a broad sea-floor platform extending far eastward to the American continent. The northern platform or Albatross Plateau, may even continue beyond the isthmus of Panama, into the floor of the Caribbean Sea as far as the Lesser Antilles. The dominantly volcanic, southern part of Central America is then merely incidental upon the platform. Even western North America to Alaska is bordered by the western half of the platform under the ocean and the eastern half would seem to lie beneath the continent itself. Menard (1960) has shown that this region exhibits abnormally high heat flow and shallow seismicity such as characterize the main suboceanic ridge to the south and a crestal rift is present into the Gulf of California where it links up with the San Andreas megashear (Fig. 228). Ultimately, off Oregon and Washington, the ridge, very much broken up by rifting, becomes again wholly submarine as the " Ridge and Trough " sea-floor province. The southern platform, which shows a curious alignment with the island-dotted Tuamotu Ridge (Fig. 250), affords a similar foundation for an independent high-standing ridge linking Ambrose Island and Juan Fernandez parallel to the coast of Chile and distant some 350 miles from it; and could well disappear eastwards beneath South America in the region where the Andes are cleft by a summit rift valley (p. 520, note). All three broad platforms are not known in detail. Views on their origin can be only speculative; they may represent submarine out-wellings of basalt akin to the well known plateau lavas of the Deccan and other continental regions, but some cross-sections show a closely corresponding rise in elevation of the subcrust also (Menard 1960). Indeed, the oceanic crust actually *thins* over the active East Pacific Ridge. Few islands rise from the Ridge, only Galapagos, Easter Island and Sala y Gomez with Scott Island and Balleny Islands in the extreme southwest. Gravity anomalies are close to zero, indicating that compensation is provided " by changes in the upper mantle under the Rise " for which Talwani (1964) has suggested 35 km. of anomalous mantle of seismic velocity 7·5 km./sec.

South of the insertion into the Gulf of California *there is no continuous median rift* (p. 634), compared with the mid-Atlantic median rift " Nothing comparable exists on the East Pacific Rise " (Menard 1964) nor are the flanks regularly terraced like those of the Atlantic Ridge.

Much of the East Pacific Ridge is aseismic.

The south-western Pacific Ocean displays two semi-concentric ridges reaching from New Zealand northwards to Lord Howe Island and to New Caledonia respectively. The latter island also resembles New Zealand geologically. A third ridge radiates from the North Island of New Zealand to Kermadec Islands and Tonga. This Tonga-Kermadec Ridge is bordered on the east by a new feature, a deep trench in the ocean floor, in which respect it compares with island arcs of the north-western Pacific Ocean. Minor ridges on which stand the New Hebrides and Fiji Islands (the latter ridge recurved) rise in the north between Tonga and New Caledonia and afford a link through the Solomon Islands and Louisiade Archipelago with New Guinea. With the New Zealand block extending to the outlying islands of the Dominion (Auckland, Campbell, Antipodes and Chatham) the ridges of the south-west Pacific Basin make a remarkable assemblage.

In the Central Pacific Basin, several rows of islands cap straight ridges rising from the ocean floor. These ridges, on which stand the Hawaiian, Tuamotu, Austral and Marquesas island chains, are all similar and nearly parallel to one another, so that the description of the " Hawaiian Islands " by Dietz and Menard (1953) would probably serve equally well for all. No trace of rock that is not derivable by differentiation from oceanic basalt, or is not coral rock, appears upon these islands, and very little consideration is necessary to convince one that these ridges are distinct in type and composition (and probably in origin) from certain of the ridges we have mentioned hitherto which have continental affinities.

ROCK CONSTITUTION OF SUBOCEANIC RIDGES

Rocks dredged from the suboceanic ridges are relatively scarce, and of small range in composition. Thus basaltic rocks only have been dredged from the Carlsberg Ridge of the Indian Ocean.

Rocks from the mid-Atlantic Ridge, described by Shand (1949), confirmed the predominance of basalt and made " two notable additions to the record, namely, an abundance of serpentine and a mylonitised anorthositic gabbro. The latter, together with the dunite-mylonite of St. Paul Rocks, provides evidence of strong shearing stresses during or after the formation of the Ridge. Wiseman (1965) has described from St. Paul several unusual rock types consisting of forsterite, brown hornblende, enstatite, clino-pyroxene and spinel, which he regards as possibly derived from the upper mantle. The much more extensive hydration of the serpentines as compared with the relative freshness of the basalts is interesting and suggests that the serpentines are older ". The serpentines, in fact, may be coeval with the formation of the Ridge, *cf.* Hess (1938; 1949); the basalts may be largely of subsequent emission.

Occasionally the suboceanic ridges are surmounted by islands such as Ascension, Bouvet or Reunion, the rocks of which are basalts, usually lime-bearing and often non-olivinic, in marked contrast to all the basalts from the adjacent deep oceanic floor where in addition to olivine they carry a single clinopyoxene. Included as xenoliths in the island basalts are abundant magnesian dunites and peridotites, often with auxiliary spinel (*e.g.* upon Madeira, Gran Canaria, Lanzarote, Gough and Ascension in the Atlantic) which hint at a derivation in some levitated mantle beneath the submarine ridge. Several islands have intrusions or enclaves of acid material in small quantity, but Tilley (1951) has taken the view that, as most of the acid rocks are small in volume and are alkali-rich (*e.g.* the granite of Ascension), they have been derived from primitive basalt by processes of fractional crystallisation, and do not signify the presence of truly sialic (continental) material in the ridges upon which the islands stand. In instances such as the obsidian

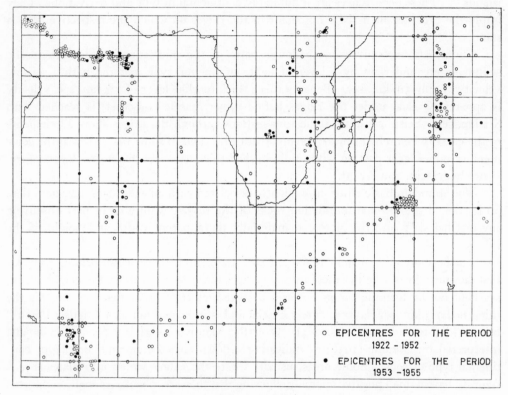

FIG. 219. Earthquakes in southern Africa and the surrounding Atlantic and Indian Oceans, showing the general association of oceanic shocks with submarine ridges. This perhaps indicates continental-type earth-materials in the ridges, and follows uparchings on both the continents and sea floors. *after J. Oliver.*

of Easter Island discussed by Bandy (1937), Tilley's view is undoubtedly correct; nevertheless there remain occurrences such as the late Precambrian granites and early Cainozoic normal syenites of Seychelles (Baker 1963) on the Mascarene Ridge, " coarse gneisses and granite of Santa Maria in the Azores with red sandstone, thick limestone, quartz and tourmaline granite on the east side of Texeira in the same group (Gagel 1910) standing upon the mid-Atlantic ridge ", and boulders of hornblende granite on Kermadec Island, which do apparently reflect a continental etiology. Kerguelen has schist and siliceous slates, as does also the much smaller Macquarie Island; for the Solomon Islands group, Reed (1949) quoted evidence " undoubtedly of continental origin " and the same is probably true of the basement of New Hebrides; Fiji has sodic granites and discordant diorites showing low-rank metamorphic effects. The Viti formation, several thousands of feet thick, was there folded by the Viti revolution. Madagascar and New Zealand are truly " continental islands ". These occurrences are indubitably continental in type and derivation. They imply the presence of a sialic basement in the ridges on which the respective islands stand.

Confirmation comes from shallower parts of the mid-Atlantic ridge where the sediments are underlain by a layer of light, continental-type material with a seismic velocity of only 5·6 km./sec. Beneath this a thick rootlike layer of 7·4 km./sec. velocity is apparently usual under the ridges before upper mantle (subcrust) is reached with 8·1 km./sec. Seismic studies indicating sections through the ridges show all elements of the crust to be arched upwards sympathetically,* and in some places reveal the sedimentary upper layer passing with undiminished thickness over the crest. Cymatogeny is surely evident, and recent.

The abundant basic effusions evidently associated with all the ridges have doubtless (a) blanketed the original foundation rocks of the ridges, wholly or in part obscuring any original sial; and (b) increased materially the apparent width and height of the ridges.

Furthermore, the major ridges are essentially in isostatic equilibrium, showing that they must be of a lighter medium and achieve their elevation above the neighbouring sea-floor not by tectonic action but as a balanced effect of lesser density. In this the thickened 7·5 km./sec. layer is surely crucial and is indicated not as a " denser basalt " but as " lighter subcrust " (p. 664). Over the Maldive Ridge is a negative anomaly, interpreted by Glennie (1936) as indicating a downwarped fragment of a light, continental type of rock. Some areas, usually where the ridges widen into plateaus (e.g. Azores), have a small positive anomaly, showing that they are in part regionally supported (isobary rather than isostasy).

Earthquake shocks follow closely the mid-Atlantic and mid-Indian Ridges, showing that they are under a certain amount of stress (Fig. 219): but in the Atlantic this stress is not general and the shocks are usually shallow and of only weak to moderate intensity (Tolstoy and Ewing 1949). The mid-Indian Ridge displays a moderate earthquake intensity along most of its length, but the east-west sector is of relatively low seismic intensity.

Subdivision of the suboceanic ridges into three groups, based on composition and occurrence, is probably valid: (a) high-standing, lesser ridges demonstrably of continental origin such as Madagascar, New Zealand, Seychelles, New Caledonia, Fiji. These are sometimes curved or distorted, e.g. Seychelles, Fiji, indicating horizontal movement. (b) Huge transoceanic ridges such as the mid-Atlantic, mid-Indian and East Pacific ridges which from their elevation and isostatic state appear to contain a

---

* e.g. Menard for the East Pacific Ridge.

proportion of lighter material than at comparable levels beneath the adjacent oceanic basin floors. Superficially they are known by dredging to consist largely of basaltic rock and at depth appear to have characteristically a layer of material of velocity in the 7·1-7·9 km./sec. range (p. 582). (c) Deeper ridges of moderate or lesser magnitude, straight or

FIG. 220. Tentative classification of submarine ridges by composition into continental ridges, volcanic ridges and mixed ridges.

curved, and consisting apparently wholly of basic and ultrabasic rocks erupted along major fractures extending down into the subcrust. Such are the Central Pacific ridges, the Crozets and, probably, the Carlsberg Ridge. The first and third categories appear distinct in origins, the second category may be of mixed derivation, and includes, apparently, the most active ridges of modern times.

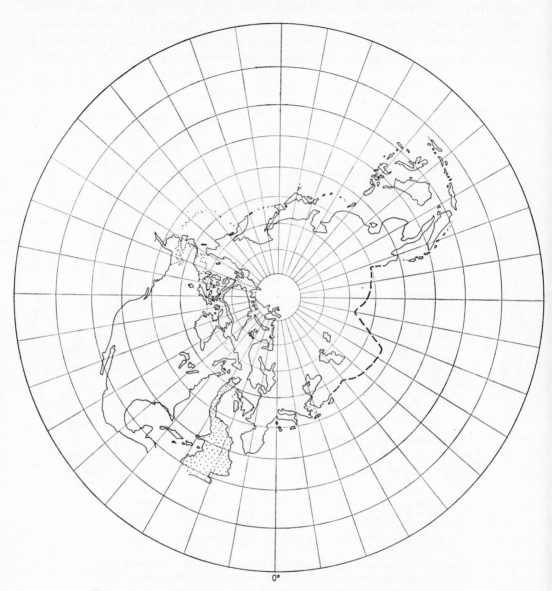

Fɪɢ. 221.   Reconstruction of Laurasia incorporating the mid-Atlantic and
Lomonosov Ridges.   For location on the graticule, the mid-Atlantic
Ridge is in its present position and the rest of the reconstruction brought to
it.   The position is thought to be correct for mid-Mesozoic time.   (All
the reconstructions (Figs. 221-226 and 240) were made with perspex
shapes upon a globe and were plotted in stereographic projection by
Mrs. V. Gorsky under the direction of the author.)

The pattern of those suboceanic ridges and plateaus *known or suspected to be of continental affinity* is peculiar and needs to be related to the continental masses. If this is done with respect to Laurasia and Gondwana, the pattern of such ridges is seen to fit into the spaces between the continents already postulated upon stratigraphic data (du Toit 1937). They then complete the reassemblies in the most remarkable way (Figs. 221, 222). *All sialic material of the earth's crust is then embodied in these two simple, oval, primitive supercontinents.*

The major suboceanic ridges may then be understood as originating successively on the dismemberment of the primitive supercontinents (King 1958), and as marking by their positions the sites of the reassemblies at the several epochs of disruption (Figs. 222-226). These epochs may be dated from stratigraphic and palæoclimatic evidence (Chapter II). The congruence of all the data from many and varied sources expressed in these diagrams passes the limits of fortuity, and the one principle that unites them all is the principle of continental drift.

Drift, which on the above basis becomes measurable in amount and direction for the late-Palæozoic and Mesozoic eras, seems however to have failed after the continental disruption of the late Mesozoic, by which time all the continental masses seem to have occupied their present relative positions on the globe. Of large scale continental drift during the Cainozoic and Quaternary eras no satisfactory evidence has yet been forthcoming.

As has already been emphasised, not all the existing suboceanic ridges are of the same type or origin, and when the above reassembly has been made certain features merge which imply that in modern times parts of the ridge system have been reactivated usually along pre-existing lines but occasionally departing from this. All the ridges with recent arching, crestal rift, high seismicity and high heat flow should evidently be regarded as current cymatogens (p. 656) whether guided by older tectonic zones or not.

The occurrence is remarkably similar to recently elevated zones upon the lands (pp. 67, 196). Most mountain ranges stand upon the sites of former orogenesis (*e.g.* circumvallation pp. 469, 492) which have recently been reactivated. Other arched elevations such as the rift valley system of East Africa do not necessarily follow old lines but have partaken of the same zonal vertical displacement.

Modern mountain ranges, rifted plateaus, and modern submarine ridges are therefore all comparable surface expressions of a single deep seated causal activity, a cymatogenic energy source which we have yet to seek (Chapter XIX). To sum up : the pattern of suboceanic ridges is, like that of mountain systems, basically inherited but modern reactivation differs in particular location.

With the modern vertical uplifts has gone considerable horizontal derangement. All the ridges are crossed by megashears (shown by dislocations upon magnetic surveys) which are more recent than the ridges themselves; and which demonstrate the prevalence

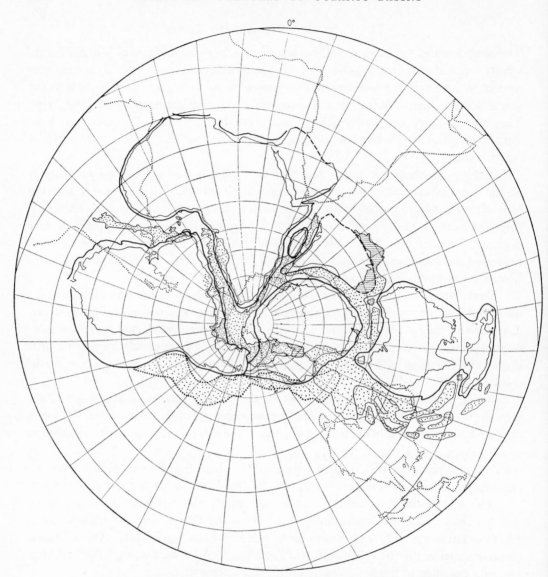

FIG. 222. Integration of suboceanic ridges known or suspected to be of
continental affinity with the Gondwana reassembly. The jig-saw fit is
obvious (the only distortion has been to fold back the branch ridge
directed towards Cape Leeuwin in the Indian Ocean), and brings into a
single ovoid continental mass all the sial of the southern hemisphere.
Volcanic ridges, obliquely ruled. Present positions of continents lightly
dotted in outline. The location upon the graticule has been decided by
bringing the whole reconstruction against the southern part of the
East Pacific Ridge, heavy dots, in its present position. Time:
(cf. Fig. 17) late Carboniferous.

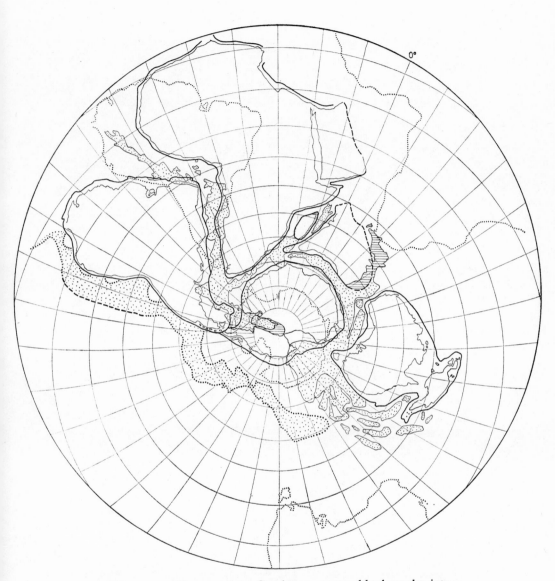

FIG. 223. The complete Gondwana reassembly brought into
juxtaposition with the northern part of the East Pacific Ridge.
Ridge in position outlined in heavy dots. Time : (*cf.* Fig. 18) early
Permian.

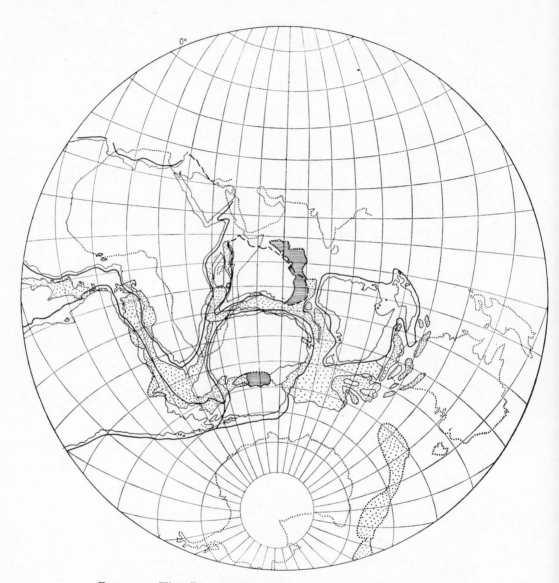

FIG. 224. The East Pacific Ridge having been left behind, the
Gondwana assembly is later oriented to the mid-Indian Ridge. Portions
of ridge in present position outlined in heavy dots. Time : (*cf.* Fig. 19)
Triassic.

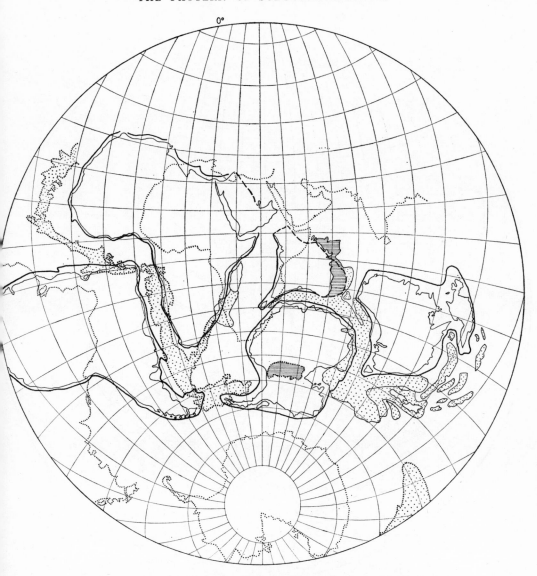

FIG. 225. The eastern half of Gondwana remaining attached to the mid-Indian Ridge, the western half has seceded (as shown by penetration of the mid-Jurassic to early-Cretaceous sea along the eastern side of Africa) and became sited with respect to the mid-Atlantic Ridge. (Parts of ridges in present positions outlined in heavy dots.) Time: (*cf.* Fig. 20) latest-Jurassic to early Cretaceous.

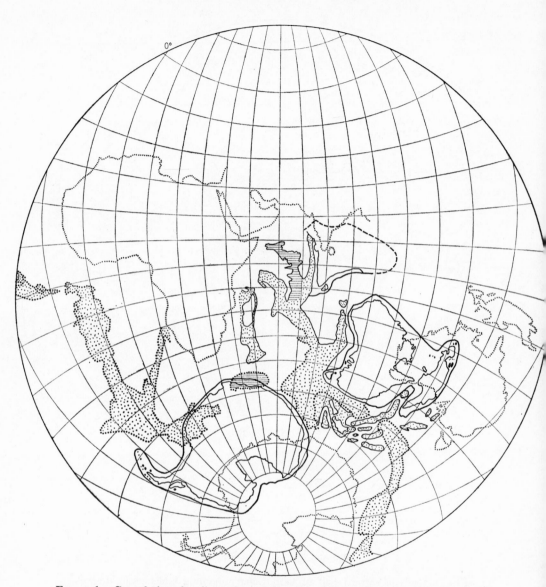

FIG. 226. Completing the disruption of Gondwanaland, Africa and South America have parted from the mid-Atlantic Ridge and assumed their present positions, Antarctica has moved south, India north and the Australian massif moved east (with 90° rotation) to the present New Zealand-Tonga line after which Australia retrograded westward to its present site, leaving beind the submarine ridges of the Tasman Sea and finally impinging on the north against Indonesia (Fig. 183). Time : (*cf*. Fig. 21) Aptian-Albian.

of crustal shear (possibly under the control of sub-crustal convection currents) since the ridges were formed. These shear displacements are minor compared with original deflections in course of the ridges, this agreeing with other evidence that Cainozoic crustal drift has been minor compared with the huge continental displacements of the Cretaceous period.

THE IMPORTANCE OF THE CRETACEOUS PERIOD

The Cretaceous appears to be an initial date in and around the oceanic basins. With a few local extensions back to the Middle Jurassic (*e.g.* Malagasy) it is the earliest date of sedimentation related to coasts of the Atlantic and Indian oceans,* where the non-geosynclinal deposits of this period are relatively thick. Outside the Pacific it is the date of the oldest sediments dredged from the walls of submarine canyons, and even along continental slopes of the Pacific older rocks are not much earlier. The oldest sediments known from submarine ridges and guyot tops are Cretaceous. Thus all the major oceanic basins existed in modern form during the Cretaceous period.

Yet for the preceding Jurassic period Arkell (1956) summarised that all the occurrences of Jurassic formations outside the Tethys and the geosynclinal ring about the Pacific (the Laurasian and Gondwana circumvallations) " amount to little more than relics of marginal lappings of the sea " across the continents. " Such transgressive seas were always shallow " . . . " nor were they contemporary everywhere ". Jurassic stratigraphy affords no evidence of the existence beyond the incipient stage of either the South Atlantic or Indian Oceans during that period, and though all workers are agreed upon the presence of sea in the Arctic regions there is no evidence that this differed from the epicontinental sea that covered Russian to the Caspian Sea.

All this is in accord with the hypothesis whereunder, following drift of two super-continental masses during late-Palæozoic and early-Mesozoic time (Chapter II), fragmentation of these parental masses during the mid-Mesozoic opened up new oceanic basins. By the end of the Mesozoic era the mutual flight of the fragments was arrested at their present positions on the globe, and from the continents at least comes no geologic evidence of further lateral changes during the Cainozoic era. Begun in the mid-Mesozoic, the present oceanic outlines were, apparently, fully established before the end of that era.

Within that interval of time many events fall sequentially into place. Thus the separation of South America and Africa from the mid-Atlantic ridge is dated as Aptian-Albian. Following drift of the former continent, unity of Caribbean structures with North America was achieved (for the first time) in the late-Cretaceous (Laramide) orogeny. Likewise the early-Cretaceous fauna of Mexico and the southern United States

---

* A few premonitary floodings date back to the Permian in India, Malagasy, Western Australia and Texas.

is similar to that of Tethyan Europe; the late-Cretaceous fauna, on the contrary, is characteristically American.

A northward movement of Africa to clear the Walvis Ridge seems to have taken it into partial collision with Eurasia (? pre-Gosau), after which retrograde movement to the south-southeast into its present position may have left the North African fold girdle attached to Europe as the Dinaric arc (p. 488).

Upon the lands, the late Mesozoic was a time of orogenesis along the circum-vallations, of initiation of new and widespread erosion cycles across the shields, and of initiation of fresh basins and foci of continental deposition some of which have continued to function until the present day.

On these data, the period appears to be unique in earth history.

CHAPTER XVII

THE ATLANTIC, ARCTIC AND INDIAN OCEANIC BASINS

Age of the North and South Atlantic Basins. The North Atlantic Basin. The Gulf of Mexico. The Caribbean Region. The South Atlantic Basin. The Scotia Arc. The Mediterranean Sea. The Arctic Ocean Basin. The Indian Ocean Basin.

AGE OF THE NORTH AND SOUTH ATLANTIC BASINS

Despite the parallelism of opposed shores for the full length of the Atlantic and the apparent continuity of the mid-Atlantic Ridge, the North and South Atlantic Basins are possibly of independent (though almost synchronous) origin, for both were seemingly generated by northward and southward gulfs from the Mesozoic Tethys into Laurasia and Gondwana respectively. For the date of formation, Arkell (1956) has noted (a) in the west the absence of Jurassic rocks for 3,500 miles between North-east Greenland and the Gulf of Mexico, and (b) in the east that the string of Jurassic outcrops between Norway and Morocco refers only to probably shallow epicontinental seas and does not prove the presence at that period of a neighbouring North Atlantic. Quite in contrast are the thick marine Cretaceous formations of the American coastal plain with Tethyan fauna in the Gulf region and the Iberian and Biscayan developments of the marine Cretaceous. Available coastal evidence therefore indicates clearly that the North Atlantic Basin did not exist prior to the Cretaceous Period; and this is borne out by marine corings wherein, from banks and guyots and the mid-Atlantic ridge, the oldest marine rocks recovered are consistently Cretaceous.

Likewise, South Atlantic coasts show no vestige of Jurassic marine deposition, and the first marine deposits related to the modern continental outlines on both sides of the ocean are of Albian age, preceded locally by littoral and lagoonal Aptian, (*e.g.* Angola). Here again islands within the area (*e.g.* South Georgia) have not yielded sediments of Atlantic fossiliferous type older than Cretaceous (Holtedahl 1929; Wilckens 1932).

G. W. Simpson has demonstrated on biological evidence that South America, which shared its Permian and Triassic reptiles and flora with Africa and not with North America, has been isolated from other continents since late-Cretaceous time at least, except for intermittent Cainozoic linkage with North America through the Isthmus of Panama where fossil faunas, both marine and continental, prove the impermanence of connection between the Americas even during Cainozoic time.

Of major structural importance is the fact that ancient fold mountain systems run out transversely to the Atlantic shores (*e.g.* Newfoundland and Brittany in the north and Sierra de la Ventana and Cape Ranges in the south). Nowhere, either, do folded ranges of Jurassic or later date extend parallel to the outlines of the basin; they have just not been created out of the continental shelf sediments. The basin is therefore disjunctive, and transects the older structures of late-Palæozoic, and even Triassic, age.

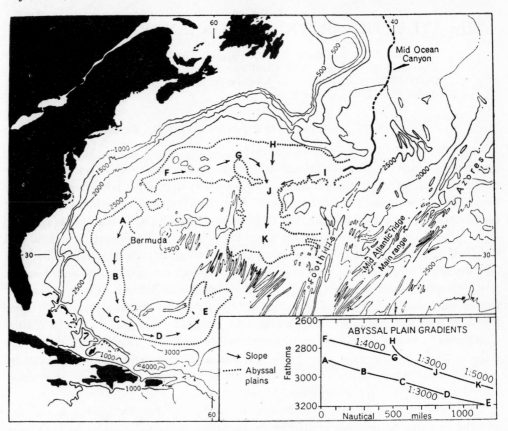

FIG. 227. Bottom topography of the North Atlantic basin.
after I. Tolstoy et al.

THE NORTH ATLANTIC BASIN

Bottom topography within the North Atlantic region has been explored extensively since 1945 by research expeditions from Wood's Hole and Lamont Observatories (Tolstoy 1951; Ewing and Heezen 1956) (Figs. 227, 248). Several independent abyssal plains have been distinguished at different depths separated by more elevated rises, or by slopes that may be either abrupt or gentle. The plains themselves are very level and are interpreted as filled or partly filled sedimentary basins. Where the sediments do not reach the sill, transition to the next basin is abrupt, but where the sediments have spilled over from a higher basin to a lower the passage is gradational. Thus the floor of the North American Basin extends from the foot of the continental slope at 2,600 fathoms with gentle slopes of 2 feet or so per mile towards the south-eastward and southward to a narrower level at depths below 2,700 fathoms, whence it changes rapidly eastward into the general floor of the North American Basin at 2,850-2,950 fathoms with a southward slope. At the base of the continental rise, from the Grand Banks to the Bahama Islands, is a continuous belt of layered, well-sorted sands, siliceous in the north and calcareous in the south, that Ericson, Ewing and Heezen (1952) interpret as carried and sorted by turbidity currents from the shelf. The sands interfinger with deep-sea clays of the oceanic basin proper. Many core samples show a sharp change from a superficial layer, 10-30 cm. thick carrying a warm water pelagic fauna to an underlying stratum of sparse cold-water fauna which is believed to represent the Wisconsin Ice epoch of the Pleistocene. " This change in lithology has been found in the equatorial Atlantic, in the Caribbean, in the Gulf of Mexico, and northward to the point where the stratigraphy is complicated by glacial marine deposits."

The abyssal plains of both eastern and western Atlantic regions, together with marginal basins such as the Gulf of Mexico and the Yucatan Basin, all yield sedimentary cores with the rapidly alternating layers of sediment typical of accumulation under turbidity currents, and remarkable indeed is the observation (Ewing and Heezen 1956) that sediments from the Magdalena River of South America are transported thus across the abyssal plain of the Caribbean Sea to the coast of Haiti. Rapidity of action and burial is here demonstrated by a deposit containing abundant organic matter from plants. Equal rapidity of deposition is indicated by 70-130 cm. of graded silt and sand overlying foraminiferal clays of abyssal facies on the deep bottom south of the Grand Banks of Newfoundland. This layer is thought to be material dislodged from the Banks by the 1929 earthquake and transported by slump and transformation into a turbidity current far out into the Atlantic. The entire area of the Gulf of Mexico too, is floored beneath a thin layer of Recent globigerina ooze, with a current-transported spread of Pleistocene sediments exceeding 30 feet in thickness.

Ewing, Heezen and others have established from core-sampling that these turbidity currents often debouch from submarine canyons of the continental shelf and carry far out on to the abyssal plains. Several submarine canyons, including that of the Hudson, are continued beyond the continental shelves into the abyssal plains where they form furrows through the plain sediments. Within the furrows, Recent sediments are relatively coarse, the finer grades being distributed, possibly as levees, over the neighbouring plains. This affords explanation too of a core recovery from the centre of the Hatteras abyssal plain of " several feet of pea-size gravel ".

Ewing and his collaborators (1953) have also traced a huge canyon (Fig. 209) following always the deepest axis of the submarine basins, from Davis Strait between Greenland and Labrador, far out beyond the Newfoundland Banks until it turns south-westward across the abyssal plains to pass eastwards of Bermuda towards the Nares Deep.   Perhaps 2,500 miles in total length, the canyon has a level or downstream gradient limited only by the distance and the maximum depth of the ocean bottom. The cross-section is box-like, with steep walls and a flat floor upon which graded silty sediment cores indicate the activity of turbidity currents. The canyon is not unique: others are known parallel with this and with the general direction of the North American coast.   All are 2-5 miles wide and lie incised 20-100 fathoms below the adjacent submarine plains.

The Iberian Basin east of the mid-Atlantic Ridge has a very irregular floor (Emery 1950) with many seamounts and a broad zone, including the Josephine and Gettysburg Banks, that rises from 2,500 fathoms to a charted depth of only 25 fathoms (Fig. 229). The southernmost tip of this rise is crowned with the volcanic island of Madeira.

The topography of the mid-Atlantic ridge in these latitudes is also very irregular, with a high central mountainland, and flanks descending between 1,600 and 2,500 fathoms, by sedimented terraces to a marginal zone of foothills.   These terraces are said to be matched by terraces at similar depths off the coast of North-west Africa; but the significance of the correlation is obscure.   The Azores Plateau, which stands immediately east of the Ridge, exhibits a linear relief directed predominantly from east-south-east or west-south-west, upon which is superimposed the normal relief trending parallel with the Ridge.   It is perhaps a truly continental fragment, preserving traces of former tectonic lineaments.   In this it partly resembles Iceland which is now known from seismic data to be a continental fragment, with a sialic foundation 15 km. thick tapering off to the east and underlain by a basaltic layer 10 km. thick.   With a thickness of erupted basalts 1·7 km. at Reykjavik increasing to 8 km. in the east an average crustal thickness of 28 km. is indicated.   Apart from these continental fragments, the crustal section in the Ridge is now believed (Le Pichon *et al.* 1965) to possess beneath the axial zone a deep root of material with seismic velocity 7·0-7·9 km./sec. the physical constitution of which is at present uncertain.   Similar material is indicated beneath parts of the East Pacific Ridge.

But quite the most remarkable topographic feature of the mid-Atlantic Ridge is a median rift valley similar in size to the rift valleys of the continents.   Coupled with a notable seismicity, this rift, which stands upon a marked arch continuous round the compound Atlantic-Indian Ridge (p. 576), may well indicate cymatogenic activity of continental type upon the Ridge during post-Cainozoic time.

At about lat. 31° N. the Ridge is transected by an east-west trench that descends to a maximum depth of 2,800 fathoms, and from which crushed and metamorphosed ultrabasic rocks have been recovered.   This plain evidence of tectonism may mark the weld between the northern and southern parts of the Ridge related to Laurasia and to Gondwana respectively.   But in the equatorial Atlantic even greater left lateral offsets of the Chain and Romanche fracture zones (Fig. 228) displace the ridge crest by 180 miles.   The Romanche Trench here plumbs 4,106 fathoms (Heezen *et al.* 1964) an indication of modern genesis which is supported by high seismicity.   Mineralogic and palæontologic examination of sediments in the trench indicates a derivation in part from the mid-Atlantic Ridge itself. Altogether a series of equatorial megashears (Fig. 228) here offsets the ridge (Heezen and Ewing).

The low gentle hills or rises between the individual Atlantic basins perhaps also owe their origin to modern cymatogeny. According to Ewing and Heezen (1956) some

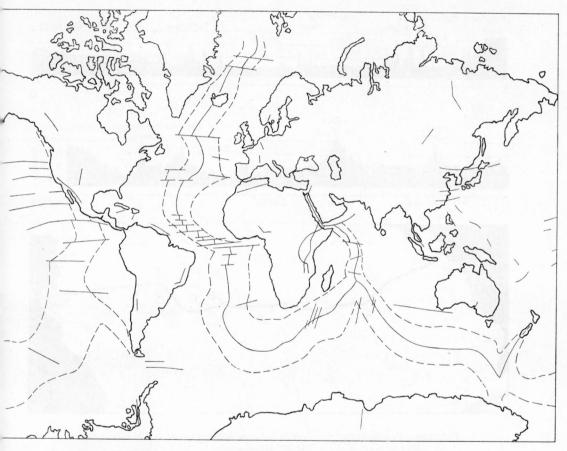

FIG. 228. The pattern of major megashears and rift valleys upon the earth. Many dislocations cross the sub-oceanic ridges, along the crest of which are also median rift valleys. Upon the continents are the following rift valley systems: Rocky Mountain Trench and Rio Grande Trough; Andean Rift, and the São Francisco and Paraiba Rifts of Brazil; in Europe the Oslo, Rhine, Rhône and Allier Grabens; Baikal and Lena Rifts of Siberia; the East African Rift system with the older Niger-Benue Rift; St. Vincent and Spencer Gulfs of South Australia; in the Antarctic are George VI Sound and Lambert Glacier Rifts. In California, Iceland, New Zealand and the Red Sea are obvious connections between the modern rifted mid-oceanic ridges and rift or transcurrent fault systems upon the lands. Some rifts date back to the Cretaceous, some to the Cainozoic, and nearly all show Recent rejuvenation (cymatogeny).

areas upon the rises have been denuded by currents and have shed sediments into adjoining basins. Core recovery from the rises generally yields Cainozoic or even Cretaceous sediments which may contain shallow-water fossil organisms (*e.g.* Bermuda Rise), and certain extraordinary cores contain " a complete succession from Oligocene foraminifera at the bottom to Pleistocene at the top ".

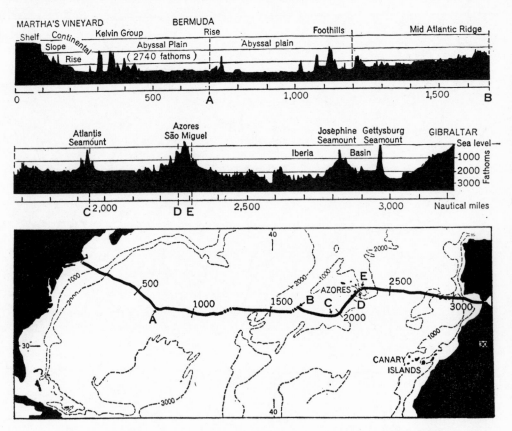

FIG. 229.   Profile across the North Atlantic sea-floor.   *after M. Ewing and B. C. Heezen.*

The Bermuda Rise, interpreted by Ewing as a truncated volcanic mass, constitutes a large area of relatively rough topography rising from the level abyssal plains of the western Atlantic. In addition to the island, which is relatively minute, the Rise bears several seamounts some of which make a chain from New England towards Bermuda and thence to the mid-Atlantic Ridge. Others continue beyond the Ridge in a chain directed from the Azores toward Gibraltar. Most of the Atlantic seamounts, indeed, are associated with the mid-Atlantic Ridge and its foothills, but some are found far out in the abyssal plains springing abruptly from the level sediment that encompasses them about the base. Every Atlantic seamount known was originally volcanic.

Cretaceous and Cainozoic sediments have been recovered from the tops of some, and Ewing is of opinion that none are older than Cretaceous in age.

Quite in contrast are the Bahamas Banks, an area which has subsided continuously since the late Jurassic but which has been constantly maintained by the accumulation of reef limestones. The deep boring on Andros Island penetrated 14,587 feet of dolomite and limestone without reaching the base of the Cretaceous, which constituted about half the entire sequence.

Where the depth of water is of the order of 2,500 fathoms or more, the bed of the North Atlantic Basin on both sides of the mid-oceanic ridge is shown by seismic refraction shooting to consist of sediment about one kilometre thick. The earth crust below this, about 5 km. thick, has a sound-wave velocity of about 6·5-7 km./sec. corresponding to a basaltic composition and a base represented by the Mohorovičić discontinuity, beneath which velocities of 8 km./sec. are encountered. Different, however, are (a) an area near Bermuda where Ewing and Press discovered basement rocks having a velocity of 7·58 km./sec. and (b) the Icelandic block which for tens of kilometres thickness has a seismic velocity of 7·4 km./sec. This was interpreted as showing a virtual absence of normal basaltic crust from these areas. The precise boundary of continental granitic material is often difficult to determine, partly because the thickness of sediments increases enormously towards the continents, e.g. to about 10 km. in the vicinity of Barbados and south of the Grand Banks. On the contrary, however, off the western approaches of the English Channel the layering suggested by 25 seismic stations follows closely the known geology of the land with semi-consolidated Cretaceo-Cainozoic formation, resting upon the New Red group over a Palæozoic system which covers a metamorphic basement. The last appears to form a long, deep trough and contouring of the layers is possible.

Beyond lat. 50° N. the floor of the Atlantic shallows progressively until the main basin is closed between Scotland-Iceland-Greenland by a narrow ridge at only 270 fathoms depth. On the western side of Greenland a similar rise connects with Baffin Land and the American continent. Northernmost elements of the Atlantic are the Norwegian and Greenland basins leading through the gap between Greenland and Spitzbergen into the Arctic Oceanic Basin (q.v.).

Extensive Eocene plateau basalts, erupted partly from fissures and partly from cones appear in Northern Ireland, West and North Scotland, Faroes, Iceland, Jan Mayen, East and West Greenland, and beyond the Icelandic sill similar basalts are widespread in Spitzbergen, Franz Joseph Land, Novaya Zemlya and finally perhaps up the Yenesei Valley into Siberia. In Iceland the basalts " are remnants of a thick plateau (thickness at least 5-6 km.) which originally must have had an extension much greater than that of the present island " . . . " The lavas are entirely sub-aerial ". On both Iceland and Jan Mayen fissure eruptions occurred. Such phenomena surely predicate a state of regional crustal tension during the early-Cainozoic.

THE GULF OF MEXICO

The Gulf of Mexico (Fig. 230) with which is considered the Yucatan Basin, has broad shelves, is flat bottomed between 1,500 and 1,900 fathoms and is tectonically quiescent. It is perhaps a part of the North American continent that has subsided gently behind the Greater Antilles-Honduras rampart and been over-flowed by the ocean; but the tendency to subside long antedates the present sedimentation cycle beginning in the Jurassic, for the Sigsbee knolls of the deep zone appear to be piercement domes of Louam salt with older Palæozoic below. These rest upon a sub-section of typical ocean basin crust, (Ewing, Worzel and Ewing 1962). The structural boundary of North America as marked by former orogenies is clearly through Mexico and Guatemala into Honduras where the fold axes curve into a strike north of east directed into the Rosalind and Pedro Banks and Jamaica. All elements of North American cordilleran structure turn here (Eardley 1962), and south of the crystalline and folded zone, through Salvador and Nicaragua, swings also a girdle of late-Cainozoic volcanoes that are believed to stand upon a foundation of Jurassic and Cretaceous formations. Even the low southern margin of Nicaragua, which includes the large lake that was formerly an arm of the sea and with neighbouring Costa Rica offered an alternative route to the Panama Canal, curves so that the Pacific coast of North America passes eastward into the Atlantic. The Isthmus of Panama is another and a foreign structure belonging neither to North nor to South America. It stands upon a portion of the Albatross submarine plateau like a higher standing version of the Cocos Ridge that, indeed, connects it with Galapagos Islands to the south-west.

One feature of the North American region needs special consideration. The Bartlett Trough is a deep trench (22,788 feet maximum) that runs in a straight line from the Gulf of Honduras to the southern end of Cuba. It is flanked on the north by the Mysteriosa Bank on which stands Grand Cayman Island, and on the south by a ridge including the Rosalind and Pedro Banks and crowned by Jamaica. Though Bartlett Trench is proportionately comparable with the oceanic deeps that parallel island arcs of the Antillean-East Asiatic type, it differs from them in several important respects. It is straight; it is without marked gravitational anomalies, departures from zero being small and either positive or negative; there is no associated volcanism; and it is situated within the continental sector as defined above by structure. The trough margins are steep and appear in part related to fault systems in Southern Cuba. The trough is thought to be a fault-trench between arching flanks to north and south (cymatogenic) and Hess has postulated 50 km. or more of transcurrent movement upon it, the north-ward side having moved relatively to the west. He writes, " The area north of the fault, Cuba, suffered only a moderate amount of late-Tertiary deformation, whereas Haiti, which was not so relieved, became very intensely folded in Miocene and Pliocene time. . . . Also it explains the abrupt disappearance of the negative strip at the east end of Cuba and its present absence from the whole length of Cuba ". " A smaller

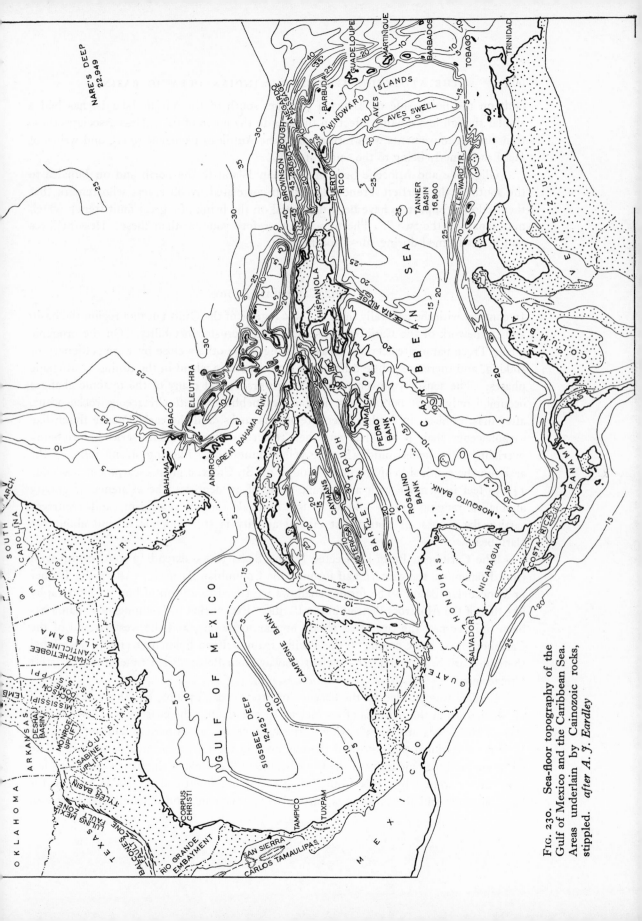

FIG. 230. Sea-floor topography of the Gulf of Mexico and the Caribbean Sea. Areas underlain by Cainozoic rocks, stippled. *after A. J. Eardley*

fault on the north side of Anegada Passage, south of the Virgin Islands, has had a similar though less striking effect on the area to the north of it." Hess associates these transcurrent movements with formation of the Antillean tectogene (q.v.), and writes of Haiti as formerly being to the south of Cuba.

Oligocene and Miocene beds on Cayman Island to the north and on Jamaica to the south of the Bartlett Trench have been correlated by observers who remark that they " do not appear to have been deposited on the brink of a great fault trench which now separates the two ". The trench is therefore younger than these: Hess believes that it was formed during late-Miocene time.

The Caribbean Region

In contrast with the generally mild tectonic regime of the Gulf-Yucatan region the basin and framework of the Caribbean display marked crustal instability. On the orogenic girdle Trechmann cites certain areas as rising while others close by were stationary or sinking, and there are subtle differences from island to island in the timing of orogenic phases. The sense of movement is often reversed, and many of the tectonic changes occupied only short periods, e.g. in Jamaica pebbles of late-Cretaceous rocks occur, after diastrophism, in further later Cretaceous rocks, and the early-Eocene flysch-like carbonaceous shale is infolded with the Cretaceous Blue Mountain series before being overlain by the lower-middle-Eocene yellow limestone. Existing strong relief of the area (on the south side of Anegada Trough off St. Croix, a great escarpment descends 14,130 feet in 5 miles with an average slope of 30 degrees), the existence of gravity anomalies ranging from +80 to −150 milligals, active volcanism, and recurrent earthquake shocks all testify that crustal activity is still endemic in and about the Caribbean.

The Caribbean Basin is bisected by the Beata Ridge extending south-south-west from Hispaniola, the western half forming the Colombian Basin, the eastern the Tanner or Venezuelan Basin. The former shallows westward to a form of bottom topography like that of the Albatross Plateau in the Pacific. Except that the Isthmus of Panama has been built across, the two areas would appear to be one, and the western end of the Caribbean may truly belong to the Pacific realm. Even Schuchert (1935) postulated that the Caribbean was a very ancient seaway from Precambrian time until the latest Cretaceous.

Eardley was puzzled by the absence of broad coastal plains, like those of the Gulf of Mexico, from the margins of so ancient an ocean; but the coast was of Pacific type and all conditions are met if, prior to the Cretaceous, the Americas had not achieved their present global positions and thereby created the Caribbean mediterranean. The structural and tectonic unity of the Caribbean-Antillean region since the Cretaceous has been demonstrated by Hess from geologic and gravimetric data. The picture for late-Cainozoic and Recent time is particularly convincing, and demonstrates how well geologic elements of diverse origins once brought together into a restricted field may behave in concert.

The structure of the Tanner Basin or eastern Caribbean, is related to the orogenic girdle that enfolds it on three sides. From the eastern floor, the Aves Bank, slightly convex eastward, rises northwards until it becomes emergent at Aves Island. Sonic soundings indicate a series of peaks on the west of the bank " parallel to the Lesser Antilles arc and 250 miles west of it ". These peaks are judged from their profiles to be submerged and extinct volcanoes, but the date of their activity is unknown.

The four sides of the Caribbean framework may be studied separately. First, the major orogenic structures of Central America have already been cited (p. 493) as curving north of east into the Greater Antilles. These islands, Cuba, Hispaniola, Puerto Rico and the Virgin Islands show a general decrease in size, and a plunge of geological structure towards the east (Woodring 1954). The oldest formations therefore appear in Cuba where, in the south-eastern extremity of the island, schists, slates and serpentinized peridotites underlie the late-Cretaceous tuff series. Eardley (1962) considers the orogenic episode represented to be in part at least Nevadan (Jurassic). The principal orogenic episode, however, is late-Cretaceous (pre-Maastrichtian), at which time the serpentine belts were intruded; and this phase is present in the Central Cordillera of Hispaniola. The high axial country of Puerto Rico has as its " older series " late-Cretaceous volcanics accumulated explosively; but older, folded beds may lie below. Cainozoic tectonic activity also declined in intensity from Cuba in the west to the Virgin Islands in the east. Crustal structure for the region has emerged from the seismic refraction studies of Officer et al. (1959) and shows what is interpreted as a great thickening downwards of the lower (basaltic) crust, with corresponding descent of the Mohorovičić discontinuity, beneath the Antilles in the St. Croix-St. Thomas section (Fig. 231).* Talwani (1964) reports that the " root " (7·0 km./sec.) is under Puerto Rico though the negative anomaly is over the Trench. The crust beneath the Trench he described as " thicker than the normal oceanic crust but thinner than a typical continental crust ". He also recorded " somewhat similar conditions " for the Tonga, Peru-Chile and Middle American Trenches ", and concluded that " geometrically the structure of the Trenches is equivalent to that of the continental margins, depressed several kilometres without a change in thickness ".

From the eastern extremity of Cuba and offshore for 500 miles past the northern coasts of Hispaniola, Puerto Rico and the Leeward Islands, extends the Puerto Rico Trench or Brownson Trough within which the sea-bottom lies below 24,000 feet, with a local maximum depth of 28,680 feet north of Puerto Rico. At the eastern end it curves past Barbuda, following the arc of the lesser Antilles but becoming progressively shallower until it joins up with the Tobago Trough at a depth of only 8,000 feet.

Layers of sand interbedded with red abyssal clays within the floor (Ewing and Worzel 1954), show that the Puerto Rico Trench has acted as a trap for sediment carried

* But see (p. 664).

outward from the Antilles by turbidity currents, a process that may have far reaching implications in the formation of island arcs.

Great deficiencies of gravity are associated with the Puerto Rico-Tobago Trench, exceeding −150 milligals between Hispaniola and Puerto Rico and seaward of the Caribbees. The same belt of deficiency anomalies bends round through Trinidad and the Sucre Province of northern Venezuela into the Los Roques Trench north of the chain of islands from la Blanquilla to Curaçao. The belt of anomalies does not everywhere follow the axis of the trough but is found in part along the Barbados Ridge (*cf.* Indonesia). Ewing and Heezen (1955) attribute the large negative anomaly to " a narrow band of exceptionally thin crust overlain by sediment of negligible or greater thickness ". They reject the older hypothesis of a sialic root below the trench. Presumably the new interpretation needs to be extended to cover the same anomaly on the Barbados Rise. Local thinning of the crust suggests tension rather than compression, and Ewing and Heezen accept this for both the Bartlett and Puerto Rico trenches. They also approve transcurrent movement, and we may note that, under the concept of continental drift, these phenomena have developed just where the westward rotation of North America is at a maximum (Fig. 236) (*cf.* Scotia Arc off South America and East Asiatic arcs).

Positive anomalies are found in zones alongside the negative strip (maximum +80 milligals at Curaçao). The open basins on either side of the Beata Ridge also show positive anomaly, about +50 milligals, and rather more (+80 milligals) was recorded by Hess over the Yucatan Basin. Generally, the deeper the basin the greater the positive anomaly.

The southern Caribbean is framed by the Colombian and Venezuelan Andes, the former continuing from the Sierra de Perija into Curaçao and the latter from the Sierra de Merida into Trinidad. Though end-Jurassic movements are reported in the Serrania de la Costa Oriental of Venezuela and the North Range of Trinidad, the chief orogeny of northern Venezuela, with adjacent parts of the Caribbean, occurred in the late Cretaceous (Laramide) with the accompaniment of ultramafic intrusion as in Margarita Island (Maxwell 1948). Regional metamorphism under continued deformation converted the geosynclinal sediments into gneisses, schists and marbles; and basaltic rocks into amphibolites (Dengo 1953). Thus the deformation parallels and synchronizes with that of the Greater Antilles, and shows that the unity of the Caribbean was already established by the late-Cretaceous period. The Central and Western Andean Cordilleras behaved, as we have seen (p. 466), independently.

On the east the Caribbean Basin is closed by the island arc of the Lesser Antilles, consisting of a double chain of islands known by their formation as the Inner or Volcanic Caribbees and Outer or Limestone Caribbees beyond which is the Brownson Trough. This is the typical arrangement of a double island arc.

Of several generally concentric zones the innermost is the Aves Bank, slightly convex to the eastward and bearing a number of apparently ancient volcanic cones

(p. 601). Next is the broad Grenada depression, not very deep and without marked relief. Next rises the inner arc of the Volcanic Caribbees crowned with a succession of Plio-Pleistocene cones from Saba in the north to Grenada in the south. Activity apparently started in early-Oligocene time and with few interruptions has continued to the present with the eruptions of Mt. Pelée and La Soufriere. As in the Cretaceous effusives of the Greater Antilles, andesite is the chief rock formed, with subordinate basalts and dacites. At the northern end of the arc, the volcanics rise from the crest of the swell, but in the south they stand 30-40 miles west of the crest.

Xenoliths in the effusives of the Caribbees were identified by Lacroix as gabbros, diabases, metamorphosed limestones, schists and cordierite rocks representing altered argillaceous sediments. The whole assemblage resembles the Cretaceous rocks of the Virgin Islands so that the basement of the island arc thus apparently dates from the Cretaceous. During the late-Cretaceous, therefore, a climax of volcanic activity extended through both the Greater and Lesser Antilles to the islands of the southern flank, Curaçao, Bonaire and Los Roques, demonstrating by its Laramide orogeny the establishment of this region as an unity before the close of the Mesozoic era.

The Limestone or Outer Caribbees, which are present only along the northern sector of the arc, are of limestone and pyroclastics shot through by hypabyssal intrusives. The larger members have a basement of volcanic rocks, possibly Cretaceous though this has been disputed, beneath Eocene and Oligocene limestones. These limestones have been disturbed and subsequently overlain by almost horizontal Miocene limestone. The only other rock type exposed is granodiorite which on Grand Terre in Guadeloupe is related to Eocene and Oligocene igneous activity. The lower-Miocene formations that follow here include tuffs with the normal limestones. In Guadeloupe the two arcs of islands converge so that the western mass, Basse Terre, stands upon the Volcanic Ridge while the eastern portion, Grand Terre belongs to the Limestone Caribbees.

Outside the arc of the Lesser Antilles, the Puerto Rico Trench is prolonged into the shallower Tobago Trough which terminates against the promontory of north-eastern Venezuela. Trinidad, Tobago and Barbados stand upon a fresh element, a submarine swell that rises east of the Tobago Trough and extends northward for a great distance at increasing depth. The axis of the " negative strip " passes along this ridge which accordingly should afford information of a typical geotectocline developed from an earlier deep. A picture of conditions obtaining at the time of deformation of an island arc is thus adduced from the Cainozoic stratigraphy of Barbados by Hess. " The Oceanic series, probably deep water sediments, are moderately deformed. They lie above the very intensely deformed Scotland series, which are shallow water or perhaps in part terrestrial sediments of quartzose character. . . . The lower part of the Oceanic series is Upper-Eocene in age according to Kugler, and the Scotland series very slightly older. Between these two formations [are] found . . . huge blocks of sandstone in a silty matrix." Noting the resemblance to a submarine landslide he had seen near Quebec, and the position of the breccia " on the junction between shallow water or

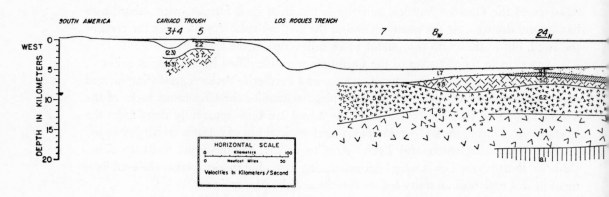

FIG. 231.   Crustal structure for the Caribbean Atlantic section through St. C

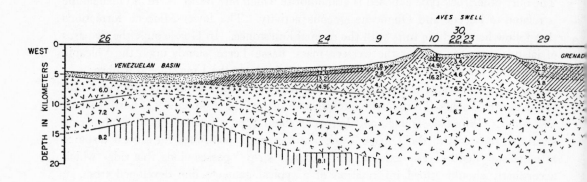

FIG. 232.   Crustal structure of the eastern Caribbean reg

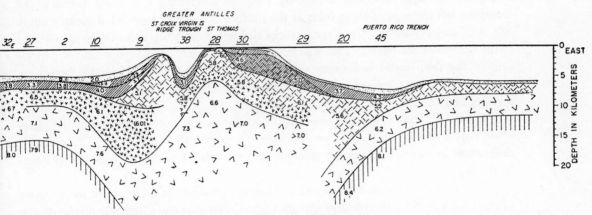

d, as interpreted from seismic wave velocities.   *after C. B. Officer* et al.

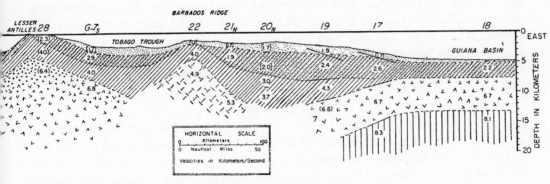

preted from seismic wave velocities.   *after C. B. Officer* et al.

terrestrial sediments below and deep sea sediments above, with practically no time interval between them " Hess thought that " in the interval of time between the deposition of the Scotland series and the Oceanics, the great deformation took place forming the tectogene. The Scotland series were squeezed up out of the core of the tectogene and thus intensely deformed, but the downward movement forming the tectogene left the tops of these folds at the bottom of a deep, steep-sided ocean trough. Silt and blocks of the Scotland series rocks slid down the steep sides covering portions of the bottom of the basin. This was followed immediately by the beginning of deposition of the deep water sediments—the Oceanics ". The Mount Moriah formation, standing upon the same swell, is equivalent to the Oceanic series and has also a great boulder bed and block conglomerate at its base.

Crustal structure for the Lesser Antillean region has been investigated by Officer *et al.* (1959) whose conclusions are summarised graphically (Fig. 232). Considerable differences in wave velocities are evident, perhaps related to former foci of deposition in the region.

The Isthmus of Panama, though lacking the characteristic island arc morphology of the Lesser Antilles nonetheless reveals a late-Cretaceous and Cainozoic history that is not dissimilar. Thus the older (andesite) rock series is of presumed Cretaceous age, below late-Eocene shallow water marine clastics, followed by Oligocene and Miocene formations. There was late-Miocene folding and intrusion (granite and syenite) with intense volcanic activity culminating in the Plio-Pleistocene. Eardley's projection of the Nevadan belt through the Isthmus has already been shown as unacceptable on the evidence available (p. 600). Though the nature of the swell on which the Isthmus stands is quite unknown, there is nothing to indicate that the Isthmus itself existed prior to the Cretaceous period, or that it has fundamentally continental associations; rather it compares with the Cocos and Carnegie Ridges that radiate to America from the Galapagos Islands (*q.v.*). About all these ridges the sea-floor stands broadly between 10,000 and 12,000 feet depth, and a similar depth and bottom topography occurs in the western Caribbean.

Seismic refraction profiles beneath the *eastern* Caribbean (Officer *et al.* 1957) reveal material of velocity 7·4 km./sec. beneath a major (but not the Mohorovičić) discontinuity at 13 km. depth. This contrasts with the 8 km./sec. of the Atlantic region but does not signify the presence of truly continental matter. The crustal velocities above also vary more widely (5·9-7 km./sec.) than beneath the Atlantic, and the thickness of material is also greater up to 4 km. All these properties consort with the hypothesis that the great submarine ridge of the eastern Pacific does not terminate at the Isthmus of Panama but continues with some structural changes beneath the Caribbean region.

THE SOUTH ATLANTIC BASIN

Exploration of the South Atlantic realm is less detailed than for the North Atlantic; but a similar grouping of basins on either side of a median ridge is evident, most of them with relatively flat bottoms; and seamounts rise within the Brazilian, South-Eastern

Atlantic and Cape Basins at least.   All those known are probably volcanic, and Discovery Tablemount, 1,200 miles south-west of the Cape of Good Hope is possibly a large guyot.   The oceanic islands Ascension, St. Helena, Trinidad, Tristan da Cunha, Gough and Bouvet are all volcanic and, except for Trinidad (Brazil), stand on or near the axis of the mid-Atlantic ridge.   According to Shand (1949), on every island basalt, generally olivine-bearing, is the dominant rock type with additionally on Gough Island essexite, trachyte, sodalite trachyte, phonolite (also andesite); on Tristan da Cunha— pyroxenite, trachyte, phonolite and a single boulder of muscovite-biotite gneiss or granite (possibly ballast from ships); on St. Helena—trachyte and phonolite; on Ascension—trachyte, rhyolite, obsidian and boulders of granite, syenite, diorite, gabbro, peridotite; on St. Paul Rocks—mylonitised dunite (with hornblendic and enstatitic facies).

Submarine canyons descend through the continental shelves to the floors of the basins upon both sides of the Ocean, one of the largest being that of the Congo which has been traced to the west for 150 miles where it was still about 5 miles wide and 3,000 feet deep.   At its sides are large natural levées.   Turbidity currents discharge the flood bed load of the river out to the Angola Abyssal Plain instead of building a delta seaward of the river mouth.

Along the coast of Namaqualand, where rivers now rarely run to the arid coast, the channel of the Saldanha River is continued basinwards for 45 miles to the limit of exploration at 400 fathoms.   Such canyons may be partly fossil, being kept open wholly by marine processes of erosion without the aid of silt-laden waters from the land.   An equatorial ocean floor canyon directed to the north between Brazil and the mid-Atlantic ridge was revealed by *Vema* cruise IX (Ewing and Heezen 1956), and another (very large) midway between la Plata and Falkland Islands.

The Scotia Arc

Remarkably similar to the island arc of the Antilles is the Scotia Arc linking Tierra del Fuego with the Antarctic Peninsula through a high submarine ridge trailing 1,500 miles backwards into the South Atlantic Basin (Fig. 233).   The northern arm trends almost due east from Staten Island through the Burdwood Bank, thence by a narrow submarine ridge to South Georgia, a large island reminiscent of the Greater Antilles. North of the ridge and eastward from the Falkland Islands is a broad submarine plateau bounded by a straight mega-scarp that descends abruptly to the floor of the Argentine Basin.   At the foot of the scarp is a straight, narrow trench resembling the Bartlett trench of the Antilles, and which is doubtless also due to transcurrent crustal movement.

Another trench on the *north* side of King George Island, after a regular descent from the north, shoals from a depth of 2,800 to 220 fathoms (15,000 feet) in 33 miles, and is also of likely transcurrent origin.   South Orkneys have a similar trench.   Between King George and Elephant Islands, too, are magnetometric and seismic discontinuities.

2 Q

FIG. 233. The Scotia Arc of islands with associated sea-floor topography.
after H. F. P. Herdman.

The geology of South Georgia is very different from that of the Greater Antilles for it contains rocks (the Sandebugten series) that are probably Palæozoic (Adie 1962) as well as the Mesozoic Cumberland Bay series that from poorly preserved plant remains has been compared with both a similar sequence in the Patagonian Andes and the richly plant-bearing Hope Bay series of Graham Land.

South Orkneys have a similar sedimentary series. All these rocks were intensely folded and cleaved by pre-Cretaceous orogeny that, from the directions of the fold axes, bore no relation to the conformation of the Scotia Arc. Upper-Cretaceous and Cainozoic glauconitic and foraminiferal deposits on South Orkney are not folded. Granodiorite and gabbro are intrusive into the Ordovician and are presumably ancient, but there are also Cainozoic eruptives and recent dacites, andesites and basalts. These last link westwards with the South Shetlands chain of small volcanic islands, built of olivine basalt with later subordinate dacite and hypersthene andesite, that finally makes a garland to Graham Land. On the north these islands are bordered by a chain of minor, linear depressions representing either an incipient trough or a trough that has been filled up. From the thick geosynclinal sediments intruded by granite, and from certain geophysical data, Matthews (1959) has concluded that areas of continental structure are probably present.

Closing the eastern end of the whole arc, and linking the northern and southern arms with their islands built largely of sedimentary formations, is the curving group of the South Sandwich Islands, wholly volcanic (basaltic) in composition and with some cones still active. Tyrrell considered that these basalts show closer petrologic affinity with lavas of the Antilles than with those of the Andes. On the oceanic side the Meteor Trench, 26,000 feet deep, curves through nearly 180°. Strongly negative anomalies are revealed by gravity surveys over the trench (Herdman 1932). The arc itself is double, with twin ridges separated by a very narrow deep (24,000 feet). The eastern ridge is incomplete.

The regional Scotia structure is indeed that of an attenuated double island arc, with some parts in *en echelon* relationship due to major transcurrent faults, which in turn find analogies in the West Indies. Most of the island groups have the Mesozoic greywacke-slate-tuff facies of the circum-Pacific geosyncline, isoclinally contorted, with occasionally a shelf facies that is not infrequently fossiliferous and may intercalate with continental beds (Fairbridge 1952). Interbedded lavas are andesites, dacites and rhyolites with their corresponding tuffs and agglomerates. But this assemblage is not known in the South Sandwich chain of islands.

Post-Mesozoic rocks of the Scotia Arc are almost exclusively volcanic, of mid-Cainozoic to Recent age.

The arc has a high seismicity: Gutenberg and Richter say higher than the Antillean arc. Shallow shocks are recorded all along the arc, but intermediate and deep shocks are recorded only from the South Sandwich area.

The Scotia Sea within the whole area embraced by the arc seldom exceeds 4,000 metres depth.

THE MEDITERRANEAN SEA

The Mediterranean Sea is but a shrunken remnant of the great Palæozoic-Mesozoic Tethys that separated Laurasia and Gondwana. At present it consists of a series of basins (*e.g.* Balearic and Tyrrhenian Abyssal Plains) divided by deep sills. The Straits of Gibraltar, its only modern outlet, are only 175 fathoms deep. Heezen and Menard have concluded that latterly the " form of the eastern Mediterranean was governed more by tectonic activity than by sedimentation ". The coasts of Southern France and Algeria have also been the sites of strong Cainozoic flexuring which may still be locally in progress.

Seismic refraction studies (Ewing and Ewing 1960) " in the Mediterranean Sea show only low-velocity sediments underlain by a refracting layer in which the average velocity is about 4·5 km./sec." This indicates absence of a true ocean basin, and close association with continental materials probably for long periods in the geologic past (*cf.* p. 592). The possible closure of the Mediterranean/Tethys temporarily during Cretaceous Period has already been noted (p. 592); and may explain the present absence of true oceanic basin.

THE ARCTIC OCEAN BASIN

The Arctic Ocean averages only 500 fathoms depth, but this includes the very wide continental shelves and shallow marginal seas that surround most of it. The true Arctic Basin, 2,000-2,500 fathoms deep (Fig. 234), is bisected by the high-standing Lomonosov Submarine Ridge extending from the New Siberian Islands directly to Ellesmere Land upon the opposite side of the North Pole. The Ridge is aseismic and has no crestal rift valley, so presumably is at present inactive. A minor rise with notable relief runs parallel 250 miles east of the Lomonosov Ridge and may be largely volcanic. North of Spitzbergen, too, a rough bottom topography recorded by echometer on submarine traverse ([88] N 578 Skate) may consist of ridges rather than conical seamounts.

The broad shelves and marginal seas (Barents, Kara, Laptev and East Siberian Seas) fringing northern Laurasia attest epeirogenic depression during late geologic time, and are matched across the basin by the gently subsided region of northern Canada with its Arctic Archipelago, perhaps a geobreccia. Seismic study by Oliver, Ewing and Press (1955) reveals that all the shallow parts of the Arctic Ocean are underlain by continental structure. The deep Arctic Basin, the Beaufort Sea and the Norwegian and Greenland Basins are devoid of continental material.

Sediments within the Arctic Basin are fine grained, almost a red clay, and there is little lime or silica in the form of organisms (Emery 1949). These characteristics accord with the low relief of surrounding lands and frigid waters.

Seismic activity is concentrated along a linear extension of the North Atlantic Ridge which trends from Iceland, between Spitzbergen and Greenland across the Arctic Basin to the Lena River in Siberia. Elsewhere the region is seismically quiescent.

Though much remains to be learned of the Arctic Basin, what is known, taken in conjunction with the geology of surrounding lands, is geotectonically important. Except where the Pacific circumvallation involving Palæozoic, Mesozoic and Cainozoic fold

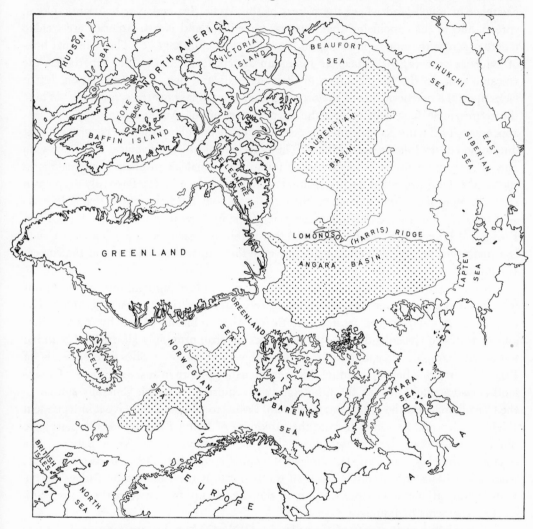

FIG. 234. Bottom topography of the Arctic Ocean Basin showing great extent of shallow continental shelves north of Eurasia and amid the Arctic Archipelago of Canada, and the two deep Arctic Basins separated by the high-standing Lomonosov Ridge.

systems, obtrudes from Alaska to Anadyr, the Arctic Ocean is girt about with stable shields—Angara, Fennoscandia, Greenland, Canada. Intracontinental orogenic belts of the Ural and Verkhoyansk ranges extend on to Arctic islands and are lost along their strike beneath the waters of the ocean, and the same is true of fold-belts upon Greenland

(Fig. 166), so that the Arctic Basin appears to be a disjunctive basin in just the same way as the North and South Atlantic.

Eardley (1962) has assembled several lines of evidence that " point to the former existence of much land where the waters of the Arctic Sea and North Atlantic Ocean spread, and to the conclusion that Eurasia, Greenland and North America are welded together across the north polar region into one great continent ". The principal lines of evidence are: (a) the Palæozoic mountain system from Alaska into Siberia has the volcanic zone on the Pacific side and then the mainland belt of sedimentation, but it lacks upon the northern side of the orogen a source landmass for the sediments. Where the source must have lain is now the deepest part of the Arctic Basin; (b) The disappearance of the intracontinental orogens into the ocean along their strike and without diminution of the folding means that " They surely project long distances into the region now covered with water ". Even so he found the Appalachian chain " anomalous in the setting if it is projected northerly into the shield province ". (c) The truly deep basin is small, more like a mediterranean than an ocean, and Eardley opined that " It looks as if the deep basin were only a sunken part of a single, great continent ". But Oliver, Ewing and Press (loc. cit.) have indicated that within the basin not a particle of any such continent remains. Eardley has made the case for land without arriving at the correct conclusion.

All difficulties seem to be solved essentially not by evoking land out of a void, but by redeploying the existent masses under the reconstruction of Laurasia (Fig. 166). The area of deep water in the western Arctic or Angara Basins (1,100 by 2,200 miles) approximates to Greenland (900 by 1,800 miles) in size, providing all the land required under stratigraphic considerations in just the right place. The severed ends of Palæozoic orogenic belts (including the Appalachians) join up in space and time. Greenland is also a shield area of the lithologic type required. Though generally similar to the Canadian Shield the Baffin and Greenland Basins to west and east give it independent shield status; and its removal from the proximity of Baffin Land solves the petrologic differences between the opposed coasts long ago pointed out by Washington. The Arctic Archipelago of Canada, somewhat compressed, then fills the eastern Arctic Laurentian Basin and precisely between the two stands the Lomonosov Ridge—as the mid-Atlantic Ridge stands perhaps, upon the site of rupture between the eastern and western segments of Laurasia.

The relative movements of Greenland and North America are rotational about a pivot in Alaska (Fig. 236), and explain also the static position of Alaska and the Aleutian island arc with respect to eastern Asia, and the " sweeping up " of Palæozoic and early-Mesozoic island arcs upon the western aspect of the North American continent from Costa Rica to Yakutat Bay.

The time of rupture may be assessed as post-Triassic from the severance of that orogenic welt through the Verkhoyansk (Siberia) and United States (Northern Greenland) Ranges (p. 447). Palæontologic evidence prescribes a Jurassic sea in Arctic regions, but there is no reason to suppose that this was more than an epicontinental flooding. Also: " The conclusion is inescapable that the Arctic Ocean in the Jurassic had no ice-cap and its waters were at least as warm as those of present temperate zones " (Arkell 1956). Along the eastern side of Greenland there was a major episode of tensional faulting during the late Jurassic and again in the Cretaceous, and " the seas of Cretaceous time were more complex than those of the Jurassic and Triassic " (Eardley). A final phase may have been prolonged into the Eocene when an enormous volume of plateau basalts was poured out along 1,200 miles of the coast. The opening of the Arctic Basin by the hinging apart of the North American and Asiatic continents thus appears to be the last stage of opening of the North Atlantic Basin, begun in the south from the ancestral Tethys early in the Cretaceous period (p. 593). Though, in contrast with Gondwana which broke into several fragments, the Atlantic-Arctic rift is the only major fragmentation of Laurasia during late-Mesozoic time, another line of Jura-Cretaceous rifting passed from the upper Rhine to Oslo, and east of this again the East Baltic-Lublin Basin is also of Cretaceous age. Here, perhaps, was an incipient twin for the Atlantic-Arctic rift.

THE INDIAN OCEAN BASIN

The boundaries of the Indian Ocean Basin resemble generally those of the Atlantic with transected geologic structures and monoclinal downwarping of ancient shields (east coast of Africa, Western Australia). It is thus a fractured basin. Nonetheless, restricted spans are of Pacific type, with mountain structures of late origin parallel with, or actually forming, the coast. These are: Mekran (Persia), Arakan (Burma) and the Indonesian island arc. The north-eastern confines must therefore be exempted from comparison with the Atlantic and classified structurally with the Pacific.

The form of the Indian Ocean Basin (Fig. 249) is particularly enlightening. As Fairbridge (1948) points out, the basin consists of two distinct parts, eastern and western, separated by the " mid-Indian " submarine ridge (p. 578) on which stand a number of islands. The western part of this ocean is shallower than the eastern, and the floor bears a number of conspicuously arcuate submarine ridges of different kinds. Thus the Carlsberg Ridge west of the Maldive Islands is a broad, low swell, whereas the Seychelles-Mauritius (Mascarene) Ridge is narrow and high, most of it being shoaler than 200 fathoms and there are several islands with rocks of continental facies appearing upon Seychelles (Baker 1963). There is the island of Malagasy with a long submarine ridge southwards to the Prince Edward-Crozet Islands and the parallel Moçambique Ridge to the west. Coasts fronting the western Indian Ocean are fractured or monoclinal edges of plateaus so that the western aspect of the ocean basin appears disjunctive between the visibly separated portions of Gondwanaland. The same may be said for the large Kerguelen-Gaussberg Plateaus (with perhaps the Crozet Plateau) of the southern Indian Ocean. These are so large and high as to have been termed microcontinents by Heezen and Tharp (1965). Eastward of the mid-oceanic ridge the

Laccadive-Maldive Ridge has also been quoted as of continental derivation: " left stranded during India's drift from Africa to Asia ", and the Chagos Archipelago stands upon a broad submerged plateau south-west of which the Vema Trench, 3,000 fathoms deep, strikes north-east across the mid-Indian Ridge.

More puzzling because insufficiently documented is the long, narrow, north-south Ninety-east Ridge standing high, aseismic, and probably of Mesozoic age. Most of the features described are aligned from north to south in contrast with features in the Atlantic most of which lie from east to west. The Wallaby and Exmouth Plateaus are marginal to Australia.

There are no islands in the eastern Indian Ocean apart from the volcanic Cocos-Keeling, the oldest rocks of which are Eocene; and the floor is smoother, with large flat areas, and deeper (to beyond 3,000 fathoms) resembling more the floor of the Pacific Basin. All these features harmonise with the Pacific structure of the Indonesian arc on the north. Here, assuredly, is a part of the proto-Pacific ocean now separated from the parent body by the drift of Australia-New Guinea against south-eastern Asia (Fig. 183).

The creation of the Indian Ocean Basin began during the Permian with the opening between India and East Africa of a rift that reached to Malagasy (then not so far south as now), and of another marine incursion (the first since the Precambrian) that appeared in Western Australia. These rifts developed slowly southward until by the end of the Jurassic all the Indian Ocean coasts were in existence, and the uniformity among land plants which had existed throughout Gondwanaland during the Triassic was substituted by an uniformity of marine life (Fairbridge 1948).

The marginal Andaman Sea between Burma and Sumatra is possibly not older than Miocene or, in part, Pliocene.

Certain biological peculiarities are explicable on the hypothesis of continental fragmentation and drift in the Indian Ocean region during late-Mesozoic time. Thus, the Jurassic molluscan faunules of New Zealand (King 1944) show considerable affinity with those of Europe and must have passed from one region to the other along the Tethys and proto-Pacific border. With the sundering of northern Gondwana during the late Jurassic and the pressing northward of India the Tethys was partly closed and newer seaways opened up in rear. The Trichinopoly molluscan types then spread southward along these new routes to New Zealand on the east and to Zululand on the west. In the late Cretaceous, with widening seaways this connection was lost; instead there was a great influx into New Zealand of Patagonian mollusca for which it has been fashionable in the past to invoke a trans-Pacific landbridge. But this is not necessary, for during the mid- or late-Cretaceous period Antarctica, which itself bears Patagonian mollusca at Snow Hill (Nordenskiold) apparently moved southward from a position in Gondwana east of Africa and for a short period then formed an almost continuous shoreline between the tip of South America and New Zealand. Such connection would soon be broken, and no molluscan invasion of New Zealand has occurred subsequently, the abundant modern species deriving, with few exceptions, from the late-Cretaceous South American invaders. Had this connection not been made anti-podean malacology might have been scanty and of Mesozoic affinity like sections of the ornithology, herpetology and botany.

Rothé (1954) has shown that the belt of seismicity which follows the South Atlantic Ridge joins with a belt from the very active South Sandwich area through the Atlantic-Antarctic Ridge to the Crozets. Thence the seismic belt continues to the mid-Indian Ridge in the vicinity of Rodriguez and northward. Where the mid-Indian Ridge bi-furcates north of the equator the plots of earthquake foci do also. The association of earthquake foci with submarine ridges is strong (Fig. 219); and Oliver (1956) remarked that on this data " it is arbitrary to consider a separation between the Indian and Atlantic Oceans ". Under the Mesozoic dismemberment of Gondwanaland this is assuredly so.

CHAPTER XVIII

THE PACIFIC BASIN

The Uniqueness of the Pacific. The Andesite Line. Pacific Islands. The Pacific as a Petrographic Province. The Floor of the Pacific Basin. Sedimentation within the Pacific Basin. The North-eastern Pacific Quadrant. The Aleutian Arc. The South-eastern Pacific Quadrant. The North-western Pacific Quadrant, including Indonesia. The Marianas Arc and the Philippine Basin. The East Asiatic Ocean Deeps. The North-western Pacific Basin. The South-western Pacific Quadrant. The Pacific Realm.

THE UNIQUENESS OF THE PACIFIC

The Pacific Basin is unique. It is the largest single feature of the earth's surface, greater in area than the combined continents, and covers nearly one third of the entire globe. In contrast with the Atlantic which is 1,700 miles wide between Brazil and Liberia, the Pacific Ocean measures 10,000 miles from New Guinea to Peru. Yet there is reason to believe that formerly it was much larger, and that before the opening of the North and South Atlantic, Arctic and Indian oceanic basins during the late-Mesozoic era, the area of the Pacific was equal to the combined scope of all the great oceans of today. Apart from the mediterranean Tethys that stretched east-west between the primitive, oval supercontinents of Laurasia and Gondwana, and the areas of those continents themselves, the Pacific Ocean covered the globe as a single, vast pan-thalassa.

But since the Palæozoic, our studies suggest, certain of the disrupted land-masses have crowded into it, opening new oceans in the rifts behind them, and circumscribing the Pacific with high ranges (developed in part from the earlier fold girdles of Laurasia and Gondwana), sometimes crowned with volcanoes, and shaken by earthquakes. No other ocean possesses a tectonically active girdle of this description, so clearly related to its form and history. The central region of the Basin is no less interesting. Crowded with seamounts, guyots and islands it has a record of Cretaceous-early Cainozoic activity accompanied by volcanism perhaps unequalled upon earth.

As a structure the Pacific Basin is vast, homogeneous and unique.

THE ANDESITE LINE

Petrologists early remarked the abundance of rocks of the andesite clan about the borders of the Pacific (Fig. 4), associated in many instances with mountain ranges and island festoons. Andesites continue also for some hundreds of miles into the continents, and they occur locally in small quantity upon certain of the oceanic islands, but the distribution is clearly zonal, girdling the Pacific Basin. This zone is known as the Andesite Line, and it is petrographically and tectonically of the highest significance. It marks essentially the boundary between the sialic masses of the continents and their outliers with the basaltic floor of the ocean basin. As such it constitutes one of the fundamental geological boundaries of the earth.

Upon the western aspect of the Pacific the track of the Andesite Line is located from the Aleutian Islands past Kamchatka and the Kurile Islands to Japan, probably nowhere extending seaward beyond the offshore ocean deeps. The marginal seas (Bering, Okhotsk and even the relatively deep Sea of Japan) which lie behind this line belong to the continental structure of Asia, of which they represent subsided elements. From central Japan the Andesite Line swings outward, following the island arcs of Bonin and Marianas to the Palaus, so that once again the continental boundary may be plotted outside these arcs. So defined, the deep basin of the Philippine Sea is excluded from the Pacific realm; clearly it calls for further investigation and explanation (p. 637). The Yellow Sea, East China Sea and even the South China Sea, however, are readily assignable to subsided portions of the Asiatic mainland.

South-eastwards, some authors place the Andesite Line east of the Caroline Islands, others including Hess place it west, and continue it thence to the northward of New Guinea. Ancient sedimentary rocks, quartzite and slate on San Cristobal in the Solomon Islands, and a Mesozoic limestone possibly associated with peridotite on Guadalcanal reveal continental affinity, and Reed summarizes the whole group of the Solomons as " undoubtedly of continental origin ", so that the Andesite Line passes to the north of them. The Coral Sea, east of Queensland, has a floor known to have subsided in recent geological time like the marginal seas of eastern Asia, and several Australian geologists have claimed it as a sunken fragment of their continent (Bryan 1944). The Solomon Islands presumably rise from the outer edges of this platform, of which a further fragment lies still farther east below and beyond the New Hebrides. The Andesite Line agrees with this interpretation passing due eastwards past Fiji to a point near Samoa, and leaving the Marshall, Gilbert and Ellice islands within the ambit of the Pacific as true oceanic islands. From Samoa the line bends through a right angle and passes southwards along the eastern edge of the Tonga and Kermadec Troughs (the islands are volcanic with Cainozoic limestones) towards New Zealand where it traverses east of Chatham Islands, and thence away to the Antarctic.

Several islands of the south-west Pacific sector, west of the Andesite Line, exhibit rock formations of continental affinity. Fiji, with granites, diorites, and the folded Viti formation several thousand feet thick was described by Woolnough (1903) as a microcosmic continent. New Zealand, of course, is continental; while to the southward schist pebbles appear with Cainozoic limestone upon Campbell Island, and Speight has recorded in a conglomerate at Carnley Harbour, Auckland Islands, pebbles of granites, gneisses and contorted schists. These islands rise from a high submarine platform, evidently of continental derivation. Biotite granite is recorded from Bounty Islands on the edge of the same platform, but the Antipodes Islands in a similar situation appear to be entirely volcanic. Basalt and basaltic glasses here contain little olivine and recall the first Hawaiian eruptive stage of Tilley.

In the Antarctic the Andesite Line may be presumed to pass offshore from King Edward VII Land to the Antarctic Peninsula.

By South America the line probably follows close to the steep continental slope and into the vicinity of the Peru-Chile Trench. It certainly passes eastward of Juan Fernandez and San Ambrosio Islands. The Line also leaves Galapagos to the Pacific realm and probably hugs the edge of the narrow continental shelf and slope nearly to Panama. Data from Central and North America are scarcely adequate for precise location, but the Andesite Line is thought to parallel the coasts at a general distance of about 100 miles until it turns in the Gulf of Alaska to complete the circuit of the Pacific Basin in or about the Aleutian Trench. The Line encompasses the true basin of the Pacific Ocean with a consistently deep though irregular floor, below 4,000 metres depth except where the submarine plateaus of the eastern sector stand 1000 metres above this.

The Andesite Line is of profound geotectonic significance. Outside it bulk the sialic masses of the continents, within it (with the possible exception of part of the East Pacific submarine Ridge) true continental matter is unknown. Evidence of strong lateral movement in parts of the Pacific floor during the last few hundred million years (p. 628), coupled with the apparent deficiency of sediments on the deep ocean floor (p. 627), has led some authors to postulate a renewal of the sea bed under the influence of sub-crustal convection currents.

PACIFIC ISLANDS

Within the Pacific Basin, of 35 million square miles, rise 2,000 or more volcanic islands totalling only about 70,000 square miles of land, though many others have been reduced to shoals or atolls. No other ocean is so richly decked with islands and archipelagoes, alike in volcanic build and coral circlet. Perhaps this abundance testifies a much greater antiquity for the Pacific as compared with other oceanic basins.

All Pacific islands, solitary or in groups, rise as volcanic piles from the deep floor of the basin and form its most marked relief over wide areas. They contain no rock of continental derivation but consist solely of volcanic rocks, coral formations and the secondary deposits derived from these. As volcanoes their size is immense for they rise from the vasty floor of the Pacific and are perhaps 15,000 feet in height before they break the surface of the ocean; and several rise more than 10,000 feet above that. The volume of lava in a single cone may exceed 10,000 cubic miles (*e.g.* Mauna Loa, Hawaii) the sea-floor base of which exceeds 5,000 square miles. Not all attain the surface: the ocean floor is dotted with smaller, but still great, cones that have died in the depths, where they remain as seamounts or as guyots. Oval in plan, flat-topped and with an outward-sloping rim, the latter are found throughout a great range of depth and size, even when close together, and some are built upon older guyots. Their summit bevellings are deemed to have been accomplished by marine agencies; and the differences of depth are probably due more to vertical tectonic movements of the oceanic floor than to changes of sea level. Some guyots are surrounded by a depressed zone as though the foundations had subsided isostatically. Little sediment collects upon the summits of most guyots though Cainozoic and even Cretaceous deposits have been dredged from some in mid-Pacific (Lees 1953). Most of the islands and guyots arise in the west and centre of the Pacific, eastern waters have relatively few.

The extreme youth of many Pacific islands is attested by their ruggedness, and upon some of them active volcanicity is still in progress. Wentworth states that none of the larger Hawaiian islands, as a whole, has reached mid-maturity in the erosion cycle. But eroded cones are not seldom rebuilt, wholly or in part, and on Oahu some ridges in the Koolaupoko district have been greatly lowered and may be called " old ". Other islands have been reduced under erosion to mere shoals.

Since the initiation of the islands and seamounts, the development of each island or group has proceeded with a considerable measure of independence. Yet most evolve upon a common history, even if they do not complete it. Stearns (1945) has distinguished (a) a youthful phase when a dome-shaped shield volcano is constructed from flows of primitive olivine basalt poured out in rapid succession. This dense material is quite like normal oceanic crust; (b) a mature phase marked by collapse of the summit with rifting of the dome. If the volcano stands high relative to the ocean floor, vesicular basalt and ash may be produced; (c) an old age phase when less-basic differentiated rock types are emitted, and the summit caldera is filled. Sometimes, after deep erosion of the mountains and renewed uplift, scattered eruptions of diverse lava types appear. most of the visible effusives are dated as late-Cainozoic or Recent, though the lower parts of the islands may conceivably be older and Marshall has reported a Cretaceous or Eocene basalt from Mangaia. The coral and foraminiferal limestones that occur on many islands are seldom of an age greater than Miocene. This is perhaps because of the marked subsidence to which many island groups have been subjected during Quaternary time.

Evidence of late subsidence, sometimes associated with enhanced volcanic activity of more differentiated type, is one of the most notable features of Pacific islands, recorded in innumerable barrier reefs and atolls; the familiar island of Oahu has subsided 1,500 feet since the reef was at sea level in Miocene time, and more than one geologist has postulated sinking of the order of 5,000-10,000 feet in late-Cainozoic time. Data from the Funafuti boring showed the dolomitic limestone continued without much change beyond 1,100 feet, and the Bikini boring (2,556 feet) in the Marshall Islands was drilled through calcareous sandstone and soft foraminiferal limestones of Pliocene and Miocene age. Seismic survey indicated that low velocity rock persisted to 7,000 feet depth, and below that a velocity of 5·5 km./sec. was encountered down to 13,000 feet.

Stearns, recording a general absence of pillow lavas from the islands of the Pacific Basin, concluded that the islands, as visible, were formed prior to the main submergence; whereas the basement rocks of islands west of the Andesite Line are characterized by pillow lavas and marine fossiliferous tuffs of Cainozoic age, and hence are submarine volcanoes elevated above sea level. The oceanic floor goes down, the surrounding framework rises.

Pacific islands constitute considerable excess loads upon foundations already weakened by withdrawal of huge quantities of lava, and evidence of subsidence accrues from all over the Pacific Basin. Whether the necessary isostatic adjustments are achieved beneath groups of islands, or are distributed more widely over the Pacific floor remains uncertain. In either case, no considerable changes of ocean level (eustasy) are necessarily entailed for within limited areas the displacements of igneous material constitute a closed system.

In the central Pacific, islands are frequently disposed in straight or very gently curving chains as exemplified in the Line Islands, Tuamotu and the Gilbert Islands. Presumably the islands of each chain have come into being along some line of weakness in the ocean floor at about the same time, though a progression of volcanism from west to east is perceptible in the Caroline, Hawaiian, Society and Revilla Gigedo island chains (Dietz 1954). Best studied of these straight island chains is the Hawaiian group trending west-north-west 1,500 miles from Hawaii to Midway Island. All the islands stand upon the submarine Hawaiian Ridge, which itself surmounts the axis of a much lower, broad rise—the Hawaiian Swell. The swell is prolonged for a further 600 miles beyond Midway and is studded with seamounts, but no islands. All the features are genetically related upon their linearity and close association. To the southward is a similar swell directed east-west and intersecting the first at a point south-south-east of Hawaii. From this second swell rise the seamounts of the Mid-Pacific Mountains (Dietz and Menard 1953), though no islands. The researches of Hamilton (1956) have shown that during pre-Aptian to Cenomanian (Cretaceous) time, however, these guyots did constitute a chain of basaltic islands that were wave-eroded to flat banks upon which flourished a shallow-water coral and rudistid fauna possessing affinities with the Tethyan fauna of the Gulf Coast. Paleocene and Eocene foraminifera were recovered from the flat tops of four guyots, but subsidence had apparently already carried the tops below the depth limits of coral-reef growth, and of later Cainozoic life there was no recovery. Though many seamounts rise in the area defined by parallels 10° and 35° N., and the meridians 170° E. and 145° W., nearly all are on the swells and few interrupt the ocean plains which lie deeper than 3,000 fathoms. The same is true of the two seamount chains in the Gulf of Alaska described by Menard and Dietz (1951).

The eastern half of the Hawaiian chain is bordered on its northern side and about its eastern end by a sea-floor depression or minor " deep ". This is not like the profound narrow trenches found about island arcs that plumb depths of perhaps 30,000 feet, (*e.g.* Philippine, Puerto Rico Trenches) but is broad and open and scarcely attains 20,000 feet depth. Curiously, at about half the length of the chain the " deep " changes its situation to the southern side. Such a relationship can surely be due only to trans-current movement on opposite sides of a crustal fracture represented by the line of islands. Betz and Hess (1942) were of this opinion, and quoted the straightness and great length of the line in support. The swell they thought to be related to volcanicity in which, because of vesicularity, the eruptives have a density deficiency of 0·4 compared with the normal crust of the Pacific floor. The fundamental activity possibly lies in convection currents in the sub-crust.

Dietz and Menard (1951) have demonstrated the presence of a further structure in the Hawaiian region. The " deep " is paralleled upon the north by a low, broad arch that also curves around the eastern end of the island chain. Relief from the bottom of the deep to the crest of the arch exceeds 3,000 feet. In some sections the arch is slightly asymmetrical with the west side steeper than the east except where, in some sections, the eastern boundary appears to be a fault 1,800 feet high.

The history of the whole vast, central Pacific region has been synthesized by Menard (1964) who viewed it rising as a huge bulge of the subcrustal mantle (the Darwin Rise) sometime during the Mesozoic. The surface of the bulge was torn by faults and megashears into ridges and troughs.

Then mighty volcanic cones grew above aprons of extruded rock that buried much of the previous faulted topography " in a paroxysm of volcanism which may be un-equalled in the geological record ". So the mid-Cretaceous sea was replete with banks, islands and active volcanoes already showing sands and cobbles as the upstanding masses were worn away, and coral growths beneath the level of the sea. These developments continued into the early Cainozoic so that the volcanism culminated between 100 and 60 million years ago, when the whole vast structure began to subside, which it has continued to do to a total depth of 2,000 metres at the present day.

THE PACIFIC AS A PETROGRAPHIC PROVINCE

More than 90 per cent. of the volcanic rocks of Pacific islands are undifferentiated olivine basalts. The remainder according to Stearns (1945) include: " nepheline basalts, nepheline-melilite basalts, picrite basalts, basaltic andesites, andesitic basalts, oligoclase andesites and soda trachytes, all of them differentiation products of isolated magma reservoirs underlying individual volcanoes ". Dunites, gabbros and related rock types found in the eroded cores of some of the volcanoes, however, may be original and derived independently from sub-crustal peridotite. With two exceptions, there are no true andesites, dacites, rhyolites or other rock types that require for their formation admixture of sialic, or continental, material; though sporadic occurrences of certain alkaline rocks (phonolite) infer perhaps local assimilation of limestone, possibly of reef derivation.

The unity of the Pacific as a petrographic province of which olivine basalt is the primary rock type is thus clearly established.*

The only Pacific islands whereon rocks foreign to the province crop out are Easter Island and the nearby Sala-y-Gomez, where dacite and rhyolite additional to the normal olivine basalt, trachy-andesite and trachyte suite suggest affinity with the calc-alkaline rocks of the Andes. These islands stand upon the high South-east Pacific Plateau

TABLE XIV

TYPES OF VOLCANIC ROCKS IN CENTRAL PACIFIC ISLANDS

	Olivine Basalt	Basalt	Picrite Basalt Types			Limburgitic Basalt	Basanite	Monchiquite	Nepheline Basalt	Melilite-nepheline Basalt	Andesine Andesite	Oligoclase Andesite	"Shoshonite"	Trachyte	Phonolite	Dacite	Rhyolite
			Oceanite	Ankaramite	Mimosite												
Hawaii	+	+	+	+	+	...	+	...	+	+	+	+	...	+	...	...	...
Clipperton	...	...	...	...	...	...	...	...	...	...	...	...	...	+	...	...	...
Caroline (eastern)	+	+	...	...	...	...	+	+	+	...	...	...	...	+	...	...	...
Cocos	+	...	...	...	...	...	...	...	...	...	...	...	...	...	?	...	...
Galapagos	+	...	...	...	...	...	...	...	...	...	+	+	...	+	...	...	...
Marquesas	+	+	+	+	...	+	...	...	...	...	+	...	...	+	+	...	...
Wallis	+	...	...	...	...	...	...	...	...	...	...	+	...	...	...	...	...
Samoa	+	+	+	...	...	+	...	...	...	...	+	+	...	+	...	...	...
Tuamotu	+	...	+	+	...	...	...	...	...	...	+	...	...	...	...	...	...
Society (Leeward)	+	...	+	+	...	...	...	...	...	...	...	+	...	+	...	...	...
Society (Windward)	+	+	+	+	...	+	+	+	...	...	+	+	+	+	+	...	...
Cook	+	+	...	+	...	...	...	...	+	...	+	...	...	...	+	...	...
Tubuai (Austral)	...	+	+	+	...	...	+	...	...	...	+	...	...	...	+	...	...
São Ambrosio	...	+	...	...	...	...	+	...	...	...	...	...	...	+	...	...	...
Easter	+	...	...	...	...	...	...	...	...	...	+	...	...	+	...	+	+
Juan Fernandez	+	+	...	+	...	...	+	...	...	...	...	...	...	+	...	...	...

(*from* G. A. *Macdonald*)

where, according to Gutenberg and Richter, the observed speed of earthquake waves suggests " a thin tongue of continental rock ".

Also upon Easter Island is a small quantity of obsidian, amounting to no more than 0·011 cubic mile on a basaltic mass of 55 cubic miles. Bandy (1937) has pointed out that such a small quantity could be derived from basalt by several processes. " There is no necessity to assume any process other than normal differentiation of the ocean basalt as it crystallized. The presence of olivine in every extrusive rock, almost up to the last flow, points to a late and relatively rapid change in the nature of the source magma."

* Recent studies of the origins of contrasted basaltic types—olivinic and tholeiitic—are by: B. C. King (1965), Poldervaart (1962), Kushiro and Kuno (1963) and Yoder and Tilley (1962).

The average Hawaiian basalt, according to Macdonald (1949), is very similar in composition to plateau basalt, with a little more magnesia and lime, and a little less alumina, iron and alkalis. It is thus somewhat more basic. The primitive olivine basalts probably correspond closely in composition with the crustal floor of the Pacific Basin, and their eruption as the parent lava of every volcanic island over that area testifies the uniform simplicity of the Pacific as a petrographic province. Gravitational differentiation does occur in it, and an interesting example is provided by the lava flows which were extruded from the flanks of Kilauea in 1840. Flows erupted from vents above 3,000 feet contained few phenocrysts of olivine; flows from vents at 800 feet contained 30 *per cent* of olivine phenocrysts and were picrite basalts of oceanite type. Evidently gravitational differentiation was signally effective in the lava column of Kilauea.

Though lava flows are extruded from centralized vents throughout the Pacific, the vents themselves (as also the islands) seem often to be aligned along fissures. Thus visible flows on Koolau volcano issued from vents along a fissure system 30 miles long and trending parallel to the main axis of the Hawaiian chain. The fissure system is marked by swarms of sub-parallel dykes in a band 2-5 miles wide.

Some of the Hawaiian volcanoes (Mauna Loa, Kilauea) have not passed beyond the early stage of the shield volcano, and continue to erupt primitive olivine basalt. Two others, Lanai and West Molokai, are apparently extinct. Several of the Hawaiian volcanoes have resumed activity after a long period of quiescence and erosion. The newer lavas are usually differentiated trachy-andesites or trachytes. Such differentiation is deemed to have taken place by crystallization in isolated magma reservoirs. Perhaps settling of olivine crystals enriched the lower olivine basalt to picrite basalt or oceanite and left a non-olivinic basalt in the upper part of the reservoir. Removal of calcic plagioclase, hypersthene, diopside and olivine could have left a salic residuum of trachy-andesite or even trachyte (Macdonald 1949). Small bodies of trachyte interbedded with olivine basalts without intervening basalt at Hualalai Volcano in the Waianae Range of Oahu suggest differentiation there in small parasitic magma chambers. More usually the complete differentiated sequence is developed in the main magma chambers. Olivine basalt may, however, be erupted at any stage of the volcanic cycle, proving the repeated addition of fresh primitive magma from below.

These olivine basalt-trachyte associations that have been further studied by Tilley (1951) may occur in the volcanic piles of other ocean basins, or rarely upon the lands. They are said to occur in quiescent areas where differentiation can proceed without assimilation of sialic material. They cannot occur in orogenic areas, where contamination by sial gives rise to calc-alkaline rocks. Tilley compared the unmixed differentiation of Pacific basalts with the Cainozoic basaltic effusions of western Scotland, with the differentiation of the great layered basic intrusions and with achondritic meteorite differentiation and concluded that it was a fundamental process. The essential simplicity of the Pacific petrographic province is thus no less impressive than its uniformity and extent.

2 R

The Floor of the Pacific Basin

In 1921 Angenheister observed from Samoa that the transmission of earthquake waves through the Pacific floor was very rapid and concluded therefrom that it was made of dense, heavy basaltic material. This conclusion has been verified by all subsequent workers, and is confirmed by the observations of positive gravity anomalies across the North Pacific by Vening Meinisz. Except for the Easter Island region, no mass of likely sialic material is known anywhere within the andesite line. Despite the abundant abyssal hills (volcanic in origin but sometimes bearing early or middle Cainozoic sediments upon their flat tops) that strew more than 80 *per cent* of its floor, the central Pacific Basin has never, so far as can be ascertained, had any portion of its true floor heaved into continental land by tectonic agencies. The hypothetical Pacific continents once so fashionable in geologic texts must one and all be rejected. Most of them purported to explain the distribution of plants and animals, but so vast an area as the Pacific with its warm and cold currents, regular and irregular wind systems and garlands of volcanic islands has its own agents of, and barriers to, organic dispersal. The utmost elevation of the simatic floor that has been achieved has been the building of volcanic cones only the highest of which broach the ocean surface as meagre islands.

Oliver, Ewing and Press (1953) express this conclusion in geophysical terms, " First mode Love and Rayleigh waves on seismograms from the Honolulu station indicate that no submerged land-masses of continental proportions underlie the Pacific Ocean as outlined by the earthquake belt. . . . The method, however, is insensitive to relatively small or thin structures. The Easter Island Rise is anomalous and possibly includes a thin layer of continent-like material ". Gutenberg (1951) also deduced geophysically that the area about and east of Easter Island contained a continental structure 20-30 km. in thickness.

The studies of Raitt and others indicate a thickness of bottom sediment 0·4 km. north of Honolulu increasing to 1·2 km. in the south-west quadrant where island groups are plentiful. Beneath the sediments refraction shooting suggests 5-6 km. of rock with compressional velocity of 6·5 km./sec. This is called the " second layer ". It is very widely distributed but is apt to be variable in thickness. Though much is undoubtedly of volcanic rock some, which thickens towards California, may be of consolidated sediment, probably limestones.

Ubiquitous below is the 8·1 km./sec. upper mantle. Greater mantle depths have been suspected in the western Pacific, but need verification.

The primitive uniformity of the Pacific Basin as a petrographic province, the dense nature of its floor and absence of past continents might infer a considerable measure of uniformity in its morphology. The four quadrants of that vast region together with their contiguous continents possess, however, considerable geomorphic independence, of which we must shortly take cognizance.

Because of the very great size of the ocean and the close proximity of the continental divides to its margins with relatively small influx of sediment-bearing river water, the Pacific Basin escapes much of the spreading of terrigenous sediment that is so characteristic of the Atlantic sea-bed. Whereas core sampling of sediments on the floor of the Atlantic Ocean revealed (Ericson, Ewing and Heezen 1952) a high proportion of sediment distributed by turbidity currents, the marginal deeps around much of the Pacific Basin have probably trapped much of the circumferential detritus. As at Bermuda, however, turbidity currents have operated to distribute calcareous debris from the erosion of coral islands to considerable distances over the ocean bed. Only off the north-western coast of North America are deposits laid down abundantly by slumping and turbidity currents, though minor occurrences are indicated by graded bedding and mixtures of Cainozoic and Quaternary fossils near isolated topographic highs such as the Marquesas and Tuamotu Archipelagoes and the Mid-Pacific Mountains (q.v.). The proportion of pyroclastics is also higher in the Pacific than in the Atlantic Basin. The area covered by red clay is conversely very large, and its accumulation long-continued. Chemical analyses indicate that some of the older clays are richer in manganese, iron and phosphorus relative to nickel, titanium and aluminium than the younger clays.

The combination of deep alkaline waters containing high concentrations of silicate and phosphate with a well developed equatorial current system results in high plankton production near the Equator in the east Pacific, and large areas of siliceous ooze, radiolarian or diatomaceous, have been determined in the warmer and colder water areas respectively.

Deposition appears to be slow, uniform and continuous in topographic lows, but upon even slight rises non-deposition, and even erosion, may be evident from core samples and Cainozoic calcareous oozes not infrequently crop out in such situations. " Seismic-refraction and reflection profiles suggest sediment thickness of approximately 200 metres in the clay areas and 400 metres beneath the equatorial calcareous oozes " (Revelle et al. 1955).

Curiously, neither the sedimentary floor nor the " second layer " beneath it (as determined by seismology) thickens toward the margins of the basin (Menard 1964), which indicates that the basin outlines are not of primordial origin but are probably not much older than Cretaceous.

THE NORTH-EASTERN PACIFIC QUADRANT

Charts reveal that the north-eastern Pacific has the most consistently deep floor and the fewest islands of any quadrant (Fig. 250). Throughout, the most impressive feature in the bottom topography is its linearity. Everywhere, the quadrant is crossed by ridges and troughs measuring hundreds and even thousands of feet in height and nearly all directed from east, or a little north of east, to west. A similar bottom relief continues over half the north-western quadrant leaving the observer with a strong impression that it is a fundamental global structure, perhaps controlled by convection currents directed from east to west in the substratum, and that it is primitive and probably ancient in the North Pacific Basin.

Four mighty topographic features with this trend have been explored by Menard (1953b); three are escarpments, one is a trough, all are on approximate great circles and they are spaced at intervals of 600-1,200 miles. " From north to south, approximate positions and dimensions are:

1) Mendocino Escarpment 5,000 feet high, 1,400 miles long.
2) Between southern California and the central Hawaiian Islands, an escarpment 4,000 feet high and 1,600 miles long.
3) West of the Revilla Gigedo Islands, a narrow trough 2,000-5,000 feet deep and 1,800 miles long.
4) Between Christmas and Clipperton Islands, an escarpment 1,000 feet high and 3,300 miles long."

" The trends mark great [left-lateral] shear zones. Between each pair of shear zones the crust appears to be deformed as a block, and alternate blocks appear to be compressed and stretched." Displacement along the Mendocino Fracture Zone is of an opposite sense at opposite ends (640 miles left displacement at the west end, 55 miles right at the east end); this is not so along the fracture zones of the equatorial Atlantic (p. 596).

The whole pattern of the North Pacific bears the impress of deformation in a thin skin over sub-crustal flow, much like the linearity induced in the skin of fluid lava flows. Significant in this connection is Menard's correlation of all four of these great features with easterly-trending structures on the American continent that extend transversely to the general north-westerly grain of the cordillera. The corresponding features are:

" 1) a major east-trending gorge zone; southern limit of the Cascade volcanoes;
2) Channel Islands; transverse ranges; northern limit of block-faulted continental borderland;
3) east-trending Revilla Gigedo Islands and volcanoes of Central Mexico; southern limit of continental borderland; northern limit of Acapulco Trench and associated volcanoes and earthquakes;
4) southern limit of Acapulco Trench and associated structures ".

Left lateral movement on these faults is shown by displacements upon the north-south pattern of magnetic anomalies to involve 1,420 km. displacement (Vacquier *et al.* 1961).

Minor lineations trend pinnately (Menard 1959) suggesting large-scale wrench faulting (Fig. 235).

These observations by Menard suggest that subcrustal conditions existing beneath North America may be similar to those inferred for the North Pacific, namely a latitudinal streaming from east to west with different speeds in separate flow streams causing shear phenomena along their margins. Maybe through the relatively uncomplicated floor of the North Pacific Basin geologists are permitted a glimpse of what is going on beneath the crust, and to surmise what is either hidden beneath continents or too obscurely presented in their visible structure for practical interpretation.

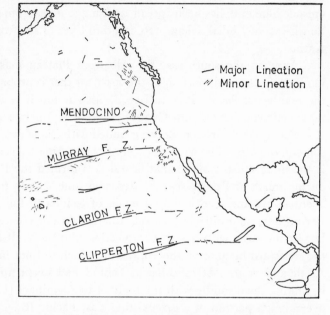

FIG. 235

Minor lineations trending pinnately to major linear features of the Pacific floor, and suggesting large-scale wrench faulting. *after W. H. Menard.*

Only on the west, in mid-ocean, do island chains arise from great ridges and swells (Hawaiian Islands, Necker Rise, Line Islands) in typical Pacific fashion (p. 622). On the east the few oceanic islands (Guadalupe, Islas Revilla Gigedo and Clipperton) rise as seamounts from near the edge of the Albatross Plateau, nor are other seamounts more than rare in this sector. They are abundant only in the Gulf of Alaska (Fig. 215) where Menard and Dietz (1951) have surveyed 35 major examples rising 3,000-12,400 feet above the smooth ocean bed. These they have divided into two types characterized by contrasted topography. The first type have the form of volcanoes truncated at depths normally of 400-500 fathoms, though one apparently subsided on the axis of the Aleutian Trench has a flat top at 1,380 fathoms (Fig. 214). Seamounts of the second type are elongate, asymmetrical and irregular. Standing upon low ridges, none are flat-topped and they rise to varied heights. " By reason of their topography and their relation to the trend of a Pliocene-Pleistocene orogenic belt, [these] seamounts are thought to be orogenic mountains."

The sea floor in the Gulf of Alaska is very flat and from bottom sampling is evidently sedimentational. It slopes south-westward from the base of the continental slope at

1,400-1,700 fathoms to 2,600 fathoms with a slope between 10 and 12 feet per mile
On the north it is warped down into the eastern end of the Aleutian Trench, on the south
it is limited by the Mendocino Escarpment. Menard (1953) showed that glacial marine
drift was deposited over several hundred thousand square miles of the north-eastern
Pacific floor during Pleistocene time, and ice-rafted pebbles were dropped into manganese deposits on top of Gilbert Seamount. Gentle currents winnowed the finer grades
of sediment from the tops of seamounts leaving only pebbles and sand. After the glacial
episode blue mud has been spread, and at 250 miles from the shore is still 125 cm. thick.
South-east of Kodiak Island, too, is a thin layer of ash from the 1912 eruption of Mount
Katmai.

Away in the south-east the Albatross Plateau makes a very large, though only
moderately elevated, portion of the sea-floor that is probably connected genetically with
the South-east Pacific Plateau (q.v.) which it much resembles. Conceivably it bears
no genetic connection with Central and North America which it now borders (p. 634).

Pacific coasts are generally garlanded with island arcs or bordered by deep trenches,
sometimes both. The western coast of North America is peculiarly free of either, which
is the more remarkable in that island arcs formed the Pacific aspect of that continent
during much of Palæozoic and Mesozoic time. Only from southern Alaska does the
Aleutian arc and trench fling a chain of islands to link with Asia across the shallow
Bering Sea; and only in Central America do the Guatemala and Acapulco Trenches
border the coast with possible connection into the Gulf of California. It as is though
the westward hinging of the continent (which did not include Alaska) to open up the
Arctic and western Atlantic Basins behind, had swept up the earlier island arcs before
it, uniting them solidly with the body of the continent (Fig. 236), and at the same time
overriding a portion of a pre-existing East Pacific Ridge (p. 579). Since these events
sub-crustal conditions have not been favourable to the initiation of offshore trenches
except by Mexico and Guatemala. The form of this interesting continental margin
was discussed by Eardley (1962) who demonstrated that the great slope leading from the
continental shelf to the ocean floor does not conform with the trends of Cretaceous or
Cainozoic orogeny, and concluded that it was younger than these, perhaps Pleistocene.
Others, including Shepard, have postulated a fault like that along the western Sierra
Nevada which is of the same size. This does not explain, however, the fundamental
geophysical difference between the materials of the continent and the ocean floor
respectively.

THE ALEUTIAN ARC

Springing from the Alaska Peninsula the Aleutian Arc is an integral portion of the
North American cordillera and both the elevations of the islands and the floor of the
trench descend in sympathy from Mount Spurr in the east to Attu Island in the west
the descent being of the order of 6,000 feet on the lands and 8,500 feet along the floor
of the trench. Between the mountain tops and the floor of the trench which plumbs a

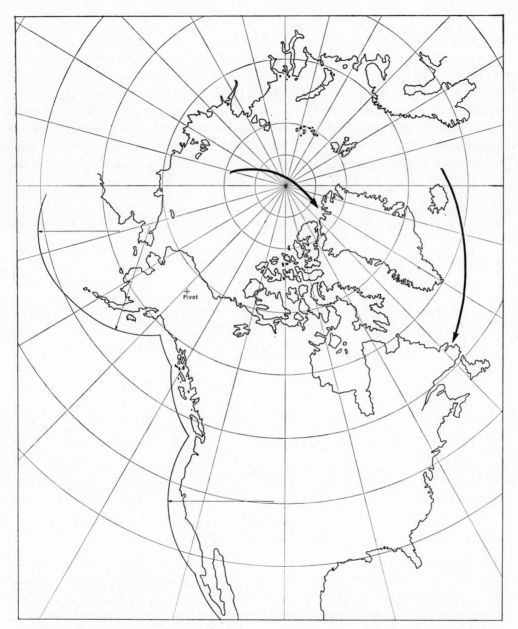

FIG. 236. Suggested movements under continental drift of North America relative to Eurasia. With rotation about a pivot in Alaska the Arctic Archipelago of Canada and Greenland moved out of the eastern and western Arctic Basins respectively. The former has broken into a geobreccia, the latter remained entire. Eastern North America withdrew from a position nearer the mid-Atlantic Ridge. The western aspect of the continent swept up and incorporated the island arcs which formerly fringed it in Palæozoic and early-Mesozoic time, and overrode part of the East Pacific suboceanic Ridge (p. 630 ; Fig. 228).

maximum of 25,000 feet, is an average relief of 30,000 feet. On the north, about half
the area of the Bering Sea is continental shelf and half is basin with a maximum depth
of 14,000 feet (Fig. 237). From the narrow ridge rises the chain of small, partly volcanic
islands dotted along the 90° sector of a small circle. Granite is known in the western
members, dacite and rhyolite are widely erupted, and the geology of the islands in general
is described as " an extension of the Alaska Peninsula geology ". This makes the islands
"continental" like the Kuriles and Japan, and the Bering Basin is then an intracontinental depression like the Sea of Japan. Nonetheless, the present structure of the

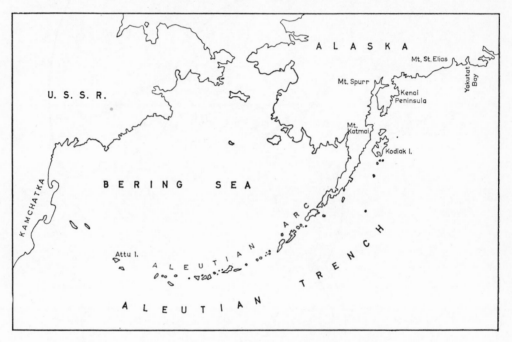

FIG. 237. The Aleutian Arc carrying the east Asiatic garland of islands
into the North American mainland.

arc and trench, with displacements due to wrench faulting, are modern oceanic features
like other arcs and trenches of eastern Asia. Trench and insular garland diverge
towards the mainland to admit further structural elements in Kodiak Island and
Kenai Peninsula which represent a filled Mesozoic trench. The Mesozoic trench of
Kodiak Island, containing upwards of 20,000 feet of sediment, underwent orogenesis
at the middle of the Cretaceous period and again at its close, since when it has
experienced only minor movements, with marine deposition mainly during the Miocene
period.

    The arc, single for most of its length, thus becomes double towards its eastern
end. In this transition it compares with the Kurile Arc of Eastern Asia. Hess and
Umbgrove have independently suggested that such transitions occur where one end of

an ancestral trench lay near a source of sediment, was filled and evolved into major islands, while the remote end failed in this evolution and persisted when a fresh trough was generated alongside the proximal earlier site.

The geological history of Southern Alaska suggests that the eastern part of the Aleutian Trench originated in early-Cainozoic time; but the exact point of its insertion into the mainland between Cape St. Elias and Yakutat Bay is obscured by a submarine canyon. Late tectonic movements have been spectacular hereabout. Plio-Pleistocene sediments 1,800 feet thick have been elevated by as much as 5,000 feet in the hills south of Mt. St. Elias (Smith 1939); and the earthquake of 1899 which raised parts of Yakutat Bay 20-47 feet shows that movements are still continuing. Yet the eastern extremity of the Aleutian Trench is only shallowly depressed below the level of the sea-floor plain; perhaps it is largely filled with sediment.

THE SOUTH-EASTERN PACIFIC QUADRANT

Mailship travellers from New Zealand to Panama appreciate the vast emptiness of this quadrant for in the three weeks voyage they are fortunate if they see, as the only land, Pitcairn Island. The ocean basin is immense and islands are numerous only in the Polynesian groups of the north-west sector. These volcanic and coral islands stand in lines upon high sea-floor ridges directed to the north-west so that they point towards further groups—Tuamotu towards the Line Islands, Society Islands towards Tokelau and the Phœnix Islands, and the Cook Islands towards Samoa; but the ridges are not continuous. This is the region of the Darwin Rise (p. 623).

South of the Polynesian Islands is the main south-eastern Pacific Basin with a deep floor and no islands though a few small ridges rise to the status of reefs. The latest charts reveal in the bottom topography, however, a faint lineation westerly or west-north-westerly. This is probably the oldest and least modified part of the ocean floor within this quadrant, and the lineation possibly reflects some aspect of subcrustal streaming like the swell and furrow topography of the North Pacific Basin.

By far the most remarkable feature of the south-eastern Pacific Quadrant is the enormous submarine ridge (p. 579) that sprawls across its eastern half from the Balleny Islands and Victoria Land in the Antarctic to Easter Island. According to Menard " Along its crest, marked in some places by a broken blocky topography with ridges and troughs running parallel to the axis, the earth's crust is significantly thinner than elsewhere. The crest is a region of high earthquake intensity and also of abnormally high rate of heat flow from the interior. On the flanks of the rise the heat flow is below average."

" At regular intervals straight cracks thousands of miles long cross the flanks of the rise in an east-west direction. There is evidence that across these fracture zones huge slabs of the earth's crust have shifted horizontally with respect to each other by hundreds of miles. Yet the slabs themselves are virtually undistorted; they are simply tilted a bit."

The chief displacement is dextral, in latitude 55° S where the pattern of earthquake epicentres is offset about 1,000 km.

A crestal rift is not continuous: in some places are a number of parallel rifts and ridges, but Menard (1964) emphasises: " South of the Gulf of California . . . the crest of the rise has no pronounced or special fault trough ".

At Easter Island the Ridge spreads out in a huge plateau that spans 50 meridians between Pitcairn Island and the coast of South America. Depths of less than 4,000 metres prevail over large areas of this submarine plateau the most westerly point of which may indeed lie amid the Tuamotu Archipelago which is an outlier of the Polynesian coral island system. Lavas from these islands are nepheline-free, distinct from the nepheline-bearing rocks to the north, as though they had assimilated continental matter in the island foundations before eruption. From Easter Island the Ridge continues northerly though with some deepening beyond the usual 3,000-4,000 metres over the South-eastern Pacific Basin, into the Albatross Plateau, the coast of Mexico and Baja California. Its area is larger than some continents, placing it in a class of phenomena almost apart from the mid-Atlantic and mid-Indian submarine ridges of the lesser oceans. Indeed in two regions the topography of the ridge seems to exceed the modern limits of the Pacific Basin, for the same bottom topography extends past the Isthmus of Panama (which may well be younger) into the western Caribbean, while the south-eastern branch that reaches Chile appears as though continued in the submerged plateau within, and north of, the Scotia arc. Both these prolongations into the Atlantic are terminated by island arcs and trenches.

From the foundation of the ridge few islands rise to the surface of the ocean, and geophysical information regarding the constitution of the ridge and plateau is as yet meagre. In the foundations about Easter Island, seismologists agree (p. 626), material of a continental nature is indicated. The twin ridges that connect Galapagos Islands with the Isthmus of Panama and with Ecuador respectively, resemble the isthmus topographically and feasibly contain similar rock formations.

If the other submarine ridges that we have reviewed have significant relationship with nearby continents (p. 585) then surely this ridge has too, and we must seriously consider whether there may not have been a connection with South America in the geologic past (Figs. 222, 223).

The west coast of South and Central America is bordered for thousands of miles by deep-sea trenches evidently of Cainozoic or Quaternary origin. All these features are topographically younger than the giant Ridge and Plateau of the South-eastern Pacific on which, indeed, they occur. Between Ecuador and Southern Nicaragua where youthful ridges stand upon the plateau the trenches are significantly absent.

For 1,260 miles the northern (Middle America) trenches parallel the tectonically active west coast of Guatemala and Mexico at a short distance offshore. The Guatemala Trench descends to depths of 20,000 feet, the Acapulco Trench to 16,000 feet and beneath them the main oceanic layer increases in thickness by 50 *per cent*, and the Moho is flexed down. South of the Tropic of Cancer the latter Trench shallows and disappears, but its structural continuation may be assessed in the Gulf of California and along the San Andreas megashear.

Much more profound are the deeps of the Peru-Chile Trench the bottom of which plumbs 25,000 feet. With the neighbouring Andes is here developed the greatest relief on earth. A cross-section in the vicinity of Taltal, Northern Chile, where the crest of the Andes stands above 16,000 feet reveals a total descent of over 40,000 feet in 175 miles. Of this descent 32,600 feet is accomplished in 75 miles. So close is the trench to the coast that from North-western Peru to Southern Chile the 4,000 metre isobath stands never beyond 125 miles from the coast, and is generally half that distance.

Three hundred miles offshore rises a high submarine ridge crowned by the islands of Juan Fernandez, San Felix and San Ambrosio. Little is known of the constitution of this ridge or of its origins and relation to the Richards-Haeckel deep. It appears to be collinear with the rise upon which stand the Tuamotu and Line Islands.

Strangely enough, the coast of Graham Land has no deep trench, but the Bentley Trench (-2,538 metres) behind the Eights Coast (Fig. 179) is apparently a megashear. Much further geophysical exploration of the South-eastern Pacific Quadrant is necessary.

The North-western Pacific Quadrant, including Indonesia

The Aleutian pattern of moated island arc with continental affinities in its structure, bordering a shelf which is in part deeply sunken (Bering Sea), is continued along the whole length of the east Asiatic maritime region to Indonesia (Fig. 217) where it rounds the south-eastern corner of the continent and *via* Sumatra and the Nicobar-Andaman Islands is finally integrated with the mainland structure in Burma. The tectonics of this maritime belt belong to the Pacific type so only brief reference is made here. Like the Aleutians, the Kurile arc bridging from Kamchatka to Hokkaido begins as a double arc but for most of its length is single. Islands at the northern end bear detrital sediments that could not possibly derive with the present distribution of land and sea and the islands must represent the former edge of the mainland. The ridge upon which they stand is thought to be granitic, and granite is reported to crop out on the islands Kunashir, Urup and Paramushiro. The enclosed Okhotsk Sea is mostly shallow shelf, but includes in the outer part a deep basin which Yabe thought might even be Quaternary in age.

Japan is a continental island possessing curious links with the mainland. Thus granite cobbles are present in a Permian conglomerate though no source for them seems to have existed at that time on the island. Kobayashi believed the cobbles might have come from a batholith near Vladivostock. The islands now lock in the Japanese Sea, a basin 3,600 metres deep with oceanic-type floor and shallow sills at both ends. The southern sill was dry land during the Pleistocene, permitting the migration of elephants into Japan. Beneath the sea of Japan rise two large banks with extensive flat tops at 300 and 500 metres depth respectively. Dredgings by Niino produced thereon well-rounded rocks of continental types resembling formations in Japan. The flat floor of the basin also indicates a thick infill of terrigenous muds and sands. Consensus of opinion dates the principal subsidence of the basin at mid and late Cainozoic.

The Riu Kiu arc to Formosa is separated from the very shallow, flat floor of the East China Sea only by a curvilinear sea-floor depression 2,500 feet deep and a score or two of miles wide. Of the function of the arc as a mere outer rampart of continental Asia there is no doubt. Both the zone of Cainozoic limestone, and the zone of volcanism are present, revealing, with the outer accompanying trench, the typical island-arc structure.

Formosa is joined to the northernmost Philippines (Luzon) by a high, though irregular ridge. This does not quite close the basin of the South China Sea because a submarine gorge 16,000 feet deep passes through the ridge and permits exit even of bottom waters. This Bashi Channel may be partly erosional in origin serving as the submarine outlet for a mighty drowned river system of which Dickerson (1941) wrote, " About thirty thousand years ago a great Mississippi-like river flowed northwards between Cochin-China and Borneo. This stream was about one thousand miles long, rising in Sumatra. Like the Mississippi this river had an even longer branch, the Pleistocene Mekong River, which rises on the north slope of the Himalaya Mountains about 2,000 miles westerly from its mouth in the South China Sea . . . Molengraaf Valley was about 700-800 miles wide between Borneo and Cochin-China ". Over the wide area between Borneo, Malaya and Java where the water is not 100 metres deep, the tributary stream channels of Molengraaf River are still unfilled, attesting the recency of the drowning (Fig. 13). The 11 major and 7,000 small islands of the Philippines belong to a vast area subsided in late-Cainozoic time, but subsidence has been far from regular and while twin south-west ridges connect the main sigmoidal Philippine arc with north-west Borneo, the Sulu and Celebes Seas occupy deeply sunken basins. Both ridges are thought (Irving 1952) to consist of the foundation rocks (? Mesozoic) of the Archipelago. From the southern tip of Mindanao a third submarine ridge connects with the northern arm of Celebes in a great reflex continuing the inner island arc structure, while lastly the Davao Peninsula of south-eastern Mindanao is continued by a submerged ridge to Talaud Island before disappearing in the Molucca Straits between Celebes and Halmahera. Structurally, therefore, the Philippines are tied in at many points with Indonesia—more so than to Formosa or the Riu Kiu arc.

The double arc of Indonesia encloses the Banda Sea Basin, west of New Guinea, an austral element that intrudes from the east; and this is the last of the marginal sea basins of eastern Asia. Java and Sumatra stand upon slightly submerged shelf across which can still be traced the Pleistocene extended courses of the headwaters of Molengraaf River. Throughout the early-Cainozoic era this region was continuous land, with local shallow epicontinental seas, but in the Miocene idiogeosynclines developed in Sumatra and Borneo and a much less stable regime supervened (p. 510) (Fig. 197).

Though situated on the geographic margin of the Indian Ocean, the remaining boundaries of which are very different, being fractured coasts transverse to the geologic structures of propinquent lands, the whole sector from the island of Timor to Burma is of characteristically Pacific " island arc " type, even to the presence of deep, bordering trenches (Java Trench, Nicobar deep).

Beyond Sumatra the mainland broke down once more, and the Andaman Basin behind the exiguous chain of Nicobar-Andaman Islands sinks to below 14,000 feet. In the Arakan Yoma of Burma the structural margin of Asia is, however, finally reunited with the mainland.

The geology of all the major islands reviewed is complex compared with that of oceanic islands: they contain sedimentary sequences of terrigenous type orogenically folded and many are invaded by plutons of granodiorite proclaiming their association with Asia. The pear-shaped basins behind them, from the Bering Sea to the Andaman Basin are therefore open tears, now flat floored with abundant sediment and with their continental slopes canyoned and irregular. They are indigenous to Asia and must be excluded from the Pacific realm though the basin floors beneath the sediment are of basalt, oceanic in type. The chain of arcuate trenches which parallels these islands, descending far below the normal level of the ocean floor, may be recognised as analogues of the trenches that follow the coasts of Mexico and Guatemala, Peru and Chile. They are probably recent, tensional, fault troughs.

THE MARIANAS ARC AND THE PHILIPPINE BASIN

Between Japan and New Guinea, to east and west of the 140° meridian, rise further arcuate and linear structures whose relationship to the great continent is less clear, though they stand definitely upon the landward side of the Andesite Line and certain of the islands are said to be founded upon metamorphic rocks. There are several sea-floor ridges arranged en échelon with the outermost ridge defining the eastern limit of the Philippine Sea; beyond it is the main North Pacific Basin.

The structural significance of these most interesting features has been assessed by Hess (1948) (Fig. 238). From a syntaxis near Tokio Bay a great submarine swell extends to the Marianas, first as a single then for most of its length as a double ridge. The northern end of the inner line carries a chain of youthful andesitic islands which line up with Fujiyama, and though the islands disappear beyond lat. 30° N. conical seamounts rise at intervals for the length of the ridge. Iwo Jima is the only emergent exception.

The northern end of the eastern Honshu-Mariana ridge begins near the Bonin Islands and is devoid of recent volcanism. The Bonins, however, have older andesitic lavas and agglomerates with Eocene and Oligocene limestones. Suzuki has reported

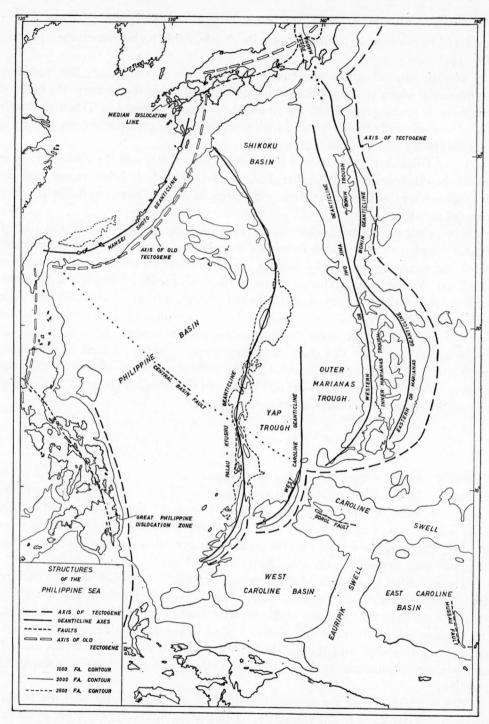

FIG. 238. Major structures of the Marianas island arc and Philippine sea.
after H. H. Hess.

serpentinised peridotite, but the field relations are uncertain. " Probably, as on Yap, it belongs to a basement series and is older than Eocene Nummulitic limestone " (Hess). Recent volcanism does appear upon the eastern geanticline, however, for this geanticline itself becomes double in the Marianas, the northerly islands of the group from Farallon de Parajos to Anatahan being andesitic and including several active members. This volcanic chain submerges and passes westwards of the larger (southern) Marianas which, like the Bonins, are built of limestones dating back to the Oligocene period and resting upon a foundation of older andesite. Serpentine has been reported from Tinian.

The southern extremities of both eastern and western geanticlines curve sharply westward (Fig. 238) before being terminated at the Marianas Trench. Another geanticline that emerges from the floor of the eastern Philippine Sea then rises into prominence is the Yap arc. The islands of this group are remarkable for the metamorphic quality and variety of their foundation rocks. Amphibolite and schist are known *in situ*, and among the pebbles of a lower-Miocene conglomerate Tayama lists amphibolite, actinolite schist, talc schist, gabbro, norite, diallage peridotite and leuco-granite. The strike of schistosity is north-eastward. Either vertical tectonics of a remarkable nature have affected this narrow submarine ridge, or else it and the associated islands formerly had direct continental connection. The Yap arc also curves westward in its southern extremity towards a third geanticline which spans the distance from Kyushu (Japan) to the Palau Islands in two consecutive arcs with a re-entrant at their junction in lat. 13° N. In the triangle between the northern end of the Palau-Kyushu geanticline and Okinawa on the Riu Kiu arc a host of seamounts rise from the sea-floor, those which break the surface being known as the Daito Islands. Borings on these islands revealed organic limestones, calcareous muds and sandstones of shallow, warm-water accumulation, and ranging probably through upper Oligocene at 1,422 feet, lower Miocene at 1,300 feet and Plio-Pleistocene (upper) stages. Progressive drowning is therefore indicated. The Daito Islands group are about the only large seamounts within the Philippine Sea that do not arise from geanticlines. At mid-length Parece Vela Reef breaks through, otherwise the whole geanticline is submerged except for the Palau Islands in the extreme south where the geanticline bends westward towards the Moluccas. The Palaus are mainly reef, but " volcanic rocks, chiefly pyroclastic, were erupted from a centre on western Babelthuap during late-Eocene and possibly Oligocene time ". Basalt, andesite and dacite are present, and " to the south, reef and lagoonal limestones, ranging from Miocene to Pleistocene in age, overlap the volcanic rocks " (Mason and Corwin 1953).

Thus the sedimentary islands of these geanticlines have sequences of tuff, agglomerate and limestone from Eocene to Recent in age *implying little change in their environment throughout the Cainozoic era.* The presence of older rocks, considerably metamorphosed, on Yap; and of serpentinised peridotites on Yap, two of the Marianas and one of the Bonins raises suspicion of a different and more active environment at some earlier epoch. No fossiliferous Mesozoic rocks have been identified on any of the islands, but it would not be difficult to relate the deformation of the rocks to some phase of Cretaceous diastrophism (p. 507). As the earlier, Jurassic tectogenesis is still related to the mainland and major offshore islands (*e.g.* Japan and Riu Kiu arc), profound geographical changes are implied between the Jurassic and the Eocene, and perhaps associated with the supposed Cretaceous diastrophism. Why should this diastrophism appear a thousand miles out in the ocean, divorced from the mainland; why was there no Cainozoic orogenesis though it is present for instance in Japan and the Philippines? Put another way, why is the presumed Cretaceous diastrophism absent from the Kyushu-Philippine sector of eastern Asia where the Jurassic and Cainozoic phases are developed? These matters call in question the nature and origin of the Philippine Basin.

The Philippine Basin is unusually deep, the western portion descending below 6,000 metres. Bottom topography is rough in detail with smooth sedimented basins between the groups of seamounts.

Investigating the nature of the basin floor Oliver, Ewing and Press (1953) reported that " The slightly low velocity for paths [of the long Rayleigh waves] crossing the Philippine Sea would admit at most the possibility of a thin low-velocity layer, but Love wave data show no indication of its presence. . . . Although this study indicates that the oceans on either side of the andesite line are similar with respect to the propagation of surface waves, it does not preclude the possibility of petrologic changes providing the dimensions of the rocks involved are thin " (or scattered).

Fundamentally, the floor of the Philippine Basin behaves like that of the Pacific but there is some indication of lighter material within it, perhaps as though the area had formed part of the path over which a sector of Asia had passed during drift. The time is, significantly, Cretaceous.

Bearing in mind (a) that the Jurassic-Cretaceous was a time of active continental drift and fragmentation; (b) the possibility of some continental material in the floor and geanticlinal ridges of the Philippine Sea; and (c) the suggestion that the planes upon which earthquake shocks of increasing depth dip continentward and are feasibly tensional in origin (p. 6: Fig. 2), the possibility arises that the Marianas arc represents a former (Mesozoic) site of the eastern margin of Asia, and that the basal structures of the several geanticlines (Fig. 238) include sialic material left behind under tension at stages in a westward withdrawal of Eurasia. For purposes of reconstruction (Fig. 239) the Indonesian arc is refitted into the Marianas (involving rotation of Laurasia about a point in the northwestern U.S.S.R.). This gives a possible earlier position either for Laurasia as a whole, or for Eurasia alone (Fig. 239) if the Atlantic rift had opened prior to drift from the outer arcs. Chronological data establish the Atlantic rift as existing by the mid-Cretaceous, whereas the serpentine belt of the outer island arc is late-Cretaceous (Fig. 196), so that the latter hypothesis seems sounder and is embodied in Fig. 239.

The suggested rotational withdrawal of Eurasia from the site of the outer island arcs may be compared with the suggested retrograde motion of Australia (also in the mid or late Cretaceous) from an extreme easterly position near New Zealand (pp. 648, 668).

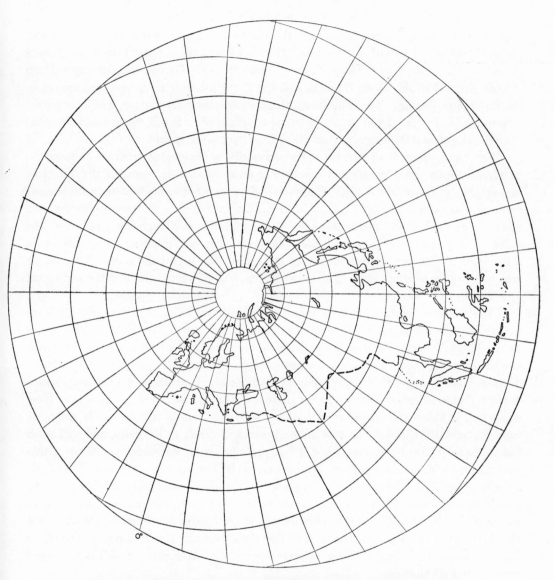

FIG. 239. Suggested position of Eurasia during the Cretaceous period
with the eastern curve of the Indonesian arc along the present line of
the Marianas island arc. Withdrawal to present longitudes is achieved
by rotation about a point in the north-western U.S.S.R.   This rotational
westward withdrawal is similar to a suggested retrograde movement of
Australia (also in the mid or late Cretaceous) from an extreme easterly
position near New Zealand (Fig. 247).

2 S

The East Asiatic Ocean Deeps

The great system of fosses surrounding the Pacific Basin attains maximal development alongside the island arcs of eastern Asia. Here are found the deepest parts of the oceans including the Challenger Deep (10,863 metres) near Guam, the Ramapo Deep (10,680 metres) in the Japan Trench, and the Cape Johnson Deep (10,479) metres in the Philippine Trench. These profound trenches are relatively narrow, with the steeper side to the landward. Even so, the bottoms are generally flat indicating sedimentation, though geophysical data signify that the sedimentary layer is thin.

For 5,000 miles from Alaska to Palau a series of connected trenches follows the outermost limits of the coasts and islands in a series of arcuate segments that intersect one another at re-entrant angles. Several of the trenches approach mathematical arcs: through most of its length the Aleutian Trench approximates the arc of a circle with radius of 750 miles, and the almost semi-circular Marianas Trench has a radius of 400 miles. Lake therefore suggested that they represent the intersection of low-angle thrust planes with the curved surface of the globe, and found the poles of successive arcs to lie upon simple lines. This concept has not, however, clarified the geological problems of the trenches.

The trenches, named for their associated island arcs (Fig. 217), successively from the north are: the Aleutian Trench, the Kamchatka Trench, the Kurile Trench, the North Japan Trench, the Izu-Bonin Trench, the Mariana Trench, the Yap Trench, and the Palau Trench. Curiously, a great straight-sided trench also borders the Philippines and dies away south-eastward only off Halmahera. It probably marks a megashear. A weak (Nansei-Shoto) trench also parallels the Riu-Kiu island arc. This last, Hess suggested, is older, associating it with a mid-Mesozoic trench that evidently extended from Kamchatka, through the axis of the Japanese Islands to Formosa, and to Luzon and Palawan in the Philippines, but it has probably been rejuvenated. Most of this originally mid-Mesozoic trench has been converted by orogeny into land; and Hess finds a chain of peridotite intrusions that are presumed to mark a tectogene. Many of the trenches possess a broad low swell upon the oceanic side, *e.g.* from Kamchatka to Japan and outside the southern portion (Mindanao) of the Philippine Trench. Worzel and Shurbet (1955) have demonstrated that the crust beneath the Philippine Trench is thinner than in the oceanic sector adjacent to it. The Marianas Trench is also sited above a crustal thinning.

Seismicity associated with the trenches is strong, and earthquake shocks are distributed in depth as though related to a plane of discontinuity, apparently tensional (pp. 6, 575), dipping landward from the sites of the trenches (Fig. 2). The strong seismicity indicates a recent origin for the trenches; a conclusion that is supported by their youthful topography, high gravity anomalies and the fact that they invariably transect other structures but are not themselves transected. South of Japan they even transect the seamount groups, and in the Carolines do so where the seamounts have maximal development (Dietz 1953). Judged on their seismicity the trenches are still developing.

Stratigraphic evidence, on the other hand, sometimes requires an earlier date for the initiation, at least, of the trenches. Alaskan structures indicate that the Aleutian Trench had begun to form in early- to mid-Cainozoic time, and the Java Trench is thought from the neighbouring stratigraphy to have existed in the late-Miocene period. Conceivably, trenches in existence earlier have experienced strong Plio-Pleistocene rejuvenation continuing into modern time (*cf.* rift valleys).

Island arcs and trenches do not, of course, occur independently. Not only are they juxtaposed but their geologic developments are closely interrelated. Perhaps the best interpretation would be that the arcs represent originally Cretaceous deeps that were filled with sediment, later lithified and elevated into geanticlines and islands, while the present trenches are mostly of no earlier date than Pleistocene.

THE NORTH-WESTERN PACIFIC BASIN

The floor of the north-western Pacific (Fig. 250) is the deepest of all the main oceanic basins, part of it lying below −6,000 metres. The principal topographic features are the swells, furrows and basins aligned towards the west or west-south-west. They are generally 200-300 miles broad and many hundreds of miles long with a relief of the order of 1,000 metres. These undulations of the sea-floor are apparently in isostatic equilibrium, and may be cymatogenetic in origin. Few seamounts appear in the basins, they are mostly on the swells as though these were the seat of primary tectonic activity.

Seamounts, some piercing the surface, others deeply submerged, form the most conspicuous relief of the north-western Pacific Basin. Many are truly enormous, and from their conical form virtually all may be judged volcanic in origin, and probably basaltic in substance. This is demonstrably so for islands like Truk, but few confirmatory dredgings are available for those submerged. On Japanese Bathymetric Chart No. 6901 seamounts are seen to be distributed not at random but in groups. The Emperor Sea-mounts, for instance, form a chain of huge cones extending southward for a distance of 1,500 miles from the convergence of the Aleutian and Kamchatka trenches to the western end of the Hawaiian swell. Four of them exceed 5,000 metres relief and still remain deeply submerged; five have flat tops and may be classed as guyots.

On the more usual east-west lineation stands a broad zone of seamounts between Marcus Island and Wake Island in lat. 17°-21° N. This group rising from a swell, continues the trend of mid-Pacific seamounts from Hawaii along the Necker Rise all the way to the Bonin-Marianas trench system. These seamounts are submerged by 1,000 metres or more, yet several of them are flat-topped guyots capped by mid- and late-Cretaceous sediments. " Several sounding lines show that the southern margin of the Marcus-Wake group is terminated by an abrupt east-west escarpment which may mark a major fracture zone in the Pacific Basin " (Dietz 1953).

Immediately east of the Marianas Trench rise the Magellan Seamounts, a group including 14 major and about 20 minor cones curiously distributed in a semicircle 400 miles in diameter. The western members, connected by a continuous ridge and adjacent to the Trench are deeply submerged, the eastern are less so and three of them are guyots. The sea-floor basin enclosed by these seamounts is smooth and almost featureless.

The Marshall and Gilbert Islands are merely the visible members of a large assemblage of seamounts. All are coral islands and foundation rock is nowhere exposed, but all reveal the familiar conical volcanic form on the chart. Several guyots are present and the group covers a broad zone trending from north-west to south-east. The Caroline Islands are less thickly grouped, and most of the larger members lie along a line from the Yap Trench to the Marshall Islands.

Data fixing the ages of Pacific seamounts are difficult to obtain. The development of volcanic mountain chains on land is usually confined to a short span of geologic time and the dating of one gives a general clue to the others. The same is probably true of volcanic seamounts. Fossiliferous sediments of mid-Cretaceous age from the summits of guyots on the Necker Ridge thus probably give the general age of seamounts along the zone from Marcus Island to Hawaii (Deitz 1953); and Hess (1948) on the basis of structural relations has suggested a late-Cretaceous age for the northernmost of the Emperor guyots. Drilling on Eniwetok Atoll in the Marshall Islands has encountered Eocene sediment in contact with olivine basalt foundation at 4,154 feet indicating there a very early Cainozoic age. The youngest group, on the evidence, is the Carolines where deeply submerged guyots are unknown and volcanic islands (Truk, Ponape and Kusaie) persist. In the absence of Miocene fossils Hanzawa (quoted by Dietz) considers these islands a result of Pliocene volcanism.

Deep-sea sediments of the north-western Pacific Basin are both terrigenous and pelagic. Blue, grey and green muds cover the shelf areas and basin floors down to depths of 4,000 metres. Volcanic detritus is strongly admixed, or even dominant, on the island-bearing ridges and in several of the trenches. Calcareous muds and sands, on the other hand, invest the flanks of atolls and other coasts where little terrigenous waste is supplied. But farther out in the ocean basins pelagic sediments are typical including inorganic red clay and globigerina, radiolarian, diatom and pteropod oozes. Red clay covers most of the bottom in depths below 4,000 metres, giving way to oozes on the swells, and towards warmer tropical waters.

THE SOUTH-WESTERN PACIFIC QUADRANT

The fourth quadrant of the Pacific Basin (Fig. 250) is quite different from the other three in that it is replete with submerged ridges and islands many of which display continental affinities in their geology. Only eastward of the New Zealand-Tonga line is the oceanic basin of importance and there the usual east-west trend of Pacific sea-floor topography is evident.

Virtually all the island groups of the south-western quadrant fall landward of the Andesite Line, and several (Fiji, New Caledonia, and New Zealand) exhibit thick formations of sedimentary type. The bottom topography, of very broad submarine plateaus and ridges, is very different from the normal Pacific floor. Making a far-flung series of outworks about eastern and northern Australia, these ridges create the impression of a dismembered former landmass. But before we can discuss this concept further data must be reviewed.

Though remote, the Carolines are possibly the northernmost integrals of the quadrant. The islands are Pliocene volcanic seamounts (p. 644), but they rise from a large swell and ridge and another major (Eauripik) swell (Fig. 238) unites the group with New Guinea and divides the east and west Caroline Seas like the minor seas of Southeast Asia. Hess has compared the bottom topography with the South Atlantic. From its geographic position, sited on the landward side of the Andesite Line, and the continuation of the swell with other parts of the island-rise complex within the south-west Quadrant (New Guinea and the Solomon Islands), the Carolines region may be regarded as indigenous within that quadrant, and extraneous both to Asia and the north-western Pacific Basin.

New Guinea is, of course, part of Australia. Its western relationships are intriguing for in New Guinea it impinges upon Indonesia where that arc doubles back upon itself between Ceram and Halmahera (Celebes) (Fig. 183). Such re-entrant structures as appear here cannot be fortuitous, and together they imply that a subcrustal current carried New Guinea into the broadly submerged platform of south-eastern Asia, which the subcrustal current also under-ran, at some date prior to the early Cainozoic (p. 479). The intrusive serpentines (Late Jurassic or Cretaceous) of Celebes, which are perhaps associated, are believed to be the largest occurrences of this rock yet explored.

The northern front of New Guinea bears the only part of the Cainozoic orogen now attached to the Australian continent (*sensu lato*), and Cretaceous and later sediments continue upon New Britain. The outer islands of the Bismarck, Solomon and New Hebrides groups are largely volcanic, of andesitic composition, but sedimentary rocks of Cainozoic age do occur. The north-western district of New Ireland, for instance " is composed of sedimentary rock possibly resting upon an older basement," and Guadalcanal has metamorphosed schists penetrated by serpentinised peridotite intrusions. Seemingly, these islands are not without continental affinity, and the two larger islands of Fiji also possess central cores of plutonic and sedimentary rocks (including red sandstones and quartzites, shales and granular limestones) overlain by more than one younger series of marine strata which have partaken of folding and which resemble folded beds of presumed Miocene age (Mawson) in New Hebrides. Structural linkage between Fiji and New Hebrides is provided by the submerged Hunter Ridge.

The structure of the Bismarck-Solomon-New Hebrides island groups is remarkable (Fig. 240). The main double chain of the Solomon Islands from Bougainville to San Cristobal (Fig. 202) carries its volcanism upon the inner, southerly line of islands

(Grover 1958); but it is paralleled upon the north by the coral and volcanic garland from Lord Howe Atoll to Santa Cruz Island. Ultrabasic intrusives, associated with sub-parallel fault zones, are arranged *en échelon* upon Guadalcanal, Choiseul, Florida, Santa Ysabel and San Cristobal, and some of these, particularly upon Santa Ysabel, " have probably suffered semi-continuous plastic intrusion up to the present. A provisional estimate of the age of initial emplacement is upper Oligocene—the same for all the islands on which they have been found " (Coleman *et al*. 1965). Upon the southern side (landward with respect to Australia) a series of trenches plunges to great depths in the ocean floor; the structure is therefore like that of an east Asiatic island arc *in reverse* (even the deeper focus earthquakes occur upon the Pacific, not the landward, side).* Indeed all three island festoons are linear or appear arcuate with the convexity towards the south or south-west (Fig. 241). The trenches are, however, conspicuously straight except for sharp right-angled bends between New Britain and Bougainville, and San Cristobal and Santa Cruz respectively; and a further straight trench in the East Caroline Sea has an extraordinarily steep side, 15,000 feet high, presumed by Hess (1938) to be a fault-scarp. Provisionally, all these trenches may be classed as megashears like the Bartlett Trench of the Caribbean region, and as such play an important rôle in the tectonics of the region eastward of New Guinea Fig. 201). Hess and Maxwell (1953) have also postulated a transcurrent fault offsetting the belt of Cretaceous-Cainozoic orogeny between New Hebrides and Fiji (Fig. 240).

At Fiji the high submarine ridge upon which stand the 250 islands of the group is hook-shaped and bent sharply southward to unite with the Tonga-Kermadec-New Zealand ridge. Both the Tonga and Kermadec island chains are largely of volcanic origin, though the Island of Eua is thought to have a plutonic base and to represent, with the islands and reefs from Va Va'u to Tongatapu, the coralline non-volcanic arc (Raitt *et al*. 1955). This is the Cretaceous-Cainozoic orogenic girdle found also in New Zealand through the East Cape-Gisborne region.

The geologic status of New Zealand has long been assessed as a continental island the visible structure being chiefly of isoclinally folded Trias-Jura greywackes the volume of which is much too great to have been derived from the islands and adjoining submarine ridges. A source highland must be sought beyond the present confines of New Zealand. The structures of the greywackes are related to the continuous Norfolk Island-New Caledonia-Papua submarine swell. Nowadays, two parallel ridges upon this swell shoal to less than 1,000 metres and break surface in the islands of New Caledonia and Lord Howe. The former represents the ruins of the Mesozoic fold-girdle of Australasia, the latter appears to be part of the belt of Palæozoic orogeny still extant upon the east Australian mainland and on the western aspect of the South Island of New Zealand (Fig. 175).

---

* The structure of the Solomons is not truly that of an island arc in reverse, but is due to linear folding and faulting accompanied by megashearing. Its seismic characteristics, too, are those of the Pacific circumvallation rather than an island arc.

On the northern side of the swell lie several deep-sea basins that resemble in form and geological setting the Sulu, Celebes and Banda sea-basins that stand within the margin of the South-east Asian Platform, and like them seem to be tensional basins induced by withdrawal westwards of major landmasses.

Australian geologists, long pondering the origin of the successive island-capped ridges and the deep-sea basins between them, have argued the disappearance of part

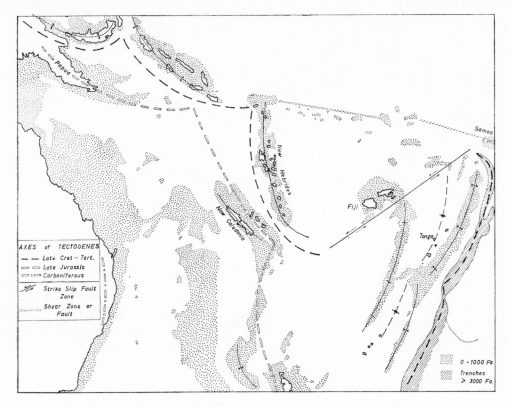

FIG. 240. Major structures of the south-western quadrant of the Pacific region. *after H. H. Hess and J. C. Maxwell.*

of the Australian landmass to the east, possibly by foundering. Hereupon the nature of the Tasman sea-floor is crucial, and has been the subject of geophysical study by Officer (1955) who concluded, " The crustal thickness of the Tasman Basin . . . is the same, five to ten km., as that for the south Pacific Basin to the east of New Zealand. The thickness of the East Cape-Kermadec-Tonga Ridge bordering the south Pacific Basin on the west and that of the Lord Howe Rise bordering the Tasman on the north-east is 36 km. A crustal refraction profile over New Zealand gives a thickness of 20 km. The interior region of ridges and troughs, north-east of New Zealand has an average thickness of 15-20 km. The results are indicative of an origin from successive orogenic

belts built out over an oceanic crust. The area is not part of an extensive continent ".
So there is no foundered continent, but how are such " successive orogenic belts " to
be built up in mid-ocean?

The solution is provided by a westerly withdrawal of Australia from a former

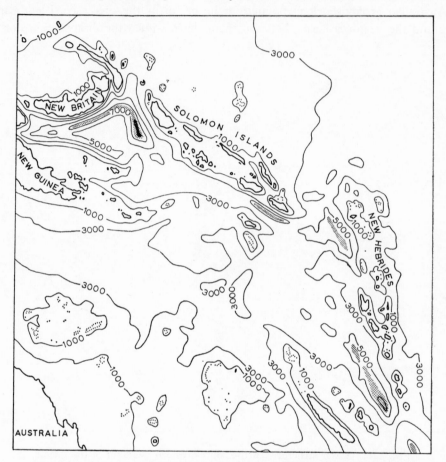

FIG. 241. Island arcs of the Bismarck-Solomon-New Hebrides region on
which the convexity of the volcanic and non-volcanic arcs and the
oceanic trenches are situated upon the *continental* side of the insular
garlands. Depth of earthquake foci also increases progressively on the
oceanic side. These are reversals of the order normal in east Asiatic arcs.

easterly situation defined by the outer arc of islands, leaving behind first its peripheral
zone which became locally bent (Fiji) and offset between New Guinea and the Solomon
Islands and between the Solomons and New Hebrides in the process. This series of
ridges thus may represent the most easterly position of the Australasian landmass on its
eastward drift from Gondwana as it rotated and curled westwards to impinge against
the promontory of South-east Asia (Figs. 183, 247). In mid-retreat it peeled off also

its eastern Mesozoic fold-girdle with Palæozoic foundation (Macpherson 1946) represented by the Louisiade-New Caledonia and Lord Howe-New Zealand double ridge.
Here are the lost portions of eastern Australia, and Bryan even notes that " New Caledonia
has all the appearance of being an outlier of the main Australian mass. It fits perfectly
into the geological picture " with an ancient north-easterly strike in schists like that of
the opposed Queensland coast. The New Zealand Alpine fault, of appropriate age
though still active, may also record part of the dislocations. Newer fold trends are, of
course, north-north-westward. Nowadays the area between Australia and the island
chains is seismically stable (Bryan 1944). What then would have been the date of the
movements envisaged?

Apparently the great bulk of Trias-Jura greywackes and argillites of the New
Zealand-New Caledonia ridge was derived from the Lord Howe Rise and adjacent
Australia, unified at that date. There are no Triassic or Jurassic marine faunas in
eastern Australia. But after the end of the Mesozoic " the various portions of
Australasia ceased to have any striking unity of geological history " (Benson 1923).
Instead, " at the beginning of the Tertiary era there were then, in the Australian region,
a number of independent geographical units which, by that time, appear to have achieved
some geological independence as well " (Bryan 1944). Despite the geographic propin-
quity, also, Cainozoic faunas of Australia and New Zealand are remarkably distinct, so
that the present distribution of continental matter in the south-east Pacific Quadrant
was plainly assumed during the Cretaceous period. Quaternary foundering along the
eastern coast of Australia has nothing to do with the basining of the Tasman Sea, nor
even in Queensland does it extend beyond the Great Barrier Reef into the Coral Sea
Basin.

Standard (1961), who considered that " The Tasman Basin is not, and never has
been, a part of the Australian continent " recorded also that seamounts and guyots, of
volcanic origin, were common in the Tasman Basin. Three of them show a relief of
more than 14,000 feet, shoaling to between 69 and 150 fathoms. " The shoalest guyot,
Taupo Bank, is thought to be Pleistocene, whereas the deeper guyots, Barcoo and
Derwent Hunter, are thought to be mid- to late Tertiary ".

Eastward of the Kermadec-Tonga submarine ridge and extending to Christchurch
(Fig. 179) is a Quaternary trench that descends 10,000 metres below sea level (Raitt
et al. 1955). It is extremely narrow, almost straight and topographically resembles the
Philippine Trench. Cross-sections through Tonga show the western flank typically
steeper, with increase of slope at greater depths except where seamounts constrict the
eastern flank. Capricorn seamount is very large and broadly bevelled in guyot fashion.
There appears to be little sediment, perhaps because the trench is far from large or
high-standing land masses. Associated earthquake foci are, as usual, progressively
deeper towards the island ridge on the west.

Beneath the Tonga Trench the Mohorovičić discontinuity sinks from its normal
south-west Pacific depth of 12km. to 20 km. in a distance of 50 km. Only at the

northern extremity does the trench curve westward towards the Wallis Islands, thereby avoiding Samoa which otherwise would stand directly in its path. Notwithstanding, other structures stand upon the farther side of Samoa that continue the strike of the Tonga Trench for another 2,000 miles, almost to Hawaii. These structures are: an eastward-facing scarp that passes closely east of Swain's Island, the Hilgard deep (7,316 metres) off the Phoenix Islands in mid-Pacific, an offset that cuts directly across the Line Islands beyond Kingman Reef, and a further linear deep half-way between that reef and Hawaii. Except for the interruption at Samoa this is probably the longest rectilinear structure in the earth's crust, extending north-north-east for 4,000 miles in all. Any origin other than by shear seems inconceivable, yet nothing is known of sub-crustal forces that might have produced it.

THE PACIFIC REALM

The immense realm of the Pacific Basin is almost completely engirdled by lands or island festoons the grain of which parallels the margins of the basin. In this it contrasts with the disruptive outlines and truncated structures of most other oceanic basins. It has a marine Mesozoic girdle and predominant Jurassic-Cretaceous marginal orogeny, not found elsewhere on the globe, that conveys an impression of Mesozoic unity around the whole tectonic framework. Lesser-Cainozoic circumvallation and present day volcanism and high seismicity continue the impression of uniformity around the Pacific Basin into Recent time. Yet the uniformity is in many ways more apparent than real and all four quadrants differ markedly, as we have seen, from one another.

In nothing does the western aspect of the Pacific differ so much from the eastern as in the abundance of island festoons and minor seas with marginal deep trenches that occupy an ever-widening zone from Kamchatka and Japan to New Zealand. Contemplation of a modern chart of this vast region creates in the observer an indelible impression of repeated ridge and basin as though these were the subtrahends left on the withdrawal westwards of the Asiatic and Australian continents. The larger of these belts from which more sediment was available (*e.g.* New Zealand) have been sites of Cainozoic mountain-making far out in the ocean, the smaller had more restricted evolution (*e.g.* Marianas Arc).

Conversely the Americas, pressing into the Pacific on the east, have welded their Palæozoic and Mesozoic island arcs (known in the cordilleran structures) firmly on to the continental masses and have developed a semi-continuous belt of Cainozoic mountain structures near the shore. The manner in which the western side of North America has apparently ridden over the northern segment of the East Pacific Ridge (Menard 1960) is surely one of the greatest geological discoveries of recent years.

Several of those apparent movements about the Pacific margins are dated by stratigraphy as Cretaceous or late Mesozoic, though some were foreshadowed as early as Permian. Within the oceanic basin no rocks older than Cretaceous are known. The

Cretaceous was also the date at which the outlines of the Atlantic, Arctic and Indian oceans were first prescribed by fracturing, and those oceanic basins were opened by continental drift. It is, perhaps, somewhat surprising to find great ocean basins so recently generated but the stratigraphic and tectonic evidence leaves little room for doubt; and the Pacific realm at least affords evidence of contemporary changes of great magnitude leading to the assumption of its modern form. Changes since the late Mesozoic have been relatively slight. All this corresponds with topographic changes upon the lands and calls for synthesis upon a global scale.

PART F

REVIEW

CHAPTER XIX

TOWARDS A MODEL OF THE EARTH

The Enquiry. From Surface Data. Cymatogeny and Isostatic Anomalies. The Suboceanic Ridge System and Modern Global Tectonics. The Time Factor. The Source of Crustal Activity. The Nature of the Subcrust. The Rôle of Occluded Volatiles. Some Evidence from Volcanism. The Atmosphere and Hydrosphere. The Last Word.

THE ENQUIRY

Our review of the earth's surface features has shown how many of them are dependent upon tectonic forces for the creation of new states. This being so, the research must now be directed to the definition of fundamental forces available within the earth to produce the crustal phenomena with which preceding chapters have made us familiar. These phenomena include continental drift and megashears with a hundred miles or more of horizontal displacement, vertical movements within the earth's crust as represented by epeirogeny, cymatogeny and orogeny (both local and world-wide in a short time dimension), volcanism and igneous intrusion, and the characteristic metamorphism of deep-seated rocks. The general nature and behaviour of continents and ocean basins needs to be contrasted with special features such as island arcs and great submarine ridges, if these have not already received explanation when reviewed in the text. The whole vast synthesis of the earth's surface and subsurface is now before us requiring activation; what we need is a functioning model of the globe.

Already in the first chapter were indicated, under the title " Dead Wood ", some current beliefs of wide acceptance that have outstayed their leave as geological opinions : a cooling and shrinking earth, imaginary continents, growing continents, migrating island arcs, and the permanence of continents and ocean basins were some of these. With much humility and awareness of our own fate that must follow in due course, we in turn pursue the enquiry " What makes the earth's crust *work*? " on a non-cooling, non-shrinking, non-expanding earth, without omnipresent tangential compression in its outer layers, and probably lacking significant addition of continental matter throughout geologic time : in other words, on an uniformitarian earth just as the geological evidence indicates it to have been ever since geologic time began (as we wrote on page 1).

FROM SURFACE DATA

All classes of topographic and geologic data from every realm of the earth's surface emphasise the ubiquity and persistence in time of radial (vertical) tectonic elevations and depressions of the earth's surface. Where movements involving lateral translation of earth materials do occur, they are due primarily to gravitational stresses self-induced in super-elevated crustal masses.* Radial, or vertical, displacement therefore appears to be the most common and fundamental activity of the planetary crust, and our first enquiry must be directed to ascertaining more clearly the nature of its accomplishment and underlying cause. For this purpose the simplest regions for study are the great crustal arches or cymatogens of which such numerous modern examples have been adduced in the text. Cymatogeny affects both shield areas and earlier orogenic welts alike, and in suitable geosynclinal environments could itself conceivably pass over into orogeny. It is also a likely underlying cause of certain of the sub-oceanic ridges as we see them today.

Notwithstanding the general independence of cymatogeny and crustal composition implied above, which immediately suggests a subcrustal origin for the primary forces involved, the visible cores of many of the greatest cymatogens (especially those which have been rejuvenated at intervals during geologic time) are characterized by extensive belts of coarse-grained, quartzo-feldspathic (microline) gneisses with parallel, steeply-inclined lamination. These gneisses are non-magmatic; they are devoid of pegmatites, pneumatolytic ore deposits and commonly also of granitisation effects. *They are purely tectonic in origin*, caused by steeply-inclined laminar movements in a confined crust associated with production of fresh minerals of low-temperature formation (commonly 450°-600° C). The mineral transformations may be brought about by diffusion in the solid: (a) through voids in the crystal lattices, (b) from one lattice point to another within the crystal, and (c) along the boundaries of closely-packed crystal grains. This characteristic facies, found in the Natal, Angola, Mt. Kosciusko, Rio de Janeiro and many other rejuvenated monoclines, demonstrates the mechanism of cymatogeny at intermediate depth, corresponding to surface warpings involving thousands of feet of vertical displacement over widths sometimes of hundred of miles.

Of course, the gneisses now exposed at surface do not correspond with Quaternary flexings but with earlier movements upon closely similar axes, for cymatogeny is a phenomenon that may be repeated from age to age, back even into Precambrian time, as Dixey has shown in Zambia.†

---

* This does not apply to continental drift or the megashears of continents and oceanic basins which may reflect differential " streaming " in the sub-crust.

† Without ruling out the likelihood of renewed sub-crustal activity as being responsible for repeated cymatogeny along earlier established lines, isostatic recovery along denuded axes combined with a tendency to sink in depressions loaded with sediment would itself tend to renew cymatogenic displacements at the surface—with fresh formation of gneisses at appropriate depths.

If it seems strange to " hard-rock " geologists that superficial causes involving erosion and deposition could in this way influence rock metamorphism deep within the crust, may we remind them that heat energy received from the sun is more than 5,000 times the heat lost at the surface by conduction from the earth's interior, and that therefore much more energy is available " above " than " below " the zone of mineral transformation.

The geostatic load theory of igneous intrusion (p. 24) likewise relates such events, even at the greatest depths, to relatively superficial changes of load on the earth's crust ! It may further be no accident that the mightiest system of continental accumulation known—the Karroo-Gondwana system (Chapter II)—is everywhere, and simultaneously, terminated in five continents by the largest known complex of basic dykes and sills and the greatest effusions of basaltic lava.

Important to note is that these gneissic belts show few or no traces of lateral compression or " crustal shortening ". Some have associated tensional rift valleys. Most of the laminar displacements have, with due regard for heterogeneity in the original materials, been nearly vertical, or radial with respect to the globe.

The number of active laminae in such a gneiss may be very large and the differential movement upon each lamina very small. With a laminar thickness of perhaps a quarter inch which is fairly typical of gneisses (over a quarter of a million laminae per mile)

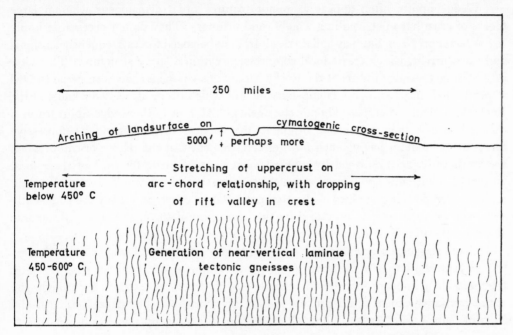

FIG. 242. Diagrammatic crustal section through a typical continental cymatogen relating major arching and rifting of the surface to formation of tectonic gneisses at intermediate crustal depth. Displacements are in the vertical sense only. At great depth, levitated mantle (pp. 664, 672) may be the active agent of the cymatogen.

very great displacement can be achieved over the hundred miles or more which is the normal breadth of a cymatogenic arch. Thus for a surface tilt of one degree the differential movement on each lamina need be less than one two-hundredth of an inch; but cumulative displacement of the surface would amount to 9,000 feet in 100 miles.

Arguing from comparison with bedded rocks which are laid down horizontally and have thereafter been folded and even steeply inclined under the action of tectonic forces, geologists have widely accepted that the characteristically steep lamination of gneisses implies great displacement of rock masses. But if, as is suggested, the near-vertical lamination is a metamorphic structure developed in that attitude, no great

2 T

displacement is implied; a vertical gneiss is almost as undisturbed as a horizontal sediment. To measure angular displacements we must use the dip for sediments, the hade for gneisses.

Of tectonic significance also are the extrusions of basic rocks, sometimes accompanied by dike swarms, upon several coastal monoclines with gneissic cores: western India, eastern Greenland, south-east Africa, and south-eastern Australia. Their rise certainly implies contemporaneous tension, not compression, in the crust.*

Wedge uplifts often appear as minor features upon cymatogens wherein large blocks of crust have behaved in a wholly rigid manner. They do not necessarily imply regional compression, but may and do result from unbalanced forces, frequently tensional and transcurrent, which create local compression within a larger structure. This view is applicable to wedge uplifts of the Rocky Mountains—northern Bighorn, western Owl Creek massif, Beartooth and Phillipsburg—all of which occur at bends or knots in the Rocky Mountain structure. Thom's statement: " All four of the wedge-uplift features referred to owe their immediate origin to the application of tangential compressive forces to rock bodies having such form or arrangement that the release of compression was most easily accomplished by upward movement " is true for each of these local occurrences but does not require a general compression of the whole Rocky Mountain region. Nor do wedge uplifts of the Basin and Range province. They are sufficiently explained as minor effects produced by the overriding of the East Pacific sub-oceanic Ridge by Western North America (p. 631).

Upon exaggeration cymatogeny passes over into orogeny. Clay model experiments by Gzovsky show that in addition to a rift valley high upon the arch, deep-reaching fractures then appear beneath the flanks. Such fractures extending through the entire crustal thickness could provide passageways for the ascent of peridotite (maybe in twin belts: see Belussoff 1960, Pl. 1, Fig. 2) and orogeny then really gets under way.

This is perhaps the place to formulate a definition of cymatogeny: Cymatogeny is a mode of major vertical (radial) deformation of the earth's crust wherein the fundamental structure induced at intermediate depths is a steeply inclined tectonic gneiss, with or without minor igneous activity, which is usually basic only. At the earth's surface it is expressed by arching sometimes thousands of feet in height and hundreds of miles in width. Rift valleys due to tension, and wedge uplifts due to unbalanced forces, are frequent minor attributes.

Cymatogeny has been the characteristic tectonic activity of late-Cainozoic and

---

* More remarkable still is the association of alkaline rocks both potassic and sodic, with rift valleys and cymatogens. Lava floods are backed also by carbonatite centres, many with cores of primary carbonate, of which a modern eruptive example is Ol Doinyo Lengai in Tanganyika. Clearly the alkalis of the carbonatite magma leak into the walls on the way up so that the residue consists increasingly of $CaCO_3$, but what is the source of the original carbon dioxide? Is it among the volatiles occluded in the mantle? Carbonatites seem to be much more abundant in Africa than elsewhere and are " strikingly more numerous during the last 200 million years than at any previous time ". This relative abundance may be not unconnected with the break up and subsequent cymatogenesis of Gondwanaland (p. 674).

Quaternary time, and its effects are apparent now in the most striking scenery of our planet. Its primary source of energy is still to be sought—below, in the substratum or upper mantle (p. 669).

CYMATOGENY AND ISOSTATIC ANOMALIES

Curious results sometimes accrue from a comparison of cymatogenic and isostatic data. A well-studied cymatogen is the Natal Monocline (p. 246), a marginal flexure that originated at the close of the Jurassic and has been rejuvenated at intervals since. The latest rejuvenation occurred about the beginning of the Pleistocene period when on the landward side a late-Cainozoic erosional surface was elevated to 5,000 feet above sea level, and the early-Cainozoic surface to 1,000 feet above that (Figs. 95, 96) (King and King 1959).

Gravity anomalies (Bouguer) within the region are marked and follow the Quaternary deformation so closely as to leave no doubt that the two sets of phenomena are inter-related (Figs. 96, 243). The axis of no anomaly passes inland of the slightly drowned coast where positive anomalies appear, and the negative anomalies increase progressively inland until the zone of maximum upwarp (Great Escarpment) is reached. In Zululand the trends of both topographic and isostatic contours change together from north-east to north. There can be no question: the gravity anomalies are linked not with the distribution of crustal rock masses but with the Quaternary deformation.

In eastern Australia, also a recently cymatogenic region, Marshall and Narain (1954) made a gravity survey and interpreted the anomalies in orthodox terms of crustal structure (batholiths) (Fig. 244). But the data appear to be equally well explained (Fig. 245) by correlation with the known Quaternary cymatogenic deformation of that area (Figs. 138, 139; p. 355). Specifically, (a) the steep gradient to −40 milligals behind Cairns corresponds to the exceptionally steep uplift to the Atherton Tableland, (b) the −50 to −60 anomalies north-westwards from Roma correspond with the zone of high ground probably produced by Pleistocene warping, (c) the −70 anomalies over the New England highlands about Armidale and the −50 milligals over the Jenolan area correspond with highs on the Pleistocene Kosciusko cymatogeny just as much as they do to granite masses, (d) Mount Kosciusko, where the gradient is from +50 at Bega to −50 near the mountain, is another Pleistocene topographic high, (e) the elevated region between Broken Hill and Cobar, evidently of Pleistocene arching, shows anomalies down to −40 milligals, and (f) the West Victoria highlands record strong elevation of late date again with marked negative anomalies.

On the gravity anomaly map of the United States the coastal monocline of California, broken by faults though it is, displays a set of isograds like those of Natal, and many recent uplifts such as the Uinta Range, the Bighorn Mountains and the western Sierra Nevada are also expressed clearly in the gravity data.

All these, and many other, observations introduce into geophysical interpretation a new principle: that departures from the isostatic state often appear related not to crustal rock composition, as is demonstrable in certain instances (*e.g.* Trompsburg subjacent basic body) and as has been assumed generally, but to *recent crustal deformation* of

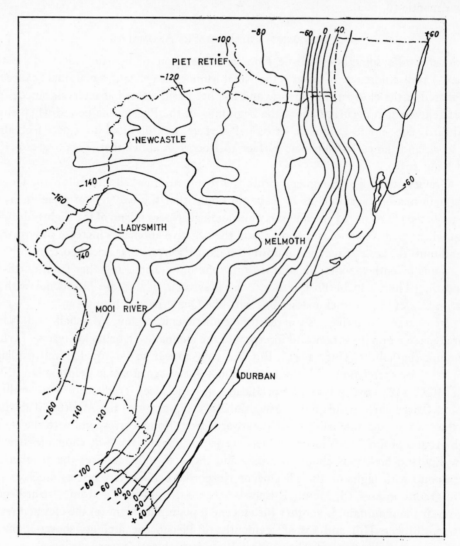

FIG. 243. Gravity anomalies (Bouguer) over the Natal Monocline showing the close relationship between the anomalies and deformation of the land-surface during Quaternary time (Figs. 95, 96). The pattern of anomalies bears no direct relationship to the geological constitution of Natal. *Republic of South Africa Geological Survey.*

cymatogenic type, which argument takes us back to the discussion (Chapter IV) on the physical nature of tectogenes and whether they are sited in the crust or subcrust. For if, in at least some instances, gravity anomalies are independent of crustal composition, then the cymatogens to which they *are* related may well be controlled from the sub-crust* and the anomalies reside therein also.

Hence arises " a most ingenious paradox ". The negative anomalies which have been cited from Africa, Australia and America appear in association with the recently most elevated strips of country. All along the western Pacific margin, however, maximum negative anomalies are associated with deep oceanic troughs where profound depression has occurred into an oceanic floor known to be of minimal thickness ! The troughs are also of very recent origin, so once again observed negative anomalies seem to be independent of crustal rock composition but are directly related to recent, maximal crustal deformation, though in the opposite sense in sectors of continental and oceanic nature !† The isostatic state, after due allowance for local abnormalities, is related not to crustal composition but to crustal *mobility*. Surely the cause of such anomalies which are so clearly modern and tectonic in type, should reside not in the crust—but in the subcrust. Anomaly belts can even be found passing from beneath a trench to beneath a ridge *e.g.* Puerto Rico Trench to Barbados Ridge. Structures continue, the negative anomaly zone wanders beneath.

This throws further grave doubt upon both the " constitutional " and " survival " aspects of formerly suspected " roots of mountains ". As an example: to explain extensive negative anomaly fields recorded from Ontario (Garland 1950) and Quebec (Innes 1957) upon suggested sites of Precambrian mountain chains, both authors invoked " roots of mountains " preserved even from a thousand million years ago ! The latter area at least experienced relatively recent uplift, as attested by the attitudes of its Cainozoic landsurfaces (p. 371) and a reappraisal of these gravity anomalies on a basis of *recent* tectonics might provide an interesting conclusion.

For good measure we now record from Ewing and Ewing: " There are many areas in the world where there are large anomalies of one sign but no apparent vertical movements as would be required by isostatic balance ". These anomalies, too, surely reside *below* the crust—perhaps they are regions of potential tectonic and isostatic function.

THE SUBOCEANIC RIDGE SYSTEM AND MODERN GLOBAL TECTONICS

We are now due to take another look at the system of suboceanic ridges (p. 575), together with systems involving axial uplifts upon the lands. In Chapter XVI two fundamental

---

* But see footnote regarding rejuvenated cymatogens on p. 656.

† A similar observation is that Bouguer anomalies normally increase with depth of water offshore, but decrease inversely within the island-arc trenches.

Captions for Figures 244 and 245 on pp. 662 and 663:

FIG. 244. Gravity anomalies over eastern Australia, with orthodox interpretation in terms of crustal composition. *after C. E. Marshall and H. Narain.*

FIG. 245. Gravity anomalies over eastern Australia with tentative re-interpretation in terms of recent crustal warping.

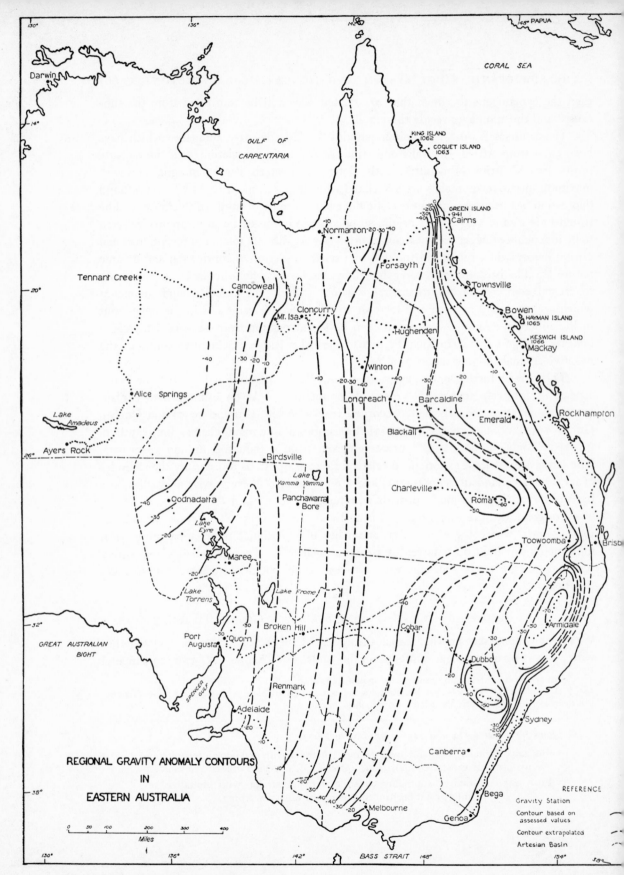

REGIONAL GRAVITY ANOMALY CONTOURS
IN
EASTERN AUSTRALIA

REFERENCE

Gravity Station

Contour based on
assessed values

Contour extrapolated

Artesian Basin

Fig. 244

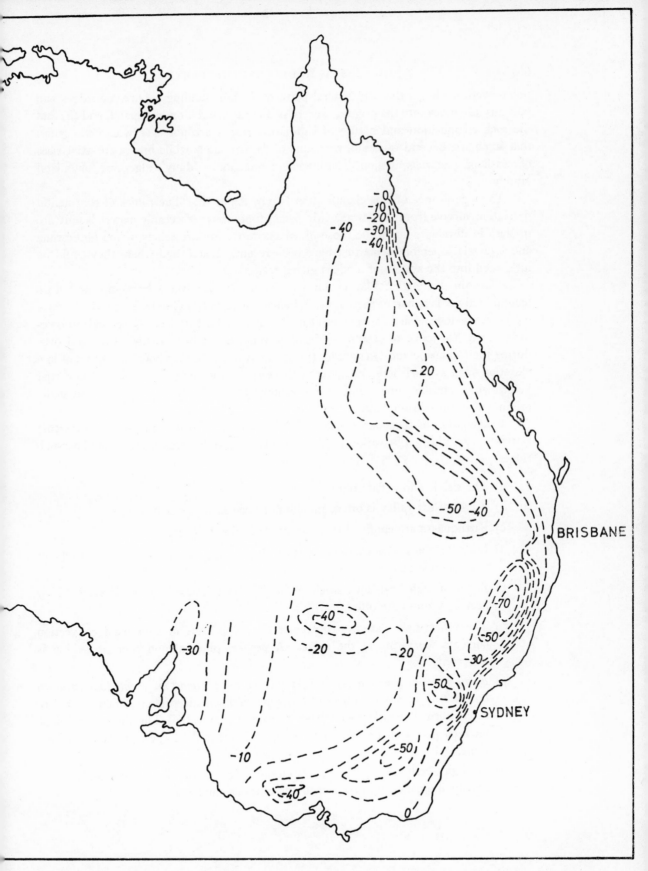

FIG. 245

points were made (a) that the general pattern of high-standing suboceanic ridges and plateaus integrates into the original pattern of Laurasia and Gondwanaland, and (b) that the rock composition and nature of submarine ridges are not everywhere the same: that some are, beyond question, remnants of former lands while others are axial rises of sea-floor materials without continental connection. Many ridges are of mixed affinity.

The significance of this classification is now apparent. The ridges of continental derivation survive from Gondwana (Mesozoic) time, those of oceanic materials only are modern in development, while those of mixed derivation are relicts of the Gondwana and Laurasia supercontinents that have been recently reactivated where they could be integrated into the system of modern global tectonics.

Thus the Kerguelen Plateau survives from the Gondwana break-up, and little tectonic activity is apparent there now. Malagasy is equally a Gondwana survival whose modern cymatogenic activity matches that of adjacent East Africa. New Zealand owes little but its existence to events of Mesozoic time, it has been remade over and over during the Cainozoic and Quaternary (p. 475). While certain suboceanic ridges of low elevation such as Carlsberg and parts of the East Pacific Ridge probably did not exist before late Cainozoic time. They are presumed to be wholly of modern cymatogenic origin within the oceanic basins.

Examination of these latter ridges should yield a picture of modern cymatogenic activity uncomplicated by earlier geologic events. Many features are associated on such ridges:

a) The rise is a low, flat arch.

b) A crestal rift valley is often, though not necessarily, present.

c) Earthquakes are confined to a narrow zone along the crest.

d) Fracture zones often transect the ridge, and earthquakes are particularly frequent at such crossings.

e) Zones of high heat-flow, single or double, sometimes lie near the crest. Low heat-flow zones are often nearby.

f) These heat-flow patterns contradict the hypothesis of subcrustal convection currents separating at the ridge. A *vertical* phenomenon such as dyking is indicated.

g) *Earth-material of seismic velocity $7 \cdot 2$-$7 \cdot 6$ km./sec. is almost invariably found beneath the crests of suboceanic ridges of this type*, and seismic probes sometimes fail to reach normal mantle rock ($8 \cdot 1$-$8 \cdot 2$ km./sec.) beneath. The light, anomalous material may well be levitated mantle (p. 675) and be the active cause of the ridge.

h) Though nearly compensated, mid-ocean ridges sometimes have small positive gravity anomalies with respect to adjacent oceanic basins.

i) Like island arcs, which sometimes continue into orogenic welts upon the lands, some of the modern suboceanic ridges are collinear with modern continental cymatogens (with rift valleys or megashears) *e.g.* Carlsberg Ridge into Gulf of Aden.

A pattern of modern global tectonics is emerging from these data.

An older pattern has also emerged. The text has adduced a host of widely diverse geologic facts relating to the distribution of the present continents and oceanic basins and their major topographic features that find simple rational explanation in terms of the working hypothesis of continental drift. During the late-Palæozoic and Mesozoic eras this operated upon two parent super-continents, Gondwana and Laurasia, which are thought to have fragmented during the late Mesozoic with dispersal of the fragments to their present global positions as continents. Of Cainozoic drift we have found no clear evidence; but the existence, in both continental and oceanic sectors, of active megashears at the present day warns that appropriate forces may be building up again. With slices of the crust 600 miles in length (San Andreas) and not more than 20 or so miles in thickness affected, the inference is plain that subcrustal currents are implicated.

Particularly impressive is the stratigraphic unity in Gondwanaland of continental Palæozoic and Mesozoic formations thousands of feet thick in five continents and constituting in their undisturbed attitude the most widespread and magnificently displayed geological system on earth. The amazing diversities of lithology (and palæoclimatic implications) which the Gondwana-Karroo system clearly displays find rational solution by slow, majestic drift through a series of climatic girdles identical with those of the present day (Chapter II). Without this reassembly and drift the facts of southern hemisphere intercontinental stratigraphic geology remain random in space, if not also in time.

Continental drift is proved, if by the Gondwana-Karroo system alone, but our present problem is to unite with the fact of drift a motive force capable of bringing it about. Clearly the successive positions assumed by the continents are not controlled by merely superficial forces inherent in the continents themselves. The motive force must reside in an active substratum, capable at a maximum activity of floating the parent super-continents either separately or together to new positions in the net of meridians and parallels, and capable at least once in geologic time (and perhaps more then once for Laurasia) of disrupting both super-continents within a short period of geologic time and dispersing the continental fragments relatively rapidly to regions remote from each other by thousands of miles. Certain of these movements require also rotation of individual continental blocks that in Australia reaches a maximum of 90°. Some system of global convection, indeed, becomes necessary, at least for the times when drift is active though it is doubtful whether any simple system of convection cells with material rising beneath the mid-oceanic ridges and sinking beneath the continents (or the reverse !) is adequate. Rather a global system needs to be envisaged like Fig. 246 depicting atmospheric circulation for the month of July. Certainly the substratum must at times possess a mobility in the lateral sense that amounts to active fluidity.

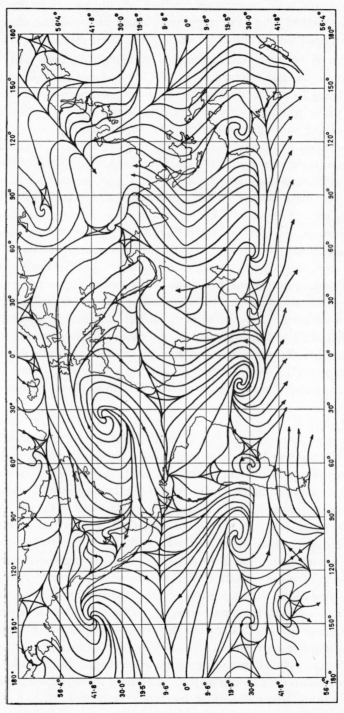

FIG. 246. An example of global convection. Atmospheric circulation during the
month of July. *after Mintz and Dean.*

Truly the commitments laid upon the substratum by continental drift are heavy, but inescapable. Indeed, a temptation exists for the geologist to reconstruct the movements involved in the mutual flight of the continents and to deduce therefrom the responsible system of global subcrustal currents for at least Mesozoic time (*e.g.* Fig. 247).

THE TIME FACTOR

Review of many classes of surface features through the preceding chapters cannot have failed to emphasize the essentially world-wide synchroneity of *major* tectonic events giving rise to new states through epeirogenesis, cymatogenesis, and orogenesis, coupled in some instances with volcanism, seismicity and other crustal activities.

Thus the sequence of major cyclic denudations upon all the continents alternating with episodes of elevation and mountain building (Chapters IX-XV), together with the relations of both phases, through coastal plain and shelf deposits, with major events in the oceanic basins, are not distributed haphazardly through geologic time but are in broad temporal conformity one with another.

This conclusion for the geologic past is confirmed for the present by Benioff's (1955) discovery from earthquake data that, *on a world basis*, " periods of high activity alternate with periods of relatively low activity. The singularity of this characteristic is interpreted as indicating that all shallow earthquakes of magnitude 8 and larger are somehow involved in a single tectonic system ".

Seen in such context, compression and tension in the earth's crust appear secondary upon global forces expressed radially within the earth-body. Both compression and tension arise simultaneously from, (a) heterogeneity of the crust with juxtaposition of materials with different physical properties, (b) deviations (curvature) of tectonic axes (folds and faults) in both horizontal and vertical dimensions, and (c) unequal application of fundamental subcrustal forces. This is so for all scales of magnitude from the opening and closing of an ore-body along a curvilinear fault to upcast block mountains such as Ruwenzori and whole orogenic zones like the Alps.

Orogenesis is then understood as a radial (or vertical) phenomenon, entirely independent of tangential (or lateral) phenomena such as continental drift. This is indicated also by temporal relations. Thus though westward drift of South America presumably took place (Chapter II) during most of the early part of the Cretaceous period, the Andes uplifts were not initiated until late in that period. Again, there is no geological evidence of continental drift during the Cainozoic era though orogenesis was then widespread.

Despite confusions introduced by local earth movements or heterogeneities of crustal structure, global tectonic control of many diverse phenomena is discernable. Only by global interpretation, indeed, does the pattern of local tectonic events become manifest and comprehensible, as Chapters IX-XVIII should have made clear.

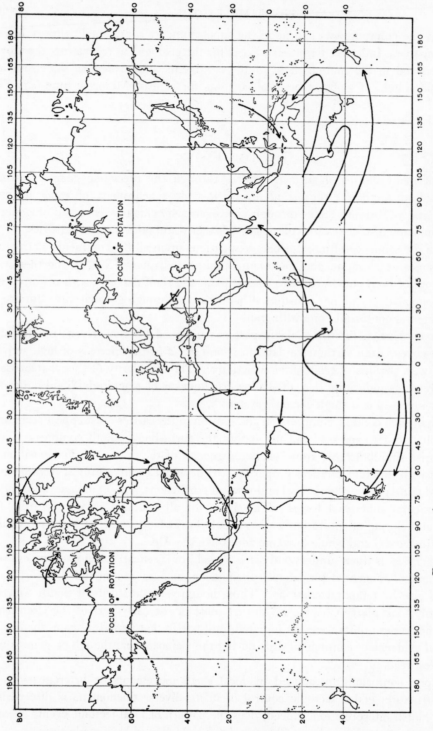

Fig. 247. Apparent movements of continental masses during the Cretaceous Period suggesting the existence of a system of subcrustal convection currents at that time. Lengths and directions of arrows show displacements.

Crustal rocks are mostly dead. In the solid state they may transmit stresses, dissipate stress by folding and fracturing, produce local stress by heterogeneity when a more general stress is applied; but they do not create stress.

Review of the surface features and their tectonic controls makes apparent, however, the existence of a major source of tectonic energy shallowly within the subcrust. This energy is manifested largely as heat; and the abundance of volcanic activity, with the levitation of vapour-charged serpentine and other magmatic bodies through the entire thickness of the crust, together with the abundance of pneumatolytic and hydrothermal effects in the depths of orogenic zones testify that the heat operates largely in conjunction with the water vapour which is probably an important agent conferring local mobility within the global crust. Indeed orogenic and cymatogenic zones may simply be zones of the crust weakened by access of intratelluric heat and volatiles (cf. Bucher's (1956) experiments), amplified in the former case by the pre-existing extreme weakness of geosynclinal sediments. These are basic assumptions with which we shall now work.

We may bear in mind that though stresses vary most in short term and at low temperatures, they are not ruled out even under pressures of 10,000 atmospheres and temperatures exceeding 1,000° C. that may be expected to exist at and below the "Moho" where it is deeply situated below continental masses. Evidently pressures necessary to deform rocks at depth are much less than has hitherto been supposed, especially if water vapour is present. But whereas " wetness " is generally conceded to reduce rigidity in discrete media, stress being transferred more and more to the fluid phase as the proportion of that phase increases, until the material becomes " quick ",—a converse phenomenon (dilatancy) exists when a small proportion only of the fluid phase is present interstitially (" dampness "). Rigidity in a medium of discrete particles may then *increase* (e.g. damp sand *vis-a-vis* dry sand). The importance of this phenomenon in relation to earthquakes originating deep within the mantle has recently been reported (Frank 1965). This is a field for research that opens up endless possibilities.

Furthermore, as Ramberg (1955) studying the thermodynamics and kinetics of petrogenesis has pointed out, " If a certain kind of process runs as an isolated event it generally starts relatively violently and then gradually quietens down as the driving force becomes exhausted and equilibrium is approached. This appears not to be true of many geologic processes, however, the violence of which is often cyclic. The reason is that the various kinds of geologic processes are intimately interconnected, hence progress in one process commonly creates potential energies which start or maintain other types of processes ".

As processes that may operate at depth, Ramberg quoted mechanical transport, chemical process, thermal transport process, electric transport process and nuclear process. Put another way, the variables of chemical potential, pressure, temperature, time and space interact with one another at depth; much of the energy released on the relaxation of time-dependent strain, for instance, appears as heat. Amid so many, and perhaps other, variables it may be difficult to provide an unambiguous solution to the problem of subcrustal activity. Nonetheless, accepting the view that the motive force for much, and especially local, crustal activity is sited in the subcrust, we now assemble some facts concerning the nature and behaviour of subcrustal material.

The Nature of the Subcrust

The properties and behaviour of subcrustal matter are not directly ascertainable by the human senses; and the data so far amassed by indirect physical exploration are scarcely comprehensive. From seismic wave velocities its density appears between 3·0 and 3·3. From continental temperature gradients its temperature below the Mohorovičić discontinuity may be estimated around 1,000° C. though modern estimates below the oceans give perhaps half of this. From certain plutonic intrusions, and by analogy with meteorites, its composition is thought to resemble that of ultramafic rocks. The implications of isostatic theory require that it should behave, over appreciable intervals of geologic time, as a fluid probably deforming in the solid state under rheidity. This is about all, and the picture it gives is of a heavy, inert or highly viscous medium in which continents could be suspended by flotation and whose response to stress is by slow laminar flow. A passive isostatic response to surface loading and unloading is about the only function assigned by some geological opinion to the subcrust. How correct is this picture? Possibly the subcrust is no more uniform and inactive than the ocean depths, formerly thought to be eternally quiet and still but now known to be the seat of powerful currents and internal waves. Indeed modern seismological evidence clearly shows that the upper part of the mantle (subcrust) varies in physical (and possibly mineral) nature from place to place. This heterogeneity is especially important as studies at the Geophysical Institute of Washington indicate that under high pressure mineralogical mutations may appear relatively rapidly.

At long time-intervals and under suitable orogenic conditions elongated masses of peridotite or serpentine irrupt the uppercrust, arriving apparently direct from the substratum. The action is violent, and involves (p. 112) an apparent contradiction. How does material now of density 3·3 rise continuously through superincumbent layers of density 3·0 to 2·7 and a score or more kilometres in thickness? Is it squirted up by deep, phenomenal pressures, or did it rise of its own volition because *temporarily* its density was less than 2·7? The phenomena of intrusion suggest that it is begun by the former and continued by the latter (p. 23).

Large-scale hydrothermal alteration of primitive peridotite to serpentine is characteristic of these intrusive belts and testifies the immense quantities of water vapour accompanying and released by these irruptions. There is no adequate source for this water on the way up through the lower crust, so seemingly it must have been occluded in the parent material *while it was still in the substratum.* Under the immense pressures prevailing at such depths the quantities of occluded vapour could be enormous. Shear, acting upon a sub-crustal medium in which vapours were thinly dispersed would cause concentration into distinct entities and enhance mobility, so long as the volatiles were not lost (pp. 669; 680). The activity responsible for the rise of peridotite belts through the continental crusts then becomes understandable in terms of geyser action of the air-lift pump. With weakening of the crust above by geosynclinal sedimentation, or perhaps rarely by unusual thinning under erosion, any initial impulse raising the vapour-charged subcrust brings it into a zone wherein pressure is lessened and water-vapour would tend to be released, which would lower the density still further. This enables the peridotite mass, generating its own energy like a rocket, to rise continuously upward. Every factor then conspires towards rapid and increasing rise, so long as further vapour be released. When the vapour is used up, or the surface is attained, the activity ceases, and hence the field observations that irruption is brief and is not repeated, and also that it accompanies an early stage of orogenesis, are confirmed in theory.

Towards, but significantly below the earth's surface, where temperatures fall below 500° C. (Bowen and Tuttle 1949), a brake is applied for serpentinization of the original peridotite, taking place according to the rule that hydrous minerals tend to form where temperatures are low and pressures still high, uses up the vapour in great quantity and limits any explosive activity.

Seemingly, accumulations of heavily occluded rock still below the crust could be detected at surface by negative gravity anomalies. Such anomalies have been interpreted hitherto by the postulation of " sialic roots ", supposed deep infolds of the crust down into subcrustal matter. But there are several instances where the " negative strip " does not coincide with the mountain ranges supposed to stand upon a sialic root. Notably the negative strip of Europe (p. 573) forsakes the Alps; and in isolated island festoons such as the Antilles or the Marianas Islands, which have anomalies approaching 150 milligals, the geologist is hard put to imagine any reasonable source of sial to form a root. On this basis the " sialic root " explanation of Airy and Vening Meinisz must fail, and the explanation of negative strips must be sought not in crustal but in subcrustal phenomena.

If this is so, then the conventional estimate of the subcrust as possessing great uniformity must apply only to very short time-intervals and considerable distances as are involved in the transmission of earthquake shocks; and our model of the earth in geologic time must conceive a substratum with local centres or belts of potentially high activity, and local large differences of density. Indeed, in attempting to gauge the activity of the substratum we must not think in terms of " rock of density 3·3 and a viscosity in the very high range " but of a medium in which both density and viscosity may and do have great local variation.

Considerable importance attaches therefore to certain areas in which, beneath the basaltic lower crust, are local developments of earth-materials with a seismic velocity of 7·0 to 7·9 km./sec. The wide range of velocity is noteworthy as indicating that the ̦materials are likely to be mixtures rather than entities with critical physical properties.

First discovered beneath California (Gutenberg) and later identified beneath several of the suboceanic plateaus and ridges where it appears to be standard (Heezen and Ewing), the material has been inferred by some authorities to be a dense basaltic root, but an alternative hypothesis now finding favour is that it is an anomalous levitated subcrust or activated upper mantle, for it always appears beneath regions of marked crustal and surface activity. Our mental picture visualizes it as mantle rock, locally charged with occluded volatiles under great pressure and in such quantity as to reduce its density and increase its mobility beyond certain critical levels, which may enable it to concentrate and rise.

Some occurrences may be potential serpentine belts or nascent tectogenes, others less charged or less favourably situated may cause cymatogeny along either modern suboceanic ridges (p. 579) or continental rift-valley belts. Some may merely abort. Iceland and Puerto Rico have thick subjacent accumulations, continental margins may have it (Bermuda) and it underlies Western North America extensively (Thompson and Talwani 1964). Always the regions are geomorphologically active. Arches, rifts, megashears and strong topographic contrasts are typically associated and the conviction grows that this material, levitated sub-crust or activated mantle, is the prime energy source of much major crustal deformation.

Its composition may be thought of as analogous to limburgite, reverting to normal mantle peridotite of velocity 8·1-8·2 km./sec. when the volatiles have been lost and the geomorphic activity is completed.* The density of limburgites is generally less than 2·9; they may be crystalline or partly glassy, and some contain nepheline, perhaps an indication of CO_2 in the volatile fraction. Silica percentages vary (as they do in basalts) from 42 to 50% with perhaps an optimum at 48%; but the silica percentage, which is dependent largely on the volatiles (p. 677) is probably less important than the " wetness " due to occluded water vapour. This " wetness " could indeed be the critical factor governing shearing and behaviour of subcrustal materials. With solid and fluid states co-existing like crystals and mesostasis in a lava, resultant activity could range from elastic rigidity to spontaneous liquifaction or to dilatancy (Frank 1965).

Of further interest are the experiments by Vinogradov (1964) on the zonal melting of stony meteorites whose composition of " silicate (chondrules), iron sulphide (troilite), chromites, and carbonaceous and phosphide phases " is considered to be like that of the earth's mantle. The material was heated in a narrow zone to 1,500° C. and then the heater moved slowly in one direction. " During this procedure, materials reducing fusion transfer to the liquid, whilst those raising fusion remain in the solid phase ". . . " The easily fusible phase . . . solidified as a glassy basaltic mass . . . The unmelted

* As beneath the granite-gneiss belts of old cymatogens (Fig. 242).

phase was dunite with large columnar olivine crystals ". Silica formed in the process migrates from the dunite fraction where it originates into the easily-fusible phase. This gives a very clear picture of expectable processes in a mantle of originally stony meteorite composition.

Furthermore, " complete melting is unnecessary in zonal fusion. The liquid, easily fusible phase of the mantle traverses a long diffusion path and continually changes its composition as it becomes enriched with different constituents from the unlimited volume of the mantle ". These processes are deemed to originate at depths of 800-900 km.—close to the region of deep-focus earthquakes.

Changes are associated with temperature maxima or pressure minima. Noting that " a great rôle was played by H_2O ", with which the volatiles HCl, S, $B(OH)_3$, and CO_2 were associated, Vinogradov noted that " very little sulphur was degassed and this remains an enigma ". We note (p. 682) that most of it is apparently trapped as sulphide ores, particularly pyrites, in the earth's crust.

Lastly, the facility with which supercooled lavas are known to flow at temperatures well below the normal melting range is an indication that, at depth too, shearing by internal movement or by earth shocks from external sources could exercise greater effect upon crystallization of magma bodies than slow cooling. Such crystallization would be rapid throughout the magma body (p. 680).

THE RÔLE OF OCCLUDED VOLATILES

The serpentine belts provide first-hand evidence of the abundance of water vapour occluded in subcrustal matter for the transformation from olivine to serpentine requires the presence of 13 per cent. of water, representing an immense volume of vapour. Locally this must alter both the density and viscosity of subcrustal matter and render the substratum non-homogeneous. If fluxing with water vapour could lower the viscosity to the point where non-laminar flow, involving turbulence, is possible many other consequences could follow. Basaltic lava flows, both in the field and in micro-section, certainly exhibit turbulent structures, and both serpentine belts and kimberlite pipes are brecciated and have sometimes been highly explosive. It is therefore not to be supposed that turbulence could not develop in heavily-occluded subcrustal matter; and turbulence means the presence of mighty forces of rapidly changing application.*

In this connection a principle of special importance is that while water vapour might diffuse and distribute itself so that the chemical potential was the same throughout there would be a tendency to concentration in regions of lowest pressures and temperatures. Thus the partial pressure could be the same throughout the subcrustal host but the quantity of water would be very different from point to point (Kennedy 1955).

Also, according to Daly (1933) an increase of water content from 0 per cent. to

* Orshear: see " swimming bath illustration " (p. 130).

2 U

7 per cent. would lower the melting point of a basic magma from 1,100° C. to 600° C. and thus generate fluidity at temperatures well below those required for dry melts. According to Tomkeieff dolerite pegmatites indicate " wet patches in the magma "; and Frankel found 3 per cent. to 8 per cent. water in Karroo dolerite glass. True, volcanic glasses in the weathered zone often absorb water, but here fluxes Cl' and SO4" were also present. Goranson melted granite under a pressure of 1,000 atmospheres of water vapour at 700° C., which temperature " accords much better with field evidence on the intrusion temperature of granite than does its dry ' melting point ' of 1,050° C." Finally, crystallization of olivine can be retarded by water vapour from 1,600° C. to 1,000° C. Results of laboratory experiments thus support field observations (p. 24) as to the probably abundant presence of water vapour in igneous phenomena generally, thereby greatly lowering the viscosity of magmas. Profound changes of melting point and fluidity are thus to be anticipated also in subcrustal matter wherein water vapour is present.

Of the rôle of water in chemical and free energy transformations in basic and ultrabasic rocks little is known, though the abundance of zeolite amygdales in plateau basalts shows that it must be very active. The thermochemical properties of hydrous minerals—heat of formation, entropy, and high-temperature heat-capacity (MacDonald (1955), Coombs et al. (1959))—offer a field of research that could open up new concepts of subcrustal activity.

Nor should the potential of carbon dioxide in the mantle be overlooked. True, carbonatite magmas (p. 658) are rarely manifested at the earth's surface, but then so are peridotites. Takemouche and Kennedy (1964) investigating the binary system H_2O-CO_2 at high temperatures and pressures concluded: " At low pressures the CO_2 rich phase is the light phase, but at higher pressures an inversion in density takes place and the CO_2 rich phase becomes the denser phase ". The critical curve has a minimum temperature of 265° C. approximately with a pressure of 2,150 bars.

This means that the CO_2-rich phase would tend to be retained at depth, and only rarely appear at high levels, where water-vapour emanations would be normal. Kimberlite intrusions, derived from unusual depths, are typically endowed with carbonate presumed to be of primary origin; and the new hypabyssal rock, ngurumanite, from Kenya which has " iron-rich mesostasis and vug-like patches of primary calcite, analcime and zeolites " is thought by Saggerson and Williams (1964), who described it, to be derived ultimately from peridotite. It occurs in the same region as the soda-carbonate volcano Ol Doinyo Lengai.

Even more remarkable are intrusive magnetite ores (of melting point around 1,500° C.), and magnetite-hematite flows at 15,000 feet in the Andes, with only " tiny needles of apatite and a few small blebs and patches of silica " as impurities. The flow exhibited both *aa* and *pahoehoe* types of extrusion and evidence of abundant gas flux (Park 1961). Four areas of extrusion occurred upon a mountain range with several volcanoes. How easily does gas-fluxed magnetite move around within the mantle? It is certainly widespread in curious bodies within basic and ultrabasic rocks. And chromite acts peculiarly therein too.

With the large differences both of fluidity and density that may be induced by the presence of water vapour in ultramafic rocks, vast potentialities for tectonic activation must exist within the substratum. In a tentative way certain of these may now be visualized.

With a low concentration of substratal volatiles the superincumbent crust may be expected to behave as a stable (shield) area. As the volatiles migrate slowly upward into the crust, broad arching or doming of cymatogenic type might follow where the migrating volatiles caused expansion and lightening of the crust, but with the substratum itself relatively inactive, fresh accessions of volatiles in depth should be few and the region could remain stable for a long period of time.

Where a vapour-rich portion of the substratum has concentrated beneath a continental mass, the density of the substratum might be lowered and the continent tend to sink into it isostatically. With a broad regional distribution of the vapour-rich substratum, regional surface subsidence could permit the spread of shallow epeiric seas across the continent as in Hudson Bay and south-east Asia or, earlier, the Paris Basin. In course of time, with the volatiles migrating into the crust above, the crust would become lighter and the substratum denser (unless the spontaneous accumulation of volatiles continued below) so that the earth's surface would rise gently and regionally (epeirogenesis). Specially vapour-rich and mobile portions of the substratum* might become liable to " streaming " below the Mohorovičić discontinuity and there the crust might show a tendency to sink linearly if the volatiles remained in the substratum or to rise if they were discharged into the crust itself. Hence, perhaps, arise the cymatogenic arches of Africa, or the linear depressions that border one third of the world's undersea continental slopes.

Where vapour-rich portions are concentrated into still narrower zones, probably by active flow as the substratum becomes more mobile, an orogenic cycle becomes feasible (*cf*. the Undation Theory of van Bemmelen 1949). In response to marked lowering of density along flow-lines in the substratum, zonal subsidence of the crust may reach geosynclinal proportions, with appropriate deficiency of gravity.

Then migration of heated volatiles from the substratum into the lower, basaltic layer of the continents, already at a temperature little below melting, mobilises some of this material and enables it to invade the lower geosynclinal sediments as the floor reaches the nadir of subsidence. With high vapour concentration in a narrow zone, a peridotite belt may then blast its way briefly upwards, and the full orogenesis gets under way.

If continued rise of heat-bringing volatiles and fluxes later reaches the sialic envelope they there create batholiths, not by melting of a root folded into the substratum but by migmatization at normal or even shallow crustal levels, aided by

---

* The vapour fraction need not be free. It can be represented by combined water as in amphibolites, the physical properties of which are very different from those of analogous basalts.

accessions of connate water from the geosynclinal sediments themselves that may help still further to depress the melting points of primary magmatic minerals. Thus Steinmann in Peru and van Bemmelen in Indonesia have estimated the original depth of plutonic granite intrusions at from 2 km. to 6 km. and on the island of Wetar the top of the late-Cainozoic granodiorite seems to have been only 1 km. below the surface. The andesitic effusions of strato-volcanoes are considered by many authorities to be " basic fronts " in advance of the migmatization process of granite emplacements below. Other fronts (*e.g.* of silica) exist, and in regions where rock-types are varied what is expelled from one type (*e.g.* potash or alumina) may be just what is required to meta-morphose another. Generally such a system requires sodium to begin, and possibly ends with a silica excess.

Plutonism does not, however, always accompany orogenesis, as Gilluly (1963) has observed in the North American cordillera (p. 114). " Plutonism must depend on processes whose time scale is of an entirely different order of magnitude from those of volcanism or tectonism ". Perhaps, as an over-simplification, tectonism is the response of a relatively thin crustal load to changes in a fluid substratum, volcanism generally marks invasion of the upper crust by activated basaltic layer under static load, while plutonism marks the much rarer occasions when large masses of volatiles invade higher levels of the crust.

Wegmann (1935, 1948) has done much to show that batholiths have been formed not from granitic melts but from volatiles or " ion migrations "* soaking into country rock and rendering portions of the transformed rock mobile enough to behave as intrusions without creating a " space problem ". Indeed, it becomes a cardinal principle that the lowering of melting points by accession of volatiles may be no less important in granitization than the rise of temperature that they bring with them. G. Macgregor, J. T. Wilson and H. H. Read agree that *complete fluidity* of a granite has never been demonstrated: that injection takes place as a mush with pore fluids or volatiles constituting perhaps only one quarter of the volume. This can be accomplished at any level to which sufficient volatiles can rise.

A further agency that may be available is the " fluidization " process discussed by Reynolds (1954) wherein aggregates of fine solid particles are available for intrusion or extrusion (*e.g.* the outrush of pumice in the early stages of volcanism, and perhaps the production of ignimbrites) when mobilized by volumes of gas permeating the aggregate at suitable speeds. It may be likened, perhaps, to the generation of quicksand.

Unlike the injection of serpentine bodies, granitic intrusion is often repeated upon similar lines, *e.g.* the Palæozoic Murrumbidgee batholith of New South Wales has five phases of granitic intrusion amid its encompassing Ordovician-Silurian sediments.

---

* During the 1940's some transformists moved in thought away from " juices or ichors " towards a concept of " ion migrations ", and placed emphasis upon changes of crystal structure rather than crystal melt equilibria as the main controlling phenomena; but as this concept does not meet all the facts of intrusion, pegmatites and so forth, this text quotes merely " vapour or volatiles " leaving the precise nature of these substances to be defined later by geochemists.

Some evidence suggests that primitive volatiles may occasionally be very siliceous.

a) The siliceous waters of hot springs and geysers.

b) Highly explosive eruptions of great magnitude producing huge quantities of acid tuff but little or no lava seem to be largely aqueous, *e.g.* the Valley of Ten Thousand Smokes (eruption of Mt. Katmai, 1912) in Alaska, the New Zealand ignimbrites (in part) and the Lebombo acid tuffs. The last are associated with abundant amygdaloidal basalts which were clearly the heat and water bringers.

c) The enormous quantity of agate and related silica minerals in plateau basalts (*e.g.* Drakensberg, São Bento basalts).

d) The highly siliceous nature of many sulphide-bearing bodies seemingly derived from depth by pneumatolytic action.

e) Patches of tholeiitic, not olivinic, basalt even in the ocean basins where contamination by continental matter is difficult to explain,* and

f) Silicification of the lower crust could perhaps make the requisite " thickening of the crust " which, for instance, Drake, Ewing and Sutton regard as the only process necessary to form mountains out of the offshore geosyncline north of Cape Hatteras. Gilluly (1963) also remarks that " the vast masses of siliceous plutonic and volcanic rock now occupying the former eugeosynclinal area near the Pacific cannot have been formed by mobilizing merely the material of the geosyncline and its pristine basement; they demand accretion from a differentiating mantle or from former sialic lands to the west ".

Quartz-rich rocks have a high thermal conductivity as compared with feldspathic or ferromagnesian media which might explain their evidently freer association with evidences of hydro-thermal action.

Sederholm, Wegmann, Read and others have considered the source of volatile emanations to lie at great depth, and support is lent to this view by the relationship existing between ore deposits and earth volatiles. The hydrothermal theory of ore-genesis postulates that ores have been concentrated by progressive enrichment during the consolidation of igneous rocks, and that they have been expelled upwards in residual aqueous liquors in the final stages of cooling. While the general association with volatiles seems well established, the derivation by concentration within melts needs to be queried. Similar associations of ores occur in many parts of the world, yet the association is not infrequently independent of the type of intrusive. These points indicate a derivation not from local concentrations but from a common source independent of and deeper than the visible intrusions. Indeed, even in areas of deepest erosion the sources of ore-bearing magmas are never revealed.

The most serious weakness of the magmatic derivation theory, however, is the relative insolubility of most ore minerals, especially sulphides, in water—either hot or

---

* These oceanic tholeiites have isotopic ratios similar to those of achondritic meteorites which indicates their primitive nature (Engel *et al.* 1956).

cold, liquid or vapour. Either, therefore, much greater quantities of water must have been present than are indicated for an ordinary igneous melt, or the hydrothermal theory is wrong and needs to be supplanted by some other explanation such as the metallurgical theory propounded by Brown (1950). Unless, indeed, the sources of both ore minerals and volatiles lie deeper than the intrusives, which may be only secondary effects due to excess heat brought to higher levels as the volatiles ascended through the crust. An abyssal source for ores, and the genesis of sulphide ores in particular, has recently been discussed by Williams (1960).

At still higher levels, hydrous metamorphism may be accomplished in accordance with the principles enunciated by Yoder (1955) and at this stage probably occur also the chief topographic changes involved in the rise of orogenic mountain systems. Later as the volatiles escape or are dispersed at higher levels the " negative gravity anomaly may be dissipated and the orogen become 'compensated'". The location of centres or belts of high substratal occlusion beneath the continents may either be due to substratal flow on the global scale or be decided initially by the form of the continental base above the Mohorovičić discontinuity. Not improbably this base is corroded and hollowed like the roof of a limestone cavern, and the accumulation of light substratum abundantly charged with occluded gas would be natural in such situations.

Conditions beneath the oceanic basins may be very differently expressed. The oceanic floors are of basalt only 5 km. to 10 km. thick, and are presumed to be underlain by thousands of kilometres of peridotite. In the absence of continental matter there is little or no opportunity for the orogenic cycle of vertical tectonics to develop. Instead the potency of the substratum is perhaps exhibited on a grand scale by a bottom topography of east-west swells and furrows that emphasise *horizontal* displacement in the thin crust, *e.g.* Pacific Basin (p. 628). This topography conceivably reflects a sub-crustal streaming from east to west of very large magnitude. With horizontal streaming in a mobile subcrust, lateral drift of a thin crust becomes an almost inevitable corollary. From this it is only a step to drifting of the continental rafts at times when substratal flow is especially active.

Some Evidence from Volcanism

Before we get lost in hypothetical details of the substratum we now devote some attention to information that is available from the study of active volcanoes. Herein, can be no better guides than the bold volcanologists of Iceland, led by Trausti Einarsson whose researches at the eruptions of Hekla (1947-1948) and Surtsey (1963-1965) shed fresh light upon the processes operating when magmas reach the earth's surface. Lavas do not truly represent the fluid materials of the lower crust and subcrust for during ascent they have differentiated and have often absorbed waters of meteoric origin, and upon emission their gases react exothermically with the atmosphere. Nonetheless, information from direct observation of gas content, viscosity, shearing phenomena, ash formation, contrasted types of composition and mode of emission from a single vent, and so forth cannot be without value in visualizing the behaviour of magmas and mohos at greater depth.

After an initial outrush of bombs and pumice due to access of meteoric waters, the eruption of Hekla in 1947-48 produced a vesicular basaltic lava whereof Einarsson (1949; 1951) recorded temperatures between 1,130° and 1,150° at many places. Within the crater temperatures of 1,000° C. were measured, the higher temperatures outside, flames and explosions with block showers being due to burning of gases mixed with the atmosphere. At the lava fronts the maximum temperature measured was 930° C. A lava viscosity of 10^7 poises at about this temperature permitted either fracture or flow according to the rapidity of application of the forces, some broke off as blocks (glowing inside), some formed extrusion tongues. This gave rise to much differential flow.*

Flow was more rapid in the upper levels so that the action at the front was like the caterpillar of a tank. Cold blocks from the surface were thus cast to the ground in front and the flow rode over them. Such was the insulating power of this carpet of blocks that lava, which in the front could not be approached with uncovered face closer than 5m., actually " flowed over a snow sheet [30 metres wide] without melting it ".

The density of lava varied greatly, from 1 or even less on emission as spongy lava to 2 for dense lava flowing plastically at a distance of 6 km. from the crater. The difference was due to loss of volatiles, chiefly water vapour. On analysis the Hekla lavas were found to be very low (0·35%) in water, even the fresh spongy lava at the point of emission. Yet it was all very fluid. By personal tests Einarsson determined viscosities of :

5×10^5 poises on the most fluid lava,

$1·3 \times 10^6$ poises on the porous plastic lava front,

$1·5 \times 10^7$ poises on the most viscous dense lava.†

In such lavas turbulence was developed at Hekla.

Primary lava flooding at the points of extrusion, Einarsson noted, was spongy with densities as low as 0·6 or 0·8. In the light, foam-like rock, gas-filled vesicles were small, with thin walls. Flowing lava remained of this type. Consolidated blocks some short distance down the flow, however, were dense (2·0) and lacking in vesicles the gas bubbles having coalesced and left the lava. At an intermediate stage the lava possessed " relatively thick walls separating largely intercommunicating cavities ". This is an important stage in the solidification of the lava, marked by a shearing movement by which the gas bubbles coalesce, thus enabling steam to pass at pressure through the many conduits which replace the original small vesicles. Some of the conduits are lined with small points produced by tearing. These points, near the end of flows, also show melting

---

* Fluidity control is difficult to define. It includes a factor other than temperature and even viscosity, for a lava, once slowed, never regains its former rate of flow.

† These compare with 10^4 poises for the most fluid Hawaiian lavas.

which can only have been caused by the passage of very hot gases (1,260°-1,200° C.). Such additional heat is available from exothermic reactions, or perhaps from the latent heat of crystallization.

Consolidation of the lava is thus not a simple freezing of a normal fluid. " Other factors than cooling seemed to be of greater importance ". At Hekla, indeed, the temperature of the lava was *raised* during crystallization to about 1,150° C., with " very hot gases " at 1,250° C. In neither the light spongy lava, nor the dense blocks was crystallinity related to rate of cooling. The lava, indeed, showed a strong reluctance to crystallize. *When it did crystallize, which it probably did suddenly it did so in relation to shearing and loss of the gas vesicles.*

To quote Einarsson (1949): " We can find spongy lava 1,000° C. or less which does not crystallize even though it flows for days in an undercooled state, whereas . . . dense, crystalline lava may be formed a short distance from the crater . . . probably only a matter of a few minutes after its appearance on the surface ". Glass is not a result of rapid cooling, nor is much water necessary for its formation. It is the natural end state of porous lava that has not undergone stirring. In glasses from Hekla three types were distinguished by Einarsson:

a) A light yellow translucent glass like palagonite tuff, in which little iron is in the ferric state (1·85-2·75% out of total iron 9-11%). Phenocrysts were few.

b) Vesicles grow larger and the glass gets darker, and in the centres of bombs and moving masses it is torn into threads (Pele's Hair) by shearing. There is progressive oxidation of iron *within* the mass and the glass darkens by crystallization of submicroscopic magnetite.

c) A clear yellow glass with well developed cubes of magnetite and sometimes plenty of microlites.

Some rocks, however, do not show this prior crystallization of magnetite, and become a dense aggregate of microlites.

The magnetite flows noted in the Andes (p. 674) may be related to such crystallization without shearing. Crystallization is " closely connected with the coalescence and disappearance of the innumerable small gas bubbles suspended in the lava when it leaves the crater. It appears that only with the disappearance of the vesicle gases can the lava crystallize beyond the formation of magnetite ". " A freely flowing, considerably undercooled lava does not crystallize unless markedly stirred " (Einarsson 1949).

When it occurs, crystallization is rapid and viscosity increases markedly. With a latent heat of 90 cal./gr. a rise of temperature due to crystallization could by be 360° C. An observed rise is 200° C.*

The production of ash also follows from the shearing process within the lava. Whereas pumice is a light-coloured translucent glassy froth produced only in the initial

---

* The same principle presumably applies to crystallization at depth within the earth.

explosive stages of eruption, the Hekla ash was grey, opaque and crowded with microlites corresponding with the lava. It was produced at the stage of shearing (p. 679) in
the movement of the lava, when small teeth were produced upon the disjunctive surfaces.
These Einarsson found to be ash *in statu nascendi*, grinding between blocks at this stage
producing quantities of glowing sand and gravel. Some of this became consolidated
into " a red-brown conglomerate made of clay, sand and worn, crudely rounded pebbles,
firmly welded together and consolidated ". The iron of the conglomerate, unlike the
lava, was mostly in the ferric state.

Such ash is, of course, basic but the introduction of much silica in the magmatic
waters (of which much evidence exists in the amygdales of basalts) could well during
the same process provide an acid ash of ignimbrite type. Such ash, often called rhyolite
ash, is however truly an acidified basic ash. The order of appearance of crystals is
different from that in granites: quartz and feldspar often come first and corrosion of
these suggests remelting during formation, perhaps in a temporary access of heating.
In the Lebombo of Southeast Africa so-called rhyolites not only contained 8% iron ores
corresponding with associated basalts, but parts of the acid materials were themselves
shown by Mrs E. Gorsky, formerly of the University of Natal (in Frankel 1960) to be
metasomatized basalt. The waters active in this process are of course highly heated
juvenile waters forming part of the lava column itself. The actual explosion of ash at
the surface is attributed to contact with meteoric water which is heated only to between
200 and 300° C.

Repetitive emissions of different lava types from a single vent are quite usual. Amid
the old Eocene basalts of Iceland tholeiites, olivine basalts and porphyritic basalts have
poured out with change of magma composition more than 50 times during the whole
15,000 feet of the volcanic pile. No rhythm is apparent though each type was erupted
widely for a prolonged period before the composition of the magma changed and a fresh
group was emitted.

More striking are the instances where magma contrasts are extreme, as where
basalt and rhyolite share the same vent successively time and again. Inclusions show that
the acid phase succeeds the basic. Where andesites are present they are not intermediate but hybrids, and several lines of evidence indicate not mixing but co-existence
of basic and acid magma types. Though mutual solution among silicate melts is generally
assumed, non-mixing between magmas may be as real as non-mixing between turbid
and clear, saline and non-saline waters.

The proportion of acid materials is often much too high to permit of explanation
on differentiation of a basaltic parent alone. In Iceland 20% of the total post-glacial
tephra are rhyolite.

The lessons learned from the solidifying of lava, especially the relatively low
importance of cooling and the very high importance of shearing at certain critical viscosities, the crystallization of magnetite and the several types of glasses all have importance
to be assessed in the behaviour of plutonic and subcrustal magmas also (p. 671).

The Atmosphere and Hydrosphere

During geologic history the earth's more easily fusible and volatile materials have been transferred from the mantle towards the surface where, the process being irreversible, they have accumulated. Some products (CO_2, SiO_2) have by chemical reactivity been partly locked away in mineral combinations leaving the relatively inactive nitrogen to make up four-fifths of the earth's atmosphere. Water is also a stable substance and in vast quantities makes the hydrosphere, wherein large quantities of salt concentrate two further light elements sodium and chlorine. Carbon dioxide, known from carbonatites to exist in the mantle, has a chequered history, with much being locked away in carbonate rocks or withdrawn by plant physiology which has added oxygen to the atmosphere.

Hydrogen sulphide, indicated to be abundant in earth volatiles, is scarce in the atmosphere, much having been oxidised to SO_2 (apparent in volcanism) and still more having been abstracted to make pyrites and perhaps other sulphide minerals.

As the primitive earth can not have held an atmosphere the materials have clearly been supplied by differentiation of the mantle after the earth had attained a critical size sufficient to retain such active particles. But as we have noted of so many earth phenomena, a stable state involving quantities was reached relatively early (during the first thousand million years) of earth history (p. 1). This is before the earliest rocks yet dated by radioactivity.

An interesting calculation by Rubey (1951), after showing that the materials of the atmosphere and oceans had derived from volcanism, is that all these materials could have been derived from " crystallization of a shell of igneous rock 40 km. thick and having a magmatic volatile content of 4%, which is normal in igneous rocks.

Atmosphere, hydrosphere and lithosphere are thus differentiated products of primitive mantle substance, or, put another way, the crust is " defluidified " mantle. The whole scheme is of segregation based upon gravity, across which cuts occasionally the aberrant principle of chemical affinity (molar forces acting upon atoms in close proximity).

The Last Word

Our initial review of the earth's crust (Chapter I) noted the necessity for great mobility in the substratum and this has been borne out by almost every succeeding chapter. That mobility, in an otherwise dense and highly viscous material can only be conferred by admixture of one of the most highly mobile of all media—volatiles, mostly water-vapour, added or created from depth in immense quantities during geologic time.

In the present state of ignorance concerning the earth's interior, the source of this activating water-vapour is quite unsurmisable. Whether it is primordial or has been produced progressively from the mantle during earth history is quite unknown. That " UNKNOWN " is for the present the last word.

SELECTED BIBLIOGRAPHY

ADAMS, F. D.   1929   Geology of Ceylon. *Canad. Journ. Res.*, Vol. 1, pp. 425-511.

ADIE, R. J.   1962   The Geology of Antarctica. *Antarc. Res., Geophys. Monog.*, No. 7, pp. 26-39.

ADKIN, G. L.   1949   The Tararua Range as a Unit of the Geological Structure of New Zealand. *Roy. Soc. N.Z., Rept. 6th Sci. Cong.*, pp. 260-272.

ALEXANDRE, J.   1959   Les Terrasses des bassins superior de l'Ourthe et de la Lesse. *Bull. Soc. Géol. de Belgique*, Vol. 80, pp. 317-332.

AMBROSE, J. W.   1964   Exhumed Paleoplains of the Precambrian Shield of North America. *Am. J. Sci.*, Vol. 262, pp. 817-857.

ANDREW, G.   1949   *Geology in the Sudan* 1948, pp. 84-128.

ARGAND, E.   1922   La Tectonique de l'Asie. *C. R. XIII Internat. Geol. Cong.*, Vol. 1, pp. 171-372.

ARKELL, W. J.   1956   *Jurassic Geology of the World*, Edinburgh, pp. 706.

ARKHANGUELSKY, A. D.   1937   Structure Geologique et Histoire Geologique de l'U.R.S.S. *C. R. XVII Internat. Geol. Cong.*, Vol. 2, pp. 285-304.

ATWOOD, W. W.   1940   *The Physiographic Provinces of North America*, Boston, pp. 536.

BAILEY, E. B.   1929   The Palæozoic Mountain Systems of Europe and America. *Brit. Assn. Adv. Sci.*, Glasgow, pp. 57-76.

BAILEY, E. B. and
   HOLTEDAHL, O.   1936   Northwest Europe (Caledonides), *Reg. Geol. der Erde.*, Vol. 2, pp. 1-76.

BAILEY, T. L.   1943   Late Pleistocene Coast Range Orogenesis in Southern California. *Bull. Geol. Soc. Am.*, Vol. 54, pp. 1549-1568.

BAKER, B. H.   1963   Geology and Mineral Resources of the Seychelles Archipelago. *Geol. Surv. Kenya*, Mem. No. 3, 140 pp.

BALCHIN, W. G. and
   PYE, N.   1955   Piedmont Profiles in the Arid Cycle. *Proc. Geol. Assn.*, Vol. 66, pp. 167-182.

BALME, B. E. and
   CHURCHILL, D. M.   1959   Tertiary Sediments at Coolgardie, Western Australia. *J. Roy. Soc. W. Aust.*, Vol. 42, pp. 37-43.

BANDY, M. C.   1937   Geology and Petrology of Easter Island. *Bull. Geol. Soc. Am.*, Vol. 48, pp. 1589-1610.

BARBOUR, G. B.   1929   The Geology of the Kalgan Area. *Mem. Geol. Surv. China*, Series A, No. 6, pp. 148.

——   1933   The Loess of China. *XVI Internat. Geol. Cong., Wash.*, pp. 777-778.

BARTH, T. F.   1956   Studies in Gneiss and Granite. *Skrifter utgitt av Det Norske Videnskaps—Akademie i Oslo, Met. Nat. Klasse* No. 1.

BAULIG, H.   1926   Le Relief de la Haute-Belgique. *Ann. Geog.*, Vol. 35, pp. 206-235.

——   1928   *Le Plateau Central de la France*, Paris, pp. 650.

——   1931   Presentation de deux cartes morphologique du Plateau Central de la France. *C. R. Cong. Internat. Geog.* Vol. 2, pp. 1-11.

BELOUSSOFF, V. V.   1959   Les Divers Types de Plissements et leurs Modes de Formation. *Rev. Geog. Phys. et Geol. Dyn.*, Vol. 2, pp. 97-112.

BEMMELEN, R. W. VAN   1949   *The Geology of Indonesia,* The Hague, 2 Vols., pp. 260 and 732.

BENFIELD, A.   1947   A Heat-Flow Value for a Well in California. *Am. J. Sci.*, Vol. 245, pp. 1-18.

BENIOFF, H.   1954   Orogenesis and Deep Crustal Structure. *Bull. Geol. Soc. Am.*, Vol. 65, pp. 385-400.

——   1955   Seismic Evidence for Crustal Structure and Activity in the crust of the Earth. *Geol. Soc. Am., Spec. Pap.*, 62, pp. 61-73.

BENSON, W. N.   1935   Notes on the Geographical Features of South-Western New Zealand. *Geog. Journ.*, Vol. 86, pp. 393-401.

——   1936   Some Landforms in Southern New Zealand. *Austral. Geographer*, Vol. 2, pp. 1-23.

BENTOR, Y. K. and VROMAN, A.   1954   A Structural Contour Map of Israel. *Geol. Inst. Heb. Univ., Jeru.*, Publ. 7, pp. 125-135.

BERKEY, C. and MORRIS, F. K.   1927   The Geology of Mongolia Vol. 2. *Am. Mus. Nat. Hist.*, 474 pp.

BERRY, L. and RUXTON, B. P.   1961   Mass Movement and Landform in New Zealand and Hong Kong. *Tr. Roy. Soc. N.Z.*, Vol. 88, pp. 623-629.

BETZ, F. and HESS, H. H.   1942   The Floor of the North Pacific Ocean. *Geog. Rev.*, Vol. 32, pp. 99-116.

BIRD, J. B.   1959   Recent Contributions to the Physiography of Northern Canada. *Zeit. f. Geomorphologie*, Vol. 3, pp. 151-174.

BIROT, P.   1949   *Essai sur quelques Problemes de Morphologie Generale*, Lisbon, pp. 176.

BIROT, P. and JOLY, F.   1952   Observations sur la Morphologie de l'Anti-Atlas Oriental. *Bull. Lab. de l'Inst. Cherifienne.*

BIROT, P., CAPOT-REY, R. and DRESCH, J.   1955   Recherches morphologiques dans le Sahara central. *Trav. de l'Inst. de Recherches Sahariennes*, Vol. 13, pp. 13-74.

DE BÖCKH, H., LEES, G. M.
and RICHARDSON, F. D. 1929 Contribution to the Stratigraphy and Tectonics of the
                              Iranian Ranges. *The Structure of Asia.* Ed. J. W.
                              Gregory, pp. 58-176. *Methuen.*

BOGDANOFF, A.   1957 Traits fondamentaux de la Tectonique de l'U.R.S.S. *Rev.
                              Geog. Phys. et Geol. Dyn.,* Vol. 1, pp. 134-166.

BOND, G.   1952 The Karroo System in Southern Rhodesia. *XIX Internat.
                              Geol. Cong., Sympos. Gondwana,*   pp. 209-223.

BOSTOCK, H. S.   1948 Physiography of the Canadian Cordillera. *Canad. Geol.
                              Surv. Mem.,* pp. 106-247.

———   1964 A Provisional Physiographic Map of Canada. *Geol. Surv.
                              Canada,* Pap. 64-35, 24 pp.

BOURCART, J. and
GLANGEAUD, L.   1954 Morphotectonique de la Marge Continentale Nord-
                              Africaine. *Bull. Soc. Geol. France,* Ser. 6, Vol. 4, pp.
                              751-772.

BOWEN, N. L.   1947 Magmas. *Bull. Geol. Soc. Am.,* Vol. 58, pp. 263-280.

BOWEN, N. L. and TUTTLE
O. F.   1949 The System $MgO-SiO_2-H_2O$. *Bull. Geol. Soc. Am.,* Vol.
                              60, pp. 439-460.

BRADLEY, W. H.   1936 Geomorphology of the north flank of the Uinta Mountains,
                              Utah. *U.S. Geol. Survey. Profess. Paper.,* 185-1, pp.
                              163-199.

BRETZ, J. H.   1942 Vadose and Phreatic Features of Limestone Caverns.
                              J. Geol., Vol. 50, pp. 675-811.

———   1965 Geomorphic History of the Ozarks of Missouri. *Geol. Surv.
                              Missouri,* Vol. 41, 147 pp.

BROWN, E.   1957 The Physique of Wales. *Geog. Journ.,* Vol. 123, pp. 208-
                              230.

BROWN, J. S.   1950 *Ore Genesis.* T. Murby, London.
BRYAN, K.   1922 Erosion and Sedimentation in the Papago Country,
                              Arizona. *U.S.G.S. Bull.* 730, pp. 19-90.

BRYAN, W. H.   1930 The Physiography of Queensland. *Handbook for Queens-
                              land, Aust., N.Z. Ass. Adv. Sci.,* pp. 17-20.

———   1944 The Relationship of the Australian Continent to the
                              Pacific Ocean. *Journ. Roy. Soc. N.S.W.,* Vol. 78,
                              pp. 42-62.

———   1946 The Geological Approach to the Study of Soils. *Rep.
                              Aust. N.Z. Ass. Adv. Sci.,* pp. 52-70.

VON BUBNOFF, S.   1926-36 *Geologie von Europa,* 2 Vols., Borntraeger.
BUCHER, W. H.   1956 Rôle of Gravity in Orogenesis. *Bull. Geol. Soc. Am.,* Vol.
                              67, pp. 1295-1318.

BULLARD, E. C. and
GASKELL, T. F.   1941 Submarine Seismic Investigations. *Proc. Roy. Soc.
                              Lond.,* Vol. 177, pp. 476-499.

BUTLER, B. E.   1956 Parna—An Æolian Clay. *Journ. Sci.,* Vol. 18, pp. 145-151.
———   1959 Periodic Phenomena in Landscapes as a basis for Soil
                              Studies. *C.S.I.R.O., Austr., Soil Publ.,* No. 14, 20 pp.

BÜTLER, H. 1922 Contributions à la Geologie de l'Ahaggar. *C. R. XIII Internat. Geol. Cong.*, Vol. 2, pp. 819-848.

CAHEN, L. 1954 *Geologie du Congo Belge*, Liège, 577 pp.
CAHEN, L. and
LEPERSONNE, J. 1952 Équivalence entre le Système du Kalahari du Congo Belge et les Kalahari Beds d'Afrique australe. *Soc. Belge de Geol.*, Ser. 8, No. 4, pp. 1-64.

CAIRE, A. 1954 L'Atlas tellien meridional entre la chaine du Djurdjura et la partie occidentale des monts du Hodna (Algerie). *Ann. Sci. Univ. Besançon*, 2nd ser., Geol., Vol. 1, pp. 35-82.

—— 1957 Etude Geologie de la Région des Biban. *Serv. Carte Geol. de l'Algerie. Bull. No.* 16, 772 pp.
CAORSI, J. H. and
GONI, J. C. 1958 Geologia del Uruguay.

CAREY, S. W. 1954 The Rheid Concept in Geotectonics. *Bull. Geol. Soc. Austr.*, Vol. 1, pp. 67-117.

—— 1955 The Orocline Concept in Geotectonics. *Proc. Roy. Soc. Tasmania*, Vol. 89, pp. 255-288.

—— 1958 The Tectonic Approach to Continental Drift. *Symp. Cont. Drift Tasmania*, 1956, pp. 75-212.

CARSON, R. 1953 *The Sea Around Us*, London, 230 pp.
CARTER, W. D. and
LUIS AGUIRRE, LE B. 1965 Central Valley Graben in Chilean Andes between Procuro and Los Angeles fault zones. *Bull. Geol. Soc. Amer.*, Vol. 76, pp. 651-664.

DE CARVALHO, G. S. 1961 Geologia do Deserto de Moçâmedes (Angola) Porto, pp. 227.

CASTER, K. E. 1952 Stratigraphic and Palæontologic Data relevant to the Problem of Afro-American Ligation during the Palæozoic and Mesozoic. *Bull. Amer. Mus. Nat. Hist.*, Vol. 99, pp. 105-158.

CHATTERJEE, N. D. 1962 The Alpine Metamorphism in the Simplon Area, Switzerland and Italy. *Geol. Rund.*, Vol. 51, pp. 1-72.

CHIBBER, H. L. 1934 *Geology of Burma*, London, 530 pp.
CLARKE, E. DE C., TEICHERT,
C. and McWHAE, J. R. H. 1948 Tertiary Deposits near Norseman, Western Australia. *Journ. Roy. Soc. W. Austr.*, Vol. 32, pp. 85-103.

COLBERT, E. H. 1948 Pleistocene of the Great Plains. *Bull. Geol. Soc. Am.*, Vol. 50, pp. 541-588.

COLEMAN, P. J. 1962 An Outline of the Geology of Choiseul, British Solomon Islands. *Journ. Geol. Soc. Austr.*, Vol. 8, pp. 135-158.

COLEMAN, P. J., GROVER, J. C.,
STANTON, R. L. and
THOMPSON, R. B. 1965 A First Geological Map of the British Solomon Islands, 1962. *Repts* Nos. 28 and 29. *Brit. Solomon Is. Geol. Record*, Vol. 2, pp. 16-31.

CONDRA, G. E., REED, E. C.
and GORDON, E. D.   1950   Correlation of the Pleistocene Deposits of Nebraska. *Geol. Surv. Nebraska, Bull. No.* 15-*A*, 74 pp.

COOKE, H. C.   1929-   Physiography of the Canadian Shield. *Trans. Roy. Soc.*
                   30-31   *Canada*. Vols. 23, sect. IV, pp. 91-120 ; 24, sect. IV, pp. 51-88 ; 25, sect. IV, pp. 85-99.

——   1947   The Canadian Shield. *Econ. Bull. No.* 1, *Geol. Surv. Canada*, pp. 11-32.

COOMBS, D. S., ELLIS, A. J.,
Fyfe, W. S. and
TAYLOR, A. M.   1959   The Zeolite Facies. *Geochim. Cosmochim. Acta.*, Vol. 17, pp. 53-107.

COOPER, W. G. G.   1936   The Bauxite Deposits of the Gold Coast. *Gold Coast Geol. Surv. Bull. No.* 7, 35 pp.

COORAY, P. G.   1956   Geological Foundations of Ceylon's Scenery. *Bull. Ceylon Geog. Soc.*, Vol. 10, pp. 20-29.

COTTON, C. A.   1944   *Volcanoes as Landscape Forms*, Wellington, 416 pp.
COTTON, C. A.   1949   A Review of Tectonic Relief in Australia. *Journ. Geol.*, Vol. 57, pp. 280-296.

——   1957   Geomorphic Evidence and Major Structures associated with Transcurrent Faults in New Zealand. *Rev. Geog. Phys. et Geol. Dyn.*, Vol. 1, pp. 16-30.

——   1957*a*   Geomechanics of New Zealand Mountain Building. *N.Z. Journ. Sci. and Tech.*, Vol. 38, pp. 187-200.

COTTON, C. A. and
TE PUNGA, M. T.   1955   Solifluxion and Periglacially Modified Landforms at Wellington, New Zealand. *Tr. Roy. Soc. N.Z.*, Vol. 82, pp. 1001-1031.

CRADOCK, C., ANDERSON, J. J.
and WEBERS, G. F.   1965   Geologic Outline of the Ellsworth Mountains, West Antarctica. *Antarctic Geology*, pp. 155-170.

CRADOCK, C., BASTIEN, T. W.
and RUTFORD, R. H.   1965   Geology of the Jones Mountains Area, West Antarctica. *Antarctic Geology*, pp. 171-187.

CRAFT, F. A.   1931-32   The Physiography of the Shoalhaven River Valley. Parts I-VI. *Proc. Linn. Soc. N.S.W.*, vols. 56 and 57.

——   1933   The Surface History of Monaro, New South Wales. *Proc. Linn. Soc. N.S.W.*, Vol. 58, pp. 229-244.

——   1933*a*   The Coastal Tablelands and Streams of New South Wales. *Proc. Linn. Soc. N.S.W.*, Vol. 58, pp. 437-460.

CREER, K. M.   1964   A Reconstruction of the Continents for the Upper Palæozoic from Palæomagnetic Data. *Nature*, Vol. 203, pp. 1115-1120.

CROHN, P. W.   1959   A Contribution to the Geology and Glaciology of the Western Part of Australian Antarctic Territory. *Austr. Bur. Min. Res. Geol. and Geop. Bull.* 52, 101 pp.

CROOKSHANK, H.   1952   A Note on the Western Margin of Gondwanaland. *XIX Internat. Geol. Cong., Sympos. Gondwana*, pp. 175-179.

688 SELECTED BIBLIOGRAPHY

DALRYMPLE, G. B. 1963 Potassium-argon dates of some Cenozoic volcanic rocks of the Sierra Nevada, California. *Bull. Geol. Soc. Amer.*, Vol. 74, pp. 379-390.

DAPPLES, E. C., KRUMBEIN, W. C., and SLOSS, L. L. 1948 Tectonic Control of Lithologic Associations. *Bull. Amer. Assoc. Pet. Geol.*, Vol. 32, pp. 1924-1947.

DAVID, T. W. E. 1950 *The Geology of the Commonwealth of Australia.* 3 vols., Arnold.

DAVIS, G. L. and HESS, H. H. 1949 Radium Content of Ultramafic Igneous Rocks. *Am. J. Sci.*, Vol. 247, pp. 856-882.

DAVIS, W. M. 1922 Peneplains and the Geographical Cycle. *Bull. Geol. Soc. Am.*, Vol. 33, pp. 587-598.

—— 1930 Rock Floors in Arid and in Humid Climates. *Journ. Geol.*, Vol. 38, pp. 1-27.

—— 1932 Piedmont Benchlands and Primärrumpfe. *Bull. Geol. Soc. Am.*, Vol. 43, pp. 113-171.

DEMANGEOT, J. 1960 Essai sur le Relief du Nord-est Brésilien. *Ann. Geog.*, Vol. 69, pp. 157-176.

DEMOREST, M. 1937 Glaciation of the upper Nugssauk Peninsula, West Greenland. *Zeits. Gletsch.*, Vol. 25, pp. 36-56.

DENGO, G. 1953 Geology of the Caracas Region, Venezuela. *Bull. Geol. Soc. Am.*, Vol. 64, pp. 7-40.

DICKERSON, R. E. 1941 Molengraaf River : a Drowned Pleistocene Stream and other Asian Evidences bearing upon the lowering of sea level during the Ice Age. *Univ. Pennsyl. Bicent. Conf.*, pp. 13-30.

DIETZ, R. S. 1954 Marine Geology of Northwestern Pacific : Description of Japanese Bathymetric Chart, 6901. *Bull. Geol. Soc. Am.*, Vol. 65, pp. 1199-1224.

DIETZ, R. S. and MENARD, H. W. 1953 Hawaiian Swell, Deep and Arch, and subsidence of the Hawaiian Islands. *Journ. Geol.*, Vol. 61, pp. 99-113.

VAN DIJK, D. C. 1959 Soil Features in relation to erosional history in the vicinity of Canberra. *C.S.I.R.O. Aust., Soil Publ. No. 13.*

DIXEY, F. 1938 Some Observations on the physiographical development of Central and Southern Africa. *Tr. Geol. Soc. S. Afr.*, Vol. 41, pp. 113-170.

—— 1946 Erosion and Tectonics in the East African Rift System. *Quart. Journ. Geol. Soc. Lond.*, Vol. 102, pp. 339-388.

—— 1948 Geology of Northern Kenya. *Geol. Surv. Kenya, Report No. 15*, 43 pp.

—— 1956 Some Aspects of the Geomorphology of Central and Southern Africa. *Tr. Geol. Soc. S. Afr.* Annexure to Vol. 58, 58 pp.

—— 1956b The East African Rift System. *Colonial Geol. and Min. Res.*, Supplement No. 1, 71 pp.

DIXEY, F.   1960   The Geology and Geomorphology of Madagascar and a comparison with Eastern Africa. *Quart. Journ. Geol. Soc. Lond.*, Vol. 116, pp. 255-268.

DRAKE, C. L., EWING, M. and SUTTON, G. H.   1959   Continental Margins and Geosynclines : the East Coast of North America north of Cape Hatteras. *Physics and Chemistry of the Earth*, Vol. 3, pp. 110-198.

DRAKE, C. L. and GIRDLER, R. W.   1964   A Geophysical Study of the Red Sea. *Geophy. Journ. Roy. Astronom. Soc.*, Vol. 8, pp. 473-496.

DRESCH, J.   1941   *Recherches sur l'Evolution du Relief dans le Massif Central du Grand Atlas*, Paris, 708 pp.

——   1953   Plaines Soudanaises. *Rev. Géomorph. Dyn.*, Vol. IV, pp. 39-44.

——   1957   Les Problèmes Morphologiques du Nord-Est Brésilien. *Bull. de l'Assoc. de Géographes Français*, No. 263, pp. 48-60.

——   1959   Problèmes Morphologique des Andes Centrales. *Ann. de Geog.*, Vol. 67, pp. 130-151.

EARDLEY, A. J.   1962   *Structural Geology of North America*, 2nd Ed. New York, 624 pp.

EINARSSON, T.   1949   *The Eruption of Hekla* 1947-1948. Parts IV, 2, 3.

——   1951   *The Eruption of Hekla* 1947-1948. Part V, 2. Icelandic Scientific Society. Reykjavik.

EMERY, K. O.   1949   Topography and sediments of the Arctic Basin. *Journ. Geol.*, Vol. 57, pp. 512-521.

EMERY, K. O. and SHEPARD, F. P.   1945   Lithology of the Sea Floor off Southern California. *Bull. Geol. Sci. Am.*, Vol. 56, pp. 431-478.

ENGEL, A. E. J., ENGEL, C. G. and HAVENS, R. G.   1965   Chemical Characteristics of Oceanic Basalts and the Upper Mantle. *Bull. Geol. Soc. Amer.*, Vol. 76, pp. 719-733.

ERICSON, D. B.   1952   North Atlantic Deep-Sea Sediments and Submarine Canyons. *Tr. N.Y. Acad. Sci.*, Ser. II, Vol. 15, pp. 50-53.

ERICSON, D. B., EWING, M. and HEEZEN, B. C.   1952   Turbidity Currents and Sediments in North Atlantic. *Bull. Am. Ass. Petrol. Geol.*, Vol. 36, pp. 489-511.

ERICSON, D. B. and WOLLIN, G.   1956   Correlation of Six Cores from the Equatorial Atlantic and the Caribbean. *Deep-Sea Research*, Vol. 3, No. 2, pp. 104-125.

ESKOLA, P.   1949   The Problem of Mantled Gneiss Domes. *Quart. Journ. Geol. Soc. Lond.*, Vol. 104, pp. 461-476.

2 X

EWING, J. and EWING, M.   1960   Seismic Refraction Measurements in the Atlantic Ocean Basins, . . . in the Mediterranean Sea, on the Mid-Atlantic Ridge, and in the Norwegian Sea. *Bull. Geol. Soc. Am.*, Vol. 70, pp. 291-318.

EWING, J. I., WORZEL, J. L., and EWING, M.   1962   Sediments and Oceanic Structural History of the Gulf of Mexico. *J. Geophys. Res.*, Vol. 67, pp. 2509-2527.

EWING, M., CRARY, A. P. and RUTHERFORD, H. M.   1937   Geophysical Investigations in the emerged and submerged Atlantic Plain, methods and results. *Bull. Geol. Soc. Am.*, Vol. 48, pp. 753-802.

EWING, M., WOOLLARD, G. P. and VINE, A. C.   1940   Geophysical Investigations in the emerged and submerged Atlantic coastal plain. Part IV. *Bull. Geol. Soc. Am.*, Vol. 51, pp. 1821-1840.

EWING, M. *et al.*   1953   Exploration of the Northwest Atlantic mid-Ocean Canyon. *Bull. Geol. Soc. Am.*, Vol. 64, pp. 865-868.

EWING, M. and WORZEL, J. L.   1954   Gravity Anomalies and Structure of the West Indies. *Bull. Geol. Soc. Am.*, Vol. 65, pp. 165-174, 195-200.

EWING, M. and HEEZEN, B. C.   1955   Puerto Rico Trench Topographic and Geophysical Data. *Spec. Pap.* 62, *Geol. Soc. Am.*, pp. 255-268.

FAIR, T. J.   1948   Slope Form and Development in the Coastal Hinterland of Natal. *Tr. Geol. Soc. S. Afr.*, Vol. 51, pp. 33-47.

——   1948a   Hillslopes and Pediments of the Semi-arid Karroo. *S.A. Geog. Journ.*, Vol. 30, pp. 71-79.

FAIRBRIDGE, R. W.   1950   Problems of Australian Geotectonics. *Scope*, Vol. 1, No. 5, pp. 22-29.

——   1952   The Geology of the Antarctic in *The Antarctic Today*, Wellington, N.Z., pp. 56-101.

FLINT, R. F.   1947   *Glacial Geology and the Pleistocene Epoch*, New York, 589 pp.

FRANK, F. C.   1965   On Dilatancy in Relation to Seismic Sources. *Rev. of Geophys.*, Vol. 3, pp. 485-503.

FRANKEL, J. J. and KENT, L. E.   1937   Grahamstown Surface Quartzites (Silcretes). *Tr. Geol. Soc. S. Afr.*, Vol. 40, pp. 1-42.

FRYE, J.   1949   Use of Fossil Soils in Kansas Pleistocene Stratigraphy. *Tr. Kansas Acad. Sci.*, Vol. 52, pp. 478-482.

——   1955   The Erosional History of the Flint Hills. *Tr. Kansas Acad. Sci.*, Vol. 58, pp. 79-86.

FRYE, J. C. and LEONARD, A. B.   1952   Pleistocene Geology of Kansas. *Geol. Surv. Kansas, Bull.* No. 99, 230 pp.

GAGE, M. 1949 Late Cretaceous and Tertiary Geosynclines in Westland. *Tr. Roy. Soc. N.Z.*, Vol. 77, pp. 325-337.

GAIR, H. 1965 Geology of the Upper Rennick, Campbell and Aviator Glaciers, Northern Victoria Land, Antarctica. *Antarctic Geology*, pp. 188-198.

GARLAND, G. D. 1950 Interpretations of Gravimetric and Magnetic Anomalies on traverses in the Canadian Shield in Northern Ontario. *Publ. Domin. Obs. Ottawa*, Vol. 16, pp. 1-57.

DE GEER, G. 1923 *Measurement of Arc of Meridian in Spitzbergen*, t. II, s. ix.

GEVERS, T. W. 1942 The Morphology of the Windhoek District. *S. Afr. Geog. Journ.*, Vol. 24, pp. 45-64.

GIBSON, W. G. 1960 Topography in the Gulf of Alaska. *Bull. Geol. Soc. Amer.* Vol. 71, pp. 1087-1108.

GIGNOUX, M. 1948 La Tectonique d'ecoulement par gravite et la Structure des Alpes. *Bull. Soc. Geol. France*, Vol. 18, pp. 739-761.

—— 1950 Comment des geoloques des Alpes francaises conçoivent la Tectonique d'ecoulement. *Geol. en Mijn.*, Vol. 12, pp. 342-346.

GILL, W. D. 1952 The Tectonics of the sub-Himalayan Fault Zone in the Northern Potwar Region and in the Kangra District of the Punjab. *Quart. Journ. Geol. Soc. Lond.*, Vol. 107, pp. 395-421.

GILLULY, J. 1949 Distribution of Mountain Building in Geologic Time. *Bull. Geol. Soc. Am.*, Vol. 60, pp. 561-569.

—— 1963 The Tectonic Evolution of the Western United States. *Quart. Journ. Geol. Soc. Lond.*, Vol. 119, pp. 133-174.

GLAESSNER, M. F. 1950 Geotectonic Position of New Guinea. *Bull. Am. Assoc. Petrol. Geologists*, Vol. 34, pp. 856-881.

—— 1947 Geosynclines: a fundamental concept in Geology. *Am. Journ. Sci.*, Vol. 245, pp. 465-482, 571-591.

GLANGEAUD, L. 1953 Tectonophysique comparee de chaines Telliennes et Rifaines. *Bull. Soc. Geol. de France*, Ser. 6, Vol. 2, pp. 619-639.

—— 1957 Essai de Classification Geodynamique des Chaines et des Phenomenes Orogenique. *Rev. Geog. Phys. et Geol. Dyn.*, Vol. 1, pp. 200-220.

GOHAN, G. and VESLIN, J. 1959 Un Example de Morphotectonique en Haute-Provence. *Rev. Geog. Phys. et Geol. Dyn.*, Vol. 2, pp. 189-192.

GOLDTHWAIT, J. W. 1924 Physiography of Nova Scotia. *Geol. Surv. Canada*, Mem. 140, 179 pp.

GOULD, L. M. 1940 Glaciers of Antarctica. *Proc. Am. Philos. Soc.*, Vol. 82, pp. 835-877.

GRIGGS, D. 1939 A Theory of Mountain Building. *Am. J. Sci.*, Vol. 237, pp. 611-650.

GRINDLEY, G. W. 1963 The Geology of the Queen Alexandra Range, Beardmore Glacier, Ross Dependency, Antarctica. *N.Z. Journ. Geol. and Geophys.*, Vol. 6, pp. 307-347.

GRINDLEY, G. W.   1963*a*   Structure of the Alpine Schists of South Westland, Southern Alps, New Zealand. *N.Z. Journ. Geol. and Geophys.*, Vol. 6, pp. 872-930.

GRINDLEY, G. W., McGREGOR,
V. R. and WALCOTT, R. I. 1965   Outline of the Geology of the Nimrod-Beardmore-Axel Heiberg Region, Ross Dependency, Antarctica. *Antarctic Geology*, pp. 206-219.

GRINDLEY, G. W. and
WARREN, G.   1965   Stratigraphic Nomenclature and Correlation in the Western Ross Sea Region, Antarctica. *Antarctic Geology*, pp. 314-333.

GROVE, A. T.   1952   Land Use and Soil Conservation on the Jos Plateau. *Bull. Geol. Surv. Nigeria*, No. 22, 63 pp.

GROVER, J. C.   1958   *The Solomon Islands—Geological Exploration and Research.* London, 151 pp.

GUIMARÃES, D.   1951   Arqui-Brasil e sua Evolucão Geologico. *Dept. Nac. da Producão Min. Brazil, Bull. No.* 88, 317 pp.

GUNN, B. M. and
WALCOTT, R. I.   1962   The Geology of the Mt. Markham region, Ross Dependency, Antarctica. *N.Z. Journ. Geol. and Geophys.* Vol. 5, pp. 407-426.

GUNN, B. M. and
WARREN, G.   1962   Geology of Victoria Land between the Mawson and Mulock Glaciers, Antarctica. *Bull. N.Z. Geol. Surv.*, No. 71, 157 pp.

GUNN, R.   1949   Isostasy-Extended. *Journ. Geol.*, Vol. 57, pp. 263-279.

GUSSOW, W. C.   1962   Energy Source of Intrusive Masses. *Trans. Roy. Soc. Canada*, Vol. 56, sec. 3, pp. 1-19.

GUTENBERG, B.   1936   Structure of the Earth's Crust and the spreading of the Continents. *Bull. Geol. Soc. Am.*, Vol. 47, pp. 1587-1610.

GUTENBERG, B. and
RICHTER, C. F.   1954   Structure of the Crust : Continents and Oceans. *Internal Constitution of the Earth*, 2nd ed., New York, 431 pp.

GUZMAN, E. J.   1952   Volumes of Mesozoic and Cenozoic Sediments in Mexican Gulf Coastal Plain. *Bull. Geol. Soc. Am.*, Vol. 63, pp. 1201-1220.

HAMELIN, L-E.   1961   Périglaciaire du Canada. *Cah. géog. Quebec.*, Vol. 5, pp. 1-65.

HAMILTON, E. L.   1956   Sunken Islands of the Mid-Pacific Mountains. *Geol. Soc. Am.*, Mem. 64, 97 pp.

HAMILTON, W.   1962   Antarctic Tectonics and Continental Drift, *Publ. Am. Assoc. Geol.*, pp. 74-93.

HARLAND, W. B.   1961   An Outline Structural History of Spitzbergen in *Geology of the Arctic*. pp. 68-132.

HARRINGTON, H. J. *et al.*   1965   The Geology of Cape Hallett-Tucker Glacier District. *Antarctic Geology*, pp. 220-228.

HARRISON, J. V.   1943   The Geology of the Central Andes in part of the Province of Junin, Peru. *Quart. Journ. Geol. Soc. Lond.*, Vol. 99, pp. 1-36.

HARRISON, J. V. and
FALCON, N. L.   1936   Gravity Collapse Structures and Mountain Ranges, as exemplified in Southwestern Iran. *Quart. Journ. Geol. Soc. Lond.*, Vol. 92, pp. 91-100.

HAUGHTON, S. H.   1952   The Karroo System in the Union of South Africa. *XIX Internat. Geol. Cong., Sympos. Gondwana*, pp. 254-255.

HEALD, K. C. and
MATHER, K. F.   1922   Reconnaissance of the Eastern Andes between Cochabamba and Santa Cruz, Bolivia. *Bull. Geol. Soc. Am.*, Vol. 33, pp. 553-570.

HEEZEN, B. C., BUNCE, E. T.,
HERSEY, J. B., and
THARP, M.   1964   Chain and Romanche fracture zones. *Deep-Sea Research*, Vol. II, pp. 11-33.

HEEZEN, B. C. and
EWING, M.   1952   Turbidity Currents and Submarine Slumps, and the 1929 Grand Banks Earthquake. *Am. J. Sci.*, Vol. 250, pp. 849-873.

HEEZEN, B. C. and
THARP, M.   1965   Descriptive Sheet to Accompany Physiographic Diagram of the Indian Ocean. *Lamont Observ. Contrib.* No. 778.

HEPWORTH, J. V.   1964   Explanation of the Geology of Sheets 19, 20, 28 and 26 (Southern West Nile) *Geol. Surv. Uganda*, Rept. No. 10, 128 pp.

HERDMAN, H. F. P.   1932   Report on Soundings taken during the Discovery Investigations, 1926-1932. *Discovery Reports*, Vol. 6, pp. 207-236.

——   1953   Soundings taken during the Discovery Investigations 1932-39. *Discovery Reports*, Vol. 25, pp. 41-106.

HESS, H. H.   1938   Gravity Anomalies and Island Arc Structure. *Proc. Am. Philos. Soc.*, Vol. 79, pp. 71-95.

——   1946   Drowned Ancient Islands of the Pacific Basin. *Am. Journ. Sci.*, Vol. 244, pp. 772-791.

——   1948   Major Structural Features of the Western North Pacific, an interpretation of H.O. 5485, Bathymetric Chart, Korea to New Guinea. *Bull. Geol. Soc. Am.*, Vol. 59, pp. 417-446.

——   1955   Serpentines, Orogeny and Epeirogeny. *Geol. Soc. Am. Spec. Pap.* 62, pp. 391-408.

HESS, H. H. and
MAXWELL, J. C.   1953   Major Structural Features of the South-west Pacific. *Proc. 7th Pacific Sci. Cong.*, Vol. 2, pp. 14-17.

HILL, D.   1952   The Gondwana System in Queensland. *XIX Internat. Geol Cong. Algeria, Sympos. Gondwana*, pp. 153-174.

HILLS, E. S.   1945   Some Aspects of the Tectonics of Australia. *Journ. Proc. Roy. Soc. N.S.W.*, Vol. 79, pp. 67-91.

HILLS, E. S.   1963   *Elements of Structural Geology.* London, 483 pp.

HOLMES, A.   1927   Some Problems of Physical Geology and the Earth's
                                           Thermal History. *Geol. Mag.*, ser. v, Vol. 64, pp.
                                           263-277.

————   1929   Radioactivity and Earth Movements. *Tr. Geol. Soc.
                                           Glasgow*, Vol. 18, pp. 559-606.

————   1933   The Thermal History of the Earth. *Journ. Wash. Acad.
                                           Sci.*, Vol. 23, pp. 169-195.

————   1964   *Principles of Physical Geology.* London, 1288 pp.

HOLTEDAHL, O.   1939   Correlation Notes on Scottish-Norwegian Caledonian
                                           Geology. *Norsk. geol. tids.*, Vol. 19, pp. 326-339.

HOLTZSCHERER, J. J. and
   ROBIN, G. DE Q.   1954   Depth of Polar Ice Caps. *Geog. Journ.*, Vol. 144, pp. 193-202.

HORBERG, L.   1950   Bedrock Topography of Illinois. *Geol. Surv. Ill., Bull.* 73,
                                           111 pp.

HORTON, R. E.   1945   Erosional Development of Streams and their Drainage
                                           Basins. *Bull. Geol. Soc. Am.*, Vol. 56, pp. 275-370.

HOSPERS, J.   1955   Rock Magnetism and Polar Wandering. *Journ. Geol.*,
                                           Vol. 63, pp. 59-74.

HOWARD, A. D.   1942   Pediment Passes and the Pediment Problem. *Journ.
                                           Geomorph.*, Vol. 5, pp. 1-31, 95-136.

HUANG, T. K.   1945   On Major Tectonic Forms of China. *Mem. Geol. Surv.
                                           China*, Ser. A, No. 20, pp. 165.

————   1959   New Studies on the Geotectonic Subdivisions of Eastern
                                           China and their characteristics. Internat. Geol. Rev. 1,
                                           Oct. 73-88.

INNES, M. J. S.   1957   Gravity and Isostasy In Central Quebec. *Trans. Am.
                                           Geop. Un.*, Vol. 38, pp. 156-165.

IRVING, E.   1964   *Palæomagnetism and its Application to Geology and
                                           Geophysical Problems.* New York. 399 pp.

IRVING, E. and GREEN, R.   1957   Palæomagnetic Evidence from the Cretaceous and Caino-
                                           zoic. *Nature*, Vol. 179, pp. 1064-1065.

IRVING, E. M.   1952   Geological History and Petroleum Possibilities of the
                                           Philippines. *Bull. Am. Ass. Petrol. Geologists*, Vol. 36,
                                           pp. 437-476.

JAMES, P. E.   1933   The Surface Configuration of Southeastern Brazil. *Ann.
                                           Assn. Amer. Geog.*, Vol. 23, pp. 165-193.

————   1952   Observations on the Physical Geography of Northeast
                                           Brazil. *Ann. Assn. Amer. Geog.*, Vol. 42, pp. 153-176.

JENKS, W. F., ed.   1956   Handbook of South American Geology. *Geol. Soc. Am.*,
                                           Mem. 65, 378 pp.

JESSEN, O.   1936   *Reisen und Forchungen in Angola*, Berlin, 397 pp.

JOHNSON, D. W.   1929   Geomorphologic Aspects of Rift Valleys. *C. R. XV
                                           Internat. Geol. Cong.*, S. Africa, pp. 354-373.

————   1931   *Stream Sculpture on the Atlantic Slope*, Columbia, 142 pp.

JOLY, F. 1962 Études sur le Relief du Sud-est Marocain. *Trav. Inst. Sci. Chérifien*, ser. Geol. No. 10, 563 pp.

JONES, O. T. 1924 The Upper Towy Drainage System. *Quart. Journ. Geol. Soc. Lond.*, Vol. 80, pp. 568-609.

—— 1938 On the Evolution of a Geosyncline. *Quart. Journ. Geol. Soc. Lond.*, Vol. 94, pp. lx-cvi.

DE JUANA, C. G. 1947 Elements of Diastrophic History of North-Eastern Venezuela. *Bull. Geol. Soc. Am.*, Vol. 58, pp. 689-702.

JUNNER, N. 1940 The Geology of the Gold Coast and Western Togoland. *Gold Coast Geol. Surv.*, Bull. No. 11, 40 pp.

JUTSON, J. T. 1934 Physiography of Western Australia. *Geol. Surv. W. Aust. Bull. No.* 10, 170 pp.

KAY, G. M. 1948 Palæozoic Volcanic Geosynclines. *Bull. Geol. Soc. Am.*, Vol. 59, pp. 1332.

—— 1951 North American Geosynclines. *Mem. Geol. Soc. Amer.*, Vol. 48, 143 pp.

KELLAWAY, G. A. and
TAYLOR, J. H. 1953 Early Stages in the Physiographic Evolution of a portion of the East Midlands. *Quart. Journ. Geol. Soc. Lond.*, Vol. 108, pp. 343-376.

KENLEY, R. 1954 The Occurrence of Cretaceous Sediments in South-Western Victoria. *Proc. Roy. Soc. Vict.*, Vol. 66, pp. 1-16.

KENNEDY, G. C. 1955 Some Aspects of the Rôle of Water in Rock Melts. *Geol. Soc. Amer. Spec. Pap.* 62, pp. 489-504.

KING, B. C. 1965 The Nature of Basic Igneous Rocks and their relations with Associated Acid Rocks. Parts I-VI. *Sci. Prog.*, Vols. 50-54.

KING, L. C. 1930 Raised Beaches and other features of the South-east Coast of the North Island of New Zealand. *Tr. N.Z. Inst.*, Vol. 61, pp. 498-523.

—— 1941 The Monoclinal Coast of Natal, South Africa. *Journ. Geomorph.*, Vol. 3, pp. 144-153.

—— 1948 A Theory of Bornhardts. *Geog. Journ.*, Vol. 112, pp. 83-87.

—— 1953 Canons of Landscape Evolution. *Bull. Geol. Soc. Am.*, Vol. 64, pp. 721-752.

—— 1953a Necessity for Continental Drift. *Bull. Am. Assn. Petrol. Geol.*, Vol. 37, pp. 2163-2177.

—— 1956 A Geomorfologia do Brasil Oriental. *Rev. Geog. Bras.*, Vol. 18, pp. 147-265.

—— 1957 The Uniformitarian Nature of Hillslopes. *Tr. Geol. Soc. Edinb.*, Vol. 17, pp. 81-102.

—— 1959 Denudational and Tectonic Relief in South-eastern Australia. *Tr. Geol. Soc. S. Afr.*, Vol. 62, pp. 113-138.

—— 1962 *The Morphology of the Earth.* Edinburgh 699 pp.

—— 1963 *South African Scenery*, 3rd ed., Edinburgh, 308 pp.

KING, L. C.   1965   The Pre-Glacial Geomorphology of Alexander Island, Antarctica. *Antarctic Geology*, pp. 55-64.

——   1966   Since du Toit: Geological Relationships between South Africa and Antarctica. 9th Alex. L. du Toit Memorial Lect. 1965. *Geol. Soc. S. Afr.*, in press.

KING, L. C. and
KING, L. A.   1959   A Reappraisal of the Natal Monocline. *S. Afr. Geog. Journ.*, Vol. 41, pp. 15-30.

KING, R. E.   1939   Geological Reconnaissance in northern Sierra Madre Occidental of Mexico. *Bull. Geol. Soc. Am.*, Vol. 50, pp. 1652-1722.

KING, W. B. R.   1954   The Geological History of the English Channel. *Quart. Journ. Geol. Soc. Lond.*, Vol. 110, pp. 77-101.

KINGMA, J. T.   1959   The Tectonic History of New Zealand. *N.Z. Journ. Geol. and Geophys.*, Vol. 2, pp. 1-55.

KLIMOV, L. V., RAVICH, M. G.
and SOLOVIEV, D. S.   1965   Charnockites of East Antarctica. *Antarctic Geology*, pp. 455-462.

KORN, H. and MARTIN, H.   1959   Gravity Tectonics in the Naukluft Mountains of South-West Africa. *Bull. Geol. Soc. Am.*, Vol. 70, pp. 1047-1078.

KOVACH, R. L.   1959   Surface Wave Dispersion for an Asio-African and a Eurasian Path. *Journ. Geophys. Res.*, Vol. 64, pp. 805-813.

KRISHNAN, M. S.   1953   The Structural and Tectonic History of India. *Mem. Geol. Surv. India*, Vol. 81, pp. 1-109.

KRAUSE, D. C.   1965   Submarine Geology North of New Guinea. *Bull. Geol. Soc. Amer.*, Vol. 76, pp. 27-41.

KUENEN, PH. H.   1953   Origin and Classification of Submarine Canyons. *Bull. Geol. Soc. Am.*, Vol. 64, pp. 1295-1314.

KULARATNAM, K.   1952   The Face of Ceylon. *Proc. 9th Sess. Ceylon Ass. Adv. Sci.*, pp. 1-11.

KUSHIRO, I. and KUNO, H.   1963   Origin of Primary Basalt Magmas and Classification of Basaltic Rocks. *Journ. Petrology*, Vol. 4, pp. 75-89.

LAMOTTE, M., ROUGERIE, G.
et al.   1955   La Chaine du Nimba. *Mem. de l'I.F.-A.N.*, No. 43, fasc. III.

LANGBEIN, W. B. and
SCHUMM, S. A.   1958   Yield of Sediment in Relation to Mean Annual Precipitation. *Tr. Am. Geop. U.*, Vol. 39, pp. 1076-1084.

LEE, J. S.   1939   *The Geology of China*, Murby, 528 pp.

LEES, G. M.   1952   Foreland Folding. *Quart. Journ. Geol. Soc. Lond.*, Vol. 108, pp. 1-34.

LENCEWICZ, S.   1933   Surfaces d'aplanissement tertiare dans les monts Lysogory. *C. R. Intern. Geog. Cong.*, Warsaw, Vol. 2, pp. 477-491.

LEOPOLD, L. B. and
MADDOCK, T.   1952   The Hydraulic Geometry of Stream Channels and some Physiographic Implications. *U.S. Geol. Surv. Prof. Pap.* 252, 57 pp.

LEPERSONNE, J.   1949   Concerning Peneplains in the South West of the Congo Basin and their superficial Formations. *Kon. Belg. Kolon. Inst.*, Vol. 20, pp. 664-676.

——   1956   Les aplanissements d'erosion du nord-est du Congo Belge et des régions voisines. *Acad. Roy. Sc. Coloniales*, Vol. 4, pt. 7, pp. 1-110.

LIDDLE, R. A.   1946   *The Geology of Venezuela and Trinidad*, 2nd ed., New York, 890 pp.

LILLIE, A. R.   1951   Notes on the Geological Structure of New Zealand. *Tr. Roy. Soc. N.Z.*, Vol. 79, pp. 218-259.

LINTON, D. L.   1931   On the relations between the early and mid-tertiary planation surfaces of S.E. England. *C. R. Internat. Géog. Cong.*, Paris, Vol. 2, pp. 1-6.

——   1951   Problems of Scottish Scenery. *Scot. Geog. Mag.*, Vol. 67, pp. 65-85.

LISTER, L.   1966   Erosion Surfaces in Malawi. *Malawi Geol. Surv. Bull.*, (in the press).

LOMBARD, A.   1953   La Tectonique du Népal Oriental. *Bull. Soc. Géol. de France*, Sec. 6, Vol. 3, pp. 321-327.

LONG, W. E.   1962   Permo-Carboniferous Glaciation in Antarctica. *Geol. Soc. Amer.* Abstracts for 1961, p. 314.

——   1962a   Sedimentary Rocks of the Buckeye Range, Horlick Mountains, Antarctica. *Science*, 136, pp. 319-321.

LORD, C. S., HAGE, C. O. and STEWART, J. S.   1957   Geology and economic minerals of Canada, 4th ed. *Can. Geol. Survey, Econ. Geol. Sec.* 1, pp. 220-260.

LOVERING, J. F.   1958   The Nature of the Mohorovičić Discontinuity. *Am. Geop. U.*, Vol. 39, pp. 947-955.

MABBUTT, J. A.   1955   Erosion Surfaces in Little Namaqualand. *Tr. Geol. Soc. S. Afr.*, Vol. 58, pp. 1-18.

——   1965   The Weathered Land Surface in Central Australia. *Zeit.f. Geomorph.*, Vol. 9, pp. 82-114.

MACAR, P.   1936   Quelques remarques sur la Geomorphologie des Cornuailles et du Sud de Devonshire. *Ann. Soc. Géol. de Belg.*, Vol. 60, pp. 152-169.

——   1955   Appalachian and Ardennes Levels of Erosion Compared. *Journ. Geol.*, Vol. 63, pp. 253-267.

McCARTHY, W. R. and TRAILL, D. S.   1965   The High Grade Metamorphic Rocks of the Mac-Robertson Land and Kemp Land Coast. *Antarctic Geology*, pp. 473-481.

MACDONALD, G. A.   1949   Hawaiian Peteographic Province. *Bull. Geol. Soc. Am.*, Vol. 60, pp. 1541-1596.

MACDONALD, G. J. F.   1955   Gibbs Free Energy of Water at elevated Temperatures and Pressures. *Journ. Geol.*, Vol. 63, pp. 244-252.

698   SELECTED BIBLIOGRAPHY

McGee, W. J.   1897   Sheetflood Erosion. *Bull. Geol. Soc. Am.*, Vol. 8, pp. 87-112.

Mackin, J. H.   1948   Concept of the Graded River. *Bull. Geol. Soc. Am.*, Vol. 59, pp. 463-512.

McCutcheon, W. R.   1957   A Treatment of Self-Gravitational Strains in the Earth. *Am. Geop. U.*, Vol. 38, pp. 95-98.

McLaughlin, D. H.   1924   Geology and Physiography of the Peruvian Cordillera, Departments of Junin and Lima. *Bull. Geol. Soc. Amer.*, Vol. 35, pp. 591-632.

McLeod, I. R.   1965   An Outline of the Geology of the Sector from Longitude 45° to 80° E., Antarctica. *Antarctic Geology*, pp. 237-247.

Macpherson, E. O.   1946   An Outline of Late Cretaceous and Tertiary Diastrophism in New Zealand. *Dept. Sci. Ind. Res. Geol. Mem.* No. 6, 100 pp.

Machatschek, F.   1955   *Das Relief der Erde*, Vol. 1 and 2, Berlin, pp. 530-594.
Marshall, C. E. and
    Narain, H.   1954   Regional Gravity Investigations in the Eastern and Central Commonwealth. *Univ. Sydney Dept. Geol. Mem.* 2, 98 pp.

Martin, H.   1961   The Hypothesis of Continental Drift in the Light of Recent Advances of geological knowledge in Brazil and in South-West Africa. *Trans. Geol. Soc. S. Afr.*, Vol. 64 (Annexure) pp. 1-47.

——   1964   The Directions of Flow of the Itararé Ice Sheets in the Paraná Basin, Brazil. *Bol. Paranaense de Geog.*, Nos. 10-15, pp. 25-76.

Mason, A. C. and
    Corwin, G.   1953   Geology of the Palau Islands. *Bull. Geol. Soc. Amer.*, Vol. 64, p. 1451.

Mather, K. F.   1922   Front Ranges of the Andes between Santa Cruz, Bolivia and Argentina. *Bull. Geol. Soc. Amer.*, Vol. 33, pp. 703-764.

Matthews, D. H.   1959   Aspects of the Geology of the Scotia Arc. *Geol. Mag.*, Vol. 96, pp. 425-441.

Maud, R. R.   1961   A Preliminary Review of the Structure of Coastal Natal. *Tr. Geol. Soc. S. Afr.*, Vol. 64, pp. 247-256.

Maxwell, J.   1948   Geology of Tobago, British West Indies. *Bull. Geol. Soc. Am.*, Vol. 59, pp. 801-854.

Maze, W. H.   1944   The Geomorphology of the central eastern area of New South Wales. *Journ. Roy. Soc. N.S.W.*, Vol. 78, pp. 28-44.

Menard, H. W.   1953   Pleistocene and Recent Sediment from the Floor of the Northeastern Pacific Ocean. *Bull. Geol. Soc. Am.*, Vol. 64, pp. 1279-1293.

——   1953*b*   Shear Zones of the Northeastern Pacific Ocean and Anomalous Structural Trends of Western North America. *Bull. Geol. Soc. Am.*, Vol. 64, p. 1512.

MENARD, H. W.   1959   Minor Lineations in the Pacific Basin. *Bull. Geol. Soc. Am.*, Vol. 70, pp. 1491-1495.

——   1961   The East Pacific Rise. *Science*, Vol. 132, pp. 1737-1746.

——   1961a   The East Pacific Rise. *Scientific American*, Vol. 205, pp. 52-61.

——   1964   *Marine Geology of the Pacific.* New York. 271 pp.

MENARD, H. W. and
DIETZ, R. S.   1951   Submarine Geology of the Gulf of Alaska. *Bull. Geol. Soc. Am.*, Vol. 62, pp. 1263-1286.

MENCHIKOFF, N.   1957   Les Grandes Lignes de la Géologie Saharienne. *Rev. Géog. Phys. et Géol. Dyn.*, Sec. 2, Vol. 1, pp. 37-45.

MERLA, G.   1951   Geologia dell'Appennino Settentrionale. *Soc. Geol. Ital. Boll.*, Vol. 70, pp. 95-382.

MESCHERIAKOV, J. A.   1959   Secular Crustal Movements of the East European Plain and associated problems. *Bull. Géod.*, No. 52, pp. 69-75.

——   1961   Surfaces d'aplanissements polygenetique et leur importance pour l'Analyse des Mouvements Néotectoniques. *Inst. Geog. Studies*, Vol. 5, pp. 25-26.

——   1961a   Problems and methods of geological and geomorphological researches in studying recent tectonic movements. *Acad. Sci. Geomorph. Comm., Rept. Recent Tectonic Movements.* 159 pp.

——   1963   Major Cycles in the Development of the Relief of Platform Plains. *Soviet Geog.*, Vol. 4, pp. 3-16.

MICHEL, P.   1962   L'evolution géomorphologique des bassins du Senégal et de la Haute-Gambie. *Rev. Géomorph. Dynam.*, Vol. 5, pp. 117-143.

MISCH, P.   1945   Remarks on the Tectonic History of Yunnan. *Bull. Geol. Surv. China*, Vol. 25, pp. 47-153.

——   1949   Metasomatic Granitization of Batholithic Dimensions. *Am. Journ. Sci.*, Vol. 247, pp. 209-245.

MITCHELL, R. C.   1959   The Tectonic Foundation and Character of S.W. Asia. *Egypt. Journ. Geol.*, Vol. 3, pp. 1-70.

——   1960   Structural Studies in Northern Iraq and their bearing on Zagros Tectonics. *Bull. Soc. Geog. Egypt.*, Vol. 33, pp. 53-72.

MOHR, P. A.   1963   The Ethiopian Rift System. *Bull. Geophys. Obs., Addis Abbaba*, Vol. 3, pp. 33-62.

MOUTA, F.   1954   *Noticia Explicativa do Esbosço Geologico de Angola*, Lisbon, 148 pp.

MULCAHY, M. J. and
HINGSTON, F. J.   1961   The Development and Distribution of the Soils of the York-Quairading Area, Western Australia, in Relation to Landscape Evolution. *C.S.I.R.O. Aust., Soil Publ.* No. 17, 43 pp.

MURRAY, G. E.   1947   Cenozoic Deposits of Central Gulf Coastal Plain. *Bull. Amer. Ass. Petrol. Geologists*, Vol. 31, pp. 1825-1850.

MURRAY, G. E.   1952   Volume of Mesozoic and Cenozoic Sediments in Central Gulf Coastal Plain of United States. *Bull. Geol. Soc. Amer.*, Vol. 63, pp. 1177-1192.

MURRAY, H. W.   1941   Submarine Mountains in the Gulf of Alaska. *Bull. Geol. Soc. Am.*, Vol. 52, pp. 333-362.

NAIRN, A. E. M.   1960   A Palæomagnetic Survey of the Karroo System. *Overseas Geol. and Min. Resources*, Vol. 7, pp. 398-410.

NALIVKIN, D. V.   1960   *The Geology of the U.S.S.R. : a short outline*, London. Trans. S. I. Tomkeieff, 170 pp.

NISKANEN, E.   1948   On the Deformation of the Earth's Crust under the Weight of a Glacial Ice-load, and Related Phenomena. *Ann. Acad. Sci. Finland*, Sci. A, Vol. 3, pp. 1-59.

NOLAN, T. B.   1943   The Basin and Range Province in Utah, Nevada and California. *U.S. Geol. Surv. Prof. Pap.* 197-D, pp. 141-196.

OBRUCHEV, W. A.   1926   *Geologie von Sibirien*, Borntraeger, 572 pp.

ODELL, N. E.   Air Survey of the New Zealand Alps. *Geol. Journ.*, Vol. 122, pp. 450-455.

OFFICER, C. B.   1955   South-West Pacific Crustal Structure. *Tr. Am. Geop. U.*, Vol. 36, pp. 449-459.

OFFICER, C. B., EWING, J. I.,
EDWARDS, R. S. and
JOHNSON, H. R.   1957   Geophysical Investigations in the Eastern Caribbean. *Bull. Geol. Soc. Am.*, **Vol.** 68, pp. 359-378.

OFFICER, C. B. *et al.*   1959   Geophysical Investigations in the Eastern Caribbean : Summary of 1955 and 1956 Cruises. *Physics and Chem. of Earth*, Vol. 3, pp. 17-109.

DE OLIVEIRA, A. I. and
LEONARDOS, O. H.   1943   *Geologia do Brasil*, Rio de Janeiro, 813 pp.

OLIVER, J.   1956   South African Earthquakes—January 1953 to December 1955. *Tr. Geol. Soc. S. Afr.*, Vol. 59, pp. 123-134.

OLIVER, J., EWING, M.
and PRESS, F.   1955   Crustal Structure of the Arctic Regions from the Lg phase. *Bull. Geol. Soc. Am.*, Vol. 66, pp. 1063-1074.

OPPENHEIM, V.   1947   Structural Evolution of the South American Andes. *Amer. J. Sci.*, Vol. 245, pp. 158-174.

PALLISTER, J. W.   1954   Erosion Levels and Laterite in Buganda Province Uganda. *XIX Internat. Geol. Cong.*, Section XXI, pp. 193-199.

———   1963   Notes on the Geomorphology of the Northern Region, Somali Republic. *Geog. Journ.*, Vol. 129, pp. 184-187.

PARK, C. F.   1961   A Magnetite " Flow " in Northern Chile. *Econ. Geol.*, Vol. 56, pp. 431-441.

PASCOE, E. H.	1950	*A Manual of the Geology of India and Burma*, Calcutta, 484 pp.
PEACOCK, M. A.	1935	Fiordland of British Columbia. *Bull. Geol. Soc. Am.*, Vol. 46, pp. 633-696.
PELTIER, L. C.	1950	The Geographic Cycle in Periglacial Regions as it is related to Climatic Geomorphology. *Ann. Ass. Amer. Geog.*, Vol. 40, pp. 214-236.
PENCK, W.	1925	The Piedmont Flats of the Southern Black Forest. *Zeit. Ges. f. Erdkunde*, pp. 83-108.
——	1953	*Morphological Analysis of Land Forms*, London, 429 pp.
PERRET, R.	1935	Le Relief du Sahara. *Rev. Géogr. Phys.*, Vol. 8, p. 211.
PICARD, L.	1937	On the Structure of the Arabian Peninsula. *C. R. Internat. Geol. Cong. Moscow*, Vol. 2, pp. 415-423.
——	1943	The Structure and Evolution of Palestine. *Bull. Geol. Dept. Hebrew Univ.*, Vol. 4, pp. 1-134.
PICHON, X. LE, HOUTZ, R. E. DRAKE, C. L. and NAFE, J. E.	1965	Crustal Structure of the Mid-Ocean Ridges. *Journ. Geophys. Res.*, Vol. 70, pp. 319-339.
PLUMSTEAD, E.	1962	Fossil Floras of Antarctica. *Sci. Repts. Trans-Antarc. Exped.* 1955-58, No. 9, 153 pp.
POLDEVAART, A.	1962	Aspects of Basalt Petrology. *Journ. Geol. Soc. India*, Vol. 3, pp. 1-21.
POLKANOV, A. A.	1937	Pre-Quaternary Geology of the Kola Peninsula and Karelia. *Rept. XVII Internat. Geol. Cong.*, Vol. 2, pp. 22-56.
PRESS, F. and BECKMANN, W.	1954	Geophysical Investigations in the Emerged and Submerged Atlantic Coastal Plain. *Bull. Geol. Soc. Am.*, Vol. 65, pp. 299-314.
PUGH, J. C.	1954	High-level Surfaces in the Eastern Highlands of Nigeria. *S. Afr. Geog. Journ.*, Vol. 36, pp. 31-42.
PULFREY, W.	1960	Shape of the sub-Miocene Erosion Bevel in Kenya. *G. S. Kenya, Bull. No.* 3, pp. 1-18.
PUTNAM, W. C.	1942	Geomorphology of Ventura, Region, California. *Bull. Geol. Soc. Am.*, Vol. 53, pp. 691-754.
QUENNELL, A. M.	1958	The Structural and Geomorphic Evolution of the Dead Sea Rift. *Quart. Journ. Geol. Soc. Lond.*, Vol. 114, pp. 1-24.
RADHAKRISHNA, B. P.	1952	The Mysore Plateau. *Bull. Mysore Geol. Assn.*, No. 3, pp. 1-56.
RAITT, R. W., FISHER, R. L. and MASON, R. G.	1955	Tonga Trench. *Geol. Soc. Am., Spec. Publ.* 62, pp. 237-254.

RAMBERG, H.   1955   Thermodynamics and Kinetics of Petrogenesis. *Geol. Soc. Am., Spec. Publ.* 62, pp. 431-448.

RAOUL, C. M.   1952   Resume des Communications. *XIX Internat. Geol. Cong.,* p. 124.

READ, H. H.   1955   Granite Series in Mobile Belts. *Geol. Soc. Am., Spec. Publ.* 62, pp. 409-430.

REAY, A. and HARRIS, P. G.   1963   The Partial Fusion of Peridotite. *Bull. Volcanique, de l'Union Géodes. et geophys. internat.,* Vol. 27, pp. 3-15.

REVELLE, R., BRAMLETTE, M., ARRHENIUS, G. and GOLDBERG, E. D.   1955   Pelagic Sediments of the Pacific. *Geol. Soc. Am. Spec. Publ.* 62, pp. 221-236.

REYNOLDS, D. L.   1949   Observations concerning Granite. *Geol. en Mijn.,* Vol. 11, pp. 241-253.

————   1954   Fluidization as a Geological Process and its Bearings on the Problem of Intrusive Granites. *Amer. Journ. Sci.,* Vol. 252, pp. 577-614.

————   1958   Granite : Some Tectonic, Petrological and Physico-Chemical Aspects. *Geol. Mag.,* Vol. 95, pp. 378-396.

RICHARDS, H. C.   1945   Subsurface Stratigraphy of Atlantic Coastal Plain between New Jersey and Georgia. *Bull. Am. Assoc. Petrol. Geol.,* Vol. 29, pp. 885-955.

RICKWOOD, F. K.   1955   The Geology of the Western Highlands of New Guinea. *J. Geol. Soc. Aust.,* Vol. 2, pp. 63-82.

ROOTS, E. F.   1953   Preliminary Note on the Geology of Western Dronning Maud Land. *Saert. Norsk. geol. tids.,* Vol. 32, pp. 18-33.

ROTHÉ, I. P.   1954   La Zone Seismique median Indo-Atlantique. *Proc. Roy. Soc. A.,* Vol. 222, pp. 387.

RUBEY, W. W.   1951   Geologic History of Sea Water. *Bull. Geol. Soc. Amer.,* Vol. 62, pp. 1111-1148.

RUHE, V.   1954   Erosion Surfaces of Central African Interior High Plateaus. *Publ. Inst. Nat. Agron. do Congo Belge,* No. 59, pp. 1-40.

RUNCORN, S. K.   1956   Palæomagnetic Comparisons between Europe and North America. *Proc. Geol. Assn. Canada,* Vol. 8, pp. 77-85.

————   1956   Palæomagnetism, Polar Wandering and Continental Drift. *Geol. v. Mijnb.,* Vol. 18, pp. 253-256.

RUSSELL, L. S.   1951   Age of the Front Range Deformation in the North American Cordillera. *Trans. Roy. Soc. Canada,* Vol. 45, pp. 47-69.

SAGGERSON, E. P. and BAKER, B. H.   1965   Post Jurassic erosion surfaces in Eastern Kenya and their deformation in relation to rift structure. *Quart. Journ. Geol. Soc. Lond.,* Vol. 121, pp. 51-72.

SAGGERSON, E. P. and WILLIAMS, L. A.   1964   Ngurumanite from Southern Kenya and its bearing on the Origin of Rocks in the Northern Tanganyika Alkaline District. *Journ. Petrology,* Vol. 5, pp. 40-81.

SANDFORD, K. S.   1937   Observations on the Geology of Northern Central Africa. *Quart. Journ. Geol. Soc. Lond.*, Vol. 93, pp. 534-580.

SCHEIDEGGER, A. E.   1959   *Principles of Geodynamics.* Berlin.

——   1961   *Theoretical Geomorphology.* Berlin.

SCHUCHERT, C.   1935   *Historical Geology of the Antillean-Caribbean Region,* New York, 811 pp.

SCHULTZ, C. B., LUENING-HOENER, G. C. and FRANKFORTER, W. D.   1951   A Graphic Resumé of the Pleistocene of Nebraska. *Bull. Univ. Nebraska State Mus.*, Vol. 3, No. 6, pp. 1-37.

SCHUMM, S. A.   1956   The Rôle of Creep and Rainwash on the Retreat of Badland Slopes. *Amer. Journ. Sci.*, Vol. 254, pp. 693-706.

——   1956a   Evolution of Drainage Systems and Slopes in Badlands at Perth Amboy, New Jersey. *Bull. Geol. Soc. Am.*, Vol. 67, pp. 597-646.

——   1962   Erosion on miniature Pediments in Badlands National Monument, South Dakota. *Bull. Geol. Soc. Amer.*, Vol. 73, pp. 719-724.

SEDERHOLM, J. J.   1923 1926   On Migmatites and associated pre-Cambrian Rocks of South-western Finland. *Bull. Comm. Geol. Finlande*, Nos. 58 and 77.

SHAND, S. J.   1949   Rocks of the mid-Atlantic Ridge. *Journ. Geol.*, Vol. 57, pp. 89-92.

SHARP, H. S.   1958   Resurrected Peneplanes of the Eastern United States. *XVIII Internat. Geog. Cong.* Comm. Study Erosion Surfaces around Atlantic, Vol. 4, pp. 10-21.

SHARPE, C. F. S.   1938   *Landslides and Related Phenomena* : a study of mass movements of soil and rock, New York, 137 pp.

SHEPARD, F. P.   1949   Terrestrial Topography of Submarine Canyons Revealed by Diving. *Bull. Geol. Soc. Am.*, Vol. 60, pp. 1597-1612.

SHEPARD, F. P. and EMERY, K. O.   1941   Submarine Topography off the California Coast. *Geol. Soc. Am., Spec., Pap.* No. 31, pp. 1-171.

SINGLETON, F. A.   1939   The Tertiary Geology of Australia. *Proc. Roy. Soc. Vict.*, Vol. 53, pp. 1-70.

SINGLETON, O. P.   1954   The Tertiary Stratigraphy of Western Australia. *Proc. Pan. Ind. Oc. Sci. Cong.*, Perth 1954, pp. 59-65.

DE SITTER, L. U.   1952   Pliocene Uplift of Tertiary Mountain Chains. *Am. Journ. Sci.*, Vol. 250, pp. 297-307.

——   1956   *Structural Geology*, McGraw-Hill, 552 pp.

SPREITZER, H.   1951   Die Piedmont Treppen in der Regionalen Geomorphologie. *Erdkunde*, Vol. 5, pp. 294-305.

SPRIGG, R. C.   1952   The Geology of the South East Province, South Australia. *Geol. Surv. S. Austr., Bull.* No. 29, 120 pp.

STANDARD, J. C.   1961   Submarine Geology of the Tasman Sea. *Bull. Geol. Soc. Am.*, Vol. 72, pp. 1777-1788.

STANDER, W.   1960   Focal Mechanism of three Kamchatka Earthquakes. *Bull. Geol. Soc. Am.*, Vol. 71, pp. 2077.

STANLEY, G. A. V.   1927   The Physiography of the Bowen District and of the northern Islands of the Cumberland Group (Whitsunday Passage). *Rept. Gt. Barrier Reef Committee*, No. 2, pp. 1-51.

STEARNS, H. T.   1945   Late Geologic History of the Pacific Basin. *Am. Journ. Sci.*, Vol. 243, pp. 614-626.

VER STEEG, K.   1940   Geomorphology of the Catoctin Belt. *Amer. Journ. Sci.*, Vol. 238, pp. 685-709.

STEINMANN, G.   1929   *Geologie von Peru*, Heidelberg, 448 pp.

STEVENS, G. R.   1956   Stratigraphy of the Hutt Valley, New Zealand. *N.Z. Journ. Sci. and Tech.*, Vol. 38, pp. 201-235.

STILLE, H.   1924   *Die Vergleichende Tektonik*, Berlin, 443 pp.

STOCKLEY, G. M.   1948   The Geology and Mineral Resources of Tanganyika Territory. *Geol. Surv. Tang., Bull.* No. 20, p. 42.

STOSE, G. W. and STOSE, A. J.   1951   Blue Ridge Front—a Fault Scarp. *Bull. Geol. Soc. Am.*, Vol. 62, pp. 1371-1373.

STRAHLER, A. N.   1950   Equilibrium Theory of Erosional Slopes Approached by Frequency Distribution of Analysis. *Am. J. Sci.*, Vol. 248, pp. 673-696.

STRØM, K.   1948   The Geomorphology of Norway. *Geog. Journ.* Vol. 112, pp. 19-27.

——   1960   The Norwegian Coast. *Norsk. Geog. Tids.*, Vol. 17, pp. 132-137.

SUESS, E.   1885-1904   *The Face of the Earth*, 4 vols. Oxford.

SUGGATE, R. P.   1963   The Alpine Fault. *Tr. Roy. Soc. N.Z., n. s.*, Vol. 2, pp. 105-129.

DE SWARDT, A. M. J.   1964   Lateritisation and Landscape Development in Parts of Equatorial Africa. *Zeit. f. Geomorph.*, Vol. 8, pp. 313-333.

TAKEMOUCHE, S. and KENNEDY, G. C.   1964   The Binary System H_2O-CO_2 at High Temperatures and Pressures. *Amer. Journ. Sci.*, Vol. 262, pp. 1055-1074.

TALIAFERRO, N. L.   1943   Geologic History and Structure of the Central Coast Ranges of California. *State Div. Mines, Dept. Nat. Resources, Calif., Bull.* 118, pp. 119-162.

TALWANI, H.   1964   A Review of Marine Geophysics in *Marine Geology*, pp. 28-80.

TANNI, L.   1942   On the Isostatic Structure of the Earth's Crust in the Carpathian Countries. *Ann. Acad. Sci. Finland, Ser. A*, Vol. 3, pp. 1-100.

TATEL, H. E. and TUVE, M. A.   1955   Seismic Exploration of a Continental Crust. *Geol. Soc. Am. Spec. Pap.* No. 62, pp. 35-51.

TEALE, E. O. and HARVEY, E.   1933   A Physiographical Map of Tanganyika. *Geog. Rev.*, Vol. 23, pp. 402-413.

TEMPERLEY, B. N.   1952   Review of the Gondwana rocks of Kenya Colony. *XIX Intern. Geol. Cong., Algeria, Sympos. Gondwana*, pp. 195-208.

TE PUNGA, M. T.   1957   Live Anticlines in Western Wellington. *N.Z. Journ. Sci. and Tech.*, Vol. 38, pp. 433-446.

DE TERRA, H.   1930   Geomorphologische Studien Zwischen oberen Industal und sudlichen Tarimbecken. *Zeitf. Geomorph.*, Vol. 5, pp. 79-131.

————   1933   Himalayan and Alpine Orogenies. *C. R. XVI Internat. Geol. Cong.*, pp. 859-871.

THOMAS, R. G.   1951   An example of Re-intrusion of Serpentine. *Tr. Amer. Geophys. U.*, Vol. 32, pp. 462-465.

THOMAS, M. F.   1965   Some Aspects of the Geomorphology of domes and tors in Nigeria. *Zeit. f. Geomorph.*, Vol. 9, pp. 63-81.

THOMPSON, G. A. and TALWANI, M.   1964   Geology of the Crust and Mantle, Western United States. *Science*, Vol. 146, pp. 1539-1549.

THORARINSSON, S.   1960   The Tephralayers and Tephrachronology. Geology and Geophysics of Iceland. *21st Internat. Geol. Cong.*, *Guide book Excursion A2*, pp. 55-60.

THORNBURY, W. D.   1965   *Regional Geomorphology of the United States.* New York, 609 pp.

THORP, J.   1945   Significance of Loess in Classification of Soils. *Amer. Journ. Sci.*, Vol. 243, pp. 263-270.

TILLEY, C. E.   1951   Some Aspects of Magmatic Evolution, Vol. 106. *Quart. Journ. Geol. Soc. Lond.*, pp. 37-61.

DU TOIT, A. L.   1937   *Our Wandering Continents*, Edinburgh, 366 pp.

————   1954   *The Geology of South Africa*, 3rd ed., Edinburgh, 611 pp.

TOLSTOY, I.   1951   Submarine Topography in the North Atlantic. *Bull. Geol. Soc. Am.*, Vol. 62, pp. 441-450.

TOLSTOY, I. and EWING, M.   1949   North Atlantic Hydrography and the mid-Atlantic Ridge. *Bull. Geol. Soc. Am.*, Vol. 60, 1527-1540.

TOZER, E. T., and THORSTEINSSON, R.   1964   Western Queen Elizabeth Islands, Arctic Archipelago. *Geol. Surv. Canada Mem.*, No. 332, 242 pp.

TRENDALL, A. F.   1959   The Topography under the northern part of the Kadam volcanics. *Rec. Geol. Surv. Uganda*, 1955-56, pp. 1-8.

TREVISAN, L.   1950   L'Elba orientale e sua tettonica di scivolamento per gravita. *Padua Univ. Inst. Geol. Mem.*, Vol. 16, pp. 1-40.

TRICART, J. L. F.   1949   *La Partie Orientale du Bassin de Paris*, Vol. 1, Paris, 471 pp.

TURNER, F. S. and WEISS, L. E.   1963   *Structural Analysis of Metamorphic Tectonites.* New York, 545 pp.

TWENHOFEL, W. H. and MACLINTOCK, P.   1940   Surface of Newfoundland. *Bull. Geol. Soc. Amer.*, Vol. 51, pp. 1665-1727.

2 Y

TWIDALE, C. R.   1956   Chronology of Denudation in Northwest Queensland. *Bull. Geol. Soc. Am.*, Vol. 67, pp. 867-882.

——   1956a   The Physiography of Northwest Queensland. *Geog. Studies*, Vol. 3, pp. 1-11.

——   1964   A Contribution to the General Theory of Domed Inselbergs. *Tr. and Pap. Inst. Brit. Geog.*, Publ. No. 34, pp. 91-113.

TYRRELL, G. W.   1926   *Principles of Petrology*, London, 349 pp.

UMBGROVE, J. H. F.   1947   *The Pulse of the Earth*, Hague, 358 pp.
——   1949   *Structural History of the East Indies*, Cambridge, 63 pp.

VACQUIER, V., RAFF, A. D.,
and WARREN, E.   1961   Horizontal Displacements in the Floor of the Northeastern Pacific Ocean. *Bull. Geol. Soc. Amer.*, Vol. 72, pp. 1251-1258.

VEATCH, A. C.   1935   Evolution of the Congo Basin. *Geol. Soc. Am., Mem.* 3, 183 pp.

VINOGRADOV, A. P.   1964   Geochemical Aspects of the Earth's Crust and Upper Mantle. *I.C.S.U. Review of World Sci.*, Vol. 6, pp. 131-136.

WADIA, D. N.   1937   *The Geology of India*, London, 460 pp.
——   1937b   Tectonics of North India. *C. R. XVII Internat. Geol. Cong.*, Moscow, Vol. 2, pp. 425-442.

——   1943   The Three Superposed Peneplains of Ceylon. *Rec. Dept. Min., Ceylon, Prof. Paper*, No. 1, pp. 25-31.

WAGER, L.   1937   Geological Investigations in East Greenland. *Medd. om Grönland*, Vol. 134, No. 5, pp. 1-64.

WAHL, W.   1949   Isostasy and the origin of Sial and Sima and of Parental Rock Magmas. *Am. Journ. Sci.*, Vol. 247, pp. 145-167.

WALKER, E. H.   1949   Andean Uplift and Erosion Surfaces near Uncia, Bolivia. *Amer. Journ. Sci.*, Vol. 247, pp. 646-663.

WALKER, F. and
NICOLAYSEN, L. O.   1954   The Petrology of Mauritius. *Colonial Geology and Mineral Resources*, Vol. 4, No. 1, pp. 3-43.

WALKER, F. and
POLDERVAART, A.   1949   Karroo Dolerites of the Union of South Africa. *Bull. Geol. Soc. Am.*, Vol. 60, pp. 591-706.

WALSH, P. T.   1966   Cretaceous Outliers in south-west Ireland and their implications for Cretaceous palaeo-geography. *Quart. Journ. Geol. Soc. Lond.*, Vol. 122, pp. 63-84.

WARD, W. H.   1945   The Stability of Natural Slopes. *Geog. Journ.*, Vol. 105, pp. 170-197.

WATERS, R. S.   1961   The Bearing of Superficial Deposits on the Age and Origin of the Upland Plain of East Devon, West Dorset and South Somerset. *Tr. and Pap. Inst. Brit. Geog.*, Publ. No. 28, pp. 89-97.

WEEKS, L. G.   1948   Palæography of South America. *Bull. Geol. Soc. Am.*, Vol. 59, pp. 249-282.

WEGENER, A.   1924   *The Origin of Continents and Ocean Basins*, London, 212 pp.

WEGMANN, C. E.   1935   Zur Deutung der Migmatite. *Geol. Rund.*, Vol. 26, pp. 305-350.

——   1948   Transformations Metasomatiques et Analyse tectonique. *XVIII Internat. Geol. Cong.*, Lond.

——   1962   Remarks on the Structure of the Jura Mountains. *Internat. Field Inst., Dept. Geol., Univ. Neuchatel*, 10 pp.

WELLINGTON, J. H.   1937   The Pre-Karroo Peneplain in the South-Central Transvaal. *S. Afr. Journ. Sci.*, Vol. 33, pp. 281-295.

WELLMAN, H. W.   1956   Structural Outline of New Zealand. *N.Z. Dept. Sci. and Ind. Res., Bull.* No. 121, 38 pp.

WELLMAN, H. W. and
WILLETT, R. W.   1942   The Geology of the West Coast from Abut Head to Milford Sound. *Tr. Roy. Soc. N.Z.*, Vol. 71, pp. 282-306.

WHITEHOUSE, F. W.   1940   The Lateritic Soils of Western Queensland. *Univ. Queensl. Papers Geol.* No. 2, pp. 1-22.

——   1941   The Surface of Western Queensland. *Proc. Roy. Soc. Queensland*, Vol. 53, pp. 2-19.

WILLIAMS, D.   1960   Genesis of Sulphide Ores. *Pr. Geol. Assn.*, Vol. 71, pp. 245-284.

WILLIAMS, H.   1953   Problems and Progress in Vulcanology. *Quart. Journ. Geol. Soc. Lond.*, Vol. 109, pp. 311-332.

WILLIS, B.   1907   Research in China, Vols. 1 and 2. *Carnegie Instit. Washington Public.* No. 54, 353 pp.

——   1914   Physiography of the Cordillera de los Andes between latitudes 39° and 44° South. *C. R. XII Internat. Geol. Cong.*, pp. 733-756.

WILSON, A. F.   1954   Charnockitic Rocks in Australia—A Review. *Proc. Pan-Ind. Oc. Cong. Perth*, Sec. C, pp. 10-17.

——   1959   The Charnockitic Rocks of Australia. *Geol. Rund.*, Vol. 47, pp. 491-510.

WILSON, A. W. G.   1903   The Laurentian Peneplain. *Journ. Geol.*, Vol. XI, pp. 615-669.

WILSON, C. C. and
BIRCHWOOD, K. M.   1965   The Trinidad mud volcano island of 1964. *Proc. Geol. Soc. Lond.*, No. 1626, pp. 169-174.

WILSON, J. T.   1948   Some Aspects of Geophysics in Canada with special reference to Structural Research in the Canadian Shield. *Tr. Amer. Geophys. U.*, Vol. 29, pp. 691-725.

——   1949   Some Major Structures of the Canadian Shield. *Canad. Min. and Metal. Bull.*, Vol. 52, pp. 231-242.

WISEMAN, J. D. H.   1965   Petrography, mineralogy, chemistry and mode of origin of St. Paul Rocks. *Proc. Geol. Soc. Lond.*, No. 1626, pp. 146-147.

WISEMAN, J. D. H. and
  SEWELL, R. B.   1937   The Floor of the Arabian Sea.   *Geol. Mag.*, Vol. 74,
                                  pp. 219-230.

WOOD, A.   1942   The Development of Hillside Slopes.   *Proc. Geol. Assn.*,
                                  Vol. 53, pp. 128-140.

WOODFORD, A. O.   1951   Stream Gradients and Monterey Sea Valley.   *Bull. Geol.
                                  Surv. Am.*, Vol. 62, pp. 799-852.

WOODRING, W. P.   1954   Caribbean Land and Sea through the Ages.   *Bull. Geol.
                                  Soc. Am.*, Vol. 65, pp. 719-732.

WOOLDRIDGE, S. W. and
  KIRKALDY, J. F.   1936   River Profiles and Denudation Chronology in Southern
                                  England.   *Geol. Mag.*, Vol. 73, pp. 1-16.

WOOLDRIDGE, S. W. and
  LINTON, D. L.   1938   Influence of Pliocene Transgression on the Geomorphology
                                  of South East England.   *Journ. Geomorph.*, Vol. 1,
                                  pp. 40-54.

———   1938a   Some Episodes in the Structural Evolution of S.E. England
                                  considered in Relation to the Concealed Boundary of
                                  Meso-Europe.   *Proc. Geologists Assn.*, Vol. 49, pp.
                                  264-291.

WOOLNOUGH, W. G.   1903   The Continental Origin of Fiji.   *Proc. Linn. Soc. N.S.W.*,
                                  Vol. 28, pp. 457-495.

WOOLNOUGH, F.   1927   On the Duricrust of Australia.   *Journ. Roy. Soc. N.S.W.*,
                                  Vol. 61, pp. 17-53.

WORZEL, J. L. and
  SHURBET, G. L.   1955   Gravity Interpretations from Standard Oceanic and
                                  Continental Crustal Sections.   *Geol. Soc. Am.*, *Spec.
                                  Publ.* 62, pp. 87-100.

YELISEYEVA, V. K.   1959   Stratigraphy and Palaeography of the Carboniferous and
                                  Permian Formations of Sikhote Alin.   *Internat. Geol.
                                  Rev.* 1, Dec. 1-20.

YODER, H. S.   1955   Rôle of Water in Metamorphism.   *Geol. Soc. Amer. Sp.
                                  Publ.* 62, pp. 505-524.

YODER, H. S. and
  TILLEY, C. E.   1962   Origin of Basaltic Magmas: An Experimental Study of
                                  Natural and Synthetic Rock Systems.   *Journ. Petrol.*,
                                  Vol. 3, pp. 342-532.

ZEUNER, F. E.   1945   *Dating the Past*, London, 516 pp.

                                  Addenda

DINIZ, A. C. and
  AGUIAR, F. Q. DE B.   1965   Geomorfologia, Solos e Ruralismo do Região Central
                                  Angolana.   *Rep. Inst. Investig Agronom. de Angola*,
                                  64 pp.

DOLLFUS, O.   1965   Les Andines Centrales du Pérou et leurs Piémonts. *Trav.*
                                 Inst. Franc. d'Etudes Andines, Vol. 10, 404 pp.

HATORI, K., *et. al.* 1964   Quaternary Tectonic Map of Japan. *Journ. Geodetic Soc.*
                                 Japan, Vol. 10, pp. 111-115.

RUNCORN, S. K.   1965   Changes in the convection pattern in the Earth's mantle
                                 and continental drift: evidence for a cold origin of the
                                 Earth. *Phil. Trans. Roy. Soc. Lond.*, Vol. 258, pp.
                                 228-251.

AUTHOR INDEX

SUBJECT INDEX

PRINTED IN GREAT BRITAIN BY
OLIVER AND BOYD LTD., EDINBURGH